THE WRITER'S HANDBOOK 1999

Barry Turner has worked on both sides of publishing, as an editor and marketing director and as an author. He started his career as a journalist with *The Observer* before moving on to television and radio. He has written over twenty books including *A Place in the Country*, which inspired a television series, and a best-selling biography of the actor, Richard Burton.

His recent work includes a radio play, travel articles, serializing books for *The Times*, editing the magazine *Country* and writing a one-man show based on the life of the legendary theatre critic, James Agate. This is his twelfth year as editor of *The Writer's Handbook* and his first as editor of *The Statesman's Yearbook*.

THE WRITER'S COMPANION

The essential guide to being published

Barry Turner

The Writer's Companion is a route map through the media jungle, an indispensable guide for established writers and newcomers alike who seek to make the best commercial use of their talents.

Drawing on the cumulative experiences of its sister volume, *The Writer's Handbook,* which is now in its twelfth year, *The Writer's Companion* is packed with a wealth of practical advice taking in:

- book publishing
- freelance journalism
- film and television
- radio drama
- theatre and poetry

Everyday concerns, financial and legal, from how to avoid contractual pitfalls to minimising the risk of libel are given full coverage and there is up-to-date advice on raising funds for creative projects on stage and screen.

THE
WRITER'S
HANDBOOK
1999

EDITOR
BARRY TURNER

First published 1988
This edition published 1998 by
MACMILLAN
an imprint of Macmillan Publishers Ltd,
25 Eccleston Place, London SW1W 9NF
and Basingstoke
Associated companies throughout the world

10 9 8 7 6 5 4 3 2 1

A CIP catalogue record for this book is available from the British Library

ISBN 0–333–71925-5

Typeset by Heronwood Press
Printed and bound in Great Britain
by Mackays of Chatham plc, Kent

If you would like an entry in *The Writer's Handbook 2000*,
please write or send a fax to:
The Writer's Handbook,
34 Ufton Road,
London N1 5BX.
Fax 0171 241 0118

Contents

Preface

The media revolution rolls on. To look back from the current *Writer's Handbook* to the first edition twelve years ago is to rediscover a lost world in which each sector of the communication and entertainment industry was neatly cordoned off under a familiar heading. With a modest amount of homework, any writer with words to sell soon discovered where best to set out his stall. Now that same writer needs an understanding of chaos theory to sort out the profusion of media interests, many of them overlapping and with no clear idea of what they are trying to achieve. There is more of everything; more publishers, production companies, hours of broadcasting and acres of newsprint. More writers, too.

The purpose of *The Writer's Handbook* is to restore a sense of order to an otherwise confused and complex industry. *The Writer's Handbook* does not tell you how to write but for those who *can* write, it does provide the essential knowledge for channelling talent in the right direction. To this end, feedback from readers is an invaluable compliment to in-house research. All experiences, observations and opinions are welcome. But, sadly, not manuscripts. If I gave a considered judgement on all the unpublished work that comes my way I would do little else in life. The same must be said of my assistant Jill Fenner whose desk is even more crowded than mine. Her patience and dedication are exemplary but there is a limit. I thank her for her attention to detail (spotting what I invariably miss) and for keeping me on the editorial straight and narrow. Thanks also to Clare Thomas who looks after our interests at Macmillan and Jayne Jenkinson who takes the stress out of production. If anyone spots an error, factual or stylistic, they must feel free to throw a brick in my direction.

Barry Turner

THE MACMILLAN GOOD ENGLISH HANDBOOK

Compiled by
Godfrey Howard

'Only a fool would be without this …' *The Guardian*

'I do not often read reference books straight through
cover to cover – but this one I did!'
Sir John Hanson, Director-General, The British Council

This completely new handbook is written and designed
for the 21st century. Writers can turn to it whenever
there's a moment's hesitation over grammar or
the use of a word – and find *at a glance* a
clearcut and authoritative answer.

The Macmillan Good English Handbook uses a consensus
of over a hundred writers to offer a reliable and
sensitive balance between traditional grammar
and what is out of touch with the language
on the brink of the new millennium.

384pp   Hardback £9.99   Paperback £5.99

Aiming for the Bestseller

One way of making money is to write a bestseller. Another and easier way of making money is to tell others how to write a bestseller. The promoter of literary stardom starts with little knowledge and even less practical experience but what he does know he puts across with huge enthusiasm and conviction. Anyone can do anything. It is not true, of course, but long before realism sets in the guru has banked his fees and is back on the lecture circuit.

It is easy to see why so many newcomers to the writing trade are attracted to the concept of bestsellerdom. It looks so easy. Why should anyone want to do a proper job when they could be emulating Jeffrey Archer, Danielle Steele or Barbara Taylor Bradford? Or, indeed, improving on the work of these and a dozen other bestselling fiction writers. It would not be difficult. One could start by sharpening up the dialogue, making it less like Dalek-speak. This would be followed by a cull of platitudes and clichés leading to a saving on space which could then be used to develop believable characters who relate in some small way to real life. The result – better books. But would they still be bestsellers? Ah, there's the rub.

Hard though it is to believe, many of the reading public, those who are not constrained by the traditional standards of literary excellence, are unfazed by stilted dialogue, appreciate clichés (the simplest way to state fundamental truths, as someone once said) and have no trouble in identifying with one-dimensional characters. No surprise in that. No harm, either. The fault is more in ourselves that we insist on judging every novel by the same criteria; criteria, moreover, that consistently ignore the virtue possessed of all bestseller writers of pulp fiction – the ability to tell a good story.

The great and good G. K. Chesterton said it all in his *Defence of Penny Dreadfuls*, written at the turn of the century.

> 'One of the strangest examples of the degree to which ordinary life is undervalued is the example of popular literature, the vast mass of which we contentedly describe as vulgar ... In former centuries the educated class ignored the ruck of vulgar literature. They ignored and therefore did not, properly speaking,

despise it ... Today, however, we have reversed this principle. We despise vulgar compositions, and we do not ignore them. We are in some danger of becoming petty in our study of pettiness.'

Chesterton took comfort in the knowledge that popular story tellers – the pulp novelists of their day – were on the side of morality.

'The vast mass of humanity, with their vast mass of idle books and idle words, have never doubted that courage is splendid, that fidelity is noble, that distressed ladies should be rescued, and vanquished enemies spared.'

Nothing much has changed. So let us not be hard on Jeffrey Archer *et al.* Their simple tales give simple pleasure. For the most part, they write themselves out at an early stage and are soon forgotten.

But there is more, much more, to the bestseller market than pulp fiction. To jump to the other extreme, some of the finest writers in English feature in the bestseller lists, Evelyn Waugh, Graham Greene and P. G. Wodehouse, to take examples at random, are by no means past their sell-by date. Among the current crop of quality bestsellers is Bill Bryson, a humorist of such potency that he has normally reserved British readers laughing out loud on trains and buses.

The Bryson books may not become classics. Humour tends to fade with time (though *England, Their England* and *Diary of a Nobody*, not to mention all those Wodehouse titles, have kept their appeal). What can be said with confidence is that there are many titles now regarded as classics that were early bestsellers. Dickens never had trouble selling his books any more, say, than Stephenson, Trollope and Conrad. Equally, there have been bestselling authors marked out for classical status who have faded from the public imagination. Hugh Walpole, Harrison Ainsworth, Mrs Humphrey Ward and, more recently, C. P. Snow spring to mind.

Good, bad or indifferent, fiction bestsellers have one thing in common, apart from their ability to sell in excess of 100,000 copies. They are all in tune with their period. Somehow they catch on to a social anxiety or aspiration that gives them their momentum. Remember all those Cold War thrillers by writers who, for the most part, now find it hard to get their books published at all?

'The younger members of my family, though brought up in a house crammed with books, are intellectually and enthusiastically devoted to music, art, ballet, film, but seem to care little for literature. ... Young people appear to me to be living far more through the eye and ear than we did at their time of life.
... I rarely find young people arguing about poets, novelists, essayists, as we used to do. The bookshop has many new competitors.'
J. B. Priestley

Spy story heroes, fanciful though they may have been, were a reassurance that the good guys would win in the end. A nervous public took them to its collective heart. Similarly, an earlier generation, facing up to the prospect of another German war, found comfort in the adventure stories of John Buchan and Sapper. Who now reads *them* with a straight face?

Not quite fiction but close enough are the 'flight from reality' bestsellers which do particularly well in times of economic gloom. A feature of the last recession was the success of Peter Mayle with his *Year in Provence* and *Toujours Provence*. Interestingly, the Mayle phenomenon had its parallel in the 1930s. Then it was the splendidly named Lady Winifred Fortescue whose books about idyllic Provence, all sun, wine and long lunches, proved a popular antidote to urban despondency.

This recurrence of circumstances which favour a particular type of bestseller is worthy of further study. The relationship between time and book is not always clear. What, if any, is the link between Dick Francis whose annual output is virtually guaranteed bestseller status and the now forgotten Nat Gould, the Manchester-born racing journalist who sold more books in his lifetime than any previous British or American author? One possible explanation is that books about racing appeal to both sexes which enhances their sales at a time when most popular novels are male or female orientated. This was true of the turn of the century and may be true now. A hard and fast rule relationship would be hard to establish but the fact remains that every bestseller must catch on to a popular mood and that trends can and do recur. Instead of listening to fatuous advice from self-appointed writing experts, the prospective bestselling authors would be better occupied studying literary history. Long-dead and forgotten authors can still teach us a thing or two.

One of the paradoxes of the book business is that the least known authors are among the biggest earners. You find them in the shelves of non-fiction, often in obscure corners where specialist interests like dog breeding, DIY or learning a foreign language are catered for. Textbooks can be licences to print money. As a fresh undergraduate at the London School of Economics more than 40 years ago I went straight out to buy Paul Samuelson's textbook on *Economics*, then as hitherto regarded as essential reading for students hoping to grasp the obscure science. Today, though the book has many

'Talk about there being far too many writers. You can't of course prevent people writing any more than copulating, but there ought to be some sort of contraception to prevent publication.'
James Lees-Milne,
Midway on the Waves

rivals, it is still a steady bestseller. Since its first edition in 1948, Samuelson's *Economics* has sold more than four million copies and has been translated into 41 languages. There is never any scarcity of academic young turks ready to challenge Samuelson. The latest is a Harvard economist who secured an advance of $1.4 million against the publication of his *Principles of Economics*.

Every academic discipline, indeed every school subject, can be linked to a publishing success story in which a fortunate author, knee deep in royalty cheques, can pass unnoticed by the literary establishment. In the wider reaches of self-instruction, we all know of the triumphal climb of Delia Smith who can sell a million copies of one of her recipe collections within a week of its publication but how many of us show proper respect to Dr David Hessayon, said to be the biggest selling non-fiction author in history, whose gardening books, currently nudging 40 million sales worldwide, have earned him £20 million?

Not long ago the bestseller list in Japan was led in the first six places by anonymous guides to computer games, all making fortunes for their compilers. It hasn't happened here. Yet.

Publishers can help to make bestsellers. A much favoured gimmick is to attach a book to a high profile name thereby hoping to ride to fortune on the back of a reputation wholly divorced from literary excellence. So it is that a senior Royal will sell more books on virtually any subject than an author, however notable, who does not feature in the gossip columns. Famous personalities – actors, models, politicians – who cannot write have no cause to despair. There is always a skilled editor on hand to assist in putting the words in the right order. The formula is not sure fire. A novel purporting to be by the famous Naomi Campbell but in fact written largely by the unknown Caroline Upcher came and went rather faster than the publisher had anticipated.

Two years ago, Random House made an ass of itself by demanding the return of the $1.2 million advance it had paid to Joan Collins for what turned out to be a 'very primitive, dated, dull, clichéd' novel called *A Ruling Passion*. Miss Collins' lawyer countered by arguing that she was accustomed to 'face-to-face, line-by-line, page-by-page' editorial help which Random had failed to provide. In other words, the publisher had bought a name, not a book. The jury agreed and Miss Collins got rich on *A Ruling Passion* without selling a single copy.

'Nobody ever writes a nasty review of a book by somebody they think might be helpful to them, and so giving a bad notice is a way of asserting status, like a baboon displaying its bottom to a rival in the jungle.'
Ben Pimlott

Bestsellers beget bestsellers. An author who pulls off one success can usually rely on his publisher's marketing team to help him repeat the trick. While it is only the super earners who qualify for an advertising campaign (publishers are notoriously cynical when it comes to advertising, believing that it does more for an author's ego than for hard sales), there will be bookshop promotions with eye-catching displays conveniently close to the till. Then there are the literary editors to be solicited for reviews and the feature pages to fill with author interviews. In the week of publication the author will be taken off round the country to talk about his 'number one bestseller' on radio and television. Outrageous hype is part of the game and has been with us for a long time. The publisher of Rider Haggard's *King Solomon's Mines* billed it unashamedly as 'the most amazing story ever written'. And that was in 1885. The latest ruse is called 'piggybacking' which is to market an up and coming writer as the natural heir to a famous predecessor. So it is that a first novel by a Washington lawyer (*The Superlative Man*) is said to be 'in the spirit of Raymond Chandler'.

'A writer doesn't write to help humanity, but to help himself.'
Graham Greene

Sometimes it works; sometimes not. Publishers are only too well aware that the most powerful weapon in the promotional armoury is controlled by the readers. Word of mouth recommendation is what really sells books. Which is why publishers are forever being caught out by the ducklings that turn into swans. Last year, the dull sounding *Longitude* was in the *Sunday Times'* bestseller list for over 50 weeks and sold more than 300,000 copies in hardback. Yet when it was first on offer all the big publishing houses gave it a miss. It was left to Fourth Estate to take up the challenge but even there, it seems, no one suspected a bestseller in the making. It was much the same with *Captain Corelli's Mandolin*, said by the agent Cat Ledger to have 'the worst 50 page start I've ever read' which nevertheless built up over two years to 'must have' status and is still going strong.

These are not isolated examples. Publishers and authors are forever being caught out by success. As Cyril Connolly observed in *Enemies of Promise* there is an abundance of writers who 'without knowing it, have hit upon the contemporary chemical combination of illusion and disillusion which makes books sell well'. Writing from a pre-war perspective, Connolly identified *The Bridge of St Luis Rey*, *Decline and Fall*, *Brave New World*, *The Postman Always Rings Twice* and *Goodbye Mr Chips* as books that were expected to sell respectably but were never treated as bestsellers, least of all by their creators, before the floodgates opened.

So there it is. If those who aim at bestsellerdom often fall short of the target, it is equally true that others who don't even claim to shoot straight nonetheless hit the bullseye. There is hope for us all.

UK Publishers

AA Publishing
The Automobile Association, Fanum House, Basingstoke, Hampshire RG21 4EA
☎0990 448866   Fax 01256 491555
Managing Director *John Howard*
Editorial Director *Michael Buttler*

Publishes maps, atlases and guidebooks, motoring and leisure. About 100 titles a year.

Authors' Rating The tour guides keep coming but, with reports of the AA reverting to core activities, the list may take on a harder commercial edge.

Abacus
See **Little, Brown & Co (UK)**

ABC-Clio Ltd
Old Clarendon Ironworks, 35a Great Clarendon Street, Oxford OX2 6AT
☎01865 311350   Fax 01865 311358
Managing Director *Tony Sloggett*
Editorial Director *Dr Robert G. Neville*

Formerly Clio Press Ltd. *Publishes* academic and general reference works, social sciences and humanities. Markets, outside North America, the CD-ROM publications of the American parent company. Art Bibliographies *S. Pape.* SERIES *World Bibliographical; International Organisations; World Photographers; Clio Montessori.*
Royalties paid twice-yearly.

Abington Publishing
See **Woodhead Publishing Ltd**

Absolute Classics
See **Oberon Books**

Absolute Press
Scarborough House, 29 James Street West, Bath BA1 2BT
☎01225 316013   Fax 01225 445836
Managing/Editorial Director *Jon Croft*

FOUNDED 1979. *Publishes* food and wine-related subjects as well as travel guides and the *Streetwise Maps* series of city maps. About 10 titles a year. Lead title for 1998: *Christie's Encyclopedia of Champagne and Sparkling Wine* Tom Stevenson. *Outlines*, launched in summer 1997, is a new series of monographs on gay and lesbian creative artists. No unsolicited mss. Synopses and ideas for books welcome.
Royalties paid twice-yearly.

Abson Books London
5 Sidney Square, London E1 2EY
☎0171 790 4737   Fax 0171 790 7346
Chairman *M. J. Ellison*

FOUNDED 1971 in Bristol. *Publishes* language glossaries, literary quizzes and puzzles. No unsolicited mss; synopses and ideas for books welcome.
Royalties paid twice-yearly.

Academic Press
See **Harcourt Brace and Company Ltd**

Academy Group Ltd
42 Leinster Gardens, London W2 3AN
☎0171 262 5097   Fax 0171 262 5093
Chairman *John Jarvis*
Managing Editor *Maggie Toy*
Approx. Annual Turnover £2 million

FOUNDED 1969. Became part of John Wiley & Sons, Inc. group in 1997. *Publishes* architecture and design. Welcomes unsolicited mss, synopses and ideas.
Royalties paid annually.

Acair Ltd
Unit 7, 7 James Street, Stornoway, Isle of Lewis, Scotland HS1 2QN
☎01851 703020   Fax 01851 703294

Specialising in matters pertaining to the Gaidhealtachd, Acair publishes books on Scottish history, culture and the Gaelic language. 75% of their children's books are targeted at primary school usage and are published exclusively in Gaelic.
Royalties paid twice-yearly.

Actinic Press
See **Cressrelles Publishing Co. Ltd**

Addison Wesley Longman Ltd
Edinburgh Gate, Harlow, Essex CM20 2JE
☎01279 623623   Fax 01279 431059
Contracts & Copyrights Department
   Brenda Gvozdanovic

FOUNDED 1724 by Thomas Longman. Restructured in 1994 to focus solely on educational publishing. A subsidiary of Pearson plc. *Publishes* a range of curriculum subjects, including English language teaching for students at primary and secondary school level, college and university. All unsolicited mss should be addressed to the Manager, Contracts and Copyrights Department.

Royalties paid twice-yearly. *Overseas associates* worldwide.

Authors' Rating Last year saw a reorganisation of the company to improve international marketing (particularly for the fast growing ELT sector) and to increase investment in product development. The prospective growth areas are Europe and China. Acquisitions or possibly a merger with another like-minded publishing group should not be ruled out. Either way, authors can only benefit. ELT is one of the fastest money spinners. Louis Alexander, who publishes with AWL, has even appeared in *The Guinness Book of Records* as a world bestseller.

Adelphi
See **David Campbell Publishers Ltd**

Adlard Coles Nautical
See **A & C Black (Publishers) Ltd**

Adlib
See **Scholastic Ltd**

African Books Collective
The Jam Factory, 27 Park End Street, Oxford OX1 1HU
☎01865 726686   Fax 01865 793298
FOUNDED 1990. Collectively owned by its 17 founder member publishers. Exclusive distribution in N. America, UK, Europe and Commonwealth countries outside Africa for 50 African member publishers. Aims to promote and disseminate African-published material outside Africa. No unsolicited mss.

Age Concern Books
1268 London Road, London SW16 4ER
☎0181 679 8000   Fax 0181 679 6069
Approx. Annual Turnover £500,000
Publishing arm of Age Concern England. *Publishes* related non-fiction only. No fiction. About 18 titles a year. Unsolicited mss, synopses and ideas welcome.

Airlife Publishing Ltd
101 Longden Road, Shrewsbury, Shropshire SY3 9EB
☎01743 235651   Fax 01743 232944
Chairman/Managing Director
  A. D. R. Simpson
Editorial Head *Peter Coles*
Approx. Annual Turnover £3 million
IMPRINTS
Airlife Specialist aviation titles for pilots, historians and enthusiasts. Also naval and military history. About 60 titles a year. TITLES *Flightwise – Aircraft Stability and Control; Progressive Flying; Restoring Museum Aircraft; U Boat Tankers.*

Swan Hill Press Country pursuits, horse riding, mountaineering, fishing, natural history and decorative art. About 35 titles a year. TITLES *Nutrition and the Feeding of Horses; Falconry for Beginners; Tree Heritage of Britain and Ireland.*

Waterline Books Practical sailing books for yachtsmen, nautical history and narrative. About 10 titles a year. TITLES *Marine Electronics Handbook; Handbook of Marine Surveying; Compass Correction.* Unsolicited mss, synopses and ideas for books welcome.

Royalties paid annually, twice-yearly by arrangement.

Ian Allan Ltd
River Dene Estate, Molesey Road, Mersham, Surrey KT12 4RG
☎01932 266600   Fax 01932 26601
Chairman *David Allan*
General Manager *Tony Saunders*
Specialist transport publisher – atlases, maps, railway, aviation, road transport, military, maritime, reference. About 80 titles a year. Send sample chapter and synopsis (with s.a.e.). Manages distribution and sales for third party publishers.
IMPRINT **Dial House** sporting titles.

J. A. Allen & Co. Ltd
1 Lower Grosvenor Place, Buckingham Palace Road, London SW1W 0EL
☎0171 834 0090   Fax 0171 976 5836
Executive Director *Caroline Burt*
Marketing Manager *Hugh Davie*
Editor *Jane Lake*
Approx. Annual Turnover £750,000
FOUNDED 1926 as part of J. A. Allen & Co. (The Horseman's Bookshop) Ltd, and became a separate independent company in 1960. *Publishes* equine and equestrian non-fiction. About 20 titles a year. Mostly commissioned, but willing to consider unsolicited mss of technical/instruc-

tional material related to all aspects of horses and horsemanship.

Royalties paid twice-yearly.

Allen Lane
See **Penguin UK**

Allison & Busby
114 New Cavendish Street, London W1M 7FD
☎0171 636 2942   Fax 0171 323 2023
Publisher *Peter Day*
Editor *Vanessa Unwin*
Editor *David Shelley*

FOUNDED 1967. *Publishes* literary fiction and non-fiction, writers' guides, crime and translations, particularly from the Spanish. About 60 titles a year. Send synopses with two sample chapters. No replies without s.a.e.

Amber Lane Press Ltd
Cheorl House, Church Street, Charlbury, Oxfordshire OX7 3PR
☎01608 810024   Fax 01608 810024
Chairman *Brian Clark*
Managing Director/Editorial Head
  Judith Scott

FOUNDED 1979 to publish modern play texts. *Publishes* plays and books on the theatre. About 4 titles a year. TITLES *Strange Fruit; Bent; A Letter of Resignation* (play texts); *Sir Donald Wolfit – His Life and Work in the Unfashionable Theatre* Ronald Harwood; *Christopher Hampton: Dramatic Ironist* Francis Ben. 'Expressly *not* interested in poetry.' No unsolicited mss. Synopses and ideas welcome.

Royalties paid twice-yearly.

AMCD (Publishers) Ltd
PO Box 182, Altrincham, Cheshire WA15 9UA
☎0161 434 5105   Fax 0161 434 5105
E-mail: 100625.3570@compuserve.com
Managing Director *John Stewart Adams*

FOUNDED 1988. *Publishes* financial directories, books on China, local history, business books. Took over the Jensen Business Books imprint in 1993 and is well placed in electronic reference after developing its own software. In conjunction with JHC (Technology) Ltd, AMCD offers publishers access to the electronic book market with their reference, dictionary and directory Pop-Up© software packages which can handle most languages. About 5 titles a year. TITLES *Financing China's Electricity; Around Haunted Croydon; Buying and Selling a Shop; Depression Challenges.* Ideas for business

books and books on China or the Far East welcome in synopsis form (no mss). No poetry, fiction or historical romance. Final mss must be on disk.

Royalties paid twice yearly.

Amsco
See **Omnibus Press**

Andersen Press Ltd
20 Vauxhall Bridge Road, London SW1V 2SA
☎0171 840 8701/840 8700 (editorial)
Fax 0171 233 6263
Managing Director/Publisher *Klaus Flugge*
Editorial Director *Janice Thomson*
Editor, Fiction *Audrey Adams*

FOUNDED 1976 by Klaus Flugge and named after Hans Christian Andersen. *Publishes* children's high-quality picture books and hardback fiction. Seventy per cent of their books are sold as co-productions abroad. TITLES *Elmer* David McKee; *Greyfriars Bobby* Ruth Brown; *I Want My Potty* Tony Ross; *Badger's Parting Gifts* Susan Varley; *Teddy, Where Are You?* Ralph Steadman; *Jack's Fantastic Voyage* Michael Foreman; *Suddenly!* Colin McNaughton; *Junk* Melvin Burgess. Unsolicited mss welcome for picture books; synopsis in the first instance for books for young readers up to age 12.

Royalties paid twice-yearly.

Anness Publishing Ltd
Hermes House, 88–89 Blackfriars Road, London SE1 8HA
☎0171 401 2077   Fax 0171 633 9499
Chairman/Managing Director *Paul Anness*
Publisher/Partner *Joanna Lorenz*

FOUNDED 1989. Successful, small entrepreneurial publisher of highly illustrated co-edition titles. *Publishes* illustrated general non-fiction: cookery, crafts, interior design, gardening, photography, decorating, lifestyle and children's. About 400 titles a year. Unsolicited summaries and proposals welcome, no manuscripts. IMPRINTS **Lorenz Books**; **Old Forge Gift Collection**; **Hermes House**; **Sebastian Kelly**.

Antique Collectors' Club
5 Church Street, Woodbridge, Suffolk IP12 1DS
☎01394 385501   Fax 01394 384434
Managing Director *Diana Steel*
Director *Brian Cotton*

FOUNDED 1966. Has a five-figure membership spread over the United Kingdom and the world. The Club's magazine *Antique Collecting* is sold on a subscription basis (currently £19.50 p.a.) and is published 10 times a year. It is sent free to members who may also buy the Club's books at special pre-publication prices. *Publishes* specialist books on antiques and collecting. The price guide series was introduced in 1968 with the first edition of *The Price Guide to Antique Furniture*. Subject areas include furniture, silver/jewellery, metalwork, glass, textiles, art reference, ceramics, horology. Also books on architecture and gardening. RECENT TITLES *Opera Houses of Europe* Andras Kaldor; *Farm Animal Portraits* Elspeth Moncrieff; *Understanding Antique Silver Plate* Stephen Helliwell; *Lucy Kemp Welch* Laura Wortley. Unsolicited synopses and ideas for books welcome. No mss.

Royalties paid quarterly as a rule, but can vary.

Anvil Press Poetry Ltd
Neptune House, 70 Royal Hill, London SE10 8RT
☎0181 469 3033   Fax 0181 469 3363
Editorial Director *Peter Jay*

FOUNDED 1968 to promote English-language and foreign poetry, both classic and contemporary, in translation. English list includes Peter Levi, Dick Davis and Carol Ann Duffy. Translated books include Bei Dao, Celan, Dante, Lalic. Preliminary enquiry required for translations. Unsolicited book-length collections of poems are welcome from writers whose work has appeared in poetry magazines.

Authors' Rating Celebrating 30 years of independent publishing, Peter Jay has achieved wonders in opening up English poetry to new work. Immune to the dictates of short-lived fashions, Anvil has had great success in building the reputation of younger poets.

Apollos
See **Inter-Varsity Press**

Apple
See **Quarto Publishing** under **UK Packagers**

Appletree Press Ltd
19–21 Alfred Street, Belfast BT2 8DL
☎01232 243074   Fax 01232 246756
Managing Director *John Murphy*
Creative Manager *Rob Blackwell*

FOUNDED 1974. *Publishes* cookery and other small-format gift books, plus general non-fiction of Irish and Scottish interest. TITLES *Little Cookbook* series (about 40 titles); *Ireland: The*

Complete Guide. No unsolicited mss; send initial letter or synopsis.

Royalties paid twice-yearly in the first year, annually thereafter. For the *Little Cookbook* Series, a standard fee is paid.

Arc Publications
Nanholme Mill, Shaw Wood Road, Todmorden, Lancashire OL14 6DA
☎01706 812338   Fax 01706 818948
Publishers *Rosemary Jones, Angela Jarman, Tony Ward*
General Editor *Tony Ward*
Associate Editors *Michael Hulse* (International), *David Morley* (UK)

FOUNDED in 1969 to specialise in the publication of contemporary poetry from new and established writers both in the UK and abroad. Runs the annual **Arc Short Story Competition** and *publishes* an anthology of winning entries. AUTHORS include John Kinsella (Australia), Glyn Maxwell, Tariq Latif, C. K. Stead (New Zealand), Donald Atkinson, Tomas Saluman (Slovenia), Jacqueline Brown, Gail Dendy (S. Africa), Robert Gray (Australia). 8 titles a year. Authors submitting material should ensure that it is compatible with the current list and should enclose s.a.e. if they wish mss to be returned.

Aris & Phillips Ltd
Teddington House, Warminster, Wiltshire BA12 8PQ
☎01985 213409   Fax 01985 212910
Managing/Editorial Director *Adrian Phillips*
Editor, Hispanic Classics *Lucinda Phillips*

FOUNDED 1972 to publish books on Egyptology. A family firm which has remained independent. *Publishes* academic, classical, oriental and hispanic. About 20 titles a year. TITLES *The God Min* A. McFarlane; *The Reign of Ramesses IV* A. J. Peden; *The Third Intermediate Period in Egypt (1100–650BC)* K. A. Kitchen. With such a highly specialised list, unsolicited mss and synopses are not particularly welcome, but synopses will be considered.

Royalties paid twice-yearly.

Arkana
See **Penguin UK**

Arms & Armour Press
See **Cassell**

Arnefold
See **George Mann Books**

Edward Arnold
See **Hodder Headline plc**

Arrow
See **Random House UK Ltd**

Artech House
Portland House, Stag Place, London
SW1E 5XA
☎0171 973 8077   Fax 0171 630 0166
Managing Director (USA) *William M. Bazzy*
Senior Commissioning Editor *Dr Julie*
Lancashire
Website: artech-house.com
FOUNDED 1969. European office of Artech
House Inc., Boston. *Publishes* electronic engi-
neering, especially telecommunications, com-
puter communications, computing, optoelec-
tronics, signal processing, digital audio and
video, intelligent transportation systems and
technology management (books, software and
videos). 50–60 titles a year. Unsolicited mss
and synopses considered.
Royalties paid twice-yearly.

Ashgate Publishing Co. Ltd
Gower House, Croft Road, Aldershot,
Hampshire GU11 3HR
☎01252 331551   Fax 01252 344405
Chairman *Nigel Farrow*
FOUNDED 1967. *Publishes* in social sciences,
business, arts and humanities under the **Gower**
imprint for professional books and **Ashgate**
imprint for academic books.
DIVISIONS
Julia Scott Business and management; *Sarah
Markham* Social sciences; *John Irwin* Political sci-
ence, international relations and legal studies;
Alec McAulay History; *John Smedley* Variorum
collected studies; *Rachel Lynch* Music and literary
studies; *Pamela Edwardes* Art history; *John Hindley*
Aviation studies; *Jo Gooderham* Social work.

Ashmolean Museum Publications
Ashmolean Museum, Beaumont Street,
Oxford OX1 2PH
☎01865 278009   Fax 01865 278018
Publisher/Editorial Head *Ian Charlton*
Website: http://www.ashmol.ox.ac.uk
The Ashmolean Museum, which is wholly
owned by Oxford University, was founded in
1683. The first publication appeared in 1890 but
publishing did not really start in earnest until the
1960s. *Publishes* European and Oriental fine and
applied arts, European archaeology and ancient

history, Egyptology and numismatics, for both
adult and children's markets. About 8 titles a
year. No fiction, American/African art, ethnography, modern art or post-medieval history.
Most publications are based on and illustrated
from the Museum's collections.
IMPRINTS **Ashmoleum Museum Publications** and **Griffith Institute** (Egyptology
imprint). Recent TITLES *Miniatures; Samuel
Palmer; Medieval England; Atlas of Anglo-Saxon
Coin Finds; The Art of the Japanese Folding Screen.*
No unsolicited mss.
Royalties paid annually.

Associated University Presses (AUP)
See **Golden Cockerel Press Ltd**

The Athlone Press
1 Park Drive, London NW11 7SG
☎0181 458 0888   Fax 0181 201 8115
E-mail: athlonepress@btinternet.com
Managing Director *Doris Southam*
Editorial Head *Brian Southam*
FOUNDED 1949 as the publishing house of the
University of London. Now wholly independent, but preserves links with the University via
an academic advisory board. *Publishes* archaeology, architecture, art, economics, film studies,
history, history-of-ideas, history-of-science, law,
eating disorders, psychiatry, literary criticism,
psychic, medical, Japan, philosophy, politics,
religion, science, sociology, women's/feminist
issues. Anticipated developments in the near
future: more emphasis on cultural studies, history
of ideas, women's/feminist studies and environmental issues, including medicine. About 35
titles a year. Unsolicited mss, synopses and ideas
for academic books welcome.
Royalties paid annually. *Overseas associates*
The Athlone Press, 165 First Avenue, Atlantic
Highlands, NJ 07716, USA.

Atlantic Europe Publishing Co. Ltd
Greys Court Farm, Greys Court, Nr Henley
on Thames, Oxon RG9 4PG
☎01491 628188   Fax 01491 628189
E-mail: info@AtlanticEurope.com
Website: AtlanticEurope.com/info
Directors *Dr B. J. Knapp, D. L. R. McCrae*
Closely associated, since 1990, with Earthscape
Editions packaging operation. *Publishes* full-
colour, highly illustrated children's non-fiction
in hardback for international co-editions. Not
interested in any other material. Main focus is

on National Curriculum titles, especially in the fields of mathematics, science, technology, social history and geography. About 25 titles a year. Unsolicited synopses and ideas for books welcome but s.a.e. essential for return of submissions.

Royalties or fees paid depending on circumstance.

Attic Books

The Folly, Rhosgoch, Painscastle, Builth Wells, Powys LD2 3JY
☎01497 851205

Managing Director/Editorial Head
Jack Bowyer

FOUNDED 1984 by its architect owners. *Publishes* books on building crafts, architecture and engineering. Mostly technical books for the industry, dealing mainly with restoration and conservation.

Royalties paid annually.

AUP (Associated University Presses)

See **Golden Cockerel Press Ltd**

Aurum Press Ltd

25 Bedford Avenue, London WC1B 3AT
☎0171 637 3225   Fax 0171 580 2469

Chairman *André Deutsch*
Managing Director *Bill McCreadie*
Editorial Director *Piers Burnett*
Approx. Annual Turnover £1.89 million

FOUNDED 1977. Formerly owned by Andrew Lloyd Webber's Really Useful Group, now owned jointly by Piers Burnett, Bill McCreadie and Sheila Murphy, all of whom worked together in the '70s for André Deutsch. Committed to producing high-quality, illustrated/non-illustrated adult non-fiction in the areas of general human interest, art and craft, lifestyle, sport and travel. About 40 titles a year. TITLES *Charlie Chaplin and His Times* Kenneth S. Lynn; *The Watercolour Artist's Palette* Tom Robb; *The Feng Shui Garden* Gill Hale; *The Caledonian Canal* Anthony Burton.

Royalties paid twice-yearly.

Autumn Publishing Ltd

North Barn, Appledram Barns, Birdham Road, Near Chichester, West Sussex PO20 7EQ
☎01243 531660   Fax 01243 774433

Managing Director *Campbell Goldsmid*
Editorial Director *Ingrid Goldsmid*

FOUNDED 1976. Publisher of highly illustrated

non-fiction: mainly children's, including activity books. About 20 titles a year. Unsolicited synopses and ideas for books welcome if they come within relevant subject areas.

Payment varies according to contract; generally a flat fee.

B & W Publishing Ltd

233 Cowgate, Edinburgh EH1 1NQ
☎0131 220 5551   Fax 0131 220 5552

Joint Managing Directors *Campbell Brown, Steven Wiggins*

FOUNDED 1990. *Publishes* fiction, memoirs, sport and guidebooks. 15 titles in 1997. Unsolicited mss, synopses and ideas for books welcome. No children's books.

Royalties paid twice-yearly.

Baillière Tindall

See **Harcourt Brace and Company Ltd**

Bantam/Bantam Press

See **Transworld Publishers Ltd**

Barefoot Books Ltd

Editorial: PO Box 95, Kingswood, Bristol BS15 5BH
☎0117 9328885   Fax 0117 9328881
E-mail: info@barefoot-books.com
Website: www.barefoot-books.com

Rights & Management: 18 Highbury Terrace, London N5 1UP
☎0171 704 6492   Fax 0171 359 5798

Managing Director *Nancy Traversy*
Publisher *Tessa Strickland (at Bristol office)*
Approx. Annual Turnover £1 million

FOUNDED in 1993. *Publishes* high-quality children's picture books, particularly new and traditional stories from a wide range of cultures. 25 titles in 1998. TITLES *The Greatest Gift* Susan Summers; *Tales of Wisdom and Wonder* Hugh Lupton; *The Barefoot Book of Mother and Daughter Tales* Josephine Evetts-Secker. No unsolicited mss.

Royalties paid twice-yearly.

Authors' Rating Barefoot gives a whole new meaning to home publishing. Founding partners Nancy Traversy and Tessa Strickland live 100 miles apart but keep in constant and profitable contact by telephone, fax and e-mail. The result is an exciting new publisher of quality books for children which looks set to break into the American market.

Barny Books

The Cottage, Hough on the Hill, Near
Grantham, Lincolnshire NG32 2BB
☎01400 250246
Managing Director/Editorial Head *Molly
Burkett*
Business Manager *Tom Cann*
Approx. Annual Turnover £10,000
FOUNDED with the aim of encouraging new
writers and illustrators. *Publishes* mainly children's
books. TITLES *The Rutland Osprey* Molly
Burkett; *Crossover* Susan Slater; *Diamond's Quest*
Lillian Gillard; *Kangaroo Slow* Shealee Inglehart.
Too small a concern to have the staff/resources
to deal with unsolicited mss. Writers with strong
ideas should approach Molly Burkett by letter in
the first instance. Also runs a readership and advisory service for new writers (£10 fee for short
stories or illustrations; £20 fee for full-length
stories).
Royalties division of profits 50/50.

Authors' Rating A cheerful and enthusiastic
publisher with an eye for popular offbeat subjects.

Barrie & Jenkins
See **Random House UK Ltd**

Bartholomew
See **HarperCollins Publishers Ltd**

B. T. Batsford Ltd
583 Fulham Road, London SW6 5BY
☎0171 471 1100   Fax 0171 471 1101
E-mail: info@batsford.com
Website: http://www.batsford.com
Chairman *Gerard Mizrahi*
Chief Executive *Jules Perel*
Approx. Annual Turnover £5 million
FOUNDED in 1843 as a bookseller, and began
publishing in 1874. An independent publisher
until 1996 when it was bought by Labyrinth
Publishing UK Ltd. A world leader in books
on chess, arts and craft. *Publishes* non-fiction:
archaeology, cinema, crafts and hobbies, fash-
ion and costume, graphic design and garden-
ing. Acquired Faber chess list in 1994 and
Rushmere Wynne business books list in 1997.
About 120 titles a year.
DIVISIONS
Arts & Crafts; **Archaeology & Ancient
History**; **Business**; **Chess**; **Film and Media**;
Graphic Design; **Horticulture**.
Royalties paid twice in first year, annually
thereafter.

Bay View Books Ltd

The Red House, 25–26 Bridgeland Street,
Bideford, Devon EX39 2PZ
☎01237 479225/421285   Fax 01237 421286
Managing Directors *Charles Herridge, Bridgid
Herridge*
FOUNDED 1986. *Publishes* transport books only,
including series: all-colour classic car restora-
tion guides; A–Zs of cars, motorcycles and rac-
ing cars. About 15 titles a year.
Payment varies according to contract.

BBC Penguin
See **BBC Worldwide Ltd**

BBC Worldwide Ltd
80 Wood Lane, London W12 0TT
☎0181 576 2623   Fax 0181 576 2858
Editorial Director *Sheila Ableman*
Approx. Annual Turnover £30 million
Publishes TV tie-in titles, including books
which, though linked with BBC television or
radio, may not simply be the 'book of the series'.
Books with no television or radio link are of no
interest. About 80 titles a year. TITLES *Delia
Smith's Winter Collection; Shooting Stars; Rhodes'
Around Britain.* Unsolicited mss (which come in
at the rate of about 15 weekly) are rarely read.
However, strong ideas well expressed will
always be considered, and promising letters
stand a chance of further scrutiny.
    IMPRINTS **Network Books** Non-fiction tie-
ins to TV programmes broadcast on channels
other than BBC1 or BBC2. Includes cookery,
gardening, crafts, plus some children's fiction.
BBC Penguin A co-publishing deal which
gives BBC Books a mass-market paperback
outlet.
    Royalties paid twice-yearly.

Authors' Rating At long last the BBC is
putting some beef into its marketing. Instead of
relying on a few bestsellers to carry the rest, the
technique now is to link books, videos and
cassettes under four genre headings – children's;
drama; music and arts; and factual and leisure.
On the Continent, where they are supposed to
know nothing about marketing, multimedia
publishers have been doing this for at least a
decade.

Bedford Square Press
See **NCVO Publications**

Belair
See **Folens Ltd**

Bellew Publishing Co. Ltd

Nightingale Centre, 8 Balham Hill, London
SW12 9EA

☎0181 673 5611   Fax 0181 675 3542

Chairman *Ian McCorquodale*
Managing Director *Ib Bellew*
Approx. Annual Turnover £600,000

FOUNDED 1983. Publisher and packager.
Publishes craft, art and design, fiction, illustrated
non-fiction, general interest, religion and poli-
tics. About 15 titles a year. TITLES *We Believe*
Alfred Gilbey; *Chronicle* Alan Wall; *The
Awakening of Willie Ryland* Tom Hart; *On
Depiction: Critical Essays on Art* Avigdor Arikha.
No unsolicited mss. Synopses with specimen
chapters welcome.
Royalties paid annually.

Berg Publishers

150 Cowley Road, Oxford OX4 1JJ
☎01865 245104   Fax 01865 791165

Editorial Director *Kathryn Earle*
Production Director *Sara Everett*
Approx. Annual Turnover £600,000

Also **Oswald Wolff Books** imprint. *Publishes*
scholarly books in the fields of history, social
sciences and humanities. About 45 titles a year.
No unsolicited mss. Synopses and ideas for
books welcome.
Royalties paid annually.

Berkswell Publishing Co. Ltd

PO Box 420, Warminster, Wiltshire
BA12 9XB
☎01985 840189   Fax 01985 840189

Managing Director *John Stidolph*
Approx. Annual Turnover £250,000

FOUNDED 1974. *Publishes* illustrated books,
royalty, heritage, country sports, biography and
books about Wessex. No fiction. About 4 titles
a year. Unsolicited mss, synopses and ideas for
books welcome.
Royalties paid according to contract.

Berlitz Publishing Co. Ltd

4th Floor, 9–13 Grosvenor Street, London
W1X 9FB
☎0171 518 8300   Fax 0171 518 8310

Chairman *H. Yokoi*
Managing Director *R. Kirkpatrick*

FOUNDED 1970. Part of Berlitz International,
which also comprises language instruction and
translation divisions. *Publishes* travel and lan-
guage-learning products only: travel guides,
phrasebooks and language courses. TITLES

*Pocket Guides; Berlitz Complete Guide to Cruising
and Cruise Ships; Business Phrase Books; Berlitz
Live.* No unsolicited mss.

BFI Publishing

British Film Institute, 21 Stephen Street,
London W1P 2LN
☎0171 255 1444   Fax 0171 436 7950

Head of Publishing *Andrew Lockett*
Head of Sales *John Atkinson*
Approx. Annual Turnover £500,000

FOUNDED 1982. Part of the **British Film
Institute**. *Publishes* academic and general film/
television-related books. About 30 titles a year.
TITLES *Film Classics* (series); *Modern Classics*
(series); *The Avengers* Toby Miller; *The British
Cinema Book* Robert Murphy; *BFI Film &
Television Handbook* (annual) Eddie Dyja. Unsoli-
cited synopses and ideas preferred to complete
mss.
Royalties paid annually.

BFP Books

Focus House, 497 Green Lanes, London
N13 4BP
☎0181 882 3315   Fax 0181 886 5174

Chief Executive *John Tracy*
Commissioning Editor *Stewart Gibson*

FOUNDED 1982. The publishing arm of the
Bureau of Freelance Photographers. *Publishes*
illustrated books on photography, mainly
aspects of freelancing and marketing pictures.
No unsolicited mss but ideas welcome.

Clive Bingley Books

See **Library Association Publishing Ltd**

A. & C. Black (Publishers) Ltd

35 Bedford Row, London WC1R 4JH
☎0171 242 0946   Fax 0171 831 8478

Chairman *Charles Black*
Deputy Chairman *David Gadsby*
Managing Directors *Charles Black,
   Jill Coleman*
Approx. Annual Turnover £7.1 million

Publishes children's and educational books,
including music, for 3–15-year-olds, arts and
crafts, ceramics, fishing, ornithology, nautical,
reference, sport, theatre and travel. About 125
titles a year. Acquisitions brought the Herbert
Press' art, design and general books, Adlard
Coles' sailing list and Christopher Helm's natural history and ornithology lists into A. & C.
Black's stable.

IMPRINTS **Adlard Coles Nautical; The
Herbert Press; Christopher Helm.** TITLES

New Mermaid drama series; *Who's Who; Writers' & Artists' Yearbook; Know the Game* sports series; *Blue Guides* travel series. Initial enquiry appreciated before submission of mss.

Royalties payment varies according to contract.

Black Ace Books

PO Box 6557, Forfar DD8 2YS
☎01307 465096   Fax 01307 465494
Managing Director *Hunter Steele, Boo Wood*
FOUNDED 1991. *Publishes* new fiction, Scottish and general; some non-fiction including biography, history, philosophy and psychology. 32 titles in print. IMPRINTS **Black Ace Books, Black Ace Paperbacks** TITLES *Succeeding at Sex and Scotland, Or the Case of Louis Morel* Hunter Steele; *Spitfire Girls* Carol Gould; *Count Dracula (The Authorized Version)* Hagen Slawkberg. Completed books only. No unsolicited mss. No submissions from outside UK. 'Send only: 1-page covering letter, 1-page synopsis, 1 full page of text and large s.a.e. If possible, include 1-page recommendation from suitable referee such as published author, book reviewer or university teacher of literature. No poetry, children's, cookery, DIY, religion.'
Royalties paid twice-yearly.

Black Dagger Crime

See **Chivers Press Ltd**

Black Lace

See **Virgin Publishing Ltd**

Black Spring Press Ltd

2nd Floor, 126 Cornwall Road, London SE1 8TQ
☎0171 401 2044   Fax 0171 401 2055
Directors *Simon Pettifar, Maja Prausnitz*
FOUNDED 1986. *Publishes* fiction, literary criticism, biography, theatre and cinema studies. About 5 titles a year. TITLES *King Ink 2* Nick Cave; *The Mortdecai Trilogy* Kyril Bonfiglioli; *The Lost Weekend* Charles Jackson; *Beautiful Losers* Leonard Cohen; *The Terrible News* collection of Russian short stories by Zamyatin, Babel, Kharms, *et al.* No unsolicited mss.
Royalties paid twice-yearly.

Black Swan

See **Transworld Publishers Ltd**

Blackstaff Press Ltd

3 Galway Park, Dundonald, Belfast BT16 0AN
☎01232 487161   Fax 01232 489552
Director/Editorial Head *Anne Tannahill*

FOUNDED 1971. *Publishes* mainly, but not exclusively, Irish interest books, fiction, poetry, history, politics, illustrated editions, natural history and humour. About 25 titles a year. Unsolicited mss considered, but preliminary submission of synopsis plus short sample of writing preferred. Return postage *must* be enclosed.
Royalties paid twice-yearly.

Authors' Rating Past winner of the *Sunday Times* Small Publisher of the Year Award, this Belfast publisher is noted for a strong backlist, 'wonderfully well-presented catalogues and promotional material'.

Blackwell Publishers Ltd

108 Cowley Road, Oxford OX4 1JF
☎01865 791100   Fax 01865 791347
Chairman *Nigel Blackwell*
Managing Director *René Olivieri*
Approx. Annual Turnover £23.7 million
FOUNDED 1922. Rapid growth since the 1970s included the establishment of a wholly owned distribution company, Marston Book Services, a joint venture with **Polity Press** (see entry). The focus is on international research journals and undergraduate textbooks in social sciences, business and humanities; computer-aided instruction on p.c. applications. About 300 titles a year and over 150 journals.

DIVISIONS
Books *Philip Carpenter, Stephan Chambers*
Journals *Sue Corbett, Claire Andrews.* Unsolicited synopses with specimen chapter and table of contents welcome.
Royalties paid annually. *Overseas associates* Blackwell Publishers Inc., Cambridge, Massachusetts; InfoSource Inc., Orlando, Florida.

Authors' Rating Investing heavily in computer-based training for the further and higher education markets, Blackwell is putting its faith in a booming US market where is owns InfoSource, a computer training company. The US now accounts for more than half of the company's turnover.

Blackwell Science Ltd

Osney Mead, Oxford OX2 0EL
☎01865 206206   Fax 01865 721205
Chairman *Nigel Blackwell*
Managing Director *Robert Campbell*
Editorial Director *Peter Saugman*
Approx. Annual Turnover (Group) £105 million
FOUNDED 1939. Rapid growth since the 1970s culminated with expansion into Europe in the

late 1980s with the acquisition of Medizinische Zeitschriften Verlagsgesellschaft (MZV), Vienna; Ueberreuter Wissenschaft Verlag (now Blackwell Wissenschafts-Verlag), Berlin; more recently, Grosse Verlag, Germany; and the academic publishing of Paul Parey. Also 75% owner of Danish general publisher Munksgaard. *Publishes* medical, professional and science. About 300 titles a year, plus 225 journals. TITLES *Diseases of the Liver and Biliary System* Sherlock; *Essential Immunology* Roitt; *Textbook of Dermatology* Rook. Unsolicited mss and synopses welcome.

Royalties paid annually. *Overseas subsidiaries* in USA, Australia, Japan, Paris, Berlin and Vienna; editorial offices in London and Edinburgh.

Authors' Rating Blackwell Science's main business is in scientific journals, mostly produced in partnership with learned societies, and medical publishing. Much of the growth is in mainland Europe where Blackwell Science has offshoots in Berlin, Paris and Vienna.

Blake Publishing
3 Bramber Court, 2 Bramber Road, London W14 9PB
☎0171 381 0666   Fax 0171 381 6868
Chairman *David Blake*
Managing Director *John Blake*
Approx. Annual Turnover £1 million
FOUNDED 1991 and rapidly expanding. Bought the assets of **Smith Gryphon Ltd** in 1997 when that publishing house went into receivership. *Publishes* mass-market non-fiction. No cookery, children's, specialist or non-commercial. About 22 titles a year. No unsolicited mss; synopses and ideas welcome. Please enclose s.a.e.
Royalties paid twice-yearly.

Authors' Rating Unashamedly mass-market with its celebrity titles, Blake has taken another step towards the big time with the acquisition of the Smith Gryphon list.

Blandford Press
See **Cassell**

Bloodaxe Books Ltd
PO Box 1SN, Newcastle upon Tyne NE99 1SN
☎01830 520590   Fax 01830 520596
Chairman *Simon Thirsk*
Managing/Editorial Director *Neil Astley*
Publishes poetry, literature and criticism, and related titles by British, Irish, European,

Commonwealth and American writers. 95 per cent of their list is poetry. About 50 titles a year. TITLES include two major anthologies, *The New Poetry* Hulse, Kennedy and Morley (eds); *Sixty Women Poets* Linda France (ed); *The Gaze of the Gorgon* Tony Harrison – winner of the **Whitbread Award** for poetry in 1992; *No Truth With the Furies* R. S. Thomas (**Nobel Prize** nominee); *Selected Poems* Jenny Joseph; recent collections by Selima Hill, Helen Dunmore and Peter Reading. Unsolicited poetry mss welcome; send a sample of no more than 10 poems, 'but if you don't read contemporary poetry, don't bother'. Authors of other material should write in the first instance.
Royalties paid annually.

Authors' Rating Assisted by regional Arts Council funding, Bloodaxe is one of the liveliest and most innovative of poetry publishers with a list that takes in some of the best of the younger poets.

Bloomsbury Publishing Plc
38 Soho Square, London W1V 5DF
☎0171 494 2111   Fax 0171 434 0151
Chairman/Managing Director *Nigel Newton*
Publishing Directors *Liz Calder, David Reynolds, Kathy Rooney, Alan Wherry Matthew Hamilton, Sarah Odedina*
Approx. Annual Turnover £13.7 million
FOUNDED 1986 by Nigel Newton, David Reynolds, Alan Wherry and Liz Calder. Over the following years Bloomsbury titles were to appear regularly on *The Sunday Times* bestseller list and many of its authors have gone on to win prestigious literary prizes: in 1991 Nadine Gordimer won the **Nobel Prize for Literature**; Michael Ondaatje's *The English Patient* won the 1992 **Booker Prize**; Tobias Wolff's *In Pharaoh's Army* won the Esquire/Volvo/Waterstone Non-Fiction Award in 1994; in 1997 Anne Michaels' *Fugitive Pieces* won both the **Orange Prize for Fiction** and the **Guardian Fiction Prize**, Joanna Traynor's *Sister Josephine* won the **SAGA Prize**, J.K. Rowling's *Harry Potter and the Philosopher's Stone* won the **Smarties Book Prize** and Jane Urquhart's *The Underpainter* won the Governor General's Prize in Canada.
Publishes literary fiction and non-fiction, including general reference. AUTHORS include Margaret Atwood, T. Coraghessan Boyle, Daniel Goleman, David Guterson, John Irving, Jay McInerney, Will Self, Hunter S. Thompson, Rupert Thomson and Joanna

Trollope. Unsolicited mss and synopses welcome; no poetry.

Royalties paid twice-yearly.

Authors' Rating A tough home market might be expected to squeeze a middle-range company like Bloomsbury but it has beaten the trend by scaling back the general list to invest in a few bestsellers while nurturing the bread and butter publishing such as reference and children's books.

Boatswain Press
See **Kenneth Mason Publications Ltd**

Bobcat
See **Omnibus Press**

Bodley Head
See **Random House UK Ltd**

The Book Guild Ltd
Temple House, 25 High Street, Lewes, East Sussex BN7 2LU
☎01273 472534   Fax 01273 476472
E-mail: info@bookguild.co.uk
Website: www.bookguild.co.uk
Chairman *George M. Nissen CBE*
Managing Director *Carol Biss*

FOUNDED 1982. *Publishes* fiction, human interest, children's fiction, academic, naval and military, autobiography, art. Approx. 90 titles a year. Expanding mainstream list, plus developing the human interest genre.

DIVISIONS/TITLES
Children's *Underneath the Underground Books 1&2* Anthea Turner and Wendy Turner. **Human Interest** *A Matter of Timing: Dealing with Alzheimer's* Audrey Brown. **Biography** *Tony Hancock's Last Stand* Edward Joffe; **Cookery** *The Absolutely Animal-Free Cookbook* Wendy Turner. **Travel** *History & Legends of European Waterways* Roger Pilkington. **Fiction** *An Ecstasy of Fumbling* Mark Stewart-Jones; *The Printer's Daughter* Valerie Gray. **Military** *Keep Your Head Down* Bernie Bruen. ·IMPRINTS **Temple House Books** Nonfiction: *The Fitzroy* Sally Fiber; *Colditz, Last Stop* Jack Pringle. Unsolicited mss, ideas and synopses welcome.

Royalties paid twice-yearly.

Authors' Rating Regularly advertises for authors who may be asked to cover their own production costs. But in promoting its services, The Book Guild is more up-front with its clients than the typical vanity publisher who promises the earth and delivers next to nothing.

The Book Guild has even been known to turn down large cheques attached to manuscripts. Last year, a novel called *Percy Longprong* was rejected because it was 'full of gratuitous sex and violence', a decision which prompted the disappointed author, who had offered £7,500 towards production costs, to stage a protest outside the publisher's office.

Boulevard Books & The Babel Guides
8 Aldbourne Road, London W12 0LN
☎0181 743 5278   Fax 0181 743 5278
E-mail: raybabel@dircon.co.uk
Website: www.raybabel.users.dircon.co.uk
Managing Director *Ray Keenoy*

Specialises in contemporary world fiction by young writers in English translation. Existing or forthcoming series of fiction from Brazil, Italy, Latin America, Low Countries, Greece, and elsewhere. The Babel Guides series of popular guides to fiction in translation started in 1995.

DIVISIONS
Latin American *Ray Keenoy* TITLE *Hotel Atlantico* J. G. Noll. **Italian** *Fiorenza Conte* TITLE *The Toy Catalogue* Sandra Petrignani. **Brazil** *Dr David Treece* TITLE *From the Heart of Brazil* (anthology). **Low Countries** *Prof. Theo Hermans*. **Greece** *Marina Coriolano-Likourezos*. **Babel Guides to Fiction in Translation** *Ray Keenoy* Series Editor *Titles Babel Guide to Italian Fiction in Translation; Babel Guide to the Fiction of Portugal, Brazil & Africa in Translation; Babel Guide to French Fiction in English Translation; Babel Guide to Jewish Fiction.*

Suggestions and proposals for translations of contemporary fiction welcome. Also seeking contributors to forthcoming Babel Guides (all literatures).

Royalties paid twice-yearly.

Bowker–Saur Ltd
Maypole House, Maypole Road, East Grinstead, West Sussex RH19 1HU
☎01342 330100   Fax 01342 330191
Group Publishing Director *Gerard Dummett*
Managing Director *Charles Halpin*
Publishers *Geraldine Turpie, Yolanda Dolling*

Owned by Reed Elsevier, Bowker-Saur is part of Reed Business Information in the UK. *Publishes* library reference, library science, bibliography, biography, African studies, politics and world affairs, business and professional directories. Unsolicited mss will not be read. Approach with ideas only.

Royalties paid annually.

Boxtree
See **Macmillan Publishers Ltd**

Marion Boyars Publishers Ltd
24 Lacy Road, London SW15 1NL
☎0181 788 9522   Fax 0181 789 8122
Managing Director/Editorial Director
Marion Boyars
Editor, Non-fiction *Ken Hollings*
FOUNDED 1975, formerly Calder and Boyars.
Publishes biography and autobiography, economics, fiction, literature and criticism, medical, music, philosophy, poetry, politics and world affairs, psychology, sociology and anthropology, theatre and drama, film and cinema, women's studies. About 30 titles a year. AUTHORS include Georges Bataille, Ingmar Bergman, Heinrich Böll, Hortense Calisher, Jean Cocteau, Clive Collins, Warwick Collins, Carlo Gébler, Julian Green, Ivan Illich, Pauline Kael, Ken Kesey, Kenzaburo Oe, Michael Ondaatje, Hubert Selby, Igor Stravinsky, Frederic Tuten, Eudora Welty, Judith Williamson, Tom Wiseman. Unsolicited mss not welcome for fiction; submissions from agents preferred. Unsolicited synopses and ideas welcome for non-fiction.
Royalties paid annually. *Overseas associates* Marion Boyars Publishers Inc., 237 East 39th Street, New York, NY 10016, USA.

Authors' Rating Marion Boyars caters exclusively for the intellectual top end of the book market. Authors who favour blockbusters should look elsewhere.

Boydell & Brewer Ltd
PO Box 9, Woodbridge, Suffolk IP12 3DF
☎01394 411320

Publishes non-fiction only, principally medieval studies. All books commissioned. No unsolicited material.

BPS Books
St Andrews House, 48 Princess Road East, Leicester LE1 7DR
☎0116 2549568   Fax 0116 2470787
Publications Manager *Joyce Collins*
Editor *Susan Pacitti*
Book publishing division of The British Psychological Society. *Publishes* a wide range of academic and applied psychology, including specialist monographs, textbooks for teachers, managers, doctors, nurses, social workers, and schools material; plus general psychology and some electronic publishing. 10–15 titles a year. Proposals considered.

Bradt Publications
41 Nortoft Road, Chalfont St Peter, Buckinghamshire SL9 0LA
☎01494 873478   Fax 01484 873478
E-mail: bradtpublications@compuserve.com
Managing Director *Hilary Bradt*
Editorial Head *Tricia Hayne*
Approx. Annual Turnover £300,000
FOUNDED in 1974 by Hilary Bradt. *Specialises* in travel guides to off-beat places. 13 titles in 1997. TITLES *Guide to Ethiopia; Madagascar; Zanzibar; Cuba* etc.; *Wildlife Guide to Madagascar; Antarctica; Rail Guide to USA; Greece; India; Backpacking Guides; By Road Guides; Climbing and Hiking in Ecuador.* No unsolicited mss; synopses and ideas for travel guidebooks welcome.
Royalties paid twice-yearly.

Authors' Rating Winner of the 1997 *Sunday Times* **Small Publisher of the Year** award.

Brampton Publications
See **SB Publications**

Brassey's (UK) Ltd
583 Fulham Road, London SW6 5BY
☎0171 471 1100   Fax 0171 471 1101
Chief Executive *Jules Perel*
Approx. Annual Turnover £2.5 million
Began life as *Brassey's Naval Annual* in 1886 to become the most important publisher of serious defence-related material in the world. Acquired by Batsford Communications, parent company of **B. T. Batsford**, in April 1998. *Publishes* books and journals on defence, international relations, military history, maritime and aeronautical subjects and defence terminology. Further sports titles are being published under the **Brassey's Sports** imprint in both the UK and US.
IMPRINTS **Brassey's (UK)**; **Brassey's Inc**; **Brassey's Sports**; **Conway Maritime Press** Naval history and ship modelling; **Putnam Aeronautical Books** Technical and reference.
Royalties paid annually.

Nicholas Brealey Publishing Ltd
36 John Street, London WC1N 2AT
☎0171 430 0224   Fax 0171 404 8311
Managing Director *Nicholas Brealey*
Website: http://www.nbrealey-books.co
FOUNDED 1992 with a backlist of major titles from The Industrial Society. Independent non-fiction publisher focusing on high-profile, practical books for business that inspire, enable,

inform and entertain. *Publishes* on the 'big picture', management, training and human resources. 20 titles a year. TITLES *Coaching for Performance; The 80/20 Principle; Reengineering the Corporation; NLP at Work; Megatrends Asia; The Fifth Discipline Fieldbook; China Wakes; Rethinking the Future; Intellectual Capital.* No fiction, poetry or leisure titles. No unsolicited mss; synopses and ideas welcome.
Royalties paid twice-yearly.

Authors' Rating A recent entry into the booming management book market, Nicholas Brealey looks to be succeeding in breaking away from the usual computer-speak business manuals to publish information and literate texts. Lead titles have a distinct trans-Atlantic feel.

The Breedon Books Publishing Co. Ltd
44 Friar Gate, Derby DE1 1DA
☎01332 384235   Fax 01332 292755
Chairman/Managing Director
   A. C. Rippon
Approx. Annual Turnover £1 million
FOUNDED 1983. *Publishes* autobiography, biography, local history, old photographs, heritage and sport. 40 titles in 1997. Unsolicited mss, synopses and ideas welcome if accompanied by s.a.e. No poetry or fiction.
Royalties paid annually.

Breese Books Ltd
164 Kensington Park Road, London W11 2ER
☎0171 727 9426   Fax 0171 229 3395
E-mail: MBreese999@aol.com
Chairman/Managing Director *Martin Ranicar-Breese*
FOUNDED 1975 to produce specialist conjuring books and then went on to establish a more general list. Breese Books has now closed its general publishing division and is concentrating on two specific areas: conjuring/sleight of hand/illusions and Sherlock Holmes pastiches. There is little point in submitting material on any subjects other than the above.

Authors' Rating Having cut back on his publishing programme, Martin Breese is offering a **Critical Eye Service** to advise authors on how to make their work saleable. There are no guarantees of publication and there is a charge but for some, straight practical advice may be useful.

Brimax Books
See **Reed Books**

Bristol Classical Press
See **Gerald Duckworth & Co. Ltd**

British Academic Press
See **I. B. Tauris & Co. Ltd**

The British Academy
10 Carlton House Terrace, London SW1Y 5AH
☎0171 969 5200   Fax 0171 969 5300
Publications Officer *J. M. H. Rivington*
Publications Assistant *J. English*
FOUNDED 1901. The primary body for promoting scholarship in the humanities, the Academy publishes many series stemming from its own long-standing research projects, or series of lectures and conference proceedings. Main subjects include history, philosophy and archaeology. About 10–15 titles a year. SERIES *Auctores Britannici Medii Aevi; Early English Church Music; Fontes Historiae Africanae; Records of Social and Economic History.* Proposals for these series are welcome and are forwarded to the relevant project committees. The British Academy is a registered charity and does not publish for profit.
Royalties paid only when titles have covered their costs.

The British Library
96 Euston Road, London NW1 2DB
☎0171 412 7704   Fax 0171 412 7768
Managing Director *Jane Carr*
Publishing Manager *David Way*
Approx. Annual Turnover £750,000
FOUNDED 1979 as the publishing arm of The British Library's London Collections to publish works based on the historic collections and related subjects. *Publishes* bibliographical reference, manuscript studies, illustrated books based on the Library's collections, and book arts. TITLES *The Illuminated Page: Ten Centuries of Manuscript Paintings; New Found Lands: Maps in the History of Exploration; The British Library Writers' Lives Series; Medieval Medicine in Illuminated Manuscripts.* About 30 titles a year. Unsolicited mss, synopses and ideas welcome if related to the history of the book, book arts or bibliography. No fiction or general non-fiction.
Royalties paid annually.

British Museum Press
46 Bloomsbury Street, London WC1B 3QQ
☎0171 323 1234   Fax 0171 436 7315
Managing Director *Patrick Wright*
Head of Publishing *Emma Way*

The book publishing division of The British Museum Company Ltd. FOUNDED 1973 as British Museum Publications Ltd; relaunched 1991 as British Museum Press. *Publishes* ancient history, archaeology, ethnography, art history, exhibition catalogues, guides, children's books, and all official publications of the British Museum. Around 50 titles a year. TITLES *The Discovery of the Past; Making Faces; Money: a History; Pottery in the Making; Early Celtic Designs.* Synopses and ideas for books welcome.
Royalties paid twice-yearly.

The Brockhampton Press
See **Hodder Headline plc**

John Brown Publishing Ltd
The New Boathouse, 136–142 Bramley Road, London W10 6SR
☎0171 565 3000   Fax 0171 565 3053
Chairman/Managing Director *John Brown*

FOUNDED 1986. *Publishes* adult comic annuals; *Viz* magazine; strange phenomena. 10 titles in 1997.

DIVISION **Fortean Times Books** *Mike Dash* TITLES *Book of Weird Sex; Book of Strange Deaths; Book of Inept Crime; Book of Exploding Pigs; Weird Year 1999; Fortean Studies Vol 4; UFO Mystery.* Does not welcome unsolicited mss.
Royalties paid twice-yearly.

Brown, Son & Ferguson, Ltd
4–10 Darnley Street, Glasgow G41 2SD
☎0141 429 1234   Fax 0141 420 1694
E-mail: info@skipper.co.uk
Website: http://www.skipper.co.uk
Chairman/Joint Managing Director *T. Nigel Brown*

FOUNDED 1850. *Specialises* in nautical textbooks, both technical and non-technical. Also Boy Scout/Girl Guide books, and Scottish one-act/three-act plays. Unsolicited mss, synopses and ideas for books welcome.
Royalties paid annually.

Bucknell University Press
See **Golden Cockerel Press Ltd**

Burns & Oates
See **Search Press**

Business Education Publishers Ltd
Leighton House, 10 Grange Crescent, Sunderland, Tyne & Wear SR2 7BN
☎0191 567 4963   Fax 0191 514 3277
Managing Director *P. M. Callaghan*
Approx. Annual Turnover £400,000

FOUNDED 1981. *Publishes* business education, economics and law for BTEC and GNVQ reading. Currently expanding into further and higher education, computing, community health services, travel and tourism, occasional papers for institutions and local government administration. Unsolicited mss and synopses welcome.
Royalties paid annually.

Butterworth-Heinemann International
See **Reed Educational & Professional Publishing**

Cadogan Books plc
3rd Floor, 27–29 Berwick Street, London W1V 3RF
☎0171 287 6555   Fax 0171 734 1733
Managing Director *Bill Colegrave*
Publisher, Cadogan Guides & Chess *Rachel Fielding*
Approx. Annual Turnover £4.4 million

Publishes the *Cadogan Travel Guide* series and chess titles. About 55 titles a year. No unsolicited mss; send introductory letter with synopsis only. Synopses and ideas welcome. Merged with **David Campbell Publishers Ltd** in 1995 (see entry).
Royalties paid twice-yearly.

Calder Publications Ltd
126 Cornwall Road, London SE1 8TQ
☎0171 633 0599
Chairman/Managing Director/Editorial Head *John Calder*

Formerly John Calder (Publishers) Ltd. A publishing company which has grown around the tastes and contacts of John Calder, the iconoclast of the literary establishment. The list has a reputation for controversial and opinion-forming publications; Samuel Beckett is perhaps the most prestigious name. The list includes all of Beckett's prose and poetry. *Publishes* autobiography, biography, drama, literary fiction, literary criticism, music, opera, poetry, politics, sociology. AUTHORS Roy Calne, Marguerite Duras, Erich Fried, Trevor Hoyle, P. J. Kavanagh, Robert Pinget, Alain Robbe-Grillet, Nathalie

Sarraute, Julian Semyonov, Claude Simon, Howard Barker (plays), ENO opera guides. *No new material accepted.*
Royalties paid annually.

Authors' Rating Operating in Paris and London and points between, John Calder is said to be 'overflowing with geniuses and eccentric talents'. But according to the publisher, times are hard and there is never enough money to pay all the bills. He is much revered in France as a free and far-ranging intellectual.

California University Press
See **University Presses of California, Columbia & Princeton Ltd**

Cambridge University Press
The Edinburgh Building, Shaftesbury Road, Cambridge CB2 2RU
☎01223 312393   Fax 01223 315052
Chief Executive *A. K. Wilson*
Managing Director, Publishing
  R. J. Mynott

The oldest printer and publisher in the world with established branches in the USA and Australia. Winner of The Queen's Award for Export Achievement in 1998. Over the last ten years, Cambridge has opened 15 new offices around the world and established a new branch in Madrid. Its books are sold in more than 200 countries. Publications include the Cambridge Histories and Companions, encyclopedias and dictionaries; the **Canto** series; popular science and scientific and medical reference; major ELT courses; coursebooks for the National Curriculum; Cambridge Reading; and Cambridge Low Price Editions for the developing world. *Publishes* academic/educational and reference books for English-language markets worldwide, at all levels from primary school to postgraduate. Also ELT, Bibles and over 140 academic journals. Over 23,000 authors in 106 different countries and about 1800 new titles a year.

PUBLISHING GROUPS
Bibles *C. J. Wright* **ELT** *C. J. F. Hayes* **Education** *A. C. Gilfillan* **Humanities and Social Sciences** *A. M. C. Brown* **Medical and Professional Publishing** *R. W. A. Barling* **Journals** *C. Guettler* **Science Publishing** *A. E. Crowden.* Synopses and ideas for educational, ELT and academic books are welcomed (and preferable to the submission of unsolicited mss). No fiction or poetry.
Royalties paid twice-yearly.

Authors' Rating Not so many monographs from the obscure corners of academia but CUP has adapted to changing times and shrinking library budgets by expanding into reference, English Language Teaching and foreign language publishing.

Camden Large Print
See **Chivers Press Ltd**

David Campbell Publishers Ltd
79 Berwick Street, London W1V 3PF
☎0171 287 0035   Fax 0171 287 0038
Chairman *Alewyn Birch*
Managing Director *David Campbell*
Approx. Annual Turnover £3.5 million

FOUNDED 1990 with the acquisition of **Everyman's Library** (established 1906) bought from **J. M. Dent.** Now merged with **Cadogan Books plc.** *Publishes* classics of world literature, pocket poetry anthologies, music companion guides and travel guides. AUTHORS include Bulgakov, Bellow, Borges, Forster, Grass, Mann, Nabokov, Orwell, Rushdie, Updike and Waugh. No unsolicited mss. IMPRINT **Adelphi** Illustrated books.
Royalties paid annually.

Campbell Books
See **Macmillan Publishers Ltd**

Candle Books
See **Angus Hudson** under **UK Packagers**

Canongate Books Ltd
14 High Street, Edinburgh EH1 1TE
☎0131 557 5111   Fax 0131 557 5211
Joint Managing Directors *Jamie Byng, Hugh Andrew*
Approx. Annual Turnover £1.5 million

FOUNDED 1973. Independent again, following a management buyout in September 1994. *Publishes* a wide range of fiction and non-fiction. There is a strong Scottish slant to part of the house. Also have an audio list (see entry under **Audio Books**).

IMPRINTS **Canongate Classics** Adult paperback series dedicated solely to important works of Scottish literature; **Kelpie** Children's paperback fiction series; **Payback Press** Afro-American, Black orientated fiction and non-fiction; music, history, politics, biography and poetry; **Rebel Inc.** promotion of new writing – fiction, poetry and non-fiction – as well as underground and neglected classics. About 60 titles a year. Prefers to see synopses rather than complete mss.

Royalties paid twice-yearly.

Authors' Rating A company led by young talent with enthusiasm for bright and original ideas.

Canterbury Press Norwich
See **Hymns Ancient & Modern Ltd**

Canto
See **Cambridge University Press**

Capall Bann Publishing
Freshfields, Chieveley, Berkshire
RG20 8TF
☎01635 247050/248711
Fax 01635 247050/248711

Chairman *Julia Day*
Editorial Head *Jon Day*

FOUNDED 1993 with three titles and now have over 100 in print. Family-owned and -run company which *publishes* British traditions, folklore, computing, boating, animals, environmental, Celtic lore, mind, body and spirit. 40 titles in 1997. TITLES *Practical Spirituality; Celtic Lore; Handbook of Fairies; Talking to the Earth; Bruce Roberts' Boatbuilding.* Synopses and ideas for books welcome. No fiction or poetry.

Royalties paid quarterly.

Jonathan Cape Ltd
See **Random House UK Ltd**

Carcanet Press Ltd
Conavon Court, 12–16 Blackfriars Street, Manchester M3 5BQ
☎0161 834 8730   Fax 0161 832 0084

Chairman *Kate Gavron*
Managing Director/Editorial Director
Michael Schmidt

Since 1969 Carcanet has grown from an undergraduate hobby into a substantial venture. Robert Gavron bought the company in 1983 and it has established strong Anglo-European and Anglo-Commonwealth links. *Publishes* poetry, academic, literary biography, fiction in translation and translations. About 50 titles a year, including the *P. N. Review* (six issues yearly). AUTHORS John Ashbery, Edwin Morgan, Elizabeth Jennings, Iain Crichton Smith, Natalia Ginzburg, Eavan Boland, Stuart Hood, Leonardo Sciascia, Christine Brooke-Rose, Pier Paolo Pasolini, C. H. Sisson, Donald Davie.

Royalties paid annually.

Authors' Rating One of the four leading poetry publishers, Carcanet combines quality with profit. William Boyd says of Carcanet that it is 'everything an independent publisher should be'.

Cardiff Academic Press
St Fagans Road, Fairwater, Cardiff CF5 3AE
☎01222 560333   Fax 01222 554909

Marketing Manager *Mary de Lange*
Academic publishers.

Carlton Books Ltd
20 St Anne's Court, Wardour Street, London W1V 3AW
☎0171 734 7338
Fax 0171 434 1196/0171 734 7371

Managing Director *Jonathan Goodman*
Approx. Annual Turnover £11 million

FOUNDED 1992. Owned by Carlton Communications, Carlton books are aimed at the mass market for subjects such as computer games, sport, health, puzzles, popular science and rock'n'roll. *Publishes* illustrated leisure and entertainment. Prime UK customers include the Book Club and W H Smith. A second arm of the company, established late 1992, was set up to create a promotional books business. No unsolicited mss; synopses and ideas welcome.

Royalties paid twice-yearly.

Authors' Rating Linked to the largest programme producer in the ITV network, Carlton Books has built a reputation on co-editions for the international market. Now it is moving into television tie-ins. Noted for speed of taking a book from first idea to publication.

Frank Cass & Co Ltd
Newbury House, 890–900 Eastern Avenue, Newbury Park, Ilford, Essex IG2 7HH
☎0181 599 8866   Fax 0181 599 0984

Managing Director *Frank Cass*
Managing Editor *Andrew Humphrys (Book Editor)*

Publishes books and journals in the fields of politics, international relations, military and security studies, history, Middle East and African studies, economics, development studies and law. TITLES *Central Asia Meets the Middle East* ed. David Henashin; *In Pursuite of Military Excellence* Shimon Naveh; *Knowing Your Friends* Martin S. Alexander; *Nothing Sacred* David Alvarez and Robert A. Graham; *The Liberian Civil War* Mark Huband; *Regional Dynamics* William Field.

DIVISIONS
Woburn Press Educational list TITLES *Her Majesty's Inspectorate of Schools Since 1944* John E. Dunford; *Going Comprehensive in England and Wales* Alan C. Kercknoff. **Vallentine Mitchell/ Jewish Chronicle Publications** Books of Jewish interest TITLES *The Library of Holocaust Testimonies* series; *The Jewish Yearbook 1998* ed. Stephen Massil; *The Jewish Travel Guide; Soldier of Jerusalem* Uzi Narkiss. Unsolicited mss considered but synopsis with covering letter preferred.
Royalties paid annually.

Cassell
Wellington House, 125 Strand, London WC2R 0BB
☎0171 420 5555   Fax 0171 240 7261
Chairman/Managing Director *Philip Sturrock*
Approx. Annual Turnover £25 million
FOUNDED 1848 by John Cassell. Bought by Collier Macmillan in 1974, then by CBS Publishing Europe in 1982. Finally returned to independence in 1986 as Cassell plc and a string of acquisitions followed: Tycooly's book publishing division; Link House Books (now Blandford Publishing Ltd); Mansell; then Mowbray and Ward Lock, publisher of Mrs Beeton, (in print continuously since 1861); Victor Gollancz Ltd in 1992 and Pinter Publishers Ltd in February 1995. *Publishes* business, education and academic, general non-fiction, primary and secondary school books, poetry, religion. About 800 titles a year.

IMPRINTS
Cassell General Books *Alison Goff* TITLES *Poems on the Underground; Cordon Bleu Complete Cookery Techniques; Cacti: The Illustrated Dictionary; Shaker.* PAPERBACK IMPRINTS **Indigo** *Mike Petty;* **Vista** *Humphrey Price.*
    Cassell Academic Books *Janet Joyce, Naomi Roth* TITLES *Cassell Guide to Literature in French; Supervisory Management; Reflective Teaching in Primary Schools.*
    Mansell *Janet Joyce* TITLES *Index of English Literary Manuscripts; Facts About the Prime Ministers.*
    Arms & Armour Press *Alison Goff* TITLES *First World War Sourcebook; Napoleonic Weapons & Warfare; Great Battles of the Royal Navy.*
    Blandford Press *Alison Goff* TITLES *Make Your Own Electric Guitar; Celebration of Maritime Art; Spiders of the World; Celtic Art Sourcebook.*
    Ward Lock *Alison Goff* TITLES *Mrs Beeton's Book of Cookery and Household Management; Home & Garden Style; Ward Lock Gardening Encyclopedia.*

Victor Gollancz *Jane Blackstock* TITLES *Lost Gardens of Heligan; High Fidelity* Nick Hornby; *Hogfather* Terry Pratchett.
    Geoffrey Chapman *Ruth McCurry* TITLES *New Jerome Biblical Commentary; The Catechism of the Catholic Church; Storykeepers.*
    Mowbray *Ruth McCurry* TITLES *Why God* Bishop of Bath & Wells, Mervyn Stockwood.
    Leicester University Press *Janet Joyce* TITLES *Museums and Popular Culture; Language of Displayed Art; Medieval Fortifications.*
    Pinter *Janet Joyce* TITLES *States and Markets; European Union, Work for All?.*

Authors' Rating Notwithstanding a profitable sale of the children's list to **Penguin**, Cassell has had a difficult year with disappointing results for its midlist titles. Expect renewed emphasis on lead titles.

Castle Publications
See **Nottingham University Press**

Kyle Cathie Ltd
20 Vauxhall Bridge Road, London SW1V 2SA
☎0171 973 9710   Fax 0171 821 9258
Publisher/Managing Director *Kyle Cathie*
Sales/Marketing Director *Julia Scott*
FOUNDED 1990 to publish and promote 'books we have personal enthusiasm for'. *Publishes* non-fiction: history, natural history, health, biography, food and drink, craft, gardening and reference. TITLES *A Passion for Cheese* Paul Gayler; *The Beauty Bible* Sarah Stacey and Josephine Fairley; *The Handbook of Ayurveda* Dr Shantha Godagama. About 25 titles a year. No unsolicited mss. 'Synopses and ideas are considered in the fields in which we publish.'
Royalties paid twice-yearly.

Catholic Truth Society
40–46 Harleyford Road, London SE11 5AY
☎0171 640 0042   Fax 0171 640 0046
Chairman *Rt. Rev. Peter Smith*
General Secretary *Fergal Martin*
Approx. Annual Turnover £500,000
FOUNDED originally in 1869 and re-founded in 1884. *Publishes* religious books – Roman Catholic and ecumenical; a variety of doctrinal, moral, biographical, devotional and liturgical publications, including a large body of Vatican documents and sources. Unsolicited mss, synopses and ideas welcome if appropriate to their list.
Royalties paid annually.

Causeway Press Ltd

PO Box 13, 129 New Court Way, Ormskirk, Lancashire L39 5HP
☎01695 576048   Fax 01695 570714
Chairman/Managing Director *M. Haralambos*
Approx. Annual Turnover £2 million

FOUNDED in 1982. *Publishes* educational textbooks only. 15 titles in 1997. TITLES *Causeway Maths Series; Discovering History Series; Economics/ Business Studies; Sociology in Focus; Politics; Causeway GNVQ; Design and Technology.* Unsolicited mss, synopses and ideas welcome.
Royalties paid annually.

CBA Publishing

Bowes Morrell House, 111 Walmgate, York YO1 2UA
☎01904 671417   Fax 01904 671384
Managing Editor *Christine Pietrowski*
Approx. Annual Turnover £25,000

Publishing arm of the **Council for British Archaeology**. *Publishes* academic archaeology reports, practical handbooks, yearbook, *British Archaeology* (monthly magazine), *Young Archaeologist* (magazine of the Young Archaeologists' Club), monographs, archaeology and education. TITLES *Grave Concerns; St Bartholomew's Hospital; Excavations at Upwich; Recording Graveyards; Archaeology in the English National Curriculum.*
Royalties not paid.

CBD Research Ltd

Chancery House, 15 Wickham Road, Beckenham, Kent BR3 5JS
☎0181 650 7745   Fax 0181 650 0768
Chairman *G. P. Henderson*
Managing Director *S. P. A. Henderson*
Approx. Annual Turnover £300,000

FOUNDED 1961. *Publishes* directories and other reference guides to sources of information. About 6 titles a year. No fiction.
IMPRINT **Chancery House Press** Non-fiction of an esoteric/specialist nature for 'serious researchers and the dedicated hobbyist'. Unsolicited mss, synopses and ideas welcome.
Royalties paid quarterly.

Centaur Press

Fontwell, Arundel, West Sussex BN18 0TA
☎01243 543302
Managing Director *Jon Wynne-Tyson*

FOUNDED 1954. A one-man outfit publishing some 20 titles a year at its peak. Then became increasingly preoccupied with humane education and reduced output to around 5 titles a year. After a semi-dormant period in the 1980s, Centaur went on to launch *The Kinship Library*, a series on the philosophy, politics and application of humane education, with special focus on the subject of animal rights and its relevance to the human condition.
IMPRINT **Linden Press** TITLES *Life of H. D. Thoreau; The Universal Kinship; Publishing Your Own Book; Animals' Rights: a Symposium.*

Century

See **Random House UK Ltd**

Chadwyck-Healey Ltd

The Quorum, Barnwell Road, Cambridge CB5 8SW
☎01223 215512   Fax 01223 215513
Chairman *Sir Charles Chadwyck-Healey*
Managing Director *Steven Hall*
Approx. Annual Turnover £9.7 million

FOUNDED 1973. *Publishes* literary full-text and humanities reference databases on microform, CD-ROM and the World Wide Web. No monographs. About 50 titles a year. TITLES *Literature Online; The English Poetry Full-Text Database; Periodical Contents Index.* No unsolicited mss. Synopses and ideas welcome for reference works only.
Royalties paid annually.

Authors' Rating Another success story for niche publishing, Chadwyck-Healey has won two Export Achievement awards for its high price CD-ROM reference list aimed at the world library market. Now heavily occupied with on-line subscription services.

Chambers Harrap Publishers Ltd

See **Kingfisher Publications plc**

Chameleon

See **André Deutsch Ltd**

Chancery House Press

See **CBD Research Ltd**

Chansitor Publications Ltd

See **Hymns Ancient & Modern Ltd**

Geoffrey Chapman

See **Cassell**

Paul Chapman Publishing Ltd

See **Sage Publications Ltd**

Chapman Publishing

4 Broughton Place, Edinburgh EH1 3RX
☎0131 557 2207   Fax 0131 556 9565
Managing Editor *Joy Hendry*

A venture devoted to publishing works by the best of the Scottish writers, both up-and-coming and established, published in *Chapman* magazine, Scotland's leading literary quarterly. Has expanded publishing activities considerably over the last two years and is now publishing a wider range of works though the broad policy stands. *Publishes* poetry, drama, short stories, books of contemporary importance in 20th-century Scotland. About 4 titles a year. TITLES *Carlucco & the Queen of Hearts; The Blasphemer* George Rosie; *Gold of Kildonan; Songs of the Grey Coast; Whins* George Gunn; *The Collected Shorter Poems* Tom Scott; *Alien Crop* Janet Paisley; *Good Girls Don't Cry* Margaret Fulton Cook. No unsolicited mss; synopses and ideas for books welcome.
Royalties paid annually.

Chapmans Publishers
See **The Orion Publishing Group Ltd**

Chatham Publishing
See **Gerald Duckworth & Co Ltd**

Chatto & Windus Ltd
See **Random House UK Ltd**

Cherrytree Press Children's Books
See **Chivers Press Ltd**

Child's Play (International) Ltd

Ashworth Road, Bridgemead, Swindon, Wiltshire SN5 7YD
☎01793 616286   Fax 01793 512795
E-mail: allday@childs-play.com
Chairman *Michael Twinn*

FOUNDED in 1972, Child's Play is an independent publisher specialising in learning through play, whole child development, life-skills and values. *Publishes* books, games and A-V materials. TITLES *Big Hungry Bear; There Was An Old Lady; Puzzle Island; Children of the Sun; Ten Beads Tall; Pocket Pals and Great Pals*. Unsolicited mss welcome. Send s.a.e. for return or response. Expect to wait 2 months for a reply.
Royalties Outright or royalty payments are subject to negotiation.

Chivers Press Ltd

Windsor Bridge Road, Bath BA2 3AX
☎01225 335336   Fax 01225 310771
Managing Director *Julian R. Batson*

Approx. Annual Turnover £8.8 million

Part of the Gieves Group. *Publishes* reprints for libraries mainly, in large-print editions, including biography and autobiography, children's, crime, fiction and spoken word cassettes. No unsolicited material.

IMPRINTS **Chivers Large Print; Gunsmoke Westerns; Galaxy Children's Large Print; Camden Large Print; Paragon Softcover Large Print; Cherrytree Press Children's Books; Windsor Large Print; Black Dagger Crime. Chivers Audio Books** (see entry under **Audio Books**.

Royalties paid twice-yearly.

Christian Focus Publications

Geanies House, Fearn, Tain, Ross-shire IV20 1TW
☎01862 871541   Fax 01862 871699
Chairman *R. W. M. Mackenzie*
Managing Director *William Mackenzie*
Editorial Head *Malcolm Maclean*
Children's Editor *Hazel Scrimshire*
Approx. Annual Turnover £750,000

FOUNDED 1979 to produce children's books for the co-edition market. Now a major producer of Christian books. *Publishes* adult and children's books, including some fiction for children but not adults. No poetry. About 70 titles a year. Unsolicited mss, synopses and ideas welcome from Christian writers. Publishes for all English-speaking markets, as well as the UK. Books produced for Australia, USA, Canada, South Africa.

IMPRINTS **Christian Focus** General books; **Mentor** Specialist books; **Christian Heritage** Classic reprints.
Royalties paid twice-yearly.

Churchill Livingstone
See **Harcourt Brace and Company Limited**

Cicerone Press

2 Police Square, Milnthorpe, Cumbria LA7 7PY
☎015395 62069   Fax 015395 63417
Managing Director *Dorothy Unsworth*
Editorial Director *Walt Unsworth*

FOUNDED 1969. Guidebook publisher for outdoor enthusiasts. About 30 titles a year. No fiction or poetry. TITLES *A Trekker's Handbook*; various *Country Walking* guides; *LD Footpath Guides*. No unsolicited mss; synopses and ideas considered.
Royalties paid twice-yearly.

Citron Press

Suite 106, Business Design Centre,
52 Islington Green, London N1 0QH
☎0171 288 6024   Fax 0171 288 6196
E-mail: citronpress.co.uk
Managing Director *Nikki Connors*
Approx. Annual Turnover £700,000

The Citron Press New Authors' Co-operative
is a new venture established to enable a limited
number of previously unpublished authors of
fiction to see their books in print. Publications
are marketed by The Citron Press Book Club.
A membership fee of £399.95 is paid by
authors who join the Co-operative although
membership is not automatic. 'All submitted
mss are sub-edited and scored to evaluate quality of the work. If an author is not successful,
the membership fee is refunded in full.'
Royalties paid twice yearly.

Authors' Rating It might work. Citron Press is
an exercise in self publishing, albeit one that is
professionally managed and backed by some of
the best names in the business – Martin Amis,
John Mortimer and Michael Holroyd amongst
them. The idea is simple enough. If I have a
manuscript that has been rejected elsewhere, I
can sign up with Citron for £399.95 (my first
worry starts here; am I being played as a sucker
who does not know £400 when I see it?) for
which sum I will receive a considered judgement
on the book's commercial prospects. If the
answer is favourable, Citron will sell it as a paperback through its own book club. I get 20 free
copies, 15% discount on further copies and a
royalty of 7½% on however many copies other
members of the club are prepared to buy. The
deal has to be more attractive than anything the
vanity publishers can offer but there remains the
nagging doubt that an operation based exclusively on marketing new writing is viable in the
long term.

Clarendon Press
See **Oxford University Press**

Claridge Press
33 Canonbury Park South, London N1 2JW
☎0171 226 7791   Fax 0171 354 0383
Chairman/Managing Director/
 Editorial Head *Roger Scruton*
Managing Editor *Merrie Cave*
FOUNDED 1987. Developed from the quarterly
Salisbury Review (see entry under **Magazines**).
Publishes current affairs – political, philosophi-
cal and sociological – from a right-wing view-
point. SERIES *Thinkers of our Time.* TITLES

*Falsification of the Good; Understanding Youth;
KGB Lawsuits; Edmund Burke and Our Present
Discontents.* Unsolicited mss welcome within
given subject areas.
Royalties paid according to contract.

Clarion
See **Elliot Right Way Books**

T. & T. Clark
59 George Street, Edinburgh EH2 2LQ
☎0131 225 4703   Fax 0131 220 4260
Managing Director/Editorial Head
 Geoffrey Green
FOUNDED 1821. *Publishes* religion, theology, law
and philosophy, for academic and professional
markets. About 35 titles a year, including jour-
nals. TITLES *Church Dogmatics* Karl Barth; *A
Textbook of Christian Ethics* ed. Robin Gill;
*Scottish Law Directory; The Law of Contracts and
Related Obligations in Scotland* David M. Walker.
Unsolicited mss, synopses and ideas for books
welcome.
Royalties paid annually.

James Clarke & Co.
PO Box 60, Cambridge CB1 2NT
☎01223 350865   Fax 01223 366951
E-mail: lutterworth.pr@dial.pipex.com
Website: http://dialspace.dial.pipex.com/
 lutterworth.pr/
Managing Director *Adrian Brink*

Parent company of **The Lutterworth Press**.
Publishes scholarly and academic works, mainly
theological, directory and reference titles. TITLES
*The Encyclopedia of the Early Church; Faith and
Doubt: Religion and Secularisation in Literature from
Wordsworth to Larkin; The Libraries' Directory.*
Approach in writing with ideas in the first
instance.

Richard Cohen Books Ltd
The Basement Offices, 7 Manchester Square,
London W1M 5RE
☎0171 935 2099   Fax 0171 935 2199
Chairman/Managing Director
 Richard Cohen
Approx. Annual Turnover £1 million

FOUNDED in 1994. *Publishes* fiction, biography,
current affairs, travel, history, politics, the arts,
and sport. First titles published in 1995 with
plans to expand from 20 books a year to 30.
No erotica, DIY, children's, reference, science
fiction, fantasy, or historical romance.
 DIVISION **RCB General Books** *Richard
Cohen* TITLES *Memoirs* Al Alvarez; *Married Alive*

Julie Burchill; *Running Free* Robin Knox-Johnston; *Alastair Cooke* Nick Clarke. No unsolicited mss.

Royalties paid twice-yearly.

Authors' Rating Having by his own admission 'bought ahead too ambitiously', Richard Cohen has had to struggle to keep his fledgling list alive. But there is much sympathy and support for a gifted publisher who gets on well with authors.

Peter Collin Publishing Ltd

1 Cambridge Road, Teddington, Middlesex TW11 8DT
☎0181 943 3386   Fax 0181 943 1673
Chairman *P. H. Collin*

FOUNDED 1985. *Publishes* dictionaries only, including specialised dictionaries in English for students and specialised bilingual dictionaries for translators (French, German, Swedish, Spanish, Greek, Chinese, Hungarian). About 5 titles a year. Synopses and ideas welcome. No unsolicited mss; copy must be supplied on disk.

Royalties paid twice-yearly.

Collins

See **HarperCollins Publishers Ltd**

Collins & Brown

London House, Great Eastern Wharf, Parkgate Road, London SW11 4NQ
☎0171 924 2575   Fax 0171 924 7725
Chairman *Cameron Brown*
Publisher *Mark Collins*
Approx. Annual Turnover £12.3 million

FOUNDED 1989. Independent publisher. Acquired **Pavilion Books Ltd** in 1997 and **David Bennett Books** in 1998 (see entries). *Publishes* illustrated non-fiction: practical photography, crafts, gardening, decorating, lifestyle and cookery. No fiction, children's, poetry or local interest. About 40 titles a year. No unsolicited mss; outlines with s.a.e. only.

Royalties paid twice-yearly.

Colonsay Books

See **House of Lochar**

Columbia University Press

See **University Presses of California, Columbia & Princeton Ltd**

Concorde House Books

See **Angus Hudson** under **UK Packagers**

Condé Nast Books

See **Random House UK Ltd**

Condor

See **Souvenir Press Ltd**

Conran Octopus

See **Reed Books**

Constable & Co. Ltd

3 The Lanchesters, 162 Fulham Palace Road, London W6 9ER
☎0181 741 3663   Fax 0181 748 7562
Chairman/Managing Director
    Benjamin Glazebrook
Editorial Director *Carol O'Brien*
Approx. Annual Turnover £3 million

FOUNDED in 1890 by Archibald Constable, a grandson of Walter Scott's publisher. Controlling interest was bought by Benjamin Glazebrook in 1967 and the remaining 48% was purchased by Hutchinson, now owned by **Random House**, in 1968. A small but select publisher whose list includes Muriel Spark and Francis King. *Publishes* archaeology, architecture and design, biography and autobiography, celtic interest, crime fiction, guidebooks, history and military, natural history, psychology, sociology and anthropology, travel and topography, food and wine. About 80 titles a year. Unsolicited sample chapters, synopses and ideas for books welcome. No fiction except crime. Enclose return postage.

Royalties paid twice-yearly.

Authors' Rating Keeping its distance from the conglomerates, even with Random holding a minority stake, Constable is highly regarded by authors who recognise a straight deal when they see it.

Consultants Bureau

See **Plenum Publishing Ltd**

Consumers' Association

See **Which? Books/Consumers' Association**

Context Limited

Grand Union House, 20 Kentish Town Road, London NW1 9NR
☎0171 267 8989   Fax 0171 267 1133

FOUNDED 1986. Electronic publisher of UK and European legal and offical information on CD-ROM and on-line. TITLE *JUSTIS* cartoons CD-ROM, developed jointly with **The Centre for the Study of Cartoons and Caricature** at the University of Kent (see entry under **Library Services**), contains over 18,000 political cartoons published in British newspapers from 1912 to 1990. No unsolicited mailshots; enquiries only.

Conway Maritime Press
See **Brassey's (UK) Ltd**

Thomas Cook Publishing
PO Box 227, Peterborough PE3 6PU
☎01733 503571   Fax 01733 503596
Head of Publishing *Kevin Fitzgerald*
Approx. Annual Turnover £1.7 million

Part of the Thomas Cook Group Ltd, publishing commenced in 1873 with the first issue of Cook's Continental Timetable. *Publishes* guidebooks, maps and timetables. About 20 titles a year. No unsolicited mss; synopses and ideas welcome as long as they are travel-related.
Royalties paid annually.

Leo Cooper/
Pen & Sword Books Ltd
190 Shaftesbury Avenue, London WC2H 8JL
☎01226 734734   Fax 0171 240 9247
Chairman *Sir Nicholas Hewitt*

FOUNDED 1990 following the acquisition of the Leo Cooper imprint from Octopus Publishing. *Publishes* military history, naval and aviation history, autobiography and biography. About 40 titles a year. IMPRINT **Wharncliffe Publishing** (see entry). Unsolicited synopses and ideas welcome; no unsolicited mss.
Royalties paid twice-yearly. *Associated company* **Wharncliffe Publishing Ltd**.

Authors' Rating Leo Cooper has now gone to **Orion** to build up a military list but his imprint stays.

Corgi
See **Transworld Publishers Ltd**

Cornwall Books
See **Golden Cockerel Press Ltd**

Coronet
See **Hodder Headline plc**

Countryside Books
2 Highfield Avenue, Newbury, Berkshire RG14 5DS
☎01635 43816   Fax 01635 551004
Publisher *Nicholas Battle*

FOUNDED 1976. *Publishes* local interest paperbacks on regional subjects, generally by English county. Local history, genealogy, walking and photographic, some transport. Over 250 titles

available. Unsolicited mss and synopses welcome but, regretfully, no fiction, poetry, natural history or personal memories.
Royalties paid twice-yearly.

Cressrelles Publishing Co. Ltd
10 Station Road Industrial Estate, Colwall, Malvern, Worcestershire WR13 6RN
☎01684 540154
Managing Director *Leslie Smith*

Publishes a range of general books, drama and chiropody titles.
IMPRINTS **Actinic Press** Specialises in chiropody; **J. Garnet Miller Ltd** Plays and theatre texts; **Kenyon-Deane** Plays and drama textbooks.

Cromwell Publishers
Eagle Court, Concord Business Park, Manchester M22 0RR
☎0161 932 6402   Fax 0161 932 6001
Chairman *James Lansbury*
Senior Editor *Hope Dubé*

FOUNDED 1995. *Publishes* fiction and non-fiction in paperback format; memoirs, biography, autobiography, religion/inspirational, popular sciences, young children, health, Millennium. 'May consider some poetry.' No cookery, academic, manuals, playscripts or erotica. 45 titles in 1997. No unsolicited mss; send synopsis and one sample chapter with return postage.
Royalties paid annually.

Authors' Rating Liable to ask authors to contribute towards costs of publication.

Croom Helm
See **Routledge**

Crossway
See **Inter-Varsity Press**

The Crowood Press Ltd
The Stable Block, Crowood Lane, Ramsbury, Marlborough, Wiltshire SN8 2HR
☎01672 520320   Fax 01672 520280
Chairman *John Dennis*
Managing Director *Ken Hathaway*

Publishes sport and leisure titles, including animal and land husbandry, climbing and walking, maritime, country sports, equestrian, fishing and shooting; also chess and bridge, crafts, dogs, gardening, natural history, aviation and motoring. About 70 titles a year. Preliminary letter preferred in all cases.
Royalties paid annually.

James Currey Publishers
73 Botley Road, Oxford OX2 0BS
☎01865 244111   Fax 01865 246454
Chairman/Managing Director *James Currey*
FOUNDED 1985. A small specialist publisher.
Publishes academic books on Africa, the Caribbean and Third World: history, anthropology, economics, sociology, politics and literary criticism. Approach in writing with synopsis if material is 'relevant to our needs'.
Royalties paid annually.

Curzon Press Ltd
15 The Quadrant, Richmond, Surrey
TW9 1BP
☎0181 948 4660   Fax 0181 332 6735
Managing Director *Malcolm G. Campbell*
Specialised scholarly publishing house. *Publishes* academic/scholarly books on history and archaeology, languages and linguistics, philosophy, religion and theology, sociology and anthropology, cultural studies and reference, all in the context of Africa and Asia. IMPRINT **Japan Library**.

Cygnus Arts
See **Golden Cockerel Press Ltd**

Dalesman Publishing Co. Ltd
Stable Courtyard, Broughton Hall, Skipton,
West Yorkshire BD23 3AE
☎01756 701381   Fax 01756 701326
Editor *Terry Fletcher*
Publishers of *Dalesman, Cumbria* and *Peak and Pennine* magazines and regional books covering Yorkshire, the Lake District and the Peak District. Subjects include crafts and hobbies, geography and geology, guidebooks, history and antiquarian, humour, travel and topography. Unsolicited mss considered on all subjects. About 20 titles a year.
Royalties paid annually.

Terence Dalton Ltd
Water Street, Lavenham, Sudbury, Suffolk
CO10 9RN
☎01787 247572   Fax 01787 248267
Director/Editorial Head *Elisabeth Whitehair*
FOUNDED 1967. Part of Lavenham Holdings plc, a family company. *Publishes* non-fiction: aviation and maritime history, river series and East Anglian interest. TITLE *Imperial Airways and the First British Airline* Capt. Archie Jackson. No unsolicited mss; send synopsis with two or three sample chapters. Ideas welcome.
Royalties paid annually.

The C. W. Daniel Co. Ltd
1 Church Path, Saffron Walden, Essex
CB10 1JP
☎01799 521909   Fax 01799 513462
Managing Director *Ian Miller*
Approx. Annual Turnover £1 million
FOUNDED in 1902 by a man who knew Tolstoy, the company was taken over by its present directors in 1973. Output has increased following the acquisition in 1980 of health and healing titles from the Health Science Press, and the purchase of Neville Spearman Publishers' metaphysical list in 1985. *Publishes* New Age: alternative healing and metaphysical. About 15 titles a year. No fiction, diet or cookery. Unsolicited synopses and ideas welcome; no unsolicited mss.
Royalties paid annually.

Darf Publishers Ltd
277 West End Lane, London NW6 1QS
☎0171 431 7009   Fax 0171 431 7655
Chairman/Managing Director
   M. B. Fergiani
Editorial Head *A. Bentaleb*
Approx. Annual Turnover £500,000
FOUNDED 1982 to publish books and reprints on the Middle East, history, theology and travel. *Publishes* geography, history, language, literature, oriental, politics, theology and travel. About 10 titles a year. TITLES *Moslems in Spain; Travels of Ibn Battuta; The Barbary Corsairs; Elementary Arabic; Travels in Syria and the Holy Land* Burckhardt.
Royalties paid annually. *Overseas associates* Dar Al-Fergiani, Cairo and Tripoli.

Darton, Longman & Todd Ltd
1 Spencer Court, 140–142 Wandsworth High Street, London SW18 4JJ
☎0181 875 0155   Fax 0181 875 0133
Editorial Director *Morag Reeve*
Approx. Annual Turnover £1 million
FOUNDED by Michael Longman, who broke away from Longman Green in 1959 when they cut their religious list. In July 1990 DLT became a common ownership company, owned and run by staff members. The company is a leading ecumenical, predominantly Christian, publisher, with a strong emphasis on spirituality and the ministry and mission of the Church. About 50 titles a year. TITLES include *Jerusalem Bible; New Jerusalem Bible; God of Surprises; Audacity to Believe*. Sample material for books on theological or spiritual subjects considered.
Royalties paid twice-yearly.

David & Charles Publishers

Brunel House, Forde Road, Newton Abbot, Devon TQ12 4PU

☎01626 323200   Fax 01626 323317

Publishing Director *Piers Spence*
Managing Director *Neil Page*
Approx. Annual Turnover £16.8 million

FOUNDED 1960 as a specialist company. Bought back from **Reader's Digest** in 1997 by a management team. *Publishes* illustrated non-fiction for international markets, specialising in crafts and hobbies, art techniques, DIY and interiors, gardening, equestrian and countryside, mind, body and spirit. No fiction, poetry, memoirs or children's. About 60 titles a year. TITLES *Just Junk; The Glass Painting Book; The Complete Cross Stitch Course; The Plantfinder's Guides; Tales From the Countryside; Pevensey Island Guide.* Unsolicited mss will be considered if return postage is included; synopses and ideas welcome. Acquired **Levinson Children's Books** in November 1997 (see entry).

Royalties paid twice-yearly.

Authors' Rating After a management buyout from Reader's Digest in 1997, David & Charles got itself together in remarkably quick time. Better marketing has brought increased rewards all round. The children's list has expanded with the purchase of Levinson's children's titles and there is the promise of further development in this area.

Christopher Davies Publishers Ltd

PO Box 403, Swansea, West Glamorgan SA1 4YF

☎01792 648825   Fax 01792 648825

Managing Director/Editorial Head
   Christopher T. Davies
Approx. Annual Turnover £100,000

FOUNDED 1949 to promote and expand Welsh-language publications. By the 1970s the company was publishing over 50 titles a year but a subsequent drop in Welsh sales led to the establishment of a small English list which has continued. *Publishes* biography, cookery, history, sport and literature of Welsh interest. About 4 titles a year. TITLES *English/Welsh Dictionaries; Famous Cricketers of Glamorgan; Historic Gower; Who's Who in Welsh History.* No unsolicited mss. Synopses and ideas for books welcome.

Royalties paid twice-yearly.

Authors' Rating A favourite for Celtic readers and writers.

Giles de la Mare Publishers Ltd

3 Queen Square, London WC1N 3AU

☎0171 465 7607/0045   Fax 0171 465 0034

Chairman/Managing Director *Giles de la Mare*
Approx. Annual Turnover £45,000

FOUNDED 1995 and commenced publishing in April 1996. *Publishes* mainly non-fiction, especially art and architecture, biography, history, music. TITLES *William Nicholson, Painter* ed. Andrew Nicholson; *Inherit the Truth 1939–1945* Anita Lasker-Wallfisch; *Short Stories 1895–1926* Walter de la Mare; *Sir John Soane, Architect* Dorothy Stroud; *The Weather of Britain* Robin Stirling; *Vermeer* Lawrence Gowing. Unsolicited mss, synopses and ideas welcome after initial telephone call.

Royalties paid twice-yearly.

Debrett's Peerage Ltd

73–77 Britannia Road, PO Box 357, London SW6 2JY

☎0171 736 6524   Fax 0171 731 7768
E-mail: people@debretts.co.uk
Website: www.debretts.co.uk

Chairman *Christopher Haines*
Managing Director *Simone Kesseler*

FOUNDED 1769. The company's main activity (in conjunction with **Macmillan**) is the quinquennial *Debrett's Peerage and Baronetage* (published in 1995) and annual *Debrett's People of Today* (also available on CD-ROM). Debrett's general books are published under licence through **Headline**.

Royalties paid twice-yearly.

Dedalus Ltd

Langford Lodge, St Judith's Lane, Sawtry, Cambridgeshire PE17 5XE

☎01487 832382   Fax 01487 832382

Chairman *Juri Gabriel*
Managing Director *George Barrington*
Approx. Annual Turnover £175,000

FOUNDED 1983. *Publishes* contemporary European fiction and classics and original literary fiction in the fields of magic realism, surrealism, the grotesque and bizarre. 14 titles in 1997. TITLES *The Decadent Gardener; The Arabian Nightmare* Robert Irwin; *Bad to the Bone* James Waddington; *Memoirs of a Gnostic Dwarf* David Madsen; *Music in a Foreign Language* Andrew Crumey (winner of the **Saltire Best First Book Award** in 1994). Welcomes submissions for original fiction and books suitable for its list but 'most people sending work in have no idea what kind of books Dedalus publishes and merely waste their efforts'. Particularly interested in intellectually clever and unusual fiction. A letter about the author should always accompany any submission. No replies without s.a.e.

DIVISIONS/IMPRINTS **Original Fiction in Paperback**; **Contemporary European Fiction 1992–1998**; **Dedalus European Classics**; **Surrealism**; **Empire of the Senses**; **Literary Concept Books**.
Royalties paid annually.

Authors' Rating A small publisher triumphing against powerful competition by the simple expedient of putting quality first.

University of Delaware
See **Golden Cockerel Press Ltd**

JM Dent
See **The Orion Publishing Group Ltd**

André Deutsch Ltd
76 Dean Street, London W1V 5HA
☎0171 316 4450   Fax 0171 316 4499
Managing Director *T. J. Forrester*
Editorial Manager *Louise Dixon*
Website: www.vci.co.uk

FOUNDED in 1950 by André Deutsch, who sold the company between 1984 and 1987 and ended his long association with it in 1991. By then a major fiction list had been established, with writers such as V. S. Naipaul, Philip Roth and Norman Mailer. In 1995 the company was acquired by audio and video publisher and distributor VCI Plc, of which it is now a wholly owned but separately managed subsidiary whose editorial policy remains enduringly successful. Since the VCI acquisition, five defined imprints have developed, two for children: **André Deutsch Classics**, a range of hardback classic books at paperback prices, and **Madcap**, offering innovative, fun and accessible titles. For adults there is **Chameleon**, the commercial label covering film, TV tie-ins, music, comedy and sport, and the **André Deutsch** imprint which covers hardback fiction, biography, politics and current affairs, photography and music. In 1996, the VCI Group also acquired the publishing interests of Manchester United Football Club and created the **Manchester United Books** imprint.

Authors' Rating Having succeeded beyond wildest dreams with *Girl Power, The Official Book* by the Spice Girls, this one-time home for literary novelists is now a leading contender for the children's market. Up to 100 new titles

are planned for the next two years, mostly in the Madcap imprint. TV tie-ins will feature prominently.

Dial House
See **Ian Allan Ltd**

Disney
See **Ladybird Books Ltd**

Dolphin Book Co. Ltd
Tredwr, Llangrannog, Llandysul SA44 6BA
☎01239 654404   Fax 01239 654002
Managing Director *Martin L. Gili*
Approx. Annual Turnover £5000

FOUNDED 1957. A small publishing house specialising in Catalan, Spanish and South American books for the academic market. TITLES *Proceedings of the First Conference on Contemporary Catalan Studies in Scotland* ed. Chris Dixon; *Elegies de Bierville/Bierville Elegies* Carles Riba, Catalan text with English translation by J. L. Gili; *The Discerning Eye Studies presented to Robert Pring-Mill*; *The Late Poetry of Pablo Neruda* Christopher Perriam; *Hispanic Linguistic Studies in Honour of F. W. Hodcroft*; *Salvatge cor/Savage Heart* Carles Riba; Catalan text with English translations by J. L. Gili. Unsolicited mss not welcome. Approach by letter.
Royalties paid annually.

John Donald Publishers Ltd
73 Logie Green Road, Edinburgh EH7 4HF
☎0131 558 8282   Fax 0131 558 8383
Publishing & Production *Donald Morrison*
Commissioning Editor *Russell Walker*

Publishes academic and scholarly, agriculture, archaeology, architecture, economics, textbooks, guidebooks, local, military and social history, religious, sociology and anthropology. About 30 titles a year.
Royalties paid annually.

Donhead Publishing Ltd
Lower Coombe, Donhead St Mary, Shaftesbury, Dorset SP7 9LY
☎01747 828422   Fax 01747 828522
Contact *Jill Pearce*

FOUNDED 1990 to specialise in publishing how-to books for building practitioners; particularly interested in architectural conservation material. *Publishes* building, architecture and heritage only. 6 titles a year. TITLES *Encyclopaedia of Architectural Terms*; *A Good Housekeeping Guide to Churches and their Contents*; *Cleaning Historic Buildings*; *Conservation of Timber Buildings*; *Surveying Historic*

Buildings; Heritage, Conservation, Interpretation; Journal of Architectural Conservation (3 issues a year). Unsolicited mss, synopses and ideas welcome.

Dorling Kindersley Ltd

9 Henrietta Street, London WC2E 8PS
☎0171 836 5411   Fax 0171 836 7570
Chairman *Peter Kindersley*
Deputy Chairman *Christopher Davis*
Approx. Annual Turnover
    UK £29.1 million; US £36.5 million

FOUNDED 1974. Packager and publisher of illustrated non-fiction: cookery, crafts, gardening, health, travel guides, atlases, natural history and children's information and fiction. Launched a US imprint in 1991 and an Australian imprint in 1997. About 175–200 titles a year.

DIVISIONS
Adult; Children's; Multimedia; Vision (video). TITLES *Eyewitness Guides*; *BMA Complete Family Health Encyclopedia*; *RHS A–Z Encyclopedia of Garden Plants*; *Children's Illustrated Encyclopedia*; *The Way Things Work*. Unsolicited synopses/ideas for books welcome.

Authors' Rating While still heavily committed to multimedia, Dorling Kindersley acknowledged that it may have been moving too fast for the market with the announcement of management restructuring, staff cutbacks and fewer titles to be produced in-house. This follows the downturn in the US market which accounts for 40% of DK sales. But the company has a firm base of popular titles with international appeal, and innovation, it is said, brings its own rewards. Writers who sign up with DK must be ready to work as part of an editorial and design team. Loners had best look elsewhere.

Doubleday

See **Transworld Publishers Ltd**

Ashley Drake Publishing Ltd

Market House, Market Place, Deddington, Oxford OX15 0SE
☎01869 338240   Fax 01869 338310
Managing Director *Norman Drake*
Approx. Annual Turnover £70,000

FOUNDED 1995. *Publishes* academic and Welsh-language books. 8 titles in 1997. No unsolicited mss; synopses and ideas for the Welsh Academic Press imprint welcome. No non-academic, scientific or computing books.

IMPRINTS
Welsh Academic Press English language academic, scholarly humanities and social sciences.

TITLES *The Path to Freedom*; *Who's Who in Scottish History*; *The Basques*; *Ivor Novello – A Biography*. **Gwasg Addysgol Cymru** Welsh-language titles. TITLES *Dyddiadur Anne Frank* (*Diary of Anne Frank*). **Y Ddraig Fach** Welsh-language titles for children. TITLES *Llew Frenin* (*Lion King*); *Pocahontas*.
Royalties paid annually.

Drake Educational Associates

St Fagans Road, Fairwater, Cardiff CF5 3AE
☎01222 560333   Fax 01222 554909
Contact *R. G. Drake*
Educational publishers.

Dryden Press

See **Harcourt Brace and Company Limited**

Gerald Duckworth & Co. Ltd

The Old Piano Factory, 48 Hoxton Square, London N1 6PB
☎0171 729 5986   Fax 0171 729 0015
Managing Director *Robin Baird-Smith*
Editorial Director *Deborah Blake*

FOUNDED 1898. A joint ownership company. Some of the company's early credits include authors like Hilaire Belloc, August Strindberg, Henry James and John Galsworthy. *Publishes* academic material in the main, with some trade books, including fiction. About 80 titles a year.
    IMPRINTS **Bristol Classical Press** Classical texts and modern languages; **Chatham Publishing** Maritime history. No unsolicited mss; synopses and sample chapters only. Enclose s.a.e. or return postage for response/ return.
    Royalties paid twice-yearly at first, annually thereafter.

Duncan Petersen Publishing Limited

31 Ceylon Road, London W14 0PY
☎0171 371 2356   Fax 0171 371 2507
Directors *Andrew Duncan, Mel Petersen*

FOUNDED 1986. Publisher and packager of childcare, business, antiques, birds, nature, atlases, walking and travel books. SERIES *Charming Small Hotel Guide*; *Walker's Britain*; *Versatile Travel Guide*. Unsolicited synopses and ideas for books welcome.
    Fees paid.

Martin Dunitz Ltd

The Livery House, 7–9 Pratt Street, London NW1 0AE
☎0171 482 2202   Fax 0171 267 0159
Chairman/Managing Director *Martin Dunitz*

FOUNDED 1978. Dunitz sold the successful *Positive Health Guides* series to former Macdonald in the '80s and now concentrates solely on specialist medical and dental titles aimed at an international market, with co-editions for the USA and Europe. The company won the Queen's Award for Export Achievement (1991). 50–60 titles a year. Unsolicited synopses and ideas welcome but no mss. Publisher of *Journal of Dermatological Treatment; International Journal of Psychiatry in Clinical Practice; Journal of Cytokines and Molecular Therapy.*

Royalties paid twice-yearly.

Eagle
See **Inter Publishing Ltd**

Earthlight
See **Simon & Schuster**

Earthscan Publications
See **Kogan Page Ltd**

Ebury Press
See **Random House UK Ltd**

Edinburgh University Press
22 George Square, Edinburgh EH8 9LF
☎0131 650 4218   Fax 0131 662 0053
Chairman *David Martin*
Editorial Director *Jackie Jones*

Publishes academic and scholarly books (and journals): gender studies, geography, history – ancient, classical, medieval and modern, Islamic studies, linguistics, literary criticism, media and cultural studies; philosophy, politics, Scottish studies, theology and religious studies. About 100 titles a year.

IMPRINTS **Polygon** Marketing *Jeanie Scott*, Freelance Fiction Editor *Marion Sinclair*. *Publishes* fiction and poetry, general trade books, Scottish literary, cultural and oral history. SERIES *Determinations* (Scottish cultural polemics); *Living Memory* (oral history). **Keele University Press** Commissioning Editor *Nicola Carr* American studies. *Publishes* landscape history.

No unsolicited mss for EUP or KUP titles; mss welcome for Polygon but must be accompanied by s.a.e. for reply/return; letter/synopsis preferred in the first instance.

Royalties paid annually.

Element Books
The Old School House, The Courtyard, Bell Street, Shaftesbury, Dorset SP7 8BP
☎01747 851448   Fax 01747 855721
Chairman/Publisher *Michael Mann*

Editorial/Managing Director *Julia McCutchen*
Approx. Annual Turnover £13 million

FOUNDED 1978. An independent general publishing house whose policy is 'to make available knowledge and information to aid humanity in a time of major transition'. *Publishes* general non-fiction in hardback and paperback, including full-colour, illustrated and gift books and children's books. 'We are interested in publishing in the areas of health and complementary therapies; self-help and personal development; psychology; world religions and spiritual traditions; divination and related areas.' TITLES *The Family Encyclopedia of Health; Learn to Meditate Kit; The Complete Book of Colour.* Unsolicited mss, synopses and ideas welcome. No fiction or poetry. 'We are always interested to hear from authors who have an original contribution to make based on quality and integrity.'

Royalties paid twice-yearly.

Authors' Rating Having found itself languishing at the bottom of the Society of Authors' league of publishers and, following a royalty inspection, agreeing to hand over £8000 to an underpaid author, Element has revised its system for checking royalty information. Growth, meanwhile, remains impressive. The popularity of New Age titles will push Element sales to around £25 million by 2000. A children's list was launched early this year.

Elliot Right Way Books
Kingswood Buildings, Lower Kingswood, Tadworth, Surrey KT20 6TD
☎01737 832202   Fax 01737 830311
Managing Directors *Clive Elliot, Malcolm G. Elliot*

FOUNDED 1946 by Andrew G. Elliot. *Publishes* how-to titles and instruction books on a multifarious list of subjects including cookery, DIY, family financial and legal matters, family health, fishing, looking after pets and horses, motoring, popular education, puzzles, jokes and quizzes. All the early books were entitled *The Right Way to . . .* but this format became too restrictive. No fiction.

IMPRINTS **Right Way** Instructional paperbacks in B format; **Clarion** Promotional/bargain series of 'how-to' books. Unsolicited mss, synopses and ideas for books welcome.

Royalties paid annually.

Ellipsis London Ltd
55 Charlotte Road, London EC2A 3QT
☎0171 739 3157   Fax 0171 739 3175
Contact *Tom Neville*

FOUNDED 1992. Formerly a subsidiary of Zurich-based Artemis Verlags AG but now an independent publishing house. *Publishes* architecture and music; contemporary art on CD-ROM. About 25 titles a year. No unsolicited mss, synopses or ideas.

Royalties paid annually.

Aidan Ellis Publishing

Whinfield, Herbert Road, Salcombe, South Devon TQ8 8HN
☎01548 842755   Fax 01548 844356
E-mail: aidan@aepub.demon.co.uk
Website: http://www.demon.co.uk/aepub
Partners/Editorial Heads *Aidan Ellis, Lucinda Ellis*
Approx. Annual Turnover £150,000

FOUNDED in 1971. *Publishes* gardening, fiction and general trade books. About 6 titles a year.

DIVISIONS **Non-Fiction** TITLES *A Chef at Your Elbow* (endorsed by Le Creuset) Ian Lye; *A Fool in the Garden* Josephine Saxton; *Presumed Dead* Eunice Chapman; *Autobiography III* Marguerite Yourcenar. **Fiction** AUTHORS include José Miguel Roig, Jonathan Maslow and Alan Bloom. Unsolicited non-fiction synopses (with s.a.e.) welcome.

Royalties paid twice-yearly. *Overseas associates worldwide.*

Elm Publications

Seaton House, Kings Ripton, Huntingdon, Cambridgeshire PE17 2NJ
☎01487 773254   Fax 01487 773359
Managing Director *Sheila Ritchie*

FOUNDED 1977. *Publishes* textbooks, teaching aids, educational resources, educational software and languages, in the fields of business and management for adult learners. Books and teaching/training resources are generally commissioned to meet specific business, management and other syllabuses. 'We are actively seeking good training materials for business/ management, especially tested and proven.' About 30 titles a year. Ideas are welcome; first approach in writing with outline or by a brief telephone call.

Royalties paid annually.

Elsevier Science Ltd

The Boulevard, Langford Lane, Kidlington, Oxford OX5 1GB
☎01865 843000   Fax 01865 843010
Managing Director *Chris Blake*
Website: http://www.elsevier.nl

Parent company **Elsevier**, Amsterdam. Now incorporates Pergamon Press. *Publishes* academic and professional reference books, scientific, technical and medical books, journals, CD-ROMs and magazines.

DIVISIONS **Elsevier Trends Division** *David Bousfield*; **Elsevier and Pergamon** *Barbara Barrett, Michael Mabe, Chris Lloyd, Jim Gilgunn-Jones, Gerry Dorey*. Unsolicited mss, synopses and ideas for books welcome.

Royalties paid annually.

Authors' Rating An offshoot of the largest Dutch publisher. Refreshingly open with authors in the tradition of northern European publishers – early news on print runs and royalties paid promptly.

Emissary Publishing

PO Box 33, Bicester, Oxfordshire OX6 7PP
☎01869 323447   Fax 01869 324096
Editorial Director *Val Miller*

FOUNDED 1992. *Publishes* mainly humorous paperback books; no poetry or children's. Runs a biennial Humorous Novel Competition in memory of the late Peter Pook and publishes the winning novel (s.a.e. for details). No unsolicited mss or synopses.

Royalties paid twice-yearly.

Enitharmon Press

36 St George's Avenue, London N7 0HD
☎0171 607 7194   Fax 0171 607 8694
Director *Stephen Stuart-Smith*

FOUNDED 1968 by Alan Clodd. An independent company with an enterprising editorial policy, Enitharmon has established itself as one of Britain's leading poetry presses. Patron of 'the new and the neglected', Enitharmon prides itself on the success of its collaborations between writers and artists. *Publishes* poetry, literary criticism, fiction, art and photography. About 20 titles a year. TITLES include *Selected Prose 1934–1996* David Gascoyne; *Lighting a Slow Fuse* Nicki Jackowska; *Heart of a Deer* Pascale Petit; *The Panic Bird* Myra Schneider; *Remembering the Earlier Auden* Edward Upward. No unsolicited mss.

Royalties paid according to contract. *Distribution in Europe by Signature Book Representation, Manchester; in the USA by Dufour Editions Inc., Chester Springs, PA 19425.*

Epworth Press

c/o Methodist Publishing House, 20 Ivatt Way, Peterborough, Cambridgeshire PE3 7PG
☎01733 332202   Fax 01733 331201
Chairman *Dr John A. Newton, CBE*

Editor *Gerald M. Burt*

Publishes Christian books only: philosophy, theology, biblical studies, pastoralia and social concern. No fiction, poetry or children's. A series based on the text of the *Revised Common Lectionary*, entitled *Companion to the RCL*, will be launched in 1998 and the two new series *Exploring Methodism* and *Thinking Things Through* continue. About 10 titles a year. TITLES *Written on the Flyleaf* Peter Bishop; *Why Evil and Suffering?* C. S. Rodd; *Acts of the Apostles* James Dunn. Unsolicited mss considered but write to enquire in the first instance. Authors wishing to have their mss returned must send sufficient postage.

Royalties paid annually.

Eros Plus
See **Titan Books**

Euromonitor
60–61 Britton Street, London EC1M 5NA
☎0171 251 8024   Fax 0171 608 3149

Chairman *R. N. Senior*
Managing Director *T. J. Fenwick*
Approx. Annual Turnover £7 million

FOUNDED 1972. International business information publisher specialising in library and professional reference books, market reports, electronic databases, journals and CD-ROMs. *Publishes* business reference, market analysis and information directories only. About 200 titles a year.

DIVISIONS **Market Direction & Reports** *S. Holmes*; **Reference Books & Directories** *S. Hunter*. TITLES *Credit & Charge Cards: The International Market*; *Europe in the Year 2000*; *European Marketing Handbook*; *European Directory of Trade and Business Associations*; *World Retail Directory and Sourcebook*.

Royalties Payment is generally by flat fee.

Europa Publications Ltd
18 Bedford Square, London WC1B 3JN
☎0171 580 8236   Fax 0171 636 1664

Chairman *C. H. Martin*
Managing Director *P. A. McGinley*
Approx. Annual Turnover £5 million

Owned by MPG Ltd. FOUNDED 1926 with the publication of the first edition of *The Europa Year Book*. *Publishes* annual reference books on political, economic and commercial matters. About 3 titles a year. No fiction, biography or poetry. Enquiries in writing only.

Royalties paid annually.

Evangelical Press of Wales
See **Gwasg Bryntirion Press**

Evans Brothers Ltd
2A Portman Mansions, Chiltern Street, London W1M 1LE
☎0171 935 7160   Fax 0171 487 5034
E-mail: evansbrothers.co.uk

Managing Director *Stephen Pawley*
International Publishing Director *Brian Jones*
Managing Editor *Su Swallow*
Approx. Annual Turnover £3 million

FOUNDED 1908 by Robert and Edward Evans. Originally published educational journals, books for primary schools and teacher education. After rapid expansion into popular fiction and drama, both were sacrificed to a major programme of educational books for schools in East and West Africa. A new UK programme was launched in 1986 followed by the acquisition of **Hamish Hamilton**'s non-fiction list for children in 1990. *Publishes* UK children's and educational books, and educational books for Africa, the Caribbean and Latin America. About 70 titles a year. Unsolicited mss, synopses and ideas for books welcome.

Royalties paid annually. *Overseas associates* in Kenya, Cameroon, Sierra Leone; Evans Bros (Nigeria Publishers) Ltd.

Everyman
See **The Orion Publishing Group Ltd**

Everyman's Library
See **David Campbell Publishers Ltd**

University of Exeter Press
Reed Hall, Streatham Drive, Exeter, Devon EX4 4QR
☎01392 263066   Fax 01392 263064
E-mail: uep@exeter.ac.uk
Website: http://www.ex.ac.uk/uep/

Publisher *Simon Baker*

FOUNDED 1956. *Publishes* academic books: archaeology, classical studies, history, maritime studies, English literature (especially medieval), linguistics, European studies, modern languages and literature, American studies, film history, Arabic studies and books on Exeter and the South West. About 40 titles a year. Unsolicited mss welcomed in the subject areas mentioned above.

Royalties paid annually.

Exley Publications Ltd
16 Chalk Hill, Watford, Hertfordshire
WD1 4BN
☎01923 248328   Fax 01923 818733
Managing/Editorial Director *Helen Exley*

FOUNDED 1976. Independent family company. *Publishes* gift books, quotation anthologies, social stationery and humour. All in series only – no individual titles. About 65 titles a year.

DIVISIONS
Gift Series TITLES *To a Very Special Friend, Daughter, Mother, ...; Golf, Book Lovers, Dog, Friendship Quotations.* **Cartoon Series** TITLES *The Fanatics Guide to Golf, Cats, Dads, etc.* **Words on Series** TITLES *Courage, Joy, Hope, Serenity, Wisdom, etc.* No unsolicited mss. 'Joke and gag writers are very badly needed. Also writers who can create personal thank you and loving messages. Emotion that's never sugary or sentimental.'

Faber & Faber Ltd
3 Queen Square, London WC1N 3AU
☎0171 465 0045   Fax 0171 465 0034
Chairman *Matthew Evans*
Managing Director *Toby Faber*
Approx. Annual Turnover £10 million

Geoffrey Faber founded the company in the 1920s, with T. S. Eliot as an early recruit to the board. The original list was based on contemporary poetry and plays (the distinguished backlist includes Eliot, Auden and MacNeice). *Publishes* poetry and drama, art, children's, fiction, film, music, politics, biography, wine.

DIVISIONS
Children's *Suzy Jenvey* AUTHORS Gene Kemp, Russell Stannard, Susan Price; **Wine** *Toby Faber* TITLES *Burgundy; Bordeaux;* **Fiction** *Jon Riley* AUTHORS P. D. James, Peter Carey, William Golding, Milan Kundera, Mario Vargas Llosa, Garrison Keillor, Caryl Phillips, Paul Auster; **Plays** *Peggy Butcher;* **Film** *Walter Donohue.* AUTHORS Samuel Beckett, Alan Bennett, David Hare, Harold Pinter, Tom Stoppard, John Boorman, Woody Allen, Martin Scorsese, Quentin Tarantino; **Music** *Belinda Matthews* AUTHORS Humphrey Burton, Alexander Goehr, Donald Mitchell, Mark Steyn; **Poetry** *Christopher Reid* AUTHORS Seamus Heaney, Ted Hughes, Douglas Dunn, Tom Paulin, Simon Armitage; **Non-fiction** *Julian Loose* AUTHORS John Carey, Adam Phillips, Darian Leader. *Royalties* paid twice-yearly.

Authors' Rating Faber moved at a slower pace last year blaming the fall in profit on the lack of a bestselling title and the drop in royalty income from *Cats.* The emphasis now seems to be on niche publishing in drama and film with biographies of actors and directors leading the list.

Fairleigh Dickinson University Press
See **Golden Cockerel Press**

Falmer Press
1 Gunpowder Square, London EC4A 3DE
☎0171 583 0490   Fax 0171 583 0581
Senior Commissioning Editor *Anna Clarkson*

Part of **Taylor & Francis Group**. *Publishes* educational books/materials for all levels. Largely commissioned. Unsolicited mss considered.
Royalties paid annually.

Farming Press Books & Videos
Wharfedale Road, Ipswich, Suffolk IP1 4LG
☎01473 241122   Fax 01473 242222
Manager *Alison Stevens*

Owned by United News & Media Plc. *Publishes* specialist books and videos on farming/agriculture. About 15 books and videos a year. No unsolicited mss; synopses and ideas on technical and machinery titles considered.
Royalties paid twice-yearly.

Fernhurst Books
Duke's Path, High Street, Arundel, West Sussex BN18 9AJ
☎01903 882277   Fax 01903 882715
Chairman/Managing Director *Tim Davison*

FOUNDED 1979. For people who love watersports. *Publishes* practical, highly-illustrated handbooks on sailing and watersports. No unsolicited mss; synopses and ideas welcome.
Royalties paid twice-yearly.

Financial Times Management
128 Long Acre, London WC2E 9AN
☎0171 447 2000   Fax 0171 240 5771
Managing Director *Rod Bristow*
Website: ftmanagement.com

Part of Financial Times Professional Ltd. Publisher and supplier of business education and management development materials. Portfolio of products and services includes books, journals, directories, looseleafs, distance learning programmes, corporate training, CD-ROMS aimed at business education and management development in both private and public sectors. About 250 titles a year.

IMPRINTS **Financial Times Pitman Publishing; Institute of Management; NatWest Business Handbooks; Allied Dunbar; Investors Chronicle; Frameworks; Fairplace Institute of Banking & Finance; The Open College; Training Direct; HDL Training & Development**. Unsolicited mss, synopses and ideas for books and other materials welcome.

Royalties paid annually.

Findhorn Press
The Park, Findhorn, Moray IV36 0TZ
☎01309 690582   Fax 01309 690036

Partners *Karin Bogliolo, Thierry Bogliolo*
Approx. Annual Turnover £320,000

FOUNDED 1971. *Publishes* mind, body, spirit, new age and healing. 14 titles in 1997. Unsolicited synopses and ideas welcome if they come within their subject areas.

Royalties paid twice-yearly.

Firefly Publishing
See **Helter Skelter Publishing**

First & Best in Education Ltd
Unit K, Earlstrees Court, Earlstrees Road, Corby, Northamptonshire NN17 4AX
☎01536 399004   Fax 01536 399012

Publisher *Tony Attwood*
Senior Editor *Katy Charge*

Publishers of over 700 educational books of all types for all ages of children and for parents and teachers. All books are published as being suitable for photocopying and/or as electronic books. Currently launching 10 new titles a month and 'keenly looking for new authors all the time'. TITLES *The Perfect Assembly; Children, Their Discipline and Behaviour; From Failure to Excellence.* IMPRINT **Multi-Sensory Learning** (see entry) and **School Improvement Reports**. In the first instance send s.a.e. for details of requirements and current projects to Julia Perkins, Editorial Dept. at the above address.

Royalties paid twice-yearly.

Fitzgerald Publishing
PO Box 804, London SE13 5JJ
☎0181 690 0597

Managing Editor *Tim Fitzgerald*
General Editor *Andrew Smith*

FOUNDED 1974. *Specialises* in scientific studies of insects and spiders. 1–2 titles a year. TITLES *Stick Insects of Europe & The Mediterranean; Baboon*

Spiders of Africa; Tarantula Classification and Identification Guide. Unsolicited mss, synopses and ideas for books welcome. Also considers video scripts for video documentaries. New video documentary: *Desert Tarantulas; Tarantulas of the USA and Mexico; The Tarantula* Prof. Baerg; *Scorpions of Medical Importance* Prof. Keegan.

Fitzjames Press
See **Motor Racing Publications**

Fitzroy Dearborn Publishers
11 Rathbone Place, London W1P 1DE
☎0171 636 6627   Fax 0171 636 6982
E-mail: 100420.3277@compuserve.com

Managing Director *Daniel Kirkpatrick*
Publishers *Lesley Henderson, Roda Morrison*
Commissioning Editors *Mark Hawkins-Dady, Carol Jones*

Publishes reference books: the arts, history, literature, business, science and the social sciences. About 30 titles a year. TITLES *Reader's Guide to American History* ed. Peter J. Parish; *Encyclopedia of Latin American Literature* ed. Verity Smith; *Encyclopedia of the Essay* ed. Tracy Chevalier; *Encyclopedia of Interior Design* ed. Joanna Banham. IMPRINT **Glenlake Business Books**. Unsolicited mss, synopses and ideas welcome for reference books.

Royalties twice yearly. *US associate* Fizroy Dearborn Publishers, 70 East Walton Street, Chicago, IL 60611.

Fitzwarren Publishing
PO Box 6887, London N19 3SG
☎0171 686 4129   Fax 0171 686 4129

Contact *Emma Prinsley*

Publishes two or three books a year, mainly layman's handbooks on legal matters. All books published so far have followed a rigid 128-page format. Written approaches and synopses from prospective authors welcome. Authors, although not necessarily legally qualified, are expected to know their subject as well as a lawyer would.

Royalties paid twice a year.

Flamingo
See **HarperCollins Publishers Ltd**

Flicks Books
29 Bradford Road, Trowbridge, Wiltshire BA14 9AN
☎01225 767728   Fax 01225 760418

Publishing Director *Matthew Stevens*

FOUNDED 1986. Devoted solely to publishing books on the cinema and related media. 10 titles

in 1997. TITLES *Queen of the 'B's: Ida Lupino Behind the Camera* ed. Annette Kuhn; *By Angels Driven: The Films of Derek Jarman* ed. Chris Lippard. Unsolicited mss, synopsis and ideas within the subject area are welcome.
Royalties paid annually and twice yearly.

Flint River Press Ltd
See **Philip Wilson Publishers Ltd**

Floris Books
15 Harrison Gardens, Edinburgh EH11 1SH
☎0131 337 2372   Fax 0131 346 7516
Managing Director *Christian Maclean*
Editors *Christopher Moore, Tony Jacobs-Brown*
Approx. Annual Turnover £350,000
FOUNDED 1977. *Publishes* books related to the Steiner movement, including arts & crafts, children's, the Christian Community, history, religious, science, social questions and Celtic studies. No unsolicited mss. Synopsis and ideas for books welcome.
Royalties paid annually.

Fodor's
See **Random House UK Ltd**

Folens Limited
Albert House, Apex Business Centre, Boscombe Road, Dunstable, Bedfordshire LU5 4RL
☎01582 472788   Fax 01582 472575
Chairman *Dirk Folens*
Managing Director *Malcolm Watson*
FOUNDED 1987. Leading educational publisher. About 150 titles a year. IMPRINTS **Folens**; **Framework**; **Belair**. Unsolicited mss, synopsis and ideas for educational books welcome.
Royalties paid annually.

Fortean Times Books
See **John Brown Publishing Ltd**

G. T. Foulis & Co Ltd
See **Haynes Publishing**

W. Foulsham & Co.
The Publishing House, Bennetts Close, Cippenham, Berkshire SL1 5AP
☎01753 526769   Fax 01753 535003
Chairman *R. S. Belasco*
Managing Director *B. A. R. Belasco*
Approx. Annual Turnover £2.2 million
FOUNDED 1816 and now one of the few remaining independent family companies to survive takeover. *Publishes* non-fiction on most subjects including astrology, gardening, cookery, DIY,

business, hobbies, sport, health and marriage. No fiction. IMPRINT **Quantum** Mind, Body and Spirit titles. Unsolicited mss, synopsis and ideas welcome. Around 60 titles a year.
Royalties paid twice-yearly.

Fount
See **HarperCollins Publishers Ltd**

Fountain Press Ltd
2 Gladstone Road, Kingston-upon-Thames, Surrey KT1 3HD
☎0181 541 4050   Fax 0181 547 3022
Managing Director *H. M. Ricketts*
Approx. Annual Turnover £750,000
FOUNDED 1923 when it was part of the Rowntree Trust Group. Owned by the British Electric Traction Group until 1982 when it was bought out by the present managing director. *Publishes* mainly photography and natural history. About 25 titles a year. TITLES *Photography Yearbook*; *Wildlife Photographer of the Year*, *Antique and Collectable Cameras*; *Camera Manual* (series). Unsolicited mss and synopsis are welcome.
Royalties paid twice-yearly.

Authors' Rating Highly regarded for production values, Fountain has the reputation for involving authors in every stage of the publishing process.

Fourth Estate Ltd
6 Salem Road, London W2 4BU
☎0171 727 8993   Fax 0171 792 3176
Chairman/Managing Director
   Victoria Barnsley
Publishing Director *Christopher Potter*
Approx. Annual Turnover £17 million
FOUNDED 1984. Independent publisher with strong reputation for literary fiction and up-to-the-minute non-fiction. *Publishes* fiction, popular science, current affairs, biography, humour, self-help, travel, reference. About 100 titles a year. DIVISIONS **Literary Fiction/Non-fiction**; **General Fiction/Non-Fiction** TITLES *Fermat's Last Theorem* Simon Singh; *Nigel Slater's Real Food* Nigel Slater; *The Giant, O'Brien* Hilary Mantel; *Me and the Fat Man* Julie Myerson; *The Intruder* Peter Blauner; *The Perfect Storm* Sebastian Junger; *The Diving Bell and the Butterfly* Jean-Dominique Bauby. No unsolicited mss; synopsis welcome.
IMPRINT **Guardian Books** in association with *The Guardian*.
Royalties paid twice-yearly.

Authors' Rating Fourth Estate has the wonderful knack of identifying non-fiction bestsellers which other publishers would be disinclined to touch with a barge pole. Think only of *Longitude*. Rapid growth is forecast. Authors praise the attention to detail and friendly editorial.

Framework
See **Folens Limited**

Free Association Books Ltd
57 Warren Street, London W1P 5PA
☎0171 388 3182   Fax 0171 388 3187
Managing Director *T. E. Brown*
Publishing Director *Gill Davies*

Publishes psychoanalysis and psychotherapy, cultural studies, sexuality and gender, women's studies, applied social sciences. TITLES *The Dialectics of Schizophrenia; The Healing Drama; Freely Associated; The Psychoanalytical Mystic.* Always send a letter in the first instance accompanied by a book outline.
Royalties paid twice-yearly. *Overseas associates* New York University Press, USA; Astam, Australia.

W. H. Freeman
Macmillan Press, Houndsmill, Basingstoke, Hampshire RG21 6XS
☎01256 329242   Fax 01256 330688
President *Robert Beiwen* (New York)
Sales Director *Elizabeth Warner*

Part of W. H. Freeman & Co., USA. *Publishes* academic, agriculture, animal care and breeding, archaeology, artificial intelligence, biochemistry, biology and zoology, chemistry, computer science, economics, educational and textbooks, engineering, geography and geology, mathematics and statistics, medical, natural history, neuroscience, palaeontology, physics, politics and world affairs, psychology, sociology and anthropology, and veterinary. Freeman's editorial office is in New York (Basingstoke is a sales and marketing office only) but unsolicited mss can go through Basingstoke. Those which are obviously unsuitable will be sifted out; the rest will be forwarded to New York.
Royalties paid annually.

Samuel French Ltd
52 Fitzroy Street, London W1P 6JR
☎0171 387 9373   Fax 0171 387 2161
Chairman *Charles R. Van Nostrand*
Managing Director *John Bedding*

FOUNDED 1830 with the object of acquiring acting rights and publishing plays. *Publishes* plays only. About 50 titles a year. Unsolicited mss considered only after initial submission of synopsis and specimen scene. Such material should be addressed to the Performing Rights Department.
Royalties paid twice-yearly for books; performing royalties paid monthly, subject to a minimum amount.

Authors' Rating Thrives on the amateur dramatic societies who are forever in need of play texts. Editorial advisers give serious attention to new material but a high proportion of the list is staged before it goes into print. Non-established writers are advised to try one-act plays, much in demand by the amateur dramatic societies but rarely turned out by well-known playwrights.

David Fulton (Publishers) Ltd
Ormond House, 26/27 Boswell Street, London WC1N 3JD
☎0171 405 5606   Fax 0171 831 4840
E-mail: fultonbooks@mail.easynet.co.uk
Chairman/Managing Director *David Fulton*
Editorial Director *John Owens*
Approx. Annual Turnover £900,000

FOUNDED 1987. *Publishes* non-fiction: books for teachers and teacher training at B.Ed and PGCE levels for early years, primary, secondary and virtually all aspects of special education; geography for undergraduates. In 1995, David Fulton set up a Fulton Fellowship in Special Education (see under **Bursaries, Fellowships and Grants**). About 65 titles a year. No unsolicited mss; synopses and ideas for books welcome.
Royalties paid twice-yearly.

Authors' Rating David Fulton has shown how niche publishing can succeed even in a difficult market. Known chiefly for books on learning difficulties, he gets most of his ideas and authors by going to education conferences.

Funfax Limited
Marsh House, Tide Mill Way, Woodbridge, Suffolk IP12 1AN
☎01394 380622   Fax 01394 380618
Publisher *Roger Priddy*
Managing Editor *Lucy Bater*
Approx. Annual Turnover £7 million

FOUNDED 1990. Bought by **Dorling Kindersley** in 1995 and now a wholly-owned subsidiary of Dorling Kindersley Holdings plc. Formerly Henderson Publishing Ltd. *Publishes* children's books for the international mass markets; non-fiction information, novelty, puzzle and some fiction books. All ideas are generated in-house to specific formats across the range of imprints. Freelance writers are commissioned to write to an agreed brief with strict guidelines. Texts are then edited in-house to suit a particular style. Unsolicited synopses and ideas for books welcome. No mss. New authors welcome (send c.v. and introductory letter to Lucy Bater).

IMPRINTS include **Funfax**; **Fun Files**; **Quiz Quest**; **The Lettermen**; **Make a Model**; **Microfax**; **FX Pax**; **Mad Jack**; **Activity Packs**; **Magic Jewellery**.

Gaia Books Ltd
66 Charlotte Street, London W1P 1LR
☎0171 323 4010   Fax 0171 323 0435
Also at: 20 High Street, Stroud,
Gloucestershire GL5 1AS
☎01453 752985   Fax 01453 752987
Managing Director *Joss Pearson*
FOUNDED 1983. *Publishes* ecology, health, natural living and mind, body & spirit, mainly in practical self-help illustrated reference form for Britain and the international market. About 12 titles a year. TITLES *Heritage Vegetables; Reiki – Healing and Harmony Through the Hands; The Family Guide to Reflexology; The Personal Feng Shui Manual.* Most projects are conceived in-house but outlines and mss with s.a.e. considered. 'From submission of an idea to project go ahead may take up to a year. Authors become involved with the Gaia team in the editorial, design and promotion work needed to create and market a book.'

Gairm Publications
29 Waterloo Street, Glasgow G2 6BZ
☎0141 221 1971   Fax 0141 221 1971
Chairman *Prof. Derick S. Thomson*
FOUNDED 1952 to publish the quarterly Gaelic periodical *Gairm* and soon moved into publishing other Gaelic material. Acquired an old Glasgow Gaelic publishing firm, Alexander MacLaren & Son, in 1970. *Publishes* a wide range of Gaelic and Gaelic-related books: dictionaries, grammars, handbooks, children's, fiction, poetry, biography, music and song. TITLES *The Companion to Gaelic Scotland; Derick Thomson's collection of poems, Meall Garbh/The Rugged Mountain.* Catalogue available.

Galaxy Children's Large Print
See **Chivers Press Ltd**

J. Garnet Miller Ltd
See **Cressrelles Publishing Co. Ltd**

Garnet Publishing Ltd
8 Southern Court, South Street, Reading,
Berkshire RG1 4QS
☎0118 9597847   Fax 0118 9597356
Managing Director *Ken Banerji*
FOUNDED 1992 and purchased Ithaca Press in the same year. *Publishes* art, architecture, photography, archive photography, cookery, travel classics, travel, comparative religion, Islamic culture and history, foreign fiction in translation. Core subjects are Middle Eastern but list is rapidly expanding to be more general. Published about 30 titles 1997.

IMPRINTS

Ithaca Press *Adel Kamal* Specialises in postgraduate academic works on the Middle East, political science and international relations. About 20 titles in 1997. TITLES *Palestine and the Law; The Israeli Labour Party; Abbas Hilmi II: Memoirs of the Last Khedive of Egypt; Islamist and Leftist Forces in Jordan; Oman and the Southern Shore of the Persian Gulf.* **Garnet Publishing** *Sue Coll* TITLES *Arab Women Writers* series (winner of the 1995 WiP New Venture Award); *Traditional Spanish Cooking; Architecture of Oman; Jerusalem: Caught in Time* series; *World Fiction* series. Unsolicited mss not welcome – write with outline and ideas first.

Royalties paid twice-yearly. *Sister companies*: All Prints, Beirut; Garnet France, Paris.

The Gay Men's Press
(GMP Publishers Ltd)
PO Box 247, Swaffham, Norfolk PE37 8PA
☎01366 328101   Fax 01366 328102
Directors *David Fernbach, Aubrey Walter*
Publishes primarily books by gay authors about gay-related issues: art, photography, biography and autobiography, literary fiction and popular (historical romance to crime and science fiction), health and leisure. No poetry. Works should generally be submitted by the author on disk.

DIVISIONS

Art & Photography *Aubrey Walter*; **General Books** (including **Fiction**) *David Fernbach*. TITLES *Safe as Houses* Alex Jeffers; *A Friendship of Convenience* Rufus Gunn; *Skin Deep* John R. Gordon; *A Cage of Bones* Jeffrey Round; *Tokyo Vanilla* Thomas Boggs; *White Rose of Night* Mel Keegan; *Love Sucks* Ken Shakin; *Byron & Greek Love* Louis Crompton; *Adonis: The Male Physique Pin-up* David Chapman. Send synopsis with sample chapters rather than complete mss. *Royalties* negotiable.

Gazelle Books
See **Angus Hudson** under **UK Packagers**

Geddes & Grosset Ltd
David Dale House, New Lanark ML11 9DJ
☎01555 665000   Fax 01555 665694
Managing Director R. *Michael Miller*
Approx. Annual Turnover £3.2 million
FOUNDED 1989. Publisher and packager of children's and reference books. Unsolicited mss, synopses and ideas welcome. No adult fiction.

Authors' Rating Geddes & Grosset came to success with Tarantula, a children's imprint launched four years ago which sells almost exclusively through supermarket chains.

Stanley Gibbons Publications
5 Parkside, Christchurch Road, Ringwood, Hampshire BH24 3SH
☎01425 472363   Fax 01425 470247
Chief Executive A. M. *McQuillan*
Operation Director A. J. *Pandit*
Editorial Head D. *Aggersberg*
Approx. Annual Turnover £3 million
Long-established force in the philatelic world with over a hundred years in the business. *Publishes* philatelic reference catalogues and handbooks. Approx. 15 titles a year. Reference works relating to other areas of collecting may be considered. TITLES *Stanley Gibbons British Commonwealth Stamp Catalogue; Collect British Stamps; How to Arrange and Write Up a Stamp Collection; Stamps of the World; Collect Aircraft on Stamps*. Foreign catalogues include Japan and Korea, Portugal and Spain, Germany, Middle East, Balkans, China. Monthly publication *Gibbons Stamp Monthly* (see entry under **Magazines**). Unsolicited mss, synopses and ideas welcome.
Royalties by negotiation.

Robert Gibson & Sons Glasgow Limited
17 Fitzroy Place, Glasgow G3 7SF
☎0141 248 5674   Fax 0141 221 8219
Chairman/Managing Director R. G. C. *Gibson*
FOUNDED 1850 and went public in 1886. *Publishes* educational books only, and has been agent for the Scottish Certificate of Education Examination Board since 1902 which, in 1997, became the Scottish Qualification Authority. About 40 titles a year. Unsolicited mss preferred to synopses/ideas.
Royalties paid annually.

Ginn & Co
See **Reed Educational & Professional Publishing**

Mary Glasgow Publications
See **Stanley Thornes (Publishers) Ltd**

Glenlake Business Books
See **Fitzroy Dearborn Publishers**

Godsfield Press Ltd
Laurel House, Station Approach, Alresford, Hampshire SO24 9JH
☎01962 735633   Fax 01962 735320
Approx. Annual Turnover £1.5 million
Publishes mind/body/spirit titles in colour for adults.

Golden Cockerel Press Ltd
16 Barter Street, London WC1A 2AH
☎0171 405 7979   Fax 0171 404 3598
E-mail: lindesay@btinternet.com
Directors *Tamar Lindesay, Andrew Lindesay*
FOUNDED 1980 to distribute titles for US-based Associated University Presses Inc., New Jersey. *Publishes* academic titles mostly: art, film, history, literary criticism, music, philosophy, sociology and special interest. About 120 titles a year. IMPRINTS **AUP: Bucknell University Press; University of Delaware; Fairleigh Dickinson University Press; Lehigh University Press; Susquehanna University Press**. Also: **Cygnus Arts** Non-academic books on the arts; **Cornwall Books** Trade hardbacks. Unsolicited mss, synopses and ideas for appropriate books welcome.

Authors' Rating Very much attuned to American interests with trans-Atlantic spelling and punctuation predominating. Some writers may find the process wearisome but those who persevere win through to a wider market.

Victor Gollancz
See **Cassell**

Gomer Press
Wind Street, Llandysul, Ceredigion SA44 4BQ
☎01559 362371   Fax 01559 363758
Chairman/Managing Director J. H. *Lewis*
FOUNDED 1892. *Publishes* adult fiction and non-fiction, children's fiction and educational material in English and Welsh. About 100 titles a year (65 Welsh; 35 English).
IMPRINTS **Gomer Press** *Dr D. Elis-Gruffydd;*

Pont Books *Mairwen Prys Jones.* No unsolicited mss, synopses or ideas.

Royalties paid twice-yearly.

Gower

See **Ashgate Publishing Co. Ltd**

GPC Books

See **University of Wales Press**

Graham & Trotman

See **Kluwer Law International**

Graham & Whiteside Ltd

Tuition House, 5–6 Francis Grove, London SW19 4DT

☎0181 947 1011   Fax 0181 947 1163

Managing Director *Alastair M. W. Graham*

FOUNDED 1995. *Publishes* annual directories for the business and professional market with titles dating back to 1975 originally published by Graham & Trotman. TITLES 22 annual directories, including: *Major Companies of Europe; Major Companies of the Arab World; Major Companies of the Far East and Australasia.* Proposals for new projects welcome.

Royalties paid annually.

Graham-Cameron Publishing

The Studio, 23 Holt Road, Sheringham, Norfolk NR26 8NB

☎01263 821333   Fax 01263 821334

Editorial Director *Mike Graham-Cameron*
Art Director *Helen Graham-Cameron*

FOUNDED 1984 as a packaging operation. *Publishes* illustrated factual books for children, institutions and business; also biography, education and social history. TITLES *Up From the Country; In All Directions; The Holywell Story; Let's Look at Dairying.* Do not send unsolicited mss, please.

Royalties paid annually. *Subsidiary company*: Graham-Cameron Illustration (agency).

Granta Books

2–3 Hanover Yard, Noel Road, London N1 8BE

☎0171 704 9776   Fax 0171 354 3469

Publisher *Frances Coady*

FOUNDED 1979. *Publishes* literary fiction and general non-fiction. About 35 titles a year. No unsolicited mss; synopses and sample chapters welcome.

Royalties paid twice-yearly.

Authors' Rating Backed by American media mogul Rae Hederman, publisher of the *New York Review of Books*, Granta has relaunched with 'a mix of new and established writers' while putting out the welcome sign for 'good writing and challenging ideas'.

W. Green (Scotland)

See **Sweet & Maxwell Ltd**

Green Books

Foxhole, Dartington, Totnes, Devon TQ9 6EB

☎01803 863843   Fax 01803 863843

Chairman *Satish Kumar*
Managing Editor *John Elford*
Approx. Annual Turnover £150,000

FOUNDED in 1987 with the support of a number of Green organisations. Closely associated with *Resurgence* magazine. *Publishes* high-quality books on a wide range of Green issues, particularly ideas, philosophy and the practical application of Green values. No fiction or books for children. TITLES *Forest Gardening* Robert A. de J. Hart; *Eco-Renovation* Edward Harland; *The Growth Illusion* Richard Douthwaite; *The Living Tree* John Lane; *The Organic Directory* ed. Clive Litchfield. No unsolicited mss. Synopses and ideas welcome.

Royalties paid twice-yearly.

Greenhill Books/ Lionel Leventhal Ltd

Park House, 1 Russell Gardens, London NW11 9NN

☎0181 458 6314   Fax 0181 905 5245

Managing Director *Lionel Leventhal*

FOUNDED 1984 by Lionel Leventhal (ex-**Arms & Armour Press**). *Publishes* aviation, military and naval books, and its Napoleonic Library series. Synopses and ideas for books welcome. No unsolicited mss.

Royalties paid twice-yearly.

Gresham Books

See **Woodhead Publishing Ltd**

Gresham Books Ltd

PO Box 61, Henley on Thames, Oxfordshire RG9 3LQ

☎01734 403789   Fax 01734 403789

Managing Director *Mary V. Green*
Approx. Annual Turnover £175,000

Bought by Mary Green from Martins Publishing Group in 1980. A small specialist publishing house. *Publishes* hymn and service books for schools and churches, also craftbound choir and orchestral folders and Records of Achievement. TITLES include music and melody editions of *Hymns for Church and School;*

The School Hymnal; Praise and Thanksgiving. No unsolicited material but ideas welcome.

Griffith Institute
See **Ashmolean Museum Publications Ltd**

Grisewood & Dempsey
See **Kingfisher plc**

Grove's Dictionaries of Music
See **Macmillan Publishers Ltd**

Grub Street
The Basement, 10 Chivalry Road, London SW11 1HT
☎0171 924 3966   Fax 0171 738 1009
Managing Director *John Davies*
FOUNDED 1982. *Publishes* cookery, health and aviation history books. About 20 titles a year. TITLES *Complete Asian Cookbook; Everyday Diabetic Cookbook; Above the Trenches; Aces High.* Unsolicited mss and synopses welcome in the above categories.
Royalties paid twice-yearly.

Grune & Stratton
See **Harcourt Brace and Company Limited**

Guardian Books
See **Fourth Estate Ltd**

Guild of Master Craftsman Publications Ltd
166 High Street, Lewes, East Sussex BN7 1XU
☎01273 477374   Fax 01273 487692
Chairman *A.E. Phillips*
Approx. Annual Turnover £2 million
FOUNDED 1979. Part of G.M.C. Services Ltd. *Publishes* woodworking and craft books, magazines and videos. 40 titles in 1998. Unsolicited mss, synopses and ideas for books welcome. No fiction.
Royalties paid twice-yearly.

Guinness Publishing Ltd
338 Euston Road, London NW1 3BD
☎0171 891 4567   Fax 0171 891 4501
E-mail: Guinness_Publishing@guinness.com
Chairman *Colin Storm*
Managing Director *Christopher Irwin*
Publishing Director *Ian Castello-Cortes*
Television Director *Michael Feldman*
Approx. Annual Turnover £7 million
FOUNDED 1954 to publish *The Guinness Book of Records,* now the highest-selling copyright book in the world, published in 35 languages.

The list has now expanded to about 12 major titles a year in international four-colour popular reference, music and film titles. Ideas and synopses welcome as is contact from projective researchers, editors and designers.

Authors' Rating Guinness has cut back on the number of new titles, choosing instead to concentrate on reinvigorating the *Book of Records.* Each of the 6 new titles to appear in the year will have to justify a minimum print run of 100,000.

Gunsmoke Westerns
See **Chivers Press Ltd**

Gwasg Addysgol Cymru
See **Ashley Drake Publishing Ltd**

Gwasg Bryntirion Press (formerly Evangelical Press of Wales)
Bryntirion House, Bridgend, Mid-Glamorgan CF31 4DX
☎01656 655886   Fax 01656 656095
Chairman *Reverend S. Jones*
Managing Editor *David Kingdon*
Approx. Annual Turnover £85,000
Owned by the Evangelical Movement of Wales. *Publishes* Christian books in English and Welsh. 11 titles in 1997. TITLES *Encounters with God; Fire in the Thatch; Following the Shepherd; Pursued by God; Taught to Serve; Sally Jones – Rhodd Duw I Charles.* No unsolicited mss; synopses and ideas welcome.
Royalties paid annually.

Gwasg Carreg Gwalch
12 Iard Yr Orsaf, Llanrwst, Conwy LL26 0EH
☎01492 642031   Fax 01492 641502
Managing Editor *Myrddin ap Dafydd*
FOUNDED in 1990. *Publishes* Welsh language; English books of Welsh interest – history, folklore, guides and walks. 50 titles in 1997. Unsolicited mss, synopses and ideas welcome.
Royalties paid.

Gwasg Prifysgol Cymru
See **University of Wales Press**

Peter Haddock Ltd
Pinfold Lane Industrial Estate, Bridlington, East Yorkshire YO16 5BT
☎01262 678121   Fax 01262 400043
Managing Director *Peter Haddock*
Contact *Pat Hornby*
FOUNDED 1952. *Publishes* children's picture story and activity books. About 200 series a

year. Ideas for picture books welcome.

Royalties Payments vary according to each contract.

Authors' Rating Cheap end of the market. Writers need to work fast to make a living.

Peter Halban Publishers

42 South Molton Street, London W1Y 1HB
☎0171 491 1582   Fax 0171 629 5381

Directors *Peter Halban, Martine Halban*

FOUNDED 1986. Independent publisher. *Publishes* biography, autobiography and memoirs, history, philosophy, theology, politics, literature and criticism, Judaica and world affairs. 4–5 titles a year. No unsolicited material. Approach by letter in first instance.

Royalties paid twice-yearly for first two years, thereafter annually in December.

Robert Hale Ltd

Clerkenwell House, 45–47 Clerkenwell Green, London EC1R 0HT
☎0171 251 2661   Fax 0171 490 4958

Chairman/Managing Director *John Hale*

FOUNDED 1936. Family-owned company. *Publishes* adult fiction (but not interested in category crime, romance or science fiction) and non-fiction. No specialist material (education, law, medical or scientific). Acquired **NAG Press Ltd** in 1993 with its list of horological, gemmological, jewellery and metalwork titles. Over 200 titles a year. TITLES *How to Make Enchanting Teddy Bears* Debbie Kesling; *Textile Techniques in Metal* Arline M. Fisch; *A Year with Rudolf Nureyev* Simon Robinson with Derek Robinson; *The Art of Survival* Steven Marshall; *The Hay Poisoner* Martin Beales; *Constable at the Dam* Nicholas Rhea; *The Adventurer* Barbara Cartland. Unsolicited mss, synopses and ideas for books welcome.

Royalties paid twice-yearly.

Authors' Rating Takes good care of authors but can be tough on advances. Favours the popular end of the fiction market.

Halsgrove

Halsgrove House, Lower Moor Way, Tiverton, Devon EX16 6SS
☎01884 243242   Fax 01884 243325

Joint Managing Directors *Simon Butler, Steven Pugsley*

Approx. Annual Turnover £1.5 million

FOUNDED in 1990 from defunct Maxwell-owned publishing group. Grown into the region's largest publishing and distribution group, specialising in books, video and audio tapes. *Publishes* local history, cookery, biography. 100 titles in 1997. No fiction or poetry. Unsolicited mss, synopses and ideas for books of regional interest welcome.

Royalties paid annually.

The Hambledon Press

102 Gloucester Avenue, London NW1 8HX
☎0171 586 0817   Fax 0171 586 9970

Chairman/Managing Director/Editorial Head *Martin Sheppard*

FOUNDED 1980. *Publishes* British and European history from post-classical to modern. Currently expanding its list to include history titles with a wider appeal including more biographies. 25–30 titles a year. TITLES *Jane Austen and Food* Maggie Lane; *Victorian Girls: Lord Lyttelton's Daughters* Sheila Fletcher; *A Muse of Fire: Literature, Art and War* A. D. Harvey. No unsolicited mss; send preliminary letter. Synopses and ideas welcome.

Royalties paid annually. *Overseas associates* **The Hambledon Press (USA)**, Ohio.

Hamilton & Co (Publishers)

10 Stratton Street, Mayfair, London W1X 5FD
☎0171 546 8646   Fax 0171 546 8570

Managing Editor *James Dalton*
Editor *Max Hoffman*

FOUNDED 1997. *Publishes* fiction and non-fiction: memoirs, autobiography, biography, war, poetry, children's and historical. Around 40 titles a year. TITLES *A Rainbow of Tales* Nicola Hasting; *Knowing Strangers* Jo Howard; *Head's Tales* George Nicholls. No unsolicited mss; synopses and sample chapters with return postage only.

Royalties paid annually.

Authors' Rating Liable to ask authors to contribute towards costs of publication.

Hamish Hamilton/Hamish Hamilton Children's

See **Penguin UK**

Hamlyn/Octopus

See **Reed Books**

Harcourt Brace and Company Limited

24–28 Oval Road, London NW1 7DX
☎0171 424 4200 Fax 0171 482 2293/485 4752

Managing Director *Peter H. Lengemann*

Owned by US parent company. *Publishes* scientific, technical and medical books, college textbooks, educational & occupational test. No unsolicited mss.

IMPRINTS **Academic Press; Baillière Tindall; Dryden Press; Churchill Livingstone; Holt Rinehart and Winston; Mosby International** (see entry); **T. & A. D. Poyser; W. B. Saunders & Co. Ltd.; Saunders Scientific Publications**.

Harlequin Mills & Boon Ltd

Eton House, 18–24 Paradise Road, Richmond, Surrey TW9 1SR
☎0181 288 2800   Fax 0181 288 2899
Managing Director F. Gejrot
Editorial Director Karin Stoecker
Approx. Annual Turnover £20.3 million

FOUNDED 1908. Owned by the Canadian-based Torstar Group. *Publishes* romantic fiction and historical romance. Over 600 titles a year.

IMPRINTS
Mills & Boon Presents (50–55,000 words) Contemporary romances with international settings, focusing intensely on hero and heroine, with happy endings assured. **Mills & Boon Enchanted; Mills & Boon Medical Romance** *Elizabeth Johnson* (50–55,000 words) Modern medical practice provides a unique background to love stories. **Mills & Boon Historical Romance** *Elizabeth Johnson* (75–80,000 words) Historical romances. **MIRA** *Linda Fildew* (minimum 100,000 words) Individual women's fiction. **Silhouette Desire, Special Edition, Sensation** and **Intrigue** imprints are handled by US-based **Silhouette Books** (see under **US Publishers**). Please send query letter in the first instance. Tip sheets and guidelines for the Mills & Boon series available from Harlequin Mills & Boon Editorial Dept. (please send s.a.e.).
Royalties paid twice-yearly.

Authors' Rating Fighting back against the raunchy romanticism of **Virgin** and **Black Lace**, Harlequin Mills & Boon launched a £2 million advertising campaign to prove that it is keeping up with current trends in women's fiction. There is also talk of launching historical and adventure books for men. But there is no question of trying to beat Black Lace at its own game. Research has found that most women, or M&B readers, want 'warm sex' where the full mechanics are left to the imagination.

Harley Books

Martins, Great Horkesley, Colchester, Essex CO6 4AH
☎01206 271216   Fax 01206 271182
Managing Director Basil Harley

FOUNDED 1983. Natural history publishers specialising in entomological and botanical books. Mostly definitive, high-quality illustrated reference works. TITLES *Aquatic Plants in Britain and Ireland; Songs of Grasshoppers and Crickets of Western Europe; The Moths and Butterflies of Great Britain and Ireland; Spiders of Great Britain and Ireland; Dragonflies of Europe; The Flora of Hampshire*.
Royalties paid twice-yearly in the first year, annually thereafter.

HarperCollins Publishers Ltd

77–85 Fulham Palace Road, London W6 8JB
☎0181 741 7070   Fax 0181 307 4440
Also at: Freepost PO Box, Glasgow G4 0NB
☎0141 772 3200   Fax 0141 306 3119
Chief Executive *Jane Friedman*
Executive Chairman/Publisher *Eddie Bell*
Group Managing Director *Les Higgins*
Approx. Annual Turnover £200 million

Publisher of high-profile authors like Jeffrey Archer, James Herbert, Fay Weldon and Len Deighton. Owned by News Corporation. Since 1991 there has been a period of consolidated focus on key management issues within the HarperCollins empire. This has led to various imprints being phased out in favour of others, among them Grafton and Fontana, which have been merged under the HarperCollins paperback imprint. Title output has been reduced by about 20%. **Booker Prize** and **Pulitzer Prize** winners in 1997.

DIVISIONS
Trade *Adrian Bourne*, Deputy Managing Director, *Susan Watt* Publishing Director. **Fiction** *Nick Sayers*; **Non-Fiction** *Michael Fishwick*. IMPRINTS **Collins Crime; Flamingo** (literary fiction, both hardback and paperback); **HarperCollins Paperbacks; Tolkien; Voyager** (science fiction/fantasy); **Fontana Press; HarperCollins**. Over 650 titles a year, hardback and paperback. No longer accepts unsolicited submissions.

Thorsons *Eileen Campbell,* Divisional Managing Director. Health, nutrition, business, parenting, popular psychology, positive thinking, self-help, divination, therapy, recovery, feminism, women's issues, mythology, religion, yoga, tarot, personal development, sexual politics, biography, history, popular culture. About 250 titles a year.

Children's *Kate Harris*, Divisional Managing Director. IMPRINTS **Picture Lions; HarperCollins Audio** (see entry under **Audio Books**);

Jets; **Collins Tracks**; **Collins Non-Fiction** Quality picture books and book and tape sets for under 7s; all categories of fiction for the 6–14 age group; dictionaries and general reference for preschool and primary. About 250 titles a year. No longer accepts unsolicited mss.

Reference *Stephen Bray*, Divisional Managing Director. IMPRINTS **HarperCollins**; **Collins New Naturalist Library**; **Collins Gems**; **Collins Willow** (sport); **Janes** (military) Encyclopedias, guides and handbooks, phrase books and manuals on popular reference, art instruction, cookery and wine, crafts, DIY, gardening, military, natural history, pet care, Scottish, sports and pastimes. About 120 titles a year.

Educational *Kate Harris*, Divisional Managing Director. Textbook publishing for schools and FE colleges (5–18-year-olds): all subjects for primary education; strong in English, history, geography, science and technology for secondary education; sociology, business studies and economics in FE. (Former Holmes McDougall, Unwin Hyman, Mary Glasgow Primary Publications, and part of Harcourt, Brace & Co. educational imprints have been incorporated under Collins Educational.) About 90 titles a year.

Dictionaries *Kate Harris*. IMPRINTS **Collins**; **Collins Cobuild**; **Collins Gem** Includes the *Collins English Dictionary* range with dictionaries and thesauruses, *Collins Bilingual Dictionary* range (French, German, Spanish, Italian, etc.), and the *Cobuild* series of English dictionary, grammars and EFL books. About 50 titles a year.

HarperCollege *Kate Harris*. IMPRINT **Harper-Collins College** Selected US academic titles, mostly imported from College Division, Basic Books, Harper Business and Harper Perennial. Most of the titles stocked are university-level texts, previously published under the Harper & Row and Scott Foresman imprints. A programme to publish UK editions of some of these commenced in 1994. Strength areas are economics, psychology, allied health and business. About 550 titles stocked in the UK.

HarperCollins World IMPRINTS **Harper-Collins US**; **Australia**; **New Zealand**; **Canada**; **India** General trade titles imported into the UK market.

Religious *Eileen Campbell*, Divisional Managing Director. A broad-based religious publisher across all denominations. IMPRINTS **HarperCollins**; **Fount**; **Marshall Pickering** Extensive range covering both popular and academic spirituality, music and reference. Marshall Pickering, bibles, missals, prayer books, and hymn books. About 150 titles a year.

HarperCollins Cartographic *Stephen Bray*. The cartographic division, with Bartholomew and Times Books now joined as one division. IMPRINTS **Bartholomew**; **Collins**; **Harper-Collins Audiobooks** (see entry under **Audio Books**); **Invincible Press**; **Longman Nicholson**; **Nicholson/Ordnance Survey**; **Sun Crosswords**; **Times Atlases**; **Times Books**; **Times Crosswords** Maps, atlases and guides (Bartholomew; Collins; Collins Longman; Times Atlases); leisure maps, educational titles (Collins Longman); London titles (Nicholson); waterway guides (Nicholson/Ordnance Survey); sports titles for *The Sun* and *News of the World* (Invincible Press); reference and non-fiction (Times Books). About 30 titles a year.

Broadcasting Consultancy *Eileen Campbell* Newly formed to exploit TV and film rights across the country.

Authors' Rating After an expensive restructuring and a cutback on its forward publishing list, a necessary preliminary, some said, to Rupert Murdoch shifting this loss-making side of his business into another media conglomerate, HarperCollins came in for a right rollicking from its rivals for daring to backtrack on a deal to publish Chris Patten's memoirs. It was said that the former Hong Kong governor's criticisms of China were in conflict with Mr Murdoch's ambitions to spread his television empire across Asia. True, but the stench of hypocrisy arising from the suggestion that other media moguls would never presume to put their own best interests first was overwhelming. Loss or no loss, HarperCollins is by far Britain's largest consumer book publisher. Children's books, with the emphasis on new authors, represent a growth area.

Harrap
See **Kingfisher Publications plc**

Harvard University Press
Fitzroy House, 11 Chenies Street, London WC1E 7ET
☎0171 306 0603   Fax 0171 306 0604

Director *William Sisler*
General Manager *Ann Sexsmith*

Part of **Harvard University Press**, USA. *Publishes* academic and scholarly works in history, politics, philosophy, economics, literary criticism, psychology, sociology, anthropology, women's studies, biological sciences, astronomy, history of science, art, music, film, reference. All mss go to the American office: 79 Garden Street, Cambridge, MA 02138.

The Harvill Press Ltd
2 Aztec Row, Berners Road, London
N1 0PW
☎0171 609 1119   Fax 0171 609 2019
Chairman *Christopher MacLehose*
Managing Director *John Mitchinson*
Editorial Director *Guido Waldman*

FOUNDED in 1946, the list was bought by Collins in 1959, of which it remained an imprint until returning to its original independent status in early 1995. *Publishes* literature in translation (especially Russian, Italian and French), literature, quality thrillers, illustrated books and Africana, plus an occasional literature anthology. 60–70 titles in 1997. AUTHORS Mikhail Bulgakov, Raymond Carver, Richard Ford, Alan Garner, Peter Høeg, Robert Hughes, Giuseppe T. di Lampedusa, Peter Matthiessen, Cees Nooteboom, Boris Pasternak, Georges Perec, Aleksandr Solzhenitsyn, Marguerite Yourcenar. Mss usually submitted by foreign publishers and agents. Synopses and ideas welcome. No educational or technical books.
Royalties paid twice-yearly.

Authors' Rating The buy-out from HarperCollins is beginning to look like a gamble that will pay off handsomely. What Harvill does best, fiction in translation, does not seem to fit comfortably in a conglomerate but can thrive with an independent publisher. The two-way traffic means that Harvill's English language writers tend to do well in Europe. Relations with authors are said to be close and friendly.

Haynes Publishing
Sparkford, Near Yeovil, Somerset BA22 7JJ
☎01963 440635   Fax 01963 440825
Chairman *John H. Haynes, OBE*
Approx. Annual Turnover £27 million

FOUNDED in 1960 by John H. Haynes. A family-run business. The mainstay of its programme has been the *Owners' Workshop Manual*, first published in the mid 1960s and still running off the presses today. Indeed the company maintains a strong bias towards motoring and transport titles. *Publishes* DIY workshop manuals for cars and motorbikes, railway, aviation, military, maritime, model-making and general leisure.
IMPRINTS **G. T. Foulis & Co.** Cars and motoring-related books; **J. H. Haynes & Co.**

Ltd *Scott Mauck* Workshop manuals; **Patrick Stephens Ltd** *Darryl Reach* Motoring, rail, aviation, military, maritime, model-making; **Oxford Illustrated Press** Photography, sports and games, gardening, travel and guidebooks; **Haynes** Home and leisure titles; **Oxford Publishing Co.** Railway titles. Unsolicited mss welcome if they come within the subject areas covered.
Royalties paid annually. *Overseas subsidiaries* Haynes Publications Inc., California, USA, Editions Haynes S.A., France, Haynes Publishing Nordiska AB, Sweden.

Hazar Publishing Ltd
147 Chiswick High Road, London W4 2DT
☎0181 742 8578   Fax 0181 994 1407
Managing Director *Gregory Hill*
Editorial Head *Marie Clayton*
Approx. Annual Turnover £700,000

FOUNDED 1993, Hazar is an independent publisher of high-quality illustrated books. *Publishes* children's and adult non-fiction: picture books and pop-up books, design and architecture. About 15 titles a year.
Royalties paid twice-yearly.

Hazleton Publishing
3 Richmond Hill, Richmond, Surrey
TW10 6RE
☎0181 948 5151   Fax 0181 948 4111
Publisher/Managing Director *R. F. Poulter*

Publisher of the leading Grand Prix annual *Autocourse*, now in its 48th edition. *Publishes* high-quality motor sport titles including annuals. TITLES *Motocourse; Rallycourse; British Motorsport Year; Federal Express Championship Yearbook*. About 13 titles a year. No unsolicited mss; synopses and ideas welcome. Interested in all motor sport titles.
Royalties payment varies.

Headline/Headstart/Headway
See **Hodder Headline plc**

Health Education Authority
Publishing Department, Trevelyan House, Great Peter Street, London SW1P 2HW
☎0171 413 1846   Fax 0171 413 8912
General Manager (Publishing) *Simon Boyd*
Approx. Annual Turnover £600,000

Publishes public information leaflets, training manuals, professional guides and open learning material for the Health Education Authority. Over 500 titles in print. TITLES cover nutrition, physical activity, cancer, sexual health, oral health, immunisation, alcohol, smoking, primary health care, accidents, mental health and drugs. No unsolicited mss; synopses and ideas welcome.

William Heinemann
See **Random House UK Ltd**

Heinemann Educational
See **Reed Educational & Professional Publishing**

Heinemann Young Books
See **Reed Books**

Helicon Publishing Ltd
42 Hythe Bridge Street, Oxford OX1 2EP
☎01865 204204   Fax 01865 204205
E-mail: admin@helicon.co.uk
Managing Director *David Attwooll*
Publishing Director *Michael Upshall*
Editorial Director, Subject Reference
   Anne-Lucie Norton
Editorial Director, General Reference
   Hilary McGlynn
Approx. Annual Turnover £3.5 million

FOUNDED 1992 from the management buy-out of former Random Century's reference division. Led by David Attwooll, the buy-out included the Hutchinson encyclopedia titles and databases, along with other reference titles. The Helicon list, which is now distributed by Penguin, is increasing the range of reference titles, particularly in history, science and current affairs and is maintaining its lead in electronic publishing. TITLES *The Hutchinson Encyclopedia; The Hutchinson Almanac; Chronology of World History.* ELECTRONIC TITLES: *The Hutchinson Multimedia Encyclopedia; The Penguin Hutchinson Reference Library.*

Authors' Rating It is not long ago that Helicon was a loss-making company in the Random House Group. Now, following a successful buyout and an injection from Microsoft which has a 40% stake, Helicon is churning out reference databases for science, business, music and, latterly, history and current affairs.

Christopher Helm Publishers Ltd
See **A. & C. Black (Publishers) Ltd**

Helter Skelter Publishing
4 Denmark Street, London WC2H 8LL
☎0171 836 1151   Fax 0171 240 9880
E-mail: helter@skelter.demon.co.uk
Contact *Sean Body*

FOUNDED 1995. *Publishes* books on music and film. About 8–10 titles a year. IMPRINTS **Helter Skelter Publishing; Firefly Publishing**. Unsolicited mss, synopses and ideas welcome.

Henderson Publishing Ltd
See **Funfax Limited**

Ian Henry Publications Ltd
20 Park Drive, Romford, Essex RM1 4LH
☎01708 749119   Fax 01708 749119
Managing Director *Ian Wilkes*

FOUNDED 1976. *Publishes* local history, transport history and Sherlockian pastiches. 8–10 titles a year. TITLES *Sherlock Holmes and the Strange Events at the Bank of England; Uncle Fred's History of Westcliff; History of Hadlow; Colchester, 1835–1992.* No unsolicited mss. Synopses and ideas for books welcome.
   Royalties paid twice-yearly.

The Herbert Press
See **A. & C. Black (Publishers) Ltd**

Hermes House
See **Anness Publishing Ltd**

Nick Hern Books
The Glasshouse, 49a Goldhawk Road, London W12 8QP
☎0181 749 4953   Fax 0181 746 2006
E-mail: info@nickhernbooks.demon.co.uk
Chairman/Managing Director *Nick Hern*
Approx. Annual Turnover £300,000

FOUNDED 1988. Fully independent since 1992. *Publishes* books on theatre and film: from how-to and biography to plays and screenplays. About 30 titles a year. No unsolicited playscripts. Synopses, ideas and proposals for other theatre material welcome. Not interested in material unrelated to the theatre or cinema.

High Risk Books
See **Serpent's Tail**

Hippo
See **Scholastic Ltd**

HMSO
See **The Stationery Office Publishing**

Hobsons Publishing
Bateman Street, Cambridge CB2 1LZ
☎01223 354551   Fax 01223 323154
Chairman *Martin Morgan*
Managing Director *Christopher Letcher*

Approx. Annual Turnover £17.7 million
Founded 1973. A division of Harmsworth Publishing Ltd, part of the Daily Mail & General Trust. *Publishes* course and career guides, under exclusive licence and royalty agreements for CRAC (Careers Research and Advisory Bureau); computer software; directories and specialist titles for employers, government departments and professional associations. Titles *Graduate Employment and Training; The Student HelpBook Series; Degree Course Guides; The Which Degree Series; Which University* (CD-ROM); *The POSTGRAD Series: The Directory of Graduate Studies; The Directory of Further Education.*

Hodder & Stoughton
See **Hodder Headline plc**

Hodder Headline plc
338 Euston Road, London NW1 3BH
☎0171 873 6000   Fax 0171 873 6024
Group Chief Executive *Tim Hely Hutchinson*
Deputy Chief Executive *Mark Opzoomer*
Approx. Annual Turnover £93.2 million
Formed in June 1993 through the merger of **Headline Book Publishing** and **Hodder & Stoughton**. Headline was formed in 1986 and had grown dramatically, whereas Hodder & Stoughton was 125 years old with a diverse range of publishing. 2,200 titles in 1997.

Divisions
Headline Book Publishing Managing Director *Amanda Ridout*. **Non-fiction** *Heather Holden-Brown*; **Fiction** *Jane Morpeth*. *Publishes* commercial fiction (hardback and paperback) and popular non-fiction including biography, cinema, design and film, food and wine, countryside, TV tie-ins and sports yearbooks. Imprints **Headline**; **Headline Feature**; **Headline Review**; **Headline Delta Liaison** (erotic fiction). Authors Raymond Blanc, Harry Bowling, Martina Cole, Josephine Cox, John Francome, Dean Koontz, Richard Layman, Lyn Macdonald, James Patterson and Ellis Peters.

Hodder & Stoughton General Managing Director *Martin Nield*, Deputy Managing Director *Sue Fletcher*. **Non-fiction** *Roland Philipps*; **Sceptre** *Carole Welch*; **Fiction** *Carolyn Mays, Carolyn Caughey*; **Audio** (See entry under **Audio Books**). *Publishes* commercial and literary fiction; biography, autobiography, history, self-help, humour, travel and other general interest non-fiction; audio. Imprints **Hodder & Stoughton**; **Coronet**; **New English Library**; **Sceptre**. Authors

Melvyn Bragg, John le Carré, James Clavell, Elizabeth George, Stephen King, Stephen Leather, Gavin Lyall, Ed McBain, Malcolm Gluck and Mary Stewart, Terry Waite.

Hodder & Stoughton Educational Managing Director *Philip Walters*. **Humanities, Science & Mathematics** *Liz Wright*; **Language, Business and Psychology** *Tim Gregson-Williams*; **Teach Yourself**; **Headway** *Lucy Purkis*. Textbooks for the primary, secondary, tertiary and further education sectors and for self-improvement. Imprint **Hodder & Stoughton Educational**.

Hodder Children's Books Managing Director *Mary Tapissier*. Imprints **Hodder & Stoughton**; **Knight**; **Picture Knight**; **Hodder Dargaud**; **Headstart**; **Test Your Child**. Authors Goscinny & Uderzo (*Asterix*), Rolf Harris, Mick Inkpen, Christopher Pike.

Hodder & Stoughton Religious Managing Director *Charles Nettleton*. **Bibles & Liturgical** *Emma Sealey*; **Christian paperbacks** *Judith Longman*. Bibles, commentaries, liturgical works (both printed and software), and a wide range of Christian paperbacks. Imprints **New International Version of the Bible**; **Hodder Christian paperbacks**.

Edward Arnold Managing Director *Richard Stileman*. **Humanities** *Chris Wheeler*; **Medical, Science and Engineering** *Nicki Dennis*; **Health Sciences** *Georgina Bentliff*. Academic and professional books and journals.

The Brockhampton Press Managing Director *John Maxwell*. Promotional books.
Royalties paid twice-yearly.

Authors' Rating A record year for sales saw a decline in the number of mainline trade titles but better results for those still on the list. Strong marketing has led to the appearance of more Hodder Headline books on the supermarket shelves. New writing is encouraged and talent nurtured.

Holmes McDougall
See **HarperCollins Publishers Ltd**

Holt Rinehart & Winston
See **Harcourt Brace and Company Limited**

Honeyglen Publishing Ltd
56 Durrels House, Warwick Gardens, London W14 8QB
☎0171 602 2876   Fax 0171 602 2876
Directors *N. S. Poderegin, J. Poderegin*
Founded 1983. A small publishing house

whose output is 'extremely limited'. *Publishes* history, philosophy of history, biography and selective fiction. No children's or science fiction. TITLES *The Soul of India; A Child of the Century* Amaury de Riencourt; *With Duncan Grant in South Turkey* Paul Roche; *Vladimir, The Russian Viking* Vladimir Volkoff; *The Dawning* Milka Bajic-Poderegin; *Quicksand* Louise Hide. Unsolicited mss welcome.

House of Lochar
Isle of Colonsay, Argyll PA61 7YR
☎01951 200232   Fax 01951 200232
E-mail: Lochar@colonsay.org.uk
Chairman *Kevin Byrne*
Managing Director *Georgina Hobhouse*
Approx. Annual Turnover £80,000

FOUNDED 1995 on the basis of some 24 titles formerly published by Thomas and Lochar of Nairn. *Publishes* Scottish fiction and non-fiction – history, topography, transport. IMPRINTS **House of Lochar** *Kevin Byrne* TITLES *Country Houses of Scotland; The Light in the Glen; The Rise and Fall of the Puffer Trade.* **Colonsay Books** *Georgina Hobhouse* TITLES *Summer in the Hebrides; Place Names of Colonsay and Oronsay; Antiquities of Colonsay.* No poetry or books unrelated to Scotland or Celtic theme. Unsolicited mss, synopses and ideas welcome if relevant to subjects covered.
Royalties paid annually.

How To Books Ltd
3 Newtec Place, Magdalen Road, Oxford OX4 1RE
☎01865 247711   Fax 01865 248780
Managing Director *Giles Lewis*

There are well over 200 titles in the How To Books series, many in revised and updated new editions. TITLES take the form of 'how to achieve a specific goal or benefit' in the areas of employment, business, education, general reference, international opportunities, computer basics, personal finance, writing and self-development: *Getting A Job In America; Managing Budgets and Cash Flows; Thriving On Stress.* Well-structured proposals from qualified and experienced writers welcome.
Royalties paid annually.

The University of Hull Press/ The Lampada Press
Cottingham Road, Hull, East Yorkshire HU6 7RX
☎01482 466532   Fax 01482 466858
E-mail: g.m.innes@admin.hull.ac.uk

Publisher *Glen Innes*

Publishes books of academic interest principally in the fields of history (maritime, medieval and colonial), literary and media studies, British art, music and regional studies. Also publishes the series *EastNote, Hull Studies in Jazz* and *Swerving East,* a new poetry imprint. TITLES *Larkin at Work* Trevor Tolley; *Dimensions of Sea Power* eds. Dr Eric Grove and Capt. Peter Hore RN; *The Devon Gentleman, A Life of Sir Peter Carew* John Wagner; *Les Lieux Interdit, Transgressions in French Literature* eds. Larry Duffy and Adrian Tudor. **The Lampada Press** *publishes* work of a more general interest. TITLES *Thank God I'm Not A Boy, the letters of Dora Willat 1915–18* ed. Alan Wilkinson; *Musicians in Time* Jenny Boyd. Welcomes unsolicited mss, synopses and ideas for books.
Royalties paid annually. *Overseas representatives*: Paul & Co., USA; St Clair Press, Australia.

Human Horizons
See **Souvenir Press Ltd**

Human Science Press
See **Plenum Publishing Ltd**

Hunt & Thorpe
Deershot Lodge, Park Lane, Ropley, Nr Alresford, Hampshire SO24 0BE
☎01962 773063   Fax 01962 772475
E-mail: Hunt&Thorpe@compuserve.com
Approx. Annual Turnover £1.5 million

Publishes children's and religious titles only – about 25 a year. Unsolicited material welcome.

C. Hurst & Co.
38 King Street, London WC2E 8JZ
☎0171 240 2666   Fax 0171 240 2667
Chairman/Managing Director
  Christopher Hurst
Editorial Heads *Christopher Hurst, Michael Dwyer*

FOUNDED 1967. An independent company, cultivating a concern for literacy, detail and the visual aspects of the product. *Publishes* contemporary history, politics and social science. About 20 titles a year. TITLES *The Origins of Japanese Trade Supremacy; The Rwanda Crisis – History of a Genocide; Listening People, Speaking Earth: Contemporary Paganism; Yugoslavia's Bloody Collapse; Following Ho Chi Minh – Memoirs of a North Vietnamese Colonel.* No unsolicited mss. Synopses and ideas welcome.
Royalties paid twice in first year, annually thereafter.

Hutchinson
See **Random House UK Ltd**

Hymns Ancient & Modern Ltd
St Mary's Works, St Mary's Plain, Norwich, Norfolk NR3 3BH
☎01603 616563   Fax 01603 624483
Chairman *Very Rev. Dr Henry Chadwick KBE*
Chief Executive *G. A. Knights*
Publisher, The Canterbury Press Norwich *Christine Smith*
Publisher, RMEP *Mary Mears*
Approx. Annual Turnover £4 million

Publishes hymn books for churches, schools and other institutions. All types of religious books, both general and educational. Owns **SCM Press Ltd** (see entry).
IMPRINTS **The Canterbury Press Norwich** General religious books TITLES *The Desert; Stars and Angels; Every Gate; Pilgrim Guides.* **Chansitor Publications Ltd** TITLES *The Sign; Home Words* – two monthly, nationwide parish magazine inserts. **Religious and Moral Education Press (RMEP)** Religious books for schools, primary, middle secondary, assembly material, etc. **G. J. Palmer & Sons Ltd** TITLES *Church Times* (see entry under **Magazines**). Ideas welcome; no mss.
Royalties paid annually.

Icon Books Ltd
Grange Road, Duxford, Cambridge CB2 4QF
☎01763 208008   Fax 01763 208080
Managing Director *Peter Pugh*
Editorial Head *Richard Appignanesi*
Publishing Director *Jeremy Cox*

FOUNDED 1992. SERIES **Beginners** Cartoon introductions to the key figures and issues in the history of science, psychology, philosophy, religion and the arts TITLES *Psychology for Beginners; Western Philosophy for Beginners;* **Critical Guides** Student guides to critical writings TITLES *James Joyce's Ulysses; Virginia Woolf's To the Lighthouse and The Waves.* **Critical Dictionaries** 'The most recent thinking and the issues under debate in key areas of current thought.' TITLES *The New Cosmology; Global Economics.* Launched **Spectator Guides to the Major Sports** in 1998 TITLES *Football; Cricket; Golf; Boxing.* 63 titles in print. No unsolicited mss; synopses and ideas for information non-fiction welcome.
Royalties paid twice yearly. *Overseas associates* Totem Books, USA.

Idol
See **Virgin Publishing Ltd**

Indigo
See **Cassell**

The Industrial Society
Robert Hyde House, 48 Bryanston Square, London W1H 7LN
☎0171 479 2000   Fax 0171 723 7375
E-mail: infoserve@undusoc.demon.co.uk
Head of Publishing *Carl Upsall*
Approx. Annual Turnover (publishing division)£1.6 million

Industrial Society Publications, which is part of The Industrial Society (a registered charity committed to making work fulfilling), has been publishing books for approximately 20 years. *Specialises* in business, management, self-development, training, staff development, human resources – both books and special reports. 10 titles in 1997. TITLES *Communication Skills – A Practical Handbook; Fifty Ways to Personal Development; Body Talk – Skills of Positive Image.* Unsolicited mss, synopses and ideas welcome. No fiction or illustrated non-fiction.
Royalties paid annually.

Institute of Personnel and Development
IPD House, Camp Road, London SW19 4UX
☎0181 263 3387

Part of IPD Enterprises Limited. *Publishes* management and training. 30 titles in 1997. Unsolicited mss, synopses and ideas welcome.
Royalties paid annually.

Inter Publishing Ltd
St Nicholas House, The Mount, Guildford, Surrey GU2 4HN
☎01483 306309   Fax 01483 579196
Managing Director *David Wavre*
Approx. Annual Turnover £500,000

FOUNDED 1990. *Publishes* religious plus some gift and art books. About 24 titles a year. IMPRINT **Eagle**. Unsolicited mss, synopses and ideas for books welcome.
Royalties paid quarterly.

Inter-Varsity Press
38 De Montfort Street, Leicester LE1 7GP
☎0116 2551754   Fax 0116 2542044
Chairman *Ralph Evershed*
Chief Executive *Frank Entwistle*

FOUNDED mid-30s as the publishing arm of Universities and Colleges Christian Fellowship, it has expanded to wider Christian markets worldwide. *Publishes* Christian belief and lifestyle, reference and bible commentaries. About 50 titles a year. No secular material or anything which fails to empathise with orthodox Protestant Christianity.

IMPRINTS **IVP**; **Apollos**; **Crossway** TITLES *The Bible Speaks Today; Sociology through the Eyes of Faith* Campolo & Fraser. No unsolicited mss; synopses and ideas welcome.

Royalties paid twice-yearly.

Intrigue
See **Harlequin Mills & Boon Ltd**

Invincible Press
See **HarperCollins Publishers Ltd**

Isis Publishing Limited
7 Centremead, Osney Mead, Oxford OX2 0ES
☎01865 250333   Fax 01865 790358
Managing Director *John Durrant*

Publishes large-print books – fiction and non-fiction; audio books (see entry under **Audio Books**). TITLES *The Colour of Magic* Terry Pratchett; *Return to Sunset House* Lady Fortescue; *Christine* Stephen King. No unsolicited mss as Isis undertakes no original publishing.

Royalties paid twice-yearly.

Ithaca Press
See **Garnet Publishing Ltd**

IVP
See **Inter-Varsity Press**

JAI Press Ltd
38 Tavistock Street, London WC2E 7PB
☎0171 379 8834   Fax 0171 379 8835
E-mail: jai@cix.co.uk
Chairman *Herbert M. Johnson*
Managing Director *Piers R. Allen*

FOUNDED 1976. Subsidiary of JAI Press Inc., USA. *Publishes* research-level scholarly publications in business, economics, social sciences, education, language and psychology, communication sciences, chemistry and life sciences, library and information sciences under JAI Press and Ablex imprints. *Specialises* in the publication of research serials and monograph series, as well as journals. About 220 book titles a year. TITLES *Advances in Biosensors; Research in Organizational Behavior; Research in Accounting in Emerging Economies; Studies in Qualitative Methodology; The Hundred Languages of Children.*

No undergraduate texts. Unsolicited mss discouraged. Synopses and ideas welcome.

Royalties paid annually. *Overseas associates* JAI Press Inc./Ablex Publishing Corp., Greenwich, Connecticut, USA.

Arthur James Ltd
40 Lower Kings Road, Berkhamsted, Hertfordshire HP4 2AA
☎01442 877511   Fax 01442 873019
E-mail: 101666.2033@compuserve.com

Editorial Office: Deershot Lodge, Park Lane, Ropley, Nr Alresford, Hampshire SO24 0BE
Managing Director *Ian Carlile*
Editorial Director *Mr J. Hunt*
Approx. Annual Turnover £250,000

FOUNDED in 1944 by a Fleet Street journalist, A. J. Russell. *Publishes* day books, devotional classics, psychological, healing, religious, social work and *New Testament* translations. AUTHORS include Karen Armstrong, William Barclay, Jacques Duquesne, Laurence Freeman, Monica Furlong, Rosemary Harthill, Sara Maitland, Mary McAleese, Chuck Spezzano, Angela Tilby, Robert Van de Weyer, Marina Warner, John Woolley. No unsolicited mss.

Royalties paid annually. *Overseas associates* Morehouse Publishing, USA; Buchanan, Australia; Omega, New Zealand.

Jane's Information Group
163 Brighton Road, Coulsdon, Surrey CR5 2NH
☎0181 700 3700   Fax 0181 763 1006
Managing Director *Alfred Rolington*

FOUNDED 1898 by Fred T. Jane with the publication of *All The World's Fighting Ships*. Now part of The Thomson Corporation. In recent years management, has been focusing on growth opportunities in its core business and in enhancing the performance of initiatives like Jane's yearbooks on CD-ROM. *Publishes* magazines and yearbooks on defence, aerospace and transport topics, with details of equipment and systems; plus directories and strategic studies. Also *Jane's Defence Weekly* (see entry under **Magazines**).

DIVISIONS
Magazines *Janine Boxall* TITLES *Jane's Defence Weekly; Jane's International Defense Review; Jane's Airport Review; Jane's Defence Upgrades; Jane's Navy International.* **Publishing** *Alan Condron* TITLES *Defence, Aerospace Yearbooks; Jane's Intelligence Review; Foreign Report; Jane's Sentinel* (regional security assessment). **Transport** *Harry*

Puckering TITLES *Transportation Yearbooks*; CD-ROM and electronic development and publication. Unsolicited mss, synopses and ideas for reference/yearbooks welcome.

Royalties paid twice-yearly. *Overseas associates* Jane's Information Group Inc., USA.

Janus Publishing Company Ltd

Edinburgh House, 19 Nassau Street, London W1N 7RE
☎0171 580 7664   Fax 0171 636 5756
E-mail: publisher@januspublishing.co.uk

Managing Director *Ronald Ross Stanton*

Publishes fiction, human interest, memoirs/biography, mind, body and spirit, religion and theology, social questions, popular science, history, spiritualism and the paranormal, poetry and young adults. About 70 titles. TITLES *World Cup 1998 – A definitive history and guide* Simon Shirley; *The Essential Guide to Learning Martial Arts* Carol Anne Strange; *Anarchists in the Spanish Civil War* Prof. Robert Alexander; *To Be A Saudi* Hani A. Z. Yamani; *Philby – The Hidden Years* Morris Riley. Unsolicited mss welcome.

Royalties paid twice-yearly. Agents in the USA, Australia, South Africa and Asia.

Authors' Rating Authors may be asked to cover their own productions costs.

Japan Library
See **Curzon Press Ltd**

Jarrold Publishing

Whitefriars, Norwich, Norfolk NR3 1TR
☎01603 763300   Fax 01603 662748

Chairman *Peter Jarrold*
Managing Director *Paul Bullen-Smith*

Part of Jarrold & Sons Ltd, the printing and publishing company FOUNDED in 1770. *Publishes* cookery, UK tourism and travel, sports and leisure, history, gift books and calendars. Material tends to be of a high pictorial content. About 30 titles a year. Unsolicited mss, synopses and ideas welcome but before submitting anything, approach in writing to Donald Greig, Managing Editor.

Royalties paid twice-yearly.

Jensen Business Books
See **AMCD (Publishers) Ltd**

Jets
See **HarperCollins Publishers Ltd**

Jewish Chronicle Publications
See **Frank Cass & Co Ltd**

Michael Joseph
See **Penguin UK**

Kahn & Averill

9 Harrington Road, London SW7 3ES
☎0181 743 3278   Fax 0181 743 3278

Managing Director *Mr M. Kahn*

FOUNDED 1967 to publish children's titles but now specialises in music titles. A small independent publishing house. *Publishes* music and general non-fiction. No unsolicited mss; synopses and ideas for books considered.

Royalties paid twice-yearly.

Karnak House

300 Westbourne Park Road, London W11 1EH
☎0171 243 3620   Fax 0171 243 3620

Chairman *Dimela Yekwai*
Managing Director *Amon Saba Saakana*

FOUNDED 1979. *Specialises* in African and Caribbean studies. *Publishes* anthropology, education, Egyptology, history, language and linguistics, literary criticism, music, parapsychology, prehistory. No poetry, humour or sport. About 12 titles a year. No unsolicited mss; send introduction or synopsis with one sample chapter. Synopses and ideas welcome.

Royalties paid twice-yearly. *Overseas subsidiaries* The Antef Institute, and Karnak House, Illinois, USA.

Keele University Press
See **Edinburgh University Press**

Sebastian Kelly
See **Anness Publishing Ltd**

Kelpie
See **Canongate Books Ltd**

Kenilworth Press Ltd

Addington, Buckingham, Buckinghamshire MK18 2JR
☎01296 715101   Fax 01296 715148
E-mail: editorial@kenilworthpress.co.uk

Chairman/Managing Director *David Blunt*
Approx. Annual Turnover £500,000

FOUNDED 1989 with the acquisition of Threshhold Books. The UK's principal instructional equestrian publisher, producing the official books of the British Horse Society, the famous *Threshold Picture Guides*, and a range of authoritative titles sold around the world. About 10 titles a year.

IMPRINTS **Kenilworth Press** TITLES *British*

Horse Society Manuals; Endurance Riding: From First Steps to 100 Miles; A Modern Horse Herbal; Learn to Ride Using Sports Psychology; Threshold Picture Guides 1–41. Unsolicited mss, synopses and ideas welcome but only for titles concerned with the care or riding of horses or ponies.
Royalties paid twice-yearly.

Kenyon-Deane
See **Cressrelles Publishing Co. Ltd**

Laurence King
71 Great Russell Street, London WC1B 3BN
☎0171 831 6351   Fax 0171 831 8356
Chairman *Robin Hyman*
Managing Director *Laurence King*
E-mail: calmann_king@compuserve.com
FOUNDED 1991. Publishing imprint of UK packager **Calmann & King Ltd** (see entry under **UK Packagers**). *Publishes* full-colour illustrated books on art history, the decorative arts, carpets and textiles, graphic design, architecture and interior design. Unsolicited material welcome.
Royalties paid twice-yearly.

Kingfisher Publications plc
New Penderel House, 283–288 High Holborn, London WC1V 7HZ
☎0171 903 9999   Fax 0171 242 4979
Chairman *Bertil Hessel*
Formerly known as Larousse plc, the name was changed to Kingfisher Publications plc in 1997. FOUNDED 1994 when owners, Groupe de la Cité (also publishers of the Larousse dictionaries in France), merged their UK operations of **Grisewood & Dempsey** and **Chambers Harrap Publishers Ltd**.
DIVISIONS
Kingfisher *Ann-Janine Murtagh*, Publishing Director, Fiction, *Gill Denton* Non-fiction. Founded in 1973 by **Grisewood & Dempsey Ltd**. *Publishes* children's fiction and non-fiction in hardback and paperback: story books, rhymes and picture books, fiction and poetry anthologies, young non-fiction, activity books, general series and reference.
Chambers, Harrap Publishers IMPRINT **Chambers** *Maurice Shepherd* Editorial offices: 7 Hopetoun Crescent, Edinburgh EH7 4AY. ☎0131 556 5929 Fax: 0131 556 5313. *Publishes* dictionaries, reference, and local interest. The imprint was founded in the early 1800s to publish self-education books, but soon diversified into dictionaries and other reference works. Acquired by Groupe de la Cité in 1989. The acquisition of Harrap Publishing Group's core business strengthened its position in the dictionary market, adding bilingual titles, covering almost all the major European languages, to its English-language dictionaries. Send synopsis with accompanying letter rather than completed mss.
Royalties paid bi-annually where applicable.

Jessica Kingsley Publishers Ltd
116 Pentonville Road, London N1 9JB
☎0171 833 2307   Fax 0171 837 2917
Managing Director *Jessica Kingsley*
Senior Editor *Charles Catton*
Editor *Helen Parry*
FOUNDED 1987. Independent publisher of books for professionals and academics on social and behavioural sciences, including special needs arts therapies, child psychology, psychotherapy (including forensic psychotherapy), psycho-analysis, social work, regional studies and higher education policy. About 75 titles a year. TITLE *Asperger Syndrome – A Guide for Parents and Professionals* Tony Attwood. 'We are actively publishing and commissioning in autism and Asperger Syndrome. We welcome suggestions for books and proposals from prospective authors. Proposals should consist of an outline of the book, a contents list, assessment of the market, and author's c.v. and should be addressed to Jessica Kingsley. Complete manuscript should not be sent.' No fiction or poetry.
Royalties paid twice-yearly.

Kingsway Publications
Lottbridge Drove, Eastbourne, East Sussex BN23 6NT
☎01323 437740   Fax 01323 411970
Chairman *Peter Fenwick*
Managing Director *John Paculabo*
Editorial Contact *Mrs L. Truesdale*
Approx. Annual Turnover £1.5 million
Part of Kingsway Communications Ltd, a charitable trust with Christian objectives. *Publishes* Christian books: Bibles, Christian testimonies, renewal issues. No poetry please. About 35 titles a year.
IMPRINT **Kingsway** TITLES *The Life Application Bible; Will God Heal Me?* Ron Dunn; *The Sermon on the Mount* Rob Warner; *The Heart of Revival* Nicky Gumbel. Partial submissions/synopses preferred. Return postage appreciated; all submissions should be addressed to the Editorial Department.
Royalties paid twice-yearly.

Kluwer Law International
Sterling House, 66 Wilton Road, London
SW1V 1DE
☎0171 821 1123   Fax 0171 630 5229
Director of Operations *Marcel Nieuwenhuis*
FOUNDED 1995. Parent company: Wolters
Kluwer Group. Kluwer Law International con-
sists of three components: the law list of Graham
& Trotman, Kluwer Law and Taxation and
Martinus Nyhoff. *Publishes* international law.
Plans to publish 200 titles a year. Unsolicited
synopses and ideas for books on law at an inter-
national level welcome.
   Royalties paid annually. North American
sales and marketing: Kluwer Law International,
675 Massachusetts Avenue, Cambridge, MA
02139.

Knight
See **Hodder Headline plc**

Charles Knight Publishing
See **Tolley Publishing Co Ltd**

Kogan Page Ltd
120 Pentonville Road, London N1 9JN
☎0171 278 0433   Fax 0171 837 3768/6348
Managing Director *Philip Kogan*
Approx. Annual Turnover £8 million
FOUNDED 1967 by Philip Kogan to publish *The
Industrial Training Yearbook*. In 1992 acquired
Earthscan Publications and launched a new
management research series. *Publishes* business
and management reference books and monographs, education and careers, marketing, personal finance, personnel, small business, training
and industrial relations, transport, plus journals.
Further expansion is planned, particularly in the
finance and high-tech, EC publications areas,
yearbooks and directories, and international
business reference. About 240 titles a year.
DIVISIONS **Kogan Page** *Pauline Goodwin,
Philip Mudd, Peter Chadwick.* TITLE *Single Market
Review* (39 vols.). **Earthscan Publications**
Jonathan Sinclair Wilson Has close associations
with the International Institute for Environment
and Development and with the Worldwide
Fund for Nature. *Publishes* Third World issues
and their global implications, and general envi-
ronmental titles, both popular and academic.
About 50 titles a year. TITLE *European
Environmental Technology Directory.* Unsolicited
mss, synopses and ideas for books welcome.
   Royalties paid twice-yearly.

Authors' Rating The biggest and the best

independent publisher of business books thrives
on strong marketing particularly in airports and
other gathering places for hungry executives.

Ladybird Books Ltd
Beeches Road, Loughborough, Leicestershire
LE11 2NQ
☎01509 268021   Fax 01509 234672
Chair *Michael Lynton*
Managing Director *L. F. A. James*
Publishing Director *M. Herridge*
International Director *D. King*
Approx. Annual Turnover £20 million
FOUNDED in the 1860s. Introduced just before
the First World War, the Ladybird name and
format was fully established as a result of the
development of a children's list during the
Second World War. In the early 1960s the
commercial print side of the operation was
abandoned in favour of publishing Ladybird
titles only and in 1971 the company was
bought by the Pearson Longman Group. From
1st January 1995, Ladybird has been integrated
into the Penguin Group. *Publishes* children's
consumer books for the mass market internationally, with an emphasis on the 0–3, 1–3,
3–5 and 5–8 age range. About 200 titles a year.
   IMPRINTS **Ladybird**; **Picture Ladybird**;
Disney. TITLES *Stories for Bedtime; Gulliver's
Travels; Teddy Bear Storytime; Alphabet Songs;
The Railway Children; Whales and Dolphins; Big
Machines; The Victorians; Jemima Puddleduck;
The Borrowers; Winnie the Pooh*; plus the
Ladybird audio cassette/book series (see entry
under **Audio Books**). No unsolicited mss;
synopses and ideas welcome; no poetry.

The Lampada Press
See **The University of Hull Press**

Larousse plc
See **Kingfisher Publications plc**

Lawrence & Wishart Ltd
99A Wallis Road, London E9 5LN
☎0181 533 2506   Fax 0181 533 7369
Managing Director *Sally Davison*
Editors *Sally Davison, Bertie Vitry*
FOUNDED 1936. An independent publisher with
a substantial backlist. *Publishes* current affairs, cultural politics, economics, history, politics and
education. 15–20 titles a year. TITLES *Between
War and Peace: The Political Future of Northern
Ireland; Forever England: Reflections on Masculinity
and Empire; After Maastricht: A Guide to European*

Monetary Union. Synopses preferred to complete mss. Ideas welcome.

Royalties paid annually, unless by arrangement.

Authors' Rating One of the few genuine left-wing publishers. Authors should expect to surrender profit to principles.

Lehigh University Press
See **Golden Cockerel Press Ltd**

Leicester University Press
See **Cassell**

Lennard Associates Ltd
Windmill Cottage, Mackerye End, Harpenden, Hertfordshire AL5 5DR
☎01582 715866   Fax 01582 715121
Chairman/Managing Director
Adrian Stephenson

FOUNDED 1979. Publisher of sporting yearbooks, personality books, and television associated titles. TITLES *The Cricketers' Who's Who; Official PFA Footballers' Factfile; Wooden Spoon Society Rugby World; British Boxing Yearbook.* No unsolicited mss.

IMPRINTS **Lennard Publishing; Queen Anne Press.** Acquired the latter and most of its assets in 1992.

Payment Both fees and royalties by arrangement.

Charles Letts
See **New Holland (Publishers) Ltd**

Levinson Children's Books
Winchester House, 259–261 Old Marylebone Road, London NW1 5XJ
☎0171 616 7200   Fax 0171 616 7201
Editorial Director *Neil Burden*

FOUNDED 1994. Acquired by **David & Charles Publishers** in 1997. *Publishes* novelty and picture books for the under-sevens. Unsolicited mss, synopses and ideas welcome.

Royalties paid twice-yearly.

Liaison
See **Hodder Headline plc**

John Libbey & Co. Ltd
13 Smiths Yard, Summerley Street, London SW18 4HR
☎0181 947 2777   Fax 0181 947 2664
E-mail: libbey@earlsfield.win-uk.net
Chairman/Managing Director *John Libbey*

FOUNDED 1979. *Publishes* medical books and cinema/animation books and journals. *Specialises*

in epilepsy, neurology, nuclear medicine, nutrition, obesity and oncology. Synopses and ideas welcome. *Overseas subsidiaries* John Libbey Eurotext Ltd, France; John Libbey & Co. Pty. Ltd, Australia.

Librapharm Ltd
3 Thames Court, High Street, Goring–on–Thames, Reading, Berkshire RG8 9AR
☎01491 875252   Fax 01635 875200
Chairman *Dr R. B. Smith*
Managing Director *Dr P. L. Clarke*
Approx. Annual Turnover £500,000

FOUNDED 1995 as a partial buyout from Kluwer Academic Publishers (UK) academic list. *Publishes* medical and scientific books and periodicals. 25 titles a year. IMPRINT **Petroc Press.** TITLES *Fry's Common Diseases; Neighbour: The Inner Consultation; Current Medical Research and Opinion* (journal). Unsolicited mss, synopses and ideas for medical books welcome.

Royalties paid twice-yearly.

Library Association Publishing
7 Ridgmount Street, London WC1E 7AE
☎0171 636 7543   Fax 0171 636 3627
Chairman *Michael Curtis*
Managing Director *Janet Liebster*

Publishing arm of **The Library Association.** *Publishes* library and information science, monographs, reference, IT books and bibliography. About 35 titles a year.

IMPRINTS **Library Association Publishing; Clive Bingley Books** Over 200 titles in print, including *Walford's Guide to Reference Material* and *AACR2.* Unsolicited mss, synopses and ideas welcome provided material falls firmly within the company's specialist subject areas.

Royalties paid annually.

Frances Lincoln Ltd
4 Torriano Mews, Torriano Avenue, London, NW5 2RZ
☎0171 284 4009   Fax 0171 267 5249
Managing Director *Frances Lincoln*

FOUNDED 1977. *Publishes* highly illustrated non-fiction: gardening, interiors, health, crafts, cookery; children's picture and information books, art and religion books; and stationery. About 45 titles a year.

DIVISIONS
Adult Non-fiction *Erica Hunningher* TITLES *Penelope Hobhouse's Garden Designs* Penelope Hobhouse; *Charleston* Virginia Nicholson and

Quentin Bell; *Healthy Indian Cooking* Shehzad Husain; **Children's General Fiction and Non-fiction** *Janetta Otter-Barry* TITLES *The Wanderings of Odysseus* Rosemary Sutcliffe, illus. Alan Lee; *Amazing Grace, Grace & Family* Mary Hoffman, illus. Caroline Binch; **Children's Art and Religion** *Kate Cave* TITLES *My Sticker Art Gallery* Carole Armstrong; *Stories from the New Testament* illustrated with paintings from the National Gallery; *The Illuminated Haggadah* illustrated with ancient haggadot from the collection at the British Museum. Synopses and ideas for books considered.
Royalties paid twice-yearly.

Linden Press
See **Centaur Press**

Lion Publishing
Peter's Way, Sandy Lane West, Oxford OX4 5HG
☎01865 747550   Fax 01865 747568
Managing Director *Paul Clifford*
Approx. Annual Turnover £6.4 million
FOUNDED 1971. A Christian book publisher, strong on illustrated books for a popular international readership, with rights sold in over 100 languages worldwide. *Publishes* a diverse list with Christian viewpoint the common denominator. All ages, from board books for children to multi-contributor adult reference, educational, paperbacks and colour co-editions and gift books.

DIVISIONS
Adult *Lois Rock*; **Children's** *Su Box*; **Giftlines** *Meryl Doney*. Unsolicited mss welcome provided they have a positive Christian viewpoint intended for a wide general and international readership. Synopses, proposals and ideas also welcome.
Royalties paid twice-yearly.

Little, Brown & Co. (UK)
Brettenham House, Lancaster Place, London WC2E 7EN
☎0171 911 8000   Fax 0171 911 8100
Chief Executive/Publisher *Philippa Harrison*
Approx. Annual Turnover £34.6 million
FOUNDED 1988. Part of Time-Warner Inc. Began by importing its US parent company's titles and in 1990 launched its own illustrated non-fiction list. Two years later the company took over former Macdonald & Co. *Publishes* hardback and paperback fiction, literary fiction, crime, science fiction and fantasy; and general non-fiction, including illustrated: architecture and design, fine art, photography, biography and autobiography, cinema, gardening, history, humour, travel, crafts and hobbies, reference, cookery, wines and spirits, DIY, guidebooks, natural history and nautical.

IMPRINTS **Abacus** *Richard Beswick* Literary fiction and non-fiction paperbacks; **Orbit** *Tim Holman* Science fiction and fantasy; **Little Brown/Warner** *Alan Samson, Barbara Boote, Hilary Hale* Mass-market fiction and non-fiction; **X Libris** *Helen Pisano* Women's erotica; **Illustrated** *Julia Charles* Hardbacks; **Virago** (see entry). Approach in writing in the first instance. No unsolicited mss.
Royalties paid twice-yearly.

Authors' Rating Combines editorial inspiration with strong marketing, living proof that quality can thrive in a highly competitive market.

Liverpool University Press
Senate House, Abercromby Square, Liverpool L69 3BX
☎0151 794 2233   Fax 0151 794 2235
Managing Director/Editorial Head
  Robin Bloxsidge
The principal activity of LUP, since its foundation in 1899, has been in the humanities and social sciences. *Publishes* academic and scholarly hardback and paperback books in the fields of archaeology, education, geography, ancient and modern history, science fiction criticism, modern French literature, English literature, Hispanic languages and literature, town planning and veterinary medicine. 30–40 titles a year. TITLES *Life of the Ancient Egyptians; Form and Fancy: Factories and Factory Buildings by Wallis, Gilbert & Partners; Public Sculpture of Liverpool; Behold the Hero: General Wolfe and the Visual Arts in the Eighteenth Century; If the Isish ran the World: Montserrat, 1630–1730; An Atlas of Victorian Mortality.* Unsolicited mss, synopses and ideas for books welcome.
Royalties paid annually.

Livewire Books for Teenagers
See **The Women's Press**

Living Books
Allen House, Station Road, Egham, Surrey TW20 9NT
☎01784 431000   Fax 01784 431382
Vice President (Europe) *Jo Wood*
Vice President (Europe) *Pilar Cloud*
FOUNDED 1994. Subsidiary of the US leading producer of children's multimedia storybooks

on CD-ROM. Part of Broderbund Software Ltd.

IMPRINT **Living Books/TAG Developments** TITLES *Dr Seuss' ABC; The Cat in the Hat; Green Eggs and Ham; Sheila Rae; The Brave; Just Grandma and Me; Harry and the Haunted House, Teacher's Guide; Little Monster at School, Teacher's Guide; The Tortoise and the Hare, Teacher's Guide; Arthur's Birthday, Teacher's Guide.* No unsolicited mss.

Lorenz Books
See **Anness Publishing Ltd**

Peter Lowe (Eurobook Ltd)
PO Box 52, Wallingford, Oxfordshire OX10 0XU
☎01865 858333   Fax 01865 858263
Managing Director *Peter Lowe*
FOUNDED 1968. *Publishes* children's natural history, popular science and illustrated adult non-fiction. No unsolicited mss; synopses and ideas (with s.a.e.) welcome. No adult fiction.

Lund Humphries Publishers Ltd
Park House, 1 Russell Gardens, London NW11 9NN
☎0181 458 6314   Fax 0181 905 5245
Chairman *Lionel Leventhal*
Editorial Director *Lucy Myers*
Publisher of fine art books. First title appeared in 1895. *Publishes* art, architecture, photography, design and graphics. Publishers of exhibition catalogues in association with museums and galleries, and of the annual *Calendar of Art Exhibitions*. About 20 titles a year. Unsolicited mss welcome but initial introductory letter preferred. Synopses and ideas for books considered.
Royalties paid twice-yearly.

The Lutterworth Press
PO Box 60, Cambridge CB1 2NT
☎01223 350865   Fax 01223 366951
E-mail: lutterworth.pr@dial.pipex.com
Website: http://dialspace.dial.pipex.com/lutterworth.pr
Managing Director *Adrian Brink*
The Lutterworth Press dates back to the 18th century when it was founded by the Religious Tract Society. In the 19th century it was best known for its children's books, both religious and secular, including *The Boys' Own Paper*. Since 1984 it has been an imprint of **James Clarke & Co**. *Publishes* religious books for children and adults, children's fiction and non-fiction, adult non-fiction. TITLES *Lutterworth*

Dictionary of the Bible; Bravo, Persevere!; OU Men: Work Through Lifelong Learning. Approach in writing with ideas in the first instance.
Royalties paid annually.

Authors' Rating The list is expanding but it still has its anchor in evangelical publishing. Imaginative children's list.

Lynx
See **Society for Promoting Christian Knowledge**

Macdonald & Co.
See **Little, Brown & Co. (UK)**

Macdonald Young Books
See **Wayland Publishers Ltd**

McGraw-Hill Publishing Company
McGraw-Hill House, Shoppenhangers Road, Maidenhead, Berkshire SL6 2QL
☎01628 502500   Fax 01628 770224
Group Vice President, Europe *Italo Raimondi*
FOUNDED 1899. Owned by US parent company. Began publishing in Maidenhead in 1965. *Publishes* business and economics, accountancy, finance, computer science, and business computing for the academic, student and professional markets. Around 50 titles a year. Unsolicited mss, synopses and ideas welcome.
Royalties paid twice-yearly.

Macmillan Publishers Ltd
25 Eccleston Place, London SW1W 9NF
☎0171 881 8000   Fax 0171 881 8001
Chairman *Nicholas Byam Shaw*
Chief Executive *Richard Charkin*
Approx. Annual Turnover £90 million (Book Publishing Group)
FOUNDED 1843. Macmillan is one of the largest publishing houses in Britain, publishing approximately 1400 titles a year. In 1995, Verlagsgruppe Georg von Holtzbrink, a major German publisher, acquired a majority stake in the Macmillan Group. In 1996, Macmillan bought Boxtree, the successful media tie-in publisher and, in 1997, purchased the Heinemann English language teaching list from Reed Elsevier. Unsolicited proposals, synopses and mss are welcome in all divisions of the company (with the exception of Macmillan Children's Books). Authors who wish to send material to Macmillan General Books should note that there is a central submissions procedure in operation. Send a synopsis

and the first 3–4 chapters (sorry, we can't accept submissions on disk) with a covering letter and return postage to the Submissions Editor, 25 Eccleston Place, London SW1W 9NF.

DIVISIONS

Macmillan Press Ltd Brunel Road, Houndsmill, Basingstoke, Hampshire RG21 6XS ☎01256 29242 Fax 01256 479476 Managing Director *Dominic Knight*. **Academic** *T. M. Farmiloe*; **College** *S. Kennedy*; **Business and Economics** *S. Rutt*. *Publishes* textbooks and monographs in academic, professional and vocational subjects; medical and scientific journals; directories. Publications in both hard copy and electronic format.

Macmillan Education Basingstoke (address as for Macmillan Press). Managing Director *Chris Harrison*, Publishing Director *Alison Hubert*. *Publishes* regional ELT titles and a wide list for the international education market.

Macmillan General Books (Eccleston Place address). Managing Director *Ian S. Chapman*, Editor-in-Chief *Clare Alexander*. Publishes under **Macmillan, Pan, Picador, Papermac, Sidgwick & Jackson**

Macmillan (FOUNDED 1865) Editorial Directors (fiction) *Suzanne Baboneau, Beverley Cousins*. *Publishes* novels, detective fiction, sci-fi, fantasy and horror. Editors (non-fiction) *Georgina Morley, Tanya Stobbs, Catherine Whitaker*. *Publishes* autobiography, biography, business and industry, economics, gift books, health and beauty, history, humour, natural history, travel, philosophy, politics and world affairs, psychology, film and theatre, gardening and cookery, encyclopedias, popular science.

Pan (FOUNDED 1947) Publisher *Clare Harington*. *Publishes* fiction: novels, detective fiction, sci-fi, fantasy and horror. Non-fiction: general non-fiction, sports and games, film and theatre, travel, gardening and cookery.

Papermac (FOUNDED 1965) Senior Editor *Tanya Stobbs*. Serious non-fiction: history, biography, science, political economy, cultural criticism and art history.

Picador (FOUNDED 1972) Publisher *Peter Straus*, Editorial Director *Ursula Doyle*. *Publishes* literary international fiction and non-fiction.

Sidgwick & Jackson (FOUNDED 1908) Senior Editor *Gordon Wise*. *Publishes* popular non-fiction with strong personality or marketable identity, from celebrity and showbusiness to ancient mystery, music and true-life adventure to illustrated lifestyle and branded books. Also military history list.

Macmillan Children's Books (Eccleston Place address) Publisher *Kate Wilson*; **Black** *Marion Lloyd*; **Full Colour** *Alison* IMPRINTS **Macmillan, Pan, Campbell** *Publishes* novels, board books, picture non-fiction (illustrated and non-illustrated), poetry and novelty books in paperback and hardback. No unsolicited material.

Macmillan Reference Ltd (Eccleston Place address) Managing Director *Ian Jacobs*. **Science** *Gina Fullerlove*; **Grove's Dictionaries of Music** *Margot Levy*. *Publishes* works of reference in academic, professional and vocational subjects, dictionaries. *The New Grove Dictionary of Music and Musicians* ed. Stanley Sadie; and *The Dictionary of Art* ed. Jane Turner.

Boxtree (Eccleston Place address) Managing Director *Adrian Singleton*, **Editorial Directors** *Susanna Wadeson, Clare Hulton*. *Publishes* books linked to and about television and film; also video, football and music. About 150 titles a year. TITLES *Dilbert; Coronation Street; Chelsea FC; Godzilla; Father Ted*, also Robert Carrier and Eric Idle.

Royalties paid annually or twice-yearly depending on contract.

Authors' Rating With Richard Charkin, formerly of **OUP** and **Reed**, taking over from long-running Nicholas Byam Shaw as chief executive there was an expectation of a shakeup which, so far, has not materialised. In expansionist mood, Macmillan has bought the Heinemann English language teaching list from Reed and Boxtree has won the contract to be the exclusive publisher for Channel 4 under the Channel 4 Books imprint. In early 1998 Macmillan's consumer CD-ROM imprint was sub-licensed to Marshall Media, part of **Marshall Editions**, who are now responsible for marketing, sales and distribution of new CD-ROMs. A few titles have remained with Macmillan – the Realtime Language Teaching series has transferred to Macmillan Press. The latest mega project to follow the *Macmillan Dictionary of Art* and *Grove's Dictionary of Music* is a multi-volume *Encyclopaedia of Life Science*.

Julia MacRae
See **Random House UK Ltd**

Mad Jack
See **Funfax Limited**

Madcap
See **André Deutsch Ltd**

Magi Publications

22 Manchester Street, London W1M 5PG
☎0171 486 0925   Fax 0171 486 0926
Publisher *Monty Bhatia*
Editor *Linda Jennings*
Approx. Annual Turnover £2.5 million

FOUNDED 1987. *Publishes* children's picture books only. About 24 titles a year. Unsolicited mss, synopses and ideas welcome, but please telephone first.

Royalties paid annually.

Magic Jewellery

See **Funfax Limited**

Magpie

See **Robinson Publishing Ltd**

Mainstream Publishing Co. (Edinburgh) Ltd

7 Albany Street, Edinburgh EH1 3UG
☎0131 557 2959   Fax 0131 556 8720
Directors *Bill Campbell, Peter MacKenzie*
Approx. Annual Turnover £2.75 million

Publishes art, autobiography/biography, current affairs, health, sport, history, illustrated and fine editions, photography, politics and world affairs, popular paperbacks. Over 80 titles a year. Ideas for books considered, but they should be preceded by a letter, synopsis and s.a.e. or return postage.

Royalties paid twice-yearly.

Authors' Rating A Scottish company aiming for a British profile. Keen on finding authors who 'can develop with us'.

Mammoth Paperbacks

See **Reed Books**

Management Books 2000 Ltd

Cowcombe House, Cowcombe Hill, Chalford, Gloucestershire GL6 8HP
☎01285 760722   Fax 01285 760708
Managing Director *Nicholas Dale-Harris*
Marketing *Nicholas Murphy*
Approx. Annual Turnover £500,000

FOUNDED 1993 to develop a range of books for executives and managers working in the modern world of business, supplemented with information through other media like seminars, audio and video. *Publishes* business and management and sponsored titles. About 30 titles a year. Unsolicited mss, synopses and ideas for books welcome.

Manchester United Books

See **André Deutsch Ltd**

Manchester University Press

Oxford Road, Manchester M13 9NR
☎0161 273 5539   Fax 0161 274 3346
E-mail: mup@man.ac.uk
Website: http://www.man.ac.uk/mup
Publisher/Chief Executive *David Rodgers*
Approx. Annual Turnover £2 million

FOUNDED at the turn of the century and now Britain's third largest university press, with a list marketed and sold internationally. Originally based on history, MUP's list has expanded to cover the humanities, social sciences and academic books from A-level texts to research monographs. *Publishes* academic and educational books in literature, cultural and media studies, history, art and architecture, politics, international law, economics, modern languages, religion and philosophy. About 120 titles a year, plus journals. Launched a new paperback imprint in 1997, **Mandolin**, to publish new work and reprints with a trade/mass-market appeal while retaining academic authority.

DIVISIONS **Humanities** *Matthew Frost*; **History/Art History/Religion** *Vanessa Graham*; **Politics and Economics** *Nicola Viinikka*. Unsolicited mss welcome.

Royalties paid annually.

Mandolin

See **Manchester University Press**

George Mann Books

PO Box 22, Maidstone, Kent ME14 1AH
☎01622 759591   Fax 01622 759591
Chairman & Managing Director
George Mann

FOUNDED 1972, originally as library reprint publishers, but has moved on to other things with the collapse of the library market. *Publishes* original non-fiction and selected reprints. Until further notice, not considering new fiction for publication. Launched a new imprint called Recollections in 1992 for subsidised publication of books of an autobiographical/biographical nature, for which unlimited editorial advice and assistance can be made available.

IMPRINTS **George Mann**; **Arnefold**; **Recollections**. No unsolicited mss; send preliminary letter with synopsis. Material not accompanied by return postage will be neither read nor returned.

Royalties paid twice-yearly.

Mansell
See **Cassell**

Manson Publishing Ltd
73 Corringham Road, London NW11 7DL
☎0181 905 5150   Fax 0181 201 9233
E-mail: manson@man-pub.demon.co.uk
Chairman/Managing Director
   Michael Manson
Approx. Annual Turnover £600,000
FOUNDED 1992. *Publishes* scientific, technical, medical and veterinary. 20 titles in 1997. No unsolicited mss; synopses and ideas will be considered.
   Royalties paid twice-yearly.

Marc
See **Monarch Publications**

Marshall Pickering
See **HarperCollins Publishers Ltd**

Marston House
Marston House, Marston Magna, Yeovil, Somerset BA22 8DH
☎01935 851331   Fax 01935 851331
Managing Director/Editorial Head
   Anthony Birks-Hay
FOUNDED 1989. Publishing imprint of book packager Alphabet & Image Ltd. *Publishes* fine art, architecture, ceramics. 4 titles a year.
   Royalties paid twice-yearly, or flat fee in lieu of royalties.

Mask Noir
See **Serpent's Tail**

Kenneth Mason Publications Ltd
Dudley House, 12 North Street, Emsworth, Hampshire PO10 7DQ
☎01243 377977   Fax 01243 379136
Chairman *Kenneth Mason*
Managing Director *Piers Mason*
Approx. Annual Turnover £500,000
FOUNDED 1958. *Publishes* diet, health, fitness, nutrition and nautical. No fiction. 15 titles in 1996. Initial approach by letter with synopsis only. IMPRINT **Boatswain Press**.
   Royalties paid twice-yearly (Jun/Dec) in first year, annually (Dec) thereafter.

Kevin Mayhew Ltd
Rattlesden, Bury St Edmunds, Suffolk IP30 0SZ
☎01449 737978   Fax 01449 737834
Chairman *Kevin Mayhew*

Managing Director *Gordon Carter*
Approx. Annual Turnover £4 million
FOUNDED in 1976. One of the leading sacred music and Christian book publishers in the UK. *Publishes* religious titles – liturgy, sacramental, devotional, also children's books and school resources. 300 titles in 1997. TITLES *Hymns Old & New (Anglican Edition); More Things to do in Children's Worship.* Unsolicited synopses and mss welcome; telephone prior to sending material, please.
   IMPRINT **Palm Tree Press** *Kevin Mayhew* Bible stories, colouring/activity and puzzle books for children.
   Royalties paid annually.

Melrose Press Ltd
3 Regal Lane, Soham, Ely, Cambridgeshire CB7 5BA
☎01353 721091   Fax 01353 721839
Chairman *Richard A. Kay*
Managing Director *Nicholas S. Law*
Approx. Annual Turnover £2 million
FOUNDED 1960. Took on its present name in 1969. *Publishes* biographical who's who reference only (not including *Who's Who*, which is published by **A. & C. Black**).
   DIVISIONS **International Biographical Centre** *Sean Tyler.* TITLES *International Authors and Writers Who's Who; International Who's Who in Music; Who's Who in Australasia and the Pacific Nations; International Who's Who in Poetry; International Who's Who in Popular Music.*

Mentor
See **Christian Focus Publications**

Mercat Press
53 South Bridge, Edinburgh EH1 1YS
☎0131 556 6743   Fax 0131 557 8149
E-mail: mercat@jthin.co.uk
Chairman/Managing Director *D. Ainslie Thin*
Editorial Heads *Tom Johnstone, Seán Costello*
FOUNDED 1971 as an adjunct to the large Scottish-based bookselling chain of James Thin. Began by publishing reprints of classic Scottish literature but has since expanded into publishing new non-fiction titles. In 1992 the company acquired the bulk of the stock of Aberdeen University Press, a victim of the collapse of the Maxwell empire. The backlist expanded greatly as a result and now stands at around 300 titles. New titles are added regularly. *Publishes* Scottish classics reprints and non-fiction of Scottish interest, mainly historical and literary. TITLES *An*

Arran Anthology Hamish Whyte; *The Scots Herbal* Tess Darwin; *Scottish Mysteries* Donald Fraser; *The Mercat Anthology of Early Scottish Literature* eds. R. Jack and P. Rozendaal; *The Scots Kitchen* F. Marian McNeill. Unsolicited synopses of non-fiction Scottish interest books, preferably with sample chapters, are welcome. No new fiction or poetry.

Royalties paid annually.

Merehurst
Ferry House, 51–57 Lacy Road, London SW15 1PR
☎0181 355 1480   Fax 0181 355 1499
CEO/Publisher *Anne Wislon*
General Manager *David Meads*
Approx. Annual Turnover £3 million

Owned by Australian media group Murdoch Magazines Pty Ltd. *Publishes* full-colour non-fiction: homes and interiors, gardening, cookery, craft, cake decorating and DIY. About 40 titles a year. Synopses and ideas for books welcome; no unsolicited mss.

Royalties paid twice-yearly.

The Merlin Press Ltd
2 Rendlesham Mews, Rendlesham, Nr Woodbridge, Suffolk IP12 2SZ
☎01394 461313   Fax 01394 461314
Directors *Martin Eve, P. M. Eve, Julie Millard*

FOUNDED 1956. *Publishes* economics, history, philosophy, left-wing politics. AUTHORS Georg Lukács, Ernest Mandel, Istvan Meszaros, Ralph Miliband, E. P. Thompson. About 20 titles a year. No fiction.

IMPRINTS **Seafarer Books** Sailing titles, with an emphasis on the traditional. No unsolicited mss; preliminary letter essential before making any type of submission.

Royalties paid twice-yearly.

Methuen
See **Random House UK Ltd**

Methuen & Co.
See **Routledge**

Methuen Children's Books
See **Reed Books**

Metro Books
Metro Publishing Ltd, 19 Gerrard Street, London W1V 7LA
☎0171 734 1411   Fax 0171 734 1811
Chairman *Alan Brooke*
Managing Director *Susanne McDadd*

Editorial Manager *Mary Remnant*

FOUNDED 1995. *Publishes* general non-fiction – popular psychology, health, cookery, gardening and travel. 15 titles in 1998. TITLES *Staying Sane* Raj Persaud; *Real Fast Vegetarian Food* Ursula Ferrigno; *Big Living* Angela Sandler; *Roddy Llewellyn's Gardening Year.* No unsolicited mss. Send outline, sample chapter, c.v., sales and marketing ideas plus s.a.e. in the first instance.

Royalties paid twice-yearly.

Authors' Rating Big advances are out and ideas are likely to be developed in-house. But authors should be encouraged by the promise to fill out royalty statements with information on where titles are selling and at what discount. Draft marketing plans are included with contracts and authors are encouraged to attend marketing meetings.

Michelin Tyre plc
The Edward Hyde Building, 38 Clarendon Road, Watford, Hertfordshire WD1 1SX
☎01923 415000   Fax 01923 415052

FOUNDED 1900 as travel publisher. *Publishes* travel guides, maps and atlases, children's I-Spy books. Travel-related synopses and ideas welcome; no mss.

Midland Publishing Ltd
24 The Hollow, Earl Shilton, Leicester LE9 7NA
☎01455 847256   Fax 01455 841805
Director *N. P. Lewis*

Publishes aviation, military and railways. No wartime memoirs. No unsolicited mss; synopses and ideas welcome.

Royalties paid quarterly.

Harvey Miller Publishers
Knightsbridge House, 8th Floor, 197 Knightsbridge, London SW7 1RB
☎0171 584 7676   Fax 0171 823 7969
Editorial Director *Mrs Elly Miller*

FOUNDED 1974. *Publishes* serious studies in the history of art only. Approx. 6 titles a year. No unsolicited mss; synopses and ideas welcome.

Royalties paid annually.

Mills & Boon Ltd
See **Harlequin Mills & Boon Ltd**

Minerva Press Ltd
195 Knightsbridge, London SW7 1RE
☎0171 225 3113   Fax 0171 581 9237
Managing Directors *A. Anton, K. Dale*

FOUNDED in 1992, the Minerva Press imprint dates back to 1792. *Publishes* fiction and non-fiction; biography, poetry, children's and historical. Specialises in new authors. 250 titles in 1997. Unsolicited mss, synopses and ideas for books welcome.

Royalties paid twice-yearly.

Authors' Rating Liable to ask authors to contribute towards costs of publication.

MIRA
See **Harlequin Mills & Boon Ltd**

The MIT Press Ltd
Fitzroy House, 11 Chenies Street, London WC1E 7ET
☎0171 306 0603   Fax 0171 306 0604
Director *F. Urbanowski*
General Manager *A. Sexsmith*

Part of **The MIT Press**, USA. *Publishes* academic, architecture and design, art history and theory, bibliography, biography, business and industry, cinema and media studies, computer science, cultural studies and critical theory, economics, educational and textbooks, engineering, environment, linguistics, medical, music, natural history, philosophy, photography, physics, politics and world affairs, psychology, reference, scientific and technical, neurobiology and neuroscience. All mss go to the American office: 55 Hayward Street, Cambridge, Mass. 02142.

Mitchell Beazley
See **Reed Books**

Mitre
See **Monarch Publications**

Monarch Publications
Broadway House, The Broadway, Crowborough, East Sussex TN6 1HQ
☎01892 652364   Fax 01892 663329
Directors *Tony & Jane Collins*

Now in association with Angus Hudson Ltd (see entry under **UK Packagers**). *Publishes* an independent list of Christian books across a wide range of concerns. About 30 titles a year. In 1994 took on *Renewal* and *Healing and Wholeness* magazines and in 1998 launched *Celebrate*, an independent magazine for the Church of England.

IMPRINTS **Monarch** Upmarket, social concern issues list covering a wide range of areas from psychology to future studies, politics, etc., all with a strong Christian dimension; **Marc** Leadership, mission and church growth titles; **Mitre** Creative writing imprint: humour and drama with a Christian dimension. Unsolicited mss, synopses and ideas welcome. 'Regretfully, no poetry or fiction.'

Monitor Press Ltd
Suffolk House, Churchfield Road, Sudbury, Suffolk CO10 6YA
☎01787 378607   Fax 01787 880201
Website: http://www.monitorpress.co.uk
Managing Director *Mary Ann Bonomo*

Owned by International Business Communications (Holdings) plc. *Publishes* a range of legal, tax, financial, management and business to business newsletters, special reports and books aimed at senior management and professional practices. 34 newsletter titles a year. Unsolicited synopses and ideas welcome. Initial approach in writing.

Mosby International
Lynton House, 7–12 Tavistock Square, London WC1H 9LB
☎0171 388 7676   Fax 0171 391 6555
Managing Director *Derrick Holman*

Part of **Harcourt Brace and Company Limited** following its acquisition by US professional publisher Harcourt General in May 1998. Acquired Wolfe Publishing in the late '80s, and acquired Gower Medical Publishing in 1993. *Publishes* medical and nursing books.

IMPRINTS **Mosby**; **Mosby Wolfe Publishing** TITLES *Immunology; A Colour Atlas & Text of Clinical Medicine; A Colour Atlas of Human Anatomy; Rheumatology; Head and Neck Surgery.* Synopses and ideas for books welcome.

Royalties paid twice-yearly.

Motor Racing Publications
Unit 6, The Pilton Estate, 46 Pitlake, Croydon, Surrey CR0 3RY
☎0181 681 3363   Fax 0181 760 5117
Chairman/Editorial Head *John Blunsden*
Approx. Annual Turnover £500,000

FOUNDED soon after the end of World War II to concentrate on motor-racing titles. Fairly dormant in the mid '60s but was reactivated in 1968 by a new shareholding structure. John Blunsden later acquired a majority share and major expansion followed in the '70s. About 10–12 titles a year. *Publishes* motor-sporting history, classic car collection and restoration, road transport, motorcycles, off-road driving and related subjects.

IMPRINTS **Fitzjames Press**; **Motor Racing**

Publications TITLES *Cars in the UK, Vol 2: 1971 to 1995* G. Robson; *Morgans to 1997* R. Bell; *Sporting Peugeot 205s* D. Thornton; *No Time to Lose: The Fast Moving World of Bill Ivy* A. Peck. Unsolicited mss, synopses and ideas in specified subject areas welcome.

Royalties paid twice-yearly.

Mowbray
See **Cassell**

Multi-Sensory Learning Ltd
34 Nene Valley Business Park, Oundle, Peterborough PE8 4HL
☎01832 274714   Fax 01832 275281

Senior Editor *Philippa Attwood*
Course Co-ordinator *Anna Robinson*

Part of **First and Best in Education Ltd**. *Publishes* materials and books related to dyslexia; the multi-sensory learning course for dyslexic pupils needing literacy skills development, plus numerous other items on assessment, reading, maths, music, etc. for dyslexics. Keen to locate authors able to write materials for dyslexic people and for teachers of dyslexics.

John Murray (Publishers) Ltd
50 Albemarle Street, London W1X 4BD
☎0171 493 4361   Fax 0171 499 1792

Chairman *John R. Murray*
Managing Director *Nicholas Perren*

FOUNDED 1768. Independent publisher. *Publishes* general trade books, educational (secondary school and college textbooks) and Success Study-books.

DIVISIONS **General Books** *Grant McIntyre*; **Educational Books** *Nicholas Perren*. Unsolicited material discouraged.

Royalties paid twice yearly.

Authors' Rating Having been hit by the downturn in the education market, John Murray is back on form with what must surely be one of the finest quality non-fiction lists. The Murray logo is as close as you are likely to get to a guarantee of a good read.

NAG Press Ltd
See **Robert Hale Ltd**

National Museums of Scotland (NMS Publishing)
Chambers Street, Edinburgh EH1 1JF
☎0131 247 4026   Fax 0131 247 4012

Chairman *Mark Jones*
Approx. Annual Turnover £130,000

FOUNDED 1987 to *publish* non-fiction related to the National Museums of Scotland collections: academic and general; children's – archaeology, history, decorative arts worldwide, history of science, technology, natural history and geology. 12 titles in 1997. **NMS Publishing** *Helen Kemp* TITLES *Scotland's Past in Action* series; *The Scottish Home; Domestic Culture in the Middle East; Agates; Harmony and Contrast: A Journey Through East Asian Art; Thistle at War; Precious Cargo; Tartan Pocket Biographies of Famous Scots*. No unsolicited mss; only interested in synopses and ideas for books which are genuinely related to NMS collections and to Scotland in general.

Royalties paid twice-yearly.

NCVO Publications
Regent's Wharf, 8 All Saints Street, London N1 9RL
☎0171 713 6161   Fax 0171 713 6300

Publications Manager *David Cameron*
Approx. Annual Turnover £140,000

FOUNDED 1992. Publishing imprint of the National Council for Voluntary Organisations, embracing former Bedford Square Press titles and NCVO's many other publications. The list reflects NCVO's role as the representative body for the voluntary sector. *Publishes* directories, management and trustee development, legal, finance and fundraising titles of primary interest to the voluntary sector. TITLES *The Voluntary Agencies Directory; Grants from Europe; The Good Trustee Guide; The Good Campaigns Guide*. No unsolicited mss as all projects are commissioned in-house.

Royalties paid twice-yearly.

Thomas Nelson & Sons Ltd
Nelson House, Mayfield Road, Walton on Thames, Surrey KT12 5PL
☎01932 252211   Fax 01932 246109

CEO/Managing Director *Nigel G. Hall*
Approx. Annual Turnover £21.8 million

FOUNDED 1798. Part of the Thomson Corporation. Major educational publisher of printed and electronic product, from pre-school to Higher Education, with emphasis on requirements of National Curriculum, GCSE, A Level, GNVQ and NVQ. Publisher of *The Arden Shakespeare* imprint, and of a range of material for the Caribbean market. TITLES *GAIA: Geography, An Integrated Approach; The Wider World; Nelson English; Nelson Maths; Wellington Square; Route Nationale; Encore*

Tricolore; Zickzack Neu; World of Sport Examined; New Balanced Science; Bath Science; Foundations of Psychology
Royalties paid twice-yearly.

Authors' Rating At number three in the UK education market (behind **Stanley Thornes** and **Heinemann Educational**), Nelson's strength is in modern languages, geography, primary English, maths and science.

Network Books
See **BBC Worldwide Ltd**

The New Adventures
See **Virgin Publishing Ltd**

New English Library
See **Hodder Headline plc**

New Holland (Publishers) Ltd
24 Nutford Place, London W1H 6DQ
☎0171 724 7773   Fax 0171 724 6184
Chairman *Gerry Struik*
Managing Director *John Beaufoy*
Editorial Heads *Charlotte Parry-Crooke, Yvonne McFarlane*
Approx. Annual Turnover £5 million
FOUNDED 1956. Relaunched 1987 with new name and editorial identity. New directions and rapid expansion transformed the small specialist imprint into a publisher of illustrated books for the international market. In 1993, they diversified further with the acquisition of the **Charles Letts Publishing Division** list. In 1997, their parent company (Struik Publishers, S. Africa) acquired Southern Book Publishers, and their sister company (New Holland Australia) acquired the natural history and lifestyle divisions of Reed Australia. *Publishes* non-fiction, specialising in natural history, travel, cookery, cake decorating, crafts, gardening and DIY. TITLES *Dive Sites Series; Top Dive Sites of the World; Climber's Handbook; Globetrotter Travel Guides and Maps; Bill Oddie's Birds of Britain and Ireland; Seabirds of the World; Design and Decorate Series; No-Time Party Cakes.* No unsolicited mss; synopses and ideas welcome.
Royalties paid twice-yearly.

Authors' Rating This South African-owned company produces superbly illustrated books. Authors need to know what looks good on the coffee table.

Nexus
See **Virgin Publishing Ltd**

Nexus Special Interests
Nexus House, Boundary Way, Hemel Hempstead, Hertfordshire HP2 7ST
☎01442 66551   Fax 01442 66998
Manager *Beverly Laughlin*
Argus Consumer Magazines and Argus Books were bought out by Nexus Media Communications in 1995 and the Nexus Special Interests imprint was established in the spring of that year. *Publishes* aviation, engineering, leisure and hobbies, modelling, electronics, health, craft, wine and beer making, woodwork. Send synopses rather than completed mss.
Royalties paid twice-yearly.

NFER-NELSON Publishing Co. Ltd
Darville House, 2 Oxford Road East, Windsor, Berkshire SL4 1DF
☎01753 858961   Fax 01753 856830
Managing Director *Michael Jackson*
FOUNDED 1981. Jointly owned by the Thomson Corporation and the National Foundation for Educational Research. *Publishes* educational and psychological tests and training materials. Main interest is in educational, clinical and occupational assessment and training material. Unsolicited material welcome.
Royalties vary according to each contract.

Nicholson
See **HarperCollins Publishers Ltd**

James Nisbet & Co. Ltd
78 Tilehouse Street, Hitchin, Hertfordshire SG5 2DY
☎01462 438331   Fax 01462 431528
Chairman *E. M. Mackenzie-Wood*
FOUNDED 1810 as a religious publisher and expanded into more general areas from around 1850 onwards. The first educational list appeared in 1926 and the company now specialises in educational material and business studies. About 5 titles a year. No fiction, leisure or religion. No unsolicited mss; synopses and ideas welcome.
Royalties paid twice-yearly.

NMS Publishing
See **National Museums of Scotland**

No Exit Press
See **Oldcastle Books Ltd**

Nonesuch Press
See **Reinhardt Books Ltd**

Northcote House Publishers Ltd

Plymbridge House, Estover Road, Plymouth, Devon PL6 7PY
☎01752 202368   Fax 01752 202330
Managing Director *Brian Hulme*

FOUNDED 1985. Recently launched a new series of literary critical studies, in association with the British Council, called *Writers and their Work*. *Publishes* education management, literary criticism, educational dance and drama. 25 titles in 1997. 'Well-thought-out proposals, including contents and sample chapter(s), with strong marketing arguments welcome.'
Royalties paid annually.

Northern Writes

4 Pilton Road, Pilton Park, Westerhope Village, Tyne & Wear NE5 4PP
☎0191 2145449   Fax 0191 2434910
E-mail: n.write@cableinet.co.uk
Chairman *Carole Wilkinson*
Managing Director *Richard Brailey*

FOUNDED 1997. *Publishes* fiction, humour and children's books. No unsolicited mss; synopses and ideas for books welcome. No erotic, science fiction or technical books.

DIVISIONS **Fiction** *Richard Brailey* TITLE *Viking Burial Fund;* **Humour** *Carole Wilkinson* TITLE *Bar Persons Guide;* **Children's** *Richard Brailey, Carole Wilkinson* TITLE *The Fairy Kettle.*
Royalties paid annually.

W. W. Norton & Co. Ltd

10 Coptic Street, London WC1A 1PU
☎0171 323 1579   Fax 0171 436 4553
Managing Director *R. A. Cameron*

Owned by US parent company. *Publishes* non-fiction and academic. No unsolicited material. Enquiries only in writing.

Notting Hill Electronic Publishers

31 Brunswick Gardens, London W8 4AW
☎0171 937 6003   Fax 0171 937 0003
Chairman *Andreas Whittam Smith*
Managing Director *Ben Whittam Smith*

FOUNDED 1994. Award-winning electronic publisher created by Andreas Whittam Smith, founder of *The Independent*. *Publishes* (on CD-ROM) arts, sport, popular science, food and wine. TITLES *International Athletics; Wine, Spirits & Beer; The Art of Singing; The Evolution of Life; Dancer DNA.* Welcomes synopses and ideas for CD-ROMs; no pornography or fiction.

Nottingham University Press

Manor Farm, Main Street, Thrumpton, Nottingham NG11 0AX
☎0115 9831011   Fax 0115 9831003
E-mail: editor@nup.com
Managing Editor *Dr D. J. A. Cole*
Approx. Annual Turnover £150,000

Initially concentrated on agricultural and food sciences titles but now branching into new areas including engineering, lifesciences, medicine, law and sport. Sports books published under newly-formed subsidary, Castle Publications. TITLES *Global 2050; Lung Function Tests; Diet, Lipoproteins and Coronary Heart Disease; Chinese Herbs in Animal Nutrition; Progress in Pig Science.* **Castle Publications** TITLES *The Mental Game of Golf; The Natural Sportsman; Worldwide Directory of Distilleries.*
Royalties paid twice-yearly.

Oak

See **Omnibus Press**

Oberon Books

521 Caledonian Road, London N7 9RH
☎0171 607 3637   Fax 0171 607 3629
Publishing Director *James Hogan*
Managing Director *Charles D. Glanville*

Publishes play texts (usually in conjunction with a production) and theatre books. *Specialises* in contemporary plays and translations of European classics. IMPRINTS **Oberon Books; Absolute Classics.** AUTHORS/TRANSLATORS Rodney Ackland, Michel Azama, Simon Bent, Ranjit Bolt, Ken Campbell, Barry Day, Marguerite Duras, Dario Fo, Jonathan Gems, Trevor Griffiths, Giles Havergal, Rolf Hochhuth, Michael Kilgarriff, Robert David MacDonald, Kenneth McLeish, Adrian Mitchell, Sheridan Morley, Gregory Motton, Stephen Mulrine, Jimmy Murphy, Meredith Oakes, Stewart Parker, David Pownall, Roland Rees, Colin Winslow, Charles Wood.

Octagon Press Ltd

PO Box 227, London N6 4EW
☎0181 348 9392   Fax 0181 341 5971
Managing Director *George R. Schrager*
Website: http://www.clearlight.com/octagon
Approx. Annual Turnover £100,000

FOUNDED 1972. *Publishes* philosophy, psychology, travel, Eastern religion, translations of Eastern classics and research monographs in series. 4–5 titles a year. Unsolicited material not welcome. Enquiries in writing only.
Royalties paid annually.

Old Forge Gift Collection
See **Anness Publishing Ltd**

Oldcastle Books Ltd
18 Coleswood Road, Harpenden,
Hertfordshire AL5 1EQ
☎01582 761264   Fax 01582 712244
E-mail: noxitpress@aol.com
Managing Director *Ion S. Mills*
FOUNDED 1985. *Publishes* crime fiction and
gambling non-fiction. 20 titles in 1997. *No
unsolicited mss*; synopses and ideas for books
within the two areas of interest welcome.
IMPRINTS **No Exit Press** TITLES *Burglar In
the Library* Lawrence Block; *No Beast So Fierce*
Eddie Bunker; **Oldcastle Books** TITLES
Biggest Game in Town Al Alvarez.
Royalties paid twice-yearly.

Oldie Publications
45/46 Poland Street, London W1V 4AU
☎0171 734 2225   Fax 0171 734 2226
Chairman *Richard Ingrams*
FOUNDED in 1992. Book publishing arm of
The Oldie magazine. *Publishes* compilations
from the magazine, including cartoon books.
TITLES *I Once Met; Dictionary For Our Time;
The Third Oldie Annual; The World According to
Enfield Senior* Edward Enfield; *Jennifer's Diary:
By One Fat Lady* Jennifer Paterson.

OM Publishing
See **Paternoster Publishing**

Michael O'Mara Books Ltd
9 Lion Yard, Tremadoc Road, London
SW4 7NQ
☎0171 720 8643   Fax 0171 627 8953
Chairman *Michael O'Mara*
Managing Director *Lesley O'Mara*
Approx. Annual Turnover £5 million
FOUNDED 1985. Independent publisher. *Pub-
lishes* general non-fiction, royalty, history,
humour, anthologies and reference. TITLES
Diana: Her True Story Andrew Morton; *The
Seven Wonders of the World* John Romer; *I
Don't Believe It!* Richard Wilson. Unsolicited
mss, synopses and ideas for books welcome.
Royalties paid twice-yearly.

Authors' Rating Buoyed up by phenomenal
sales for Andrew Motion's latest reflections on
Diana, Michael O'Mara has plenty of scope to
publish a few more of the less populist titles
that grace his list.

Omnibus Press
Book Sales/Music Sales Ltd, 8–9 Frith Street,
London W1V 5TZ
☎0171 434 0066   Fax 0171 734 2246
Editorial Head *Chris Charlesworth*
FOUNDED 1971. Independent publisher of
music books, rock and pop biographies, song
sheets, educational tutors, cassettes, videos and
software. IMPRINTS **Amsco**; **Bobcat**; **Oak**;
Omnibus; **Wise Publications**. Unsolicited
mss, synopses and ideas for books welcome.
Royalties paid twice-yearly.

Oneworld Publications
185 Banbury Road, Oxford OX2 7AR
☎01865 310597   Fax 01865 310598
Editorial Director *Juliet Mabey*
FOUNDED 1986. Distributed worldwide by
Penguin Books. *Publishes* adult non-fiction
across a range of subjects from world religions
and social issues to psychology and self-help. 20
titles in 1997. TITLE A series on world religions
was launched in 1994 with *A Short History of
Buddhism* and *A Short History of Islam*. AUTHORS
include Geoffrey Parrinder, Keith Ward,
William Montgomery Watt, Alfred Adler, Kahlil
Gibran. No unsolicited mss; synopses and ideas
welcome, but should be accompanied by s.a.e.
for return of material and/or notification of
receipt. No autobiographies, fiction, poetry or
children's.
Royalties paid annually.

Onlywomen Press Ltd
40 St Lawrence Terrace, London W10 5ST
☎0181 960 7122   Fax 0181 960 2817
Editorial Director *Lilian Mohin*
FOUNDED 1974. *Publishes* radical feminist lesbian
books only: fiction, poetry and non-fiction.
About 6 titles a year. In 1995/96, published the
first three titles in a new crime novel list, original
paperbacks set in contemporary England with
lesbian protagonists. TITLES *Burning Issues*
Maggie Kelly; *Dirty Work* Vivien Kelly; *A
Fearful Symmetry* Tash Fairbanks; *An Intimacy of
Equals: Lesbian Feminist Ethics* ed. Lilian Mohin.
Unsolicited mss, synopses and ideas welcome.
Submissions should be accompanied by s.a.e. for
return of material and/or notification of receipt.

Open University Press
Celtic Court, 22 Ballmoor, Buckingham,
Buckinghamshire MK18 1XW
☎01280 823388   Fax 01280 823233
Managing Director *John Skelton*

Approx. Annual Turnover £3 million

FOUNDED 1977 as an imprint independent of the Open University's course materials. *Publishes* academic and professional books in the fields of education, management, sociology, health studies, politics, psychology, women's studies. No economics or anthropology. Not interested in anything outside the social sciences. About 100 titles a year. No unsolicited mss; enquiries/proposals only.

Royalties paid annually.

Orbit
See **Little, Brown & Co. (UK)**

Orchard Books
See **The Watts Publishing Group**

The Orion Publishing Group Limited
Orion House, 5 Upper St Martin's Lane, London WC2H 9EA
☎0171 240 3444   Fax 0171 240 4822
Chairman *Nicholas Barber*
Chief Executive *Anthony Cheetham*
Managing Director *Peter Roche*
Approx. Annual Turnover £40 million

FOUNDED 1992 by Anthony Cheetham, Rosemary Cheetham and Peter Roche. Incorporates Weidenfeld & Nicolson, JM Dent and Chapmans Publishers.

DIVISIONS
Orion Managing Director *Malcolm Edwards* Publisher *Rosemary Cheetham* IMPRINTS **Orion** General Publishing Director *Jane Wood* Hardcover fiction/non-fiction; **Orion Business** *Martin Liu* Business books; **Orion Media** Publishing Director *Trevor Dolby* Film and TV; **Orion Children's** Managing Director *Judith Elliott* Children's fiction/non-fiction.

Weidenfeld & Nicolson Managing Director *Ion Trewin* IMPRINTS **Weidenfeld General** Publishing Director *Rebecca Wilson* General non-fiction, biography and autobiography; **Phoenix House** Publishing Director *Maggie McKernan* Literary fiction; **Weidenfeld Illustrated** Publisher *Michael Dover* Illustrated non-fiction.

Mass Market Managing Director *Susan Lamb* IMPRINTS **Orion**; **Phoenix**; **Phoenix Illustrated**; **Everyman**.

Authors' Rating Aiming at an annual sales growth of at least 15%, Orion is pursuing 'a vigorous commissioning programme' with an emphasis on media, business and military history. Orion's 20% stake in Double Exposure, a

television production company, suggests a move into multimedia. Plans to float the company have been put on hold.

Osprey
See **Reed Books**

Peter Owen Ltd
73 Kenway Road, London SW5 0RE
☎0171 373 5628/370 6093
Fax 0171 373 6760
E-mail: admin@peterowen.u-net.com
Chairman *Peter Owen*
Editorial Director *Antonia Owen*

FOUNDED 1951. *Publishes* biography, general non-fiction, English literary fiction and translations, sociology. 'No middlebrow romance, thrillers or children's.' AUTHORS Jane Bowles, Paul Bowles, Shusaku Endo, Anna Kavan, Fiona Pitt-Kethley, Anaïs Nin, Jeremy Reed, Peter Vansittart. 35–40 titles a year. Unsolicited synopses welcome for non-fiction material; mss should be preceded by a descriptive letter and synopsis with s.a.e.

Royalties paid twice-yearly. *Overseas associates* worldwide.

Authors' Rating Forever looking for ways of cutting costs to maintain output in the highbrow market, Peter Owen has been described as 'a publisher of the old and idiosyncratic school'. He has seven Nobel prizewinners on his list.

Oxford Illustrated Press/ Oxford Publishing Co.
See **Haynes Publishing**

Oxford University Press
Great Clarendon Street, Oxford OX2 6DP
☎01865 556767   Fax 01865 556646
Chief Executive *Henry Reece*
Approx. Annual Turnover £278.2 million

A department of the university, OUP grew from the university's printing works and developed into a major publishing business in the 19th century. *Publishes* academic books in all categories: student texts, scholarly journals, schoolbooks, ELT material, dictionaries, reference, music, bibles, electronic publishing, as well as paperbacks, poetry, general non-fiction and children's books. Around 3000 titles a year.

DIVISIONS
Academic *I. S. Asquith* Academic and college titles in all disciplines; dictionaries and non-lexical reference, trade books, journals and electronic publishing. TITLES *Concise Oxford Dictionary;*

Birds of the Western Palearctic; **Educational** *F. E. Clarke* National Curriculum courses; **ELT** *W. R. Andrewes* ELT courses and dictionaries.

IMPRINTS **Clarendon Press** Monographs in humanities, science and social science; **Oxford Paperbacks** Trade paperbacks; **Oxford Science Publications**; **Oxford Medical Publications**; **Oxford Electronic Publications**. OUP welcomes first-class academic material in the form of proposals or accepted theses.

Royalties paid twice-yearly. *Overseas subsidiaries* Sister company in USA; also branches in Australia, Canada, East Africa, Hong Kong, India, Japan, New Zealand, Pakistan, Singapore, South Africa. Offices in Argentina, Brazil, France, Germany, Greece, Italy, Mexico, Spain, Taiwan, Thailand, Turkey, Uruguay. Joint companies in Malaysia, Nigeria and Germany.

Authors' Rating By far the largest of the university presses, OUP is the market leader in dictionary publishing and in English Language Teaching. But the real strength of Oxford is its international network. It publishes in 12 countries and has offices and associated companies in 40 others.

Palm Tree Press
See **Kevin Mayhew Ltd**

G. J. Palmer & Sons Ltd
See **Hymns Ancient & Modern Ltd**

Pan Books Ltd
See **Macmillan Publishers Ltd**

Papermac
See **Macmillan Publishers Ltd**

Paragon Softcover Large Print
See **Chivers Press Ltd**

Partridge Press
See **Transworld Publishers Ltd**

The Paternoster Press
See **Paternoster Publishing**

Paternoster Publishing
PO Box 300, Kingstown Broadway, Carlisle, Cumbria CA3 0QS
☎01228 512512   Fax 01228 593388
Publishing Director *Pieter Kwant*
Editorial Manager *Mark Finnie*
Approx. Annual Turnover £2 million

A division of STL Ltd. IMPRINTS: **The Paternoster Press** FOUNDED 1936. *Publishes* religion and learned/church/life-related journals. Over 100 titles a year. TITLES *The New International Dictionary of New Testament Theology* (4 vols) ed. Colin Brown; *Acts in its 1st Century Setting* ed. Bruce Winter; *Calvin's Old Testament Commentaries.*

OM Publishing FOUNDED 1966. *Publishes* Christian books on evangelism, discipleship and mission. About 30 titles a year. TITLES *Operation World* Patrick Johnstone; *You Can Change the World* Jill Johnstone; and many titles by Elisabeth Elliot and A. W. Tozer.

Solway FOUNDED 1996. 'Tackling Christianity and Christian art from an original perspective.' About 10 titles a year. TITLES *After Eating the Apricot* John Goldingay; *Learning to Fly* Adrian Plass and Ben Ecclestone. Unsolicited mss, synopses and ideas for books welcome.

Royalties paid twice-yearly.

Pavilion Books Ltd
London House, Great Eastern Wharf, Parkgate Road, London SW11 4NQ
☎0171 924 2575   Fax 0171 924 7725
Publisher *Colin Webb*

Acquired by **Collins & Brown** in 1997. *Publishes* biography, children's, cookery, gardening, humour, art, sport and travel. Unsolicited ms not welcome. Ideas and synopses for non-fiction titles and children's fiction considered.

Royalties paid twice-yearly.

Payback Press
See **Canongate Books Ltd**

Pen & Sword Books Ltd
See **Leo Cooper**

Penguin UK
27 Wrights Lane, London W8 5TZ
☎0171 416 3000   Fax 0171 416 3099
Chairman *Michael Lynton*
Managing Director *Anthony Forbes Watson*
Managing Director, Children's *Philippa Milnes-Smith*
Approx. Annual Turnover £99.1 million

Owned by Pearson plc. The world's best known book brand and for more than 60 years a leading publisher whose adult and children's lists include fiction, non-fiction, poetry, drama, classics, reference and special interest areas. Reprints and new work.

DIVISIONS
Penguin General Books Adult fiction and non-fiction is published in hardback under Michael Joseph, Viking and Hamish Hamilton

imprints. Paperbacks come under the Penguin imprint. IMPRINTS **Viking/Penguin** Publishing Directors *Juliet Annan, Tony Lacey*; **Hamish Hamilton** Publisher *Simon Prosser*; **Michael Joseph/Penguin** Publishing Director *Tom Weldon* Unsolicited mss discouraged.

Penguin Press Publishing Director *Alastair Rolfe* Academic adult non-fiction, reference, specialist and classics. IMPRINTS **Allen Lane**; **Arkana** Mind, body and spirit; **Buildings of England**; **Classics**; **Penguin Books** Approach in writing only.

Frederick Warne Publisher *Sally Floyer* Classic children's publishing and merchandising including *Beatrix Potter™*; *Flower Fairies*; *Orlando*. **Ventura** Publisher *Sally Floyer* Producer and packager of *Spot* titles by Eric Hill.

Penguin Children's Books Hardback IMPRINTS **Hamish Hamilton Children's**; **Viking Children's**; Paperback IMPRINT **Puffin** Publishers *Jane Nissen* (fiction, poetry and picture books), *Richard Scrivener* (media and popular non-fiction). Leading children's paperback list, publishing in virtually all fields including fiction, non-fiction, poetry, picture books, media-related titles. No unsolicited mss; synopsis and ideas welcome.

Penguin Audiobooks (see entry under **Audio Books**).

Royalties paid twice-yearly. *Overseas associates* worldwide.

Authors' Rating The acquisition of Putnam Berkley last year has doubled Penguin's sales and shifted the emphasis towards new books. In its previous form Penguin relied on its backlist for at least 70% of sales. Now, the figure is closer to 50%. In the UK the company is settling down after a period of radical restructuring.

Petroc Press
See **Librapharm Ltd**

Phaidon Press Limited
Regent's Wharf, All Saints Street, London N1 9PA
☎0171 843 1000   Fax 0171 843 1010
Chairman/Publisher *Richard Schlagman*
Finance & Operating Director *Andrew Price*
Editorial Heads *David Jenkins (Architecture and Design), Pat Barylski (Art and Ideas Series), Gilda Williams (Contemporary Art), Sara Borins (General)*
Approx. Annual Turnover £8.8 million

Publishes quality books on the visual arts, including fine art, art history, architecture, design,

photography, decorative arts, music and performing arts. Recently started producing videos. About 100 titles a year. Unsolicited mss welcome but 'only a small amount of unsolicited material gets published'.

Royalties paid twice-yearly.

Authors' Rating A fast growing art book publisher, Phaidon has decided to apply the brakes just enough to transfer some attention from new titles to improving revenue from the existing list.

Philip's
See **Reed Books**

Phillimore & Co. Ltd
Shopwyke Manor Barn, Chichester, West Sussex PO20 6BG
☎01243 787636   Fax 01243 787639
E-mail: bookshop@phillimore.co.uk
Website: http://www.phillimore.co.uk
Chairman *Philip Harris*
Managing Director *Noel Osborne*
Approx. Annual Turnover £1 million

FOUNDED in 1897 by W. P. W. Phillimore, Victorian campaigner for local archive conservation in Chancery Lane, London. Became the country's leading publisher of historical source material and local histories. Somewhat dormant in the 1960s, it was revived by Philip Harris in 1968. *Publishes* British local and family history, including histories of institutions, buildings, villages, towns and counties, plus guides to research and writing in these fields. About 70 titles a year. No unsolicited mss; synopses/ideas welcome for local or family histories.

IMPRINTS **Phillimore** *Noel Osborne* TITLES *Domesday Book; A History of Essex; Carlisle; The Haberdashers' Company; Channel Island Churches; Bolton Past; Warwickshire Country Houses.*

Royalties paid annually.

Phoenix/Phoenix House/ Phoenix Illustrated
See **The Orion Publishing Group Ltd**

Piatkus Books
5 Windmill Street, London W1P 1HF
☎0171 631 0710   Fax 0171 436 7137
E-mail: info@piatkus.co.uk
Managing Director *Judy Piatkus*
Approx. Annual Turnover £4.75 million

FOUNDED 1979 by Judy Piatkus. The company is committed to continuing independence. *Specialises* in publishing books and authors 'who we feel enthusiastic and committed to as we like to build for long-term success as well as short-term!' *Publishes* self-help, biography, personal growth, business and management, careers, cookery, health and beauty, healing, Mind, Body and Spirit, popular psychology and fiction. In 1996 launched a list of mass-market non-fiction and fiction titles. About 120 titles a year (70 of which are fiction).

DIVISIONS
Non-fiction *Gill Cormode* TITLES *Creating Sacred Space With Feng Shui* Karen Kingston; *10 Day MBA* Steve Silbiger; *The New Perfect CV* Tom Jackson; *The Complete Low-Fat Cookbook* Sue Kreitzman. **Fiction** *Judy Piatkus* TITLES *Only Love* Erich Segal; *Too Close* Hilary Norman; *Bumps* Zoë Barnes; *Denial* Keith Ablow. Piatkus are expanding their range of books and welcome synopses and first three chapters.
Royalties paid twice-yearly.

Authors' Rating A small publisher which continues to do well despite hard times by focusing titles on clearly defined markets. 'Things are going really well,' says Judy Piatkus.

Picador
See **Macmillan Publishers Ltd**

Piccadilly Press
5 Castle Road, London NW1 8PR
☎0171 267 4492   Fax 0171 267 4493
E-mail: books@piccadillypress.co.uk
Chairman/Managing Director *Brenda Gardner*
Approx. Annual Turnover £600,000
FOUNDED 1983. Independent publisher of children's and parental books. 30 titles in 1997. Welcomes approaches from authors 'but we would like them to know the sort of books we do. It is frustrating to get inappropriate material. They should check in their local libraries or bookshops. We will send a catalogue (please enclose s.a.e.)'. No adult or cartoon-type material.
Royalties paid twice-yearly.

Pictorial
See **Souvenir Press Ltd**

Picture Knight
See **Hodder Headline plc**

Picture Lions
See **HarperCollins Publishers Ltd**

Pimlico
See **Random House UK Ltd**

Pinter
See **Cassell**

Pitkin Unichrome
Healey House, Dene Road, Andover, Hampshire SP10 2AA
☎01264 334303   Fax 01264 334110
Managing Director *Heather Hook*
Pitkin Guides, FOUNDED in 1947, was part of Reed Books from 1988 to April 1998 when it merged with Unichrome. *Publishes* illustrated souvenir guides.

Pitman Publishing
See **Financial Times Management**

Plenum Publishing Co. Ltd
New Loom House, 101 Back Church Lane, London E1 1LU
☎0171 264 1910   Fax 0171 264 1919
Chairman *Martin E. Tash (USA)*
Managing Director *Dr Ken Derham*
Editor *Joanna Lawrence*
FOUNDED 1966. A division of **Plenum Publishing**, New York. The London office is the editorial and marketing base for the company's UK and European operations. *Publishes* postgraduate, professional and research-level scientific, technical and medical textbooks, monographs, conference proceedings and reference books and books of general interest on scientific and social issues. About 300 titles (worldwide) a year.
IMPRINTS **Consultants Bureau; IFI Plenum Data Company; Plenum Insight; Plenum Medical Company; Plenum Press; Human Science Press**. Proposals for new publications will be considered, and should be sent to the editor.
Royalties paid annually.

Pluto Press Ltd
345 Archway Road, London N6 5AA
☎0181 348 2724   Fax 0181 348 9133
Managing Director *Roger Van Zwanenberg*
Publishing Director *Anne Beech*
FOUNDED 1970. Has developed a reputation for innovatory publishing in the field of non-fiction. *Publishes* academic and scholarly books across a range of subjects including cultural studies, politics and world affairs, social sciences and socialist, feminist and Marxist books. About 50–60 titles a year. Synopses and ideas welcome if accompanied by return postage.

Point
See **Scholastic Ltd**

The Policy Press

University of Bristol, Rodney Lodge, Grange Road, Bristol BS8 4EA
☎0117 9738797   Fax 0117 9737308
Managing Director *Alison Shaw*
Approx. Annual Turnover £250,000

The Policy Press is a specialist publisher of policy studies. Material published, in the form of books, reports, practice guides and journals, is taken from research findings and provides critical discussion of policy initiatives and their impact, and also recommendations for policy change. 45–50 titles per year. No unsolicited mss; brief synopses and ideas welcome.

Polity Press

65 Bridge Street, Cambridge CB2 1UR
☎01223 324315   Fax 01223 461385

FOUNDED 1984. All books are published in association with **Blackwell Publishers**. *Publishes* archaeology and anthropology, criminology, economics, feminism, general interest, history, human geography, literature, media and cultural studies, medicine and society, philosophy, politics, psychology, religion and theology, social and political theory, sociology. Unsolicited mss, synopses and ideas for books welcome.
   Royalties paid annually.

Polygon

See **Edinburgh University Press**

Pont Books

See **Gomer Press**

Pop Universal

See **Souvenir Press Ltd**

Portland Press Ltd

59 Portland Place, London W1N 3AJ
☎0171 580 5530   Fax 0171 323 1136

Chairman *Professor A.J. Turner*
Managing Director *G.D. Jones*
Editorial Director *Rhonda Oliver*
Approx. Annual Turnover £2.5 million

FOUNDED 1990 to expand the publishing activities of the Biochemical Society (1911). *Publishes* biochemisty and medicine for graduate, post-graduate and research students. Expanding the list to include schools and general readership. 16 titles in 1997. TITLES *Landmarks in Gene Regulation; X-ray Microanalysis for Biologists; Metabolic Regulation; Making Sense of Science* series includes *Brainbox* and *Poo, You and the Potoroo's Loo.* Unsolicited mss, synopses and ideas welcome. No fiction.

Royalties paid twice-yearly. *Overseas subsidiary* Portland Press Inc.

Authors' Rating More of Portland's output is going on-line. Hard print will decline from around twenty books a year to ten.

T. & A. D. Poyser

See **Harcourt Brace and Company Limited**

Presentations

See **Souvenir Press Ltd**

Princeton University Press

See **University Presses of California, Columbia & Princeton Ltd**

Prion Books Ltd

Unit L, 32–34 Gordon House Road, London NW5 1LP
☎0171 482 4248   Fax 0171 482 4203
Managing Director *Barry Winkleman*

Formerly a packaging operation but began publishing under the Prion imprint in 1987. *Publishes* non-fiction: humour, popular culture, historical and literary reprints, beauty, food and drink, sex, psychology and health. About 40 titles a year. Unsolicited mss, synopses and ideas welcome.
   Royalties paid twice-yearly.

Profile Books

62 Queen Anne Street, London W1M 9LA
☎0171 486 6010   Fax 0171 486 6010
Managing Director *Andrew Franklin*

FOUNDED 1996. *Publishes* serious nonfiction including current affairs, history, politics, psychology, cultural criticism, business and management. 25 titles in 1997. IMPRINTS **Profile Books** *Andrew Franklin;* **Economist Books** *Stephen Brough.* No unsolicited mss.
   Royalties paid twice-yearly.

Authors' Rating In his bid for independence, Andrew Franklin promises to be 'author friendly, fast and fleet of foot'. But anyone who expects a large advance will be disappointed.

Puffin

See **Penguin UK**

Pushkin Press Ltd

22 Cathcart Road, London SW10 9NN
☎0171 349 9367   Fax 0171 352 8139
E-mail: pushkinpressltd@compuserve.com
Chairman *Melissa Ulfane*
Editorial Head *Oliver Berggruen*
Approx. Annual Turnover £500,000

Publishes novels, essays and poetry drawn from the best of classic and contemporary European literature. 4 titles in 1997. Welcomes unsolicited mss, synopses and ideas for books which come within these areas. No popular/commercial fiction/nonfiction.

Royalties paid twice-yearly.

Putnam Aeronautical Books
See **Brassey's (UK) Ltd**

Quadrille Publishing Ltd
Alhambra House, 27–31 Charing Cross Road, London WC2H 0LS
☎0171 839 7117   Fax 0171 839 7118
Chairman *Sue Thomson*
Managing Director *Alison Cathie*
Publishing Director *Anne Furniss*

FOUNDED in 1994 by four ex-directors of Conran Octopus, with a view to producing a small list of top-quality illustrated books. *Publishes* non-fiction, including cookery, gardening, interior design and decoration, craft, health and travel. 10 titles in 1997. TITLES *Carluccio's Complete Italian Food*; *Cooked to Perfection* Anne Willan; *Sensual Home* Ilse Crawford; *Take Off 10 Years in 10 Weeks* Judith Wills; *Bewitched: Titania's Book of Love Spells*; *Country Living Soft Furnishings*. No unsolicited mss; synopses and ideas for books welcome. No fiction or children's books.

Royalties paid twice-yearly.

Quantum
See **W. Foulsham & Co.**

Quartet Books
27 Goodge Street, London W1P 2LD
☎0171 636 3992   Fax 0171 637 1866
Chairman *Naim Attallah*
Managing Director *Jeremy Beale*
Publishing Director *Stella Kane*
Approx. Annual Turnover £1 million

FOUNDED 1972. Independent publisher. *Publishes* contemporary literary fiction including translations, popular culture, biography, music, history, politics and some photographic books. Unsolicited mss with return postage welcome; no poetry, romance or science fiction.

Royalties paid twice-yearly.

Authors' Rating This year put the quarter into Quartet. The publisher which values 'people before statistics' celebrated its first 25 years. Never less than interesting, the Quartet list, with its angle towards new writing, has not found it easy to compete in a trade market dedicated to

bestsellers. But there are some strong titles coming along which should please the accountants.

Queen Anne Press
See **Lennard Associates Ltd**

Quiller Press
46 Lillie Road, London SW6 1TN
☎0171 499 6529   Fax 0171 381 8941
Managing/Editorial Director *Jeremy Greenwood*

Specialises in sponsored books and publications sold through non-book trade channels as well as bookshops. *Publishes* architecture, biography, business and industry, children's, collecting, cookery, DIY, gardening, guidebooks, humour, reference, sports, travel, wine and spirits. About 15 titles a year. TITLES *Running Racing – the Jockey Club Years* John Tyrrel; *Understanding Lloyds* Iain Simpson; *French Entrée Guides* Patricia Fenn; *Eton & Harrow at Lord's* Robert Titchener-Barrett. Most ideas originate in-house – unsolicited mss not welcome unless the author sees some potential for sponsorship or guaranteed sales.

Royalties paid twice-yearly.

Quiz Quest
See **Funfax Limited**

RAC Publishing
See **West One (Trade) Publishing Ltd**

Radcliffe Medical Press Ltd
18 Marcham Road, Abingdon, Oxon OX14 1AA
☎01235 528820   Fax 01235 528830
E-mail: medical@radpress.win-uk.net
Managing Director *Andrew Bax*
Editorial Director *Gillian Nineham*
Editorial Manager *Jamie Etherington*
Approx. Annual Turnover £1.5 million

FOUNDED 1987. Medical publishers which began by specialising in books for general practice and health service management. *Publishes* clinical, management, health policy books and CD-ROMs. 60 titles in 1997. Unsolicited mss, synopses and ideas welcome. No non-medical or medical books aimed at lay audience.

Royalties paid twice-yearly.

The Ramsay Head Press
15 Gloucester Place, Edinburgh EH3 6EE
☎0131 225 5646   Fax 0131 225 5646
Managing Directors *Conrad Wilson, Mrs Christine Wilson*

FOUNDED 1968 by Norman Wilson OBE. A

small independent family publisher. *Publishes* biography, cookery, Scottish fiction and non-fiction, plus the quarterly literary magazine *Books in Scotland*. About 3–4 titles a year. TITLES *Medusa Dozen* Tessa Ransford; *The Happy Land* Howard Denton & Jim C. Wilson. Synopses and ideas for books of Scottish interest welcome. *Royalties* paid twice-yearly.

Random House UK Ltd

Random House, 20 Vauxhall Bridge Road, London SW1V 2SA
☎0171 840 8400   Fax 0171 233 6058
Chief Executive *Gail Rebuck*
Executive Chairman *Simon Master*

Random's increasing focus on trade publishing, both here and in the US, has been well rewarded, with sales continuing to grow over the last year. Random House UK Ltd is the parent company of three separate publishing divisions following the Group's reorganisation under Gail Rebuck. These are: General Books division, the Group's largest publishing division; Children's Books, and Ebury Press Special Books division.

DIVISIONS
General Books Divided into two operating groups, allowing hardcover editors to see their books through to publication in paperback. The literary imprints Jonathan Cape, Methuen, Secker & Warburg and Chatto & Windus work side by side with paperback imprints Vintage and Pimlico to form one group; trade imprints Century, William Heinemann and Hutchinson go hand-in-hand with Arrow to form the other group.

IMPRINTS
Jonathan Cape Ltd ☎0171 840 8576 Fax 0171 233 6117 Publishing Director *Dan Franklin* Biography and memoirs, current affairs, fiction, history, photography, poetry, politics and travel.

Methuen ☎0171 840 8638 Fax 0171 233 6117 Publishing Director *Michael Earley* Plays, film, drama, humour, performing arts.

Secker & Warburg ☎0171 840 8649 Fax 0171 233 6117 Editorial Director *Geoff Mulligan* Principally literary fiction with some non-fiction.

Chatto & Windus Ltd ☎0171 840 8522 Fax 0171 233 6117 Publishing Director *Alison Samuel* Art, belles-lettres, biography and memoirs, current affairs, essays, fiction, history, poetry, politics, philosophy, translations and travel.

Century (including **Business Books**) ☎0171 840 8555 Fax 0171 233 6127 Publisher *Kate Parkin* Publishing Director, Non-fiction *Mark Booth* General fiction and non-fiction, plus business management, advertising, communication, marketing, selling, investment and financial titles.

William Heinemann ☎0171 840 8400 Fax 0171 233 6127 Publishing Director *Maria Rejt* Editorial Director *Lynne Drew* General non-fiction and fiction, especially history, biography, science, crime, thrillers and women's fiction.

Hutchinson ☎0171 840 8564 Fax 0171 233 7870 Publishing Director *Sue Freestone* General fiction and non-fiction including notably belles-lettres, current affairs, politics, travel and history.

Arrow ☎0171 840 8516 Fax 0171 233 6127 Publishing Director *Andy McKillop* Mass-market paperback fiction and non-fiction.

Pimlico ☎0171 840 8630 Fax 0171 233 6117 Publishing Director *Will Sulkin* Large-format quality paperbacks in the fields of history, biography, popular culture and literature.

Vintage ☎0171 840 8531 Fax 0171 233 6127 Publisher *Caroline Michel* Quality paperback fiction and non-fiction. Vintage was founded in 1990 and has been described as one of the 'greatest literary success stories in recent British publishing'.

Children's Books ☎0171 840 8400 Fax 0171 233 6058 Managing Director *Ian Hudson* Deputy Managing Director *Debbie Sandford* IMPRINTS **Hutchinson** Publishing Director *Caroline Roberts*; **Jonathan Cape** Publishing Director *Tom Maschler*; **Bodley Head** Publishing Director *Anne McNeil*; **Red Fox** and **Tellastory** Publishing Director *Pilar Jenkins*; **Julia MacRae** Publishing Director *Delia Huddy* Picture books, fiction, non-fiction, novelties and audio cassette (see entry under **Audio Books**).

Ebury Press Special Books ☎0171 840 8400 Fax 0171 840 8406 Managing Director *Amelia Thorpe*. Publisher *Fiona MacIntyre* Associate Publisher *Julian Shuckburgh* IMPRINTS **Ebury Press**; **Vermilion**; **Rider**; **Barrie & Jenkins**; **Condé Nast Books**; **Fodor's**. Art, antiques, biography, Buddhism, cookery, gardening, health and beauty, homes and interiors, personal development, spirituality, travel and guides, sport, TV tie-ins. About 150 titles a year. Unsolicited mss, synopses and ideas for books welcome.
Royalties paid twice-yearly for the most part.

Authors' Rating In the publishing sale of the year, the American-owned Random House was taken over by Germany-based Bertelsmann, the third largest media conglomerate after Disney and Time Warner. What this will mean for British authors is hard to assess. Bertelsmann already owns **Transworld** and while the two companies will keep their distinct features, Carole Blake of **Blake Friedmann** has warned that 'such power all in one place is not healthy'. Against this, European influence from whatever quarter on an increasingly American dominated industry has to be welcome. Strong in the fiction market, Random House was the dominant publisher last Christmas with sales close to £9 million in the four weeks to end December. Not surprisingly, Random went on to pick up the Publisher of the Year award. A number of imprints acquired from **Reed** in early 1997 have now been dropped. These include Sinclair-Stevenson and Minerva. But Gail Rebuck is committed to general trade publishing 'not just as our core activity but as our entire activity'.

Ransom Publishing Ltd
Ransom House, 2 High Street, Watlington, Oxfordshire OX9 5PS
☎01491 613711   Fax 01491 613733
Managing Director *Jenny Ertle*

FOUNDED 1995 by ex-McGraw-Hill publisher. Partnerships formed with, among others, Channel 4 and the ICL. *Publishes* educational and consumer multimedia and study packs; all titles link to the Internet. 5 CD-ROMs and 5 study packs in 1997. TITLES *Lost Animals: Living on the Edge of Extinction; The History of the Universe; Rivers; Insects: Little Creatures in a Big World; Worlds of the Reef; Sonoran Desert: A Multimedia Field Trip to the Cactus Desert of Arizona*. No unsolicited mss. Synopses and ideas for books, as well as multimedia/Internet projects, welcome. Special areas of interest: science, geography, maths, general reference, natural history and history.
Royalties paid twice yearly.

RCB General Books
See **Richard Cohen Books Ltd**

Reader's Digest Association Ltd
11 Westferry Circus, Canary Wharf, London E14 4HE
☎0171 715 8000   Fax 0171 715 8181
Managing Director *Neil McRae*
Editorial Head *Cortina Butler*

Approx. Annual Turnover £205 million
Publishes gardening, natural history, cookery, history, DIY, travel and word books. About 35 titles a year. TITLES *Family Encyclopedia of World History; Know Your Rights; New Encyclopedia of Garden Plants and Flowers; Treasures in Your Home; Foods That Harm, Foods That Heal; 30 Minute Cookbook; Country Walks and Scenic Drives.*

Authors' Rating Joining the steady march towards multimedia, Reader's Digest children's books are making a big impact with their book-plus-product deals with toymakers Fisher Price and Playmobil.

Reaktion Ltd
11 Rathbone Place, London W1P 1DE
☎0171 580 9928   Fax 0171 580 9935
E-mail: Reaktionbooks@compuserve.com
Managing Director *Michael R. Leaman*

FOUNDED in Edinburgh in 1985 and moved to its London location in 1988. *Publishes* art history, architecture, Asian studies, cultural studies, design, history, photography and travel. About 20 titles a year. TITLES *Why Wars Happen* Jeremy Black; *Animal Rights* Hilda Kean; *Terminal Architecture* Martin Pawley; *Mirror in Parchment* Michael Camille; *Grand Hotels* Elaine Denby; *Landscape and Englishness* David Matless. No unsolicited mss; synopses and ideas welcome.
Royalties paid twice-yearly.

Reardon and Rawes
11 Trowscoued Avenue, Cheltenham, Gloucestershire GL53 7BP
☎01242 245259
Editor *Julian Rawes*

FOUNDED 1996. *Publishes* re-issues of out-of-print titles in electronic/multimedia format. Non-fiction historical titles only. 4 titles in 1997. TITLES *Picture of Bristol – A Guide* Rev. John Evans; *Proverbs and Family Mottoes* J. A. Mair; *Wessex to Essex* Rosemary Barham. Unsolicited mss welcome.
Royalties not paid.

Reardon Publishing
56 Upper Norwood Street, Leckhampton, Cheltenham, Gloucestershire GL53 0DU
☎01242 231800
Managing Editor *Nicholas Reardon*

FOUNDED in the mid 1970s. Family-run publishing house specialising in local interest and tourism in the Cotswold area. Member of the

Outdoor Writers Guild. Publishes walking and driving guides, and family history for societies. 10 titles a year. TITLES *The Cotswold Way* (video); *The Cotswold Way Map; Cotswold Walkabout; Cotswold Driveabout; The Donnington Way; The Haunted Cotswolds; The Cotswold Way.* Unsolicited mss, synopsis and ideas welcome with return postage only.

Royalties paid twice-yearly.

Rebel Inc.
See **Canongate Books Ltd**

Recollections
See **George Mann Books**

Red Fox
See **Random House UK Ltd**

William Reed Directories
Merchant House, 4A Reading Road, Pangbourne, Berkshire RG8 7LL
☎0118 9844111   Fax 0118 9841579
Editorial Manager *Mrs H. Turner*
William Reed Directories, a division of William Reed Publishing, was ESTABLISHED in 1990. Its portfolio includes 13 titles covering the food, drink, non-food, catering, retail and export industries. The titles are produced as directories, market research reports, exhibition catalogues and electronic publishing.

Reed Books
Michelin House, 81 Fulham Road, London SW3 6RB
☎0171 581 9393   Fax 0171 225 9424
Chief Executive *John Holloran*
Approx. Annual Turnover £150 million
Reed Books, whose parent company is Reed Elsevier, has several offices; addresses and telephone numbers have been given if different from that above.

ILLUSTRATED NON-FICTION:
Hamlyn/Octopus Fax 0171 225 9528 Managing Director *Laura Bamford* Popular non-fiction, particularly cookery, gardening, craft, sport, film tie-ins, rock 'n' roll TITLES *Larousse Gastronomique; Sunday Times Chronicle of Sport; Hamlyn New Cookbook; Hamlyn Book of Gardening; Hamlyn Book of DIY & Decorating.*

Mitchell Beazley Fax 0171 225 9024 Managing Director *Jane Aspden* Quality illustrated reference books, particularly wine, Miller's Antiques books, gardening, craft, interior design and architecture, general reference TITLES *Hugh Johnson's Pocket Wine Book; The New Joy of Sex; Miller's Antiques Price Guide.*

Osprey Fax 0171 225 9348 Managing Director *Jonathan Parker* Militaria, aviation, automotive SERIES *Men-at-Arms; Elite Campaign; New Vanguard; Warrior; Aircraft of the Aces.* TITLES *Combat Aircraft; Stanley Classic Car Year Book; Osprey Companion to Military History; Spitfire – Flying Legend.*

Conran Octopus 37 Shelton Street, London WC2H 9HN ☎0171 240 6961 Fax 0171 836 9951 Managing Director *John Wallace* Quality illustrated books, particularly interiors, design, cookery, gardening and crafts TITLES *East Meets West* Kelly Hoppen; *The New Office* Francis Duffy; *The Essential Garden Book* Terence Conran and Dan Pearson; *Passion for Flavour* Gordon Ramsay; *The Sensuous Garden* Monty Don; *Fabric Dyeing and Printing* Kate Wells.

Philip's Fax 0171 225 9841 Managing Director *John Gaisford* World atlases, globes, astronomy, road atlases, encyclopaedias, thematic reference TITLES *Philip's Atlas of the World; Philip's Modern School Atlas; Philip's Guide to the Stars and Planets; Ordnance Survey Street Atlas; Philip's Concise Encyclopaedia; Philip's Atlas of World History.*

CHILDRENS:
Reed Children's Books Fax 0171 225 9731 Managing Director *Jane Winterbotham*, Publishing Director *Gill Evans.*

Heinemann Young Books Quality picture books, novelty books, novels and anthologies TITLES *Thomas The Tank Engine; The Jolly Postman; The Trouble With* series; **Methuen Children's Books** Quality picture books and fiction for babies to early teens TITLES *Winnie the Pooh; Tintin; The Wind in the Willows;* **Hamlyn** Illustrated non-fiction and reference books for children TITLES *Every Boy's/Girl's Handbook; Crime Files; In the Next 3 Seconds;* **Mammoth Paperbacks** Paperback imprint of the above hardback imprints; licensed characters and tie-ins TITLES *Barbie; Star Wars; Disney Playbooks.* No unsolicited mss.

Brimax Books Units 4/5, Studlands Park Industrial Estate, Exning Road, Newmarket, Suffolk CB8 7AU ☎01638 664611 Fax 01638 665220 Managing Director *Patricia Gillette* Mass-market board and picture books for children, age groups 1–10.

Royalties paid twice-yearly/annually, according to contract in all divisions.

Authors' Rating After a clumsy and expensive withdrawal from consumer books, Reed pursued an ambition to become a leading contender in information technology. But European Commission fears of a near monopoly in the professional markets of Europe put a stop to a proposed merger with Wolters Kluwer. Meanwhile, Reed sold Heinemann ELT to **Macmillan** for, it is rumoured, £35 million. Reed's magazine business IPC (excluding *New Scientist*) was sold to a management buyout team for £860 million. This left the children's list which had been on the market for three years. After **Penguin** pulled out of negotiations, Egmont (**World International**), Europe's leading publisher of children's books, took over as the hot and heavy suitor. The purchase was confirmed in May. Meanwhile, any fears that Reed children's authors may have about their future have been stilled by unfazed management. Incredibly, Reed has not only held on to its market share during a time of uncertainty but has actually increased sales.

Reed Educational & Professional Publishing
Halley Court, Jordan Hill, Oxford OX2 8EJ
☎01865 311366   Fax 01865 314641
Chief Executive *William Shepherd*

Incorporating   Butterworth-Heinemann, Heinemann Educational and Ginn in the UK; Greenwood Heinemann and Rigby in the USA; Rigby Heinemann in Australia.

This division has several offices; addresses and telephone numbers have been given if different from that above.

Heinemann Educational Fax 01865 314140 Managing Director *Bob Osborne*, Primary *Paul Shuter*, Secondary *Kay Symons*. Textbooks/literature/other educational resources for primary and secondary school and further education. Mss, synopses and ideas welcome.

Ginn & Co Prebendal House, Parson's Fee, Aylesbury, Bucks HP20 2QY ☎01296 394442 Fax 01296 393433 Managing Director *Paul Shuter*, Editorial Director *Jill Duffy*. Textbook/other educational resources for primary and secondary schools.

Butterworth Heinemann International Linacre House, Jordan Hill, Oxford OX2 8EJ ☎01865 310366 Fax 01865 310898 Managing Director *Philip Shaw*, Engineering & Technology *Neil Warnock-Smith*, Business *Kathryn Grant*, Medical *Geoff Smaldon*. Books and electronic products across business, technical, medical and open-learning fields for students and professionals.

Royalties paid twice-yearly/annually, according to contract in all divisions.

Regency House Publishing Limited
3 Mill Lane, Broxbourne, Hertfordshire EN10 7AZ
☎01992 479988   Fax 01992 479966
Chairman *Brian Trodd*
Managing Director *Nicolette Trodd*
Approx. Annual Turnover £1.3 million
FOUNDED 1991. Publisher and packager of mass-market non-fiction. 20 titles in 1997. No unsolicited mss; synopses and ideas for books welcome. No fiction.
Royalties paid twice-yearly.

Reinhardt Books Ltd
Flat 2, 43 Onslow Square, London SW7 3LR
☎0171 589 3751
Chairman/Managing Director *Max Reinhardt*
Director *Joan Reinhardt*
FOUNDED 1887 as H. F. L. (Publishers) and was acquired by Max Reinhardt in 1947. Changed its name to the present one in 1987. First publication under the new name was Graham Greene's *The Captain and the Enemy*. Also publishes under the **Nonesuch Press** imprint. AUTHORS include Mitsumasa Anno, Alistair Cooke and Maurice Sendak. New books are no longer considered.
Royalties paid according to contract.

Religious & Moral Educational Press (RMEP)
See **Hymns Ancient & Modern Ltd**

Richmond House Publishing Company
Douglas House, 3 Richmond Buildings, London W1V 5AE
☎0171 437 9556   Fax 0171 287 3463
Managing Directors *Gloria Gordon, Spencer Block*
Publishes directories for the theatre and entertainment industries. Synopses and ideas welcome.

Rider
See **Random House UK Ltd**

Robinson Publishing Ltd
7 Kensington Church Court, London W8 4SP
☎0171 938 3830   Fax 0171 938 4214
E-mail: 100560.3511@compuserve.com
Managing Director *Nicholas Robinson*
Publishing Director, Robinson *Jan Chamier*
Publishing Director, Magpie *Nova Jane Heath*
FOUNDED 1983. *Publishes* fiction: anthologies;

general non-fiction includes, health and self-help, psychology, true crime, puzzles, military history. Children's: anthologies, humour, games. 65 titles in 1997. No unsolicited fiction. Do not send mss; letters/synopses only. No e-mail submissions.

IMPRINTS **Magpie** Children's books. **Scarlet** Women's fiction: 100,000-word mss with a strong central romance. Contemporary (present-day) setting. Will consider Regency and medical romances, provided they are sensuous in tone. Guidelines are available; send s.a.e.

Royalties paid twice-yearly.

Authors' Rating Now heavily into what was once the preserve of Mills & Boon. The Scarlet series of romantic fiction is low priced and sold heavily through supermarkets and petrol stations. Authors tend to be regulars who can turn in acceptable manuscripts to tight deadlines. Also into self-help books published with the *Daily Telegraph*.

Robson Books Ltd

Bolsover House, 5–6 Clipstone Street, London W1P 8LE
☎0171 323 1223   Fax 0171 636 0798
Managing Director *Jeremy Robson*
Editorial Head *Kate Mills*

FOUNDED 1973. *Publishes* general non-fiction, including biography, cookery, gardening, guidebooks, health and beauty, humour, travel, sports and games. About 70 titles a year. Unsolicited mss, synopses and ideas for books welcome (s.a.e. essential).

Royalties paid twice-yearly.

Authors' Rating The hard-pressed gift buyers' favourite publisher. Strong on humour.

Round Hall

See **Sweet & Maxwell Ltd**

Roundhouse Publishing Group

PO Box 140, Oxford OX2 7FF
☎01865 512682   Fax 01865 559594
Editorial Head *Alan Goodworth*

ESTABLISHED 1991. *Publishes* cinema and media-related titles. TITLES *Cinema of Oliver Stone; Cinema of Stanley Kubrick; Shoot the Piano Player; Toms, Coons, Mulattoes, Mammies and Bucks*. Represents a broad range of non-fiction publishing houses throughout the UK and Europe. No unsolicited mss.

Royalties paid twice-yearly.

Routledge

11 New Fetter Lane, London EC4P 4EE
☎0171 583 9855   Fax 0171 842 2298
Managing Director *David Hill*
Publishing Director *Peter Sowden*
Publishers *Claire L'Enfant, Alan Jarvis, Anna Hodson, Edwina Welham, Phillip Read*
Approx. Annual Turnover (Group) £35.5 million

Publishes academic and professional books and journals in the social sciences, humanities, health sciences and the built environment for the international market. Routledge was formed in 1987 through an amalgamation of Routledge & Kegan Paul, Methuen & Co., Tavistock Publications, and Croom Helm. Subsequent acquisitions include the Unwin Hyman academic list from **HarperCollins** (1991), *Who's Who* and historical atlases from **Dent/Orion** (1994), archaeology and ancient history titles from **Batsford** (1996), and the E & FN Spon imprint from ITP Science (1997).

Publishes addiction, anthropology, archaeology, architecture, Asian studies, biblical studies, the built environment, business and management, civil engineering, classics, heritage, construction, counselling, criminology, development and environment, dictionaries, economics, education, environmental engineering, geography, health, history, Japanese studies, journals, language, leisure studies and leisure management, linguistics, literary criticism, media and culture, Middle East, nursing, philosophy, politics, political economy, psychiatry, psychology, reference, social administration, social studies and sociology, therapy, theatre and performance studies, women's studies. No poetry, fiction, travel or astrology. About 900 titles a year. Send synopses with sample chapter and c.v. rather than complete mss.

Royalties paid annually and twice-yearly, according to contract.

Authors' Rating Having cut free from Thomson in 1996, Routledge has continued recruiting from its previous owner with the acquisition of E & FN Spon, the environment and construction publisher founded in 1834 and, while under Thomson, responsible for around 100 titles a year.

Ryland Peters and Small Limited

Cavendish House, 51–55 Mortimer Street, London W1N 7TD
☎0171 436 9090   Fax 0171 436 9790
Managing Director *David Peters*

FOUNDED 1996 – first titles published in the

autumn. *Publishes* highly illustrated lifestyle books – gardening, cookery, craft, interior design. No fiction. No unsolicited mss; synopses and ideas welcome.
Royalties paid twice-yearly.

Authors' Rating A new list of illustrated books of eye-catching quality.

Sage Publications
6 Bonhill Street, London EC2A 4PU
☎0171 374 0645   Fax 0171 374 8741
Managing Director *Stephen Barr*
Editorial Director *Ziyad Marar*
FOUNDED 1971. *Publishes* academic books and journals in humanities and the social sciences. Bought academic and professional books publisher **Paul Champman Publishing Ltd** in April 1998.
Royalties paid twice-yearly.

Saint Andrew Press
Board of Communication, Church of Scotland, 121 George Street, Edinburgh EH2 4YN
☎0131 225 5722   Fax 0131 220 3113
Publishing Manager *Lesley Ann Taylor*
Approx. Annual Turnover £225,000
FOUNDED in 1954 to publish and promote the 17-volume series *The Daily Study Bible New Testament* by Professor William Barclay. Owned by the Church of Scotland Board of Communication. *Publishes* religious, Scottish local interest and some children's books. No fiction. 16 titles in 1997. No unsolicited mss; synopses and ideas preferred.
Royalties paid annually.

St Paul's Bibliographies
1 Step Terrace, Winchester, Hampshire SO22 5BW
☎01962 860524   Fax 01962 842409
E-mail: stpauls@stpaulsbib.com
Publishing Director *Robert Cross*
Approx. Annual Turnover £40,000
FOUNDED 1982. *Publishes* bibliographical reference books and works on the history of the book. 2–3 titles a year. TITLES *The Stationers' Company and The Book Trade* ed. Robin Myers and Michael Harris; *A New Introduction to Bibliography* Philip Gaskell; *George Orwell: A Bibliography*. Unsolicited mss, synopses and ideas welcome if relevant to subjects covered. Agent for Oak Knoll Press books.
Royalties paid twice-yearly.

St Pauls Publishers
Morpeth Terrace, London SW1P 1EP
☎0171 828 5582   Fax 0171 828 3329
E-mail: editions@stpauls.org.uk
Managing Director *Karamvelil Sebastian*
Publishing division of the Society of St Paul. Began publishing in 1914 but activities were fairly limited until around 1948. *Publishes* religious material only: theology, scripture, catechetics, prayer books, children's material and biography. Unsolicited mss, synopses and ideas welcome. About 50 titles a year.

Salamander Books Ltd
8 Blenheim Court, Brewery Road, London N7 9NT
☎0171 700 7799   Fax 0171 700 3572
Managing Director *David Spence*
FOUNDED 1973. Acquired by remainder books dealer Ramboro Books. *Publishes* collecting, cookery, interiors, gardening, music, crafts, military and aviation, pet care, sport and transport. About 30 titles a year. Unsolicited synopses and ideas for books welcome.
Royalties outright fee paid instead of royalties.

Sangam Books Ltd
57 London Fruit Exchange, Brushfield Street, London E1 6EP
☎0171 377 6399   Fax 0171 375 1230
Executive Director *Anthony de Souza*
Traditionally an educational publisher of school and college level textbooks. Also *publishes* art, India, medicine, science, technology, social sciences, religion, plus some fiction in paperback.

W. B. Saunders & Co. Ltd/ Saunders Scientific Publications
See **Harcourt Brace and Company Ltd**

SB Publications
c/o 19 Grove Road, Seaford, East Sussex BN25 1TP
☎01323 893498
Managing Director *Steve Benz*
Approx. Annual Turnover £200,000
FOUNDED 1987. *Specialises* in local history, including themes illustrated by old picture postcards and photographs; also travel, guides (town, walking), maritime history and railways. 20 titles a year.
IMPRINTS **Brampton Publications** *Steve Benz* TITLES *Potteries Picture Postcards*; *Curiosities of East Sussex*; *A Dorset Quiz Book*. Also pro-

vides marketing and distribution services for local authors.

Royalties paid annually.

Scala Books
See **Philip Wilson Publishers Ltd**

Scarlet
See **Robinson Publishing Ltd**

Scarlet Press
5 Montague Road, London E8 2HN
☎0171 241 3702   Fax 0171 275 0031

Directors *Christine Considine, Avis Lewallen*

FOUNDED 1989. Independent publishing house. *Publishes* feminist non-fiction covering politics, autobiography, social policy, arts, leisure, history, lesbian and gay studies. No fiction or any 'non-woman-centred' material. About 8 titles a year. TITLES *Patient No More: The Politics of Breast Cancer* Sharon Batt; *Idols to Incubators: Reproduction Theory Through the Ages* Julia Stonehouse; *Stolen Lives: Trading Women into Sex and Slavery* Sietske Altink. Unsolicited mss, synopses and ideas welcome.

Royalties paid twice-yearly.

Sceptre
See **Hodder Headline plc**

Scholastic Ltd
Villiers House, Clarendon Avenue, Leamington Spa, Warwickshire CV32 5PR
☎01926 887799   Fax 01926 883331

Chairman *M. R. Robinson*
Managing Director *David Kewley*
Approx. Annual Turnover £52 million

FOUNDED 1964. Owned by US parent company. *Publishes* children's fiction and non-fiction and education for primary schools.

DIVISIONS
Scholastic Children's Books *David Fickling* Commonwealth House, 1–19 New Oxford Street, London WC1A 1NU ☎0171 421 9000 Fax 0171 421 9001 IMPRINTS **Scholastic Press** (hardbacks); **Adlib** (12+ fiction); **Hippo** (paperbacks); **Point** (paperbacks) TITLES *Postman Pat; Rosie & Jim; Tots TV; Horrible Histories; Goosebumps; Point Horror.*

Educational Publishing *Anne Peel* (Villiers House address) Professional books and classroom materials for primary teachers, plus magazines such as *Child Education, Junior Education, Art & Craft, Junior Focus, Infant Projects, Nursery Projects.*

Red House Book Clubs *David Teale,*

Victoria Birkett Cotswold Business Park, Witney, Oxford OX8 5YT ☎01993 774171/771144 Fax 01993 776813 The Book Club group sells to families at home through The Red House Book Club and Book Parties, through Red House School Book Clubs (four different clubs catering for children from 4–15), and through the Red House International Schools Club.

School Book Fairs *Will Oldham* (Villiers House address) The Book Fair Division sells directly to children, parents and teachers in schools through 14,000 week-long book events held in schools throughout the UK.

Royalties paid twice-yearly.

Authors' Rating Has held up well against tough competition in a shrinking children's market. Authors benefit from strong marketing. Came out top in a recent Society of Authors survey of author-friendly publishers.

SCM Press Ltd
9–17 St Albans Place, London N1 0NX
☎0171 359 8033   Fax 0171 359 0049

Managing Director *Rev. Dr John Bowden*
Approx. Annual Turnover £1 million

Publishes religion and theology from an open perspective, with some ethics and philosophy. About 40 titles a year. Relevant unsolicited mss and synopses considered if sent with s.a.e.

Royalties paid annually.

Authors' Rating Leading publisher of religious ideas with well-deserved reputation for fresh thinking. At SCM, 'questioning theology is the norm'.

Scope International Ltd
Forestside House, Forestside, Rowlands Castle, Hampshire PO9 6EE
☎01705 631468   Fax 01705 631777

Managing Director *David Gibson*
Editor *Nicholas Pullen*

Publishes business, economics, finance, privacy, tax haven and tax planning.

IMPRINT **Scope**. No unsolicited mss; approach in writing with ideas/proposals. Additional material for existing reports welcome.

Royalties paid twice-yearly.

Scottish Academic Press
56 Hanover Street, Edinburgh EH2 2DX
☎0131 225 7483   Fax 0131 225 7662

Managing Editor *Dr Douglas Grant*

FOUNDED 1969. *Publishes* academic: architecture, biography, education, Gaelic, geology,

history, law, literature, philosophy, poetry, social sciences, theology.
Royalties paid annually.

Seafarer Books
See **The Merlin Press Ltd**

Search Press Ltd/Burns & Oates
Wellwood, North Farm Road, Tunbridge Wells, Kent TN2 3DR
☎01892 510850   Fax 01892 515903
E-mail: searchpress@searchpress.com
Managing Director *Martin de la Bédoyère*
FOUNDED 1847. *Publishes* (Search Press) full-colour art, craft, needlecrafts; (Burns & Oates) theology, history, spirituality, reference.
DIVISIONS **Academic** *Paul Burns* TITLES include *Butler's Lives of the Saints*, new full edition, 12 volumes. **Craft** *Rosalind Dace* Books on papermaking and papercrafts, painting on silk, art techniques and embroidery.
Royalties paid annually.

Secker & Warburg
See **Random House UK Ltd**

Sensation
See **Harlequin Mills & Boon Ltd**

Seren
First Floor, 2 Wyndham Street, Bridgend CF31 1EF
☎01656 767834   Fax 01656 767834
Chairman *Cary Archard*
Managing Director *Mick Feltin*
Approx. Annual Turnover £100,000
FOUNDED 1981 as a specialist poetry publisher but has now moved into general literary publishing with an emphasis on Wales. *Publishes* poetry, fiction, literary criticism, drama, biography, art, history and translations of fiction. 25 titles in 1997.
DIVISIONS
Poetry *Amy Wack* AUTHORS Robert Minhinnick, Tony Curtis, Sheenagh Pugh, Duncan Bush, Deryn Rees-Jones. **Drama** *Brian Mitchell* AUTHORS Edward Thomas, Charles Way, Lucinda Coxon. **Fiction**, **Art**, **Literary Criticism**, **History**, **Translations** *Mick Felton* AUTHORS Christopher Meredith, Leslie Norris, Gwyn Thomas.
IMPRINT **Border Lines Biographies** TITLES *Bruce Chatwin; Dennis Potter; Mary Webb; Wilfred Owen; Raymond Williams.* Unsolicited mss, synopses and ideas for books welcome.
Royalties paid twice yearly.

Serpent's Tail
4 Blackstock Mews, London N4 2BT
☎0171 354 1949   Fax 0171 704 6467
Contact *Laurence O'Toole*
Approx. Annual Turnover £650,000
FOUNDED 1986. Won the *Sunday Times* Small Publisher of the Year Award (1989) and the Ralph Lewis Award for new fiction (1992). Serpent's Tail has introduced to British audiences a number of major internationally known writers. Noted for its strong emphasis on design – including flaps on paperback covers in the continental style – and an eye for the unusual. *Publishes* contemporary fiction, including works in translation, crime, popular culture and biography. No poetry, science fiction, horror, romance or fantasy. About 40 titles a year.
IMPRINTS
Serpent's Tail TITLES *Mr Clive and Mr Page* Neil Bartlett; *Hallucinating Foucault* Patricia Duncker; *Ocean of Sound* David Toop; **Mask Noir** TITLES *A Little Yellow Dog*; *Black Betty* Walter Mosley; *Wavewalker* Stella Duffy; *Jello Salad* Nicholas Blincoe; *Jade Lady Burning* Martin Limon; **High Risk Books** *Rent Boy* Gary Indiana; *Spinsters* Pagan Kennedy; *Bombay Talkie* Armeena Meer. Send preliminary letter outlining proposal (include s.a.e. for reply). No unsolicited mss. Prospective authors who are not familiar with Serpent's Tail are advised to study the list before submitting anything.
Royalties normally paid annually.

Authors' Rating Described by publisher Peter Ayrton as 'a reference point for outlaw culture', Serpent's Tail gives a voice to writers who are outside the political, sexual or racial mainstream. Marketing is imaginative. Not for Serpent's Tail the single website listing recent titles. Key in to www.serpentstail.com and you get a questionnaire checking out your subject interests before being led ever so gently to the Serpent's Tail book that is just for you.

Settle Press
10 Boyne Terrace Mews, London W11 3LR
☎0171 243 0695
Chairman/Managing Director *D. Settle*
FOUNDED 1981. *Publishes* travel and guidebooks. About 12 titles a year. **Travel/Tourist Guides** TITLES *City Breaks Series* (Paris, Rome, Vienna, etc.); *Key To Series* (Far East, Indian Ocean, Africa, Florida, etc). Unsolicited synopses accepted but no mss.
Royalties paid by arrangement.

Severn House Publishers Ltd

9–15 High Street, Sutton, Surrey SM1 1DF
☎0181 770 3930   Fax 0181 770 3850
Chairman *Edwin Buckhalter*
Editorial *Sara Short*

FOUNDED 1974. A leader in library fiction publishing. *Publishes* hardback fiction: romance, science fiction, horror, fantasy, crime. About 130 titles a year. No unsolicited material. Synopses/proposals preferred through *bona fide* literary agents only.

Royalties paid twice-yearly. *Overseas associates* Severn House Publishers Inc., New York.

Sheffield Academic Press

Mansion House, 19 Kingfield Road, Sheffield S11 9AS
☎0114 2554433   Fax 0114 2554626
Managing Director *Mrs Jean R.K. Allen*
Approx. Annual Turnover £1.5 million

FOUNDED in 1976. Originally known as JSOT Press. Now the leading academic publisher of biblical titles. Recently expanded its list to include archaeology, literary studies, history and culture, languages, scientific, professional, reference. 110 titles in 1997. Unsolicited mss, synopses and ideas welcome. No fiction. IMPRINTS **Sheffield Academic Press** *Jean Allen*; **Subis**.

Royalties paid annually

Sheldon Press

See **Society for Promoting Christian Knowledge**

Shepheard-Walwyn (Publishers) Ltd

Suite 34, 26 Charing Cross Road, London WC2H 0DH
☎0171 240 5992   Fax 0171 379 5770
Managing Director *Anthony Werner*
Approx. Annual Turnover £150,000

FOUNDED 1972. 'We regard books as food for the mind and want to offer a wholesome diet of original ideas and fresh approaches to old subjects.' *Publishes* general non-fiction in three main areas: Scottish interest; gift books in calligraphy and/or illustrated; history, political economy, philosophy. About 5 titles a year. Synopses and ideas for books welcome.

Royalties paid twice-yearly.

The Shetland Times Ltd

Prince Alfred Street, Lerwick, Shetland ZE1 0EP
☎01595 693622   Fax 01595 694637
Managing Director *Robert Wishart*

Publications Manager *Beatrice Nisbet*

FOUNDED 1872 as publishers of the local newspaper. Book publishing followed thereafter plus publication of monthly magazine, *Shetland Life*. *Publishes* anything with Shetland connections – local and natural history, music, crafts, maritime. 10 titles in 1997. Prefers material with a Shetland theme/connection.

Royalties paid annually.

Shire Publications Ltd

Cromwell House, Church Street, Princes Risborough, Buckinghamshire HP27 9AA
☎01844 344301   Fax 01844 347080
Managing Director *John Rotheroe*

FOUNDED 1967. *Publishes* original non-fiction paperbacks. About 25 titles a year. No unsolicited material; send introductory letter with detailed outline of idea.

Royalties paid annually.

Authors' Rating You don't have to live in the country to write books for Shire but it helps. With titles like *Church Fonts, Haunted Inns* and *Discovering Preserved Railways* there is a distinct rural feel to the list. Another way of putting it, to quote John Rotheroe, Shire specialises in 'small books on all manner of obscure subjects'.

Sidgwick & Jackson

See **Macmillan Publishers Ltd**

Sigma Press

1 South Oak Lane, Wilmslow, Cheshire SK9 6AR
☎01625 531035   Fax 01625 536800
E-mail: sigma.press@zetnet.co.uk
Chairman/Managing Director *Graham Beech*

FOUNDED in 1980 as a publisher of technical books. Sigma Press now publishes mainly in the leisure area. *Publishes* outdoor, local heritage, myths and legends, sports, dance and exercise. Recently launched a popular science series. Approx. 50 titles in 1997. No unsolicited mss; synopses and ideas welcome.

DIVISIONS **Sigma Leisure** TITLES *The Celtic Way; Country and Western Line Dancing for Cowgirls and Cowboys; Feeding the Imagination – The Vegetarian Society Cookbook*; **Sigma Press** TITLES *Scrooge's Crypic Carol; Alice in Quantumland*.

Royalties paid twice-yearly.

Silhouette Desire

See **Harlequin Mills & Boon Ltd**

Simon & Schuster
West Garden Place, Kendal Street, London
W2 2AQ
☎0171 316 1900   Fax 0171 402 0639
Managing Director *Nick Webb*
Editorial Directors *Clare Ledingham, Martin
Fletcher, Helen Gummer*
FOUNDED 1986. Offshoot of the leading
American publisher. *Publishes* general fiction,
including science fiction under its **Earthlight**
imprint (Editor *John Jarrold*) and non-fiction in
hardback and paperback. The academic division
is based in Hemel Hempstead. No academic or
technical material.
Royalties paid twice-yearly.

Authors' Rating Best known in the States for
its technology list, Simon & Schuster has made
its British reputation with new fiction and children's books. But the company's single biggest
advantage is being able to take in books from
the American side of Simon & Schuster, an
economic bonus that nonetheless makes it
harder for British authors to gain a foothold.
The educational, professional and reference
publishing operations (including Prentice Hall,
Allyn & Bacon, Macmillan Publishing USA
and Macmillan Reference USA) are up for sale.

Skoob Books Ltd
11A–17 Sicilian Avenue, Southampton Row,
London WC1A 2QH
☎0171 404 3063   Fax 0171 404 4398
Editorial office: 76A Oldfield Road, London
N16 0RS
☎/Fax 0171 275 9811
Managing Director *I. K. Ong*
Editorial *M. Lovell*
Publishes literary guides, cultural studies, esoter-
ica/occult, poetry, new writing from the Orient.
No unsolicited mss, synopses or ideas. TITLES
Where We Are Lucien Stryk; *Skoob Directory of
Secondhand Bookshops*; *The Necronomicon* George
Hay; *Haunting the Tiger* K. S. Maniam.

Smith Gryphon Ltd
See **Blake Publishing**

Colin Smythe Ltd
PO Box 6, Gerrards Cross, Buckinghamshire
SL9 8XA
☎01753 886000   Fax 01753 886469
Managing Director *Colin Smythe*
Approx. Annual Turnover £1.5 million
FOUNDED 1966. *Publishes* Anglo-Irish litera-
ture, drama, and criticism, history. About 15

titles a year. No unsolicited mss. Also acts as literary agent for a small list of authors.
Royalties paid annually/twice-yearly.

Society for Promoting Christian Knowledge (SPCK)
Holy Trinity Church, Marylebone Road,
London NW1 4DU
☎0171 387 5282   Fax 0171 388 2352
Director of Publishing *Simon Kingston*
FOUNDED 1698, SPCK is the third oldest pub-
lisher in the country. IMPRINTS **Sheldon Press**
Editorial Director *Joanna Moriarty* Popular medi-
cine, health, self-help, psychology, business.
SPCK Senior Editor *Alison Barr* Theology, aca-
demic, liturgy, prayer, spirituality, Biblical stud-
ies, educational resources, mission, pastoral care,
gospel and culture, worldwide. **Triangle** Editor
Alison Barr Popular Christian paperbacks. **Lynx**
Editor *Robin Keeley* Parish resources, training and
youthwork, textbooks.
Royalties paid annually.

Authors' Rating Religion with a strong social
edge.

Solo Books Ltd
49–53 Kensington High Street, London
W8 5ED
☎0171 376 2166   Fax 0171 938 3165
Chairman/Managing Director *Don Short*
Approx. Annual Turnover (Group)
£1.3 million
Publishing arm of **Solo Literary Agency** (see
entry under **UK Agents**). *Publishes* biography
and autobiography and celebrity books, some
non-fiction and business titles. About 15 titles a
year. No fiction. Unsolicited mss not welcome;
approach in writing with synopses or ideas.
Royalties paid quarterly.

Solway
See **Paternoster Publishing**

Sotheby's Publications
See **Philip Wilson Publishers Ltd**

Souvenir Press Ltd
43 Great Russell Street, London WC1B 3PA
☎0171 580 9307/8 & 637 5711/2/3
Fax 0171 580 5064
Chairman/Managing Director *Ernest Hecht*
Senior Editor *Tessa Harrow*
Independent publishing house. FOUNDED 1951.
Publishes academic and scholarly, animal care
and breeding, antiques and collecting, archaeol-

ogy, autobiography and biography, business and industry, children's, cookery, crafts and hobbies, crime, educational, fiction, gardening, health and beauty, history and antiquarian, humour, illustrated and fine editions, magic and the occult, medical, military, music, natural history, philosophy, poetry, psychology, religious, sociology, sports, theatre and women's studies. About 55 titles a year. Souvenir's Human Horizons series for the disabled and their carers is one of the most pre-eminent in its field and recently celebrated 18 years of publishing for the disabled.

IMPRINTS **Condor; Pictorial; Presentations; Pop Universal; Human Horizons**. TITLES *Whatever Happened to ...? The Ultimate Sequels Book* Adrian Mourby; *Fairy Spells – Seeing and Communicating with the Fairies* Claire Nahmad; *Warning: When I am an Old Woman I Shall Wear Purple* Jenny Joseph; *Spineless Wonders* Richard Conniff, illus. Sally Bensusen; *In Praise of Teddy Bears, Collector's Edition* Philippa Waring; *The Sleep Book for Tired Parents* Rebecca Huntley; *Tales of Love and Loss* Knut Hamsun; *Perfect Sight the Natural Way* Janet Goodrich. Unsolicited mss considered but initial letter of enquiry preferred.
Royalties paid twice-yearly.

Authors' Rating Eclectic is the only word for Souvenir. Jokey books about knickers and bras share shelf space with translations of work by Nobel Prize winners and the Human Horizon series for and about disabled people. Ernest Hecht is foremost a showman (his company takes its name from the souvenir theatre programmes he produced as his first publishing venture). His chaotic office with books everywhere has been described as Dada out of Dickens. But he is much loved by his authors.

SPCK
See **Society for Promoting Christian Knowledge**

Neville Spearman
See **The C. W. Daniel Co. Ltd**

Special Edition
See **Harlequin Mills & Boon Ltd**

Spellmount Ltd
The Old Rectory, Staplehurst, Kent TN12 0AZ
☎01580 893730   Fax 01580 893731
Managing Director *Jamie Wilson*
Approx. Annual Turnover £450,000
FOUNDED 1983. *Publishes* non-fiction in hard-

cover; primarily history and military history. About 30 titles a year. Synopses/ideas for books in these specialist fields welcome, enclosing return postage.
Royalties six-monthly for two years, then annually.

E & FN Spon
See **Routledge**

Stainer & Bell Ltd
PO Box 110, 23 Gruneisen Road, London N3 1DZ
☎0181 343 3303   Fax 0181 343 3024
Managing Directors *Carol Y. Wakefield, Keith M. Wakefield*
Publishing Manager *Nicholas Williams*
Approx. Annual Turnover £640,000
FOUNDED 1907 to publish sheet music. *Publishes* music and religious subjects related to hymnody. Unsolicited synopses/ideas for books welcome. Send letter enclosing brief précis.
Royalties paid annually.

Harold Starke Publishers Ltd
Pixey Green, Stradbroke, Near Eye, Suffolk IP21 5NG
☎01379 388334   Fax 01379 388335
Directors *Harold K. Starke, Naomi Galinski*
Publishes adult non-fiction, medical and reference. No unsolicited mss.
Royalties paid annually.

The Stationery Office Publishing
St Crispins, Duke Street, Norwich, Norfolk NR3 1PD
☎01603 622211   Fax 01603 694313
Chief Executive *Fred J. Perkins*
Business Development Director *Kevan Lawton*
Approx. Annual Turnover £60 million
Formerly HMSO, which was FOUNDED 1786. Became part of the private sector in October 1996. Publisher of material sponsored by Parliament, government departments and other official bodies. Also commercial publishing in the following broad categories: business and professional, environment, education, heritage. Unsolicited material may be considered if suitable and should be sent in the first instance to Kim Yarwood, Editorial Coordinator.

Authors' Rating It seems that privatisation has done the world of good to the Stationery Office which now manages to operate at a modest profit. This was not achieved without pain, however. The staff has dropped by a thousand and other overheads have been slashed. The Stationery Office's chief activity is printing and office supplies with the publishing division accounting for just 20% of the total business. But this is set to grow with the development of professional, business, science and heritage publishing. On the trade side, the Stationery Office produces some excellent popular history. There may be opportunities here for authors who would not automatically think of the publisher of the *Highway Code* as their natural home.

Patrick Stephens Ltd
See **Haynes Publishing**

Stevens
See **Sweet & Maxwell Ltd**

STL Ltd
See **Paternoster Publishing**

Subis
See **Sheffield Academic Press**

Summersdale Publishers
46 West Street, Chichester, West Sussex PO19 1RP
☎01243 771107   Fax 01243 786300
E-mail: summersdale@summersdale.com

Directors *Stewart Ferris, Alastair Williams*
Editor *Claire Richardson*
Approx. Annual Turnover £1 million

FOUNDED 1990. *Publishes* non-fiction: humour, TV/film tie-ins, travel literature, self-help, biography, sport, true crime, gift books, cookery. TITLES *Don't Mention the War; The Romance Book; The Many Faces of Jack the Ripper; Bestsellers; The Great British Festival Guide; Chat-up Lines and Put Downs; The Kama Sutra For One.* 50 titles in 1998. No unsolicited mss; synopses and ideas welcome.
Royalties paid.

Susquehanna University Press
See **Golden Cockerel Press**

Sutton Publishing Ltd
Phoenix Mill, Thrupp, Stroud, Gloucestershire GL5 2BU
☎01453 731114   Fax 01453 731117
Managing Director *David Hogg*
Publishing Director *Peter Clifford*
Approx. Annual Turnover £4.1 million
FOUNDED 1978. Owned by Guernsey Press.

Publishes academic, archaeology, biography, countryside, history, regional interest, local history, pocket classics (lesser known novels by classic authors), transport. About 240 titles a year. Send synopses rather than complete mss.
Royalties paid twice-yearly.

Authors' Rating Having started as a regional publisher concentrating on historical interests, Sutton is now into general trade publishing on a national level. The new Pocket Biography series is aimed at the popular end of the market.

Swan Hill Press
See **Airlife Publishing Ltd**

Sweet & Maxwell Ltd
100 Avenue Road, London NW3 3PF
☎0171 393 7000   Fax 0171 393 7010
Managing Director *Mike Dixon*
FOUNDED 1799. Part of The Thomson Corporation. *Publishes* legal and professional materials in all media, looseleaf works, journals, law reports and on CD-ROM. About 150 book titles a year, with live backlist of over 700 titles, 75 looseleaf services and more than 80 legal periodicals. Not interested in material which is non-legal. The legal and professional list is varied and contains many academic titles, as well as treatises and reference works in the legal and related professional fields.

IMPRINTS **Sweet & Maxwell; Sweet & Maxwell Asia; Stevens; W. Green (Scotland); Round Hall/Sweet & Maxwell (Ireland)** *Anthony Kinahan* (Managing Director). Ideas welcome. Writers with legal/professional projects in mind are advised to contact the company at the earliest possible stage in order to lay the groundwork for best design, production and marketing of a project.
Royalties and fees vary according to contract.

Take That Ltd
PO Box 200, Harrogate, North Yorkshire HG1 2YR
☎01423 507545   Fax 01423 526035
Chairman/Managing Director *C. Brown*
FOUNDED 1986. Independent publisher of computing, business, humour and gambling titles (books and magazines). TITLES *Understand Financial Risk in a Day; Complete Beginner's Guide to the Internet; The Hangover Handbook; Playing Lotteries For the Big Money.* About 10 titles a year. Unsolicited synopses for books welcome; 'no novels or humour, please'.
Royalties paid twice-yearly.

Tango Books
See **Sadie Fields Productions Ltd** under **UK Packagers**

I. B. Tauris & Co. Ltd
Victoria House, Bloomsbury Square, London WC1B 4DZ
☎0171 831 9060   Fax 0171 831 9061
Chairman/Publisher *Iradj Bagherzade*
Managing Director *Jonathan McDonnell*
FOUNDED 1984. Independent publisher. *Publishes* general non-fiction and academic in the fields of international relations, current affairs, history, politics, cultural, media and film studies, Middle East studies. Joint projects with Cambridge University Centre for Middle Eastern Studies, Institute for Latin American Studies and Institute of Ismaili Studies. *Distributes* The New Press (New York) outside North America. *Represents* **The Curzon Press** in the UK. IMPRINTS **Tauris Parke Books** Illustrated books on architecture, travel, design and culture. **British Academic Press** Academic monographs. Unsolicited synopses and book proposals welcome. *Royalties* paid twice-yearly.

Tavistock Publications
See **Routledge**

Taylor & Francis Group
1 Gunpowder Square, London EC4A 3DE
☎0171 583 0490   Fax 0171 583 9581
Chairman *Angus MacDonald, CBE*
Managing Director *Anthony Selvey*
Approx. Annual Turnover £30 million
FOUNDED 1798 with the launch of *Philosophical Magazine* which has been in publication ever since (now a solid state physics journal). The company is privately owned with strong academic connections among the major shareholders. **Falmer Press** (see entry) joined the group in 1979 and it doubled its size in the late '80s with the acquisition of Crane Russak in 1986 and Hemisphere Publishing Co in 1988. In 1995, acquired Lawrence Erlbaum Associates Ltd and Brumer/Mazel in 1997, adding to the growing list of psychology publications. In 1996, UCL Press Ltd was acquired, adding further to its portfolio of publications in science and humanities. The most recent addition to the Taylor & Francis Group is Garland Publishing Inc. located in New York. *Publishes* scientific, technical, education titles at university, research and professional levels. About 600 titles a year. Unsolicited mss, synopses and ideas welcome.

Royalties paid yearly. *Overseas office* Taylor & Francis Inc., Philadelphia, PA and New York.

Teach Yourself
See **Hodder Headline plc**

Telegraph Books
1 Canada Square, Canary Wharf, London E14 5DT
☎0171 538 6826   Fax 0171 538 6064
Owner *Telegraph Group Ltd*
Manager *Susannah Charlton*
Approx. Annual Turnover £1.5 million
Concentrates on Telegraph branded books in association/collaboration with other publishers. Also runs Telegraph Books Direct, a direct mail, 24-hour phone-line bookselling service and off-the-page sales for other publishers' books. *Publishes* general non-fiction: journalism, business and law, cookery, education, gardening, wine, guides, sport, puzzles and games, maps. 66 titles in 1997. Only interested in books if a Telegraph link exists. No unsolicited material.
Royalties paid twice-yearly.

Tellastory
See **Random House UK Ltd**

Temple House Books
See **The Book Guild Ltd**

Test Your Child
See **Hodder Headline plc**

Thames and Hudson Ltd
30–34 Bloomsbury Street, London WC1B 3QP
☎0171 636 5488   Fax 0171 636 4799
Managing Director *Thomas Neurath*
Editorial Head *Jamie Camplin*
Approx. Annual Turnover £19.4 million
Publishes art, archaeology, architecture and design, biography, crafts, fashion, garden and landscape design, graphics, history, illustrated and fine editions, mythology, music, photography, popular culture, travel and topography. 200 titles a year. SERIES *World of Art; New Horizons; Chic Simple; Celtic Design; World Design; Fashion Memoir.* TITLES *The Panorama of the Renaissance; Derek Jarman's Garden; The Shock of the New; The Book of Kells; The Body; The Most Beautiful Villages of Greece; Website Graphics; The Tibetan Art of Healing; Henri Cartier-Bresson; The Complete Pyramids; The*

Chronicle of Jazz. Send preliminary letter and outline before mss.

Royalties paid twice-yearly.

Authors' Rating A multimedia and on-line division are the latest evidence of Thames and Hudson's growth. There are plans to increase title output from 200 a year to around 240

Stanley Thornes (Publishers) Ltd

Ellenborough House, Wellington Street, Cheltenham, Gloucestershire GL50 1YW
☎01242 228888   Fax 01242 221914
Managing Director *David Smith*
Approx. Annual Turnover £20.6 million

FOUNDED 1972. Part of the Wolters-Kluwer Group. Merged with Mary Glasgow Publications in 1992. *Publishes* secondary school and college curriculum textbooks and primary school resources. About 200 titles a year. Unsolicited mss, synopses and ideas for books welcome if appropriate to specialised list.

IMPRINT **Mary Glasgow Publications** foreign-language teaching materials and teacher support.

Royalties paid annually.

Thorsons

See **HarperCollins Publishers Ltd**

Times Books

See **HarperCollins Publishers Ltd**

Titan Books

42–44 Dolben Street, London SE1 0UP
☎0171 620 0200   Fax 0171 620 0032
E-mail: 101447.2455@compuserve.com
Managing Director *Nick Landau*
Editorial Director *Katy Wild*

FOUNDED 1981. Now a leader in the publication of graphic novels and in film and television tie-ins. *Publishes* comic books/graphic novels, film and television titles. About 70–80 titles a year.

IMPRINTS **Titan Books; Eros Plus** Erotic fiction. TITLES *Batman; Superman; Alien; Star Trek; Star Wars; The Simpsons; The X Files; The Avengers; Due South.* No unsolicited fiction or children's books please. Ideas for film and TV titles considered; send synopsis/outline with sample chapter. Author guidelines available.

Royalties paid twice-yearly.

Tolkien

See **HarperCollins Publishers Ltd**

Tolley Publishing Co. Ltd

Tolley House, 2 Addiscombe Road, Croydon, Surrey CR9 5AF
☎0181 686 9141   Fax 0181 686 3155
Chief Executive *Neville Cusworth*
Managing Director *Kelvin Ladbrook*
Approx. Annual Turnover £3.16 million

Owned by Reed Elsevier Legal Division.

DIVISIONS **Tolley Publishing; Charles Knight Publishing; Payroll Alliance; Butterworths Tax Publications.** Unsolicited mss, synopses and ideas welcome.

Transworld Publishers Ltd

61–63 Uxbridge Road, London W5 5SA
☎0181 579 2652   Fax 0181 579 5479
Chairman *Stephen Rubin*
Managing Director *Mark Barty-King*
Approx. Annual Turnover £43.8 million

FOUNDED 1950. A subsidiary of **Bantam, Doubleday, Dell Publishing Group Inc.**, New York, which is a wholly-owned subsidiary of Bertelsmann AG, Germany. *Publishes* general fiction and non-fiction, children's books, sports and leisure.

DIVISIONS

Adult Trade *Patrick Janson-Smith* **Adult Hardback** *Ursula Mackenzie* **Adult Paperback** *Larry Finlay* IMPRINTS **Anchor** *John Saddler;* **Bantam** *Francesca Liversidge;* **Bantam Press** *Sally Gaminara;* **Corgi, Black Swan** *Bill Scott-Kerr;* **Doubleday** *Marianne Velmans;* **Partridge Press** *Alison Barrow.* AUTHORS Kate Atkinson, Bill Bryson, Catherine Cookson, Jilly Cooper, Nicholas Evans, Frederick Forsyth, Robert Goddard, Stephen Hawking, Andy McNab, Terry Pratchett, James Redfield, Gerald Seymour, Danielle Steel, Joanna Trollope, Mary Wesley.

Children's & Young Adult Books *Philippa Dickinson* IMPRINTS **Doubleday** (hardcover); **Picture Corgi; Corgi Pups; Young Corgi; Corgi Yearling; Corgi; Corgi Freeway; Bantam** (paperback). AUTHORS Ian Beck, Malorie Blackman, Helen Cooper, Peter Dickinson, Dick King-Smith, Francine Pascal, K. M. Peyton, Terry Pratchett, Philip Pullman, Robert Swindells, Jacqueline Wilson.

Royalties paid twice-yearly. *Overseas associates* Transworld Australia/New Zealand, Transworld Book Distributors(South Africa).

Authors' Rating Judged by *The Economist* to be 'the most efficient publisher in the business', Transworld has been first in *The Guardian* fastseller chart for four years running (up to

January 1997) and one of the few trade publishers to turn in a consistently decent profit. Transworld owes its success as much to sophisticated marketing as to its choice of titles. Mainstream blockbusters dominate the catalogue but with the new Anchor list there is now a move towards literary publishing.

Trentham Books Ltd
Westview House, 734 London Road, Stoke on Trent, Staffordshire ST4 5NP
☎01782 745567   Fax 01782 745553
Chairman/Managing Director *Dr John Eggleston*
Editorial Head *Dr Gillian Klein*
Approx. Annual Turnover £1 million

Publishes education (nursery, school and higher), social sciences, intercultural studies and law for professional readers *not* for children and parents. No fiction, biography or poetry. About 25 titles a year. Unsolicited mss, synopses and ideas welcome if relevant to their interests. Material only returned if adequate s.a.e. sent.
Royalties paid annually.

Triangle
See **Society for Promoting Christian Knowledge**

Trotman & Co. Ltd
12 Hill Rise, Richmond, Surrey TW10 6UA
☎0181 940 5668   Fax 0181 948 9267
Chairman *Andrew Fiennes Trotman*
Publishing Director *Morfydd Jones*
Approx. Annual Turnover £3 million

Publishes general careers books, higher education guides, teaching support material, employment and training resources. About 70 titles a year. TITLES *Complete Degree Course Offers* (book and CD-ROM); *The Student Book; How to Complete Your UCAS Form; Students' Money Matters.* Unsolicited material welcome. Also active in the educational resources market, producing recruitment brochures.
Royalties paid twice-yearly.

Two-Can Publishing Ltd
346 Old Street, London EC1V 9NQ
☎0171 684 4000   Fax 0171 613 3371
Chairman *Andrew Jarvis*
Marketing Director *Ian Grant*
Creative Director *Sara Lynn*
Approx. Annual Turnover £6 million

FOUNDED 1987 to publish innovative, high-quality material for children. *Publishes* books and magazines, including *Young Telegraph* (weekend supplement for 9–12-year-olds; see entry under **Magazines**).

DIVISIONS **Books** *Ian Grant*; **Magazines** *Andrew Jarvis.* No unsolicited mss; send synopses and ideas in the first instance.
Royalties paid twice-yearly.

UCL Press Ltd
See **Taylor & Francis Group**

University Presses of California, Columbia & Princeton Ltd
1 Oldlands Way, Bognor Regis, West Sussex PO22 9SA
☎01243 842165   Fax 01243 842167
E-mail: lois@upccp.demon.co.uk

Publishes academic titles only. US-based editorial offices. Over 200 titles a year. Enquiries only.

Unwin Hyman
See **HarperCollins Publishers Ltd**

Usborne Publishing Ltd
83–85 Saffron Hill, London EC1N 8RT
☎0171 430 2800   Fax 0171 430 1562
Managing Director *Peter Usborne*
Editorial Director *Jenny Tyler*
Approx. Annual Turnover £13.3 million

FOUNDED 1973. *Publishes* non-fiction, fiction, puzzle books and music for children and young adults. Some titles for parents. Up to 100 titles a year. Non-fiction books are written in-house to a specific format and therefore unsolicited mss are not normally welcome. Ideas which may be developed in-house are sometimes considered. Fiction for children aged 8+ will be considered. Keen to hear from new illustrators and designers.
Royalties paid twice-yearly.

Authors' Rating 21 years in the business of 'making books that children want to read' has given the Usborne imprint a distinctive, busy look recognisable in the bookshops at several yards. Most of the writing is done by in-house editors.

Vallentine Mitchell
See **Frank Cass & Co Ltd**

Ventura
See **Penguin UK**

Vermilion
See **Random House UK Ltd**

Verso

6 Meard Street, London W1V 3HR
☎0171 437 3546   Fax 0171 734 0059

Chairman *Lucy Heller*
Managing Director *Colin Robinson*
Approx. Annual Turnover £2 million

Formerly New Left Books which grew out of the *New Left Review*. Publishes politics, history, sociology, economics, philosophy, cultural studies, feminism. TITLES *Theatres of Memory* Raphael Samuel; *The Enemy Within* Seumas Milne; *The Missionary Position* Christopher Hitchens; *City of Quartz* Mike Davis; *Senseless Acts of Beauty* George McKay; *Year 501* Noam Chomsky; *Ideology* Terry Eagleton; *The Politics of Friendship* Jacques Derrida; *The Motorcycle Diaries* Ernesto Che Guevara. No unsolicited mss; synopses and ideas for books welcome.
Royalties paid annually. *Overseas office* in New York.

Authors' Rating Dubbed by *The Bookseller* as 'one of the most successful small independent publishers'.

Viking/Viking Children's
See **Penguin UK**

Vintage
See **Random House UK Ltd**

Virago Press

Little, Brown & Co. (UK), Brettenham House, Lancaster Place, London WC2E 7EN
☎0171 911 8000   Fax 0171 911 8100

Publisher *Lennie Goodings*
Senior Editor *Sally Abbey*
Approx. Annual Turnover £2.5 million

FOUNDED 1973 by Carmen Callil, with the aim of publishing a wide range of books which illuminate and celebrate all aspects of women's lives. Bought by **Little, Brown & Co. (UK)** in 1996. Most titles are published in paperback; a distinguished reprint list makes up one third of these, with two thirds original titles commissioned across a wide range of interest: autobiography, biography, crime, fiction, history, social issues, politics, psychology, women's studies. About 50 titles a year. TITLES *Cure for Death by Lightning* Gail Anderson-Dargate; *Transgressions* Sarah Dunant; all of Maya Angelou's books. Send return postage with unsolicited material.
Royalties paid twice-yearly.

Authors' Rating Having changed the reading habits of a generation of British women, Virago has now latched on to Big Brother

who, it is hoped, will provide the resources for major growth. A new list of raunchy, popular fiction may show the way.

Virgin Publishing

332 Ladbroke Grove, London W10 5AH
☎0181 968 7554   Fax 0181 968 0929

Chairman *Robert Devereux*
Managing Director *Robert Shreeve*
Approx. Annual Turnover £10 million

The Virgin Group's book publishing company. *Publishes* non-fiction, fiction and large-format illustrated books on entertainment and popular culture, particularly music, TV tie-ins and books about film, showbiz, sport, biography, autobiography and humour. Also developing a travel list. No poetry, short stories, individual novels, children's books or cartoons.

IMPRINTS
Non-fiction: **Virgin** *Rod Green* Sport, music biography, humour, film, TV tie-ins; *Carolyn Thorne* Illustrated books on all above subjects.

Fiction: **Virgin**; **The New Adventures**; **Idol**; **Black Lace**; **Nexus** Branded series of genre novels. Publisher *Peter Darvill-Evans*. Series editors: *Kerri Sharp* (erotica, crime), *Rebecca Levene* (science fiction and TV tie-ins).
Royalties paid twice-yearly.

Authors' Rating Aiming for the popular end of the market with some sure-fire hits like the Black Lace erotic fiction for women readers. A new travel list is planned for late 1998.

Vista
See **Cassell**

Volcano Press Ltd

PO Box 139, Leicester LE2 2YH
☎0116 2706714   Fax 0116 2706714
E-mail: asafevolcano.u-net.com

Chairman *F. Hussain*
Managing Director *A. Hussain*

FOUNDED 1992. *Publishes* academic non-fiction in the following areas: Islam, women's studies, human rights, Middle East, strategic studies and cultural studies. About 15 titles a year. TITLES *Beyond Islamic Fundamentalism; Islam in Britain; Islamic Fundamentalism in Britain; Islam in Everyday Life: An Introduction; Women in the Islamic Struggle*. No unsolicited mss; synopses and ideas welcome. No fiction, poetry or plays.
Royalties paid twice-yearly.

Voyager
See **HarperCollins Publishers Ltd**

University of Wales Press
6 Gwennyth Street, Cathays, Cardiff
CF2 4YD
☎01222 231919   Fax 01222 230908
Director *Ned Thomas*
Approx. Annual Turnover £425,000

FOUNDED 1922. *Publishes* academic and scholarly books in English and Welsh in four core areas: history, Welsh and Celtic Studies, European Studies, religion and philosophy. 51 titles in 1997.

IMPRINTS **GPC Books; Gwasg Prifysgol Cymru; University of Wales Press**. TITLES *Wales and the Reformation* Glanmor Williams; *Opera House Lottery* Nicholas Crickhowell; *Minority Nationalism and European Integration* Peter Lynch; *Francis Fukuyama and the End of History* Howard Williams, David Sullivan and Gwynn Matthews. Unsolicited mss considered. *Royalties* paid annually.

Walker Books Ltd
87 Vauxhall Walk, London SE11 5HJ
☎0171 793 0909   Fax 0171 587 1123
Editors *Wendy Boase, Vanessa Clarke, Jackie Gaff, Caroline Royds, Sally Christie, Jacqui Bailey*
Approx. Annual Turnover £31.7 million

FOUNDED 1979. *Publishes* illustrated children's books, children's fiction and non-fiction. About 300 titles a year. TITLES *Where's Wally?* Martin Handford; *Five Minutes' Peace* Jill Murphy; *Can't You Sleep, Little Bear?* Martin Waddell & Barbara Firth; *Guess How Much I Love You* Sam McBratney & Anita Jeram; *MapHead* Lesley Howarth. Unsolicited mss welcome. *Royalties* paid twice-yearly.

Authors' Rating The loss of the Sainsbury own-brand deal was a setback but the leading publisher of children's books continues to grow, if more gently of late. Authors praise the friendly and efficient editors and designers.

Ward Lock
See **Cassell**

Ward Lock Educational Co. Ltd
1 Christopher Road, East Grinstead, West Sussex RH19 3BT
☎01342 318980   Fax 01342 410980
Owner *Ling Kee (UK) Ltd*
Editor *Rose Hill*

FOUNDED 1952. *Publishes* educational books (primary, middle, secondary, teaching manuals) for all subjects, specialising in maths, science, geography, reading and English.

Frederick Warne
See **Penguin UK**

Warner
See **Little, Brown & Co. (UK)**

Warner Chappell Plays Ltd
See entry under **UK Agents**

Waterline Books
See **Airlife Publishing Ltd**

Franklin Watts
See **The Watts Publishing Group**

The Watts Publishing Group
96 Leonard Street, London EC2A 4RH
☎0171 739 2929   Fax 0171 739 2318
Managing Director *Marlene Johnson*

Part of Groupe Lagardere. *Publishes* general non-fiction, reference, information and children's (fiction, picture and novelty). About 300 titles a year.

IMPRINTS **Franklin Watts** *Philippa Stewart* Non-fiction and information; **Orchard Books** *Francesca Dow* Children's fiction, picture and novelty books. Unsolicited mss, synopses and ideas for books welcome. *Royalties* paid twice-yearly. *Overseas associates* in Australia and New Zealand, US and Canada.

Wayland Publishers Ltd
(incorporating **Macdonald Young Books**)
61 Western Road, Hove, East Sussex BN3 1JD
☎01273 722561   Fax 01273 329314
Director & General Manager *Roberta Bailey*
Editorial Director *Stephen White-Thomson*
Approx. Annual Turnover £9.3 million

Part of the Wolters Kluwer Group. FOUNDED 1969. *Publishes* a broad range of subjects for children, mainly colour-illustrated non-fiction and fiction for 5 years and upwards. About 400 titles a year. No unsolicited mss or synopses as all books are commissioned. Submissions from literary agents considered. *Royalties* paid annually. *Overseas associates* Steck-Vaughn Company, USA.

Weidenfeld & Nicolson Ltd
See **The Orion Publishing Group Ltd**

Welsh Academic Press
See **Ashley Drake Publishing Ltd**

West One (Trade) Publishing Ltd
4 Great Portland Street, London
W1N 5AA
☎0171 580 6886   Fax 0171 580 9788
Chief Executive *Martin Coleman*
Approx. Annual Turnover £2 million

Publishes travel guides and cartography, including
RAC publications. TITLES *RAC Inspected Hotels
Guide to UK and Ireland; France for the Independent
Traveller; Europe for the Independent Traveller.*
Unsolicited synopses and ideas welcome.

Wharncliffe Publishing
47 Church Street, Barnsley, South Yorkshire
S70 2AS
☎01226 734222   Fax 01226 734438
Chairman *Sir Nicholas Hewitt*
Chief Executive *C. Hewitt*
Imprint Manager *Mike Parsons*

An Imprint of **Pen & Sword Books Ltd**.
Wharncliffe is the book and magazine publishing arm of an old-established, independently
owned newspaper publishing and printing
house. *Publishes* local history throughout the
UK, focusing on nostalgia and old photographs. Unsolicited mss, synopses and ideas
welcome but return postage must be included
with all submissions.
Royalties paid twice-yearly.

Which? Books/Consumers' Association
2 Marylebone Road, London NW1 4DF
☎0171 830 6000   Fax 0171 830 7660
Director *Sheila McKechnie*
Head of Publishing *Gill Rowley*

FOUNDED 1957. Publishing arm of Consumers'
Association, a registered charity. *Publishes* non-
fiction: information, reference and how-to
books on travel, gardening, health, personal
finance, consumer law, food, careers, crafts,
DIY. Titles must offer direct value or utility to
the UK consumer. 25–30 titles a year.
　IMPRINT **Which? Books** *Gill Rowley* TITLES
*Good Food Guide; Good Skiing Guide; Good
Walks Guide; Which? Travel Guides; Which?
Consumer Guides.* No unsolicited mss; send
synopses and ideas only.
Royalties, if applicable, paid twice-yearly.

Whittet Books Ltd
Hill Farm, Stonham Road, Cotton,
Stowmarket, Suffolk IP14 4RQ
☎01449 781877   Fax 01449 781898
Managing Director *Annabel Whittet*

Publishes natural history, pets, horses, rural
interest and transport. Unsolicited mss, synopses and ideas for books welcome.
Royalties paid twice-yearly.

Whurr Publishers Ltd
19B Compton Terrace, London N1 2UN
☎0171 359 5979   Fax 0171 226 5290
Chairman/Managing Director *Colin Whurr*
Approx. Annual Turnover £1 million

FOUNDED in 1987. Originally specialised in
publishing books and journals on disorders of
communication but now publishing in a number of academic and professional fields. *Publishes*
speech and language therapy, nursing, psychology, psychotherapy, business and management,
dyslexia. No fiction and general trade books. 30
titles in 1997. Unsolicited mss, synopses and
ideas welcome within their specialist fields only.
Royalties paid twice-yearly.

John Wiley & Sons Ltd
Baffins Lane, Chichester, West Sussex
PO19 1UD
☎01243 779777   Fax 01243 775878
Chairman *The Duke of Richmond*
Managing Director *Dr John Jarvis*
Publishing Director *Steven Mair*
Approx. Annual Turnover £51 million

FOUNDED 1807. US parent company. *Publishes*
professional, reference trade and text books,
scientific, technical and biomedical.
　DIVISIONS **Psychology, Business & Health-
care Management** *Sarah Stevens*; **Physical
Sciences** *Ernest Kirkwood*; **Life/Medical,
Technology & Stats** *Mike Davis*; **Finance/
Law** *David Wilson*; **Environmental/
Engineering** *Lesley Valentine*; **College
Division** *Simon Plumtree*. Unsolicited mss wel-
come, as are synopses and ideas for books.
Royalties paid annually.

Authors' Rating Voted best publisher by academic bookshops, Wiley's inexorable rise (it
now publishes more titles than OUP) is tied to
the success of its college division and to academic journals. In the US, restructuring has
disposed of the law publications division (to
Wolters Kluwer) but gained Van Nostrand
Reinhold, the US professional and STM pub-

lisher. On this side of the Atlantic, Wiley does over 30% of its business with mainland Europe.

Neil Wilson Publishing Ltd
Suite 303a, The Pentagon Centre, 36 Washington Street, Glasgow G3 8AZ
☎0141 221 1117   Fax 0141 221 5363
E-mail: nwp@cqm.co.uk
Website: http://www.nwp.co.uk/
Chairman *Gordon Campbell*
Managing Director/Editorial Director
Neil Wilson
Approx. Annual Turnover £250,000
FOUNDED 1992. *Publishes* Scottish interest and history, biography, humour and hillwalking, whisky and beer; also cookery and Irish interest. About 10 titles a year. Unsolicited mss, synopses and ideas welcome. No fiction, politics, academic or technical.
Royalties paid twice-yearly.

Philip Wilson Publishers Ltd
143–149 Great Portland Street, London W1N 5FB
☎0171 436 4490   Fax 0171 436 4403/4260
Chairman *Philip Wilson*
Managing Director *Antony White*
FOUNDED 1976. *Publishes* art, art history, antiques and collectables. 21 titles in 1997. DIVISIONS **Philip Wilson Publishers Ltd;** **Scala Books** *Anne Jackson;* **Flint River Press Ltd** *Antony White;* **Sotheby's Publications** *Anne Jackson.*

Windrow & Greene Ltd
5 Gerrard Street, London W1V 7LJ
☎0171 287 4570   Fax 0171 494 0583
Managing Director *Alan Greene*
Editorial Director *Martin Windrow*
FOUNDED 1990 by ex-conglomerate refugees wanting to publish quality books in close consultation with authors. *Publishes* military history and hobbies, cars and motorcycling, aviation and transport, directories and specialist journals. About 28 titles a year. Unsolicited mss considered; synopses and ideas preferred in first instance.
Royalties paid twice-yearly.

The Windrush Press
Little Window, High Street, Moreton in Marsh, Gloucestershire GL56 0LL
☎01608 652012/652025   Fax 01608 652125
E-mail: windrushpress@compuserve.com
Managing Director *Geoffrey Smith*
Editorial Head *Victoria Huxley*

FOUNDED 1987. Independent company. *Publishes* travel guides, biography, history, military history, humour. About 10 titles a year. TITLES *The Recollections of Rifleman Harris; Waterloo: A Near Run Thing; Lanzarote: A Windrush Island Guide; A Traveller's History of China.* Send synopsis and letter with s.a.e.
Royalties paid twice-yearly.

Windsor Large Print
See **Chivers Press Ltd**

Wise Publications
See **Omnibus Press**

Woburn Press
See **Frank Cass & Co Ltd**

Oswald Wolff Books
See **Berg Publishers**

The Women's Press
34 Great Sutton Street, London EC1V 0DX
☎0171 251 3007   Fax 0171 608 1938
Publishing Director *Kathy Gale*
Approx. Annual Turnover £1 million
Part of the Namara Group. First title 1978. *Publishes* women only: quality fiction and non-fiction. Fiction usually has a female protagonist and a woman-centred theme. International writers and subject matter encouraged. Non-fiction: subjects of general interest, both practical and theoretical, to women generally; art books, feminist theory, health and psychology, literary criticism. About 50 titles a year.
IMPRINTS **Women's Press Crime;** **Women's Press Handbooks Series;** **Livewire Books for Teenagers** Fiction and non-fiction series for young adults. Synopses and ideas for books welcome. No mss without previous letter, synopsis and sample material.
Royalties paid twice-yearly.

Woodhead Publishing Ltd
Abington Hall, Abington, Cambridge CB1 6AH
☎01223 891358   Fax 01223 893694
E-mail: woodhead@dial.pipex.com
Website: http://www.ds.dial.pipex.com/ woodhead/
Chairman *Alan Jessup*
Managing Director *Martin Woodhead*
Approx. Annual Turnover £1.2 million
FOUNDED 1989. *Publishes* engineering, materials technology, finance and investment, food technology, production and management. TITLES

The TWI Journal (welding research); *Advanced Composites Letters; The International Grain/Nickel/Zinc/Tin/Silver Trade* series; *Base Metals Handbook; Foreign Exchange Options.* About 40 titles a year.

DIVISIONS **Woodhead Publishing** *Martin Woodhead;* **Abington Publishing** (in association with the Welding Institute) *Patricia Morrison;* **Gresham Books**. Unsolicited material welcome.

Royalties paid annually.

Woodstock Books
The School House, South Newington, Banbury, Oxon OX15 4JJ
☎01295 720598   Fax 01295 720717
Chairman/Managing Director *James Price*
Approx. Annual Turnover £150,000

FOUNDED 1989. *Publishes* literary reprints only. Main series: *Revolution and Romanticism, 1789–1834; Decadents, Symbolists, Anti-Decadents: Poetry of the 1890s; Hibernia: Literature and Nation in Victorian Ireland.* No unsolicited mss.

Wordsworth Editions Ltd
Cumberland House, Crib Street, Ware, Hertfordshire SG12 9ET
☎01920 465167   Fax 01920 462267
E-mail: 101512.3577@compuserve.com

Editorial Office: 6 London Street, London W2 1HL
☎0171 706 8822   Fax 0171 706 8833
E-mail: 100434.276@compuserve.com

Directors *M. C. W. Trayler, E. G. Trayler*
Director/Editorial Head *C. M. Clapham*
Approx. Annual Turnover £4 million

FOUNDED 1987. *Publishes* reprints of English literature, paperback reference books, poetry, children's classics, classic erotica, military history, mind, body and spirit and American classics. About 150 titles a year. No unsolicited mss.

Authors' Rating A non-starter for living writers, Wordsworth is dedicated to high-run, low-cost editions of books everyone has heard of. The formula has proved a winner, particularly with young people, who don't mind paying a pound for required reading but resent the fiver charged by up-market publishers for essentially the same product.

World International Limited
Deanway Technology Centre, Wilmslow Road, Handforth, Cheshire SK9 3FB
☎01625 650011   Fax 01625 650040
Managing Director *Ian Findlay*

Publishing Manager *Nina Filipek*
Part of the Egmont Group, Denmark. *Specialises* in children's books for home and international markets: activity, sticker, baby, early learning, novelty/character books and annuals. SERIES *Mr Men; Fun to Learn; I Can Learn; Learning Rewards.* 'Unsolicited material rarely used. World International does not accept responsibility for the return of unsolicited submissions.'

X Libris
See **Little Brown & Co. (UK)**

The X Press
6 Hoxton Square, London N1 6NU
☎0171 729 1199   Fax 0171 729 1771
Chairman *Dotun Adebayo*
Managing Director *Steve Pope*

LAUNCHED in 1992 with the cult bestseller *Yardie,* The X Press is the leading publisher of Black-interest fiction in the UK. Also *publishes* general fiction and children's fiction. 11 titles in 1997. IMPRINTS **The X Press** TITLES *Yardie; Baby Father;* **Nia** TITLE *In Search of Satisfaction;* **20/20** TITLE *Curvy Lovebox.* Send mss rather than synopses or ideas (enclose s.a.e.). No poetry.

Royalties paid annually.

Y Ddraig Fach
See **Ashley Drake Publishing Ltd**

Y Lolfa Cyf
Talybont, Ceredigion SY24 5HE
☎01970 832304   Fax 01970 832782
E-mail: ylolfa@ylolfa.com
Website: http://www.ylolfa.com/
Managing Director *Robat Gruffudd*
Editor *Lefi Gruffudd*
Approx. Annual Turnover £600,000

FOUNDED 1967. Small company which publishes mainly in Welsh. It handles all its own typesetting and printing too. *Publishes* Welsh language publications; Celtic language tutors; English language books about Wales for the visitor; nationalism and sociology (English language). 30 titles in 1997. Expanding slowly. TITLES *Artists in Snowdonia* James Bogle; *The Welsh Learner's Dictionary* Heini Gruffudd; *Burning Down the Dosbarth* David Greenslade. Not interested in any English language books except political and Celtic. Write first with synopses or ideas.

Royalties paid twice-yearly.

Yale University Press (London)
23 Pond Street, London NW3 2PN
☎0171 431 4422   Fax 0171 431 3755
Managing Director/Editorial Director
John Nicoll

FOUNDED 1961. Owned by US parent company. *Publishes* academic and humanities. About 200 titles (worldwide) a year. Unsolicited mss and synopses welcome if within specialised subject areas.
Royalties paid annually.

Authors' Rating Yale is not one of the publishers dominated by its American parent. Many of the best ideas originate in this country. Unusually for a university press, the list has much of interest to the general reader.

Roy Yates Books
Smallfields Cottage, Cox Green, Rudgwick, Horsham, West Sussex RH12 3DE
☎01403 822299   Fax 01403 823012
Chairman/Managing Director *Roy Yates*
Approx. Annual Turnover £120,000

FOUNDED 1990. *Publishes* children's books only. No unsolicited material as books are adaptations of existing popular classics suitable for translation into dual-language format.
Royalties paid quarterly.

Zastrugi Books
PO Box 2963, Brighton, East Sussex
BN1 6AW
☎01273 566369   Fax 01273 566369/56270
Chairman *Ken Singleton*

FOUNDED 1997. *Publishes* English-language teaching books only. No unsolicited mss; synopses and ideas for books welcome.
Royalties paid twice-yearly.

Zed Books Ltd
7 Cynthia Street, London N1 9JF
☎0171 837 4014   Fax 0171 833 3960
Approx. Annual Turnover £1 million

FOUNDED 1976. *Publishes* international and Third World affairs, development studies, women's studies, environmental studies, cultural studies and specific area studies. No fiction, children's or poetry. About 40 titles a year.

DIVISIONS **Development & Environment** *Robert Molteno*; **Women's Studies, Cultural Studies** *Louise Murray*. TITLES *The Development Dictionary* ed. Wolfgang Sachs; *Staying Alive* Vandana Shiva; *The Hidden Face of Eve* Nawal el Saadawi. No unsolicited mss; synopses and ideas welcome though.
Royalties paid annually.

Meeting of Opposites

Why academics and publishers fail to get on

The uneasy relationship between academic writers and publishers is the product of mutual misunderstanding. Let me rephrase that. The open hostility evinced by both sides is caused by a stubborn disregard for the other person's point of view. The change of tone only goes to show how the situation is deteriorating. And how fast.

The publisher is at fault because nine times out of ten he treats the academic writer like a supplicant for commercial favours; one who should be humbly grateful for the opportunity to bring his work before a wider public. The question of a just reward for the time and effort put into researching and writing a book is barely worth consideration. Other non-fiction writers expect, and usually get, an advance against royalties. But not the academic author. Indeed, he is lucky if he is offered a standard royalty.

But look now at the other side of the coin. Though undoubtedly hard done by, academic authors are themselves partly to blame for their publishing ills. If only they would toughen up a little. All it needs is to get wise to the realities of a highly competitive, profit-led business.

Instead, what we see is a queue of innocents pathetically eager to be fleeced. A Nobel Prize should be awarded to the academic author who reads and understands a publishing contract before signing it. Except that for most years the prize would go unclaimed, so unusual is it for a cloistered writer to give attention to the small print.

The rush to publish, apparently at any cost, is not entirely irrational. We all know that a weighty volume of research can do wonders for career prospects. If the chance to publish presents itself, the instinct is to snatch at it with both hands. The details can be settled later, can't they? Sadly, no. The way a publisher looks at it, a deal is a deal. There is no allowance for second thoughts.

What, then, should an academic author do to protect his interests?

First, study the contract; yes, all 20 to 30 pages of it. If in doubt, seek expert advice. This doesn't necessarily mean hiring a lawyer (an expensive luxury) or signing up with an agent (assuming you can find one who is ready to take on an academic author). The easy option, and much the best, is to join the Society of Authors. One of its services to members is to vet contracts and to suggest amendments to dodgy clauses. It is amazing how often the Society is able to clarify that which is meant to confuse.

A sound basic rule for academic writers is to resist handing over copyright. From the publisher's point of view, it makes sense to try to persuade an author to sign up and shut up. As a leading academic publisher was once heard to say, 'The only problem with this business is having to cope with writers'. There is nothing a publisher enjoys more than the freedom to buy and sell literary properties. Such deals can be to the author's advantage also. But there is no guarantee.

Consider, for example, the vexed question of electronic rights. Even those of us who react sceptically to panic warnings of the book in terminal decline cannot doubt that the new technology is tough competition for the printed word. In most areas of science the doorstop tome is giving way to the screen image backed up by articles in learned journals. Yet publishers have been slow to grant authors a share of the profits on the exploitation of electronic rights. When asked to justify such parsimony, the typical response is to point up the risk factor in any media business. I first heard this argument in the mid-sixties from Robert Maxwell when he was making his early millions from academic journals. Enough said.

A draft book contract may very well have a clause which allows the publisher to handle all non-print and electronic rights. It may even invite an assignment of the right to publish in 'all forms of media now or hereinafter invented'. Now, it may make sense to allow the publisher to exercise his commercial acumen (after all, that is what he is there for) but only when there are safeguards to protect the author. These should start with an undertaking not to enter into any agreement without the author's consent. A useful supplementary is to rule out any attempt to incorporate a book into a 'composite work' such as a CD-ROM within, say, one year of first publication. The reason is that the royalty from a CD-ROM encompassing the work of several authors will be necessarily smaller than the royalty from a stand alone book.

Other contract pitfalls – I nearly said pratfalls – to look out for are in those clauses that specify who is to pay for what. An author who accepts responsibility for supplying an index and artwork and for obtaining permission for use of quotations or illustrations from other sources, is liable to wind up having to pay a hefty bill that could wipe out or even exceed any income from royalties. If this sounds like sharp practice I can only repeat that modern publishing is a hard-nosed business which seeks to maximise its profits.

On the other hand, publishers cannot afford to be inflexible. They need authors to make money. If pressed, they will be ready to compromise on terms. It is a rare publisher indeed and almost certainly a bad one, who will not negotiate on essential editorial expenses. An author with any punch should be able to persuade his publisher to pay for index and artwork or, at the very least, cover a substantial share of the bill.

We return now to the sins of the writer. With the contract duly signed and work in progress there is the temptation to start playing games. The delivery date for the manuscript is, say, two years ahead. But somewhere along the way interesting new lines of research require an extension of the deadline. Then, other commitments, a lecture tour here, a round of meetings there, intrude on the time that should be given over to writing. Another delay is called for. This can go on for years on end. I promise, I have a friend, an eminent linguist, who is currently twelve years late with the delivery of a finished work. Who can blame a publisher who eventually cries 'Enough' and cancels the contract? It didn't used to happen in the days when publishers were gentlemen and bank managers were a soft touch. But it does now, believe me.

Then there is the writer who, nearing completion of his masterwork, suffers delusions of grandeur. As the sentences form and the pages mount up, it is easy to be seduced by a sense of monumental achievement. After all, it is not everybody who can write a book let alone one that contains original ideas. The author thrills to images of glowing reviews, bookshop displays, an entry into the bestseller list, even, ah what joy, an interview with Melvyn Bragg. Elated by these distant and nearly always unrealisable prospects the author badgers his publisher for an attractive four colour book jacket; press advertisements and a low cover price to appeal to the general reader. When his pleas are rejected, for sound economic reasons, the feeling of let down can be severe.

The consolation is in knowing that however small the print-run or however restricted the readership, a book is still the most effective medium for imparting ideas and for building academic reputations. If it also turns in a modest profit for author and publisher, so much the better.

Irish Publishers

An Gúm

44 Sráid Uí Chonaill, Uacht, Dublin 1,
Republic of Ireland
☎00 353 1 8734700   Fax 00 353 1 8731140
E-mail: gum@educ.irlgov.ie

Editors *Dónall ó Cuill, Máire Nic Mhaoláin*

FOUNDED 1926. Publications branch of the
Department of Education. Established to provide general reading, textbooks and dictionaries in the Irish language. *Publishes* educational,
children's, music, lexicography and general.
Little fiction or poetry. About 50 titles a year.
Unsolicited mss, synopses and ideas for books
welcome. Also welcomes reading copies of first
and second level school textbooks with a view
to translating them into the Irish language.
Royalties paid annually.

Anvil Books

45 Palmerston Road, Dublin 6, Republic of
Ireland
☎00 353 1 4973628

Managing Director *Rena Dardis*

FOUNDED 1964 with the emphasis on Irish history and biography. Expansion of the list followed to include more general interest Irish
material and in 1982 The Children's Press was
established, making Anvil the first Irish publisher
of mass-market children's books of Irish interest.
Publishes illustrated books, history, biography
(particularly 1916–22), folklore and children's
fiction (for ages 8–14). No adult fiction, poetry,
short stories or illustrated books for children
under 7. About 7 titles a year. Unsolicited mss,
synopses and ideas for books welcome.

DIVISIONS **General** TITLES *Guerilla Days in
Ireland* Tom Barry; *The Workhouses of Ireland* John
O'Connor; *The Norman Invasion of Ireland*
Richard Roche. **The Children's Press** TITLES
Kids Can Cook Sarah Webb; *Riders by the Grey
Lake* Pauline Devine; *Timber Twig* Kate
McMahon.
Royalties paid annually.

Attic Press Ltd

c/o Cork University Press, Crawford Business
Park, Crosses Green, Cork, Co. Cork,
Republic of Ireland
☎00 353 1 6616128   Fax 00 353 1 6616176

Publisher *Sara Wilbourne*

FOUNDED 1988. Began life in 1984 as a forum
for information on the Irish feminist movement. *Publishes* adult and teenage fiction, and
non-fiction (history, women's studies, politics,
biography). About 10 titles a year. Unsolicited
mss, synopses and ideas for books welcome.
Royalties paid twice yearly.

Blackwater Press

c/o Folens Publishers, Broomhill Business
Park, Broomhill Road, Tallaght, Dublin 24,
Republic of Ireland
☎00 353 1 4515311   Fax 00 353 1 4520451

Chief Executive *Dirk Folens*
Managing Director *John O'Connor*

Part of Folens Publishers. *Publishes* political,
sports, fiction (*Anna O'Donovan*) and children's
(*Deidre Whelan*). 31 titles in 1997.

Brandon Book Publishers Ltd

See **Mount Eagle Publications Ltd**

Edmund Burke Publisher

Cloonagashel, 27 Priory Drive, Blackrock,
Co. Dublin Republic of Ireland
☎00 353 1 2882159   Fax 00 353 1 2834080

Chairman *Eamonn De Búrca*
Approx. Annual Turnover £100,000

Small family-run business publishing historical
and topographical and fine limited-edition
books relating to Ireland. TITLES *Annals of the
Four Masters; Ireland and the Printed Word
1475–1700* Sweeney; *An Irish Flower Garden
Replanted* Nelson and Walsh; *The Irish Fiants of
the Tudor Sovereigns; Irish Stuart Silver; Irish
Names of Places* Joyce; *History of the Kingdom of
Kerry* Cusack; *Scot's Mercenary Forces in Ireland*
G. A. Hayes-McCoy; *The Dean's Friend* Alan
Harrison; *Manners and Customs of the Ancient
Irish* Eugene O'Curry. Unsolicited mss wel-
come. No synopses or ideas.
Royalties paid twice yearly.

Butterworth Ireland Limited

26 Upper Ormond Quay, Dublin 7, Republic
of Ireland
☎00 353 1 8731555   Fax 00 353 1 8731876

Chairman *P. Woods (UK)*
Director *Gerard Coakley*

Subsidiary of Butterworth & Co. Publishers,

London, (Reed Elsevier is the holding company). *Publishes* solely law and tax books. Tax Editor *Susan Keegan*, Legal Editor *Louise Leavy*. 12 titles in 1997. Leading publisher of Irish law and tax titles. Unsolicited mss, synopses and ideas welcome for titles within the broadest parameters of tax and law.
Royalties paid twice yearly.

The Children's Press
See **Anvil Books**

Cló Iar-Chonnachta
Indreabhán, Connemara, Galway, Republic of Ireland
☎00 353 91 593307   Fax 00 353 91 593362
Chairman/Director *Micheál Ó Conghaile*
Editor *Nóirín Ní Ghrádaigh*
Approx. Annual Turnover £250,000
FOUNDED 1985. *Publishes* fiction, poetry, plays and children's, mostly in Irish but not exclusively. Also publishes cassettes of writers reading from their own works. TITLES *Aran Song* John Carter; *Facing South* Patrick Gallager; *The Village Sings* Gabriel Fitzmaurice. 10 titles in 1997.
Royalties paid annually.

The Collins Press
Carey's Lane, The Huguenot Quarter, Cork, Co. Cork, Republic of Ireland
☎00 353 21 271346   Fax 00 353 21 275489
Managing Director *Con Collins*
Editor *Maria O'Donovan*
FOUNDED 1989. *Publishes* archaeology, biography, fiction, general non-fiction, health, history, mind, body and spirit, poetry, photographic and travel guides. About 12–15 titles a year. Unsolicited mss, synopses and ideas for books welcome.
Royalties paid annually.

The Columba Press
Unit 55A Spruce Avenue, Stillorgan Industrial Park, Blackrock, Co. Dublin, Republic of Ireland
☎00 353 1 2942556   Fax 00 353 1 2942564
Chairman *Neil Kluepfel*
Managing Director *Seán O'Boyle*
Approx. Annual Turnover £750,000
FOUNDED 1985. Small company committed to growth. *Publishes* only religious titles. 30 titles in 1997. (Backlist of 225 titles.) TITLES *Nine Faces of God* Pat Collins; *Through the Year with George Otto Simms* Lesley Whiteside. Unsolicited ideas and synopses rather than full mss preferred.
Royalties paid twice yearly.

Cork University Press
Crawford Business Park, Crosses Green, Cork, Co. Cork, Republic of Ireland
☎00 353 21 902980   Fax 00 353 21 315329
Managing Director *Sara Wilbourne*
Production Editor *Eileen O'Carroll*
FOUNDED 1925. Relaunched in 1992, the Press *publishes* academic and some trade titles. Plans to publish 27 titles in 1998. Two journals, *Irish Review* (bi-annual), an interdisciplinary cultural review, and *The Irish Journal of Feminist Studies* (bi-annual), are now part of the list. Unsolicited synopses and ideas welcome for textbooks, academic monographs, belles lettres, illustrated histories and journals.
Royalties paid annually.

Flyleaf Press
4 Spencer Villas, Glenageary, Co. Dublin, Republic of Ireland
☎00 353 1 2806228   Fax 00 353 1 8370176
E-mail: ryanj@biores.irl.ie
Managing Director *Dr James Ryan*
FOUNDED 1981 to publish natural history titles. Now concentrating on family history and Irish history as a background to family history. No fiction. TITLES *Irish Records; Longford and its People; Tracing Kerry Ancestors; Tracing Dublin's Ancestors.* Unsolicited mss, synopses and ideas for books welcome.
Royalties paid twice yearly.

Four Courts Press Ltd
Fumbally Lane, Dublin 8, Republic of Ireland
☎00 353 1 4534668   Fax 00 353 1 4534672
E-mail: info@four-courts-press.ie
Website: http://www.four-courts-press.ie
Chairman/Managing Director
  Michael Adams
Director *Martin Healy*
Approx. Annual Turnover £500,000
FOUNDED 1972. *Publishes* mainly scholarly books in the humanities. About 60 titles a year. Unsolicited mss, synopses and ideas for books welcome.
Royalties paid annually.

Gill & Macmillan
Goldenbridge, Inchicore, Dublin 8, Republic of Ireland
☎00 353 1 4531005   Fax 00 353 1 4541688
Managing Director *M. H. Gill*
Approx. Annual Turnover £5 million
FOUNDED 1968 when M. H. Gill & Son Ltd

and Macmillan Ltd formed a jointly owned publishing company. *Publishes* biography/autobiography, history, current affairs, literary criticism (all mainly of Irish interest), guidebooks, cookery. Also educational textbooks for secondary and tertiary levels. About 100 titles a year. Contacts: *Hubert Mahony* (educational); *Fergal Tobin* (general); *Ailbhe O'Reilly* (tertiary textbooks). IMPRINT **Newleaf** (popular health, psychology, mind, body and spirit). Unsolicited synopses and ideas welcome. Not interested in fiction or poetry.
Royalties paid subject to contract.

Institute of Public Administration
57–61 Lansdowne Road, Dublin 4, Republic of Ireland
☎00 353 1 2697011   Fax 00 353 1 2698644
Chairman *Frank Murray*
Director General *John Gallagher*
Acting Publisher *Tony McNamara*
Approx. Annual Turnover £500,000

FOUNDED 1957 by a group of public servants, the Institute of Public Administration is the Irish public sector management development agency. The publishing arm of the organisation is one of its major activities. *Publishes* academic and professional books and periodicals: history, law, politics, economics and Irish public administration for students and practitioners. 12 titles in 1997. TITLES *Administration Yearbook & Diary; Measuring Civil Service Performance; Your Rights at Work; A Politics of the Common Good*. No unsolicited mss; synopses and ideas welcome. No fiction or children's publishing.
Royalties paid annually.

Irish Academic Press Ltd
44 Northumberland Road, Ballsbridge, Dublin 4, Republic of Ireland
☎00 353 1 6688244   Fax 00 353 1 6601610
Chairman *Frank Cass (London)*
Managing Editor *Linda Longmore*
Approx. Annual Turnover £250,000

FOUNDED 1974. *Publishes* academic monographs and humanities. 14 titles in 1997. Unsolicited mss, synopses and ideas welcome.
Royalties paid annually.

Irish Management Institute
Sandyford Road, Dublin 16, Republic of Ireland
☎00 353 1 2956911   Fax 00 353 1 2955150
Chief Executive *Barry Kenny*
Approx. Annual Turnover £8 million

FOUNDED 1952. The Institute is owned by its members (individual and corporate) and its major activities involve management education, training and development. The book publishing arm of the organisation was established in 1970. *Publishes* management practice, interpersonal skills and aspects of national macroeconomics. TITLES *The Economy of Ireland; Practical Finance; Pricing For Results; Personnel Management; Managing Your Business: A Guidebook for Small Business*. Unsolicited mss welcome provided that any case material is relevant to Irish management practice. Synopses and ideas also welcome.
Royalties paid annually.

The Lilliput Press
62–63 Sitric Road, Arbour Hill, Dublin 7, Republic of Ireland
☎00 353 1 6711647   Fax 00 353 1 6711233
Chairman *Vivienne Guinness*
Managing Director *Antony Farrell*
Approx. Annual Turnover £200,000

FOUNDED 1984. *Publishes* non-fiction: literature, history, autobiography and biography, ecology, essays; criticism; fiction and poetry. About 20 titles a year. TITLES *Ulysses: The Dublin Edition; The Growth Illusion* (ecology); *Modern Art in Ireland; Nature in Ireland; Crisis and Decline, The Fate of the Southern Unionists* (history); *My Generation – Rock 'n' Roll Remembered, An Imperfect History; The Irish Writers' Guide 1998–99*. Unsolicited mss, synopses and ideas welcome. No children's or sport titles.
Royalties paid annually.

Marino Books
See **Mercier Press Ltd**

Mercier Press Ltd
PO Box No 5, 5 French Church Street, Cork, Co. Cork, Republic of Ireland
☎00 353 21 275040   Fax 00 353 21 274969
E-mail (Dublin office): books@marino.ie
(Cork office): books@mercier.ie
Chairman *George Eaton*
Managing Director *John F. Spillane*

FOUNDED 1944. One of Ireland's largest publishers with a list of approx 250 Irish interest titles and a smaller range of religious titles. *Publishes* alternative lifestyle, folklore, women's interest, popular psychology, dual language, children's, cookery, history, politics, poetry and fiction.   No academic books. IMPRINTS

Mercier Press *Mary Feehan* **Marino Books** *Jo O'Donoghue.* TITLES *The Course of Irish History; The Field; Irish High Crosses; Irish Myths & Legends; Mortally Wounded; The Great Irish Famine; A Short History of Ireland.* Unsolicited mss, synopses and ideas welcome.
Royalties paid annually.

Mount Eagle Publications Ltd
Dingle, Co. Kerry, Republic of Ireland
☎00 353 66 51463   Fax 00 353 66 51234
Publisher *Steve MacDonogh*
Approx. Annual Turnover £300,000
FOUNDED in 1997, Mount Eagle took over Brandon Book Publishers in December of that year. Strong Irish fiction and some non-fiction. About 10 titles a year. Not seeking unsolicited mss.

Newleaf
See **Gill & Macmillan**

The O'Brien Press Ltd
20 Victoria Road, Rathgar, Dublin 6,
Republic of Ireland
☎00 353 1 4923333   Fax 00 353 1 4922777
E-mail: http://www.obrien.ie
Chairman/Managing Director
Michael O'Brien
Editorial Director *Íde Ní Laoghaire*
FOUNDED 1974 to publish biography and books on the environment. Also *publishes* business, adult fiction, crime, popular biography, music and travel. In recent years the company has become a substantial force in children's publishing, concentrating mainly on juvenile novels. No poetry or academic. About 40 titles a year. Unsolicited mss (with return postage enclosed), synopses and ideas for books welcome.
Royalties paid annually.

Oak Tree Press
Merrion Building, Lower Merrion Street,
Dublin 2, Republic of Ireland
☎00 353 1 6761600   Fax 00 353 1 6761644
E-mail: oaktreep@iol.ie
Website: www.oaktreepress.com
Managing Director *Brian O'Kane*
FOUNDED 1992. Part of Cork Publishing. Specialist publisher of business and professional books: accounting, finance, management and law, aimed at students and practitioners in Ireland and the UK. About 25 titles a year. TITLES *The Accountant's Guide to Excel; Winning*

Business Proposals; The European Handbook of Management Consultancy; Once a Customer, Always a Customer; Working and Living in Ireland. Unsolicited mss and synopses welcome; send to *David Givens*, General Manager, at the above address.
Royalties paid twice yearly.

On Stream Publications Ltd
Cloghroe, Blarney, Co. Cork, Republic of Ireland
☎00 353 21 385798   Fax 00 353 21 385798
Chairman/Managing Director
Roz Crowley
Approx. Annual Turnover £200,000
FOUNDED 1992. Formerly Forum Publications. *Publishes* academic, fiction, cookery, wine, general health and fitness, local history, railways, photography and practical guides. About 6 titles a year. TITLES *The Merchants of Ennis; On-Farm Research – The Broad Picture; Suicide: The Irish Experience.* Synopses and ideas welcome. No children's books.
Royalties paid twice yearly.

Poolbeg Press Ltd
123 Baldoyle Industrial Estate, Baldoyle,
Dublin 13, Republic of Ireland
☎00 353 1 832 1477
Fax 00 353 1 832 1430
E-mail: poolbeg@iol.ie
Managing Director *Philip MacDermott*
Approx. Annual Turnover £1 million+
FOUNDED 1976 to publish the Irish short story and has since diversified to include all areas of fiction (literary and popular), children's fiction and non-fiction, and adult non-fiction: history, biography and topics of public interest. About 100 titles a year. Unsolicited mss, synopses and ideas welcome (mss preferred). No drama.
IMPRINTS **Poolbeg** (paperback and hardback); **Children's Poolbeg**; **Wren**.
Royalties paid bi-annually.

Real Ireland Design Ltd
27 Beechwood Close, Boghall Road, Bray,
Co. Wicklow, Republic of Ireland
☎00 353 1 2860799   Fax 00 353 1 2829962
Managing Director *Desmond Leonard*
Producers of calendars, diaries, posters, greeting cards and books, servicing the Irish tourist industry. *Publishes* photography and tourism. About 2 titles a year. No fiction. Unsolicited mss, synopses and ideas welcome.
Royalties paid twice yearly.

Relay Publications

Tyone, Nenagh, Co. Tipperary, Republic of Ireland
☎00 353 67 31734   Fax 00 353 67 31734
Managing Director *Donal A. Murphy*
FOUNDED 1980; in abeyance 1985–92. *Publishes* regional history. 7 titles in 1996/7. Welcomes unsolicited mss, ideas and synopses. Not interested in adult fiction.
Royalties paid twice yearly.

Roberts Rinehart Publishers

Trinity House, Charleston Road, Dublin 6, Republic of Ireland
☎00 353 1 4976860   Fax 00 353 1 4976861
Chairman *Rick Rinehart*
Chief Executive Officer *Jack Van Zandt*
European branch of a US company first established in 1983. Particularly active in the Irish-American market. *Publishes* general non-fiction, particularly arts, environment, nature, Irish interest, photography, politics, history and biography; and colour illustrated children's books, fiction and non-fiction. No adult fiction. About 60 titles a year. TITLES *Literary Ireland; The Troubles; At Home in Ireland; Cats As Cats Can; The People Who Hugged the Trees*.

Royal Dublin Society

Science Section, Ballsbridge, Dublin 4, Republic of Ireland
☎00 353 1 6680866   Fax 00 353 1 6604014
E-mail: carol.power@rds.ie
President *Liam Connellan*
FOUNDED 1731 for the promotion of agriculture, science and the arts, and throughout its history has published books and journals towards this end. Publishers hired on contract basis. *Publishes* conference proceedings, biology and the history of Irish science. TITLES *Agricultural Development for the 21st Century; Kerry and Dexter Cattle and Other Ancient Irish Breeds – A History; The Right Trees in the Right Places; Agriculture & the Environment; Water of Life; Science, Technology & Realism*; occasional papers in *Irish Science & Technology* series.
Royalties not generally paid.

Royal Irish Academy

19 Dawson Street, Dublin 2, Republic of Ireland
☎00 353 1 6762570   Fax 00 353 1 6762346
Executive Secretary *Patrick Buckley*

Approx. Annual Turnover £50,000
FOUNDED in 1785, the Academy has been publishing since 1787. Core publications are journals but more books published in last 13 years. *Publishes* academic, Irish interest and Irish language. About 7 titles a year. Welcomes mss, synopses and ideas of an academic standard.
Royalties paid once yearly, where applicable.

Tír Eolas

Newtownlynch, Doorus, Kinvara, Co. Galway, Republic of Ireland
☎00 353 91 637452   Fax 00 353 91 37452
Publisher/Managing Director *Anne Korff*
Approx. Annual Turnover £50,000
FOUNDED 1987. *Publishes* books and guides on ecology, archaeology, folklore and culture. TITLES *The Book of the Burren; The Shannon Floodlands; Not a Word of a Lie; The Book of Aran; Women of Ireland, A Biographic Dictionary; Kinvara, A Seaport Town on Galway Bay*. Unsolicited mss, synopses and ideas for books welcome. No specialist scientific and technical, fiction, plays, school textbooks or philosophy.
Royalties paid annually.

Town House and Country House

Trinity House, Charleston Road, Ranelagh, Dublin 6, Republic of Ireland
☎00 353 1 4972399   Fax 00 353 1 4970927
E-mail: books@townhouse.ie
Managing Director *Treasa Coady*
FOUNDED 1980. *Publishes* commercial fiction, art and archaeology, biography and environment. About 20 titles a year. TITLES *A Place of Stones; Irish Painting; The Illustrated Archaeology of Ireland; Lifelines*. Good production and design standards. Unsolicited mss, synopses and ideas welcome. No children's books.
Royalties paid twice yearly.

Veritas Publications

7–8 Lower Abbey Street, Dublin 1, Republic of Ireland
☎00 353 1 8788177   Fax 00 353 1 8786507
Chairman *Diarmuid Murray*
Director *Fr Sean Melody*
FOUNDED 1969 to supply religious textbooks to schools and later introduced a more general religious list. Part of the Catholic Communications Institute. *Publishes* religious books only. About 20 titles a year. Unsolicited mss, synopses and ideas for books welcome.
Royalties paid annually.

Wolfhound Press
68 Mountjoy Square, Dublin 1, Republic of Ireland
☎00 353 1 8740354   Fax 00 353 1 8720207
Managing Director *Seamus Cashman*
FOUNDED 1974. Member of **Clé** – the Irish Book Publishers Association. *Publishes* art, biography, children's, fiction, general non-fiction, history, literature, literary studies and gift books. About 30 titles a year. TITLES *Famine; Run With the Wind; Leading Hollywood; Eye Witness Bloody Sunday; Breakfast in Babylon; Father Brown's Titanic Album.* Unsolicited mss (with synopses and s.a.e.) and ideas welcome.
Royalties paid annually.

Wren
See **Poolbeg Press Ltd**

Money Matters –
Measuring the Bottom Line

Taking the coward's way out, the last edition of *The Writer's Handbook* skirted the discussion of money matters. The market for the written word was in such turmoil that any generalisation on rates for the job was bound to mislead. Readers protested. A guideline, however imprecise, was said to be better than no guideline at all. Thus, bowing to popular demand, the latest *Writer's Handbook* details the minimum terms secured by the **Society of Authors**, the **Writers' Guild** and the **National Union of Journalists** for most sectors of broadcasting and journalism. The figures are not to be taken as gospel. As writers' organisations are the first to concede, there is much that goes on in the media that is beyond their remit. An independent production company will not necessarily follow the example of pay and conditions set by the BBC. A magazine or newspaper with a regular team of decently rewarded freelancers may mete out inferior treatment to occasional contributors.

And what of books?

There was a time when authors could rely on fundamentals such as standard royalties – 10 per cent on hardback and 7½ per cent on soft cover with built-in increases tied to volume of sales. No longer. With aggressive marketing techniques all the fashion we have such let-outs as 'high discount' sales which inevitably attract lower royalties. Some contracts even specify that no royalties at all are due on copies sold for promotional purposes. Then again, there has been a big increase in publisher inspired books involving several contributors, writers and artists. The royalty income in such cases can be derisory. Watch out for the small print.

More complications arise whenever electronic rights are involved. For some curious reason, publishers find it hard to come up with a simple, standardised clause which covers CD-ROMs and works published on the Web. A fair deal would be an 80:20 division of the proceeds in the author's favour. Publishers generally try for a 50:50 split. Anything less than 50 per cent for the author suggests that a dodgy accountant is in charge.

Exports are another contentious area. Contracts usually provide for royalties to be based not on the UK published price but on the price or net receipts received by the publishers. It is not at all unusual for an author to hear good news – that a container load of his books has joined the export drive – followed by the bad news – the deal was done at such a cheap rate that earnings will be minuscule.

Any author who wants to make a living by writing must establish early on that his publisher is prepared to make a down payment on account of royalties. The bigger the advance the more likely the publisher will be to put his back into the marketing effort. Even if he winds up hating the book, he will want to earn his money back by pushing sales.

The other virtue of an advance is that it permits an author to eat while working on a book.

Advances vary wildly between and within publishers. All that can be said with confidence is that the level of advances for the general run of authors has fallen over the last five years while those for established writers with proven economic muscle have kept their value and even increased. A novelist who is starting out on a career is lucky to get £1000 while educational academic writers have to settle for a few hundred or nothing at all. There are exceptions that prove the rule. Barely a week passes without a trumpeted discovery of a bestseller in the making, plucked from obscurity by a cheque waving publisher. But million dollar deals can prove as ephemeral as the newspapers which give them prominence. Publishers quote astronomical sums to heat up public interest; they neglect to mention that six figure advance is often conditional on the sale of rights, be they paperback, foreign, film or television. If the deals do not come through, neither does the money. One young innocent given the star treatment reappeared in the news a year later. She was spotted on the dole queue.

A reasonable advance for all but the top names is a sum equivalent to 60 per cent of the estimated royalties payable on the first edition. The advance should be non-returnable, except when the author fails to deliver a manuscript. Usually, it is split three ways, part on signature of contract, part on delivery of the manuscript, and part on publication.

A popular misconception is that if an advance is not recovered by royalties on sales, in other words if there is an unearned advance, the publisher is bound to lose money. But the correlation between royalties and profit is not precise. A publisher's margin may be 15 or 20 per cent after royalties, overheads and trade discount are taken into account. It is possible, therefore, for an unearned advance to be absorbed into costs with the publisher still coming out at a profit. It all depends on the size of the advance, the level of sales and the publisher's margin over fixed costs. There are too many variables to produce a general rule. Just do not be too quick to assume that the publisher loses out.

Another unsafe assumption is that advances are bound to be higher if negotiated by an agent. This may be so for best-selling authors who put their work up for auction but down the scale there may not be too much room for manoeuvre. Where an agent really proves his worth is in knowing the pitfalls of a publishing contract and helping his client to avoid them.

The good agent understands the small print and, to greater advantage, spots the omissions – such as the failure to allow for higher royalties beyond a certain minimum sale. The agented author has a say on bookclub deals, promotion budgets, cover design, the timing of publication, print number and on subsidiary rights – the latter capable of attracting earnings long after the book is out of print. The sheer range of potential subsidiary rights is mind-boggling – overseas publication (the publisher will try for world rights but when an agent is acting,

US and translation rights are nearly always reserved to the ultimate benefit of the author), film and television adaptations, audio cassettes, video, information retrieval – to mention only the most obvious. Above all, the good agent keeps a watching brief long after the contract has been signed, always ready to challenge the publisher to do better on behalf of his author.

There are authors who have a natural talent for wheeler-dealing and prefer to remain unagented. Others would dearly like to be represented but for the life of them cannot find an agent to suit their personality or are rejected because the agent of their choice is already overloaded with clients. Fortunately, there is a way of breaking the impasse and that is to join the Society of Authors. There is always someone there to advise on a contract and to run a cynical eye over the more abstruse clauses. You might even find a shoulder to cry on.

The Society of Authors, 84 Drayton Gardens, London SW10 9SB (☎0171 373 6642; fax 0171 373 5768).

Audio Books

Abbey Home Entertainment
1 Sussex Place, Hammersmith, London
W6 9XS
☎0181 910 5424   Fax 0181 910 5425
Managing Director *Anne Miles*

Abbey were the instigators (previously as MSD Holdings) in the development of the spoken word. With over 20 years' experience in recording, marketing and distribution of audio, book and cassette, their catalogue includes major children's story characters such as *Thomas the Tank Engine, Postman Pat, Rupert Bear* and *Winnie the Pooh*. Specialises in children's audio cassettes. 60 titles in 1997. Ideas from authors and agents welcome.

Argo
See **PolyGram Spoken Word**

BBC Radio Collection
Woodlands, 80 Wood Lane, London W12 0TT
☎0181 576 2230   Fax 0181 576 3851
Owner *BBC Worldwide Ltd*
Spoken Word Publishing Director *Jan Paterson*

ESTABLISHED in 1988 as The BBC Radio Collection, BBC Audio now releases material associated with BBC Radio and Television. *Publishes* drama, comedy, science fiction, fiction, non-fiction and sound effects. TITLES *Hancock's Half Hour; Round the Horne; Alan Bennett's Diaries; Knowing Me, Knowing You; This Sceptred Isle*. Almost all releases sourced from BBC Radio and Television. Unsolicited work not accepted.

Bespoke Audio Ltd
Unit 7, Pepys Court, 84 The Chase, London
SW4 0NF
☎0171 627 8777   Fax 0171 498 6420
Managing Director *Bob Nolan*

FOUNDED in 1994 by ex-**PolyGram** executive. Part of Total Records. *Publishes* and distributes for other publishers such as **Macmillan** and **HarperCollins**; biography, children's, fiction, comedy. AUTHORS John Cole, Patricia Cornwell, Michael Crichton, Roald Dahl, Ruth Rendell, Steve Turner, Sue Townsend. Ideas from authors not welcome as Bespoke deal with publishers only.

Canongate Audio
14 High Street, Edinburgh EH1 1TE
☎0131 557 5111   Fax 0131 557 5211
Joint Managing Directors *Jamie Byng, Hugh Andrew*

Part of **Canongate Books**. *Publishes* fiction, children's, humour, poetry, historical and Scottish titles. TITLES *The Driver's Seat* Muriel Spark, read by Judi Dench; *Lanark* read by the author, Alasdair Gray; *Parahandy* Neil Munro; *Scots Quair* Lewis Grassic Gibbon; Robert Louis Stevenson titles.

Cavalcade Story Cassettes
See **Chivers Audio Books**

Chivers Audio Books
Windsor Bridge Road, Bath BA2 3AX
☎01225 335336   Fax 01225 310771
Managing Director *Julian Batson*

Part of **Chivers Press Ltd**. *Publishes* a wide range of titles, mainly for library consumption. Fiction, autobiography, children's and crime. 270 titles in 1997. TITLES *Taken on Trust* Terry Waite; *Brideshead Revisited* Evelyn Waugh; *Behind the Scenes at the Museum* Kate Atkinson; *The 'Regeneration' Trilogy* Pat Barker; *True Ghost Stories* Terry Deary; *Famous Five Stories* Enid Blyton.

IMPRINTS **Chivers Audio Books, Chivers Children's Audio, Cavalcade Story Cassettes, Sterling Audio Books, Word-for-Word Audio Books.**

The Complete Listener Recorded Book Company
Field End Cottage Studios, 8 Apple Street, Oxenhope, Keighley, West Yorkshire
BD22 9LT
☎01535 645983
Managing Director *James D. Gillhouley*

FOUNDED 1989. One of the largest catalogues of unabridged classic titles in Europe and the only one to include the complete novels of the Brontë sisters, Henry Fielding and Charles Dickens. TITLES *War and Peace; Anna Karenina*. Recordings of contemporary works by new authors are undertaken by special arrangement. Please write for details.

Corgi Audio

Transworld Publishers Ltd, 61–63 Uxbridge Road, London W5 5SA
☎0181 579 2652   Fax 0181 231 6666
Managing Director *Mark Barty-King*
Part of **Transworld Publishers**. *Publishes* fiction, autobiography, children's and humour. 8 titles in 1997. TITLES *Discworld Series* Terry Pratchett; *Notes From a Small Island* Bill Bryson; *A Kentish Lad* Frank Muir; *The Horse Whisperer* Nicholas Evans.

Cover To Cover Cassettes Ltd

PO Box 112, Marlborough, Wiltshire SN8 3UG
☎01672 562255   Fax 01672 564634
Managing Director *Helen Nicoll*
Publishes classic 19th-century fiction – Jane Austen, Charles Dickens, Anthony Trollope, plus children's titles – *Fantastic Mr Fox* Roald Dahl; *Worst Witch* Jill Murphy; *Sheep-Pig* Dick King-Smith; *In Your Garden* Vita Sackville-West (book/cassette). 18 titles in 1997.

CSA Telltapes Ltd

101 Chamberlayne Road, London NW10 3ND
☎0181 960 8466   Fax 0181 968 0804
Managing Director *Clive Stanhope*
FOUNDED 1989. *Publishes* fiction, children's, short stories, poetry, travel, biographies. 90 titles to-date. Tends to favour quality/classic/nostalgic/timeless literature for the 40+ age group. TITLES *Carry on Jeeves* P. G. Wodehouse; *Great Trials: Oscar Wilde*; *The Third Man* Graham Greene; *Lamb's Tales from Shakespeare I & II*; *Bitter Lemons* Lawrence Durrell; *England Their England* A. G. Macdonell; *Goodbye Mr Chips* James Hilton. Ideas for cassettes welcome.

Cult Listening

See **PolyGram Spoken Word**

CYP Limited

The Fairway, Bush Fair, Harlow, Essex CM18 6LY
☎01279 444707   Fax 01279 445570
Joint Managing Directors *Mike Kitson, John Bassett*
FOUNDED 1978. *Publishes* children's material for those under 10 years of age; educational, entertainment, licensed characters (i.e. *Mr Men*; *Little Miss*). Ideas for cassettes welcome.

Faber Penguin Audiobooks

27 Wrights Lane, London W8 5TZ
☎0171 416 3000   Fax 0171 416 3289
3 Queen Square, London WC1N 3AU
☎0171 465 0045 Fax 0171 465 0108
Publishing Manager *Anna Hopkins (at Wrights Lane address)*
Publishing Director *Joanna Mackle (at Queen Square address)*
A joint venture between **Penguin Books** and **Faber & Faber**. *Publishes* 25–30 titles per year, drawing on the strength of Faber's authors. AUTHORS include Ted Hughes, Philip Larkin, Garrison Keillor, Sylvia Plath, T.S. Eliot, Wendy Cope, William Golding, Seamus Heaney, Paul Muldoon.

Funny Business

See **PolyGram Spoken Word**

Golden Days of Radio

See **Hodder Headline Audio Books**

Halsgrove

See entry under **UK Publishers**

HarperCollins AudioBooks

77–85 Fulham Palace Road, London W6 8JB
☎0181 741 7070
Fax 0181 307 4517(adult)/307 4291(child.)
The Collins audio and video company was acquired in the mid-eighties but the video section was later sold. In 1990/91 HarperCollins overhauled the audio company, dividing the adult and children's tapes into two separate divisions.
ADULT
Managing Director *Adrian Bourne*
Publisher *Rosalie George*
Publishes a wide range including popular and classic fiction, non-fiction, Shakespeare and poetry. 70 titles in 1997. TITLES *God of Small Things* Arundhati Roy; *Angela's Ashes* Frank McCourt; *Fugitive Pieces* Anne Michaels; *About a Boy* Nick Hornby; *Cold Mountain* Charles Frasier; *Memoirs of a Geisha* Arthur Golden.
CHILDREN'S DIVISION
Publishing Director *Gail Penston*
Senior Editor *Stella Paskins*
Publishes picture books/cassettes and story books/cassettes as well as single and double tapes for children aged 2–13 years. Fiction, songs, early learning, poetry etc. 60 titles in 1997. AUTHORS Roald Dahl, C. S. Lewis, Enid Blyton, Robin Jarvis, Colin and Jacqui

Hawkins, Ian Whybrow, Lynne Reid Banks, Robert Westall, Jean Ure, Nick Butterworth, Judith Kerr.

Hodder Headline Audio Books

338 Euston Road, London NW1 3BH
☎0171 873 6000   Fax 0171 873 6024
Publisher *Rupert Lancaster*
Editor *Charlotte Barton*

LAUNCHED in 1994 with 50 titles. A strong list, especially for theatre, vintage radio, film tie-ins, poetry plus fiction, non-fiction, children's, religious. Approx 120 titles in 1997. AUTHORS Enid Blyton, John LeCarré, Mick Inkpen (*Kipper* books), Stephen King, Rosamunde Pilcher, Emma Tennant, Joanna Trollope, Terry Waite, Mary Wesley.

IMPRINT **Golden Days of Radio** series of classic vintage radio broadcasts.

Isis Audio Books

7 Centremead, Osney Mead, Oxford
OX2 0ES
☎01865 250333   Fax 01865 790358
Managing Director *John Durrant*
Editorial Head *Veronica Babington Smith*

Part of **Isis Publishing Ltd.** *Publishes* fiction and a few non-fiction titles. AUTHORS Virginia Andrews, Barbara Taylor Bradford, Edwina Currie, Leslie Thomas, Douglas Adams, Terry Pratchett.

Ladybird Books Ltd

Beeches Road, Loughborough, Leicestershire
LE11 2NQ
☎01509 268021   Fax 01509 234672
Managing Director *Laurence James*

Part of the Penguin Group. Only *publishes* recordings of titles which appear on the Ladybird book list. 60 titles in 1997. TITLES *The Railway Children; Gulliver's Travels; Little Red Riding Hood; Puss in Boots; Farmyard Stories for Under Fives.*

Laughing Stock Productions

81 Charlotte Street, London W1P 1LB
☎0171 637 7943   Fax 0171 436 1646
Managing Director *Colin Collino*

FOUNDED 1991. Issues a wide range of comedy cassettes from family humour to alternative comedy. 12–16 titles per year. TITLES *Red Dwarf; Shirley Valentine* (read by Willy Russell); *Rory Bremner; Peter Cook Anthology; Sean Hughes; John Bird and John Fortune; Eddie Izzard.*

Listen for Pleasure

E.M.I. House, 43 Brook Green, London
W6 7EF
☎0171 605 5000   Fax 0171 605 5134
Director *Paul Holland*

Part of E.M.I. Records, the Listen for Pleasure label started in 1977 as part of Music for Pleasure. Also covers Virgin and E.M.I. *Publishes* humour, comedy classics, children's, fiction and non-fiction, poetry. TITLES *Morecambe & Wise; The Goon Shows; The Railway Children; The Borrowers; An Evening with Johnners; The Beiderbecke Affair; All Creatures Great and Small; Under Milk Wood; Pride and Prejudice; Every Living Thing; Smith & Jones.* Welcomes original ideas for cassettes.

Macmillan Audio Books

25 Eccleston Place, London SW1W 9NF
☎0171 881 8000   Fax 0171 881 8001
Owner *Macmillan Publishers Ltd*
Manager *Gina Rozner*

FOUNDED 1995. *Publishes* adult fiction, non-fiction and autobiography, focusing mainly on lead book titles and releasing audio simultaneously with hard or paperback publication. About 20 titles a year. AUTHORS Wilbur Smith, Ken Follett, Colin Dexter, Carl Hiaasen, Clare Francis, Minette Walters, Michael Ondaatje, Richard E. Grant, Helen Fielding, Elizabeth Jane Howard, Robyn Davidson, Andrew Neil, W. F. Deedes, Scott Adams.

MCI Spoken Word

76 Dean Street, London W1V 5HA
☎0171 396 8899   Fax 0171 396 8901
Owner *VCI Plc*
Head of Spoken Word *Steve Crickmer*

Established in 1993 and now a rapidly expanding publisher of a wide range of spoken word titles: comedy, children's, TV programmes. 150 titles to-date. TITLES *Inspector Morse; Barbie; Joe Pasquale, Eddie Izzard, Cracker; James Bond.*

Naxos AudioBooks

Unit 4, Wyllyotts Manor, Potters Bar, Hertfordshire EN6 2HN
☎01707 661961   Fax 01707 661971
Owner *HNH International, Hong Kong*
Managing Director *Nicolas Soames*

FOUNDED 1994. Part of Naxos, the classical budget CD company. *Publishes* classic and modern fiction, non-fiction, children's and junior classics, drama and poetry. 100 titles by the end of 1996. TITLES *Paradise Lost* Milton; *Ulysses* Joyce; *Kim* Kipling; *Decline and Fall of the Roman Empire* Gibbon.

Penguin Audiobooks

27 Wrights Lane, London W8 5TZ
☎0171 416 3000   Fax 0171 416 3289
Owner *Penguin Books Ltd*
Publishing Manager *Anna Hopkins*

Launched in November 1993 and has rapidly expanded since then to reflect the diversity of **Penguin Books'** list. *Publishes* mostly fiction, both classical and contemporary, non-fiction, autobiography and an increasing range of children's titles under the **Puffin Audiobooks** imprint. Approx. 110 titles a year. Contemporary AUTHORS include: Paul Theroux, Miss Reed, Dick Francis, Barbara Vine, Michael Ridpath, Anne Fine, Gillian Cross, Stephen King, John Mortimer.

PolyGram Spoken Word

1 Sussex Place, Hammersmith, London W6 9XS
☎0181 910 5000   Fax 0181 910 5400
Owner *PolyGram*
Product Manager *Alex Mitchison*

Part of PolyGram, the Spoken Word division has been in operation for two years, publishing under the **Speaking Volumes**, **Funny Business**, **Cult Listening** and **Argo** labels. *Publishes* comedy, biography, fiction, poetry and documentary titles. TITLES *Red Dwarf*; *Backwards* Rob Grant; *They Think It's All Over* Kenneth Wolstenholme; *Billy Connolly's Two Night Stand*; *The Fortean Times*; *Mark Lamarr: Live*; *Jack Dee: Live*; *Girl Force, So You Wannabe a Star*. Ideas for new releases always welcome.

Puffin Audiobooks

See **Penguin Audiobooks**

Random House Audiobooks

20 Vauxhall Bridge Road, London SW1V 2SA
☎0171 840 8400   Fax 0171 233 6127
Owner *Random House UK Ltd.*
Managing Director *Simon King*
Manager *Kate Elton*

The audiobooks division of Random House started early in 1991. Acquired the Reed Audio list in 1997. *Publishes* fiction, non-fiction and self help. 18 titles in 1998. AUTHORS include John Grisham, Stephen Fry, Charles Handy, Patricia

Cornwell, Michael Crichton and Ruth Rendell.

CHILDREN'S DIVISION IMPRINT **Tellastory** AUTHORS include Jane Hissey, Shirley Hughes, David McKee and Michael Palin. About 20 titles in 1998.

Reed Audio

See **Random House Audiobooks**

Simon & Schuster Audio

West Garden Place, Kendal Street, London W2 2AG
☎0171 316 1900   Fax 0171 262 3102
Audio Manager *Gillian Holmes*

Simon & Schuster Audio began by distributing their American parent company's audio products. Moved on to repackaging products specifically for the UK market and in 1994 became more firmly established in this market with a huge rise in turnover. *Publishes* adult fiction, self help, business, Star Trek titles. 3 titles per month. TITLES *From Potter's Field* Patricia Cornwell; *A Thousand Acres* James Smiley; *Shipping News* E. Annie Proulx; *Popcorn* Ben Elton; *My Story* Duchess of York; *Star Trek, First Contact* J. M. Dillard.

Smith/Doorstop Cassettes

The Poetry Business, The Studio, Byram Arcade, Huddersfield, West Yorkshire HD1 1ND
☎01484 434840   Fax 01484 426566
Co-directors *Peter Sansom, Janet Fisher*

Publishes poetry, read and introduced by the writer. AUTHORS Carol Ann Duffy, Simon Armitage, Les Murray, Ian McMillan, Sujata Bhatt.

Soundings

Kings Drive, Whitley Bay, Tyne & Wear NE26 2JT
☎0191 253 4155   Fax 0191 251 0662
Managing Director *Derek Jones*

FOUNDED in 1982. *Publishes* fiction and non-fiction; crime, romance, young adults. 144 titles in 1997. TITLES *Bees in My Bonnet* Angus McVicar; *A Ghost in Monte Carlo* Barbara Cartland; *The Branded Man* Catherine Cookson; *School for Love* Olivia Manning; *Gull on the Roof* Derek Tangye. Ideas for cassettes welcome.

Speaking Volumes

See **PolyGram Spoken Word**

Sterling Audio Books

See **Chivers Audio Books**

WALKfree Productions Ltd

56 Upper Norwood Street, Leckhampton, Cheltenham, Gloucestershire GL53 0DU
☎01242 231800

Managing Director *Mark Richards*
Publishing/Sales Director *Nicholas Reardon*

FOUNDED 1996. In association with the Ordnance Survey, produces *WALKfree Audio-Guides* which 'cultivate a new form of country walking experience in the countryside'. The audio tape is accompanied by a 16-page guide book containing an Ordnance Survey Travel-master map extract plus outline route maps. Each guide also offers advice on convenient places for refreshment and local contacts. 8 titles in 1996. TITLES *The Cotswolds; Peak District; Hadrian's Wall.*

Word-for-Word Audio Books

See **Chivers Audio Books**

Poetry – Perfect for Our Times

Peter Finch

You'd like to avoid poetry? You'll have a hard time; these days it's everywhere – newspapers, tv, London tubes, all over the Internet. Poets on the news because they've written vile poems about politicians; poets commissioned to re-write the Hippocratic Oath; poets uncovered faking famous works in order to get themselves into anthologies; poets taken on at law firms to help the QCs get their speeches right; poets working in zoos and public parks; poets employed as mascots by sports organisations. This all sounds as if poetry has at last found its place in society – everyday accepted – used in TV adverts, recited in clubs. Certainly true. But consumed by the population at large and actually worth real money? Unfortunately, not yet.

The irony here is the huge number of people actually engaged in poetry's creation. If you'd just landed from Mars you might imagine that almost everyone writes it, and you'd be near right. Publishers will tell you that it often seems that way. Thirty thousand poems reached the *Poetry Society's* famous *Poetry Review* last year. Almost all of them were sent back. The population at large imagine that poetry is such an easy option. Crank it out when it comes to you. Use it to fix those blobs of emotion banging round inside. Sort life out creatively and, more importantly, as fast as you can. Revise nothing. When pushed simply bash out another. 'Best thought first thoughts,' said Allen Ginsberg, and a whole generation have made that their *raison d'etre*. All would be fine if the newly literary enfranchised did not also try to publish their ragged efforts. No time served, no craft, no apprenticeship but enormous expectation. It is as if they'd all bought violins on their way home, briefly checked out a play-in-day handbook and then sent in their applications to join the LSO. No one reads anymore – I saw this the other week when I was the only person with a book among sixty in a doctor's waiting room. I worked through Simon Armitage's *CloudCuckooLand*, the other fifty-nine stared into space. If anyone else had been reading I'd lay my money that it would not be poetry. Have you checked the best-seller lists recently? Apart from fleeting appearances of things like Ted Hughes' anthology *By Heart* (poetry standards) or the BBC's *The Nation's Favourite Love Poems* (classic verse) not a scrap of poetry in sight. Cookbooks go better, thrillers, street-hip novels about sex and death and dope.

Nevertheless poetry, in this last decade of the millennium is a more popular activity than it has been for years. Strong men in pubs no longer regard its practitioners as flowery weaklings. It appears in Australian soaps. *The Sun* knows what it is. Perspectives have changed. The daily poem in *The Independent* (for which no one gets paid, by the way) and the dreadful doggerel in my local evening tabloid are testimony to that. In a decade which has seen everything from Seamus Heaney winning the Nobel prize to Ian McMillan taking up residency at Barnsley Football Club poetry has lost much of its distance.

Who are today's poets? Ask the average person in the street and you might get a real answer. John Hegley, they'll say. Benjamin Zephaniah, John Cooper Clark, Roger McGough, Wendy Cope, Carol Ann Duffy, Thom The World Poet, Lemn Sissay (remembering him from his time on *Grange Hill*). A few, driven by the publicist's hype may suggest Murray Lachlan Young. The bookstore frequenters will add Ted Hughes and Seamus Heaney or, if you are asking in Wales, R.S.Thomas. Twenty years ago the answer would have been Pam Ayres. 'Poetry is a bit like Campbell's soup. It's very concentrated and you can get your money's worth out of a very short amount,' says Henry Normal. Perfect for our times.

National Poetry Day, the annual excuse for sending verse off on balloons, has become an institution. The media participate, news-readers are asked to memorise new verse, celebs appear reciting favourites from the past. The annual Forward Prize, awarded amid huge attention at the Groucho Club, has become the rhymer's Booker. The Paul Hamlyn Foundation awards, worth £75,000, have been given to poets. The London Poetry Society has received a massive cash injection from the Lottery. Soon there will be poetry residencies at M&S and London Zoo. 200,000 passengers at Waterloo Station have been presented with poetry postcards by the Poetry Book Society. Waterstones fill their windows with verse top-sellers. Poetry Slams, where brash upstarts can get on simply by making an audience laugh, have been included in the annual Cheltenham Literature Festival. Trevor McDonald has been touring the UK telling everyone that he likes poetry too.

But at base what is it? When you get home and write yours you'll know. A private art where the participants are just you and your muse. As Don Patterson says – 'Poetry is a strange little town for which no reliable streetplan exists, full of all-night cafes, tiny specialist libraries, tango bars, Zen gardens and balti houses.' A small place, a quiet place, where big business has not yet pushed things beyond reach. You want to join in? You can.

First step

Are you up to this? Are you personally convinced that your work is ready? If you are uncertain, then most likely that will be the view of everyone else. Check your text for glips and blips. Rework it. Root out any clichés or archaic poetry expressions such as O, doeth, bewilld'd and the like. Drop any of what Peter Sansom calls 'spirit of the age' poetry words. Do without shards, lozenges, lambent patina, stippled seagulls. If you use rhymes them make them less obvious. If by this time your writing still sounds okay, then go ahead.

Commercial publishers

Despite the obvious possibilities of making something from poetry in the commercial market place the number of those conglomerate publishers involved continues to shrink. Where once there were a goodly number of mainstream imprints there are now only three or four. Poetry is increasingly seen today as the quality line which enhances a publisher's list. Never there to make profit but rather to impart class. Back to where it was forty years ago. Compared to other lines slim volumes are slow sellers. Their editors are almost always part-time or have other jobs within the company and are never allowed to publish everyone they would like.

The obvious exception to this approach is long-term market leader and envy of the whole business **Faber & Faber**. Here editor Christopher Reid, along with Jane Feaver, preside over a list which continues to be as important to the firm as when T. S. Eliot inaugurated it more than seventy years ago. And for Faber it all seems to work. This is the imprint most poets would like to join. The greats of the twentieth century are here – Pound, Eliot, Plath, Hughes, Larkin. Seamus Heaney made half-a-million in sales when he won the Nobel prize. Wendy Cope shifts at least 70,000 copies each time she goes into print. Simon Armitage regularly sells into five figures. The imprint is built on distinctively designed class and the roster of contemporary poets includes some of the best we have – Derek Walcott, Don Paterson, Glyn Maxwell, Andrew Motion, Tom Paulin, Hugo Williams, Paul Muldoon, Douglas Dunn. Reid will read all manuscripts submitted determined to continue publishing good poetry despite the vagaries of the market place. Send a brief covering letter and a sample of your writing (10-20 poems) not forgetting s.a.e. if you think this is where you'll fit in.

At the traditional centre for English verse, **Oxford University Press,** long regarded for its unbeatable anthologies and mainstream mix of Keats, Milton and Pope, the contemporary poetry list continues with ten new titles annually. Poetry editor Jacqueline Simms runs a stable which includes Sean O'Brien, Jamie McKendrick, Moniza Alvi, Fleur Adcock, D. J. Enright, Tobias Hill and Penelope Shuttle along with newcomers Greg Delanty and Antony Dunn. 'Interest may be up,' says Simms, 'but the rise in sales is a bit of a myth'. Despite this the books with their distinctive black covers remain an important part of the imprint's catalogue. Should the unpublished try here? Not at present, unsolicited mss will not be considered again until the year 2000.

The commercial editor most admired for his taste is still **Cape**'s Robin Robertson. 'You can see a clear editorial mind at work,' says former Poetry Society chairman Bill Swainson. The Cape list is by no means all things to all people. Matthew Sweeney, Mark Doty, Thomas Lynch and Michael Longley are typical. Robertson, himself a fine poet, moved into the editorial chair from **Secker & Warburg**, who abandoned their own poetry list when he went. He produces four to six titles annually – all books, no anthologies and with a number sourced from the other side of the Atlantic. The care taken in their production is obvious – fine design, significant content. Check them out, with their distinctive fold-in flaps these books look worth the money. Worth trying? Yes but potential contributors should never waste anyone's time by not looking at the list first.

At **The Harvill Press** poetry is part of the company's overall commitment to literature, although output is low. Poetry editor Christopher Maclehose manages two new books annually with Paul Durcan and Raymond Carver still cornering the sales. They'll look at new manuscripts but chances are slim. New writers would be better off starting elsewhere.

Among the other commercial houses former activity is now limited to nominal titles or back-list obligations. **Cassell** anthologises the poems from the London Underground. The **Orion** group's **Everyman** imprint repackages the past at one or two pounds per volume with a series which includes Edward Thomas, W.B. Yeats, Andrew Marvell, John Clare, and William Shakespeare. **Marion Boyars** translates Yevgeny Yevtushenko. **Hutchinson** has Dannie Abse and the inspirational attractions of Helen Steiner Rice. **Methuen** sticks to Brecht and John Hegley. **Chatto** gives poetry up then decides it might start again. Mainstream imprints may once have been the proving grounds for new voices but if recent activity is anything to go on that is certainly no longer the case.

The smaller operators

Not all commercial publishing is vast and conglomerate. Independents still exist and on their lists poetry still occurs. **Payback Press**, an imprint of **Canongate Books**, has published Lemn Sissay's anthology of black British poetry. Northern Ireland general publisher, **The Blackstaff Press**, brings out at least one poetry title annually. Joan Newmann, Frank Ormsby and Ruth Carr's anthology of women poets are typical. **Serpent's Tail** publishes Dorothy Porter's Aussie lesbian thriller in verse (but have declared that they do *not* want to see unsolicited new work), Welsh family firm **Gwasg Gomer** produces tidy editions of Jon Dressel, Nigel Jenkins and Chris Bendon. Former *Sunday Times* Small Publisher of the Year, **Polygon**, (which is an imprint of **Edinburgh University Press**) continues to mix Gaelic with English as part of its 'poetry for the new generation' policy. The press has at least half a dozen poets on the list including Donny O'Rourke, Rody Gorman, Liz Lochhead and W. N. Herbert. Try here if you are part of the Scottish renaissance.

Nominal dabbling

Poetry in the shape of single titles and the occasional anthology dots the lists of many UK publishers but this is hardly a declaration of interest or a desire to see more. Most editors do not like unsalable unknown poets dropping their life's outputs through the letterbox. **BBC Books** publishes anthologies of the nation's favourite poems but you need to have been voted there to get in. **Element** tracks the mystical. **John Murray** has George Mackay Brown, **Weidenfeld & Nicolson** re-runs W. B. Yeats. **Headline**, **Bloomsbury**, **Michael Joseph**, **Hodder & Stoughton**, **Routledge**, **Deutsch** and others publish either generic anthologies or handy reprints of the classics. The occasional new voice that gets in arrives almost by mistake. Tokenism. For the beginner these are not the places to try and it is worth remembering that the editors of commercially produced anthologies do not accept unsolicited single poems. Some specialist interests are dealt with at **Lion** (Christian verse), **Peepal Tree** (Caribbean) and **Oscars** (gay) – but it isn't a lot.

Universities

Apart from OUP, activity is sparse in the UK. Reprints and literary studies at **Cambridge** are the same as at **Manchester**. At the **University of Wales Press**, which publishes a splendid series of collected works from Welsh poets, you need to be dead. American university presses such as Nebraska, **Nevada**, Pittsburg, Ohio, Yale, Duke, **Iowa**, **Syracuse** and **California** along with **W. W. Norton** do an increasing amount of verse but exclusively by Americans. No chances there. In Austria, however, the University of Salzburg Press, run these days largely from the pocket of James Hogg, has embarked on an extensive programme of substantial poetry volumes from the less commercial. Editing is shared with Wolfgang Gortschacher and present output is twenty volumes annually. Workmanlike, if not brilliantly designed, the books fill a niche unoccupied by anyone else. James Kirkup, Peter Russell, Ian Caws, Alexis Lykiard, Alison Bielski, and William Oxley are typical authors. In addition Hogg has revived *The Poet's Voice*, a literary magazine edited by Fred Beake and produced a number of anthologies drawn from the little mags including a best of both *Stride* and *Outposts*. Despite its Austrian location the poetry is almost exclusively British in origin

Women

A spent force. Well hardly that, but as a commercial proposition poetry is not seen as the way ahead. Britain's leading feminist publishing house, **Virago** (now part of **Little, Brown**), does little more than bring out the obvious (Margaret Atwood, Jean Binta Breeze, Merle Collins, Maya Angelou) along with the occasional anthology. As the direction for UK women poets? Not a hope. At **The Women's Press**, Virago's main competitor, the situation is much the same. Original good intentions sunk into a programme which endlessly publishes Alice Walker. Women poets are better served by the poetry specialists. More of them anon.

The mass market paperback

The cheap and popular end is where many poets imagine the best starting place to be. Mass-market paperback houses were founded to publish inexpensive reprints of hard-covered originals and, despite a certain amount of innovation, to a large extent they still fulfil this role. Being neither cheap nor that popular poetry does not really fit in. Among the carrousels on station bookstalls you do not see it. Check the empires of **Arrow**, **Vista**, **Corgi**, **Headline** and **Pan**. If you discount the inspirational, you won't find a book of verse between them. **Vintage** to their credit publish the occasional anthology and run reprints of Iain Sinclair but he is also a successful novelist. Elsewhere nothing, although there are two exceptions. At **Penguin**, where things are always different, poetry plays a significant part. With a commercial ear ever to the ground the company have correctly assessed the market for contemporary and traditional verse and systematically and success-fully filled it. Reprinting important volumes pioneered by poetry presses such as **Anvil**, **Carcanet** and **Bloodaxe**, originating historic and thematic anthologies, reviving classic authors and producing a multitude of translations en route, Penguin continues to provide an almost unrivalled introduction to the world of verse. But appearances aside, this is most certainly no place for the beginner. 'As a large trade publisher, we publish only anthologies plus a handful of famous poets,' publishing director Tony Lacey told me. 'We leave the discovering of poets to the specialists. The smaller presses can take risks; we cannot.' The company acts as main publishers for a select group of sure sellers which includes James Fenton, Geoffrey Hill, Craig Raine, and Roger McGough. The main thrust remains the re-packaging of proven bards such as Simon Armitage, Carol Ann Duffy, U. A. Fanthorpe and Dannie Abse, a good range of modern poets in translation along with larger sets from the likes of Allen Ginsberg and John Ashbery. The *Penguin Modern Poets* series of loosely-connected trios has now reached Volume 13 and represents an excellent cross-section of British and Irish contemporary verse. The company's 1998 poetry blockbuster is the Simon Armitage and Robert Crawford edited *British and Irish Poetry Since the War*. Despite these obvious win-ners, Lacey sees the whole market for verse as small, despite the hype.

Penguin's nearest rival, **Picador**, the literary paperbacker from **Pan Macmillan**, has followed its successful and very non-mainstream anthology of UK outsiders *Conductors of Chaos* with a series of original volumes. Beginning with proven poets Robin Robertson, Kathleen Jamie and Ruth Sharman the list has now embraced newcomers such as Paul Farley and Peter Armstrong. Using Don Patterson as poetry talent scout and Tanya Stobbs as in-house poetry editor the imprint intends to continue an output of two to four titles annually. Their Sean O'Brien anthology of contemporary verse has certainly put them on the map. Worth trying here? 'Poets who haven't published in the magazines are dis-couraged,' is the official line. Watch this space.

The specialists

Despite having a tough time in the hands of the commercial giants poetry flour-ishes. Where? With the specialist independents, a host of semi-commercial operations scattered across the country. They are run by genuine poetry enthusiasts whose prime concern is not so much money as the furtherance of their art. Begun as classic small presses which soon outgrew the restraints of back-bedroom offices and under-the-stairs warehousing, they have emerged by stealth. A real force on the poetry scene most now have national representation, with a number using *Signature* (the old *Password* rebranded), the Arts Council subsidised poetry (and recently new fiction) specialists who issue a very useful catalogue (23 New Mount Street, Manchester M4 4DE). These presses have learned well how the business works. You can find them in Waterstones, you can see them in Dillons. Most (but not all) receive grant aid, without which their publishing programmes would be sunk. They are models of what poetry publishing should be – active, involving, alert and exciting. They promote their lists through readings, tours, web sites and broadcasts and they involve their authors in the production and sales of their books. Never before have new poets been faced with so many publishing opportunities. And if there is any criticism then this is it. Too many books jamming the market. Just how does the reader see through the flood? By the press's reputation I guess. Two have emerged well ahead of the pack – along with **Faber**, **Carcanet** and **Bloodaxe** now dominate British poetry publishing.

Regarded by many as the only verse specialist with critical clout Carcanet is almost indistinguishable from its trade competitors. Although no longer exclusively a publisher of verse, it still gives poetry pre-eminence and has over 600 titles in print and reps in 42 countries. Managing Director Michael Schmidt agrees with Auden's observation that most people who read verse read it for some reason other than the poetry. He fights the tide with his own mainstream journal *PN Review*. Despite an IRA bombing of his Manchester offices his press continues its policy of serious quality. 'I am strongly aware of the anti-modernist slant in a lot of poetry publishing, and publish to balance this,' he comments. 'Most submissions we receive come from people ignorant of the list to which they are submitting. Nothing is more disheartening than to receive a telephone call asking whether Carcanet publishes poetry.' The press concentrates on producing substantial editions which make a poet's whole oeuvre available alongside cheaper selected poems and new titles by both the untried and the famous. Typical of their list are John Ash, John Ashbery, Louise Gluck, Allen Curnow, Edwin Morgan, Les Murray, Sophie Hannah, Miles Champion, Eavan Boland and best-seller, Elizabeth Jennings. Three major millennium projects under way at present involve the bringing back into print the entire outputs of Robert Graves, Hugh MacDiarmid and Ford Madox Ford, a total in excess of fifty volumes. Carcanet has an air of purpose about it. 'We avoid the technicolour and pyrotechnic media razzmatazz,' says Schmidt. New poets are welcome to submit but check both your own past performance as well Carcanet's list before you go ahead.

The second and even larger of the pair is Neil Astley's acclaimed Bloodaxe Books. Publishing fifty titles annually the press brings out more poetry books than any other British imprint. Picking up poets dropped by the commercial operators and selling on to the world's anthologists, this is certainly one of poetry's best proving grounds. Based in the North East and begun in the early eighties, the press is unhindered by a past catalogue of classical greats or an overly regional concern. It relentlessly pursues the new. Astley presents the complete service from thematic anthologies, world greats and selecteds to slim volumes by total newcomers. The press has its own range of excellent handbooks to the scene including Paul Hyland's *Getting Into Poetry* and Peter Sansom's *Writing Poems* along with an increasing range of critical volumes. Best poetry sellers include Linda France's anthology *Sixty Women Poets*, Jenni Couzyn's *Contemporary Women Poets*, Selima Hill and Peter Reading's *Work In Regress* and the work of John Hartley Williams. Still way out ahead is the decade-framing and still controversial anthology, *The New Poetry*. With commendable concern to stay ahead Bloodaxe has been pushing *The Next Generation* with books and a reading tour from younger voices. This plus Maura Dooley's anthology *Making For Planet Alice*, thirty new women poets whose first collections have appeared since 1990. With aid from the Lottery the current thrust is multi-media – a series of poets on CD and cassette (Linton Kwesi Johnson, Glyn Maxwell, Jackie Kay), video productions in conjunction with television and a Bloodaxe website (*http://www.bloodaxebooks.demon.co.uk*). Are there too many poets out there? 'No, only too many people who think they are poets.' Nonetheless, the press welcomes newcomers but, since they receive at least 100 new collections a week, advises that you restrict yourself to sending only a dozen of your best. If Bloodaxe wants to see more, they'll ask. A simple way to taste the imprint's range is to try their anthology, *Poetry With An Edge*.

Production standards among the other specialists are just as good although annual output (and as a consequence, opportunity for the new poet) is substantially less.

At the **Anvil Press**, founder Peter Jay celebrates thirty years of independent, alternative publishing. Founded as a small press in 1968 Anvil was an early alternative to the Fabers and OUPs of the poetry scene. Jay still runs his original group of poets – Harry Guest, Peter Levi, Anthony Howell and Heather Buck – although he is adamant about avoiding cliques. If they are right for the imprint new poets will be taken on. With the assistance of Bill Swainson, Jay has expanded his abiding interest in poetry in translation. The press is justly proud of its claim of keeping British poetry open to new work from all over the world. Four Nobel Laureates are among the authors on its list. Editions have a quiet style with as much attention paid to presentation inside the book as out. Anvil's runaway best-seller is Carol Ann Duffy (who also edits their useful *Anvil New Poets* anthology). Their Matthew Sweeney and Ken Smith anthology, *Beyond Bedlam*, 'poems written out of mental distress' has also done very well. Typical poets include Michael Hamburger, Ruth Silcock, Sally Purcell and Dennis O'Driscoll.

Enitharmon Press represents quality, cares about presentation and like Anvil has a real concern for internal design. Its books, its splendid poet/artist limited edition collaborations and its occasional pamphlets are produced to the highest of standards. Enitharmon has little interest in fashion, preferring 'poetry of the human spirit' which exhibits 'moral imagination'. Owner Stephen Stuart-Smith continues a policy of publishing between eight and ten volumes annually by new, established and unjustly neglected poets. David Gascoyne's *Selected Verse Translations* sells alongside Jeremy Reed's rich and subversive *Sweet Sister Lyric*. Enitharmon is 'wary of unsolicited mss – unless, of course, those mss are of extraordinary brilliance.' Stuart-Smith considers the finding of such a work in the slush pile unlikely. Typical recent poets include Martyn Crucefix, Judith Kazantzis, Hilary Davies and Phoebe Hesketh. In a rather uncharacteristic dash for publicity Enitharmon has teamed with the Arts Council and the charity Barnados to publish *Poetry On The Ceiling*, a series of posters for display above dentists' chairs.

Seren Books (the Welsh for 'star') is a full-blown literary house publishing novels, short fiction, biographies and critical texts. Started by Cary Archard as an offshoot of the magazine *Poetry Wales* the imprint still maintains a solid interest in verse publishing at least eight new single author volumes annually. In receipt of considerable Arts Council of Wales sponsorship the bias is towards work from Wales and the border regions. Poetry editor Amy Wack reads *everything* submitted but admits that she has only ever accepted one unsolicited manuscript in her entire tenure. Editions are quality productions with plenty of attention paid to design inside and out. Typical recent poets include Duncan Bush, Deryn Rees-Jones, Paul Henry, Robert Minhinnick and Tony Curtis. Their major best-seller is Dannie Abse's *Twentieth Century Anglo-Welsh Poetry*. A good press sampler is their anthology, *Burning The Bracken*. They have also published their own guide to the scene, *The Poetry Business*.

Tony Ward's **Arc Publications**, based in Lancashire, may have declined in output from ten titles annually to seven but commitment is still high on the list. 'Although there appear to be more and more poetry volumes being published, this does not equate with a renaissance,' he remarks. 'Comprehension of literary tradition and, indeed, our native tongue, is still missing.' The imprint employs Michael Hulse and David Morley as editors and maintains a backlist of approaching 100 titles. Ivor Cutler, John Kinsella and Jackie Wills are recent successes. New poets include Robert Gray and Joel Lane. Prospective poets should expect to wait four months for a reply and most certainly familiarise themselves with the Arc list before sending. 'There are simply too many family/angst/therapy writers believing, without any hint of editing or rewriting, they are god's gift' is the official line. You have been warned.

Rupert Loydell's **Stride** began in 1982 as a wild small mag which took over the editor's life. The booklet series which spun from the magazine is now the main thrust and Stride operates as a fully fledged poetry publisher, producing well-designed, full-size volumes the equal of any commercial operation he comes up against. Based in the south west, the press publishes 20 new books annually and has a list of well over 200 titles ranging from the totally unknown to the famous. Innovative poetry, 'reinvigorated and re-explored/invented forms' form the backbone although Loydell is certain no opponent of more formal material, so long as it lives dangerously and helps 'reinvent the way we see the world'. The press runs individual collections, criticism, interviews and an increasing range of excellent, alternative anthologies. Advice to prospective contributors? 'Research your market, target your work correctly, buy poetry, make sure you know how language works.' Stride responds to submissions swiftly. Invariably within three weeks and often within three days. Recent successes include their William Burroughs memorial anthology, Charles Wright, Peter Redgrove, Evangeline Paterson and Anthony Wilson. Check Stride's anthology *Ladder To The Next Floor* for a sampler of how the press got where it is or *The Stumbling Dance*, a collection of twenty-one new poets, to discover the kind of thing Loydell likes.

Peterloo Press, based in Cornwall, represents poetry without frills, without fuss and most definitely without the avant-garde. Run by Harry Chambers the press aims to publish quality work by new and neglected poets, some of them late starters (although if you have been flogging your stuff around the circuit for years and got nowhere then Chambers is unlikely to be your saviour); to co-publish with reputable presses abroad (Goose Lane in Canada, Storyline Press and the University of Pittsburgh in the States and **Cló Iar Chonnachta** in Ireland); and to establish a Peterloo list of succeeding volumes by a core of poets of proven worth. Chambers avoids anthologies and has finished with magazines and newsletters. The press sticks to books, running an active backlist of nearly two hundred titles. Bestsellers include U. A. Fanthorpe, John Mole, John Whitworth, John Latham and Dana Gioia. Recent additions are Anna Crowe, Gary Geddes, Gabriel Fitzmaurice and Ann Drysdale. Current plans include the establishment of a Peterloo centre in a converted chapel at Calstock, a venture not without its funding difficulties. Peterloo, now in its 15th year runs its own poetry competition (£4000 first prize) and insists that prospective contributors to his press have had at least six poems in reputable magazines. Send a full mss accompanied by a stamped envelope large enough to carry your mss back to you. Chambers currently takes three to four months to reply and is full to the year 2000.

There are other presses with less prodigious outputs but whose editions can still give the poetry world a run for its money. In Newcastle, Peter Lewis's **Flambard Press** was begun in 1991 and publishes around three titles annually in the Bloodaxe style. With aid from Northern Arts the press sees a role as an outlet for new or neglected writers from the region. Gerard Benson, Geoffrey Holloway, William Scammell, Peter Mortimer and Michael Blackburn are typical names. If you think you qualify send a small sample rather than a life-time's output. Gladys Mary Coles has steadily developed her **Headland Publications** into a regular Peterloo clone. Her interest in Welsh poets is clear – Herbert Williams, Richard Poole, Joseph Clancy – although her biggest seller is Simon Rae. Like many of the smaller operators Headland have discovered that anthologies are easier to market than single author titles. *The Poet's View*, reactions to paintings at the Walker Art Gallery, has done well. A new anthology of women poets and a set of regional compilations are in the pipeline.

Hertfordshire's **Rockingham Press** run by David Perman publishes modern Turkish and Persian poetry in translation along with an increasing number of contemporary British poets. Six well-produced volumes plus two chapbooks annually featuring John Greening, Dinah Livingstone and others point to the imprint's rising significance. Ken Edwards' **Reality Street Editions**, an amalgamation of his own press with Wendy Mulford's Street Editions, specialises in 'linguistically innovative writing by women and men on both sides of the Atlantic'. Publishing solid single-author volumes, translations, ground-breaking anthologies along with a series of four-poet showcases the press takes the new poetry seriously. Typical authors include Lisa Robertson, Maurice Scully, Cris Cheek and Denise Riley. Check their *Out Of Everywhere* anthology of UK and US innovative poetry from women. The press have also published book/CD packages and run an excellent web site (*www.demon.co.uk/eastfield/reality/*).

At the self-styled poetry capital of Britain, no other place than Huddersfield, Janet Fisher and Peter Sansom run **Smith/Doorstop** the poetry imprint of their enterprising **Poetry Business** (see **Organisations**). The press produces a mixture of pamphlets, full-length collections and stylish cassettes. Duncan Curry, Martin Stannard, Jo Haslam, Carcanet Press MD Michael Schmidt and Irene Rawnsley are typical authors. Simon Armitage, Carol Ann Duffy and Ian Macmillan feature in the cassette series. **Slow Dancer Press**, an outgrowth of the now defunct *Slow Dancer* magazine begun 21 years ago, is run by detective fiction author John Harvey with the assistance of Sarah Boiling. The press long in the business of pamphlet production (Peter Sansom, Rebecca Goss, Tamar Yoseloff, Barry MacSweeney, Robert Etty, etc.) has recently launched a series of more substantial volumes including Lee Harwood, Lucille Clifton, Ruth Valentine and the late James Schuyler. The press also publishes fiction. A class operation worth checking. Send for their catalogue or access their web site (*www.mellotone.co.uk*).

From the appropriately named Coleridge Cottage in Somerset, Derrick Woolf runs the poetry publisher **Odyssey** whose editions are beginning to outgrow their home-made origins. Like Stride this is another outgrowth of a successful small mag. Odyssey's editions have a south-west bias although this doesn't prevent Woolf from casting his net where he wishes. Kerry Sowerby, Tilla Brading, Andy Brown and Tony Charles are on the list. As technology continues to make life easier for publishers it becomes harder to draw the line between the poetry specialists and the classic small presses. Maybe by now such a division does not exist at all.

The traditional outlets

Poetry has a place in our national press, albeit a small one. *The Independent* runs a daily poem, *The Guardian* features verse from time to time as do all the serious Sunday heavies. *The Times Literary Supplement* gives over considerable space on a regular basis, whole double page spreads devoted to the work of one poet or to a long single poem are not unusual although the paper does have its favourites. *The London Review of Books* shows a similar interest although neither appear very keen to use unsolicited work. *The London Magazine*, another stalwart, has the reputation for being the fastest responder in the business (you walk to the post box, mail your poems, then return home to find them rejected and waiting for you on the mat). Auberon Waugh relishes stuffy tradition at *The Literary Review*. Among other weeklies and monthlies the situation is fluid. Poetry gets in when someone on the staff shows an interest. Check your targets along the shelves at W. H. Smith's. Some local newspapers and freesheets are responding to the perceived poetry boom by devoting pages to contributions from readers, mostly dire doggerel and largely unpaid, although it is publication. If your paper hasn't joined in yet try sending your work in the form of a letter to Postbag. Start a trend. Much of this might sound quite reassuring for the poet but the truth is that were poetry to cease to exist overnight, then these publications would continue to publish without a flicker. Who, other than the poets, would notice?

Forward Press and the regional anthologies

Running in parallel with the high ground literary approach of much of the forementioned poetry publishing is an empire largely unknown to the taste-makers and ignored by the critics. Ian and Tracy Walton's ground-floor **Forward Press** in Peterborough now turns over a million and a half annually, has almost 3000 titles in print, and reckons to account for around ten percent of all verse published in the UK. Depressed with 'twenty years of not being able to enjoy poetry' because it was inevitably obscure, the couple have moved from back kitchen to factory unit in the service of 180,000 active British verse scribblers. 'A high proportion of the thousands of letters we receive tell us that many people find poetry over-complex and difficult to understand' runs one of their brochures. In the ten years since it was founded Forward Press has promoted an 'accessible, sincere poetry which everyone can relate to'. The higher realms are not for them. Publishing under a number of imprints including **Poetry Now**, **Anchor Books** and **Triumph House**, the operation receives thousands of contributions annually. Poets are sourced through free editorial copy in regional newspapers. 'Peterborough publishers are looking for contributions to their new poetry anthology *Anchor Books Inspirations From Yorkshire*' is a typical line. The contributions flow in their hundreds. 'It is a bit like amateur dramatics,' Ian told me, 'anyone can take part.'

Forward's outstanding success is built on its approachability. Perpetuating a poetry world's *Home and Away* image, the Waltons and their team of exclusively young editors include as many as two hundred and fifty poems in each anthology. Submissions under thirty lines are preferred. Costs are kept down by using in-house printing equipment coupled to serviceable bindings. If you want to see your work in print, and for most contributors this is the whole *raison d'etre* for writing, then you have to buy a copy. For many poets this will be their first appearance in book form and chances are they will buy more than a single copy. This is not a traditional vanity operation. No one is actually being ripped off nor are the publishers raking in exorbitant profits. Page for page their titles are no more expensive than those of Cape or Faber and are cheaper than the output of some little presses. However, distribution is patchy – not that many Forward titles make the shelves at Waterstones or Dillons, (although with the appointment of Vine House to handle representation this is set to improve soon). As for many of the small presses interested parties are encouraged to buy direct. Forward's critics, some of whom are quite vociferous, claim that quality is being neglected in exchange for quantity. Reduce your criteria for inclusion, cram the poems in, sell more copies. Undoubtedly the genuine literary achievement of appearing in one of these books is questionable. In mitigation though it must be said that for some people this will be a much-needed beginning and for others the only success they are going to get.

The Waltons have embellished their operation with a range of free-to-enter competitions, a rondeau workshop with attendant anthology and **Spotlight Poets**, a joint publishing project where poets published are 'asked to purchase some books and assist with marketing efforts'. Their much criticised royalty payment scheme has been replaced with the *Forward Press Top 100 Awards* which offer a total of £10,000 annually to the best poets published in their many anthologies.

Forward reckon now to have reached the UK limits for regular anthology publication and will no longer have to be as aggressive as they were. In addition to their schools and regional collections they run three magazines, *Poetry Now, Triumph Herald* (which specialises in Christian verse) and *Rhyme Arrival*, have their own bookshop, *The Garret* in Warwick, a print and design service for self-publishers, and *Poetry Now Introducing* – a series of books from single authors. **Need2Know**, their how-to imprint has a range of titles for new writers, including poets while their **Writers' Bookshop** imprint publishes a useful series of guides to the small magazines of Britain, America and Australia along with a directory of mainstream publishers and a guide to prizes, grants and bursaries. If *Poetic Enlightenment From The Midlands* sounds like your scene send for the group's newsletters (1-2 Wainman Road, Woodston, Peterborough PE2 7BU), ring them (01733 230751) or e-mail your request (pete@forwardpress.co.uk). You'll find no dubious accommodation address dealing here, but on the other hand, few literary giants either.

Envious of Forward's success at catching the hearts and minds of most of the UK's poetry hobbyists a good number of rival operations have risen in their wake. Regional poetry anthologies, Best of Britain collections, compendiums of English, Scottish, Irish and Welsh verse abound. Contributions are sourced through notices on library walls, local free-sheets, local radio and through direct mail. These operations vary from the glossy to a number of pathetically produced and, one hopes, short-lived incarnations based in the non-metropolitan sticks. No actual rip-off occurs and contributors get in whether they purchase or not. But if you want to see your work then you must buy and the books can cost upwards of twenty pounds. Before agreeing to contribute check the press's output. Do not submit blindly, research their back list. It is what Faber would demand of you. The rule applies to the whole poetry scene.

The small press and the little magazine

Hobbyist publishing ventures have been with us for quite a long time. Virginia Woolf began the **Hogarth Press** this way, quite literally on the kitchen table. But it was not until well after the Second War and the rise of the transatlantic mimeo revolution that amateur poetry magazine and pamphlet publication really took off. And recent advances have seen that revolution overturned again. Technologically literate poets are everywhere. Publishing has been stripped of its mystery. Access to laser printers and the computers that drive them are commonplace. Desk-Top Publishing and Word Processing software make it so easy to do. Disposable income has gone up. Poets in growing numbers are able and willing to establish competent one-person publishing operations, turning out neat, professional-looking titles on a considerable scale.

These are the small presses and little magazines. They sell to new and often non-traditional markets rarely finding space on bookshop shelves, where they are regarded as unshiftable nuisances. Professional distribution is still the age old problem. Instead, small mags go hand-to-hand among friends, at poetry readings, creative writing classes, literary functions, via subscriptions, and are liberally exchanged among all those concerned. The network is large. The question remains: is anyone out there not directly concerned with the business of poetry actually reading it? But that is another story.

Statistically, the small presses and the little magazines are the largest publishers of new poetry both in terms of range and circulation. They operate in a bewildering blur of shapes and sizes everywhere from Brighton to Birmingham and Aberystwyth to Aberdeen. Check out the **Association of Little Presses** (see **Professional Associations**) who produce a regular catalogue of member's output along with *PALPI*, a new publications listings magazine. Derrick Woolf's fine *Poetry Quarterly Review* (Coleridge Cottage, Nether Stowey, Somerset TA5 1NQ) carries regular reviews, as does Andy Cox's *Zene* (5 Martins Lane, Witcham, Ely, Cambs CB6 2LB) and Gerald England's *New Hope International* (20 Werneth Avenue, Gee Cross, Hyde, Cheshire). There are others. The **National Small Press Centre** (see **Organisations**) also provides information.

This country's best poetry magazines all began as classic littles. Between them *PN Review, Ambit, Agenda, Outposts, Orbis, Poetry Review, Rialto, Acumen, Staple, The North, Smiths Knoll, Envoi* and *Stand* do not come up to even half the circulation of journals like *Shooting Times* and *Practical Fishkeeping* – which says a lot about the way society values its poetry. Nonetheless, taken as a group, they will get to almost everyone who matters. They represent poetry as a whole. Read this group and you will get some idea of where the cutting edge is. In the second division in terms of kudos lie the regional or genre specialists such as *Lines Review* (Scottish poetry), *Poetry Ireland, The New Welsh Review, Poetry Wales, Queer Words* (the magazine of new lesbian and gay writing), *Psycopoetica* (psychologically based poetry), *Krax* (humorous verse), *Writing Women, Christian Poetry Review, Haiku Quarterly* and *Poetry Manchester.* All these magazines are well produced, sometimes with the help of grants, and all represent a specific point of view. In Wales there is *Barddas* for poets using the strict meters and in Scotland *Lallans* for poets working in Lowland Scots. The vast majority of small magazines, however, owe no allegiance and range from fat irregulars like *Bête Noir* (reputed to be the worst responder in the UK), quality general round ups like *Tabla, Headlock, Tears In The Fence, Obsessed With Pipework* (high-wire poetry) and *Seam* (small enough to slide up your sleeve), to pamphlets like *The Yellow Crane* (interesting new poems), *The Cadmium Blue Literary Journal* (spearhead of the romantic renaissance), *Iota* (recent poetry), *Poetry Monthly* (run by poets for poets), The *Wide Skirt* (at least 50% accepted from the mailbox), *Slipstream* (risktakers welcome) and *Pulsar* (thoughts, comments and observations). Some like *Prop* want to be both dynamic and eclectic, *Sub Voicive* doesn't like you smoking while *The News That Stays News* is a private affair. If you can't find a magazine that suits you and your style then you can't be writing poetry. On the other hand if you are really sure you are then start your own.

Among the small presses there is a similar range. **Oasis** dips its toe in the new wave; Bob Cobbing's venerable **Writers Forum** sticks to mainstream experimental; in Stockton-on-Tees, Mark Robinson has published his final issue of **Scratch** but will continue with books and booklets that track the edges of experimentalism and the Northern School poetic. **Dangaroo, Peepal Tree** and **Totem** have third world and ethnic concerns. **Staple First Editions** insists on the new and unsafe. **Mudfog** excels at twenty-page pamphlets. **Infernal Methods** works with the innovative, as do **Words Worth** and **Microbrigade**. **Redbeck** follows David Tipton's reliable ear with at least a dozen pamphlets each year. **Y Lolfa** publishes unofficial bards. For the new writer these kinds of presses are the obvious place to try first. Indeed it is where many have. Who put out T. S. Eliot's first? A small publisher. Dannie Abse, Peter Redgrove, James Fenton and Dylan Thomas, the same. R. S. Thomas, Ezra Pound and Edgar Allen Poe didn't even go that far – they published themselves.

Cash

A lot of writers new to the business are surprised to learn that their poetry will not make them much money. Being a poet is not really much of an occupation. You get better wages delivering papers. There will be the odd pound from the better heeled magazine, perhaps even as much as £40 or so from those periodicals lucky enough to be in receipt of a grant, but generally it will be free copies of the issues concerned, thank you letters and little more. Those with collections published by a subsidised, specialist publisher can expect a couple of hundred as an advance on royalties. Those using the small presses can look forward to a handful of complimentary copies. The truth is that poetry itself is undervalued. You can earn money writing about it, reviewing it, lecturing on it or certainly by giving public recitations (£100 standard here, £900 if you are Roger McGough, several thousand if you are Ted Hughes). In fact, most things in the poetry business will earn better money than the verse itself. Expect to spend a lot on stamps and a fair bit on sample copies. Most of the time all you'll get in return is used envelopes.

Readings

Since the great Beat Generation, Albert Hall reading of 1964, there has been an ever-expanding phenomenon of poets on platforms, reading or reciting their stuff to an audience that can be anywhere between raptly attentive and fast asleep. Jaci Stephen, writing in *The Daily Mirror*, reckoned readings to be like jazz. 'Both involve a small group of people making a lot of noise, and then, just when you think it's all over, it carries on.' But I believe there can be a magic in the spoken poem. Not everything, certainly. But when it's good it can be sublime. Yet for some writers the whole thing has devolved so far as to become a branch of the entertainment industry. Whichever way you view it, it is certainly an integral part of the business and one in which the beginner is going to need to engage sooner or later. Begin by attending and see how others manage. Watch out for local events advertised at your local library or ring your local arts board. Poets with heavy reputations can often turn out to be lousy performers while many an amateur can really shake it down. Don't expect to catch every image as you listen. Readings are not places for total comprehension but more for glancing blows. Treat it as fun and it will be. If you are trying things yourself for the first time, make sure you've brought your books along to sell, stand upright, drop the shoulders, gaze at a spot at the back of the hall and blow.

Competitions

Poetry competitions have been the vogue for more than a decade now with the most unlikely organisations sponsoring them. The notion here is that anonymity ensures fairness. Entries are made under pseudonyms so that if your name does happen to be Miroslav Holub, then this won't help you much. Results seem to bear this out too. The big competitions run biennially by the **Arvon Foundation** with the help of commercial sponsors, or the **Poetry Society's**

National attract an enormous entry and usually throw up quite a number of complete unknowns among the winners. And why do people bother? Cash prizes can be large – thousands of pounds – but it costs at least a pound a poem to enter, and often much more than that. If it is cash you want, then the Lottery scratch-cards are a better bet. And there has been a trend for winners to come from places like Cape Girardeau, Missouri and Tibooburra, Australia. The odds are getting longer. Who won the last Arvon? I don't remember. But if you do fancy a try then it is a pretty innocent activity. You tie up a poem for a few months and you spend a few pounds. Winners' tips include reading the work of the judges to see how they do it, submitting non-controversial middle-of-the-road smiling things, and doing this just before the closing date so you won't have to wait too long. Try two or three of your best. Huge wodges are costly and will only convince the judges of your insecurity. Watch the small mags for details, write to your regional arts board, check out *The New Writer*, *Poetry London Newsletter*, *Writer's News* or the listings in *Orbis* magazine, look on the notice board at your local library, or write for the regularly updated list from **The Poetry Library** in London (see **Organisations**).

Combining both competition and reading is the Poetry Slam. Here all-comers are given the opportunity to strut their stuff for around three closely-timed minutes before a usually not all that literary crowd. Points are awarded for performance and audience reaction. Scatology and street-wise crowd pleasing are more likely to get you through the rounds than closely-honed work. The ultimate winners get prizes, a slice of the door-take or a donated book. The events, which involve much shouting, can be a lot of fun. Slams have been mounted in places as far apart as Cardiff and Sheffield and the craze is spreading. Even the august **Cheltenham Literary Festival** ran one last year.

Radio and TV

Taking National Poetry Day as a true celebration of poetry in all its forms the BBC, both television and radio, have seen verse as a vehicle for popular entertainment. There have been annual polls for the Nation's Favourite Poem which are shown on BBC1, run on the corporation's website and generally made a huge fuss of with an array of support programmes elsewhere on radio and TV. Newscasters have been heard trying to recite verse they learned in their youth and sports commentary has found itself dotted with poetry about football. Generally, however, coverage is slight. The regular slots are all on radio, naturally enough. It is so hard to make verse visually appealing. Some TV producers have tried, notably Peter Symes who produced both *Poet's News* and *Words On Film* for BBC2. Symes' approach is to avoid the poem illustrated and to concentrate instead on documentary-style collaborations between commissioned poet and film-maker. His great successes have all been with Tony Harrison (who now makes his own films for Channel 4) although projects with Simon Armitage,

Jackie Kay, Lemn Sissay, Fred d'Aquiar and others underline his open approach. Poetry can also occasionally be found ladled between the music on MTV but inevitably by the media-promoted bards such as Murray Lachlan Young. On Radio 3, Fiona McLean produces *Best Words*, an occasional poetry magazine programme fronted by Michael Rosen. It is also worth listening out for the Sunday feature programme on Radio 3 which includes poetry in its range. Radio 1 puts poetry into some of its evening slots, showcasing poets like Simon Armitage and Ian Macmillan. Independent radio are trying verse as fillers. An enlarging but difficult market although the BBC are pretty definite about having no remit to use 'unpublished or amateur verse'. If you are determined to put your verse on air then local radio offers better possibilities. Try sending in self-produced readings on cassette (if you are any good at it) or topical poetry which regional magazine programmes could readily use. Don't expect to be paid much.

Internet

Poetry's current development is its appearance in huge quantity on the Internet. Cyberspace – the place where all this happens – is a mirror of the conventional world. The electronic replicates the real. There are on-line books, magazines, historical and contemporary archives, reference works, and news round-ups. Many dedicate themselves entirely to poetry. They also change almost as fast as the systems they run on. The Internet is enormously volatile. Addresses and providers move here at a much higher rate than they do elsewhere.

Journals – On-line magazines range from those which mirror their print based cousins (and in some cases are simply direct copies) to completely innovative, interactive compilations which mix sound and action with the text. The Net is no static place. It can provide movement, video, sound and user-defined typeface along with actual text. Some mags (e-zines, on-line journals, call them what you will) offer playable recordings of their poets performing, others give space for readers to add criticism. Most use the hyper-link, a method of moving instantly from one section of the site to another. The difference between on-line and print-based magazines becomes more apparent when you discover that what you get when you call them up is not simply the current issue but access to the entire back catalogue. All searchable, storable (put them on your hard drive, onto a floppy disk, print copies out) and, best of all, free.

Geography dissolves on-line. America is no further and no more costly to access than Britain. One of the great mags, *Isibongo*, is based in South Africa. It's just as easy to read as our own Derbyshire market leader, Sean Woodward's *Living Poets* or Mary Buechler's Sacramento *Poetic Express*. In fact, half the time, the user has no idea precisely where the site being accessed is physically based. Place ceases to matter, language takes over.

How do you contribute? Send your poems by e-mail, no s.a.e. needed. A few brave journals will accept work by snail mail from the not yet connected (*New*

Hope International insists on this method) although most prefer to deal electronically. On-line mag editors hate re-keying, it goes against the grain.

Cyberspace is huge. Some of the sites which list on-line journals, such as *Yahoo's Poetry Page* seems to go on for days. Starting your own mag is easy – frictionless, Microsoft's Bill Gates calls it – and size presents few difficulties. Standards are therefore pretty variable. Not only are the UK's computer literate newbies up there but America, Canada and Australia's too.

Competitions – Naturally there is an on-line variant to the more traditional send five pound and your best work contests. Some actively canvass entries from the un-connected and offer Net publication as the prize. For some poets this will no doubt be sufficient reward. Others accept on-line entries and chose their winners by asking readers to vote – again on-line. Once set-up, contemporary software usually allows the entire process to run automatically. The selling point for all these competitions is the enormous audience supposedly sitting around out there in front of their screens. The potential certainly is large – forty or fifty million users already connected and with more joining every day. Yet how many actually bother to access poetry remains debatable. Still, 22,500 visitors to the *Poetic Express* site every quarter is a few more than the number of *Poetry Review* readers (5000 per issue). *Poetic Express*'s competitions are free. Readers vote for the best poem on the site.

Books – If you tire of contributing to the websites of others then start your own. A whole collection of verse on-line will present relatively little difficulty. Most *ISP*s (Internet Service Providers) now offer an amount of free Web space as part of the subscription. This means that with the aid of some Web authoring software (*HotMetal Pro*, *FrontPage*) or a handbook on *Hyper-Text Mark-Up Language* (html) you can put your work on-line. Hosting your own *home page* is certainly not beyond anyone capable of using conventional computer word processing packages. If you'd like to see the kind of thing that's possible have a look at poet and singer, Labi Siffre's home page, or for that matter my own, *The Peter Finch Archive*. If you are reticent get a fan to set up a site devoted to your works. This has happened to David Gascoyne, to J. H. Prynne, Benjamin Zephaniah and others. Otherwise go to it on your own. If you have a recording of yourself doing your stuff then get one-jump ahead. Put that up there on-site too.

Groups – To reduce the poet's traditional feeling of isolation the Net presents a number of opportunities. World-wide poets, once they've got over the stunning breadth of Net facilities, are usually hard to shut up. E-mail provides one vehicle. Here bands of poets circulate their work, their criticisms and their views of world literature. Join a group (no cost, just ask) and you'll find a daily delivery of e-mails in your in-box. Some groups are moderated which means that contributions are filtered by a controlling individual although most are free-for-alls. Discussion can range from the moronic to the stimulating. *The British and Irish Poets Group* established by Ric Caddel and *Cyber Poets* set-up by Peter Howard are two worth looking at.

A variant on e-mail discussion groups are Usenet Newsgroups. Newsgroups are run through their own dedicated software (provided by your ISP as part of your subscription) and are open to contributions from anyone anywhere. Articles are delivered to your browser for consumption. If you want to contribute then type it up and it's done. The principle poetry newsgroups, *rec.arts.poems* and *alt.arts.poetry. comments*, offer pretty varied fare. By their world-wide nature they tend to be American dominated and standards of contribution are not always that high. But they are places where you can get an instant reaction to your latest poem.

Tools and resources – The Net offers a multitude of these. There are on-line spell-checkers (in many languages), thesauri, an anagram creator, a rhyming dictionary. The archives of universities (particularly in America) offer the great poetry of the past in comprehensive quantity. Download facsimile editions of *The Germ* (the first ever poetry magazine from 1850) or hear Seamus Heaney recite. Read the complete works of Blake, find out what powered the Beat generation, discover how Hardy worked, check the roots of modern verse. Not only can you find the texts themselves but entire critical apparatuses, historical contexts, biographies, bibliographies, portraits, names of lovers, and shoe sizes for most of the great poets of the world. You can access information on poetry readings or check at the British Council for data on literature festivals. Students seems to revel in posting their dissertations. Archives want their knowledge made available to everyone. Interested in a particular style? Haiku? Visual poetry? Traditional forms? They've all got their sites.

How to find them – Internet *search engines* are vast, free-to-use, on-line databases which allow users to track down their interests by either key words or subject type. The big ones, such as *Yahoo, InfoSeek, Web Crawler, Excite, AltaVista* and *Lycos* hold billions of records. To use them you need to be specific in your request. I tried keying 'poetry' in to *AltaVista* and got 149,529 results. Much easier is to log onto one of a number of poetry resource sites which run clickable lists of relevant pages. The UK Poetry Society, The Poetry Library and the *Poetry Review*'s 'web watcher' Peter Howard's home page are worth consulting.

Where next? – Change on the Net is dynamic. New forms and ideas arrive all the time. As I write, the possibilities of on-line real-time broadcasting are being explored. The Chicago based *Telepoetics* group are experimenting with video-conferencing poetry and setting up what they call 'Internet Bridges' which link audiences and poets worldwide. The *hypertext link* has given birth to a poetry form known as hyper-verse which exploits the way in which a reader moves across Internet text. The *Poetry Web Ring* links poetry pages (and parts of pages) world-wide. Follow it and you'll be up for days stuffing your head with verse. The opportunities for poets are as huge as the Net itself. Get involved now.

Some Web addresses for poets:

British Poets e-mail list   *http://www.mailbase.ac.uk/lists/british-poets/*
Chadwyck-Healey (poetry database) *http://lion.chadwyck.co.uk*
Electronic Poetry Centre   *http://wings.buffalo.edu/epc*

Isibongo (magazine)	*http://www.uct.ac.za/projects/poetry/* *isibongo/isibongo.htm*
Living Poets (magazine)	*http://dougal.derby.ac.uk/lpoets/*
New Hope International (magazine)	*http://www/nhi.clara.net/nhihome.htm*
Peter Finch Archive	*http://dialspace.dial.pipex.com/peter.finch/*
Peter Howard's Poetry Page	*http://www.hphoward.demon.co.uk*
Poetic Express (magazine)	*http://sacramento-news.com/peindex.htm*
The Poetry Library	*http://www.rfh.org.uk/poetry/index.htm*
Poetry On the Web	*http://www.geocities.com/Paris/1416/*
The Poetry Society (UK)	*http://www/poetrysoc.com/index.htm*
Yahoo Sources for Poetry	*http://www.yahoo.com/Art/Literature/* *Genres/Poetry*

Starting up

Probably the best place will be locally. Find out through the library or the nearest arts board which writers groups gather in your area and attend. There you will meet others of a like mind, encounter whatever locally produced magazines there might be and get a little direct feedback on your work. 'How am I doing?' is a big question for the emerging poet and although criticism is not all that hard to come by, do not expect it from all sources. Magazine editors, for example, will rarely have the time to offer advice. It is also reasonable to be suspicious of that offered by friends and relations – they will no doubt be only trying to please. Writers groups present the best chance for poets to engage in honest mutual criticism. But if you'd prefer a more detached, written analysis of your efforts and are willing to pay a small sum, then you could apply to *The Script,* the service operated nationally by the Poetry Society (22 Betterton Street, London WC2H 9BU), to the service run by The Arts Council of Wales (see **Arts Councils and Regional Arts Boards**) or to those run on an area basis by your local arts board. There are also a number of non-subsidised critical services which you will find advertised in writers' magazines.

If you have made the decision to publish your work – and I don't suppose you'd be reading this if you hadn't – then the first thing to do is some market research. I've already indicated how overstocked the business is with periodicals and publications, yet surprisingly you will not find many of these in your local W. H. Smith. Most new poetry still reaches its public by other routes. However, begin by reading a few newly published mainstream books. Ask at your booksellers for their recommendations. Check Waterstones or Dillons who both do a good job. *Waterstone's Guide to Poetry Books* edited by Nick Rennison is a decent map. Most shops these days carry a basic stock, but if you need a specialist then get hold of the Poetry Library's current list of shops with a specific interest in poetry. Enquire at your local library. Try selecting a recent anthology of contemporary verse. To get a broad view of what's going on, not only should you read

Hulse, Kennedy and Morley's Bloodaxe *The New Poetry* along with Ian Sinclair's *Conductors of Chaos* (Picador) and the new Simon Armitage and Robert Crawford edited Penguin *British and Irish Poetry Since the War* but the annual *Forward Book of Poetry* (Faber); Mike Horovitz's *Grandchildren of Albion* (New Departures); Bob Cobbing's *Verbi Visi Voco* (Writer's Forum); Edward Lucie Smith's Penguin *British Poetry Since 1945*; and perhaps Seamus Heaney and Ted Hughes' *The Rattle Bag* (Faber) or their *The School Bag* (Faber); Jeni Couzyn's *The Bloodaxe Book of Contemporary Women Poets*; Linda France's *Sixty Women Poets* (Bloodaxe); Tony Frazer's *A State Of Independence* (Stride); *From the Other Side of the Century – A New American Poetry 1960-1990* edited by Douglas Messerli (Sun & Moon), and *Postmodern American Poetry,* a really splendid selection edited by Paul Hoover (Norton). These last two might be harder to find but will be worth the effort. Progress to the literary magazine. Write off to a number of the magazine addresses which follow this article and ask the price of sample copies. Enquire about subscriptions. Expect to pay a little but inevitably it will not be a lot. It is important that poets read not only to familiarise themselves with what is currently fashionable and to increase their own facility for self-criticism, but to help support the activity in which they wish to participate. Buy – this is vital for little mags, it is the only way in which they are going to survive. Read; if it's all a mystery to you, try Tony Curtis' *How to Study Modern Poetry* (Macmillan); Matthew Sweeney and John Hartley Williams' *Teach Yourself Writing Poetry*, Peter Sansom's excellent *Writing Poems* (Bloodaxe) or my own *How to Publish Your Poetry* (Allison & Busby). How real poets actually work can be discovered by reading C. B. McCully's the *Poet's Voice and Craft* (Carcanet) or *How Poets Work* (Seren). After all this, if you still think it's appropriate, try sending in.

How to do it

Increase your chances of acceptance by following simple, standard procedure:

- Type or print on a single side of the paper, A4 size, single-spacing with double between stanzas, exactly as you'd wish your poem to appear when printed.
- Give the poem a title, clip multi-page works together, include your name and address at the foot of the final sheet. Avoid files, plastic covers, stiffeners and fancy clips of any sort.
- Keep a copy, make a record of what you send where and when, leave a space to note reaction.
- Send in small batches – six is a good number – with a brief covering letter saying who you are. Leave justification, apology and explanation for your writers group.
- Include a self-addressed, stamped envelope of sufficient size for reply and/or return of your work.
- Be prepared to wait some weeks for a response. Don't pester. Be patient. Most magazines will reply in the end.

- Never send the same poem to two places at the same time.
- Send your best. Work which fails to fully satisfy even the author is unlikely to impress anyone else.

Where?

Try the list which follows, sending for samples as suggested. The total market is vast – 200 or so addresses here – hundreds more in *Small Presses and Little Magazines of the UK and Ireland* (enquiries to **Academi Literature Promotion** – see **Organisations**), the *Small Press Guide* (which only covers journals – Writers' Bookshop, 7-11 Kensington High Street, London W8 5NP) and in *Light's List of Literary Magazines* which contains both UK and US addresses (John Light, The Lighthouse, 29 Longfield Road, Tring, Hertfordshire HP23 4DG), literally thousands and thousands worldwide in Christine Martin's *Poet's Market* (Writer's Digest Books) and Len Fulton's *Directory of Poetry Publishers* (Dustbooks) – the two main American directories.

Scams and cons

With poetry overpopulated by participants it is not surprising that the con artist should make an appearance. There are plenty of people out there taking money off beginner writers and offering very little in return. The traditional vanity anthology, once the staple of the trickster, is fortunately in retreat. With this scam classified small ads ask poets to contribute to a forthcoming anthology of verse. All work submitted is accepted, poets are told they have 'unusual and high potential' and are then asked to 'contribute fifty pounds to help offset ever increasing publishing costs'. There are no value judgements made yet poets are led to believe that they have in some way succeeded. The scam has been around for decades. In the sixties TV host Bernard Brayden submitted cut-ups of the local newspaper, a shopping list, two Shakespearean sonnets and the scribblings of a six-year old. The lot were accepted. More recently the **National Poetry Foundation**'s Johnathon Clifford tested the market by sending in grossly amateur items in the tradition of William McGonagall. He was amazed to receive a sheaf of letters praising him as a poet of real worth, suggesting that in 'partnership' they should go right ahead and publish his shining verses and could he find his way to stump up the odd £3000 to help pay the bills. If Clifford had been a real beginner he might have fallen for the deal, sold the family silver and invested in what sadly would have turned out to be a no-hope project where the books would languish unsold, unwanted and unread in a distant warehouse or more likely under the author's bed. Instead Clifford wrote up his experiences (*Vanity Press & The Proper Poetry Publishers*) and began a one-man campaign against the vanity industry of back-street operators, accommodation addresses, and abandoned value judgements. You get published by the vanity presses because you pay and not because you are any good. Clifford has chased doggedly after his foe recruiting supporters, including the Advertising Standards Authority, the Office of Fair Trading and the Committee of Advertising Practice. Rogue traders now find it much harder to place their adverts, newspapers, once conduits for the scheme's of vanity publishers, now run stories exposing them. Poets can once again sleep peacefully in their beds.

Wish that they could. Already variations and embellishments on the vanity press theme are surfacing. These include offers to put your poetry to music setting you off on the road to stardom, readings of your verse by actors with deep voices to help you break into the local radio market (there isn't one) and further requests for cash to have entries on you appear in leather-bound directories of world poets. Everyone appears, including your uncle. There is a huge rash of bogus competitions where entry fees bear no relation to final prize money and the advertised 'publication of winners in anthology form' often means shelling out more for what will turn out to be a badly printed abomination crammed full of weak work. Poets should look very carefully at anything which offers framed certificates, scrolls or engraved wall hangings. They should also be wary of suggestions that they have come high in the State of Florida's Laureateship Contest (or some such like) and have been awarded a calligraphed testimonial. Presentation usually occurs at a three-day festival held in one of state's most expensive hotels. To get your bit of paper you need to stay for all three days and it is you who has to settle the bill.

How do you spot the tricksters? They change their names and addresses at will. They bill themselves as Foundations, Societies, Libraries, National Associations, Guilds. They sound so plausible. If you have the slightest suspicion then check with the Poetry Society (see **Organisations**). In the poetry world genuine advertisements for contributions are rare. And if anyone asks you for money then forget it. It is not the way things should be done.

The next step

Once you have placed a few poems you may like to consider publishing a booklet. There are as many small presses around as there are magazines. Start with the upmarket professionals by all means – Jonathan Cape, Faber & Faber – but be prepared for compromise. The specialists and the small presses are swifter and more open to new work.

If all else fails you could do it yourself. Blake did, so did Walt Whitman. Modern technology puts the process within the reach of us all and if you can put up a shelf, there is a fair chance you will be able to produce a book to go on it. Read my *How to Publish Yourself* (Allison & Busby), Peter Domanski's *A Practical Guide To Publishing Books using Your PC* (Domanski-Irvine Books) and Jonathan Zeitlyn's *Print: How You Can Do It Yourself* (Journeyman). Remember that publishing the book may be as hard as writing it but marketing and selling it is quite something else. Check Alison Baverstock's *How To Market Books* (**Kogan Page**) if you really want to get ahead.

The listings

None of the lists of addresses which follow are exhaustive. Publishers come and go with amazing frequency. There will always be the brand new press on the look-out for talent and the projected magazine desperate for contributions. For up to the minute information check some of the **Organisations of Interest to Poets**. Poetry has a huge market. It pays to keep your ear to the ground. Note that not all of the presses and magazines listed welcome unsolicited contributions – enquire first (and include an s.a.e.).

Poetry Presses

Acumen Publications See also **Acumen** magazine, *Patricia Oxley*, 6 The Mount, Higher Furzeham, Brixham, S. Devon TQ5 8QY

Agenda Editions See also **Agenda** magazine, *William Cookson & others*, 5 Cranbourne Court, Albert Bridge Road, London SW11 4PE

Aireings Press See also **Aireings** magazine, *Jean Barker*, 3/24 Brudenell Road, Leeds, West Yorkshire LS6 1BD

Akros Publications *Duncan Glen*, 33 Lady Nairn Avenue, Kirkcaldy, Fife

Alfred David Editions 3a Palace Road, London SW2 3DY

Allardyce, Barnett, Publishers See under **Small Presses**

Aloes Books *Jim Pennington & others*, 110 Mountview Road, London N4 4JH

Alun Books (includes Goldleaf & Barn Owl Press) *Sally Jones*, 3 Crown Street, Port Talbot, West Glamorgan SA13 1BG

Amazing Colossal Press *Maureen Richardson*, PO Box 177, Nottingham NG3 5SU

Amra Imprint *Bill Griffiths*, 21 Alfred Street, Seaham, Co. Durham SR7 7LH

Anarcho Press *Stan Trevor*, Briagha, Badninish, Dornoch, Sutherland IV25 3JB

Angel Press See also **Anarchist Angel Youth Poetry Quarterly**, *Philip Berr*, 41 Rosewood Park, Cheslyn Hay, Staffordshire WS6 7HP

Ankle Books 153 Gwydir Street, Cambridge CB1 2LJ

Anvil Press Poetry (anvil@cix.compulink.co.uk) See under **UK Publishers**

Appliance Books *Tabitha Webb*, 1 Bolton Lane, Ipswich, Suffolk 1PX 2BX

Aramby Publishing *Mal Cieslak*, 1 Alanbrooke Close, Knaphill, Surrey GU21 2RU

Arc Publications See under **UK Publishers**

Argyll Publishing Glendaruel, Argyll PA22 3AE

Avalanche Books *Deborah Gaye*, 125 Derricke Road, Stockwood, Bristol

Aylesford Press *D. A. Ashton*, 158 Moreton Road, Upton, Wirral, Cheshire LA9 4NZ

Basil Bunting Poetry Centre Durham University Library, Palace Green, Durham HD1 3RN

The Bay Press 7 Collingwood Terrace, Whitley Bay, North Yorks NE26 2NP

BB Books See also **Global Tapestry Journal**, *Dave Cunliffe*, Springbank, Longsight Road, Copster Green, Blackburn, Lancs BB1 9EU

Bedlam Press *David Moody*, Church Green House, Old Church Lane, Pately Bridge, Harrogate, North Yorks HG3 5LZ

Bellew Publishing See under **UK Publishers**

The Benjamin Press *Douglas Clark*, 69 Hillcrest Drive, Bath BA2 1HD

Beyond the Cloister *Hugh Hellicar*, Flat 1, 14 Lewes Crescent, Brighton, East Sussex

The Black Gate Press *John Spence*, 25 York Close, Cramlington, Northumberland NE23 9RN

Blackstaff Press See under **UK Publishers**

Blackwater Press 17 Holbrook Road, Leicester LE2 3LG

Blaxland Family Press *John Jarrett* 12 Matthews Road, Taunton, Somerset TA1 4NH

Bloodaxe Books (editor@bloodaxebooks.demon.uk) See under **UK Publishers**

Blue Cage See also **Blue Cage** magazine, 98 Bedford Road, Birkdale, Southport, Merseyside PR8 4HL

Blue Nose Press 32 Northolme Road, London N5

Bogle-L'Ouverture Press Ltd *Valerie Bloom*, PO Box 2186, London W13 9ZQ

Brentham Press *Margaret Tims* 40 Oswald Road, St Albans, Herts AL1 3AQ

Businesslike Publishing See under **Small Presses**

Carcanet Press (pnr@carcanet.u-net.com) See also **PN Review** and under **UK Publishers**

Celandine Press Halford Lodge, Halford, Shipston-on-Stour, Warwickshire CV36 5DQ

Chapman Press See also **Chapman** magazine under **Magazines**, *Joy Hendry*, 4 Broughton Place, Edinburgh EH1 3RX

Cherybite Publications 45 Burton Road, Little Neston, South Wirral L64 4AE

Chilli Pepper Press Latin American Writers & Theatre Company, 4 Mawson Road, Cambridge CB1 2AC

Chotriffid Books *K. V. Bailey*, 1 Val De Mer, Alderney, Channel Islands CN9 3YR

The Chrysalis Press 11 Convent Close, Kenilworth, Warwickshire CV8 2FQ

Chudbury Books *David Southall*, 5 Fairhaven, Yate BS17 4DS

Clocktower Press 27 Alfred Street, Stromness, Orkney KW16 3DF

Cloud *Michael Thorpe*, 48 Biddleston Road, Heaton, Newcastle upon Tyne NE6 5SL

Coelecanth Press *Maurice Scully*, 21 Corrovorrin Grove, Ennis, Co Clare, Eire

The Collective (blind.cwm@aol.com) *John Jones*, Penlanlas Farm, Llantilio Pertholey, Y-fenni, Gwent NP7 7HN

Commonword See also **Crocus Books**, *Deyike Nezribe*, Cheetwood House, 21 Newton Street, Manchester M1 1FZ

Company of Poets Books Oversteps, Froude Road, Salcombe, S. Devon TQ8 8LH

The Corbie Press 57 Murray Street, Montrose, Angus DD10 8JZ

Cottage Books Publications *Patricia Batstone*, 5 Foxglove Close, Highfield, Dunkeswell, Honiton, Devon EX14 0QE

Crabflower Pamphlets See also **The Frogmore Press** and **The Frogmore Papers** magazine, *Jeremy Page*, 42 Morehall Avenue, Folkstone, Kent CT19 4EF

Creation Books 83 Clerkenwell Road, London EC1M 5RJ

Credo Publishing *Annie Manning*, 45 Melsted Road, Boxmoor, Hemel Hempstead, Herts HP1 1SX

Crescent Moon Publishing See under **Small Presses**, and **Passion** magazine

Crocus Books (Imprint of **Commonword**) *Cathy Bolton*, Cheetwood House, 21 Newton Street, Manchester M1 1FZ

Curfew Press *John Citizen*, 112 Sunnyhill Road, Streatham, London SW16 2UL

Cwm Nedd Press *Robert King*, 16 Rhydhir, Neath Abbey, Neath SA10 7HP

Dagger Press 70 Dagger Lane, West Bromwich B71 4BS

Damnation Publications (kerry@peepal.demon.co.uk) *Kerry Sowerby*, 2 Midland Road, Leeds, West Yorks LS6 1BQ

Dangaroo Press See also **Kunapipi** magazine, PO Box 20, Hebden Bridge, West Yorks HX7 5UZ

Da'th Scholarly Dervices/Darengo Publications 31b Northbury Crescent, London SW16 4JS

Day Dream Press See also **Haiku Quarterly** magazine *Kevin Bailey*, 39 Exmouth Street, Swindon, Wilts SN1 3PU

Dedalus Press/Peppercanister Books *John F. Deane*, 24 The Heath, Cypress Downs, Dublin 6, Eire

Deucalion Press *D. S. Savage*, 67 Church Street, Mevagissy, St Austell, Cornwall PL26 6SR

Diamond Press *G. Godbert*, 5 Berners Mansions, 34–36 Berners Street, London W1P 3DA

Dido Press *Diane Thomas*, 2 Pelham Street, London SW7 2NG

Diehard Publishers *Ian King & others*, Grindles Bookshop, 3 Spittal Street, Edinburgh EH3 9DY

Dilettante Publications Little Bystock, Bystock Close, Exeter, Devon EX4 4JJ

Dionysia Press Ltd See also **Understanding** magazine, *Denise Smith*, 20a Montgomery Street, Edinburgh EH7 5JS

Dissident Editions *Frederik Wolff,* 71 Ballyculter Road, Loughkeelan, Downpatrick, Co. Down BT30 7BD

Dog 32b Brakespears Road, London SE4 1JW

Dog and Bone Publishers 175 Queen Victoria Drive, Scotstown, Glasgow G12 9BP

Dragonfly Press 2 Charlton Cottages, Barden Road, Speldhurst, Kent TN3 0LH

Drasc Limited 33 Marlborough Road, Swindon, Wilts SN13 1PH

Ellerton Press PO Box 354, Newcastle under Lyme ST5 4NH

Enitharmon Press See under **UK Publishers**

Equinox Press Sinodum House, Shalford, Braintree, Essex CM7 5MW

Equipage *Rod Mengham,* Jesus College, Cambridge CB5 8BL

Eros Press See also **Interactions** magazine, *Andrew Yardwell,* PO Box 250, St Helier, Jersey, Channel Islands JE4 8TZ

Etruscan Books *Nicholas Johnson,* 24a Fore Street, Buckfastleigh, South Devon TQ11 0AA

Evelyn Press *C. Gage,* 80 Evelyn Road, Otford, Sevenoaks, Kent TN14 5PU

Farrago Collective Press 106 High Street, West Wickham, Kent BR4 0ND

Fatchance Press See also **Fatchance** magazine, Elm Court, East Street, Sheepwash, Beaworthy EX21 5NL

Feather Books See under **Small Presses** and also **The Poetry Church** magazine

Fern Publications See also **Dandelion Arts Magazine** *Jacqueline Gonzalez-Marina,* 24 Frosty Hollow, East Hunsbury, Northants NN4 0SY

Fire River Poets 19 Green Close, Holford, Bridgwater, Somerset TA5 1SB

First Class Publications PO Box 1799, London W9 2BZ

First Time Publications See also **First Time** magazine, *Josephine Austin,* 4 Burdett Place, George Street, Hastings, East Sussex TN34 3ED

Five Leaves Publications See under **Small Presses**

Five Seasons Press Wickton Court, Stoke Prior, Leominster, Herefordshire HR6 0LN

Flambard Press *Peter Elfed Lewis,* Stable Cottage, East Fourstones, Hexham, Northumberland NE47 5DY

Forest Books *Brenda Walker* 20 Forest View, Chingford, London E4 7AY

Form Books *Harry Gilonis,* 42a Lowden Road, London SE24 0BH

Forward Press *Ian Walton,* 1–2 Wainman Road, Woodston, Peterborough, Cambs. PE2 7BU

Fox Press/Winter Sweet Press *Beryl Bron,* Oak Tree, Main Road, Colden Common, Nr Winchester, Hants SO21 1TL

The Frogmore Press See also **Crabflower Pamphlets** press and **The Frogmore Papers** magazine, *Jeremy Page,* 42 Morehall Avenue, Folkestone, Kent CT19 4EF

Gallery Press *Peter Fallon,* Loughcrew, Oldcastle, County Meath, Eire

Gekko Press *Anne Bailey,* 30b Stanmer Street, Battersea, London SW11 3BG

Get Connected Press 342 Hartshill Road, Hartshill, Stoke on Trent, Staffs ST4 7NX

Gill's Verse Publications *Gillian Rose Pearce,* 25 Braden Road, Penn, Wolverhampton WV4 4JR

Gisgog Books *Natasha Vann,* 70 Sycamore Avenue, Boythorpe, Chesterfield, Derbyshire S40 2PS

Golgonooza Press *Brian Keeble,* 3 Cambridge Drive, Ipswich, Suffolk IP2 9EP

Gomer Press/Gwasg Gomer See under **UK Publishers**

Gorse Publications *Pat Earnshaw,* PO Box 214, Shamley Green, Guildford, Surrey GU5 0SW

Green Branch Press Kencot Lodge, Kencot, Lechlade, Glos GL7 3QX

Green Lantern Press 9 Milner Road, Wisbech, Cambridge PE12 2LR

Grevatt & Grevatt See under **Small Presses**

Greylag Press *Jim Vollmar,* 2 Grove Street, Higham Ferrars, Rushden, Northants NN10 8HX

Gruffyground Press *Anthony Baker,* Ladram, Sidcot, Winscombe, Somerset BS25 1PW

Gryphon Press *Barbara Beazeley,* 28 Prince Edwards Road, Lewes, East Sussex BN7 1BE

Hangman Books *Jack Ketch,* 2 May Road, Rochester, Kent ME1 2HY

Hard Pressed Poetry *Billy Mills,* 11 Watermeadow Park, Old Bawn, Tallaght, Dublin 24, Eire

Hastings Arts Pocket Press/Pickpockets *Margaret Rose,* 25 St Mary's Terrace, Hastings, East Sussex TN34 3LS

Headland Publications *Gladys Mary Coles,* Ty Coch, Galltegfa, Ruthin, Clwyd LL15 2AR

Hearing Eye *John Rety,* Box 1, 99 Torriano Avenue, London NW5 2RX

Here Now *Tom Kelly*, 69 Wood Terrace, Jarrow, Tyne & Wear NE32 5LU

Heron Press 16 Barracks Square, Newcastle under Lyme, North Staffs ST5 1LG

The Hiccup Press 160 Plantsbrook Road, Walmley, Sutton Coldfield B76 1HL

Highcliff Press See under **Small Presses**

Hillside Books See also **Linear A** magazine, *Johan De Wit*, Flat 1, Sylva Court, 81 Putney Hill, London SW15 3NX

Hilltop Press (science fiction poetry) *Steve Sneyd*, 4 Nowell Place, Almondbury, Huddersfield, West Yorks HD5 8PD

Hippopotamus Press See also **Outposts Poetry Quarterly** *Roland John*, 22 Whitewell Road, Frome, Somerset BA11 4EL

Honno *Elin Ap Hywel*, Alisa Craig, Heol Y Cawl, Dinas Powys, S. Glamorgan CF6 4AH

Hub Editions *Jill Bamber*, 9 Western Road, East Finchley, London N2 9JB

Hunter House – Anachoresis *J. E. Rutherford*, 36 Lisburn Street, Hillsborough, Co Down BT26 6AB

I*D Books *Clive Hopwood*, Connah's Quay Library, High Street, Connah's Quay, Deeside, Clwyd

Ibid Press See also **Ibid** magazine *Matthew Hollis*, Dept of English Literature, University of Edinburgh, David Hume Tower, George Square, Edinburgh EH8 9JX

Icon Press *Philip Brown*, 71 Northbourne Road, Eastbourne, East Sussex BN22 8QP

Infernal Methods See also **The Many Press** *John Welch*, 15 Norcott Road, London N16 7BJ

Ink Sculptors/Cult Productions *Patricia Scanlan*, 34 Waldemar Avenue, Fulham, London SW6 5NA

International Concrete Poetry Archive *Paula Claire*, 11 Dale Close, Thames Street, Oxford OX1 1TU

Invisible Books *B. Oenney*, BM Invisible, London WC1N 3XX

Iron Press *Peter Mortimer*, 5 Marden Terrace, Cullercoats, North Shields, Tyne & Wear NE30 4PD

Isle of Wight Poetry Society Spindrift, Heathfield Road, Freshwater, Isle of Wight PO40 9SH

Jackson's Arm See **Sunk Island Publishing** under **Small Presses** and **Sunk Island Review** magazine *Michael Blackburn*, PO Box 74, Lincoln LN1 1QG

Jayol Publications 145 Saintfield Road, Lisburn, Co. Antrim BT27 6UH

Jester Press 46 The Avenue, St George, Bristol BS5 8HW

Joe's Press See also **Passion** magazine and **Crescent Moon Publishing** under **Small Presses**

Jugglers Fingers Press See also **Uncompromising Positions** magazine, *Cheryl Wilkinson*, 92 Staneway, Leam Lane, Gateshead, Tyne & Wear NE10 8LS

Kami Kazi Publications 31 Belle Vue Street, Filey, East Yorks YO14 9HU

Katabasis *Dinah Livingstone*, 10 St Martin's Close, London NW1 0HR

Kawabata Press See also **Sepia** magazine Knill Cross House, Knill Cross, Millbrook, Near Torpoint, Cornwall PL10 1DX

Kernow Poets Press See also **Links** magazine, *Bill Headon*, Bude Haven, 18 Frankfield Rise, Tunbridge Wells, Kent TN2 5LF

Kettleshill Press PO Box 38, Wirral, Merseyside L20 6NS

King of Hearts *Aude Gotto*, 13-15 Fye Bridge Street, Norwich, Norfolk NR3 1LJ

Klinker Zoundz *Hugh Metcalfe*, 10 Malvern House, Stamford Hill Estate, London N16 6RR

The KQBX Press *Malcolm Povey*, 124 Carberry Avenue, Bournemouth BH6 3LH

Kropotkin's Lighthouse Publications *Jim Huggon* 59 Leiston Road, Knodishall, Suffolk IP17 1UQ

K. T. Publications See also **The Third Half** magazine, *Kevin Troop*, 16 Fane Close, Stamford, Lincolnshire PE9 1HG

Language Alive See also **Sound & Language** magazine, (cris@slang.demon. co.uk) *Chris Cheek*, 85 London Road South, Lowestoft, Suffolk NR33 0AS

The Lansdowne Press 33 Lansdowne Place, Hove, East Sussex BN3 1HF

Lapwing Publications *Dennis & Rene Greig*, 1 Ballysillan Drive, Belfast BT14 8HQ

Last Ever Melodic Scribble Press 35 Kearsey Road, Sheffield S2 4TE

Laurel Books 282 The Common, Holt, Wiltshire BA14 6QJ

Lewes Live Literature *Mark C. Hewitt*, All Saints Arts Centre, Friars Walk, Lewes, East Sussex BN7 2LE

Libanus Press *Christopher Driver*, 6 Church Road, London N6 4QT

Ligden Publishers See also **Pulsar** magazine, *Jill Meredith*, 34 Linacre Close, Grange Park, Swindon, Wiltshire SN5 6DA

The Lilliput Press 12 Christopher Close, Norwich, Norfolk NR1 2PQ

Lobby Press *Richard Tabor*, Simonburn Cottage, Sutton Montis, Yeovil, Somerset BA22 7HF

Lomond Press *R. L. Cook*, Whitecraigs, Kinnesswood, Kinross KY13 7JN

Lothian Press 43 Ickburgh Road, London E5 8AF

Lung Gom Press 2 Henderson Street, Kingseat, Dunfermline, Fife KY12 0TP

The Lymes Press *Alex Crossley*, Greenfields, Agger Hill, Finney Green, Newcastle under Lyme, Staffs ST5 6AA

Magenta *Maggie O'Sullivan*, Middle Fold Farm, Colden, Heptonstall, Hebden Bridge, West Yorks HX7 7PG

Mainstream See also **RWC** press and **Sub Voicive Poetry** magazine, *Lawrence Upton*, 32 Downside Road, Sutton, Surrey SM2 5HP

Making Waves *Anthony Selbourne*, PO Box 226, Guildford, Surrey GU3 1EW

Malfunction Press See also **Bardonni/Stopgap/Songs** magazine *Peter E. Presford*, Rose Cottage, 3 Tram Lane, Buckley, Clwyd

Mammon Press *Fred Beake*, 12 Dartmouth Avenue, Bath BA2 1AT

Mandeville Press *Peter Scupham & others*, Old Hall, Norwich Road, South Burlingham, Norfolk NR13 4EY

The Many Press See also **Infernal Methods** press, *John Welch*, 15 Norcott Road, London N16 7BJ

Marc Goldring Books PO Box 250, St Helier, Jersey, Channel Islands JE4 5PU

Mariscat Press *Hamish Whyte & others*, 3 Mariscat Road, Glasgow G41 4ND

Marvell Press c/o 2 Kelly Gardens, Calstock, Cornwall PL18 9SA

Maypole Editions See under **Small Presses**

Melinga Publishing *Christopher M. Balston*, 56 Yardley Court, Hemingford Road, North Cheam, Surrey SM3 8HL

Menard Press *Anthony Rudolf*, 8 The Oaks, Woodside Avenue, London N12 8AR

Microbrigade See also **Garuda** magazine, *Ulli Freer*, 7 Highwood Avenue, London N12 8QL

MidNag Publications See also **The Northern Poetry Library** under **Organisations**. Leisure Dept, Wansbeck Square, Ashington, Northumberland NE63 9XL

Morning Star Publications *Alex Finlay*, 17 Gladstone Terrace, Edinburgh EH9 1LS

Moschatel Press *Thomas A. Clarke*, Iverna Cottage, Rockness Hill, Nailsworth, Gloucester

Mr Pillow's Press See also **Apostrophe** magazine, *Diana Andersson*, 41 Canute Road, Faversham, Kent ME13 8SH

Mudflat Press *M.U. Fiorillo*, 176 Clive Street, Grangetown, Cardiff CF1 7JG

Mudfog 11 Limes Road, Linthorpe, Middlesbrough TS5 7QR

Mushroom Press 48 Dryclough Road, Beaumont Park, Huddersfield, West Yorks HD4 5JA

National Poetry Foundation See also **Pause** magazine, *Johnathon Clifford & others*, 27 Mill Road, Fareham, Hants PO16 0TH

Naturama Publications 42 Pinner Court, Pinner Road, Pinner, Middx HA5 5RJ

NDA Press *Natalie D'Arbeloff*, 6 Lady Somerset Road, London NW5 1UT

New Albion Press *David Geall*, 42 Overhill Road, London SE22 0PH

New Departures See also **New Departures** magazine, *Michael Horowitz*, Piedmont, Bisley, Gloucestershire GL6 7BU

New Hope International *Gerald England*, 20 Werneth Avenue, Gee Cross, Hyde, Cheshire SK14 5NL

New River Project See also **Writers Forum** press and **And** magazine, *Bob Cobbing & others*, 89a Petherton Road, London N5 2QT

New Writing North *Claire Malcolm*, 9 Black Swan Court, Westgate Road, Newcastle upon Tyne NE1 1SG

North and South *Peterjon & Yasmin Skelt*, 9 Grovewood Close, Chorleywood, Hertfordshire WD3 5PU

Northern House Poets See also **Stand** magazine, 19 Haldane Terrace, Newcastle upon Tyne NE2 3AN

Northgate Books *Joseph Clancy*, PO Box 106, Aberystwyth, Dyfed SY33 3ZZ

Oasis Books See also **Oasis** magazine, *Ian Robinson*, 12 Stevenage Road, London SW6 6ES

Odyssey Poets See also **PQR** magazine, *Derrick Woolf*, Coleridge Cottage, Nether Stowey, Somerset TA5 1NQ

Oldtown Books/Macprint *Graham Mawhinnes*, 185 Gulladuff Road, Bellaghy, Londonderry BT45 8LW

The Oleander Press, *Philip Ward*, 17 Stansgate Avenue, Cambridge CB2 2QZ

On the Wire Press 6 Orchard Court, Beverley Road, Barnes, London SW13 0NA

Oscars Press *Peter Daniels*, BM Oscars, London WC1N 3XX

The Other Press *Frances Presley* 19b Marriott Road, London N4 3QN

Parataxis *Drew Milne*, School of English Studies, Arts Building, University of Sussex, Falmer, Brighton, E Sussex BN1 9NQ

Pennine Pens (100342.3424@compuserve. com and http://www.eclipse.co.uk/pens) *Chris Ratcliffe*, 32 Windsor Road, Hebden Bridge, West Yorks HX7 8LF

Pennyworth Press *Douglas Evans*, 64 Rosehill Park, Emmer Green, Reading, Berks RG4 8XF

Peppercorn Books *Judith White*, 24 Cromwell Road, Ely, Cambs CB6 1AS

Permanent Press *Robert Vas Dias*, 5b Compton Avenue, Canonbury, London N1 2XD

Perpetua Press 26 Norham Road, Oxford OX2 6SF

Peterloo Poets *Harry Chambers*, 2 Kelly Gardens, Calstock, Cornwall PL18 9SA

The Phlebas Press 7 The Stables, High Park, Oxenholme, Cumbria LA9 7RE

Phoenix Press *Bruce Barnes*, 37 Wilmer Road, Bradford, West Yorks BD9 4RX

Pig Press *Richard Caddel*, 7 Cross View Terrace, Durham DH1 4JY

Pikestaff Press *Robert Roberts*, Elton House, Harpford, Sidmouth, Devon EX10 0NH

Pimp$ of the Alphabet *Glenn Carmichael*, 130c Lower Cheltenham Place, Montpelier, Bristol BS6 5LF

Piscean Press 60 Silam Road, Stevenage, Hertfordshire SG1 8BQ

Pleasure To Be Alive 52 Cissbury Road, Tottenham, London N15 5QA

Pocket Prints *Florence Williams*, 425 Footscray Road, New Eltham, London SE9 3UL

Poet and Printer *Alan Tarling*, 30 Grimsdyke Road, Hatch End, Pinner, Middlesex HA5 4PW

Poetical Histories *Peter Riley*, 27 Sturton Street, Cambridge CB1 2QG

The Poetry Business See also **Smith/Doorstop Books** and **The North** magazine, *Peter Sansom & others*, 51 Byram Arcade, Westgate, Huddersfield, West Yorks HD1 1ND

The Poetry Church Fair View, Old Coppice, Lyth Bank, Shrewsbury, Shropshire SY3 0BW

Poetry Life Publishing See also **Poetry Life Magazine**, 14 Pennington Oval, Lymington, Hants SO41 8BQ

Polygon Books See **Edinburgh University Press** under **UK Publishers** and also **Edinburgh Review** under **Magazines**

Prebendal Publications PO Box 9313. London E17 8LX

Precious Pearl Press See also **Cadmium Blue Literary Journal** and **The People's Poetry** and **Romantic Heir** magazines, *Peter Geoffrey Thompson*, 71 Harrow Crescent, Romford, Essex RM3 7BJ

The Press Upstairs *Giles Goodland*, 360 Cowley Road, Oxford OX4 2AG

Prest Roots Press *P. E. Larkin*, 34 Alpine Court, Lower Ladyes Hill, Kenilworth, Warwickshire CV8 2GP

Pretani Press *Harris Adamson*, 78 Abbey Street, Bangor, Co. Down BT20 4JB

The Previous Parrot Press See under **Small Presses**

Prospero Illustrated Poets Clarion Publishing, Neatham Mill, Holybourne, Alton, Hampshire GU24 4NP

Providence Press (Whitstable) See also **Scriptor** magazine, *John & Lesley Dench*, 22 Plough Lane, Swalecliffe, Whitstable, Kent CT5 2NZ

Psychopoetica Publications See also **Psychopoetica** magazine, *Geoff Lowe*, Dept of Psychology, University of Hull, Hull HU6 7RX

Purple Sandpiper Press *E. Tanguy*, Misson Beau Regard, Five Oaks, Jersey, Channel Islands JE2 7GR

Pyramid Press PO Box 10023, London E9 7UW

Rack Press *N. Murray*, The Rack, Kinnerton, Presteigne, Powys LD8 2PF

Raunchland Publications See also **3x4** magazine, *John Mingay*, 2 Henderson Street, Kingseat, by Dunfermline, Fife KY12 0TP

Raven Arts Press PO Box 1430, Finglass, Dublin 11, Eire

Reality Street Editions *Ken Edwards & others*, 4 Howard Court, Peckham Rye, London SE15 3PH

Red Candle Press See also **Candelabrum Poetry Magazine**, 9 Milner Road, Wisbech, Cambs PE13 2LR

Red Sharks Press *Tôpher Mills*, 122 Clive Street, Grangetown, Cardiff CF1 7JE

Redbeck Press *David Tipton*, 24 Aireville Road, Frizinghall, Bradford, West Yorks BD9 4HH

Rialto Publications See also **The Rialto** magazine, *Michael Mackmin*, PO Box 309, Aylsham, Norwich, Norfolk NR11 6LN

Rive Gauche Publishing *Sheila Yeger*, 69 Lower Redland Road, Bristol BS6 6SP

River Publishing Company, 39 Cumberland Street, London SW1V 4LU

Road Books *Judy Kravis & others,* Garravagh, Inniscarra, Co Cork, Eire

Rockingham Press *David Perman,* 11 Musley Lane, Ware, Herts SG12 7EN

Rubicon Press 57 Cornwall Gardens, London SW7 4BE

Rumney Publishing Co *Graham Jones,* 10 South View Drive, Rumney, Cardiff CF3 8LY

RWC See also **Mainstream** press and **Sub Voicive Poetry** magazine, *Lawrence Upton,* 32 Downside, Sutton, Surrey SM2 5HP

S.A.K.S. Publications 42 Chatsworth Road, London E5 0LP

S. A. Publishing See also **Premonitions, Scar Tissue** and **The Zone** magazines *Tony Lee,* 13 Hazely Combe, Arreton, Isle of Wight PO30 3AJ

S. Editions *Ray Seaford,* 11 Richmond Avenue, Feltham, Middlesex TW14 9SG

Salmon Poetry (salpub@iol.ie) *Jessie Lendennie* Knockeve, Cliffs of Moher, Clare, Eire

Satis *Matthew Mead,* Knoll Hill House, Ampleforth, West End, York YO6 4DU

Saxon Books *David Roberts,* 221 London Road, Burgess Hill, West Sussex RH15 9RN

Scottish Cultural Press See under **Small Presses**

Scratch Publications *Mark Robinson,* 9 Chestnut Road, Eaglescliffe, Stockton-on-Tees TS16 0BA

Sea Dream Music/Polyptoton *Keith Dixon,* 236 Sebert Road, Forest Gate, London E7 0NP

Seren Books See under **UK Publishers** and **Poetry Wales** magazine

Shearsman Books See also **Shearsman** magazine, *Tony Frazer,* 47 Dayton Close, Plymouth, Devon PL6 5DX

Shell Press See also **Unicorn** magazine, *Alex Warner,* 12 Milton Avenue, Millbrook, Stalybridge, Cheshire SK15 3HB

Ship of Fools See also **Pages** magazine, *Robert Sheppard,* 78 Nicander Road, Liverpool 18

Shoestring Press 19 Devonshire Avenue, Beeston, Nottingham NG9 1BS

SKB Books 115 Victoria Road, Mablethorpe LN12 2AL

Skoob Books Publishing Ltd See under **UK Publishers**

Slow Dancer Press (john@mellotone.co.uk and www.mellotone.co.uk) *John Harvey,* 59 Parliament Hill, London NW3 2TB

Smith/Doorstop Books See also **The Poetry Business** press and **The North** magazine, *Peter Sansom & others,* The Studio, Byram Arcade, Westgate, Huddersfield, West Yorks HD1 1ND

Sol Publications See also **Sol Poetry Magazine,** *Malcolm E. Wright,* 58 Malvern, Coleman Street, Southend on Sea, Essex SS2 5AD

Somniloquence Publishing *Lee Freeman,* 25 Broadwater Road, Worthing, West Sussex BN14 8AD

South Manchester Poets *Dave Tarrant,* 122 Peterburgh Road, Edgeley Park, Stockport SK3 9RB

Spanner Press See also **Spanner** magazine, *Allen Fisher,* 14 Hopton Road, Hereford HR1 1BE

Spectacular Diseases See also **Spectacular Diseases** magazine, *Paul Green,* 83b London Road, Peterborough, Cambs PE2 9BS

Spike Press 57 Spencer Avenue, Earlsdon, Coventry CV5 6NQ

Spineless Books *Keith Musgrove,* Owlsmead, Sutton Manderville, Salisbury, Wiltshire SP3 5NA

Spineless Press *Tim Allen,* 21 Overton Gardens, Mannamead, Plymouth, Devon PL3 5BX

Spout Publications Birstall Library, Market Street, Birstall, Batley, West Yorks WF17 9EN

Staple First Editions See also **Staple** magazine, Tor Cottage, 81 Cavendish Road, Matlock, Derbyshire DE4 3HD

Stingy Artist Book Co. *Bernard Hemensley,* 85 Goldcroft Road, Weymouth, Dorset DT4 0EA

Stride Publications See also **Taxus Press,** *Rupert Loydell,* 11 Sylvlan Road, Exeter, Devon EX4 6EW

Sui Generis Publishing See also **Likewise** magazine (gavin_leigh.e@virgin.net and business.virgin.net/gavin_leigh.e/) *Gavin Leigh,* 18e Marlborough Road, Roath, Cardiff CF2 5BX

Swansea Poetry Workshop *Nigel Jenkins,* 124 Overland Road, Mumbles, Swansea SA3 4EU

Tabor Press *M. A. Duxbury-Hibbert,* 2 Holyhead Road, Llanerchymedd, Ynys Mon LL71 7AB

Talking Pen Press 12 Derby Crescent, Moorside, Consett, Co Durham DH8 8DZ

Talus Editions See also **Talus** magazine, *Hanne Bramness & others,* Dept of English, King's College, Strand, London WC2R 2LS

Taranis Books See also **West Coast Magazine**, *Kenny MacKenzie*, 2 Hugh Miller Place, Edinburgh EH3 5JG

Taxus Press See also **Stride Publications**, 11 Sylvan Road, Exeter, Devon EX4 6EW

Tellet Publications 30 York Street, Broadstairs, Kent CT10 1PB

The Tenormen Press See also **Ostinato** magazine, *Stephen C. Middleton*, PO Box 552, London N8 7SZ

Torque Press *Peter Middleton*, 79 Welbeck Avenue, Southampton SO17 1SQ

Totem *Fiifi Annobil*, 55 Mercher Gardens, Cardiff CF1 7RF

Trimingham Press 30 Paddocks Lane, Cheltenham, Glos GL50 4NU

Triple Cat Publishing *R. E. Field*, 3 Back Lane Cottages, Bucks Horn Oak, Farnham, Surrey GU10 4LN

Tuba Press See also **Tuba** magazine, *Peter Ellison*, Tunley Cottage, Tunley, Nr Cirencester, Glos GL7 6LW

A Twist In The Tail *Paul Cookson*, PO Box 25, Retford, Nottinghamshire DN22 7ER

Two Rivers Press *Peter Hay*, 145 Liverpool Road, Reading, Berkshire RG1 3PN

Ulsterman Pamphlets See also **HU – The Honest Ulsterman** magazine, *Tom Clyde*, 14 Shaw Street, Belfast BT4 1PT

Underground Press *John Evans*, 9 Laneley Terrace, Maesycoed, Pontypridd, Mid Glamorgan CF37 1ER

Unusual Books 4 Colonel Road, Ammanford SA18 2HB

Ure Group Press *Gary Boswell & others*, 22 Moss Lane, Parr, St Helens WA9 3SB

Vennel Press *Richard Price*, 8 Richmond Road, Staines, Middlesex TW18 2AB

Ventus Books *Tony Breeze*, 70 Nottingham Road, Burton Joyce, Notts NG14 5AL

Ver Poets *May Badman*, 'Haycroft', 61/63 Chiswell Green Lane, St Albans, Herts AL2 3AL (See also under **Professional Associations**)

Vigil Publications See also **Vigil** magazine, *John Howard-Greaves*, 12 Priory Mead, Bruton, Somerset BA10 0DZ

Visual Associations *Michael Weller* 3 Queen Adelaide Court, Queen Adelaide Road, London SE20 7DZ

Wanda Publications See also **Doors** and **South** magazines, Word and Action, 61 West Borough, Wimborne, Dorset BH21 1LX

Weatherlight Press *David Keefe*, 34 Cornwallis Crescent, Clifton, Bristol BS8 4PH

Welford Court Press 1 Welford Court, Leicester LE2 6ER

Wellsweep Press *John Cayley*, 1 Grove End House, 150 Highgate Road, London NW5 1PD

West House Books (alan@nethedge.demon.co.uk) *Alan Halsey*, 16a Priory Road, Nether Edge, Sheffield S7 1LW

White Adder Press 14 Canongate Venture, New Street, Edinburgh EH8 8BH

White Box Publications *James Turner*, 114 Monks Road, Exeter, Devon EX4 7BQ

Wild Goose Publications Unit 15, Six Harmony Row, Glasgow GL51 3BA

Wild Hawthorn Press *Ian Hamilton Finlay*, Little Sparta, Dunsyre, Lanark ML11 8NG

Windows Publications See also **Windows Poetry Broadsheet**, *Heather Brett*, Nature Haven, Legaginney, Ballinagh, Cavan, Eire

Woodman's Press See also **Rustic Rub** magazine, *Jay Woodman*, 14 Hillfield, Selby, N Yorkshire YO8 0ND

Words Worth Books See also **Words Worth** magazine, *Alaric Sumner*, BM Box 4515, London WC1N 3XX

Writers Forum See also **And** magazine and **New River Project** press, *Bob Cobbing*, 89a Petherton Road, London N5 2QT

Wysiwyg Chapbooks *Ric Hool*, 89 Abertillery Road, Blaina, Gwent

Yorkshire Art Circus Ltd See under **Small Presses**

Young Woodchester PO Box 26, Stroud, Gloucestershire GL5 5YF

Zum Zum Books *Neil Oram*, Goshem, Bunlight, Drumnadrochit, Inverness-shire IV3 6AH

ZZZg Press See also **Symtex & Grimmer** magazine, *Chris Jones*, Clatto Bothy, Blebo Craigs, Cupar, Fife KY15 5UE

Poetry Magazines

Many poetry magazines have links with or are produced by companies listed in **Poetry Presses**

Acid Rainbow Dada Dance *Dee Rimbaud*, Ground Floor Left, 35 Falkland Street, Glasgow G12 9QZ

Acumen See also **Acumen Publications**, *Patricia Oxley*, 6 The Mount, Higher Furzeham, Brixham, Devon TQ5 8QY

The Affectionate Punch *Andrew Tutty*, 35 Brundage Road, Manchester M22 0BY

Agenda See also **Agenda Editions** press, *William Cookson*, 5 Cranbourne Court, Albert Bridge Road, London SW11 4PE

Aireings See also **Aireings Press**, *Jean Barker*, 3/24 Brudenell Road, Leeds, West Yorks LS6 1BD

Ambit *Martin Bax*, 17 Priory Gardens, London N6 5QY

Anarchist Angel Youth Poetry Quarterly See also **Angel Press**, *Liz Berry*, 41 Rosewood Park, Cheslyn Hay, Staffs WS6 7HP

And See also **New River Project** and **Writers Forum** presses, *Bob Cobbing & Adrian Clarke*, 89a Petherton Road, London N5 2QT

Angel Exhaust (http://angel-exhaust.offworld.co.uk) *Andrew Duncan & others*, 27 Sturton Street, Cambridge CB1 2QC

Anthem *Howard Roake*, 36 Cyril Avenue, Bobbers Mill, Nottingham NG8 5BA

Apostrophe See also **Mr Pillows Press**, *Diana Andersson*, Orton House, 41 Canute Road, Faversham, Kent ME13 8SH

Aquarius *Eddie S. Linden*, Flat 10, Room A, 116 Sutherland Avenue, Maida Vale, London W9

The Arcadian *Mike Boland*, 11 Boxtree Lane, Harrow Weald, Middlesex HA3 6JU

Areopagus *Julian Barritt*, 101 May Tree Close, Badger Farm, Winchester SO22 4JF

The Argotist (ragedliv.ac.uk and http://users.why.net/macabut/argotist) *Nick Watson*, 221 Chesnut House, Mulberry Street, Liverpool L7 7EZ

At Last 16 Ramsay Lane, Kincardine-on-Forth, Fife FK10 4QY

Avaganda *Albert Benson*, 51a Rodney Street, Liverpool L1 9ER

Avon Literary Intelligencer (dsr@maths.bath.ac.uk) 20 Byron Place, Clifton, Bristol BS8 1JT

Bad-Breakfast All Day *Philip Boxall*, 43 Kingsdown House, Amhurst Road, London E8 2AS

Bad Poetry Quarterly PO Box 6319, London E11 2EP

Bananas 876 Church Street, Croydon CR0 1RN

Banipal Modern Arab literature, PO Box 22300, London W13 8ZQ

The Banshee *Rachel Fones*, 16 Rigby Close, Waddon Road, Croydon CR0 4JU

Bardonni/Stopgap/Songs See also **Malfunction Press** *Peter E. Presford*, Rose Cottage, 3 Tram Lane, Buckley, Clwyd

Barfly *Jon Summers*, 96 Brookside Way, West End, Southampton SO30 3GZ

Basically Insane *Gary Greenwood & others*, Number 20 Publications, 48 St Davids Crescent, Newport, Gwent NP9 3AW

Bête Noire *John Osborne*, American Studies Dept, The University of Hull, Cottingham Road, Hull HU6 7 RX

Beyond the Brink *Ed Hackett*, PO Box 493, Sheffield S10 3YX

The Big Spoon 32 Salisbury Court, Belfast BT7 1DD

Billy Liar 7–8 Trinity Chare, Quayside, Newcastle upon Tyne NE1 3DF

Blade *Jane Holland*, Maynrys, Glen Chass, Port St Mary, Isle of Man IM9 5PN

Blithe Spirit *Jackie Hardy*, Hill House Farm, Knighton, Powys LD7 1NA

The Bloody Quill *J. Rogerson*, West Lodge, Higher Lane, Liverpool L9 7AB

Blue Cage See also **Blue Cage** press, *Paul Donnelly*, 98 Bedford Road, Birkdale, Southport, Merseyside PR8 4HL

Bogg *George Cairncross*, 31 Bellevue Street, Filey, North Yorks YO14 9HU

Borderlines *Dave Bingham*, Nant Y Brithyll, Llangynyw, Welshpool, Powys SY21 0JS

Brando's Hat 14 Vine Street, Salford, Manchester M7 3PG

Brangle *Carol Rumens*, 100a Tunis Road, London W12 7EY

Braquemard *David Allenby*, 20 Terry Street, Hull HU3 1UD

The Bridge *James Mawer*, 112 Rutland Street, Grimsby DN32 7NF

Brimstone Signatures *Isabel Gillard,*
St Lawrence Cottage, Sellman Street,
Gnosall, Stafford ST20 0EP

Brink (alexisk@zeus.sc.plym.ac.uk and
gopher://wings.buffalo.edu/hh/internet/
library/ and ejournals/ub/rift/journals/
selected/brink/.index.) *Alexis Kirke,*
22 West Park Road, Peverell, Plymouth,
Devon PL3 4NU

Butterfly & Bloomers *Maggie Allen,*
12 Wetmoor Lane, Wath-upon-Dearne,
Rotherham S63 6DF

Cadmium Blue Literary Journal See also
Precious Pearl Press and **The People's
Poetry** and **Romantic Heir** magazines,
Peter Geoffrey Thompson, 71 Harrow
Crescent, Romford, Essex RM3 7BJ

Candelabrum Poetry Magazine See also
Red Candle Press, *M. L. McCarthy,*
9 Milner Road, Wisbech, Cambs
PE13 2LR

Celtic Pen *Diarmuid O'Breaslain,* 36 Fruithill
Park, Belfast B11 8GE

Cencrastus – The Curly Snake *Raymond Ross
& others,* Unit 1, Abbeymount Techbase,
8 Easter Road, Edinburgh EH8 8EJ

Chapman See under **Magazines** and also
Chapman Press

Chasing the Dragon *Niall Griffiths,* 5 Cliff
Terrace, Aberystwyth SY23 2DN

Christian Poetry Review *Val Newbrook,*
Grendon House, 67 Walsall Road,
Lichfield, Staffs WS13 8AD

Chronicles of Disorder *Wayne Dean-
Richards,* 191 Pound Road, Oldbury,
Warley, West Midlands B68 8NF

City Writings *Megan Miranda,* The Gantry
Arts Centre, Off Blechynden Terrace,
Southampton SO15 1GW

Civil Service Author See also **Businesslike
Publishing** under **Small Presses**, *Iain
McIntyre,* 'Bluepool', Strathoykel, Ardgay,
Inverness-shire IV24 3DP

Cobweb Arts Security Press, St Patrick's
College, Maynooth, Co Kildare, Eire

Connections *Jeanne Conn,* 165 Domonic
Drive, New Eltham, London SE9 3LE

Connections – The Writers Journal *Narissa
Knights,* 13 Wave Crest, Whitstable, Kent
CT5 1EH

Critical Quarterly Blackwell Publishers,
108 Cowley Road, Oxford OX4 1JF

Cuirt Review *Trish Fitzpatrick,* Galway Arts
Centre, 47 Dominick Street, Galway,
Eire

Cyphers *Eilean NcChuilleanain,* 3 Selskar
Terrace, Ranelagh, Dublin 6, Eire

D.A.M. (Disability Arts Magazine) *Kit
Wells,* 11a Cleveland Avenue, Lupset Park,
Wakefield, West Yorks WF2 8LE

Dandelion Arts Magazine See also **Fern
Publications,** *Jacqueline Gonzalez-Marina,*
24 Frosty Hollow, East Hunsbury,
Northants NN4 0SY

The Dark Horse *Gerry Cambridge,*
19 Cunninghamhead Estate, By
Kilmarnock, Ayrshire KA3 2PY

Data Dump *Steve Sneyd,* 4 Nowell Place,
Almondsbury, Huddersfield, West Yorks
HD5 8PB

Defying Gravity *C. Turner,* 26 Tomsfield,
Hatfield, Hertfordshire

The Devil (formerly **The Printer's Devil**)
Sean O'Brien & others Top Offices,
13a Western Road, Hove, East Sussex
BN3 1AE

Dial 174 (apoet@globalnet.co.uk) *Joseph
Hemmings,* 21 Mill Road, Watlington,
King's Lynn, Norfolk PE33 0HH

Distaff *J. Brice,* London Women's Centre,
Wesley House, 4 Wild Court, Kingsway,
London WC2

Dog *David Crystal,* 32b Breakspears Road,
London SE4 1UW

Doors See also **Wanda Publications** and
South magazine, Word and Action,
61 West Borough, Wimborne, Dorset
BH21 1LX

The Echo Room *Brendan Cleary,* 45 Bewick
Court, Princess Square, Newcastle upon
Tyne NE1 8HG

Eco-runes *D. O'Ruie,* 68b Fivey Road,
Ballymoney BT53 8JH

Ecorche 17 Eastfields, Thornford, Sherborne,
Dorset DT9 6PU

Edible Society *Peter Godfrey,* 10 Lincoln
Street, Brighton, East Sussex BN2 2UH

Edinburgh Review See under **Magazines**
and also **Polygon Books**

End of Millennium (101336@compuserve.
com and ourworld.compuserve.com/
homepages/_GAC) Porcine Publications,
PO Box 7367, Kilmarnock KA3 1RA

Envoi *Roger Elkin,* 44 Rudyard Road,
Biddulph Moor, Stoke-on-Trent, Staffs
ST8 7JN

Erran Publishing See also **Poetic Hours**
magazine, *Nick Clark,* 8 Dale Road,
Carlton, Notts NG4 1GT

Exile *Herbert Marr,* 8 Snow Hill, Clare,
Suffolk CO10 8QF

Fatchance See also **Fatchance Press**, *Louise
Hudson & others,* Elm Court, East Street,
Sheepwash, Beaworthy, Devon EX21 5NL

Figments 218 York Street, Belfast BT15 1GY

First Offense *Tim Fletcher*, Syringa, The Street, Stodmarsh, Canterbury, Kent CT3 4BA

First Time See also **First Time Publications**, *Josephine Austin*, 4 Burdett Place, George Street, Hastings, East Sussex TN34 3ED

Flaming Arrows *Leo Regan*, County Sligo V.E.C., Riverside, Sligo, Eire

Force Ten *Molly McClaske*, The Model Arts Centre, The Mall, Sligo, Co. Cligo, Eire

Fragmente *Anthony Mellors*, 31 Queens Road, Skegness, Lincolnshire PE25 2ET

Freedom Rock *Mike Coleman*, 18 Sunningdale Avenue, Sale, Cheshire M33 2PH

Freestyle (formerly **Writer's Viewpoint/Caring & Sharing**) *Belinda Rance*, Wilcox Design Services, 40 Buttermere Road, Bowring Park, Liverpool L16 2NN

The Frogmore Papers See also **The Frogmore Press** and **Crabflower Pamphlets** press *Jeremy Page*, 42 Morehall Avenue, Folkstone, Kent CT19 4EF

Full Moon *Barbara Parkinson*, Church Road, Killybegs, Co. Donegal, Eire

Gairm *Derek Thomson*, 29 Waterloo Street, Glasgow G2 6BZ

Garuda See also **Microbrigade** press, *Ulli Freer*, 7 Highwood Avenue, London N12 8QL

Global Tapestry Journal See also **BB Books**, *Dave Cunliffe*, Spring Bank, Longsight Road, Copster Green, Blackburn, Lancs BB1 9EU

Granite - new verse from Cornwall *Alan M. Kent*, South View, Wheal Bull, Foxhole, St Austell, Cornwall PL26 7UA

Haiku Quarterly See also **Day Dream Press** *Kevin Bailey*, 39 Exmouth Street, Swindon, Wilts SN1 3PU

Handshake *John Francis Haines*, 5 Cross Farm, Station Road, Padgate, Warrington WA2 0QC

Headlock *Tony Charles*, The Old Zion Chapel, The Triangle, Somerton, Somerset TA11 6QP

Heart Throb (formerly **People to People**) *Mike Parker*, 95 Spencer Street, Birmingham B18 6DA

Helicon *Shelagh Nugent*, Cherrybite Publications, Linden Cottage, 45 Burton Road, Little Neston, South Wirral L64 4AE

Hjok-Finnie's Sanglines *Jim Inglis*, 8 Knockbain Road, Dingwall IV15 9NR

Hrafnhoh *Joseph Biddulph*, 32 Stryd Ebeneser, Pontypridd CF 37 5PB

HU - The Honest Ulsterman See also **Ulsterman Pamphlets** press, *Tom Clyde*, 14 Shaw Street, Belfast BT4 1PT

Ibid See also **Ibid Press**, *Matthew Hollis*, Dept of English Literature, University of Edinburgh, David Hume Tower, George Square, Edinburgh EH8 9JX

Incognito 23 St James, Hollybrook Park, Dublin 3, Eire

Interactions See also **Eros Press**, *Diane M. Moore*, PO Box 250, St Helier, Jersey, Channel Islands JE4 8TZ

The Interpreter's House *Merryn Williams*, 10 Farrell Road, Wootton, Beds MK43 9DU

Intimacy *Adam McKeown*, 11c, Elizabeth House, Alexandra Street, Maidstone, Kent ME16 2BX

Involution *A. M. Horne*, Magdelene College, Cambridge CB3 0AG

Iota *David Holliday*, 67 Hady Crescent, Chesterfield, Derbyshire S41 0EB

Issue One/The Bridge *Ian Brocklebank*, 2 Tewkesbury Drive, Grimsby, South Humberside DN34 4TL

Journal of Contemporary Anglo-Scandinavian Poetry *Sam Smith*, 11 Heatherton Park, Bradford-on-Tone, Taunton, Somerset TA4 1EV

Krax *Andy Robson*, 63 Dixon Lane, Wortley, Leeds, West Yorks LS12 4RR

Krino - the review *Gerald Dawe & others*, PO Box 65, Dun Laoghaire, Co. Dublin, Eire

Kulture Vulture *John Evans*, 9 Lanelay Terrace, Maesycoed, Pontypridd CF37 1ER

Kunapipi See also **Dangaroo Press** *Anna Rutherford*, PO Box 20, Hebden Bridge, West Yorks HX7 5UZ

Lallans *Neil MacCullum*, 18 Redford Avenue, Edinburgh EH13 0BU

Lateral Moves *Ann White*, 5 Hamilton Street, Astley Bridge, Bolton, Lancs BL1 6RJ

Lexicon *Francis Anderson*, PO Box 754, Stoke on Trent ST1 4BU

Likewise See also **Sui Generis Publishing** (gavin_leigh.e@virgin.net and business.virgin.net/gavin_leigh.e/) *Gavin Leigh*, 18e Marlborough Road, Roath, Cardiff CF2 5BX

Linear A See also **Hillside Books**, *Johan De Wit*, Flat 1, Sylva Court, 81 Putney Hill, London SW15 3NX

Lines Review *Tessa Ransford*, Macdonald Publishing, Edgefield Street, Loanhead, Mid Lothian EH20 9SY

The Link *David Pollard*, Brumus Management, PO Box 317, Hounslow, Middlesex TW3 2SD

Links See also **Kernow Poets Press**, *Bill Headdon*, Bude Haven, 18 Frankfield Rise, Tunbridge Wells, Kent TN2 5LF

Lit Up *Jeremy Rogers*, 8a Mill Street, Torrington, Devon EX38 8HQ

London Magazine - See under **Magazines**

The Long Poem Group Newsletter *William Oxley*, 6 The Mount, Higher Furzeham, Brixham, S Devon TQ5 8QY

Mad Cow *J. Whittington*, 33 Kingsley Place, Highgate, London N6 5EA

Madam X (colpress@ress.sonnet.co.uk) *M. Lollopit*, Colophon Press, 18a Prentis Road, London SW16 1QD

The Magazine *Nancy Allison*, Open Studies, Dept of Continuing Education, University of Warwick, Coventry, Warwickshire CV4 7AL

Magma *Laurie Smith & others*, The Stukely Press, The City Lit, Stukely Street, Drury Lane, London WC2B 5LJ

Magpie's Nest *Bal Saini*, 176 Stoney Lane, Sparkhill, Birmingham B12 8AN

Maquette *Andy Brown*, 3 South Street, Sheepwash, Beaworthy, Devon EX21 5LZ

Metre *David Wheatley*, Dept of English, Trinity College, Dublin, Eire

Moonstone *Talitha Clare*, SOS, The Old Station Yard, Settle BD24 9RP

Mosaic *L. Williamson*, 16 Vale Close, Eastwood, Nottingham

MPT – Modern Poetry in Translation *Daniel Weissbort*, MPT, School of Humanities, King's College London, Strand, London WC2R 2LS

Navis *Robert Bush & others*, 211 Bedford Hill, London SW12 9HQ

Never Bury Poetry *Eileen Holroy*, 12a Kirkstall Gardens, Radcliffe, Manchester M26 0JQ

New Departures See also **New Departures** press, *Michael Horowitz*, PO Box 9819, London W11 2GC

New Hope International (newhope@iname.com) *Gerald England*, 20 Werneth Avenue, Gee Cross, Hyde, Cheshire SK14 5NL

New Millennium 292 Kennington Road, London SE11 4LD

New Poetry Quarterly *Simon Brittan*, 5 Stockwell, Colchester, Essex CO1 1HP

New Scottish Epoch *Neil Mathers*, 57 Murray Street, Montrose, Angus DD10 8JZ

New Welsh Review See under **Magazines**

The New Writer (incorporating **Acclaim** & **Quartos**) See under **Magazines**

Night Dreams *Anthony Barker*, 52 Denman Lane, Huncote, Leicester LE9 3BS

Nineties Poetry *Graham Ackroyd*, 33 Lansdowne Place, Hove, East Sussex BN3 1HF

Nomad *Julie Smith*, Survivors Press, GAMH, Melrose House, 1st Floor, 15/23 Cadogan Street, Glasgow G2 6QQ

The North See also **Smith/Doorstep Books** and **The Poetry Business** presses, *Peter Sansom & Janet Fisher*, The Studio, Byram Arcade, Westgate, Huddersfield, West Yorks HD1 1ND

Northwords *Angus Dunn*, The Stable, Long Road, Avoch, Ross-shire IV9 8QR

Nova Poetica 14 Pennington Oval, Lymington, Hampshire SO41 8BQ

Novocaine (zdhu010@uk.ac.kd.cc.bay) 22 Wilderness Road, Mannamead, Plymouth, Devon PL3 4RN

Oasis See also **Oasis Books**, *Ian Robinson*, 12 Stevenage Road, Fulham, London SW6 6ES

Obsessed With Pipework 15 Market Place, Redditch B98 8AR

One *Wendy B. Cardy*, 48 South Street, Colchester, Essex CO2 7BJ

Orbis *Mike Shields*, 27 Valley View, Primrose, Jarrow, Tyne & Wear NE32 5QT

Ostinato See also **The Tenormen Press**, *Stephen C. Middleton*, PO Box 522, London N8 7SZ

Other Poetry *Peter Bennet & others*, 8 Oakhurst Terrace, Benton, Newcastle upon Tyne NE12 9NY

Otter *R. Skinner*, Little Byspock, Richmond Road, Exeter, Devon

Outposts See also **Hippopotamus Press**, *Roland John*, 22 Whitewell Road, Frome, Somerset BA11 4EL

Outreach *M. Brooks*, 7 Grayson Close, Stockbridge, Sheffield, S Yorks S30 5BJ

Oxford English *Marcus Nevitt*, Magdalen College, Oxford

Oxford Poetry *Graham Nelson*, Magdalen College, Oxford OX1 4AU

Oxford Quarterly Review *Ernie Hibert*, St Catherine's College, Oxford OX1 3UJ

Pages See also **Ship of Fools** press, *Robert Sheppard*, 78 Nicander Road, Liverpool 18

Passion See also **Crescent Moon Publishing and Joe's Press** under **Small Presses**, *Jeremy Robinson*, PO Box 393, Maidstone, Kent

Pause See also **National Poetry Foundation** *Helen Robinson*, 27 Mill Road, Fareham, Hants PO16 0TH

Peace and Freedom *Paul Rance*, 17 Farrow Road, Whaplode Drove, Spalding, Lincs PE12 0TS

Peer Poetry Magazine *Paul Amphlett*, 26 Arlington House, Bath Street, Bath BA1 1QN

Pen and Keyboard *David Stern*, SQR Publishing, 526 Fulham Palace Road, London SW6 6JE

The Pen Magazine *Pam Probert*, 15 Berwyn Place, Penlan, Swansea, West Glamorgan SA5 5AX

The Penniless Press *Alan Dent*, 100 Waterloo Road, Ashton, Preston, Lancs PR2 1EP

Pennine Platform *K. E. Smith*, 7 Cockley Hill Lane, Kirkheaton, Huddersfield, West Yorks HD5 0HH

The People's Poetry See also **Precious Pearl Press** and **Cadmium Blue Literary Journal** and **Romantic Heir** magazines, *Peter Geoffrey Thompson*, 71 Harrow Crescent, Romford, Essex RM3 7BJ

Planet *John Barnie*, PO Box 44, Aberystwyth, Dyfed

Plume Literary Magazine 15 Bolehill Park, Hove Edge, Brighouse HD6 2RS

PN Review (pnr@carcaneet.u-net.com) See also **Carcanet Press** under **UK Publishers**, *Michael Schmidt*, 4th Floor, Conavon Court, 12–16 Blackfriars Street, Manchester M3 5BQ

The Poet's Voice (Published with Univ. of Salzburg) *Fred Beake*, 12 Dartmouth Avenue, Bath BA2 1AT

Poetechniciens *Matthew Revell*, Causey Bridge End Farm, Marley Hill, Newcastle upon Tyne NE16 5EG

Poetic Hours See also **Erran Publishing** magazine *Nick Clark*, 8 Dale Road, Carlton, Notts NG4 1GT

Poetic Licence 70 Aveling Close, Purley, Surrey CR8 4DW

Poetry and Audience *Carolyn Fyffe*, School of English, University of Leeds, Leeds, West Yorks LS2 9JT

The Poetry Church See also **Feather Books** under **Small Presses** *Rev J. Waddington Feather*, Fair View, Old Coppice, Lyth Bank, Shrewsbury, Shropshire SY3 0BW

Poetry Ireland Review Bermingham Tower, Upper Yard, Dublin Castle, Dublin, Eire

Poetry Life Magazine See also **Poetry Life Publishing**, *Adrian Bishop*, 14 Pennington Oval, Lymington, Hants SO41 8BQ

Poetry London Newsletter (http://www.rmplc.co.uk/eduweb/sites/pooetry.index.html) *P. Daniels*, 35 Bethnal Road, London E16 7AR

Poetry Manchester *Sean Boustead*, 13 Napier Street, Swinton, Manchester M27 0JQ

Poetry Monthly (martinholroyd@compuserve. com and http://ourworld. compuserve.com/homepage/martinholroyd) *Martin Holroyd*, 39 Cavendish Road, Long Eaton, Nottingham NG10 4HY

Poetry Nottingham International *Cathy Grindrod*, 13 Bradmore Rise, Sherwood, Nottingham NG5 3BJ

Poetry Now *Andrew Head*, 1–2 Wainman Road, Woodston, Peterborough, Cambs PE2 7BU

Poetry Review *Peter Forbes*, Poetry Society, 22 Betterton Street, London WC2H 9BU

Poetry Scotland 3 Spittal Street, Edinburgh EH3 9DY

Poetry Wales See also **Seren Books** under **UK Publishers**, *Robert Minhinnick*, First Floor, 2 Wyndham Street, Bridgend CF31 1EF

Pomes *Adrian Spendlow*, 23 Bright Street, York YO2 4XS

PPQ *Peter Taylor*, PO Box 1435, London W1A 9LB

PQR – Poetry Quarterly Review See also **Odyssey Poets** press, *Derrick Woolf*, Coleridge Cottage, Nether Stowey, Somerset TA5 1NQ

Premonitions See also **S. A. Publishing**, **Scar Tissue** and **The Zone** magazines *Tony Lee*, 13 Hazely Combe, Arreton, Isle of Wight PO30 3AJ

Presence *Martin Lucas*, 188 Langthorne Road, London E11 4HS

The Present Tense *Michael Abbott*, 115 Princess Victoria Street, Clifton, Bristol

Prop *Stephen Blythe*, 31 Central Avenue, Farnworth, Bolton, Lancs BL4 0AU

Psychopoetica See also **Psychopoetica Publications**, *Geoff Lowe*, Dept of Psychology, University of Hull, Hull HU6 7RX

Pulsar See also **Ligden Publishers**, *David Pike*, 34 Lineacre, Grangepark, Swindon, Wilts SN5 6DA

Purge *Robert Hampson*, 11 Hillview Court, Hillview Road, Woking, Surrey GU22 7QN

Purple Patch *Geoff Stevens*, 8 Beaconview House, Charlemont Farm, West Bromwich B71 3PL

Queer Words *Michael Nobbs*, PO Box 23, Aberystwyth, Dyfed SY23 1AA

Radical Poetics (m.hrebeniak@ram.ac.uk) 23 Broadcroft Avenue, Stanmore, Middlesex HA7 1NT

Rainbow Bridge *Tricia Frances*, PO Box 136, Norwich, Norfolk NR3 3LJ

Ramraid Extraordinaire 57 Canton Court, Canton, Cardiff CF1 9BG

Raw Edge Magazine *Dave Reeves*, PO Box 4867, Birmingham B3 3HD

Reach Cherrybite Publications, Linden Cottage, 45 Burton Road, Little Neston, South Wirral L64 4AE

Reader's Feast *Jennifer Brown*, PO Box 879, Rhyl, Clwyd LL18 1TJ

The Reater *Shane Rhodes*, 1 Pilmar Lane, Roos, North Humberside HU12 0HP

Red Herring See also **MidNag Publications**, Arts Section, Central Library, The Willows, Morpeth, Northumberland NE61 1TA

The Red Shoes *Adrian Hodges*, 3 Ashfield Close, Bishops Cleeve, Cheltenham, Glos GL52 4LG

Reflections PO Box 70, Sunderland SR1 1DU

Rhyme Arrival *Trudi Ramm*, 1-2 Wainman Road, Woodston, Peterborough, Cambs PE2 7BU

The Rialto See also **Rialto Publications**, *Michael Mackmin*, PO Box 309, Aylsham, Norwich, Norfolk NR11 6LN

Rivet *Eve Catchpole & others,* 74 Walton Drive, High Wycombe, Bucks HP13 6TT

Romantic Heir See also **Precious Pearl Press** and **Cadmium Blue Literary Journal** and **The People's Poetry** magazines, *Peter Geoffrey Thompson*, 71 Harrow Crescent, Romford, Essex RM3 7BJ

Rustic Rub (formerly **And What of Tomorrow**) See also **Woodman's Press**, *Jay Woodman*, 14 Hillfield, Selby, N. Yorkshire YO8 0ND

Scar Tissue See also **S. A. Publishing**, **Premonitions** and **The Zone** magazines, *Tony Lee*, 13 Hazley Combe, Arreton, Isle of Wight PO30 3AJ

Scintilla *Anne Cluysenaar*, Little Wentwood Farm, Llantrisant, Usk, Monmouthshire NP5 1ND

Scriptor See also **Providence Press (Whitstable)**, *John & Lesley Dench*, 22 Plough Lane, Swalecliffe, Whitstable, Kent CT5 2NZ

Seam *David Lightfoot*, 1 Horncastle Road, Louth, Lincolnshire LN11 9LB

Sepia See also **Kawabata Press**, *Colin David Webb*, Knill Cross House, Knill Cross, Millbrook, Near Torpoint, Cornwall PL10 1DX

Shearsman See also **Shearsman Books**, *Tony Frazer*, 47 Dayton Close, Plymouth, Devon PL6 5DX

Sheffield Thursday *E. A. Markham*, School of Cultural Studies, Sheffield Hallam University, 36 Collegiate Crescent, Sheffield S10 2BP

Skald *Zoe Skoulding*, 2 Park Street, Bangor, Gwynedd LL57 2AY

Slipstream *Cathy Cullis*, 4 Crossways, Crookham Village, Fleet, Hampshire GU13 0TA

Smiths Knoll *Roy Blackman & others* 49 Church Road, Little Glemham, Woodbridge, Suffolk IP13 0BJ

Smoke *Dave Ward*, The Windows Project, 40 Canning Street, Liverpool L8 7NP

Sol Poetry Magazine See also **Sol Publications**, *Malcolm E. Wright*, 24 Fowler Close, Southchurch, Southend-on-Sea, Essex SS1 2RD

Sound & Language 85 London Road South, Lowestoft, Suffolk NR33 0AS

The Source *Kelly Lemaitre*, 19 Cumberland Street, Edinburgh EH3 6RT

South See also **Wanda Publications** and **Doors** magazine, Word and Action, 61 West Borough, Wimborne, Dorset BH21 1LX

Southfields *Richard Price*, 8 Richmond Road, Staines, TW18 2AB

Spanner See also **Spanner Press**, *Allen Fisher*, 14 Hopton Road, Hereford HR1 1BE

Spectacular Diseases See also **Spectacular Diseases** press, *Paul Green*, 83b London Road, Peterborough, Cambs PE2 9BS

Spice Box 1 Alanbrooke Close, Knaphill, Surrey GU21 2RU

Spokes *Alistair Wisker*, 319a Hills Road, Cambridge CB2 2QT

Stand See also **Northern House Poets** press, *Lorna Tracy*, 179 Wingrove Road, Newcastle-upon-Tyne NE4 9DA

Staple See also **Staple First Editions** press, *Bob Windsor* Tor Cottage, 81 Cavendish Road, Matlock, Derbyshire DE4 3HD

The Steeple *Patrick Cotter*, Three Spires Press, Killeen, Blackrock Village, Cork City, Eire

Still *Al Li*, 49 Englands Lane, London NW3 4YD

Stone Soup 37 Chesterfield Road, London W4 3HQ

The Storehouse Carad, The Old Pantydwr Stores, West Street, Rhayader, Powys LD6 5AF

Story Cellar *Sara Waddington*, 26 Cippenham Lane, Slough, Berkshire SL1 5BS

Sub Voicive Poetry See also **Mainstream** press, *Lawrence Upton*, 32 Downside Road, Sutton, Surrey SM2 5HP

Sunk Island Review See also **Sunk Island Publishing** and **Jackson's Arm** under **Small Presses**, *Michael Blackburn*, PO Box 74, Lincoln LN1 1QG

Super-Trouper *Andrew Savage*, 81 Castlerigg Drive, Burnley, Lancs BB12 8AT

Swagmag *Peter Thabit Jones*, Dan-y-Bryn, 74 Cwm Level Road, Brynhyfred, Swansea SA5 9DY

The Swansea Review, *Glyn Pursglove*, Dept of English, University College Swansea, Singleton Park, Swansea SA2 8PP

Symphony Bemerton Press, 9 Hamilton Gardens, London NW8 9PU

Symtex & Grimmer See also **ZZZg Press**, Clatto Bothy, Blebo Craigs, Cupar, Fife KY15 5UE

Tabla *Stephen James Ellis & others*, 13a Shirlock Road, London NW3 2HR

Talus See also **Talus Editions** *Marzia Balzani & others*, Dept of English, King's College, Strand, London WC2R 2LS

Tandem *Michael J. Woods*, 13 Stephenson Road, Barbourne, Worcester WR1 3EB

Tartarus Press *Raymond Russell*, 5 Birch Terrace, Hangingbirch Lane, Horam, East Sussex TN21 0PA

Tears In The Fence *David Caddy*, 38 Hod View, Stourpaine, Nr Blandford Forum, Dorset DT11 8TN

10th Muse *Andrew Jordan*, 33 Hartington Road, Southampton SO14 0EW

The Text 46–47 Byram Arcade, Westgate, Huddersfield HD1 1ND

The Third Alternative See also **ZENE** under **Magazines**, *Andy Cox*, 5 St Martin's Lane, Witcham, Ely, Cambs CB4 2LB

The Third Half See also **K. T. Publications**, *Kevin Troop*, 16 Fane Close, Stamford, Lincs PE9 1HG

This Is *Carol Cornish*, PO Box 16185, London NW1 8ZH

Threads *Geoff Lynas*, 32 Irvin Avenue, Saltburn, Cleveland TS12 1QH

3x4 See also **Raunchland Publications**, *John Mingay*, 2 Henderson Street, Kingseat, By Dunfermline, Fife KY12 0TP

Thumbscrew *Tim Kendall* PO Box 657, Oxford OX2 6PH

Time Haiku *Erica Facey*, 105 Kings Head Hill, London E4 7JG

Tongue to Boot *Miles Champion*, 5 Abbots Court, Thackeray Street, London W8 5ES

Tops *Anthony Cooney*, Rose Cottage, 17 Hadassah Grove, Liverpool L17 8XH

Track Marks *Dee Rimbaud*, Triangle Arts Centre, West Pilton Bank, Pilton, Edinburgh EH4 HN

Tracks See also **Dedalus Press/Peppercanister Books** 24 The Heath, Cypress Downs, Dublin 6, Eire

Triumph Herald *Chris Walton*, 1-2 Wainman Road, Woodston, Peterborough, Cambs PE2 7BU

Tuba See also **Tuba Press**, *Charles Graham*, Tunley Cottage, Tunley, Nr Cirencester, Glos GL7 6LW

Uncompromising Positions See also **Jugglers Fingers Press**, *Cheryl Wilkinson*, 92 Staneway, Leam Lane, Gateshead, Tyne & Wear NE10 8LS

Under Surveillance 60 Arnold Street, Brighton, East Sussex BN2 2XT

Understanding See also **Dionysia Press Ltd**, *Denise Smith*, 20a Montgomery Street, Edinburgh EH7 5JS

Unicorn See also **Shell Press**, *Alex Warner*, 12 Milton Avenue, Millbrook, Stalybridge, Cheshire SK15 3HB

Upstart 19 Cawarden, Stantonbury, Milton Keynes MK14 6AH

Urges *Ian Hunter*, Huntiegouke Press, 32 Caneluk Avenue, Carluke ML8 4LZ

Urthona *Chris Warren*, 3 Coral Park, Henley Road, Cambridge CB1 3EA

Various Artists *Tony Lewis Jones*, 65 Springfield Avenue, Horfield, Bristol BS7 9QS

Verse *Andrew Zawacki* University College, Oxford OX1

Vertical Images *Brian Docherty*, 10a Dickenson Road, London N8 9ET

Vigil See also **Vigil Publications**, *John Howard-Greaves*, 12 Priory Mead, Bruton, Somerset BA10 0DZ

Walking Naked *Sean Boustead*, 13 Napier Street, Swinton, Manchester M27 3JQ

Wasafiri Dept of English, Queen Mary and Westfield College, Mile End Road, London E1 4SN

West Coast Magazine See also **Taranis Books**, *Joe Murray*, Em-dee Productions, Unit 7, 29 Brand Street, Glasgow G51 1DN

Weyfarers *Martin Jones,* Guildford Poets Press, 1 Mountside, Guildford, Surrey GU2 5JD

The Whistle House *J. Wistlin,* 4 Hamilton Road, Windle, Merseyside WA10 6HG

The Wide Skirt *Geoff Hattersley,* 1a Church Street, Penistone, South Yorks S30 6AR

Windows Poetry Broadsheet See also **Windows Publications**, *Heather Brett & others,* Nature Haven, Legaginney, Ballinagh, Cavan, Eire

Wits End *Jean Turner,* 27 Pheasants Close, Winnersh, Wokingham, Berks RG11 5LS

Words Worth See also **Words Worth Books**, *Alaric Sumner,* BM Box 4515, London WC1N 3XX

Writing Women *Linda Anderson & others,* Unit 14, Hawthorn House, Forth Banks, Newcastle upon Tyne NE1 3SG

Yellow Crane *Jonathan Brookes* Flat 6, 23 Richmond Crescent, Roath, Cardiff CF2 3AH

Zed 2 0 See also **Akros Publications,** *Duncan Glen,* 33 Lady Nairn Avenue, Kirkcaldy, Fife

Zimmerframe Pileup *Stephen Jessener,* Loose Hand Press, 54 Hillcrest Road, Walthamstow, London E17 4AP

The Zone See under **Magazines,** also **S. A. Publishing, Premonitions** and **Scar Tissue** magazines, *Tony Lee,* 13 Hazely Combe, Arreton, Isle of Wight PO30 3AJ

Organisations of Interest to Poets

A survey of some of the societies, groups and other bodies in the UK which may be of interest to practising poets. Organisations not listed should send details to The Editor, *The Writer's Handbook,* 34 Ufton Road, London N1 5BX for inclusion in future editions.

Academi Literature Promotion

3rd Floor, Mount Stuart House, Mount Stuart Square, Cardiff Bay, Cardiff CF1 6DQ

☎01222 492025   Fax: 01222 492930

Director *Peter Finch*

The writers' organisation of Wales with special responsibility for literary activity, writers' residencies, writers on tour, festivals, writers' groups, readings, tours, exchanges and other development work. The Academi won the 1988 Arts Council of Wales franchise for Wales-wide literature development. It has offices in Cardiff and development workers based in North and West Wales. *Publishes* the Lottery-funded *Encyclopedia of Wales,* the Welsh-medium literary magazine *Taliesin,* the *Academi English–Welsh Dictionary* and co-publishes *The New Welsh Review.* The Academi sponsors a number of annual contests including the prestigious **Cardiff International Poetry Competition**. Publishes a newsletter of Welsh literary events – send for details.

Apples & Snakes

Unit 7, Theatre Place, 489a New Cross Road, London SE14 6TQ

☎0181 692 0393   Fax 0181 692 4551

E-mail: apples@snakes.demon.co.uk

Contacts *Roger Robinson, Karen McCarthy, Malika Booker*

A unique, independent promotional organisation for poetry and poets – furthering poetry as an innovative and popular medium and cross-cultural activity. A&S organises an annual programme of over 150 events (including their London season which actively pushes new voices), tours, residencies and festivals as well as operating a Poets-in-Education Scheme and a non-profit booking agency for relevant poets.

Arts Councils and Regional Arts Boards

For a full list of addresses see **Arts Councils and Regional Arts Boards**

The Arvon Foundation

See entry under **Professional Associations**

The Association of Little Presses

See entry under **Professional Associations**

The British Haiku Society

35 Downs Park West, Westbury Park, Bristol BS6 7QH

☎0117 962 1035

Secretary *Alan J Summers*

Formed in 1990. Promotes the appreciation and writing within the British Isles of haiku, senryu, tanka, and renga by way of tutorials, workshops, exchange of poems, critical comment and information. Provides leaders for workshops and has a travelling exhibition of posters of and about haiku and renga. *Publishes* a quarterly journal, *Blithe Spirit*, administers the annual James W. Hackett Award for haiku, and has established a mail-order members' library of related books and journals.

The Eight Hand Gang
5 Cross Farm, Station Road, Padgate, Warrington WA2 0QG

Secretary *John F. Haines*

An association of British SF poets. *Publishes Handshake*, a single-sheet newsletter of SF poetry and information available free in exchange for a s.a.e.

The Little Magazine Collection, Poetry Store and Alternative Press Collections
University College London, Gower Street, London WC1E 6BT
☎0171 380 7796   Fax 0171 380 7727
Librarian *Geoffrey Soar*

Housed at University College London Library, these are the fruits of Geoffrey Soar and David Miller's interest in UK and US alternative publishing, with a strong emphasis on poetry. The Little Magazines Collection runs to over 3600 titles mainly in the more experimental and avant-garde areas. The Poetry Store consists of over 12,200 small press items, mainly from the '60s onwards, again with some stress on experimental work. In addition, there are reprints of classic earlier little magazines, from Symbolism through to the present. Anyone who is interested can consult the collections, and it helps if you have some idea of what you want to see. Bring evidence of identity for a smooth ride. The collections can be accessed by visiting the Manuscripts and Rare Books Room at University College at the above address between 10.00am and 5.00pm on weekdays. Most items are available on inter-library loans.

The National Convention of Poets and Small Presses/Poets and Small Press Festival
Dumfries & Galloway Arts Centre, Dumfries, Scotland

Contact *Stuart A. Paterson*

An accessible, some might say disorganised, weekend jamboree of writers and poetry publishers held at a different venue each year. The quasi-amateur status of the event is celebrated and it can be good fun for those with enough stamina to last out the marathon readings. There is no central organising committee – bids to host future conventions being made in person at the event itself. So far, it has visited Liverpool, Hastings, Corby, Dartford, Stamford, Norwich, North Shields, Exeter, Stockton-on-Tees, Middlesborough, Huddersfield and Birmingham. Write to Stuart A. Paterson for information on the next convention.

National Poetry Foundation
27 Mill Road, Fareham, Hampshire PO16 0TH
☎/Fax 01329 822218
Contact Johnathon Clifford

A charitable poetry organisation (Registered Charity No: 283032) founded in 1981 administered by a board of trustees from the address above. With the financial assistance of Rosemary Arthur, who has so far put over £62,000 into the kitty, the NPF attempts to encourage new writers through a series of rather well produced poetry books. Annual reading fees cost £20 which, in addition, gives members access to *Pause*, the organisation's internal magazine. The NPF has an interest in the professional poetry recital as a fund-raising device for the furtherance of its work. Eight small mags and a number of individual poets have to-date benefited from NPF financial aid. Grants are small, unrenewable and directed at that sector of the poetry community traditionally ignored by other bodies. A good history of the NPF, together with information on poetry and the poetry scene can be found in Johnathon Clifford's self-published *Metric Feet & Other Gang Members*, available from the same address.

The National Small Press Centre
BM Bozo, London WC1N 3XX

Director *John Nicholson*
Press Officer *Cecilia Boggis*
Liaison Officers *John & Lesley Dench*
Treasurer *Andy Hopton*

A point of focus for small, self and independent publishers. Offers advice surgeries, book ordering services, publicity, help with origination and design, mounts exhibitions and workshops, holds a comprehensive reference library. Publishes *News From The Centre* (bi-monthly) and *Small Press Listings* (quarterly). Joint annual subscription to these publications is £12. The Centre's *Handbook* is available at £12 (plus

£1.50 postage). An outgrowth of the former *Small Press Group* the Centre was originally housed at Middlesex University but is currently relocating. Contact the liaison officers for more information.

The New Writer
PO Box 60, Cranbrook, Kent TN17 2ZR
☎01580 212626

Editor *Suzanne Ruthven*
Publisher *Merric Davidson*

The contemporary writing magazine resulting from the merging of *Quartos* and *Acclaim* magazines. Includes a poets' showcase edited by Abi Hughes-Edwards along with news and views from the UK poetry scene. Subscriptions £29.50 for ten issues. Best single source of information on poetry competitions. Offers an inexpensive critical service for poets, currently £12.00 for six poems. Send two first-class stamps for free back issue. (See also **Magazines**.)

The Northern Poetry Library
Central Library, The Willows, Morpeth, Northumberland NE61 1TA
☎01670 511156/512385   Fax 01670 518012
E-mail: amenities@northumberland.gov.uk

Membership available to everyone in Cleveland, Cumbria, Durham, Northumberland and Tyne and Wear. Associate membership available for all outside the region. Over 13,000 books and magazines for loan including virtually all poetry published in the UK since 1968. Access to English Poetry, the full text database of all English Poetry from 600 - 1900. Postal lending available too. In association with MidNag publishes *Red Herring*, a poetry magazine.

The Poetry Book Society
Book House, 45 East Hill, London SW18 2QZ
☎0181 870 8403   Fax 0181 877 1615

Director *Clare Brown*

For readers, writers, students and teachers of poetry. Founded in 1953 by T. S. Eliot and funded by the Arts Council, the PBS is a unique membership organisation providing up-to-date and comprehensive information about poetry from publishers in the UK and Ireland. Members receive the quarterly *PBS Bulletin* packed with articles by poets, poems, news, listings and access to discounts of at least 25% off featured titles. These range from classics to contemporary works. There are three membership packages – two of which include a number of new books specially selected by the Society's

panel of experts. Subscriptions start at £10. The PBS also runs the annual **T. S. Eliot Prize** for the best collection of new poetry.

The Poetry Business
The Studio, Byram Arcade, Westgate, Huddersfield, West Yorkshire HD1 1ND
☎01484 434840   Fax 01484 426566
E-mail: poetry-business@GEO2.poptel.org.uk

Administrators *Peter Sansom, Janet Fisher*

Founded in 1986, the Business publishes *The North* magazine, and books, pamphlets and cassettes under the Smith/Doorstop imprint. It runs an annual competition and organises monthly writing Saturdays. Send an s.a.e. for full details.

Poetry Ireland/Eigse Eireann
Bermingham Tower, Upper Yard, Dublin Castle, Dublin, Republic of Ireland
☎00 353 1 6714632   Fax 00 353 1 6714634
E-mail: poetry@iol.ie

Director *Theo Dorgan*
General Manager *Niamh Morris*

The national poetry organisation for Ireland, supported by Arts Councils both sides of the border. Publishes a quarterly magazine *Poetry Ireland Review* and a bi-monthly newsletter of upcoming events and competitions, as well as organising tours and readings by Irish and foreign poets and the National Poetry Competition of the Year, open to poets working in both Irish and English. Administers the Austin Clarke Library, a collection of over 6000 volumes and is Irish partner in the European Poetry Translation Network.

The Poetry Library
Royal Festival Hall, Level 5, London SE1 8XX
☎0171 921 0943/0664/0940
Fax 0171 921 0939
E-mail: poetrylibrary@rfh.org.uk
Website: http://www.poetrylibrary.org.uk

Librarian *Mary Enright*

Founded by the Arts Council in 1953. A collection of 45,000 titles of modern poetry since 1912, from Georgian to Rap, representing all English-speaking countries and including translations into English by contemporary poets. Two copies of each title are held, one for loan and one for reference. A wide range of poetry magazines and ephemera from all over the world are kept along with cassettes, records and videos for consultation, with many available for loan.

There is a children's poetry section with a teacher's resource collection. An information service compiles lists of poetry magazines, competitions, publishers, groups and workshops, which are available from the Library on receipt of a large s.a.e. or direct from the library's website. It also has a noticeboard for lost quotations, through which it tries to identify lines or fragments of poetry which have been sent in by other readers.

General enquiry service available. Membership is free, proof of identity and address are essential to join. Open 11.00am to 8.00pm, Tuesday to Sunday. The Library's website is one of the best poetry resources on the Net.

Beside the Library is *The Voice Box*, a performance space especially for literature. For details of current programme ring 0171 921 0906.

Poetry London Newsletter
35 Benthal Road, London N16 7AR
E-mail: pdaniels@easynet.co.uk

Contacts *Peter Daniels* (listings & subscriptions), *Katherine Gallagher* (promotions), *Pascale Petit* (poetry editor), *Greta Stoddart* (reviews).

Published three times a year, *PLN* includes poetry by new and established writers, reviews of recent collections and anthologies, features on issues relating to poetry, and an encyclopaedic listings section of virtually everything to do with poetry in the capital and the South East. The magazine also carries a limited coverage of events elsewhere.

The Poetry Society
22 Betterton Street, London WC2H 9BU
☎0171 240 4810   Fax 0171 240 4818
E-mail: poetrysoc@dial.pipex.com
Website: http://www.poetrysoc.com

Chair *Mary Enright*
Director *Chris Meade*

Founded in 1909, which ought to make it venerable, the Society exists to help poets and poetry thrive in Britain. At one time notoriously strife-ridden, it has been undergoing a renaissance lately, reaching out from its Covent Garden base to promote the national health of poetry in a range of imaginative ways. Membership costs £27.50 for individuals. Friends membership is £10. Current activities include:

● A quarterly, recently redesigned magazine of new verse, views and criticism, *Poetry Review*, edited by Peter Forbes.
● A quarterly newsletter, *Poetry News*.
● Promotions, events and co-operation with Britain's many literature festivals, poetry venues and poetry publishers.
● Competitions and awards including the

annual **National Poetry Competition** with a substantial first prize.
● A mss diagnosis service, *The Script*, which gives detailed reports on submissions. Reduced rates for members.
● Seminars, fact sheets, training courses, ideas packs.
● *Publishes* the excellent *Poetry Society Resources* files for primary level, and provides specialist information and advice on all aspects of poetry in education. Recently published are *The Young Poetry Pack*, an informative and colourful guide to reading, writing and performing poetry along with colourful poetry posters for Keystages 2 & 3. Many of Britain's most popular poets - including Michael Rosen, Roger McGough and Jackie Kay - contribute, offering advice and inspiration.
● The Café serving snacks & drink to members, friends and guests, part of *The Poetry Place*, a venue for many poetry activities - readings, poetry clinic, workshops and poetry launches.

Current developments at the Society include *Poetry Places*, a national programme of residencies, placements and projects.

Poeziecentrum
Hoornstraat 11, B-9000 Ghent, Belgium
☎00 32 9 225 22 25   Fax 00 32 9 225 90 54

Manager Willy Tibergien

Taking over some of the activities of the now defunct *European Centre For The Promotion of Poetry*, Poeziecentrum (Poetry Centre) aims to document everything to do with poetry and poetry activity. It has an archive of literary periodicals, press cuttings, information on poets, a non-book poetry collection and other data. Poeziecentrum has its own press publishing collections along with the bi-monthly journal, *Poeziekrant*. The emphasis is on suppressed genres. The Centre is keen to expand its activities on an international level by developing a European Poetry Network of activity and exchange. Like-minded organisations are asked to make contact.

Point
Apdo 119, E-03590 Altea, Spain
☎00 34 6 584 2350   Fax 00 34 6 584 2350
Brusselsesteenweg 356, B-9402 Ninove, Belgium
☎00 32 54 32 4748   Fax 00 32 54 32 4660
E-mail: elpoeta@point-editions.com
Website: www.point-editions.com

Director *Germain Droogenbroodt*

Founded as Poetry International in 1984, Point

has offices in Spain and Belgium. A multilingual publisher of contemporary verse from established poets, the organisation has brought out more than 60 titles in at least eight languages, including English. Editions run the original work alongside a verse translation into Dutch made in co-operation with the poet. The organisation's website is highly developed and features much English language verse. Point also organises an annual international poetry festival in Altea, Spain.

Regional Arts Boards
See **Arts Councils and Regional Arts Boards**

Scottish Poetry Library
Tweeddale Court, 14 High Street, Edinburgh EH1 1TE
☎0131-557 2876
E-mail: spl/queries@presence.co.uk
Librarian *Penny Duce*

A comprehensive reference and lending collection of work by Scottish poets in Gaelic, Scots and English, plus the work of international poets, including books, tapes, videos, news cuttings and magazines. Borrowing is free to all. Services include: a postal lending scheme, for which there is a small fee, a mobile library which can visit schools and other centres by arrangement, exhibitions, bibliographies, publications, information and promotion in the field of poetry. Also available is an online catalogue and computer index to poetry and poetry periodicals. There is a membership scheme costing £10 annually. Members receive a newsletter and support the library.

Survivors' Poetry
Diorama Arts Centre, 34 Osnaburgh Street, London NW1 3ND
Administration *Clare Douglas*
☎0171 916 5317   Fax 0171 916 0830
Outreach *Alison Smith* (0171 916 6637)
London Events *Patrick Fahy* (0171 916 0825)

Arts Council-funded literature/performance project managed by and for poets who have survived the mental-health system. Organises regular poetry workshops and performances in London and throughout the UK. Also runs performance training workshops led by established writers. Has published four full-length anthologies of Survivors' work. Through its Outreach Project has established fourteen groups in a UK-wide network which spreads from Bristol to Glasgow and London to Aberystwyth

Tŷ Newydd
Llanystumdwy, Cricieth, Gwynedd LL52 0LW
☎01766 522811   Fax 01766 523095
Director *Sally Baker*

Run by the Taliesin Trust, an independent, Arvon-style residential writers centre established in the one-time home of Lloyd George in North Wales. The programme (which runs in both Welsh and in English) has a regular poetry content. Fees start at £100 for weekends and £275 for week-long courses. Tutors to-date have included Gillian Clarke, Wendy Cope, Roger McGough, Carol Ann Duffy, Liz Lochhead, Peter Finch and Paul Henry. Send for their descriptive leaflets. (See also **Writers' Courses, Circles and Workshops**.)

Small Presses

Aard Press
c/o Aardverx, 31 Mountearl Gardens, London
SW16 2NL
Managing Editor D. *Jarvis, Dawn Redwood*
FOUNDED 1971. *Publishes* artists' bookworks,
experimental/visual poetry, 'zines, eonist litera-
ture, topographics, ephemera and international
mail-art documentation. TITLES: *Eos – The Arts
& Letters of Transkind* (TG & M–A 'zine); *I, Jade
Green, Jade's Ladies, Jade AntiJade* (thrillers) by A.
K. Ashe; *Actuary* Dawn Redwood (novel).
AUTHORS/ARTISTS: Dawn Redwood, Petal
Jeffery, Phaedra Kelly, Barry Edgar Pilcher
(Eire), D. Jarvis, Harry Fox. No unsolicited
material or proposals.
Royalties not paid. No sale-or-return deals.

ABCD
See **Allardyce, Barnett, Publishers**

Agneau 2
See **Allardyce, Barnett, Publishers**

AK Press/AKA Books
PO Box 12766, Edinburgh EH8 9YE
☎0131 555 5165   Fax 0131 555 5215
Managing Editor *Alexis McKay*
AK Press grew out of the activities of AK
Distribution which distributes a wide range of
radical (anarchist, feminist, etc.) literature (books,
pamphlets, periodicals, magazines), both fiction
and non-fiction. *Publishes* politics, history, situ-
ationist work, occasional fiction in both book
and pamphlet form. About 12 titles a year.
TITLES *Pen and the Sword* Edward W. Said;
Chronicles of Dissent Noam Chomsky; *Some
Recent Attacks* James Kelman; *Scum Manifesto*
Valerie Solanas; *Tales From the Clit* ed. Cherie
Matrix. Proposals and synopses welcome if they
fall within AK's specific areas of interest.
Royalties paid.

The Alembic Press
Hyde Farm House, Marcham, Abingdon,
Oxon OX13 6NX
☎01865 391391   Fax 01865 391322
E-mail: AlembicPrs@aol.com
Owner *Claire Bolton*
FOUNDED 1976. Publisher of hand-produced
books by traditional letterpress methods. Short
print-runs. *Publishes* bibliography, book arts

and printing, miniatures and occasional poetry.
Book design and production service to like-
minded authors wishing to publish in this manner. No unsolicited mss.

Allardyce, Barnett, Publishers
14 Mount Street, Lewes, East Sussex
BN7 1HL
☎01273 479393   Fax 01273 479393
Publisher *Fiona Allardyce*
Managing Editor *Anthony Barnett*
FOUNDED 1981. *Publishes* art, literature and
music, with past emphasis on contemporary
English poets. About 3 titles a year.
    IMPRINTS **Agneau 2**, **ABCD**, **Allardyce
Book**. TITLES *Poems* Andrea Zanzotto; *Desert
Sands: The Recordings and Performances of Stuff
Smith* Anthony Barnett; *The Black Heralds* César
Vallejo. Unsolicited mss and synopses cannot be
considered.

Anglo-Saxon Books
Frithgarth, Thetford Forest Park, Hockwold
cum Wilton, Norfolk IP26 4NQ
☎01842 828430   Fax 01842 828332
Managing Editor *Tony Linsell*
FOUNDED 1990 to promote a greater awareness
of and interest in early English history and culture. Originally concentrated on Old English
texts but now also publishes less academic, more
popular titles. Seeking titles for all periods of
English history. *Publishes* English history, culture, language and society. About 5–10 titles a
year. TITLES *A Handbook of Anglo-Saxon Food;
English Martial Arts; The Rebirth of England and
English: The Vision of William Barnes.* Unsolicited
synopses welcome but return postage necessary.
    Royalties standard rate.

AVERT
AIDS Education and Research Trust,
4 Brighton Road, Horsham, West Sussex
RH13 5BA
☎01403 210202   Fax 01403 211001
Managing Editor *Annabel Kanabus*
Publishing arm of the AIDS Education and
Research Trust, a national registered charity
established 1986. *Publishes* books and leaflets
about HIV infection and AIDS. About 3 titles a
year. TITLES *AIDS: The Secondary Scene;*

Guidelines for Management of Children with HIV Infection. Unsolicited mss, synopses and ideas welcome.
Royalties paid accordingly.

M. & M. Baldwin

24 High Street, Cleobury Mortimer, Kidderminster DY14 8BY
☎01299 270110   Fax 01299 270110
Managing Editor *Dr Mark Baldwin*
FOUNDED 1978. *Publishes* local interest/history and inland waterways books. Up to 5 titles a year. TITLES *Idle Women; West Midland Wanderings; Canal Coins.* Unsolicited mss, synopses and ideas for books welcome (not general fiction).
Royalties paid.

Bardon Enterprises

20 Queens Keep, Palmerston Road, Southsea, Hampshire PO5 3NX
☎01705 874900   Fax 01705 874900
E-mail: info@bardonia.softnet.co.uk
Website: www.soft.net.uk/bardonia
Managing Director *W. B. Henshaw*
FOUNDED 1996. *Publishes* music, art and academic books. 5 titles in 1997. TITLES *Bibliography of Organ Music; Dictionary of Musical Terms.* Unsolicited mss, synopses and ideas welcome. No pictorial books.

Barnworks Publishing

Asbury, Roydon Road, Launceston, Cornwall PL15 8DN
☎01566 777303   Fax 01566 777303
Managing Editor *Hazel Kelly*
Publishes interesting lives. TITLES *Together They Fly; French Resistance in Sussex; Appleford: A Berkshire Village.* 'We accept more mss for vanity publishing, offering individual, tailored advice, editing, format suggestions and aid with distribution.' Telephone in the first instance.
Royalties paid.

BB Books

See under **Poetry Presses**

Birlinn Ltd

Unit 8, Canongate Venture, 5 New Street, Edinburgh EH8 5BH
☎0131 556 6660   Fax 0131 558 1500
Managing Editor *Hugh Andrew*
FOUNDED 1992. *Publishes* Gaelic, Scottish interest and history. 80 titles planned for 1999. TITLES *Scottish Folklore* Raymond Lamont-

Brown; *Island Going* Robert Atkinson; *Drove Roads of Scotland* A. R. B. Haldane. No unsolicited mss; synopses and ideas welcome.
Royalties paid.

Black Cat Books

See **Neil Miller Publications**

The Bonaventura Press

Bagpath, Tetbury, Gloucestershire GL8 8YG
☎01453 860827   Fax 01453 860487
Managing Editor *Janet Sloss*
FOUNDED 1995 as a self-publishing venture. Synopses and ideas concerning the British connection with Menorca welcome. Shared cost publishing considered in certain circumstances. TITLES *Richard Kane, Governor of Minorca; Archive Annie or How to Solve the Mysteries of Historical Research; Menorcan Cooking; Menorcan Proverbs.*

The Book Castle

12 Church Street, Dunstable, Bedfordshire LU5 4RU
☎01582 605670   Fax 01582 662431
Managing Editor *Paul Bowes*
FOUNDED 1986. *Publishes* non-fiction of local interest (Bedfordshire, Hertfordshire, Buckinghamshire, Northamptonshire, the Chilterns). 6+ titles a year. About 50 titles in print. TITLES *Chiltern Walks* series; *The Hill of the Martyr; Journeys into Bedfordshire.* Unsolicited mss, synopses and ideas for books welcome.
Royalties paid.

The Book Gallery

Bedford Road, St. Ives, Cornwall TR26 1SP
☎01736 793545
Directors *David & Tina Wilkinson*
FOUNDED 1991. *Publishes* limited edition monographs by and about writers/painters associated with the so-called Newlyn and St Ives schools of painting. Topics include Sven Berlin, Kit Barker, Arthur Caddick, Guido Morris, Leach Pottery. Ideas welcome.
Royalties not paid; flat fee.

Book-in-Hand Ltd

20 Shepherds Hill, London N6 5AH
☎0181 341 7650   Fax 0181 341 7650
Contact *Ann Kritzinger*
Print production service for self-publishers. Includes design and editing advice to give customers a greater chance of selling in the open market. Also runs an editing service called Scriptmate.

Bookmarque Publishing

26 Cotswold Close, Minster Lovell,
Oxfordshire OX8 5SX
☎01993 775179

Managing Editor *John Rose*

FOUNDED 1987. Publishing business with aim of filling gaps in motoring history of which it is said 'there are many!' *Publishes* motoring history, motor sport and general titles. About 8 titles a year (increasing). All design and typesetting of books done in-house. TITLES *The First Motor Racing in Britain – Bexhill-on-Sea 1902; 3-Wheelers' Almanac; The 1903 Irish Gordon Bennett Race.* Unsolicited mss, synopses and ideas welcome on transport titles. S.a.e. required for reply or return of material or for advice on publishing your work. Jacket/cover design advice. *Royalties* paid.

Bozo

BM Bozo, London WC1N 3XX

Managing Editors *John & Cecilia Nicholson*

FOUNDED 1981. Began by producing tiny pamphlets (*Patriotic English Tracts*) and has gained a reputation as 'one of England's foremost pamphleteers'. *Publishes* historical analyses, apocalyptic rants, wry/savage humour and political 'filth'. Considerable expansion of titles is underway. No unsolicited mss, synopses or ideas. *Royalties* not paid.

Brantwood Books

PO Box 144, Orpington, Kent BR6 6LZ
☎01689 897520   Fax 01689 897520

Managing Editor *Philip D. Turner*

Publishes low volume runs of specialist cinema titles, ranging from Russian cinema architecture to 32-page illustrated guides to British and North American cinema circuit histories. 2 titles in 1997. DIVISIONS **Brantwood Books** and **Outline Publications** UK/US cinema circuit and film studio histories; **Brantwood Biographical** Biographies of movie moguls and directors; **Brantwood Miniature Life** Series of outline biographies of popular movie stars; **Brantwood Technical** Screen, film and camera/projector techniques. Ideas which can be adapted to a 32-page format are welcome.

Brentham Press

See under **Poetry Presses**

Brilliant Publications

The Old School Yard, Leighton Road,
Northall, Dunstable, Bedfordshire LU6 2HA
☎01525 222844   Fax 01525 221250

Publisher *Priscilla Hannaford*

FOUNDED 1993. *Publishes* books for pre-school, primary and special needs teachers. About 10–15 titles a year. SERIES *How to be Brilliant at ...* for 7–11-year-olds; *How to Sparkle at ...* for 5–7-year-olds; *Activities* for 3–5-year-olds. Submit synopsis and sample pages in the first instance. *Royalties* paid twice yearly.

Brinnoven

9 Thomson Green, Livingston, West Lothian EH54 8TA
☎01506 442846   Fax 01506 431060

Proprietor *William Murray*

FOUNDED 1991. *Publishes* Scottish interest titles specialising in local history, dialects, languages and traditional/folk music. About 3–5 titles a year. Unsolicited mss, synopses and ideas welcome but return postage must be included. *Royalties* and fees paid.

Business Innovations Research

Tregeraint House, Zennor, St Ives, Cornwall TR26 3DB
☎01736 797061   Fax 01736 797061

Managing Director *John T. Wilson*

Publishes business books and newsletters, home study courses, and guidebooks. Production service available to self-publishers.

Businesslike Publishing

'Bluepool', Strathoykel, Ardgay, Inverness-shire IV24 3DP
☎01549 441211
Website:
    http://www. dorian.blue@btinternet.com

Managing Editor *Iain R. McIntyre*

FOUNDED 1989. Provides a printing and publishing service for members of the **Society of Civil Service Authors**. *Publishes* magazines, collections of poetry, short stories (not individual poems or short stories) and Scottish history. About 6 titles a year. TITLES *Childhood Days in Glasgow; To Freedom Born* – 2nd printing (Doric Scots poetry); *Verse or Worse* (poetry); *Korea, Land of the Morning Calm* (non-fiction); *A Question of Patience; Celebrations* (2 plays). Ideas/synopses accepted. No unsolicited mss. *Royalties* generally not paid but negotiable in some circumstances.

Call Times Publications

See **Freudian Variant** under **Magazines**

Cartmel Press Associates
Old Orchard, Barber Green, Grange-over-Sands, Cumbria LA11 6HU
☎015395 36390
E-mail: dguthrie@ndirect.co.uk
Managing Editor *D. M. Guthrie*

FOUNDED in 1983 to publish art monographs and now publishing full-length biographies. TITLE *The Life and Art of John Cecil Stephenson.* No unsolicited mss; synopses and ideas welcome. *Royalties* paid.

Chameleon HH Publishing
The Quarry House, East End, Witney, Oxfordshire OX8 6QA
☎01993 880223   Fax 01993 880236
E-mail: chameleon.hh@virgin.net
Directors *David Hall, Marion Hazzledine*

FOUNDED 1997. CD-ROM and Web publishers on behalf of commercial publishers, institutes, associations and government bodies. No marketing or distribution department so no unsolicited mss but all enquiries welcome. Full editorial services also offered.

Chapter Two
13 Plum Lane, Plumstead Common, London SE18 3AF
☎0181 316 5389   Fax 0181 854 5963
Managing Editor *E. N. Cross*

FOUNDED 1976. Chapter Two's chief activity is the propagation of the Christian faith through the printed page. *Publishes* about 12 titles a year exclusively on Plymouth Brethren. No unsolicited mss, synopses or ideas. Enquiries only. *Royalties* not paid.

Charlewood Press
7 Weavers Place, Chandlers Ford, Eastleigh, Hampshire SO53 1TU
☎01703 261192
Managing Editors *Gerald Ponting, Anthony Light*

FOUNDED 1987. Publishes local history booklets on the Fordingbridge area, researched and written by the two partners. Also leaflets on local walks. TITLES *Tudor Fordingbridge; Breamore – A Short History & Guide; The Tragedies of the Dodingtons.* No unsolicited mss. *Royalties* not paid.

The Cheverell Press
Manor Studios, Manningford Abbots, Pewsey, Wiltshire SN9 6HS
☎01672 563163   Fax 01672 564301

Managing Editor *Sarah de Larrinaga*

Publishes careers, media and performing arts. No fiction. IMPRINTS **The Cheverell Press, First Hand Books**. TITLES *The Guide to Drama Training in the UK 1997/8; How To Get Into Drama School; The Guide to Careers and Training in the Performing Arts; How to Become a Working Actor; Guide to Careers & Training in the Media.* Currently using researchers/writers on a fee basis, rather than royalties. No unsolicited mss. Started as a self-publisher and has produced a self-publishers information pack. Write for details.

Chrysalis Press
7 Lower Ladyes Hills, Kenilworth, Warwickshire CV8 2GN
☎01926 855223   Fax 01926 856611
Managing Editor *Brian Boyd*

FOUNDED 1994. *Publishes* fiction, literary criticism and biography. TITLES *Two Tales; Challenge and Renewal: D.H. Lawrence and the Thematic Novel.* No unsolicited mss. *Royalties* paid.

CNP Publications
Roseland, Gorran, St Austell, Cornwall
☎01726 843501   Fax 01726 843501
Managing Editor *Dr James Whetter*

FOUNDED 1975. *Publishes* poetry, political essays, local Cornish interest/biography and Celtic design. 1–2 titles a year. TITLES *An Baner Kernewek (The Cornish Banner)* – quarterly local-interest magazine; Cornish history published under the **Lyfrow Trelyspen** imprint – *Cornish Weather and Cornish People in the 17th Century; The Bodrugans: A Study of a Cornish Medieval Knightly Family.* Unsolicited mss, synopses and ideas welcome. *Royalties* not paid.

Condor Books
78 Highland Road, Earlsdon, Coventry, West Midlands CV5 6GR
☎01203 714359
Contact *Alvaro Graña*

Condor Books was created by pan-pipes expert Alvaro Graña to publish his book *How to Make and Play Pan-Pipes.*

Copperfield Books
Hillbrook House, Lyncombe Vale Road, Bath BA2 4LS
☎01225 442835   Fax 01225 319755
Managing Director *John Brushfield*

Publishes paperback fiction and general non-fiction. No unsolicited mss; 'we only commission books to our own specification'.

Corvus Press
See **ignotus press**

The Cosmic Elk
68 Elsham Crescent, Lincoln LN6 3YS
☎01522 820922
E-mail: HevHobden@aol.com
Managing Editor *Heather Hobden*

FOUNDED 1988. For academic, specialised and local interests, in science, history and the history of science. Books, leaflets, posters, handbooks, booklets to accompany exhibitions, videos, CD-ROMs, websites, tutorial notes, etc. A4 card and comb bindings. Illustrations and colour. Future paperbacks planned. TITLES *John Harrison and the Problem of Longitude; Red Shift and the Origin of the Universe; The Telescope Revolution; Law or War – the Legal Aspects of the Cuban Missile Crisis; The Hampton Court Clock.* Enquiries welcome.

Creation Books
83 Clerkenwell Road, London EC1R 5AR
☎0171 430 9878   Fax 0171 242 5527
Managing Editor *James Williamson*

FOUNDED 1990 to publish books of extreme thought and imagination – surreal, pulp, horror, avant-garde, underground film, art, erotica. 20 titles in 1997.
Royalties paid annually.

Crescent Moon Publishing and Joe's Press
PO Box 393, Maidstone, Kent ME14 5XU
Managing Editor *Jeremy Robinson*

FOUNDED 1988 to publish critical studies of figures such as D. H. Lawrence, Thomas Hardy, André Gide, Walt Disney, Rilke, Leonardo da Vinci, Mark Rothko, C. P. Cavafy and Hélèn Cixous. *Publishes* literature, criticism, media, art, feminism, painting, poetry, travel, guidebooks, cinema and some fiction. Literary magazine, *Passion*, launched February 1994. Quarterly. Twice-yearly anthology of American poetry, *Pagan America*. About 15–20 titles per year. TITLES *Samuel Beckett Goes into the Silence; Jackie Collins and the Blockbuster Novel; Vincent Van Gogh; The Poetry of Cinema; Wild Zones: Pornography, Art and Feminism; Andrea Dworkin.* Unsolicited mss, synopses and ideas welcome but approach in writing first and send an s.a.e.
Royalties negotiable.

Crocus Books
See under **Poetry Presses**

Daniels Medica
Zetland House, Cley Next The Sea, Norfolk NR25 7RS
☎01263 740230   Fax 01263 740343
E-mail: v.daniels@dial.pipex.com
Publisher *Dr Victor G. Daniels*

Educational materials and training packs for the pharmaceutical industry.

Diamond Press
See under **Poetry Presses**

Dionysia Press
20A Montgomery Street, Edinburgh EH7 5JS
☎0131 478 0927   Fax 0131 478 2572
Managing Editor *Denise Smith*

FOUNDED 1989. Initially published the literary magazine *Understanding* which featured poetry, short stories, extracts from plays, reviews and articles, and now publishes poetry collections and translations. TITLES *Broken Angels* Susanne Roxman; *The Sand Garden* Thom Nairn; *And Here's What You Could Have Won* Paul Hullah. Unsolicited mss, synopses and ideas welcome.

Dog House Publications
18 Marlow Avenue, Eastbourne, East Sussex BN22 8SJ
☎01323 729214
Managing Editor *Silvia Kent*

FOUNDED 1990. Publishes books and booklets on dog behaviour and related subjects. Unsolicited mss, synopses and ideas welcome but must be relevant. Mss must be practical and informed; 'we get too many doggie sob stories and poetry!' TITLES: *Your Dog and Your Baby; Overcoming Dog Problems; Training Your Dog With Love; Help to Heal Your Dog.* Branching out into other doggie subjects, e.g. health and general new age dog care and training.
Royalties paid.

Dragon's Head Press
PO Box 3369, London SW6 6JN
Managing Editor *Ade Dimmick*

Founded 1993. Independent small press publishing project, specialising in dragon-lore and related themes. TITLES *The Dragon Chronicle*, a special-interest academic and literary journal devoted entirely to dragons; *Dragon Dance*, poetry anthology; *Water Dragons: A Guide to Lake Serpent Legends Around the World.* Member of the **Association of Little Presses**. Unsolicited mss welcome.

The Dragonby Press
15 High Street, Dragonby, Scunthorpe
DN15 0BE
☎01724 840645
Managing Editor *Richard Williams*
FOUNDED 1987 to publish affordable bibliography for reader, collector and dealer. About 3 titles a year. TITLES *Collins Crime Club: A Checklist*. Unsolicited mss, synopses and ideas welcome for bibliographical projects only.
Royalties paid.

Dramatic Lines
PO Box 201, Twickenham TW2 5RQ
☎0181 296 9502   Fax 0181 296 9503
Managing Editor *John Nicholas*
Founded to promote drama for young people. Publications with a wide variety of theatrical applications including classroom use and school assemblies, drama examinations, auditions, festivals and theatre group performance. TITLES *The Sieve; Cabbage* (monologues); *Pears* (duologues); *Will Shakespeare Save the King!* (one-act plays); *Drama Lessons in Action* (resource book). Unsolicited drama-related mss, proposals and synopses welcome.
Royalties paid.

Education Now Publishing Cooperative Ltd
113 Arundel Drive, Bramcote Hills,
Nottingham NG9 3FQ
☎0115 9257261   Fax 0115 9257261
Managing Editors *Dr Roland Meighan,
Philip Toogood*
A non-profit research and writing group set up in reaction to 'the totalitarian tendencies of the 1988 Education Act'. Its aim is to widen the terms of the debate about education and its choices. *Publishes* reports on positive educational initiatives such as flexi-schooling, mini-schooling, small schooling, home-based education and democratic schooling. 4–5 titles a year. TITLES *Flexischooling* Roland Meighan; *Developing Democratic Education* Clive Harber. No unsolicited mss or ideas. Enquiries only.
Royalties generally not paid.

Educational Heretics Press
113 Arundel Drive, Bramcote Hills,
Nottingham NG9 3FQ
☎0115 9257261   Fax 0115 9257261
Directors *Janet & Roland Meighan*

Non-profit venture which aims to question the dogmas of schooling in particular and education in general. TITLES *Alice Miller: The Unkind Society, Parenting and Schooling* Chris Shute; *Rules, Routines and Regimentation* Ann Sherman; *Compulsory Schooling Disease* Chris Shute; *John Holt: Personalised Education and the Reconstruction of Schooling* Roland Meighan. No unsolicited material. Enquiries only.
Royalties not paid but under review.

EKO Fund
Wedgwood Memorial College, Barlaston,
Staffs ST12 9DG
☎01782 372105   Fax 01782 372393
Managing Editor *Brian W. Burnett*
FOUNDED January 1996 to publish modern, lively books and magazines in and about Esperanto. Unsolicited mss, synopses and ideas welcome.
Royalties paid.

Enable Enterprises
150 Sadler Road, Radford, Coventry CV6 2LN
☎070209 21158   Fax 070209 21158
E-mail: enquires@enable.demon.co.uk
Website: http://www.enableonline.com
Contact *Simon Stevens*
Enable Enterprises provides accessibilty awareness publications and other material to small and medium-sized businesses. It welcomes unsolicited material, especially in terms of accessibility related materal.

estamp
204 St Albans Avenue, London W4 5JU
☎0181 994 2379   Fax 0181 994 2379
Contact *Silvie Turner*
Independent publisher of fine art books on printmaking, papermaking and artists' book–making. Books are designed and written for artists, craftspeople and designers. TITLES *British Printmaking Studios; About Prints; Europe for Printmakers; British Artists Books; Which Paper?* Approach in writing in first instance.

Feather Books
Fair View, Old Coppice, Lyth Bank,
Shrewsbury, Shropshire SY3 0BW
☎01743 872177   Fax 01743 872177
E-mail: john@feather.icom-web.com
Website: http://www.feather.icom-web.com
Managing Editor *Rev. John Waddington-
Feather*
FOUNDED 1980 to publish writers' group work.

All material has a strong Christian ethos. *Publishes* poetry (mainly, but not exclusively, religious). 10 titles a year. TITLES *The Quill Hedgehog Series; The Poetry Church Magazine; Feather Books Poets Series; Feather Books Songs & Hymns Series; Feather's Little Birthday Book Series*. No unsolicited mss, synopses or ideas. All correspondence to include s.a.e. please.

Ferry Publications Ltd
PO Box 9, Narberth, Pembrokeshire SA68 0PE
☎01834 891460   Fax 01834 891463
Managing Editor *Miles Cowsill*

FOUNDED 1987 to publish ferry and shipping books. 3–4 titles a year. TITLES *Only Britanny Ferries; P&O The Fleet; Ferries of Portsmouth*. Also publishes *European Ferry Scene* - 4 issues per year. Unsolicited mss, synopses and ideas welcome.
Royalties paid.

First Hand Books
See **The Cheverell Press**

First Rank Publishing
23 Ditchling Rise, Brighton, East Sussex BN1 4QL
☎01273 279934   Fax 01273 297128
Contact *Byron Jacobs, Andrew Kinsman*

FOUNDED 1996. Packagers and publishers of sports, games and leisure books. 12–15 titles a year. Also providers of editorial, production and typesetting services. No unsolicited mss but ideas and synopses welcome.
Fees paid.

Fisher Miller Publishing
17 The Drive, Oakley, Basingstoke, Hampshire RG23 7BA
☎01256 781050   Fax 01256 782850
Managing Editor *Joan Miller*

ESTABLISHED 1994 as a result of enquiries from an author whose book was too esoteric to warrant publication by a commercial publisher. 'We are a service publisher, passing on the costs of publishing direct to the author to facilitate self-publishing to professional standards.' Unsolicited mss, synopses and ideas welcome. TITLES *The Hibiscus Years* George Bishop; *Dear Mr Willis* Derek Wren; *A Future Beyond the Sun* Mali Klein.
Royalties not paid.

Five Leaves Publications
PO Box 81, Nottingham NG5 4ER
☎0115 9603355
Contact *Ross Bradshaw*

FOUNDED 1995 (taking over the publishing programme of Mushroom Bookshop), producing 6–8 titles a year. *Publishes* fiction, poetry, politics and Jewish interest. TITLES *The Bend in the Road: Refugees Writing* ed. Jennifer Langer; *Starkness at Noon* Richard Boston; *The Golem of Old Prague* Michael Rosen; *The Radical Twenties: Literature, Politics, Society* John Lucas. Publisher of several books by Michael Rosen. No unsolicited mss; titles normally commissioned.
Royalties and fees paid.

Flying Witch Publications
See **ignotus press**

Forth Naturalist & Historian
University of Stirling, Stirling FK9 4LA
☎01259 215091   Fax 01786 464994
E-mail: dsm2@stirling.ac.uk
Website:
  http://www.stir.ac.uk/theuni/forthnat/
Also at: 30 Dunmar Drive, Alloa, Clackmannanshire FK10 2EH
Honorary Editors *Lindsay Corbett, Neville Dix*

FOUNDED 1975 by the collaboration of Stirling University members and the Central Regional Council to promote interests and publications on central Scotland. Aims to provide a 'valuable local studies educational resource for mid-Scotland schools, libraries and people'. Runs an annual symposium: Man and the Landscape. *Publishes* naturalist, historical and environmental studies and maps. TITLES *The Forth Naturalist & Historian from 1976* (annual publication; 1997 is Vol. 20); *Doune – Historical Notes; Postcards of the Past; Central Scotland: Land, Wildlife, People* (a new survey); *The Ochil Hills: Landscapes, Wildlife, Heritage, Walks; Airthrey and Bridge of Allan; Alloa Tower and The Erskines of Mar; Lure of Loch Lomond*; 1890s maps 25" to the mile – 24 of Central Scotland areas/places with historical notes. Over 20 selected papers from the annual are published in pamphlet form. Welcomes papers, mss and ideas relevant to central Scotland. Promotes annual environment/heritage symposia – 1997 was the 23rd year.
Royalties not paid.

The Frogmore Press
See under **Poetry Presses**

Frontier Publishing
Windetts, Kirstead, Norfolk NR15 1BR
☎01508 558174   Fax 01508 550194
Managing Editor *John Black*

FOUNDED 1983. *Publishes* travel, photography

and literature. 2–3 titles a year. TITLES *Travellers on a Trade Wind; Eye on the Hill: Horse Travels in Britain; Euphonics: A Poet's Dictionary of Sounds; The Green Book of Poetry.* No unsolicited mss; synopses and ideas welcome.
Royalties paid.

Full House Productions
12 Sunfield Gardens, Bayston Hill, Shrewsbury, Shropshire SY3 0LA
☎01743 874059   Fax 01743 874059
Managing Editor *Judith A. Shone*

FOUNDED 1993 by writer/producer Judith Shone in order to supply professionally written pantomime scripts to small production companies such as operatic societies, amateur dramatic societies and other performing groups – village halls etc. *Publishes* a complete low-cost 'panto-pack' consisting of scripts, posters and tickets. Future plans are to expand into publication of plays and sketches. All titles are written and published in-house. 14 titles to date; two planned for 1998.

Galactic Central Publications
Imladris, 25A Copgrove Road, Leeds, West Yorkshire LS8 2SP
E-mail: philsp@compuserve.com
Managing Editor *Phil Stephensen-Payne*

FOUNDED 1982 in the US. *Publishes* science fiction bibliographies. About 4 titles a year. TITLES *Gene Wolfe: Urth-Man Extraordinary; Andre Norton: Grand Master of Witch World.* All new publications originate in the UK. Unsolicited mss, synopses and ideas welcome.

The Gargoyle's Head
Chatham House, Gosshill Road, Chislehurst, Kent BR7 5NS
☎0181 467 8475   Fax 0181 295 1967
Managing Editor *Jennie Gray*

FOUNDED 1990. *Publishes* a quarterly magazine and newsletter plus books and supplements on Gothic and macabre subjects. History, literary criticism, reprints of forgotten texts, biography, architecture, art etc., usually with a gloomy and black-hued flavour. About 4 titles a year. Synopses and ideas welcome. (Also see **The Gothic Society** under **Literary Societies**).
Flat fee paid.

Gateway Books
The Hollies, Wellow, Bath BA2 8QJ
☎01225 835127   Fax 01225 840012
Publisher *Alick Bartholomew*

FOUNDED 1983. *Publishes* mind, body and spirit, alternative health. No unsolicited mss; synopses and ideas for books welcome but 'authors should check our list first'. No fiction, children's or poetry. Written submissions only; no disks or e-mails considered.
Royalties paid annually.

Geological Society Publishing House
Unit 7, Brassmill Enterprise Centre, Brassmill Lane, Bath BA1 3JN
☎01225 445046   Fax 01225 442836
Managing Editor *Mike Collins*

Publishing arm of the Geological Society which was founded in 1807. *Publishes* undergraduate and postgraduate texts in the earth sciences. 25 titles a year. Unsolicited mss, synopses and ideas welcome.
Royalties not paid.

Get a Grip
See **Working Books Ltd**

Global Books
See **Neil Miller Publications**

Glosa
PO Box 18, Richmond, Surrey TW9 2AU
☎0181 948 8417
Managing Editors *Wendy Ashby, Ronald Clark*

FOUNDED 1981. *Publishes* textbooks, dictionaries and translations for the teaching, speaking and promotion of Glosa (an international, auxiliary language); also a newsletter and journal. Rapid growth in the last couple of years. TITLES *Glosa 6000 Dictionary; Introducing Euro-Glosa; Eduka-Glosa; Central Glosa; Glosa 1000 – Chinese; Glosa 1000 – Swahili Dictionary.* In 1994 launched *Sko-Glosa,* a publication for and by younger students of Glosa to be distributed to schools in different countries. Also in 1994 published several fairy stories and activity pages for school children who are learning Glosa in school. Unsolicited mss and ideas for Glosa books welcome.

Gothic Press
PO Box 542, Highgate, London N6 6BG
Managing Editor *Robin Crisp*

Specialist publisher of Gothic titles in quality, case editions. Mostly non-fiction at present (*Carmel: Authentic Sequel to Bram Stoker's Dracula* is a notable exception). *Publishes* mysticism, supernatural, history, biography, Gothic

novels. TITLES *The Vampire Hunter's Handbook;*
*The Highgate Vampire; Mad, Bad and Dangerous
to Know; From Satan to Christ; The Grail Church.*
No unsolicited mss; synopses and ideas might
be welcome.

Flat fee paid.

Grant Books

The Coach House, New Road, Cutnall
Green, Droitwich, Worcestershire WR9 0PQ
☎01299 851588   Fax 01299 851446
Managing Editor *H. R. J. Grant*

FOUNDED 1978. *Publishes* golf-related titles only:
course architecture, history, biography, etc., but
no instructional material. New titles and old, plus
limited editions. About 6 titles a year. TITLES
*Oxford and Cambridge Golfing Society; The Golf
Courses of Newbury and Cookham; Aspects of Golf
Course Architecture (1895–1924); The Amateur:
The Stories of the Amateur Championship 1885–
1995; The Golf Courses of James Braid; Golf with a
View: Broadway Golf Club 1895–1995; The
Murdoch Golf Library; Aspects of Collecting Golf
Books; The Architectural Side of Golf; British
Professional Golfers – A Register, 1887–1930.* Un-
solicited mss, synopses and ideas welcome.

Royalties paid.

Grevatt & Grevatt

9 Rectory Drive, Newcastle upon Tyne
NE3 1XT
Chairman/Editorial Head *Dr S. Y. Killingley*

FOUNDED 1981. Alternative publisher of works
not normally commercially viable. Three books
have appeared with financial backing from professional bodies. *Publishes* academic titles and
conference reports, particularly language, linguistics and religious studies. Some poetry also.
TITLES *Overhearing the Incoherent: Selected Poems;
The Sanskrit Tradition in the Modern World,* a series
of rewritten conference/lecture proceedings
launched 1988. New titles: *Sound, Speech and
Silence: Selected Poems; Divided Attention: Selected
Poems.* No unsolicited mss. Synopses and ideas
should be accompanied by s.a.e.

Royalties paid annually (after first 500 copies).

GRM Publications

34 Holmwood Avenue, Meanwood, Leeds,
West Yorkshire LS6 4NJ
☎0113 2752456   Fax 0113 2752456
Managing Editors *Graham Wade,
Elizabeth Wade*

FOUNDED 1996. Publishes monographs on
music, especially relating to the classical guitar
repertoire. About 5 titles a year. TITLES *John
Mills, Concert Guitarist – A Celebration; Distant
Sarabandes: The Solo Guitar Music of Joaquín
Rodrigo; The Guitarist's Guide to Associated Board
Examinations.*

GSSE

11 Malford Grove, Gilwern, Abergavenny,
Gwent NP7 0RN
☎01873 830872   E-mail: GSSE@zoo.co.uk
Owner/Manager *David P. Bosworth*

Publishes newsletters and booklets describing
classroom practice (at all levels of education and
training). Ideas welcome – particularly from
practising teachers, lecturers and trainers describing how they use technology in their teaching.
TITLES *OLS News* (quarterly newsletter); series:
IT in the Classroom (first title: *Databases in the
School).*

Royalties paid by arrangement.

Guildhall Press

41 Great James Street, Derry BT48 7DF
☎01504 364413   Fax 01504 372949
Managing Editor *Adrian Kerr*

FOUNDED 1979 to produce local history ma-
terial. Government funding has helped establish
the press as a community publishing house with
increased output across a wide range of subjects.
About 12 titles a year. TITLES *No Go* Barney
McMonagle; *When the President Calls* T. Burney
and J. O'Neill; *Seeing is Believing, Murals in Derry*
Oona Woods; *Perceptions: Cultures in Conflict*
Adrian Kerr; *The Road to Bloody Sunday* Dr
Raymond McClean; *The Wile Big Derry
Phrasebook* Seamus McConnell. Unsolicited mss,
synopses and ideas welcome.

Royalties negotiable.

Happy House

3b Castledown Avenue, Hastings, East Sussex
TN34 3RJ
☎01424 434778

FOUNDED 1992 as a self-publishing venture for
Dave Arnold/Martin Honeysett collaboration
of poetry and cartoons. TITLES *Out to Lunch;
Under the Wallpaper; Before and After the Shrink;
Fragile Balance; Zen Haiku; Draw a Poem; The
Wacky World of Dave and Iggy Arnold; How the
Moon Rules the Heart and the Ocean.*

Haunted Library

Flat 1, 36 Hamilton Street, Hoole, Chester,
Cheshire CH2 3JQ
☎01244 313685   Fax 01244 313685
Managing Editor *Rosemary Pardoe*

FOUNDED 1979. *Publishes* a twice-yearly ghost story magazine and booklets in the antiquarian tradition of M. R. James. The magazine publishes stories, news and articles. 2–3 titles a year. TITLE *Ghosts & Scholars*. No unsolicited mss. *Royalties* not paid.

Heart of Albion Press

2 Cross Hill Close, Wymeswold, Loughborough, Leicestershire LE12 6UJ
☎01509 880725
Managing Editor *R. N. Trubshaw*
FOUNDED 1990 to publish books and booklets on the East Midlands area. *Publishes* mostly local history. About 4–6 titles a year. TITLES *Little-known Leicestershire & Rutland; User-Friendly Dictionary of Old English*. No unsolicited mss but synopses and ideas welcome.
Royalties negotiable.

Hedgerow Publishing Ltd

325 Abbeydale Road, Sheffield, South Yorkshire S7 1FS
☎0114 2554873   Fax 0114 2509400
Managing Editor *T. Hale*
FOUNDED 1988. Publisher of local interest postcards and greeting cards. Expanded into book publishing in 1990 with the emphasis on tourist-orientated material. Ideas for books relevant to the South Yorkshire and Northern Peak District areas will be considered. Interested in photographic submissions of colour transparencies of local views. Outright purchase only. Telephone *before* sending.
Royalties negotiable.

Highcliff Press

23 Avon Drive, Guisborough, Cleveland TS14 8AX
☎01287 637274   Fax 01287 637274
Managing Editor *Robert Sampson*
FOUNDED 1994. *Publishes* fiction, short prose, prose poems and poetry. TITLES *Metaphysical Graffiti* Estill Pollock; *Lady on a Stained Glass Fire-Escape* Pete Faulkner; *For Everything Must Be Returned* Andrew Fox; *Images* Robert Sampson. Unsolicited mss welcome.

Hilmarton Manor Press

Calne, Wiltshire SN11 8SB
☎01249 760208   Fax 01249 760379
Chairman/Managing Director *Charles Baile de Laperriere*
Publishes fine art reference only.
Royalties paid.

Horseshoe Publications

PO Box 37, Kingsley, Warrington, Cheshire WA6 8DR
☎01928 787477 (Afternoons and evenings)
Managing Editor *John C. Hibbert*
FOUNDED 1994. Initially to publish work of Cheshire writers. Poetry, short stories and own writing. Shared cost publishing considered in certain circumstances. Reading fee on full mss £25. TITLES *One Boy's War; The Reincarnate; Windmills; The Travellers Series; Taxi; Golden Boy; Whistle and I'll Be There; A Scent of Violets; Italy Again and Again*. Unsolicited mss, synopses and ideas in the realm of commercial fiction welcome. S.a.e. for return.

ignotus press

BCM-Writer, 27 Old Gloucester Street, London WC1X 3XX
☎01559 371108   Fax 01559 371108
Publisher *Suzanne Ruthven*
Specialises in full length esoteric non-fiction and fiction of all traditions although writers are advised to send s.a.e. for authors' guidelines before submitting material for consideration. All mss are checked for accuracy and knowledge of subject by specialists who will reject sword-n-sorcery and idealistic New Age material. Also *publishes Comhairle*, the official journal of the Comhairli Cairde. The articles and features published in the quarterly magazine illustrate the range of material sought by any of the ignotus press imprints. Sample copies available priced £2.50 from the publisher.
IMPRINTS **Corvus Press** *Christine Sempers* Non-fiction paperbacks and booklets relating to self-help, healing, herb lore and primitive native traditions. **Flying Witch Publications** *Frances Denton* Non-fiction paperbacks and booklets on indigenous craft and arts/craft covering Anglo Saxon, Nordic and Celtic traditions.
Royalties paid.

IKON Productions Ltd

Manor Farm House, Manor Road, Wantage, Oxfordshire OX12 8NE
☎01235 767467   Fax 01235 763211
Publisher *Clare Goodrick-Clarke*
FOUNDED 1988. *Publishes* religion, countryside and self-help. TITLES *The English Religious Tradition and the Genius of Anglicanism; Setting Your Sights: A Guide to Job Hunting and Interview Technique*. No unsolicited mss. Please write first. Editorial and production consultancy also offered.

Intellect Books
E.F.A.E., Earl Richards Road North, Exeter, Devon EX2 6AS
☎01392 475110   Fax 01392 475110
Publisher *Masoud Yazdani*
Assistant Publisher *Robin Beecroft*
FOUNDED 1984. *Publishes* books and journals on social implications of writing, language learning and European cultural influence, among others. TITLES *African Theatre for Development; Signs, Symbols and Icons; Women Voice Men; Television in Europe.* Unsolicited synopses and ideas welcome. *Royalties* paid.

Iolo
38 Chaucer Road, Bedford MK40 2AJ
☎01234 270175   Fax 01234 270175
Managing Director *Dedwydd Jones*
Publishes Welsh theatre-related material and campaigns for a Welsh National Theatre. SERIES *Black Books on the Welsh Theatre.* Ideas on Welsh themes welcome; approach in writing.

JAC Publications
28 Bellomonte Crescent, Drayton, Norwich, Norfolk NR8 6EJ
☎01603 861339
Managing Editor *John James Vasco*
Publishes World War II Luftwaffe history only. TITLES *Zerstörer: The Messerschmitt 110 and its Units in 1940* John J. Vasco and Peter D. Cornwell. Unsolicited mss welcome. No synopses or ideas. *Royalties* paid.

Jackson's Arm
See **Sunk Island Publishing**

John Jones Publishing Ltd
Borthwen, Wrexham Road, Ruthin, Denbighshire LL15 1DA
☎01824 707255   Fax 01824 707255
Managing Editor *John Idris Jones*
FOUNDED 1989. *Publishes* paperbacks in English with a Welsh background – topography, biography, stories and legends, history, food. Tourist market, educational and general. No novels. TITLES *Wild Wales; I Bought a Mountain; The Son of Prophecy.* Approach in writing with s.a.e. *Royalties* paid.

The Jupiter Press
Oracle House, 1–3 Gospel End Road, Sedgley, Dudley, West Midlands DY3 3LT
☎01902 665477   Fax 01902 678655
Managing Editor *Gordon Drury*

FOUNDED 1995. Looking for niche market and information publications, particularly sport orientated (golf and soccer) – quiz, puzzles and games content. No unsolicited mss; synopses and ideas for books welcome. *Royalties* paid.

Katabasis
See under **Poetry Presses**

Richard Kay Publications
80 Sleaford Road, Boston, Lincolnshire PE21 8EU
☎01205 353231
Managing Editor *Richard Kay*
FOUNDED 1970. Non-profit motivated publisher of local interest (Lincolnshire) material: dialect, history, autobiography and biography, philosophy, medico-political and contemporary dissent on current affairs. About 6 titles a year. TITLES *Herbert Ingram, Esq., MP, Founder of the Illustrated London News; Now the Day is Over: The Life and Times of Rev. Sabine Baring-Gould; In the Wake of Captain Cook: The Life and Tides of Captain Charles Clerke, R.N., 1741-79; Wodds and Doggeybaw – A Lincolnshire Dialect Dictionary.* No unsolicited mss; synopses and ideas welcome.
Royalties paid if appropriate.

Kittiwake
3 Glantwymyn Village Workshops, Nr. Machynlleth, Montgomeryshire SY20 8LY
☎01650 511314   Fax 01650 511602
E-mail: KittiBooks@aol.com
Managing Editor *David Perrott*
FOUNDED 1986. *Publishes* guidebooks only, with an emphasis on good design/production. TITLES *Western Islands Handbook; Outer Hebrides Handbook; Local Welsh Walks Guides; Local Walks Around Machynlleth; Dolgellau; Porthmadog; New Quay,* etc. Unsolicited mss, synopses and ideas for guidebooks welcome. Specialist cartographic and electronic publishing services available. *Royalties* paid.

Lily Publications
PO Box 9, Narberth, Pembrokeshire SA68 0YT
☎01834 891461   Fax 01834 891463
Managing Editor *Miles Cowsill*
FOUNDED 1991. *Publishes* holiday guides and specialist books. TITLES *Premiere Guide to Pembrokeshire 1998; Cardiganshire 1997/8; Brecon Beacons and Heart of Wales Guide 1998; Carmarthenshire 1998/1999; Swansea and Gower 1997/1998; Isle of Man 1998/9,* tourist guide to

the island; *Isle of Man – A Photographic Journey*. Publishers of *Flagship®* for P&O European Ferries, UK. Unsolicited mss, synopses and ideas welcome. Sister company **Lily Publications (Isle of Man) Ltd.**, PO Box 1, Portland House, Ballasalla, Isle of Man. ☎/fax 01624 823848. *Royalties* paid.

The Lindsey Press
Unitarian Headquarters, 1–6 Essex Street, Strand, London WC2R 3HY
☎0171 240 2384   Fax 0171 240 3089
E-mail: ga@unitarian.org.uk
Convenor *Kate Taylor*
Established at the end of the 18th century as a vehicle for disseminating liberal religion. Adopted the name of The Lindsey Press at the beginning of the 20th century (after Theophilus Lindsey, the great Unitarian Theologian). *Publishes* books reflecting liberal religious thought or Unitarian denominational history. Also worship material – hymn books, collections of prayers etc. TITLES *Celebrating Life; Love, Sex and the Spirit; Glorious Liberty*. No unsolicited mss; synopses and ideas welcome. *Royalties* not paid.

Logaston Press
Logaston, Woonton, Almeley, Herefordshire HR3 6QH
☎01544 327344
Managing Editors *Andy Johnson, Ron Shoesmith*
FOUNDED 1985. *Publishes* walking guides, social history, rural issues and local history for Wales, the Welsh Border and West Midlands. 6–8 titles a year. TITLES *A View from Hereford's Past; Castles and Moated Sites of Herefordshire; Castles of Radnorshire; Prehistoric Sites of Monmouthshire; Arthurian Links with Herefordshire; The Man in the Moone*. Unsolicited mss, synopses and ideas welcome. Return postage appreciated. *Royalties* paid.

Luath Press Ltd
543/2 Castlehill, The Royal Mile, Edinburgh EH1 2ND
☎0131 225 4326   Fax 0131 225 4324
E-mail: gavin.macdougall@luath.co.uk
Website: www.luath.co.uk
Managing Editor *G. H. MacDougall*
FOUNDED 1981. *Publishes* mainly guidebooks and books with a Scottish connection. About 6 titles a year. TITLES *The Luath Guides; Rum: Nature's Island; Blind Harry's Wallace; The Joy of Hillwalking; Seven Steps in the Dark* (autobiogra-

phy of a Scottish miner); *Mountain Days and Bothy Nights*. Unsolicited mss, synopses and ideas welcome. *Royalties* paid.

Lyfrow Trelyspen
See **CNP Publications**

Madison Publishing Ltd
83 Albert Palace Mansions, Lurline Gardens, London SW11 4DH
☎0370 873399   Fax 0171 622 4679
Managing Director *Nathan Andrew Iyer*
FOUNDED 1995. *Publishes* British fiction. TITLES *Domino Run; The Discovery*. No unsolicited mss. Synopses (no more than 2pp) and ideas welcome.

Mandrake of Oxford
PO Box 250, Oxford OX1 1AP
☎01865 243671   Fax 01865 432929
E-mail: mandrake@mandrake.cix.co.uk
Managing Editor *Kris Morgan*
Publishes occult, surreal, magical art, sexology, heretical and radically new ideas. 3–5 titles a year. TITLE *I Crowley: almost the last confession of the beast 666* Snoo Wilson. No mss; send synopsis first with return postage. *Royalties* paid.

Marine Day Publishers
64 Cotterill Road, Surbiton, Surrey KT6 7UN
☎0181 399 7625   Fax 0181 399 1592
Managing Editor *Anthony G. Durrant*
FOUNDED 1990. Part of The Marine Press Ltd. *Publishes* local history. TITLES *Malden Old & New; Malden Old & New Revisited; Kingston and Surbiton Old & New; All Change*. *Royalties* not paid.

Matching Press
1 Watermans End, Matching Green, Harlow, Essex CM17 0RQ
☎01279 731308
Publisher *Patrick Streeter*
FOUNDED 1993. *Publishes* biography, autobiography, social history and fiction. Enquiries welcome. *Royalties* paid.

Maverick Publishing
Morris House, 5 Claremont Road, Morecambe LA4 4HJ
Managing/Editorial Director *Chancery Stone*
Art/Production *Max Scratchman*
FOUNDED 1996. *Publishes* fiction, erotica, art

and photography. Does not require unsolicited mss.

Maypole Editions
22 Mayfair Avenue, Ilford, Essex IG1 3DQ
☎0181 252 3937

Contact *Barry Taylor*

Publisher of plays and poetry in the main. 2–3 titles a year. TITLES *Snorting Mustard; Love Sonnets; Chocolate Rose Memoriam.* Plays: *Laurel Trireme; Frog; Piraeus Pelican; Cinderfield; Egretta and Lucretia.* Unsolicited mss welcome, especially plays and poetry, provided return postage is included. Poems should be approximately 30 lines long, broadly covering social concerns, ethnic minorities, feminist issues, romance, travel, lyric rhyming verse. No politics. The annual collected anthology is designed as a small press platform for first-time poets who might not otherwise get into print, and a permanent showcase for those already published. 'Please be patient when sending work because of the huge volume of submissions.'

Meadow Books
22 Church Meadow, Milton under Wychwood, Chipping Norton, Oxfordshire OX7 6JG
☎01993 831338

Managing Director *C. O'Neill*

FOUNDED 1990. Published a social history of hospitals. TITLES *A Picture of Health; More Pictures of Health* Cynthia O'Neill.

Mercia Cinema Society
19 Pinder's Grove, Wakefield, West Yorkshire WF1 4AH
☎01924 372748

Managing Editor *Brian Hornsey*

FOUNDED 1980 to foster research into the history of picture houses. *Publishes* books and booklets on the subject, including cinema circuits and chains. Books are often tied in with specific geographical areas. TITLES *Cinemas of Essex/Exeter/Lincoln/Southampton/York* (series); *How to Research the History of Cinemas; Cinema Story – The Rise, Fall and Revival of Wakefield Cinemas; Ribbon of Dreams: Remembering Cardiff Cinemas.* Unsolicited mss, synopses and ideas. *Royalties* not paid.

Meridian Books
40 Hadzor Road, Oldbury, West Midlands B68 9LA
☎0121 429 4397

Managing Editor *Peter Groves*

FOUNDED 1985 as a small home-based enterprise following the acquisition of titles from Tetradon Publications Ltd. *Publishes* local history, walking and regional guides. 4–5 titles a year. TITLES *The Navigation Way: A Hundred Mile Towpath Walk* Peter Groves & Trevor Antill; *The Monarch's Way, Books 1, 2 & 3* Trevor Antill; *Heart of England Hillwalks* John Newson; *Country Walks in Warwickshire and Worcestershire* Des Wright. New titles 1997: *Walks Around the Malverns* Roy Woodcock; *Walks to Wet Your Whistle* Roger Seedhouse. Unsolicited mss, synopses and ideas welcome if relevant. Send s.a.e. if mss is to be returned. *Royalties* paid.

Merton Priory Press Ltd
67 Merthyr Road, Whitchurch, Cardiff CF4 1DD
☎01222 521956   Fax 01222 623599

Managing Director *Philip Riden*

FOUNDED 1993. *Publishes* academic and mid-market history, especially local and industrial history; also distributes for small publishers working in the same field. About 6 titles a year. Full catalogue available. *Royalties* paid twice yearly.

Neil Miller Publications
Mount Cottage, Grange Road, Saint Michael's, Tenterden, Kent TN30 6EE

Managing Editor *Neil Miller*

FOUNDED 1994. *Publishes* tales with a twist, comedy, suspense, mystery, fantasy, science fiction, horror and the bizarre under the **Black Cat Books** imprint. **Global Books** romance tales. Also *publishes* paperbacks: classics, rare tales, tales of the unexpected. New authors always welcome. Evaluation and critique service available for large mss. 'We seek short story writers, in any genre. No unsolicited mss, please. In the first instance, send £2.75 and large s.a.e. for author's package, which includes free book. We have published 50 new authors since 1994. We will help and advise on anything well written and researched.'

Minimax Books Ltd
Broadgate House, Church Street, Deeping St James, Peterborough, Cambridgeshire PE6 8HD
☎01778 345254   Fax 01778 341198

Chairman *Bob Lavender*
Managing Director *Lynn Green*
Approx. Annual Turnover £40,000

FOUNDED in the early 1980s. *Publishes* books of

local interest and history. No academic or technical.

Royalties paid twice yearly.

Minority Rights Group

379 Brixton Road, London SW9 7DE
☎0171 978 9498   Fax 0171 738 6265
Deputy Head of Communications *Angela Warren*
Website: http://www.minorityrights.org

FOUNDED in the late 1960s, MRG works to raise awareness of minority issues worldwide. *Publishes* books, reports and educational material on minority rights. 8–10 titles a year. TITLES *The Kurds; Afro-Latins; Burundi; North Caucasus.*

Morton Publishing

PO Box 23, Gosport, Hampshire PO12 2XD
Managing Editor *Nik Morton*

FOUNDED 1994. *Publishes* fiction – genre novellas (eg crime, science fiction, fantasy, horror, western), max. 20,000 words; short story anthologies – max. 4000 words per story. TITLES *Auguries 19* (a science fiction/fantasy/horror anthology); *A Sign of Grace* and *Silenced in Darkness* both crime novellas by Robert W. Nicholson. Unsolicited synopses and ideas for books welcome. Also offers literary agent service of guidance and advice (fees on applications) *Royalties* paid annually.

Need2Know

1–2 Wainman Road, Woodston,
Peterborough PE2 7BU
☎01733 390801   Fax 01733 230751
Managing Editor *Anne Sandys*

FOUNDED 1995 'to fill a gap in the market for self-help books', Need2Know is an imprint of Forward Press Ltd. (see under **Poetry Presses**). *Publishes* self-help, reference guides for people in difficult situations. TITLES *Make the Most of Being a Carer; Forget the Fear of Food; Make the Most of Retirement; A Parent's Guide to Dyslexia; Help Yourself to a Job.* No unsolicited mss, but synopses and ideas for books welcome. It is important first to ensure the project fits in with the series and that the subject is not already covered.
Payment Advance paid plus royalties.

New Arcadian Press

13 Graham Grove, Burley, Leeds, West Yorkshire LS4 2NF
☎0113 2304608
Managing Editor *Patrick Eyres*

FOUNDED 1981 to publish artist-writer collaborations on landscape and garden themes through *The New Arcadian Journal* (limited edition collector's items). TITLES *Castle Howard; The Wentworths; A Cajun Chapbook; Hearts of Oak; Sons of the Sea; Naumachia; Landfall; The Political Temples of Stowe; Four Purbeck Arcadias.* No unsolicited mss, synopses or ideas.
Royalties not paid.

New Millennium

292 Kennington Road, London SE11 4LD
☎0171 582 1477   Fax 0171 582 4084
Managing Editor *Tom Deegan*

New Millennium is the imprint of the Professional Authors' & Publishers' Association (see entry under **Professional Associations**), established in 1993 'to provide self-publishing writers with an alternative to the vanity trade'. *Publishes* general fiction and non-fiction. 55 titles in 1997. TITLES *Fighting On; Captain Guthrie; The Ministry Syndrome; The God Shift; Nigeria 1966; Lilliburlero; Growing Pelargoniums.*

Nimbus Press

18 Guilford Road, Leicester LE2 2RB
☎0116 2706318   Fax 0116 2706318
Managing Editor *Clifford Sharp*
Assistant Editor *Justin Moulder*

FOUNDED in 1991 to encourage churches to use drama in worship. *Publishes* Christian drama and discussion booklets on Christian themes. TITLES *Let's Go To Bethlehem; Looking for a King; Angel's Counsel.* 6 titles in 1997. No unsolicited mss but an open competition for plays will be run in 1998. Synopses and ideas for plays of less than 25 minutes' length, suitable for production in a church, and plays for children welcome.

Norvik Press Ltd

School of Modern Languages & European Studies, University of East Anglia, Norwich, Norfolk NR4 7TJ
☎01603 593356   Fax 01603 250599
Managing Editors *James McFarlane, Janet Garton, Michael Robinson*

Small academic press. *Publishes* the journal *Scandinavica* and books related to Scandinavian literature. About 4 titles a year. TITLES *A Sudden Liberating Thought* Kjell Askildsen; *From Baltic Shores* ed. Christopher Moseley; *Days with Diam* Svend Åge Madsen; *My Son on the Galley* Jacob Wallenberg; *A Century of Swedish Narrative* eds. Sarah Death & Helena Forsås-Scott; *A Fighting Pig's Too Tough to Eat* Suzanne Brögger; *Witches' Rings* Kerstin Ekman; *Modus Vivendi* Gunnar

Ekelöf; *Five Swedish Poets* Robin Fulton. Interested in synopses and ideas for books within its *Literary History and Criticism* series. No unsolicited mss.
Royalties paid.

Nyala Publishing
4 Christian Fields, London SW16 3JZ
☎0181 764 6292
Fax 0181 764 6292/0115 9819418
Editorial Head *J. F. J. Douglas*

FOUNDED 1996. Publishing arm of Geo Group. *Publishes* biography, travel and general non-fiction. No unsolicited mss; synopses and ideas considered. Also offers a wide range of publishing services.
Royalties paid twice-yearly.

Oast Books
See **Parapress Ltd**

Octave Books
See **Parapress Ltd**

Open Gate Press
51 Achilles Road, London NW6 1DZ
☎0171 431 4391   Fax 0171 431 5088
Managing Directors *Jeannie Cohen,*
Elisabeth Petersdorff

FOUNDED 1989 to provide a forum for psychoanalytic social and cultural studies. *Publishes* psychology, philosophy, social sciences, politics. SERIES *Psychoanalysis and Society.* Synopses and ideas for books welcome.
Royalties paid twice yearly.

Oriflamme Publishing
60 Charteris Road, London N4 3AB
☎0171 281 8501   Fax 0171 281 8501
Managing Editor *Tony Allen*

FOUNDED 1982, originally to publish science fiction and fantasy but now concentrating on a range of educational textbooks, mainly English and mathematics. Some fiction and special interest also. About 7 titles a year. SERIES *The Rules of Maths; Help Yourself to English; The Rules of English; Succeed in Maths.* No unsolicited mss; synopses/ideas welcome but must be brief.
Royalties paid.

Orpheus Publishing House
4 Dunsborough Park Lodges, Ripley Green, Ripley, Guildford, Surrey GU23 6AL
☎01483 225777   Fax 01483 225777
E-mail: orpheuspubl.ho@btinternet.com
Managing Editors *J. S. Gordon, S. H. Francke*

FOUNDED 1996. *Publishes* 'well-researched and properly argued' books in the fields of occult science, esotericism and comparative philosophy/religion. TITLES *Self-Consistent Kosmos; Land of the Fallen Star Gods.* 'Keen to encourage good (but sensible) new authors.' In the first instance send a maximum 3-page synopsis with s.a.e.
Royalties by agreement.

Outline Publications
See **Brantwood Books**

Palladour Books
Hirwaun House, Aberporth, Nr. Cardigan, Ceredigion SA43 2EU
☎01239 811658   Fax 01239 811658
Managing Editors *Jeremy Powell/Anne Powell*

FOUNDED 1986. Started with a twice-yearly issue of catalogues on the literature and poetry of World War I. Occasional catalogues on World War II poetry have also been issued. TITLES *A Deep Cry*, a literary pilgrimage to the battlefields and cemeteries of First World War British soldier-poets killed in Northern France and Flanders; *The Fierce Light: The Battle of the Somme: July – November 1916.* No unsolicited mss.
Royalties not paid.

Pandora
See **Rivers Oram Press**

Parapress Ltd
2 St Mary's Bungalow, Perry Hill, Worplesdon, Guildford, Surrey GU3 3RD
☎01483 232504   Fax 01483 232881
Managing Director *Ian W. Morley-Clarke*

FOUNDED 1993. *Publishes* autobiography, biography, diaries, journals of military personnel, composers and sportsmen. Also books on local history. About 12 titles a year. Largely self-publishing. IMPRINT: **Oast Books** Literary and local guides; **Parapress** Militaria; **Octave Books** Music biographies.

Parthian Books
41 Skelmuir Road, Cardiff CF2 2PR
☎01222 460164   Fax 01222 460164
Chairman *Gillian Griffiths*
Managing Director *Richard Davies*
Approx. Annual Turnover £25,000

FOUNDED in 1993. *Publishes* contemporary Welsh fiction in English. TITLES *Work, Sex & Rugby* Lewis Davies; *Tilting at Windmills.* 3–4 books per year. No unsolicited; synopses and ideas welcome.
Royalties paid annually.

Partizan Press

816–818 London Road, Leigh on Sea, Essex
SS9 3NH
☎01702 73986   Fax 01702 73986

Managing Editor *David Ryan*

Caters for the growing re-enactment and war-gaming market. *Publishes* military history, with particular regard to the 17th and 18th centuries. TITLES *Winchester in the Civil War; Eye & Ear Witnesses; Discovery of Witchcraft.* Also publishes *Odyssey,* a science fiction and fantasy short-story magazine. Copies and author's notes available. *Royalties* paid.

Paupers' Press

27 Melbourne Road, West Bridgford,
Nottingham NG2 5DJ
☎0115 9815063   Fax 0115 9815063
E-mail: stan2727uk@aol.com
Website: http://members.aol.com/
stan2727uk/ pauper.htm

Managing Editor *Colin Stanley*

FOUNDED 1983. *Publishes* extended essays in booklet form (about 15,000 words) on literary criticism and philosophy. About 6 titles a year. TITLES *More on the Word Hoard: The Poetry of Seamus Heaney* Stephen Wade; *Proportional Representation: A Debate on the Pitfalls of our Electoral System* Gregory K. Vincent; *Sex and Sexuality in Ian McEwan's Work* Christina Byrnes; *Sex and the Intelligent Teenager* Colin Wilson; *Witchcraft and Misogyny* Samantha Giles; *So Far So Linear: responses to the work of Jeanette Winterson* Christopher Pressler. Limited hardback editions of bestselling titles. No unsolicited mss but synopses and ideas for books welcome. *Royalties* paid.

Peepal Tree Press Ltd

17 King's Avenue, Leeds, West Yorkshire
LS6 1QS
☎0113 2451703   Fax 0113 2468368
E-mail: hannah@peepal.demon.co.uk

Managing Editor *Jeremy Poynting*

FOUNDED 1985. *Publishes* fiction, poetry, drama and academic studies. *Specialises* in Caribbean, Black British and South Asian writing. About 18 titles a year. In-house printing and finishing facilities. AUTHORS Kamau Brathwaite, Cyril Dabydeen, Beryl Gilroy, Velma Pollard, Jan Shinebourne and **Forward Poetry Prize** winner Kwame Dawes. 'Please send an A5 s.a.e. with a 38p stamp for a copy of our submission guidelines.' Write or 'phone for a free catalogue. *Royalties* paid.

The Penniless Press

100 Waterloo Road, Ashton, Preston,
Lancashire PR2 1EP

Managing Editor *Alan Dent*

Publishes quarterly magazine with literary, philosophical, artistic and political content, including reviews of poetry, fiction, non-fiction and drama. Prose of up to 3000 words welcome. No mss returned without s.a.e. *Payment* Free copy of magazine.

Pentaxion Ltd

180 Newbridge Street, Newcastle upon Tyne
NE1 2TE
☎0191 232 6189   Fax 0191 232 6190
E-mail: pentaxion@pentaxion.force9.net

Managing Editor *Adrian Spooner*

Publishes academic, educational, medical, arts and professional studies. 11 titles in 1997. TITLES *Venice Sketchbook; Reflection and Action for Health Care Professionals; The Law of Evidence A Team Approach to School Improvement.* No unsolicited mss; synopses and ideas welcome. 'Under certain circumstances we will enter into joint ventures with authors.' *Royalties* paid.

Pipers' Ash Ltd

'Pipers' Ash', Church Road, Christian
Malford, Chippenham, Wiltshire SN15 4BW
☎01249 720563   Fax 01249 720563
E-mail: pipersash@supamasu.demon.co.uk

Managing Editor *Mr A. Tyson*

FOUNDED 1976 to publish technical manuals for computer-controlled systems. Later broadened the company's publishing activities to include individual collections of contemporary short stories, science fiction short stories, poetry, short novels, local histories, children's fiction, philosophy, biographies, translations and general non-fiction. 48 titles in 1997. TITLES *Goose Pimples* Mark Bannerman; *Romany Revenge* Jenny Williams; *So U 12 Ba Poet* Bob Griffiths; *Yowl!* Stephen Jansen. No unsolicited mss. Synopses and ideas welcome; 'new authors with potential will be actively encouraged'. *Royalties* paid annually.

Planet

PO Box 44, Aberystwyth, Ceredigion
SY23 5ZZ
☎01970 611255   Fax 01970 611197

Managing Editor *John Barnie*

FOUNDED 1985 as publishers of the arts and current affairs magazine *Planet: The Welsh*

Internationalist and branched out into book publishing in 1995. TITLES *Graffiti: Narratives* poems by Mike Jenkins; *Them & Other Stories* (trans. from Galician) by Xosé Luís Méndez Ferrín; *A Barrel of Stones – In Search of Serbia* Peter Morgan; *The Skiffle Craze* Mike Dewe. All books so far have been commissioned. Unsolicited synopses and ideas welcome. *Royalties paid.*

Playwrights Publishing Co.
70 Nottingham Road, Burton Joyce, Nottinghamshire NG14 5AL
☎0115 9313356
Managing Editors *Liz Breeze, Tony Breeze*
FOUNDED 1990. *Publishes* one-act and full-length plays. TITLES *Birthmarks* Mark Jenkins; *Lifestyles* Silvia Vaughan; *Undercoats* Roger Pinkham. Unsolicited scripts welcome. No synopses or ideas. Reading fees: £15 one act; £30 full length.
Royalties paid.

Poisonenginepress
31 Leconfield House, Champion Hill, London SE5 8AY
☎0171 787 9678
E-mail: poisonenginepress@compuserve.com
Managing Editor *Louise Barker*
FOUNDED 1994. *Publishes* mainly Black experimental writing – fiction and poetry. 2 titles in 1997. TITLES *Desafinado* and *Teragaton* Athony Joseph; *Spaces Between the Screams* Kemal Mulbocus. Unsolicited mss, synopses and ideas welcome.
Royalties paid.

Polymath Publishing
Manor Farm, Thornton Steward, Ripon, North Yorkshire HG4 4BB
☎01677 460058   Fax 01677 460059
Owner *Charles Knevitt*
FOUNDED 1989. *Publishes* general interest and technical architecture and construction industry books, postcard books, calendars, etc., also cartoon anthologies. TITLES *From Pecksniff to The Prince of Wales: 150 Years of Punch Cartoons on Architecture, Planning and Development 1851–1991; The Responsive Office: People and Change; Seven Ages of the Architect: The Very Best of Louis Hellman 1967–92; Shelter: Human Habitats From Around the World*; re-issue of *Community Architecture* (Penguin 1987). Synopses and ideas welcome.
Royalties negotiable.

Pomegranate Press
Church Cottage, Lewes Road, Westmeston, Hassocks, East Sussex BN6 8RH
☎01273 846743   Fax 01273 846743
E-mail: 106461.1316@compuserve.com
Website: http://ourworld.compuserve.com/ PomegranatePress
Managing Editor *David Arscott*
FOUNDED in 1992 to publish David Arscott's Sussex trilogy (*The Sussex Story; Living Sussex; In Praise of Sussex*) and has expanded into local interest subjects such as history and wildlife. Also publishes how-to books (eg *Good English*). No fiction. 12 titles in 1997. No unsolicited mss; synopses and ideas for books welcome.
Royalties paid twice yearly.

David Porteous Editions
PO Box 5, Chudleigh, Newton Abbot, Devon TQ13 0YZ
☎01626 853310   Fax 01626 853663
Publisher *David Porteous*
FOUNDED 1992 to produce high quality colour illustrated books on hobbies and leisure for the UK and international markets. *Publishes* crafts, hobbies, art techniques and needlecrafts. No poetry or fiction. 3–4 titles a year. TITLES *Flower Painting* Paul Riley; *Silhouettes in Cross Stitch* Julie Hasler; *Dolls' Clothes* Mette Jorgensen. Unsolicited mss, synopses and ideas welcome if return postage included.
Royalties paid twice yearly.

Power Publications
1 Clayford Avenue, Ferndown, Dorset BH22 9PQ
☎01202 875223   Fax 01202 875223
Contact *Mike Power*
FOUNDED 1989. *Publishes* local interest, pub walk guides and mountain bike guides. 2–3 titles a year. TITLES *Pub Walks in Cornwall/Hampshire/ New Forest* (every county along the south coast); *Ferndown: A Look Back; Mountain Bike Guides to the New Forest, Hampshire, Dorset and Chilterns; Famous Women in Dorset; Penstemons; A Century of Cinema in Dorset; Ancient Stones of Dorset; Parley's Past.* Unsolicited mss/synopses/ideas welcome.
Royalties paid.

Praxis Books
Sheridan, Broomers Hill Lane, Pulborough, West Sussex RH20 2DU
☎01798 873504
E-mail: 100543.3270@compuserve.com
Proprietor *Rebecca Smith*

FOUNDED 1992. *Publishes* reissues of Victorian fiction, general interest. 12 titles to date. TITLES *In Search of Life's Meaning* R. Matley and R. Smith; *The Poet's Kit* Katherine Knight; *A Book of Folklore* Sabine Baring-Gould; *By Way of Beachy Head* Joyce Tombs. Unsolicited mss accepted with s.a.e. No fiction or humour. Editing service available. Shared funding, shared proceeds. 'I am most likely to accept work with a clearly identifiable market.'

Previous Parrot Press

The Foundry, Church Hanborough,
Nr. Witney, Oxford OX8 8AB
☎01993 881260   Fax 01993 883080
Managing Editor *Dennis Hall*

Publishes limited editions with a strong emphasis on illustration. About 3 titles a year. TITLES *An Avian Alphabet* Nyr Indictor, illus. Elizabeth Rashley; *Newhaven – Dieppe* written and illus. by Frank Martin; *The Return of A. J. Raffles* Graham Green, illus. Annie Newnham.

Primrose Hill Press Ltd

58 Carey Street, London WC2A 2JB
☎0171 405 7484   Fax 0171 405 7459
Managing Director *Brian H. W. Hill*

FOUNDED in 1997, having taken over the stock and projects in progress of Silent Books Ltd. *Publishes* general art titles, wood engraving, poetry and books for the gift market, 'all high quality productions'. No fiction. About 12 titles a year. Unsolicited mss, synopses and ideas welcome.

Prism Press Book Publishers Ltd

The Thatched Cottage, Partway Lane,
Hazelbury Bryan, Sturminster Newton,
Dorset DT10 2DP
☎01258 817164   Fax 01258 817635
Managing Director *Julian King*

FOUNDED 1974. *Publishes* alternative medicine, conservation, environment, psychology, health, mysticism, philosophy, politics and cookery. About 6 titles a year. TITLES *Boundaries of the Soul* June Singer; *Soul on Fire* Stan Papenfus; *Beyond Therapy* Guy Claxton. Synopses and ideas welcome.

Royalties paid twice-yearly. *Overseas associates* Prism Press USA.

Pulp Faction

PO Box 12171, London N19 3HB
☎0171 700 3409
Website: http://www.pulpfact.demon.co.uk

Contact *Editor*

FOUNDED 1995. *Publishes* book form collections of underground/offbeat short fiction along with artwork and graphic fiction. TITLE *Technopagan, Fission, Allnighter.* Flat fee paid for short stories. (Website should be checked for themes of future compilations and deadlines.) **Pulp Books** Set up in 1996 to publish original contemporary fiction. About 8–10 titles a year. TITLES *Call Me; Their Heads Are Anonymous; Go.* 'A good first stop for ambitious new writers.' Send synopsis/sample chapters from a novel.

Royalties paid annually.

QED Books

1 Straylands Grove, York YO3 0EB
☎01904 424242   Fax 01904 424381
E-mail: qed@enterprise.net
Managing Editor *John Bibby*

Publishes and *distributes* resource guides and learning aids, including laminated posters, for mathematics and science. TITLES *Fun Maths Calendar; Maths Resource Guides; Maths and Art; Joy of Maths; Geometer's Sketchpad*™. Synopses (3pp) and ideas for books welcome. QED arranges publicity for other small presses and has many contacts overseas. Also provides publishing services for other publishers and arranges exhibitions at Frankfurt, LIBF, educational conferences etc.

Royalties by agreement.

QueenSpark Books

49 Grand Parade, Brighton, East Sussex
BN2 2QA
☎01273 571710   Fax 01273 571710

A community writing and publishing group run mainly by volunteers who work together to write and produce books. Since the early 1970s they have published 60 titles: local autobiographies, humour, poetry, history and politics. Free writing workshops and groups held on a regular basis. New members welcome.

Redstone Press

7A St Lawrence Terrace, London W10 5SU
☎0171 352 1594   Fax 0171 352 8749
E-mail: redstone.press@virgin.net
Managing Editor *Julian Rothenstein*

FOUNDED 1987. *Publishes* art and literature. About 5 titles a year. No unsolicited mss; synopses and ideas welcome but familiarity with Redstone's list advised in the first instance.

Royalties paid.

Regentlane Ltd
Devonshire Road Industrial Estate, Millom,
West Cumbria LA18 4JS
☎01229 770465   Fax 01229 770339
Managing Editor *Alan Bryant*
FOUNDED 1992. *Publishes* local and national
guide books, autobiographies and travel-orien-
tated books. 50 titles in 1997. SERIES *Travellers'
Guide; Festivals, Galas and Events of Britain;
Towns and Villages of Britain.* Unsolicited mss
welcome; no synopses or ideas.
Royalties paid.

Rivers Oram Press
144 Hemingford Road, London N1 1DE
☎0171 607 0823   Fax 0171 609 2776
Managing Director *Elizabeth Fidlon*
Editorial *Katharine Bright-Holmes*
FOUNDED 1990. *Publishes* radical political and
social sciences: social history, sociology, politics,
gender studies, women's studies. IMPRINT
Pandora *Katharine Bright-Holmes* Feminist titles
– general non-fiction: biography, arts, media,
health, current affairs, reference and sexual politics. No fiction, children's or cookery.
Royalties paid annually.

The Robinswood Press
30 South Avenue, Stourbridge,
West Midlands DY8 3XY
☎01384 397475   Fax 01384 440443
E-mail: catandrob@aol.com
Managing Editor *Christopher J. Marshall*
FOUNDED 1985. *Publishes* education, particularly
teacher resources, SEN and Waldorf. About 3–5
titles a year. TITLES *Take Time; Phonic Rhyme
Time; The Extra Lesson* (exercises for children
with learning difficulties); *Stories for the Festivals;
Spotlight on Words; The Eden Mission; Spotlight on
Blends; Teaching Children Handwriting.* Unsolici-
ted mss, synopses and ideas welcome.
Royalties paid.

Romer Publications
Smith Yard, Unit 5, 29A Spelman Street,
London E1 6LQ
☎0171 247 3581

PO Box 10120, NL–1001 EC, Amsterdam,
The Netherlands
☎/Fax 00 31 20 6769442
Managing Editor *Hubert de Brouwer*
FOUNDED 1986. *Publishes* children's books but
main tenet remains critical reflection on origins
and legitimacy of established institutions.
Specialises in history, education and law. TITLES

The Children's Kosher Funbook Rabbi L. Book;
The Decline of the House of Herod Hubert de
Brouwer; *Fascism Down the Ages: From Caesar to
Hitler* Frank A. Ridley; *African Mythology for
Children* Impendoh Dan Iyan; *Dominic Dormouse
Goes to Town* Anthony Wall. Will consider
sound, coherent and quality mss, synopses or
ideas appropriate to its list.
Royalties paid.

Sawd Books
Plackett's Hole, Bicknor, Sittingbourne, Kent
ME9 8BA
☎01795 472262   Fax 01795 422633
Managing Editor *Susannah Wainman*
FOUNDED 1989 to supply the local interests of
the people of Kent. *Publishes* local interest,
cookery, gardening and general non-fiction.
About 3 titles a year. No unsolicited mss; syn-
opses and ideas welcome (include s.a.e.). No
fiction.
Royalties paid.

Scottish Cultural Press
Unit 14, Leith Walk Business Centre,
130 Leith Walk, Edinburgh EH6 5DT
☎0131 555 5950   Fax 0131 555 5018
E-mail: scp@sol.co.uk
Chair/Managing Editor *Jill Dick*
Children's Press Administrator *Avril Gray*
FOUNDED 1992. Began publishing in 1993.
Publishes Scottish interest titles, including cul-
tural, literature, poetry, archaeology, local his-
tory, children's fiction and non-fiction.
IMPRINTS
**Scottish Cultural Press, Scottish Children's
Press.** TITLES *John Buchan's Collected Poems; A
World of Folk Tales from Multi-Cultural Scotland;
A–Z Scots Words for Younger Children; A Doric
Dictionary; Scottish Contemporary Poets Series;
Scottish Burgh Surveys Series; Classic Children's
Games; The Jimmy Shand Story; Night Visits;
Clan Fraser.* Unsolicited mss, synopses and ideas
welcome provided return postage is included.
Royalties paid.

Serif
47 Strahan Road, London E3 5DA
☎0181 981 3990   Fax 0181 981 3990
Managing Editor *Stephen Hayward*
FOUNDED 1994. *Publishes* cookery, Irish and
African studies and modern history; no fiction.
TITLES *The Crowd in History* George Rudé;
Northern Ireland 1921–1996 Paul Bew, Henry
Patterson and Peter Gibbon; *The Alice B. Toklas*

Cookbook; Bengali Cooking: Seasons and Festivals Chitrita Banerji. Ideas and synopses welcome; no unsolicited mss.
Royalties paid.

Sherlock Publications
6 Bramham Moor, Hill Head, Fareham, Hampshire PO14 3RU
☎01329 667325
Managing Editor *Philip Weller*
FOUNDED to supply publishing support to a number of Sherlock Holmes societes. *Publishes* Sherlock Holmes studies only. About 14 titles a year. TITLES *Elementary Holmes; Alphabetically, My Dear Watson; Anonymously, My Dear Lestrade; The Annotated Sherlock Holmes Cases*. No unsolicited mss; synopses and ideas welcome.
Royalties not paid.

Silver Link Publishing Ltd
The Trundle, Ringstead Road, Great Addington Kettering, Northamptonshire NN14 4BW
☎01536 330588   Fax 01536 330588
Managing Editor *Peter Townsend*
Website: http://www.slinkp-p.demon.co.uk
FOUNDED 1985 in Lancashire, changed hands in 1990 and now based in Northamptonshire. Small independent company specialising in nostalgia titles including illustrated books on railways, trams, ships and other transport subjects, also, under the Past and Present Publishing imprint, post-war nostalgia on all aspects of social history. TITLES: *Home and Distant: Forty Years of Railway Life; The River Nene From Source to Sea; Keeping House: Domestic Life Since 1945; Queen Elizabeth 2: Cruising into the Next Millennium; The Ffestiniog Railway: A Past & Present Companion*. Unsolicited synopses and ideas welcome.
Fees paid.

Spacelink Books
115 Hollybush Lane, Hampton, Middlesex TW12 2QY
☎0181 979 3148
Managing Director *Lionel Beer*
FOUNDED 1986. Named after a UFO magazine published in the 1960/70s. *Publishes* non-fiction titles connected with UFOs, Fortean phenomena and paranormal events. TITLE *The Moving Statue of Ballinspittle and Related Phenomena*. No unsolicited mss; send synopses and ideas. Publishers of *TEMS News* for the Travel and Earth Mysteries Society. Distributor of wide range of related titles and magazines.
Royalties and fees paid according to contract.

Springboard
See **Yorkshire Art Circus Ltd**

Stenlake Publishing
Ochiltree Sawmill, The Lade, Ochiltree, Ayrshire KA18 2NX
☎01290 423114   Fax 01290 423114
Publishes local history, transport, Scottish and industrial. 32 titles in 1997. Unsolicited mss, synopses and ideas welcome if accompanied by s.a.e.
Royalties paid annually.

Stride Publications
See under **Poetry Presses**

Sunk Island Publishing
PO Box 74, Lincoln LN1 1QG
☎01522 520645
E-mail: 100074.140@compuserve.com
Managing Editor *Michael Blackburn*
FOUNDED 1989. Publishes occasional paperback fiction. TITLES *Radio Activity* John Murray; *Winterman's Company* David Lightfoot. Also publishes poetry under the **Jackson's Arm** imprint. TITLES *Unlike the Buddha* Nigel Planer; *Room of Leaves* Amanda Dalton. No unsolicited mss. Now runs residential courses, a critical service for writers, and a home-study course in poetry writing.
Royalties by arrangement, on publication.

T.C.L. Publications
8 Hywel Way, Pembroke SA71 4EF
☎01646 685637
Managing Editor *Duncan Haws*
FOUNDED 1966 as Travel Creatours Limited (TCL). *Publishes* nautical books only – the Merchant Fleet series (33 vols.). 2 titles in 1997. TITLES *White Star Line; Elder Dempster Line; Cunard Line; French Line; Holland America Line*. Unsolicited mss welcome, 'provided they are in our standard format and subject matters'. No unsolicited synopses or ideas.
Royalties paid.

Tamarind Ltd
PO Box 296, Camberley, Surrey GU15 4WD
☎01276 683979   Fax 01276 685365
E-mail: TamrindLTD@aol.com
Managing Editor *Verna Wilkins*
FOUNDED 1987 to publish picture books which give Black children a high, unselfconscious, positive profile. Won Gold Award for Best Product, Nursery & Creche Exhibition, 1994.

All titles sold into both trade and educational markets. Age range: 3–9.

Tarquin Publications
Stradbroke, Diss, Norfolk IP21 5JP
☎01379 384218   Fax 01379 384289
Managing Editor *Gerald Jenkins*

FOUNDED 1970 as a hobby which gradually grew and now *publishes* mathematical, cut-out models, teaching and pop-up books. Other topics covered if they involve some kind of paper cutting or pop-up scenes. 8 titles in 1998. TITLES *Make Shapes; Sliceforms; The Chemical Helix; High Fashion in Stuart Times; Paper Automata; Mathematical Origami; Dragon Mobiles.* No unsolicited mss; letter with 1–2 page synopses welcome.
Royalties paid.

Tarragon Press
Moss Park, Ravenstone, Whithorn DG8 8DR
☎01988 850368   Fax 01988 850304
Director/Editorial Head *David Sumner*

FOUNDED 1987. *Publishes* medical and scientific for the layperson. About 3 titles a year. Unsolicited mss, synopses and ideas for books welcome.
Royalties paid annually.

Tartarus Press
5 Birch Terrace, Hangingbirch Lane, Horam, East Sussex TN21 0PA
☎01435 813224
Managing Director *Raymond Russell*

FOUNDED 1987. *Publishes* fiction, short stories, essays and local history. Also books by and about Arthur Machen. About 12 titles a year. TITLES Short story collections: *Worming the Harpy and Other Bitter Pills* Rhys Hughes; *Ritual and Other Stories* Arthur Machen; *Tales from Tartarus.* Essays: *The Secret of the Sangraal and Other Writings* Arthur Machen. Reference: *The Tartarus Press Guide to First Edition Prices.* Letters: *Containing a Number of Things* Starrett & Millard.

Thames Publishing
14 Barlby Road, London W10 6AR
☎0181 969 3579   Fax 0181 969 1465
Publishing Manager *John Bishop*

FOUNDED 1970. *Publishes* music, and books about English music and musicians, particularly of this century but not pop. About 4 titles a year. No unsolicited mss; send synopses and ideas in first instance.

Totem
55 Merches Gardens, Cardiff CF1 7RF
☎01222 377694
Managing Editor *Ishmael Fiifi Annobil*

FOUNDED 1994. *Publishes* literary novels, poetry, arts of international and Welsh origin (including photography). Also publishes the magazines *Totem* and *Circa21* (see entries under **Magazines**). Plans to publish 6 titles a year, mostly literary novels and poetry. Short print runs characterise the imprint's output but reproduction rights market explored. Book production services offered. TITLES *Pyramids, People & Piccadilly; Seven Horn Elegy; Silence of the Raised Voice.* No unsolicited mss; letter, cv and synopsis welcome.
Royalties paid.

Tuckwell Press Ltd
The Mill House, Phantassie, East Linton, East Lothian EH40 3DG
☎01620 860164   Fax 01620 860164
E-mail: tuckwellpress@sol.co.uk
Website: http://www.tuckwellpress.co.uk
Managing Director *John Tuckwell*

FOUNDED 1995. *Publishes* history, literature, ethnology, biography, architecture, gardening history, genealogy, palaeography, with a bias towards Scottish and academic texts, also north of England. 60 titles in print. No unsolicited mss but synopses and ideas welcome if relevant to subjects covered.
Royalties paid annually.

Twiddlesmith Publishing Ltd
Whitton House, 11 York Road, Beverley, East Yorkshire HU17 8DP
☎01482 860208   Fax 01482 860208
Managing Editor *Alan Twiddle*

FOUNDED 1997. *Publishes* general fiction and non-fiction, including local history. 6 titles in 1997. TITLES *Boozers Ballcocks and Bail* S. D. Smith; *Braithwell: The Village Where I Belong* J. Milnis. Unsolicited mss and synopses welcome.
Royalties paid.

Two Heads Publishing
9 Whitehall Park, London N19 3TS
☎0171 561 1606   Fax 0171 561 1607
Contact *Charles Frewin*

Independent publisher of sport, particularly football and cricket. Synopses and ideas welcome; write in the first instance.
Royalties paid quarterly.

UNKN
Highfields, Brynymor Road, Aberystwyth, Dyfed SY23 2HX
☎01970 627337   Fax 01970 627337
Managing Editor *Niall Quinn*
Publisher *Siobhán O'Rourke*

FOUNDED 1995 originally to promote the work of writers (primarily poets) engaged in the production of experimental and marginal text – its core commitment. TITLES *However Introduced to the Soles.*

Wakefield Historical Publications
19 Pinder's Grove, Wakefield, West Yorkshire WF1 4AH
☎01924 372748
Managing Editor *Kate Taylor*

FOUNDED 1977 by the Wakefield Historical Society to publish well-researched, scholarly works of regional (namely West Riding) historical significance. 1–2 titles a year. TITLES *Aspects of Medieval Wakefield; Landscape Gardens in West Yorkshire 1680–1880; Coal Kings of Yorkshire; The Aire and Calder Navigation; Right Royal – Wakefield Theatre 1776–1994.* Unsolicited mss, synopses and ideas for books welcome.
Royalties not paid.

Paul Watkins Publishing
18 Adelaide Street, Stamford, Lincolnshire PE9 2EN
☎01780 756793   Fax 01780 756793
Proprietor *Shaun Tyas*

Publishes non-fiction – medieval, academic, biography, nautical, local history. No fiction. 5 titles in 1997. Unsolicited mss, synopses and ideas for books welcome.
Royalties paid twice yearly.

Westwood Press
44 Boldmere Road, Sutton Coldfield, West Midlands B73 5TD
☎0121 354 5913   Fax 0121 355 6920
Managing Editor *Reg Hollins*

FOUNDED 1955 as a general printer and commenced local publication in the 1970s. *Publishes* local history of the Birmingham area only and specialised printing 'Know How' publications. TITLES *A History of Boldmere; The Book of Brum; Up the Terrace – Down Aston and Lozells.* No unsolicited mss; synopses and ideas welcome.
Royalties paid.

Whittles Publishing
Roseleigh House, Latheronwheel, Caithness KW5 6DW
☎01593 741240   Fax 01593 741360
E-mail: whittl@globalnet.co.uk
Managing Editor *Dr Keith Whittles*

FOUNDED 1986 to offer freelance commissioning and consulting. Started publishing a few years ago in the field of civil engineering and surveying. Also general books with a marine/Scottish theme. 12 titles in 1997. TITLES *Construction Disputes: Avoidance and Resolution; The Geological Interpretation of Well Logs; No Port in a Storm.* Unsolicited mss, synopses and ideas welcome on appropriate themes.
Royalties paid annually.

Whyld Publishing Co-op
Moorland House, Kelsey Road, Caistor, Lincolnshire LN7 6SF
☎01472 851374   Fax 01472 851374
Managing Editor *Janie Whyld*

Having taken over former ILEA titles on anti-sexist work with boys which would otherwise have vanished, Janie Whyld has gone on to publish a specialist list of educational materials for teachers, trainers and students, with an emphasis on equal opportunities and interpersonal skills. TITLES *Anti-Sexist Work with Boys and Young Men; Equal Opportunities in Training and Groupwork; Countering Objections to Anti-Sexist Work; Using Counselling Skills to Help People Learn; NVQs and the Assessment of Interpersonal Skills; Teaching Assertiveness in Schools and Colleges; The Essence of Yin and Yang; Multicultural Stories.* Would welcome being taken over by anyone/organisation interested in preserving the list.
Royalties nominal.

Witan Books & Publishing Services
Cherry Tree House, 8 Nelson Crescent, Cotes Heath, via Stafford ST21 6ST
☎01782 791673
Managing Editor *Jeff Kent*

FOUNDED in 1980 for self-publishing and commenced publishing other writers in 1991. *Publishes* general books, including biography, education, environment, geography, history, politics, popular music and sport. 1 title in 1997. TITLES *The Last Poet: The Story of Eric Burdon; The Man Who Sank the Titanic?: The Life and Times of Captain Edward J. Smith.* Witan

Publishing Services, which began as an offshoot to help writers get their work into print, offers guidance, editing, proofreading etc. Unsolicited mss, synopses and ideas welcome (include s.a.e.).
Royalties paid.

Yorkshire Art Circus Ltd

School Lane, Glasshoughton, Castleford, West Yorkshire WF10 4QH
☎01977 550401   Fax 01977 512819
E-mail: admin@artcircus.org.uk
Website: www.artcircus.org.uk
Books Coordinator *Ian Daley*

FOUNDED 1986. *Specialises* in new writing by first-time authors. *Publishes* autobiography, community books, fiction – novels and short stories – and local interest (Yorkshire and Humberside). No local history, children's, poetry, reference or nostalgia. TITLES *The Righteous Brother* Adrian Wilson; *The Story of a House, Askham Grange Women's Prison* ed. Brian Lewis and Harry Crewe; *When Push Comes to Shove, Vol 2* ed. I. Clayton, I. Daley, R. Gate. Unsolicited mss discouraged; authors should send for fact sheet first. **Springboard** fiction imprint launched 1993 mainly for Yorkshire/Humberside-based writers. Write or ring for free catalogue.
Royalties paid.

The English Language in the Year 2000

Godfrey Howard

In the 21st century the English language will be, we could say, 1600 years old. It was brought to Britain in the 5th century by Germanic tribes, as an obscure dialect spoken by a few thousand people and hardly written down at all. The name *English*, itself, has its origin in the name of one of those Teutonic peoples, the Angles. Since it arrived here, the language has been exposed to all manner of radical shake-ups and upheavals. There have been so many wide-ranging changes, that if we look at one of the few surviving Old English texts, it reads like a remote foreign language, incomprehensible without prolonged study.

Grammatical gender, with non-sexual words being 'feminine' or 'masculine' (as in French, for example), went down the drain probably between the late 8th and 10th centuries, as the inflections became too complicated for everyday usage. The Norman Conquest, after the Battle of Hastings in 1066 (the one date in history everyone remembers), brought English into the mainstream of western European languages, as the vocabulary took on board shiploads of words from Norman French, most of which had descended from Latin.

The Renaissance from the 14th century onwards introduced a revival of classical culture, which led to a renewed flood of Latin and many Greek words coming into the language. In the late 16th and early 17th century English basked and stretched in the warmth and glory of Elizabethan England, making and being made by Shakespeare and the Authorised Version of the Bible published in 1611. The scientific outlook of the 18th century brought the concept of order and correctness to language, with Samuel Johnson's *Dictionary*, published in 1755, becoming the first established authority on the use of English. Imperial expansion of British power in the late 18th and 19th centuries carried English all over the world, making it the symbol of government and civilisation.

The language had arrived, and in smug Victorian Britain was settling down complacently, which is the worst thing that can happen to any language. But before this hardening of linguistic arteries set in, along came a transfusion of vigorous new blood from America, a verbal hand-out that has been keeping the language on its toes ever since. The result of such a topsy-turvy history and such diverse influences is that writers in English inherit the most lively and flexible language in the long history of lexical communication.

The new millennium will see an ever-widening grey area between so-called 'good' and 'bad' English. There will still be tut-tutters who feel that 'good' English is the language they learned at school 30 or more years ago from a Mr Chips or a Miss Trump. The late Kingsley Amis proposed that title pages of books should by law carry the author's date of birth, so that he could avoid reading anything written by anyone born after 1945. That leaves Salman Rushdie (born in 1947) just beyond the pale, along with his contention that 'English, no longer an *English* language, now grows from many roots'.

By the end of the 20th century, aside from the discontented grumbling of a dying-off band of diehards, many of the linguistic controversies that caused so much uproar have settled down, and we hardly think twice about them any more. The 21st century will open with the language in a post-feminist age. Writers and others are more or less in the habit of avoiding sexist language. Politicians are careful to say 'he or she', some of them (with an eye on women's votes) varying that with 'she or he'. Even the fustiest of lawyers has long since abandoned the coy legal formula 'words importing the masculine gender shall be deemed to embrace females'. And there is a revised version of the Bible which replaces *man* by *one* in as many contexts as possible.

Perhaps it is still not altogether comfortable for everyone to use unisex alternatives, such as *humankind* and *chair*, or unisex forms, such as *actor*, for both sexes. But we are getting used to it, just as we have no problem with women being *masters* of colleges. After all, a great painting has always been an *old master*, whatever the sex of the artist, for we could hardly call it an 'old mistress', could we? There will be more of a give-and-take situation in the new century, and extremes of linguistic feminism will come to be regarded as silly. The attempt to call *history* 'herstory' (included in *Random House Webster's College Dictionary*) was as short-lived as calling *manholes* 'humanholes'. Reuters' style guide lays down the now accepted principle, 'language that perpetuates the stereotype of women as the weaker, inferior sex ... is offensive, out of date and simply inaccurate'.

The term *politically correct* will remain suspect, as describing linguistic nit-picking or fudging real issues by obfuscation, such as calling the *poor* 'disadvantaged' or *slums* 'inner cities', or perpetrating absurdities such as 'hair disadvantaged' for *bald* (recorded in the American *Quarterly Review of Doublespeak*). At the same time, we have come to see that the English language is loaded with prejudices, built up over centuries. Most of these will be laid aside during the next century, and not a moment too soon. Words relating to race and sex will continue to be sensitive and subject to change. *African-American*, for example, is now the preferred term, rather than 'black American', for an American of African descent.

Before the 20th century is out, writers no longer look over their shoulders if they use *four-letter words*, when they're called for. But the floodgates have opened only so far, and are not going to open any further for a long time to come. So *piss* and *shit* remain labelled 'taboo' in the latest dictionaries, although they hardly shock any more. *Fuck* will continue to cause at least a modest tightening of the lips for many people. *Cunt* will continue to give real offence, although it broke through the television barrier some years ago, when David Hockney used the word to refer to the focus of interest in a sketch by Picasso.

Such words will stay forbidden on BBC's *Today* programme, just as *The Times* will continue to soften them with dots (*f..k*, *c..t*). At the same time, fashion writers in the most respectable papers write about *fuck-me* shoes and *fuck-me* heels, without a priggish dot in sight. These double standards will remain with us well into the new century. The wind of permissiveness seems to have blown itself out for the time being. The recent new edition of Fowler's famous guide does not include a single so-called *four-letter word*, as if such words do not exist at all in *Modern English Usage*. There will be many winners of the Booker Prize during the next century who will disagree.

At the beginning of the 20th century Fowler proclaimed magisterially 'Americanisms are foreign words and should be so treated.' (*The King's English*, 1906). But by the end of the century, British dictionaries are required to include American usage and spelling. There are, after all, at least four times as many people using English in North America as there are in Britain. American English will move centre-stage in the new millennium, and cross-fertilisation with British English will gather more and more momentum.

At the same time, British English will continue to resist the simplified American spelling, much of it introduced by Noah Webster in the 19th century. The eccentricities of our spelling, loaded with multiple-choice options, belong to the antiquity and tangled roots of the language, and we are as unlikely to surrender them as we are to take up driving on the right. Much of our vocabulary will remain steadfast. *Autumn* will continue to be the standard word, even though the American *fall* was long ago used in Britain and is a more poetic and descriptive word for the 'season of mists and mellow fruitfulness'. We shall continue to go up and down in a *lift*, a good 14th century word, instead of using the rather silly word *elevator*. Nor is the American word *sidewalk* likely to catch on in Britain, where pedestrians prefer to walk on the pavement, a word that in America can mean the roadway. This difference of meaning will require sorting out well into the future, when police in London tell Americans 'not to park on the *pavement*'.

The new century will see many new words coming into the language. Some will be like autumn leaves drifting across the landscape, settling for a while, then drifting on, never to be seen again. Others will stay and eventually find a lasting home in dictionaries, as they fill a linguistic need in society and technology. The last few years of the old century saw expressions such as *road rage*, *alcopop*, *Doc Martens*, *sleaze*, *spin doctor* and inevitably *Blairite* take firm roots in the language, leaving lexicographers scrambling to catch up with them.

Other words will drop away, as they go past their sell-by date, or simply because no one under 30 will understand them. Women will go out with *men*, rather than 'chaps', just as they already *have sex* or *make love* rather than 'have intercourse'. 'Schoolmaster' and 'schoolmistress' will be superseded altogether by *schoolteacher*, as more and more gender variants are put on the shelf alongside 'sculptress', 'manageress', authoress …

In the 20th century, radio, films and television brought the spoken and written language closer together, which relaxed grammar and syntax. Writers in the 21st century will become increasingly aware that many traditional rules of English grammar and the use of words belong to the 19th century and are out of touch with the language in the new millennium. Much less fuss will be made about it all, and the disgusted grammarians of Tunbridge Wells will sooner or later become fossils. Yet for the foreseeable future some writers will prefer to hold back and continue to use *who* and *whom*, for example, according to the book of rules, either out of respect for the language or in case people think they don't know any better. For many others, the *who* and *whom* distinction, with other old usage rules, will become grammatical museum pieces. Good writers usually lean towards licence and freedom rather than orthodoxy and scholasticism.

Capital letters for most job titles (chief executive, bank manager, prime minister …) will sound pompous in the new century. *The Times* style guide already advises 'if in doubt, use lower case'. *God* will always attract a capital, but the *queen* will be seen increasingly in lower case. Even before the 20th century is out, the National Consumer Council's *Plain English for Lawyers* advises 'avoid too many capital letters … they are difficult to read'. As for eponyms, for a long time now it has shown no disrespect to the Duke of Wellington to put on our *wellies*, with a small *w*.

The line between formal and informal English will become ever more blurred, and there will be a case for a new linguistic term, *ceremonial English*. For there will always be occasions, such as the queen's speech at the opening of parliament, when language is required to have dignity and solemnity, and certain perfectly good words and expressions are excluded because they seem too casual. But in the 21st century, English will not belong to the great and the good, even less to secretaries of state for education. The language will be seen to be the property of everyone who uses it.

Our age is more linguistically uneasy than any in the past, which is a reflection of the uneasiness about every aspect of the human situation in the century that lies ahead. The language will continue to reflect society, as it has always done. But as clocks strike midnight on Friday, 31st December 1999 and we stumble bleary-eyed into the 21st century, English will still resound with the complexity, beauty, wit, cadence and poetry it had for Shakespeare and Milton, Eliot and Graham Greene. What is more, it will come during the new century to take its place as the first true lingua franca, understood by more people in more countries than any other language in the world.

All we have to do is to go on using it.

Godfrey Howard read linguistics at Oxford under C. T. Onions (the last surviving editor of the original Oxford English Dictionary), C. S. Lewis and J. R. R. Tolkien. His books The Good English Guide *and* The Macmillan Good English Handbook *have become standard works on the use of English, and the BBC has recorded his programme* The State of the Language.

UK Packagers

The Albion Press Ltd
Spring Hill, Idbury, Oxfordshire OX7 6RU
☎01993 831094   Fax 01993 831982
Chairman/Managing Director
  Emma Bradford

FOUNDED 1984 to produce high-quality illustrated titles. *Commissions* illustrated trade titles, particularly children's, English literature, social history and art. About 4 titles a year. TITLES *Christmas Fairy Tales* Isabelle Brent; *Tales of Heartsease Wood* Neil Philip & Tracey Williamson; *Odin's Family* Neil Philip & Mary Clare Foa. Unsolicited synopses and ideas for books not welcome.
  Royalties paid; fees paid for introductions and partial contributions.

Alphabet & Image Ltd
See **Marston House** under **UK Publishers**

Andromeda Oxford Ltd
11–15 The Vineyard, Abingdon, Oxfordshire OX14 3PX
☎01235 550296   Fax 01235 550330
Managing Director *Mark Ritchie*

FOUNDED 1986. *Commissions* adult and junior international illustrated reference, both single volume and series. About 30 titles a year.

DIVISIONS
Adult Books *Graham Bateman* Editorial Director; **Children's Books** *Nick Leggett* Editorial Director; **Andromeda Interactive** (CD-ROMs) TITLES *Encyclopedia of World Geography; Cultural Atlases; Science Encyclopedia; Atlas of World History; Factfiles; Interactive Space Encyclopedia; Complete Shakespeare; Classic Library; Medical Science* on CD-ROM. Approach by letter in the first instance.

Archival Facsimiles Ltd
The Old Bakery, 52 Crown Street, Banham, Norwich, Norfolk NR16 2HW
☎01953 887277   Fax 01953 888361
Chief Executive *Cris de Boos*

FOUNDED 1986. Specialist private publishers for individuals and organisations. Produces scholarly reprints for the **British Library** among others, plus high-quality limited edition publications for academic/business organisations in Europe and the USA, ranging from leather-bound folios of period print reproductions to small illustrated booklets. *Publishes* Antarctic exploration titles (about 2 a year) under the **Erskine Press** imprint. No unsolicited mss. Ideas welcome.
  Royalties paid twice yearly.

AS Publishing
73 Montpelier Rise, London NW11 9DU
☎0181 458 3552   Fax 0181 458 0618
Managing Director *Angela Sheehan*

FOUNDED 1987. *Commissions* children's illustrated non-fiction. No unsolicited synopses or ideas for books, but approaches welcome from experienced authors, editors and illustrators in this field. *Fees* paid.

BCS Publishing Ltd
1 Bignell Park Barns, Kirtlington Road, Chesterton, Bicester, Oxon OX6 8TD
☎01869 324423   Fax 01869 324385
Managing Director *Steve McCurdy*
Approx. Annual Turnover £350,000

Commissions general interest non-fiction for international co-edition market.

Belitha Press Ltd
London House, Great Eastern Wharf, Parkgate Road, London SW11 4NQ
☎0171 978 6330   Fax 0171 223 4936
Editorial Director *Mary-Jane Wilkins*

FOUNDED 1980. Part of **Collins & Brown**. *Commissions* children's non-fiction in all curriculum areas. About 50 titles a year. All titles are expected to sell in at least four co-editions. TITLES *Can You Find?; Ed Mouse Finds Out About; Fun with Numbers/Shapes/ Sizes/Patterns; What's It Like To Be?; Where Am I?; Mighty Machines; Weather; Myths and Legends; Musical Instruments of the World; The World Reacts.* No unsolicited mss. Synopses and ideas for books welcome from experienced children's writers.

Bellew Publishing Co. Ltd
See entry under **UK Publishers**

Bender Richardson White
PO Box 266, Uxbridge, Middlesex UB9 5BD
☎01895 832444   Fax 01895 835213
Partners *Lionel Bender, Kim Richardson, Ben White*

FOUNDED 1990 to produce illustrated non-fiction for children aged 7–14 for publishers in the UK and abroad. 20 titles in 1997. Unsolicited material not welcome.
Fees paid.

David Bennett Books Ltd
15 High Street, St Albans, Hertfordshire AL3 4ED
☎01727 855878   Fax 01727 864085
Publisher/Creative Director *David Bennett*
FOUNDED 1989. Acquired by **Collins & Brown** in May 1998. Producer of children's books: picture and novelty books, interactive and board books, baby gifts and non-fiction for babies and toddlers. Synopses and ideas for books welcome. Unsolicited mss may not be returned. No fiction or poetry.
Payment both fees and royalties.

BLA Publishing Ltd
1 Christopher Road, East Grinstead, West Sussex RH19 3BT
☎01342 318980   Fax 01342 410980
Owner *Ling Kee (UK) Ltd*
Packagers of multi-volume encyclopedias for younger readers, and information book series on various topics. Now only producing a minimal number of books.
Payment varies according to contract (reference books tend to be flat fees).

Book Packaging and Marketing
3 Murswell Lane, Silverstone, Towcester, Northamptonshire NN12 8UT
☎01327 858380   Fax 01327 858380
Contact *Martin F. Marix Evans*
FOUNDED 1989. Essentially a project management service, handling books demanding close designer/editor teamwork or complicated multi-contributor administration, for publishers, business 'or anyone who needs one'. Mainly illustrated adult non-fiction including travel, historical, home reference, military and coffee-table books. No fiction or poetry. 5–8 titles a year. Proposals considered; and writers are often required for projects in development. TITLES *Canals of England; Contemporary Photographers*, 3rd ed.; *Michelin's Paris in Your Pocket; The Battles of the Somme 1916–18; The Military Heritage of Britain and Ireland; Passchendale and the Battle of Ypres*.
Payment Authors contract direct with client publishers; fees paid on first print usually and royalties on reprint but this depends on publisher.

Breslich & Foss Ltd
20 Wells Mews, London W1P 3FJ
☎0171 580 8774   Fax 0171 580 8784
Directors *Paula Breslich, K. B. Dunning*
Approx. Annual Turnover £1.5 million
Packagers of non-fiction titles only, including art, children's, crafts, gardening and health. Unsolicited mss welcome but synopses preferred. Include s.a.e. with all submissions.
Royalties paid twice yearly.

Brown Wells and Jacobs Ltd
Forresters Hall, 25–27 Westow Street, London SE19 3RY
☎0181 771 5115   Fax 0181 771 9994
Managing Director *Graham Brown*
FOUNDED 1979. *Commissions* non-fiction, novelty, pre-school and first readers, natural history and science. About 40 titles a year. Unsolicited synopses and ideas for books welcome.
Fees paid.

Calmann & King Ltd
71 Great Russell Street, London WC1B 3BN
☎0171 831 6351   Fax 0171 831 8356
E-mail: calmann_king@compuserve.com
Chairman *Robin Hyman*
Managing Director *Laurence King*
Approx. Annual Turnover £4 million
FOUNDED 1976. *Commissions* books on art, the decorative arts, design, architecture, graphic design, carpets and textiles. About 30 titles a year. Unsolicited synopses and ideas for books welcome.
Royalties paid twice yearly.

Cameron Books (Production) Ltd
PO Box 1, Moffat, Dumfriesshire DG10 9SU
☎01683 220808   Fax 01683 220012
Directors *Ian A. Cameron, Jill Hollis*
Approx. Annual Turnover £350,000
Commissions contemporary art, including environmental art, film, design, collectors' reference, educational reference, conservation, natural history, social history, decorative arts, esoteric gardening and cookery. About 6 titles a year. Unsolicited synopses and ideas for books welcome.
Payment varies with each contract.

Chancerel International Publishers Ltd
120 Long Acre, London WC2E 9PA
☎0171 240 2811   Fax 0171 836 4186
Managing Director *W. D. B. Prowse*

FOUNDED 1976. *Commissions* educational books, and *publishes* language-teaching materials in most languages. Language teachers/writers often required as authors/consultants, especially native speakers other than English.

Payment generally by flat fee but royalties sometimes.

Philip Clark Ltd

53 Calton Avenue, Dulwich, London
SE21 7DF
☎0181 693 5605   Fax 0181 299 4647
Managing Director *Philip Clark*

Founder member of the **Book Packagers Association**. *Commissions* heavily illustrated titles on a variety of subjects. TITLES include *Travellers Wine Guides* series and sponsored publications.

Fees paid.

Roger Coote Publishing

Gissing's Farm, Fressingfield, Eye, Suffolk
IP21 5SH
☎01379 588044   Fax 01379 588055
Director *Roger Goddard-Coote*

FOUNDED 1993. Packager of high-quality children's and adult non-fiction for trade, school and library markets. About 24 titles a year. No fiction.

Fees paid; no royalties.

Diagram Visual Information Ltd

195 Kentish Town Road, London NW5 2JU
☎0171 482 3633   Fax 0171 482 4932
Managing Director *Bruce Robertson*

FOUNDED 1967. Producer of library, school, academic and trade reference books. About 10 titles a year. Unsolicited synopses and ideas for books welcome.

Fees paid; no payment for sample material/submissions for consideration.

Dorling Kindersley Ltd

See under **UK Publishers**

Duncan Petersen Publishing Limited

See entry under **UK Publishers**

Eddison Sadd Editions

St Chad's House, 148 King's Cross Road, London WC1X 9DH
☎0171 837 1968   Fax 0171 837 2025
Managing Director *Nick Eddison*
Editorial Director *Ian Jackson*

Approx. Annual Turnover £3.5 million

FOUNDED 1982. Produces a wide range of popular illustrated non-fiction, with books published in 25 countries. Ideas and synopses are welcome but titles must have international appeal.

Royalties paid twice yearly; flat fees paid when appropriate.

Erskine Press

See **Archival Facsimiles Ltd**

Expert Publications Ltd

Sloe House, Halstead, Essex CO9 1PA
☎01787 474744   Fax 01787 474700
Chairman *Dr. D. G. Hessayon*

FOUNDED 1993. Produces the Expert series of books by Dr. D. G. Hessayon. Currently 18 titles in the series, including *The Evergreen Expert; The NEW Vegetable & Herb Expert; The Flowering Shrub Expert; The Container Expert*. No unsolicited material.

First Rank Publishing

See entry under **Small Presses**

Geddes & Grosset Ltd

See entry under **UK Publishers**

Angus Hudson Ltd

Concorde House, Grenville Place, Mill Hill, London NW7 3SA
☎0181 959 3668   Fax 0181 959 3678
Chairman *Angus R. M. Hudson*
Managing Director *Nicholas Jones*
Approx. Annual Turnover £3.5 million

FOUNDED 1977. Management buyout from Maxwell Communications in 1989. Leading packager of religious co-editions. *Commissions* Christian books for all ages and co-editioning throughout the world. About 160 titles in 1997. Publishes under the **Candle Books**; **Concorde House Books**; **Gazelle Books** and **Monarch Books** imprints. Prototype dummies complete with illustrations welcome for consideration. No mss on their own, please.

Royalties paid.

Lexus Ltd

13 Newton Terrace, Glasgow G3 7PJ
☎0141 221 5266   Fax 0141 226 3139
Managing/Editorial Director *P. M. Terrell*

FOUNDED 1980. Compiles bilingual reference, language and phrase books. About 20 titles a year. TITLES *Rough Guide Phrasebooks; Collins*

Italian Concise Dictionary; Harrap Study Aids; Hugo's Phrase Books; Harrap Shorter French Dictionary (revised); *Impact Specialist Bilingual Glossaries; Oxford Student's Japanese Learner.* No unsolicited material. Books are mostly commissioned. Freelance contributors employed for a wide range of languages.
Payment generally flat fee.

Lionheart Books
10 Chelmsford Square, London NW10 3AR
☎0181 459 0453   Fax 0181 451 3681
Senior Partner *Lionel Bender*
Partner *Madeleine Samuel*
Designer *Ben White*
Approx. Annual Turnover £250,000

A design/editorial packaging team. Titles are primarily commissioned from publishers. Highly illustrated non-fiction for children aged 8–14, mostly natural history, history and general science. About 20 titles a year.
Payment generally flat fee.

Market House Books Ltd
2 Market House, Market Square, Aylesbury, Buckinghamshire HP20 1TN
☎01296 84911   Fax 01296 437073
Directors *Dr Alan Isaacs, Dr John Daintith*

FOUNDED 1970. Formerly Laurence Urdang Associates. *Commissions* dictionaries, encyclopedias and reference. About 15 titles a year. TITLES *Concise Medical Dictionary; Brewer's 20th Century Phrase and Fable; Oxford Dictionary for Science Writers and Editors; Oxford Dictionary of Business; Oxford Dictionary of Banking and Finance; Oxford Dictionary of Accounting; Bloomsbury Thesaurus; Larousse Thematica* (6 volume encyclopedia); *Collins English Dictionary; The Macmillan Encyclopedia; Grolier Bibliographical Encyclopedia of Scientists* (10 vols); *Oxford Paperback Encyclopedia; Oxford Dictionary for the Business World; Penguin Biographical Dictionary of Women.* Unsolicited material not welcome as most books are compiled in-house.
Fees paid.

Marshall Editions Ltd
170 Piccadilly, London W1V 9DD
☎0171 629 0079   Fax 0171 834 0785
Publisher *Barbara Anderson*

FOUNDED 1977. *Commissions* non-fiction, including thematic atlases, leisure, self-improvement, health and visual information for children. TITLES *The Marshall Illustrated Encyclopedia of Animals; Total Health; The Twentieth Century Year By Year; Fitness Handbook; Golf Handbook.*

MM Productions Ltd
33 Warner Road, Ware, Hertfordshire SG12 9JL
☎01920 466003   Fax 01920 466003
Chairman/Managing Director *Mike Moran*

Packager and publisher. TITLES *MM Publisher Database; MM Printer Database* (available in UK, European and international editions).

Oyster Books Ltd
Unit 4, Kirklea Farm, Badgworth, Axbridge, Somerset BS26 2QH
☎01934 732251   Fax 01934 732514
Managing Director *Jenny Wood*

FOUNDED 1985. Packagers of quality books and book/toy/gift items for children of pre-school age to ten years. About 20 titles a year. Most material is created in-house.
Payment usually fees.

Parke Sutton Ltd
Orchard House, Grange Farm, Ashwellthorpe, Norfolk NR16 1ET
☎01508 489212   Fax 01508 489212
Director *Ian S. McIntyre*

FOUNDED 1982. Packages books for publishers. Unsolicited synopses and ideas for books welcome. S.a.e. essential. Also publishing consultant.
Royalties paid twice yearly; fees sometimes paid rather than royalties.

Playne Books Limited
Chapel House, Trefin, Haverfordwest, Pembrokeshire SA62 5AU
☎01348 837073   Fax 01348 837063
E-mail: playne.books@virgin.net
Director *Gill Davies*
Design & Production *David Playne*

FOUNDED 1987. *Commissions* early learning titles for young children – fun ideas with an educational slant and novelty books. Also highly illustrated and practical books on any subject. Unsolicited synopses and ideas for books welcome.
Royalties paid 'on payment from publishers'. Fees sometimes paid instead of royalties.

Mathew Price Ltd
The Old Glove Factory, Bristol Road, Sherborne, Dorset DT9 4HP
☎01935 816010   Fax 01935 816310
Chairman/Managing Director
Mathew Price
Approx. Annual Turnover £1 million

Commissions high-quality, full-colour novelty

picture books and fiction for young children plus children's non-fiction for all ages.

Fees sometimes paid instead of royalties.

Quarto Publishing

The Old Brewery, 6 Blundell Street, London N7 9BH
☎0171 700 6700/333 0000
Fax 0171 700 4191/700 0077

Chairman *Laurence Orbach*

FOUNDED 1976. Britain's largest book packager. *Commissions* illustrated non-fiction, including painting, graphic design, visual arts, history, cookery, gardening, crafts. *Publishes* under the Apple imprint. Unsolicited synopses/ideas for books welcome.

Payment Flat fees paid.

Regency House Publishing Limited

See entry under **UK Publishers**

Sadie Fields Productions Ltd

3D West Point, 36–37 Warple Way, London W3 0RG
☎0181 746 1171   Fax 0181 746 1170

Directors *David Fielder, Sheri Safran*

FOUNDED 1981. Quality children's books with international co-edition potential: pop-ups, three-dimensional, novelty, picture and board books, 1500 words maximum. About 30 titles a year. Approach with preliminary letter and sample material in the first instance. *Publishes* in the UK under the Tango Books imprint.

Royalties based on a per-copy-sold rate and paid in stages.

Salariya Book Company Ltd

25 Marlborough Place, Brighton, East Sussex BN1 1UB
☎01273 603306   Fax 01273 693857
E-mail: salariya@fastnet.co.uk

Managing Director *David Salariya*

FOUNDED 1989. Children's information books – fiction, history, art, music, science, architecture, education and picture books.

Payment by arrangement.

Savitri Books Ltd

115J Cleveland Street, London W1P 5PN
☎0171 436 9932   Fax 0171 580 6330

Managing Director *Mrinalini S. Srivastava*
Approx. Annual Turnover £200,000

FOUNDED 1983. Keen to work 'very closely with authors/illustrators and try to establish long-term

relationships with them, doing more books with the same team of people'. *Commissions* high-quality, illustrated non-fiction, crafts, New Age and nature. About 7 titles a year. Unsolicited synopses and ideas for books 'very welcome'.

Royalties 10–15% of the total price paid by the publisher.

Sheldrake Press

188 Cavendish Road, London SW12 0DA
☎0181 675 1767   Fax 0181 675 7736

Publisher *Simon Rigge*
Approx. Annual Turnover £250,000

Commissions illustrated non-fiction: history, travel, style, cookery and stationery. TITLES *The Victorian House Book; The Shorter Mrs Beeton; The Power of Steam; The Railway Heritage of Britain; Wild Britain; Wild France; Wild Spain; Wild Italy; Wild Ireland; The Kate Greenaway Baby Book.* Synopses and ideas for books welcome, but not interested in fiction.

Fees or royalties paid.

Stonecastle Graphics Ltd/ Touchstone

Old Chapel Studio, Plain Road, Marden, Tonbridge, Kent TN12 9LS
☎01622 832590   Fax 01622 832592
E-mail: paul.turner2@ukonline.co.uk

Managing Director *Paul Turner*
Editorial Head *Sue Pressley*
Approx. Annual Turnover £300,000

FOUNDED 1976. Formed additional design/packaging partnership, Touchstone, in 1983. *Commissions* high-quality, illustrated non-fiction general books – motoring, health, sport, leisure, home interest and popular culture. 20 titles in 1997. TITLES *Aston Martin, The Legend; Creating a Home; The Herbal Yearbook; Essential Health for Women.* Unsolicited synopses and ideas for books welcome.

Fees paid.

Templar Publishing

Pippbrook Mill, London Road, Dorking, Surrey RH4 1JE
☎01306 876361   Fax 01306 889097

Managing Director/Editorial Head
   Amanda Wood
Approx. Annual Turnover £5 million

FOUNDED 1981. A division of The Templar Company plc. *Commissions* novelty and gift books, children's illustrated non-fiction, educational and story books, children's illustrated non-fiction. 100 titles a year. Synopses and ideas for books welcome.

Royalties by arrangement.

Toucan Books Ltd
Fourth Floor, 32–38 Saffron Hill, London EC1N 8BS
☎0171 404 8181   Fax 0171 404 8282
Managing Director *Robert Sackville-West*
Approx. Annual Turnover £1,600,000

FOUNDED 1985. Specialises in international co-editions and fee-based editorial, design and production services to film. *Commissions* illustrated non-fiction only. About 20 titles a year. TITLES *The Eventful Century; The Earth, Its Wonders, Its Secrets; Leith's Cookery Bible; Charles II; The Complete Photography Course; Journeys into the Past* series; *People and Places.* Unsolicited synopses and ideas for books welcome. No fiction or non-illustrated titles.

Royalties paid twice-yearly; fees paid in addition to or instead of royalties.

Touchstone
See **Stonecastle Graphics Ltd**

Touchstone Publishing Ltd
Gissing's Farm, Fressingfield, Eye, Suffolk IP21 5SH
☎01379 588044   Fax 01379 588055
Chairman/Managing Director
  Roger Goddard-Coote
Editorial Director *Edwina Conner*

FOUNDED 1989. Packager of children's non-fiction for trade, school and library markets. About 8 titles a year. No fiction, textbooks or adult material. Synopses and ideas welcome. Include s.a.e. for return.

Fees paid; no royalties.

Victoria House Publishing Ltd
King's Court, Parsonage Lane, Bath BA1 1ER
☎01225 463401   Fax 01225 460942
Managing Director *Clyde Hunter*
Approx. Annual Turnover £10.5 million

Part of the Reader's Digest Group. Trade imprint: Reader's Digest Children's Books. *Commissions* children's projects in novelty or interactive formats – acetate, pop-up, toy add-ons. Also religious list. About 100 titles a year.

Royalties or flat fee according to contract.

Wordwright Books
25 Oakford Road, London NW5 1AJ
☎0171 284 0056   Fax 0171 284 0041
Contact *Charles Perkins*

FOUNDED by ex-editorial people 'so good writing always has a chance with us'. *Commissions* illustrated non-fiction: social history and comment, military history, women's issues, sport. *Specialises* in military and social history, natural history, science, art, cookery, and gardening. About 4–6 titles a year. Unsolicited synopses/ideas (a paragraph or so) welcome for illustrated non-fiction.

Payment usually fees but royalties (twice-yearly) paid for sales above a specified number of copies.

Working Partners Ltd
11a Dunraven Road, London W12 7QY
☎0181 735 0888   Fax 0181 749 5013
Contact *Ben Baglio, Rod Ritchie*

Specialises in children's mass-market series fiction books. Creators of *Animal Ark; Animal Ark Pets; Jess the Border Collie; Internet Detectives; Puppy Patrol; Sheltie, Stacy & Friends and Survive!.* No unsolicited mss.

Payment both fees and royalties by arrangement.

Zoë Books Ltd
15 Worthy Lane, Winchester, Hampshire SO23 7AB
☎01962 851318   Fax 01962 843015
Managing Director *Imogen Dawson*
Director *Bob Davidson*

FOUNDED 1990. *Specialises* in full-colour information and reference books for schools and libraries worldwide. *Publishes* about 30 titles a year. Tends to generate own ideas but happy to hear from experienced freelance writers and editors of information books. Does *not* publish picture books or fiction.

Fees paid.

Book Clubs

Artists' Choice
PO Box 3, Huntingdon, Cambridgeshire
PE18 0QX
☎01832 710201   Fax 01832 710488

Specialises in books for the amateur artist at all levels of ability.

BCA (Book Club Associates)
87 Newman Street, London W1P 4EN
☎0171 637 0341   Fax 0171 291 3525

With two million members, BCA is Britain's largest book club organisation. Consists of 20 book clubs, catering for general and specific interests: Ancient & Medieval History Book Club, The Arts Guild, The Book Club of Ireland, Book of the Month Club, The Christian Book Club, Discovery The Book Club for Children, The English Book Club, Executive World, Fantasy and Science Fiction, History Guild, Home Software World, The Literary Guild, Military and Aviation Book Society, Mind, Body & Spirit, Music Direct, Mystery and Thriller Guild, The New Home & Garden Guild, Quality Paperbacks Direct, Railway Book Club, World Books.

Bookmarks Club
1 Bloomsbury Street, London WC1B 3QE
☎0171 637 1848   Fax 0171 637 3416

New and recent books of interest to Socialists at discount prices. Write, phone or fax for latest list.

Books for Children (Time-Life Entertainment Group Ltd)
4 Furzeground Way, Stockley Park, Uxbridge, Middlesex UB11 1DP
☎0181 606 3061   Fax 0181 606 3099

Editor *Sian Hardy*
Editorial Director *Shelagh Casebourne*

Hardcover and paperback books for children from newly-born to teenage. Also occasional adult fiction and non-fiction – cookery, family interest, parenting guides.

The Bookworm Club
Heffers Booksellers, 20 Trinity Street, Cambridge CB2 1TY
☎01223 568650   Fax 01223 568668
E-mail: club:heffers.co.uk

Website: http://www.heffers.co.uk

Sells paperback books for children through schools.

Cygnus Book Club
PO Box 15, Llandeilo, Carmarthenshire
SA19 6YX
☎01550 777693   Fax 01550 777569
E-mail: enquiries@cygnus-books.co.uk

'Books which make people think.' Books on spirituality, complementary healthcare, environmental issues, plus some management and education titles.

The Folio Society
44 Eagle Street, London WC1R 4FS
☎0171 400 4222   Fax 0171 400 4242

Fine editions of classic titles and reference; also some children's classics.

Letterbox Library
Children's Book Cooperative,
Unit 2D/2nd Floor, Leroy House,
436 Essex Road, London N1 3QP
☎0171 226 1633   Fax 0171 226 1768

Hard and softcover, non-sexist and multi-cultural books for children from one to teenage.

Poetry Book Society
See under **Organisations of Interest to Poets**

Readers Union Ltd
Brunel House, Newton Abbot, Devon
TQ12 2DW
☎01626 336424   Fax 01626 364463

Has nine book clubs, all dealing with specific interests: Country Review, The Craft Club, Craftsman Society, Equestrian Society, The Gardeners Society, Life Matters, Needlecrafts with Cross Stitch, Focal Point, Ramblers & Climbers Society.

Red House Book Clubs
See **Scholastic Ltd** under **UK Publishers**

The Softback Preview (Time-Life UK)
4 Furzeground Way, Stockley Park, Uxbridge, Middlesex UB11 1DP
☎0181 606 3073   Fax 0181 606 3099

Mainly serious non-fiction.

The Women's Press Book Club
The Women's Press, 34 Great Sutton Street, London EC1V 0DX
☎0171 251 3007   Fax 0171 608 1938

'Best women writers from more than 70 publishers.' Fiction, biography and autobiography; popular mind, body and spirit; health and self-help; also a collection of women's studies, social issues and current affairs.

Writers Book Society
PO Box 4, Nairn IV12 4HU
☎01667 454441   Fax 01667 454401

Specialises in books for writers.

Someone to Lean On

The author in search of an agent

Publishers are reluctant to admit it but they adore agents. Like all objects of love agents have their irritating habits such as harping on about contractual details that a publisher would prefer to ignore. But their failings are far outweighed by their qualities. Who else would give themselves selflessly to the pursuit of literary talent, thus saving publishers endless time and trouble?

There was a time, of course, when publishers did their own talent spotting. Every manuscript sent in was read assiduously for hints of a bestseller in the making. Then the accountants took over and editors were told to spend their time more productively, by attending marketing meetings and checking their computer printouts. Freelance professional readers, often retired editors, were pensioned off as part of general cost cutting.

But even the accountants admit that publishers need authors. Where are they to be found? Step forward, the agents. They have the contacts, the experience and the great virtue of charging their clients and not the publishers for their services. Writers, and particularly novelists, are quickly catching on to this change in the way the publishing business is managed. Instead of pinning their hopes on an editor plucking their work from the slush pile with a wild cry of Eureka (it happens, but the Lottery offers better odds) they scan the list of agents for someone to front up for them in the battle to be noticed.

The question then arises, how best to persuade an agent to do the decent thing by agreeing to take up the fight?

Here is some advice from the front line, an agent of 25 years' standing.

When referring to *The Writer's Handbook*, make sure you read the agent's entry carefully. Some agents don't handle certain literary material such as poetry, short stories and original dramatic works. Remember, no reputable agent charges a reading fee, and authors should never agree to pay one. This system allows agents to react as briefly or as fully to new work as they like. So don't expect a detailed report as a matter of course.

Before approaching an agent you must have *completed* the work in a draft you are happy with. No agent wants to see a draft of something you are going to rewrite, and publishers are not going to commission an unknown author to finish a book. It may sound like stating the obvious but do take care with grammar and spelling. So much of the stuff received by agents wouldn't pass a school exam.

Agents do have other work to do. So, to save their time and yours, follow this simple procedure. Write – don't telephone – to one agent at a time, sending a brief covering letter to the agent concerned. Too often

authors send photocopies addressed 'Dear Sir/Madam' so it is obvious all
the agents in this book are being approached at the same time. These go
straight into an agent's bin. (Do *you* answer all the circulars that come
through your letterbox?) The letter should state who you are and include
any writing experience you have had (especially professional work such as
journalism) and the names of the publishers (if any – the less the better)
who have already declined the work you are submitting. Don't write a
blurb. Your novel may be potentially the best since *Gone With the Wind*,
but let it speak for itself.

Secondly, send the first two chapters – no more than about 20 pages
– and a synopsis – no more than two pages – of the rest of the book,
together with a note of its total word length. A good average is 60,000 to
70,000 words. Less makes for a rather slim volume, longer is more expensive to publish though family sagas and airport novels, for instance, are
more like 120,000 words. It's no good sending only a synopsis as it gives no
idea of how you write.

All work *must* be typed double-spaced and on one side of A4 paper only,
with an inch-and-a-half margin all round, and the pages numbered straight
through (not just by chapter). Each chapter should start on a fresh sheet.
Do *not* paperclip each chapter separately.

Finally, always send return postage – preferably a stamped envelope
– and a stamped card if you want an acknowledgement. Agents cannot be
expected to subsidise a service they give free. They are not the copyright
extension of the Citizens Advice Bureau.

Always keep a copy of any material submitted – don't use registered post
or recorded delivery as this can entail collection from a distant post office
– and allow at least a month for a response.

'Become intimate with the mathematics of publishing,
get to know a lot of people and read a lot.'
Ed Victor's advice to aspiring authors.

UK Agents

The Agency (London) Ltd★
24 Pottery Lane, Holland Park, London
W11 4LZ
☎0171 727 1346   Fax 0171 727 9037

Contact *Stephen Durbridge, Leah Schmidt, Sebastian Born, Julia Kreitman, Bethan Evans, Hilary Delamere, Katie Haines*

FOUNDED 1995. *Handles* children's fiction, TV, film, theatre, radio scripts. No adult fiction or non-fiction. Unsolicited TV, film and radio scripts welcome. Send letter with s.a.e. No reading fee. CLIENTS include William Boyd, Andrew Davies, Jimmy McGovern, Sam Mendes. *Commission* Home 10%; USA various.

Aitken & Stone Ltd★
29 Fernshaw Road, London SW10 0TG
☎0171 351 7561   Fax 0171 376 3594

Contact *Gillon Aitken, Brian Stone, Antony Harwood, Emma Parry*

FOUNDED 1984. *Handles* fiction and non-fiction. No plays or scripts unless by existing clients. Send preliminary letter, with synopsis and return postage, in the first instance. No reading fee. CLIENTS include Pat Barker, Agatha Christie, Sebastian Faulks, Helen Fielding, Germaine Greer, Alan Hollinghurst, Susan Howatch, A. L. Kennedy, Douglas Kennedy, V. S. Naipul, Caryl Phillips, Piers Paul Read. *Commission* Home 10%; US 15%; Translation 20%.

Michael Alcock Management
5–7 Young Street, London W8 5EH
☎0171 937 5277   Fax 0171 937 2833
E-mail: michaelalcock@compuserve.com

Contact *Michael Alcock*

FOUNDED 1997. *Handles* general non-fiction including current affairs, biography and memoirs, history, lifestyle, health and personal development, media; and literary and commercial mainstream fiction. Film and TV scripts handled for existing clients only. No academic material, poetry or plays. No unsolicited mss; approach in writing in the first instance giving details of writing and other media experience, plus synopsis and s.a.e. (for fiction send first three chapters as well). No reading fee. CLIENTS include Vicci Bentley, Michael Brunson, Ross Burden, James Burke, James Carleton-Paget,

Lynne Crawford, Philip Dunn, Kevin Gould, Mark Griffiths, Martin Miller, Jo-Anne Richards, Lynne Robinson. *Commission* Home 15%; USA and Translation 20%.

Jacintha Alexander Associates
See **Lucas Alexander Whitley**

Alta Vista® (The Alta Vista Corporation Ltd)
186 Bickenhall Mansions, Bickenhall Street, London W1H 3DE
☎0171 224 1748   Fax 0171 224 1802
E-mail: petercox1@msn.com

Managing Director *Peter Cox*

FOUNDED in 1993 by author Peter Cox to manage a restricted number of clients. 'We are prepared to consider any author, known or unknown, with major international potential.' Sells directly to key overseas markets with particular emphasis on the USA. 'Alta Vista personnel visit New York once a month.' No radio or theatre scripts. No unsolicited mss; initial contact should be by e-mail for a brochure and submission guidelines. No reading fee. CLIENTS Stephen Twigg, Dr Danny Penman, Dr Harash Narang, Isidore Rosmarin, Marnie Inskip, Peggy Brusseau. *Commission* by negotiation.

Darley Anderson Literary, TV & Film Agency★
Estelle House, 11 Eustace Road, London SW6 1JB
☎0171 385 6652   Fax 0171 386 5571
E-mail: DAnder6652@aol.com

Contact *Darley Anderson, Kerith Biggs* (Crime/ Foreign Rights), *Gabi Chase* (Film/TV Scripts), *Elizabeth Wright* (Contemporary Women's Fiction/Love Stories/'Tear jerkers'), *Sarah Hannigan* (Non-Fiction)

Run by an ex-publisher with a sympathetic touch and a knack for spotting and encouraging talent who is known to have negotiated over £1,000,000 in advances and a Hollywood film deal for for one first-time novelist and a £350,000 UK advance for another first-time novelist. *Handles* commercial fiction & non-fiction; also scripts for film, TV and radio. No academic books or poetry. *Special interests* Fiction: all types of thrillers and all types of women's fiction including contemporary, 20th-century romantic sagas, erotica, women in jeopardy; also crime (American/hard-boiled/cosy/ historical), horror, comedy all types of American and Irish novels. Non-fiction: celebrity autobiographies, biographies, 'true life' women in jeopardy, relevatory history and science, popular psychology, self-improvement, diet, health, beauty and fashion, humour/cartoons, gardening, cookery, inspirational and religious. Send letter and outline with first 3 chapters; return postage/s.a.e. essential. CLIENTS Tessa Barclay, Paul Carson, Lee Child, Martina Cole, John Connolly, Joseph Corvo, Debbie Frank, Joan Jonker, Beryl Kingston, Frank Lean, Deborah McKinlay, Lesley Pearse, Allan Pease, Adrian Plass, Ben Richards, Fred Secombe, Julia Stephenson, Jane Walmsley. *Commission* Home 15%; US & Translation 20%; TV/Film/Radio 20%. *Overseas associates* Renaissance-Swanson Film/Book Agency (LA/ Hollywood); and leading foreign agents throughout the world.

Angels Delight Literary Agency
PO Box 3050, Christchurch, Dorset
BH23 4YW
☎01425 271173
President *Ms K. Gold*
Director *Ms H. Gold*

FOUNDED 1997. All subjects considered including TV, film, radio and theatre scripts; 'we like to try to promote new writers'. Unsolicited mss welcome; send synopsis and sample chapters with s.a.e. No reading fee. *Commission* 15–25% (negotiable).

Anubis Literary Agency
79 Charles Gardner Road, Leamington Spa,
Warwickshire CV31 3BG
☎01926 832644   Fax 01926 311607
Contact *Steve Calcutt, Maggie Heavey,*
Liam Martin

FOUNDED 1994. *Handles* mainstream adult fiction, especially historical, horror, crime and women's. Also literary fiction. No children's books, poetry, short stories, journalism, academic or non-fiction. No unsolicited mss; send a covering letter and brief (one-page) synopsis (s.a.e. essential). No reading fee. *Commission* Home 15%; USA & Translation 20%.

Author
53 Talbot Road, Highgate, London N6 4QX
☎0181 341 0442   Fax 0181 341 0442
E-mail: author@dial.pipex.com

Website: www:authors.co.uk
Contact *John Ridley Havergal*

'Agile agenting, all genres and media.' New writers welcome. For details, contact via e-mail.

The Authors Representative Co.
3 Behoes Cottage, Behoes Lane, Woodcote,
Oxfordshire RG8 0PS
☎01491 680169
Proprietor *David Sarjent*
Associate *Brenda Ralph Lewis*

FOUNDED 1997. HANDLES book-length commercial mss only. Quality original adult fiction with international sales potential and general non-fiction. 'Will suggest revisions where appropriate.' No poetry, textbooks, short stories or children's material. Send synopsis, first three chapters and author biography/c.v./credits with covering letter. '*Absolutely* no unsolicited mss will be considered unless authors phone first for discussion. S.a.e essential, please.' Reading service available (Readers Reports International); details on request. CLIENTS include Jeremy Wilson, Molly Lord, Robert Poole, D. K. Anand. *Commission* Home 10–15%; Overseas 20%.

Yvonne Baker Associates
8 Temple Fortune Lane, London
NW11 7UD
☎0181 455 8687   Fax 0181 458 3143
Contact *Yvonne Baker*

FOUNDED 1987. *Handles* scripts for TV, theatre, film and radio. Books extremely rarely. No poetry. Approach by letter giving as much detail as possible, including s.a.e. No reading fee. *Commission* Home 10%; US & Translation 20%.

Blake Friedmann
Literary Agency Ltd*
37–41 Gower Street, London WC1E 6HH
☎0171 631 4331   Fax 0171 323 1274
Contact *Carole Blake* (books), *Julian Friedmann*
(film/TV), *Conrad Williams* (original
scripts/radio), *Isobel Dixon* (books)

FOUNDED 1977. *Handles* all kinds of fiction from genre to literary; a varied range of specialised and general non-fiction, plus scripts for TV, radio and film. No poetry, juvenile, science fiction or short stories (unless from existing clients). *Special interests* commercial women's fiction, literary thrillers. Unsolicited mss welcome but initial letter with synopsis and first two chapters preferred. Letters should contain as much information as possible on previous writing experience, aims for the future, etc. No reading fee. CLIENTS include Ted Allbeury, Jane Asher, Joanna Briscoe, Elizabeth Chadwick, Teresa Crane, Barbara Erskine, Maeve Haran, John Harvey, Ken Hom, Juliet Mead, Glenn Meade, Lawrence Norfolk, Joseph O'Connor, Eve Pollard, Michael Ridpath, Tim Sebastian, Robyn Sisman. *Commission* Books: Home 15%; US & Translation 20%. Radio/TV/Film: 15%. *Overseas associates* throughout Europe, Asia and the US.

David Bolt Associates
12 Heath Drive, Send, Surrey GU23 7EP
☎01483 721118   Fax 01483 721118
Contact *David Bolt*

FOUNDED 1983. *Handles* fiction and general non-fiction. No books for small children or verse (except in special circumstances). No scripts. *Special interests* fiction, African writers, biography, history, military, theology. Preliminary letter with s.a.e. essential. Reading fee for unpublished writers. Terms on application. CLIENTS include Chinua Achebe, David Bret, Eilis Dillon, Arthur Jacobs, James Purdy, Joseph Rhymer, Colin Wilson. *Commission* Home 10%; US & Translation 19%.

BookBlast Ltd
21 Chesterton Road, London W10 5LY
☎0181 968 3089   Fax 0181 932 4087
Director *Georgia de Chamberet*

HANDLES traditional and underground literature. Also authors from the African diaspora, Asia, Europe. No poetry, plays, light romance, science fiction, horror, travel, fantasy, children's, cookery, gardening, health. No reading fee. No unsolicited mss. Will suggest revisions. Preliminary letter, biographical information and s.a.e. essential, also names of agents and publishers previously contacted. *Commission* Home 10%; USA 20%; Translation 20%.

Alan Brodie Representation Ltd (incorporating Michael Imison Playwrights Ltd)
211 Piccadilly, London W1V 9LD
☎0171 917 2871   Fax 0171 917 2872
Contact *Alan Brodie, Sarah McNair*

FOUNDED 1989. *Handles* theatre, film and TV scripts. No books. Preliminary letter plus professional recommendation and c.v. essential. No reading fee but s.a.e. required. *Commission* Home 10%; Overseas 15%.

Rosemary Bromley Literary Agency
Avington, Near Winchester, Hampshire SO21 1DB
☎01962 779656   Fax 01962 779656
Contact *Rosemary Bromley*

FOUNDED 1981. *Handles* non-fiction. Also scripts for TV and radio. No poetry or short stories. *Special interests* natural history, leisure, biography and cookery. No unsolicited mss. Send preliminary letter with full details. Enquiries unaccompanied by return postage will not be answered. CLIENTS include Elisabeth Beresford, Linda Birch, Gwen Cherrell, Teresa Collard, estate of Fanny Cradock, Cécile Curtis, Glenn Hamilton, Jacynth Hope-Simpson, David Rees, Judy Strafford, Keith West, Ron Wilson, John Wingate. *Commission* Home 10%; US 15%; Translation 20%; Illustration 20%.

Felicity Bryan★
2A North Parade, Banbury Road, Oxford OX2 6PE
☎01865 513816   Fax 01865 310055
Contact *Felicity Bryan*

FOUNDED 1988. *Handles* fiction of various types and non-fiction with emphasis on history, biography, science and current affairs. No scripts for TV, radio or theatre. No crafts, how-to, science fiction or light romance. No unsolicited mss. Best approach by letter. No reading fee. CLIENTS include John Charmley, Liza Cody, John Julius Norwich, Rosamunde Pilcher, Miriam Stoppard, Roy Strong. *Commission* Home 10%; US & Translation 20%. *Overseas associates* Lennart Sane, Scandinavia; Andrew Nurnberg, Europe; **Curtis Brown Ltd**, US.

Peter Bryant (Writers)
94 Adelaide Avenue, London SE4 1YR
☎0181 691 9085   Fax 0181 692 9107
Contact *Peter Bryant*

FOUNDED 1980. *Special interests* animation, children's fiction and TV sitcoms. Also *handles* drama scripts for theatre, radio, film and TV. No reading fee for these categories but return postage essential for all submissions. CLIENTS include Isabelle Amyes, Roy Apps, Joe Boyle, Andrew Brenner, Lucy Daniel, Jimmy Hibbert, Jan Page, Ruth Silvestre, Peter Symonds, George Tarry. *Commission* 10%. *Overseas associates* Hartmann & Stauffacher, Germany.

Bycornute Books
76A Ashford Road, Eastbourne, East Sussex
BN21 3TE
☎01323 726819   Fax 01323 649053
Contact *Asia Haleem*
FOUNDED 1987. *Handles* illustrated books on religions, art, archaeology, cosmology, symbolism and metaphysics, both ancient and modern. No scripts. *No* children's or poetry. No unsolicited mss. Send introductory letter outlining proposal. No reading fee. *Commission* 10%.

Campbell Thomson & McLaughlin Ltd★
1 King's Mews, London WC1N 2JA
☎0171 242 0958   Fax 0171 242 2408
Contact *John McLaughlin, Charlotte Bruton*
FOUNDED 1931. *Handles* book-length mss (excluding children's). No plays, film scripts, articles, short stories or poetry. No unsolicited mss. Send preliminary letter with synopsis and s.a.e. in the first instance. No reading fee. *Overseas associates* Fox Chase Agency, Pennsylvania; Raines & Raines, New York.

Carnell Literary Agency★
Danescroft, Goose Lane, Little Hallingbury, Hertfordshire CM22 7RG
☎01279 723626
Contact *Pamela Buckmaster*
FOUNDED 1951. *Handles* fiction and general non-fiction, specialising in science fiction and fantasy. No poetry. No scripts. No unsolicited mss and no phone calls. *Commission* Home 10%; US & Translation 19%. Works in conjunction with agencies worldwide.

Casarotto Ramsay Ltd
National House, 60–66 Wardour Street, London W1V 3HP
☎0171 287 4450   Fax 0171 287 9128
Film/TV/Radio *Jenne Casarotto, Tracey Smith, Rachel Swann, Charlotte Kelly*
Stage *Tom Erhardt, Mel Kenyon*
(**Books Handled by Lutyens and Rubinstein**)
Took over the agency responsibilities of Margaret Ramsay Ltd in 1992, incorporating a strong client list, with names like Alan Ayckbourn, Caryl Churchill, Willy Russell and Muriel Spark. *Handles* scripts for TV, theatre, film and radio, plus general fiction and non-fiction. No poetry or books for children. No unsolicited material without preliminary letter. CLIENTS include J. G. Ballard, Edward Bond,

Simon Callow, David Hare, Terry Jones, Neil Jordan, Willy Russell, David Yallop. *Commission* Home 10%; US & Translation 20%. *Overseas associates* worldwide.

Celia Catchpole
56 Gilpin Avenue, London SW14 8QY
☎0181 255 7200   Fax 0181 878 0594
Contact *Celia Catchpole*
FOUNDED 1996. *Handles* children's books – artists and writers. No TV, film, radio or theatre scripts. No unsolicited mss. Approach by phone in the first instance. *Commission* Home 10–15%; USA & Translation 20%. Works with associate agents abroad.

Chapman & Vincent
The Mount, Sun Hill, Royston, Hertfordshire SG8 9ATZ
☎01763 247474   Fax 01763 243033
Contact *Jennifer Chapman, Gilly Vincent*
A new, small agency whose clients come mainly from personal recommendation and write original non-fiction and quality fiction – usually with TV and film potential which the agents help to develop as necessary (although they do not handle scripts). Since the agency aims to look after only a small number of writers, it is not actively seeking clients but 'we are enthusiasts who are happy to consider really original work'. No poetry, children's, romantic fiction, science fiction or avant-garde prose. No reading fee but in the case of non-fiction a fully-developed idea is required for consideration together with confirmation that a ms is 50% complete; for fiction, send a synopsis and two sample chapters. Write, please do not telephone, and enclose s.a.e. Do not send complete ms in the first instance. CLIENTS include Leslie Geddes-Brown, Sara George, Rowley Leigh, Dorit Peleg. *Commission* Home 15%; US & Europe 20%.

Mic Cheetham Literary Agency
11–12 Dover Street, London W1X 3PH
☎0171 495 2002   Fax 0171 495 5777
Contact *Mic Cheetham*
ESTABLISHED 1994. *Handles* general and literary fiction, crime and science fiction, and non-fiction. No film/TV scripts apart from existing clients. No children's, illustrated books or poetry. No unsolicited mss. Approach in writing with publishing history, first two chapters and return postage. No reading fee. CLIENTS include Iain Banks, Anita Burgh, Laurie Graham, Janette Turner Hospital, Toby Litt, Antony Sher. *Commission* Home 10%; USA & Translation

20%. Works with **The Marsh Agency** for all translation rights.

Judith Chilcote Agency★
8 Wentworth Mansions, Keats Grove, London NW3 2RL
☎0171 794 3717   Fax 0171 794 7431
E-mail: Judybks@aol.com
Contact *Judith Chilcote*

FOUNDED 1990. *Handles* commercial fiction, TV tie-ins, health and nutrition, sport, cinema, self-help, popular psychology, biography and autobiography, cookery and current affairs. No academic, science fiction, children's, short stories or poetry. No unsolicited mss. Send letter with c.v., synopsis, three chapters and s.a.e. for return. No reading fee. CLIENTS include Jane Alexander, Richard Barker, David Emery, Vanessa Feltz, Philippa Kennedy, Maureen Paton, Douglas Thompson. *Commission* Home 15%; Overseas 20–25%. *Overseas associates* in the US and abroad.

Teresa Chris Literary Agency
43 Musard Road, London W6 8NR
☎0171 386 0633
Contact *Teresa Chris*

FOUNDED 1989. *Handles* general, commercial and literary fiction, and non-fiction: health, business, travel, cookery, sport and fitness, gardening etc. *Specialises* in crime fiction and commercial women's fiction. No scripts. Film and TV rights handled by co-agent. No poetry, short stories, fantasy, science fiction or horror. Unsolicited mss welcome. Send query letter with sample material (*s.a.e. essential*) in first instance. No reading fee. CLIENTS include J. Wallis Martin, Joan Marysmith, Marguerite Patten. *Commission* Home 10%; US 15%; Translation 20%. *Overseas associates* Thompson & Chris Literary Agency, USA; representatives in most other countries.

Serafina Clarke★
98 Tunis Road, London W12 7EY
☎0181 749 6979   Fax 0181 740 6862
Contact *Serafina Clarke*

FOUNDED 1980. *Handles* fiction: romance, horror, thrillers, literary; and non-fiction: travel, cookery, gardening and biography.

Mary Clemmey Literary Agency★
6 Dunollie Road, London NW5 2XP
☎0171 267 1290   Fax 0171 267 1290
Contact *Mary Clemmey*

FOUNDED 1992. *Handles* fiction and non-fiction – high-quality work with an international market. No science fiction, fantasy or children's books. TV, film, radio and theatre scripts from existing clients only. No unsolicited mss. Approach by letter giving a description of the work in the first instance. S.a.e. essential. No reading fee. CLIENTS include Paul Gilroy, Sheila Kitzinger, Ray Shell, Elaine Showalter, Prof. David Wiggins; US & Canadian clients: The Bukowski Agency, **Frederick Hill Associates**, Lynn C. Franklin Associates Ltd, The Miller Agency, Roslyn Targ Literary Agency Inc. *Commission* Home 10%; USA & Translation 20%. *Overseas Associate* Elaine Markson Literary Agency, New York.

Jonathan Clowes Ltd★
10 Iron Bridge House, Bridge Approach, London NW1 8BD
☎0171 722 7674   Fax 0171 722 7677
Contact *Brie Burkeman*

FOUNDED 1960. Pronounced 'clewes'. Now one of the biggest fish in the pond, and not really for the untried unless they are true high-flyers. Fiction and non-fiction, plus scripts. No textbooks or children's. *Special interests* situation comedy, film and television rights. No unsolicited mss; authors come by recommendation or by successful follow-ups to preliminary letters. CLIENTS include David Bellamy, Michael Cooney, Len Deighton, Elizabeth Jane Howard, Doris Lessing, David Nobbs, and the estate of Kingsley Amis. *Commission* Home/US 15%; Translation 19%. *Overseas associates* **Andrew Nurnberg Associates**; Sane Töregard Agency.

Elspeth Cochrane Agency
11–13 Orlando Road, London SW4 0LE
☎0171 622 0314/4279   Fax 0171 622 5815
Contact *Elspeth Cochrane*

FOUNDED 1960. *Handles* fiction, non-fiction, biographies, screenplays. Subjects have included Marlon Brando, Sean Connery, Clint Eastwood, Lord Olivier. Also scripts for all media, with special interest in drama. No unsolicited mss. Preliminary letter, synopsis and s.a.e. is essential in the first instance. CLIENTS include Royce Ryton, Robert Tanitch. *Commission* 12½% ('but this can change; the percentage is negotiable, as is the sum paid to the writer').

Rosica Colin Ltd
1 Clareville Grove Mews, London SW7 5AH
☎0171 370 1080   Fax 0171 244 6441
Contact *Joanna Marston*

FOUNDED 1949. *Handles* all full-length mss, plus theatre, film, television and sound broadcasting.

Preliminary letter with return postage essential; writers should outline their writing credits and whether their mss have previously been submitted elsewhere. May take 3–4 months to consider full mss; synopsis preferred in the first instance. No reading fee. *Commission* Home 10%; US 15%; Translation 20%.

Combrógos Literary Agency

10 Heol Don, Whitchurch, Cardiff CF4 2AU
☎01222 623359   Fax 01222 529202
Contact *Meic Stephens*

FOUNDED 1990. *Specialises* in books about Wales or by Welsh authors, including novels, short stories, poetry, biography and general. Good contacts in Wales and London. Also editorial services, arts and media research. No unsolicited mss; preliminary letter (s.a.e. essential). *Commission* 10%.

Jane Conway-Gordon★

1 Old Compton Street, London W1V 5PH
☎0171 494 0148   Fax 0171 287 9264
Contact *Jane Conway-Gordon*

FOUNDED 1982. Works in association with **Andrew Mann Ltd**. *Handles* fiction and general non-fiction, plus occasional scripts for TV/radio/theatre. No poetry or science fiction. Unsolicited mss welcome; preliminary letter and return postage essential. No reading fee. *Commission* Home 10%; US & Translation 20%. *Overseas associates* **Ellen Levine, Literary Agency, Inc.**, New York; plus agencies throughout Europe and Japan.

Rupert Crew Ltd★

1A King's Mews, London WC1N 2JA
☎0171 242 8586   Fax 0171 831 7914
E-mail (correspondence only):
rupertcrew@compuserve.com
Contact *Doreen Montgomery,*
  Caroline Montgomery

FOUNDED 1927. International representation, handling volume and subsidiary rights in fiction and non-fiction properties. No plays or poetry, journalism or short stories. Preliminary letter essential. No reading fee. *Commission* Home 10–15%; Elsewhere 20%.

The Croft Agency

13 Croft Road, Caister–on–Sea, Great Yarmouth, Norfolk NR30 5EJ
☎01493 721919
Contact *John Laity*

FOUNDED 1995. *Handles* general fiction including crime, suspense and drama, murder mysteries, adventure, thrillers and novels with 'social issues'. No poetry, children's, science fiction, occult, supernatural, cookbooks or picture books. 'The agency is always interested in hearing from new and previously unpublished authors.' No unsolicited mss. Initial enquiry by letter only (no phone calls) and s.a.e. for agency conditions and free copy of 'helpful hints' for new authors. All mss will be read; minor revisions suggested free of charge. Reading/critique fee from £10, refunded from commission. CLIENTS John Collins, Catherine Hill, B. M. Rogers, Jonathan Sparkes. *Commission* Home 10%; USA 15%; Translation 20%.

Cruickshank Cazenove Ltd

97 Old South Lambeth Road, London SW8 1XU
☎0171 735 2933   Fax 0171 820 1081
Contact *Harriet Cruickshank*

FOUNDED 1983. *Specialises* in plays and screenplays only. No unsolicited mss. Preliminary letter with synopsis and s.a.e. essential. *Commission* Home 10%; US & Translation varies according to contract. *Overseas associates* Various.

Curtis Brown Group Ltd★

Haymarket House, 28/29 Haymarket, London SW1Y 4SP
☎0171 396 6600   Fax 0171 396 0110
Chairman *Paul Scherer*
Group Managing Director *Jonathan Lloyd*
Directors *Jane Bradish-Ellames, Mark*
  Collingbourne (Finance), Tim Curnow
  (Australia), Sue Freathy, Jonny Geller, Giles
  Gordon, Diana Mackay, Nick Marston (MD,
  Media Division), Anthea Morton-Saner, Peter
  Murphy, Peter Robinson, Vivienne Schuster,
  Michael Shaw, Elizabeth Stevens

Long-established literary agency, whose first sales were made in 1899. Merged with John Farquharson, forming the Curtis Brown Group Ltd in 1989. *Handles* a wide range of subjects including fiction, general non-fiction, children's and specialist, scripts for film, TV, theatre and radio. Send synopsis with covering letter and c.v. rather than complete mss. No reading fee. *Commission* Home 10%; US & Translation 20%. *Overseas associates* in Australia, Canada and the US.

Judy Daish Associates Ltd

2 St Charles Place, London W10 6EG
☎0181 964 8811   Fax 0181 964 8966
Contact *Judy Daish, Sara Stroud, Deborah*
  Harwood

FOUNDED 1978. Theatrical literary agent. *Handles* scripts for film, TV, theatre and radio. No books. Preliminary letter essential. No unsolicited mss.

Caroline Davidson Literary Agency

5 Queen Anne's Gardens, London W4 1TU
☎0181 995 5768   Fax 0181 994 2770
Contact *Caroline Davidson, Alice Hurt*

FOUNDED 1988. *Handles* fiction and non-fiction, including archaeology, architecture, art, astronomy, biography, cookery, crafts, design, fitness, gardening, history, investigative journalism, medicine, music, natural history, photography, reference, science, self-help and how-to, TV tie-ins. Many highly illustrated books. Finished first novels positively welcomed. No occult, short stories, plays or poetry. Writers should telephone or send an initial letter giving details of the project together with c.v. and s.a.e. CLIENTS Robert Baldock, Nigel Barlow, John Brackenbury, Elizabeth Bradley, Stuart Clark, Andrew Dalby, Emma Donoghue, Willi Elsener, Anissa Helou, Paul Hillyard, Mary Hollingsworth, Tom Jaine, Andrew King, Bernard Lavery, Adrian Lyttleton, Huon Mallalieu, Simon Nolan, Marie O'Connor, Diane Purkiss, S4C (the Welsh Channel Four). *Commission* US, Home, Commonwealth, Translation 12½%; occasionally more (20%) if sub-agents have to be used.

Merric Davidson Literary Agency

12 Priors Heath, Goudhurst, Cranbrook, Kent TN17 2RE
☎01580 212041   Fax 01580 212041
Contact *Merric Davidson, Wendy Suffield*

FOUNDED 1990. *Handles* fiction, general non-fiction and children's books. No scripts. No academic, short stories or articles. Particularly keen on contemporary fiction. No unsolicited mss. Send preliminary letter with synopsis and biographical details. S.a.e. essential for response. No reading fee. CLIENTS include Valerie Blumenthal, Murray Davies, Louise Doughty, Harold Elletson, Elizabeth Harris, Alison Habens, Alison MacLeod, Allis Moss, Mark Pepper, Luke Sutherland. *Commission* Home 10%; US 15%; Translation 20%.

Felix de Wolfe

Manfield House, 1 Southampton Street, London WC2R 0LR
☎0171 379 5767   Fax 0171 836 0337
Contact *Felix de Wolfe*

FOUNDED 1938. *Handles* quality fiction only, and scripts. No non-fiction or children's. No unsolicited mss. No reading fee. CLIENTS include Jan Butlin, Robert Cogo-Fawcett, Brian Glover, Sheila Goff, Jennifer Johnston, John Kershaw, Bill MacIlwraith, Angus Mackay, Gerard McLarnon, Braham Murray, Julian Slade, Malcolm Taylor, David Thompson, Paul Todd, Dolores Walshe. *Commission* Home 12½%; US 20%.

Dorian Literary Agency (DLA)

Upper Thornehill, 27 Church Road, St Marychurch, Torquay, Devon TQ1 4QY
☎01803 312095   Fax 01803 312095
Contact *Dorothy Lumley*

FOUNDED 1986. *Handles* mainstream and commercial full-length adult fiction; specialities are women's (including contemporary and sagas), crime and thrillers; horror, science fiction and fantasy. Also, limited non-fiction: primarily self-help and media-related subjects; plus scripts for TV and radio. No poetry, children's, theatrical scripts, short stories, academic or technical. Introductory letter with synopsis/outline and first chapter (with return postage) only please. Equiries or submissions by fax or e-mail will not be acceptable. No reading fee. CLIENTS include Stephen Jones, Brian Lumley, Amy Myers, Dee Williams. *Commission* Home 10%; US 15%; Translation 20–25%. Works with agents in most countries for translation.

Anne Drexl

8 Roland Gardens, London SW7 3PH
☎0171 244 9645
Contact *Anne Drexl*

FOUNDED 1988. *Handles* commercially orientated full-length mss for women's fiction, general, family sagas and crime. Ideas welcome for business-related books, how-to, DIY, hobbies and collecting. Strong interest too in juvenile fiction, including children's games and activity books. Writers should approach with preliminary letter and synopsis (including s.a.e.). No reading fee but may ask for a contribution to admin. costs. *Commission* Home 12½%; US & Translation 20% (but varies depending on agent used).

Toby Eady Associates Ltd

9 Orme Court, London W2 4RL
☎0171 792 0092   Fax 0171 792 0879
Contact *Toby Eady, Alexandra Pringle, Victoria Hobbs*

Handles fiction, and non-fiction. No scripts. No unsolicited mss. Approach by letter first.

No reading fee. CLIENTS include Nuha Al-Radi, Elspeth Barker, Sister Wendy Beckett, Ronan Bennett, Julia Blackburn, John Carey, Jung Chang, Bernard Cornwell, Nell Dunn, Patricia Duncker, Geoff Dyer, Lucy Ellmann, Esther Freud, Kuki Gallmann, Alasdair Gray, Sean Hardie, Tobias Hill, Michael Hofmann, Tim Jeal, Rana Kabbani, Que Lei Lei, Karl Miller, Tim Pears, Sun Shuyun, Amir Taheri, Barbara Trapido, Hong Ying. *Commission* Home 10%; US & Translation 20%. *Overseas associates* La Nouvelle Agence; Mohr Books; The English Agency, Tokyo; Jan Michael; Rosemarie Buckman.

Eddison Pearson Literary Agents
44 Inverness Terrace, London W2 3JA
☎0171 727 9113   Fax 0171 727 9143
E-mail: box1@eddisonpearson.com
Contact *Clare Pearson, Tom Eddison*

FOUNDED 1995. *Handles* literary fiction and non-fiction, some quality commercial fiction, poetry for the literary market, children's books; also feature screenplays, stage plays, TV and radio scripts. Unsolicited mss with s.a.e welcome. Advisable to send sample chapters in the first instance. No reading fee. *Commission* negotiable but usually 15% for home sales for first two books/scripts and 10% thereafter; Overseas: additional 5%.

Edwards Fuglewicz
49 Great Ormond Street, London WC1N 3HZ
☎0171 405 6725   Fax 0171 405 6726
Contact *Ros Edwards, Helenka Fuglewicz*

FOUNDED 1996. *Handles* adult and children's fiction; non-fiction: biography, current affairs, business books, music and film. No scripts. Unsolicited mss welcome; approach in writing in the first instance with covering letter giving publishing history and brief c.v. (enclose s.a.e. and postage for return of mss; disks not acceptable). No reading fee. *Commission* Home 10%; USA & Translation 20%.

Faith Evans Associates★
27 Park Avenue North, London N8 7RU
☎0181 340 9920   Fax 0181 340 9410
Contact *Faith Evans*

FOUNDED 1987. Small, selective agency. *Handles* fiction and non-fiction. New clients by recommendation only; no unsolicited mss or phone calls, please. CLIENTS include Melissa Benn, Eleanor Bron, Helen Falconer, Midge Gillies, Saeed Jaffrey, Helena Kennedy, Cleo Laine, Seumas Milne, Christine Purkis, Sheila Rowbotham, Lorna Sage, Hwee Hwee Tan, Marion Urch, Harriet Walter, Elizabeth Wilson, Andrea Weiss. *Commission* Home 15%; US & Translation 20%. *Overseas associates* worldwide.

John Farquharson★
See **Curtis Brown Group Ltd**

Film Rights Ltd
See **Laurence Fitch Ltd**

Laurence Fitch Ltd
483 Southbank House, Black Prince Road, Albert Embankment, London SE1 7SJ
☎0171 735 8171
Contact *Brendan Davis*

FOUNDED 1952, incorporating the London Play Company (1922) and in association with Film Rights Ltd (1932). *Handles* scripts for theatre, film, TV and radio only. No unsolicited mss. Send synopsis with sample scene(s) in the first instance. No reading fee. CLIENTS include Judy Allen, Carlo Ardito, Hindi Brooks, John Chapman & Ray Cooney, John Graham, Glyn Robbins, Gene Stone, the estate of Dodie Smith, Edward Taylor. *Commission* 10%. *Overseas associates* worldwide.

Jill Foster Ltd
9 Barb Mews, Brook Green, London W6 7PA
☎0171 602 1263   Fax 0171 602 9336
Contact *Jill Foster, Alison Finch, Ann Foster, Kim Dockrey*

FOUNDED 1976. *Handles* scripts for TV, drama and comedy. No fiction, short stories or poetry. No unsolicited mss; approach by letter in the first instance. No reading fee. CLIENTS include Colin Bostock-Smith, Jan Etherington and Gavin Petrie, Phil Ford, Rob Gittins, Julia Jones, Peter Tilbury, Peter Tinniswood, Susan Wilkins. *Commission* Home 12½%; US & Translation 15%.

Fox & Howard Literary Agency
4 Bramerton Street, London SW3 5JX
☎0171 352 8691   Fax 0171 352 8691
Contact *Chelsey Fox, Charlotte Howard*

FOUNDED 1992. *Handles* general non-fiction: biography, popular history, current affairs, reference, business, mind, body and spirit, self-help, health. No scripts. No poetry, plays, short stories, children's, science fiction, fantasy and horror. No unsolicited mss; send letter, synopsis and sample chapter with s.a.e. for response. No reading fee. CLIENTS Sarah Bartlett, Sir Rhodes Boyson, Simon Collin, Bruce King,

Bill Laws, Tony Clayton Lea, Jane Struthers. *Commission* Home 10%; US & Translation 20%.

French's

9 Elgin Mews South, London W9 1JZ
☎0171 266 3321   Fax 0171 286 6716
Contact *Mark Taylor*

FOUNDED 1973. *Handles* fiction and non-fiction; and scripts for all media. No religious or medical books. No unsolicited mss. 'For unpublished authors we offer a reading service at £60 per ms, exclusive of postage.' Interested authors should write in the first instance. *Commission* Home 10%.

Vernon Futerman Associates★

159A Goldhurst Terrace, London NW6 3EU
☎0171 625 9601   Fax 0171 625 9601
All submissions to: 17 Deanhill Road, London SW14 7DQ
☎0181 286 4860   Fax 0181 286 4861
Academic/Politics/Current Affairs *Vernon Futerman*
Educational/Art *Alexandra Groom*
Fiction/Show Business/TV, Film & Theatre Scripts *Guy Rose*

FOUNDED 1984. *Handles* fiction and non-fiction, including academic, art, biography, autobiography, educational, politics, current affairs, show business; also scripts for film, TV and theatre. No short stories, science fiction, crafts or hobbies. No unsolicited mss; send preliminary letter with a brief biography, detailed synopsis and s.a.e. No reading fee. CLIENTS Lorraine Chase, Sir Martin Ewans KCMG, Kingsley Fielding, Susan George, Angus Graham-Campbell, Sue Lenier, Stephen Lowe, Sir Robert McCrindle, Angela Meredith, Brian Milton, Valerie Grosvenor Myer, Prof. Wu Ningkun, Dapo Odesanya, Adam Shaw, Judy Upton, Russell Warren Howe, Ernie Wise, Simon Woodham. *Commission* Literature: Home 12½%; Overseas: 17½%. Drama/Screenplays: Home 15%; Overseas 20%; Translation 20%. *Overseas associates* USA, South Africa, France (Lora Fountain), Germany/Austria/Switzerland (Brigitte Axter).

Jüri Gabriel

35 Camberwell Grove, London SE5 8JA
☎0171 703 6186   Fax 0171 703 6186
Contact *Jüri Gabriel*

Handles quality fiction, non-fiction and (mainly for existing clients) film, TV and radio rights/scripts. Jüri Gabriel worked in television, wrote books for 20 years and is chairman of

Dedalus publishers. No short stories, articles, verse or books for children. Unsolicited mss ('2-page synopsis and 3 sample chapters in first instance, please') welcome if accompanied by return postage and letter giving sufficient information about author's writing experience, aims etc. CLIENTS include Nigel Cawthorne, Diana Constance, Stephen Dunn, Miriam Dunne, Pat Gray, James Hawes, Robert Irwin, Mark Lloyd, David Madsen, David Miller, Prof. Cedric Mims, John Outram, Ewen Southby-Tailyour, Dr Stefan Szymanski, Dr Terence White, John Wyatt, Dr Robert Youngson. *Commission* Home 10%; US & Translation 20%.

Eric Glass Ltd

28 Berkeley Square, London W1X 6HD
☎0171 629 7162   Fax 0171 499 6780
Contact *Janet Glass*

FOUNDED 1934. *Handles* fiction, non-fiction and scripts for publication or production in all media. No poetry. No unsolicited mss. No reading fee. CLIENTS include Marc Camoletti, Charles Dyer, Wolf Mankowitz, Jack Popplewell and the estates of Rodney Ackland, Jean Cocteau, Philip King, Robin Maugham, Beverley Nichols, Jean-Paul Sartre. *Commission* Home 10%; US & Translation 20% (to include sub-agent's fee). *Overseas associates* in the US, Australia, France, Germany, Greece, Holland, Italy, Japan, Poland, Scandinavia, South Africa, Spain.

Christine Green Authors' Agent★

40 Doughty Street, London WC1N 2LF
☎0171 831 4956   Fax 0171 405 3935
Contact *Christine Green*

FOUNDED 1984. *Handles* fiction (general and literary) and general non-fiction. No scripts, poetry or children's. No unsolicited mss; initial letter and synopsis preferred. No reading fee but return postage essential. *Commission* Home 10%; US & Translation 20%.

Greene & Heaton Ltd★

37 Goldhawk Road, London W12 8QQ
☎0181 749 0315   Fax 0181 749 0318
Contact *Carol Heaton, Judith Murray, Antony Topping*

A small agency that likes to involve itself with its authors. *Handles* fiction (no science fiction, fantasy or children's books) and general non-fiction. No original scripts for theatre, film or TV. No unsolicited mss without preliminary letter. CLIENTS include Geraldine Bedell, Bill Bryson, Kate Charles, Jan Dalley, Colin Forbes, P. D.

James, Mary Morrissy, Conor Cruise O'Brien, William Shawcross. *Commission* Home 10%; US & Translation 20%.

Gregory & Radice Authors' Agents★

3 Barb Mews, London W6 7PA
☎0171 610 4676   Fax 0171 610 4686
Contact *Jane Gregory, Dr Lisanne Radice* (Editorial), *Pippa Dyson* (Film/TV)

FOUNDED 1987. *Handles* full-length fiction and non-fiction. *Special interest* crime, suspense, thrillers, literary and commercial fiction, politics. 'We are particularly successful in selling foreign rights.' No original plays, film or TV scripts (only published books are sold to film and TV). No science fiction, fantasy, poetry, academic or children's books. No reading fee. Editorial advice given to new authors. No unsolicited mss; send a preliminary letter with synopsis and first three chapters (plus return postage). No submissions by fax or e-mail. *Commission* Home 15%; Newspapers 20%; US & Translation 20%; Radio/TV/Film 15%. Is well represented throughout Europe, Asia and USA.

David Grossman Literary Agency Ltd

118b Holland Park Avenue, London W11 4UA
☎0171 221 2770   Fax 0171 221 1445
Contact *Material should be addressed to the company*

FOUNDED 1976. *Handles* full-length fiction and general non-fiction – good writing of all kinds and anything healthily controversial. No verse or technical books for students. No original screenplays or teleplays (only works existing in volume form are sold for performance rights). Generally works with published writers of fiction only but 'truly original, well-written novels from beginners' will be considered. Best approach by preliminary letter giving full description of the work. All material must be accompanied by return postage. No approaches or submissions by fax. No unsolicited mss. No reading fee. *Commission* Rates vary for different markets. *Overseas associates* throughout Europe, Asia, Brazil and the US.

Margaret Hanbury Literary Agency★

27 Walcot Square, London SE11 4UB
☎0171 735 7680   Fax 0171 793 0316
Contact *Margaret Hanbury*

Personally-run agency representing quality fic-

tion and non-fiction. No plays, scripts, poetry, children's books, fantasy, horror. No unsolicited mss; preliminary letter with s.a.e. essential. *Commission* Home 15%; Overseas 20%.

Roger Hancock Ltd

4 Water Lane, London NW1 8NZ
☎0171 267 4418   Fax 0171 267 0705
Contact *Material should be addressed to the Company*

FOUNDED 1961. *Special interests* drama and light entertainment. Scripts only. No books. Unsolicited mss not welcome. Initial phone call required. No reading fee. *Commission* 10%.

A. M. Heath & Co. Ltd★

79 St Martin's Lane, London WC2N 4AA
☎0171 836 4271   Fax 0171 497 2561
Contact *Bill Hamilton, Sara Fisher, Sarah Molloy*

FOUNDED 1919. *Handles* fiction and general non-fiction. No dramatic scripts or poetry. Preliminary letter and synopsis essential. No reading fee. CLIENTS include Christopher Andrew, Anita Brookner, Katie Fforde, Lesley Glaister, Graham Hancock, Hilary Mantel, Hilary Norman, Adam Thorpe. *Commission* Home 10–15%; US & Translation 20%; Film & TV 15%. *Overseas associates* in the US, Europe, South America, Japan.

Hermes The Literary Agency

5 Thames House, Manor House Lane, Datchet, Berkshire SL3 9EB
☎01753 582941
E-mail: susan@hermes-theagency.demon.co.uk
Contact *Susan Wells*

FOUNDED 1993. *Handles* full-length fiction, *specialising* in the high-concept/techno-thriller genre - manuscripts and screenplays. Unsolicited, fully revised mss accepted with return postage (also for acknowledgement), c.v., one-page synopsis, telephone numbers, and copies of all rejections. No reading fee. No telephone calls. CLIENTS include Sam Christopher. *Commission* Home 10–15%; US & Translation 20%; Motion Picture 20%.

David Higham Associates Ltd★

(incorporating **Murray Pollinger**)
5–8 Lower John Street, Golden Square, London W1R 4HA
☎0171 437 7888   Fax 0171 437 1072
Scripts *Elizabeth Cree, Nicky Lund, Georgina Ruffhead, Gemma Hirst*

Books *Bruce Hunter, Jacqueline Korn, Anthony Goff, Sara Menguc, Caroline Walsh, Daniela Bernardelle*

FOUNDED 1935. *Handles* fiction and general non-fiction: biography, history, current affairs, etc. Also scripts. Preliminary letter with synopsis essential in first instance. No reading fee. CLIENTS include John le Carré, Stephen Fry, Jane Green, James Herbert, Alice Walker. *Commission* Home 10%; US & Translation 20%.

Vanessa Holt Ltd★
59 Crescent Road, Leigh-on-Sea, Essex SS9 2PF
☎01702 473787   Fax 01702 471890
Contact *Brenda White*
FOUNDED 1989. *Handles* general adult fiction and non-fiction. No scripts, poetry, academic or technical. *Specialises* in commercial and crime fiction. No unsolicited mss. Approach by letter in first instance, although 'taking on few new clients at present'; s.a.e. essential. No reading fee. *Commission* Home 10%; US & Translation 20%; Radio/TV/Film 15%. *Overseas associates* in the US, Europe, South America and Japan.

Valerie Hoskins
20 Charlotte Street, London W1P 1HJ
☎0171 637 4490   Fax 0171 637 4493
E-mail: ValerieHoskinsAss@compuserve.com
Contact *Valerie Hoskins*
FOUNDED 1983. *Handles* scripts for film, TV and radio. *Special interests* feature films and TV. No unsolicited scripts; preliminary letter of introduction essential. No reading fee. *Commission* Home 12½%; US 20% (maximum).

Tanja Howarth Literary Agency★
19 New Row, London WC2N 4LA
☎0171 240 5553/836 4142
Fax 0171 379 0969
Contact *Tanja Howarth*
FOUNDED 1970. Interested in taking on both fiction and non-fiction from British writers. No children's books, plays or poetry, but all other subjects considered providing the treatment is intelligent. No unsolicited mss. Preliminary letter preferred. No reading fee. Also an established agent for foreign literature, particularly from the German language. *Commission* Home 15%; Translation 20%.

ICM
Oxford House, 76 Oxford Street, London W1N 0AX
☎0171 636 6565   Fax 0171 323 0101
Contact *Ian Amos, Amanda Davis, Greg Hunt, Cathy King, Michael McCoy, Alan Radcliffe, Sue Rodgers, Jessica Sykes*
FOUNDED 1973. *Handles* film, TV and theatre scripts. No books. No unsolicited mss. Preliminary letter essential. No reading fee. *Commission* 10%. *Overseas associates* ICM, New York/Los Angeles.

IMG
Pier House, Strand on the Green, Chiswick, London W4 3NN
☎0181 233 5000   Fax 0181 233 5001
Contact *Sarah Wooldridge (London), Carolyn Krupp, David Chalfant (New York)*
Part of the Mark McCormack Group. Offices in New York. *Handles* celebrity books, sports-related books, commercial fiction (New York), non-fiction, how-to business books. No TV, film, radio, theatre, children's books, poetry and academic. No unsolicited mss; send letter with c.v., synopsis, three chapters and s.a.e. CLIENTS include Tony Buzan, Pat Conroy, Mark McCormack, professional sports stars, classical musicians, broadcasting personalities. *Commission* Home & USA 20%; Translation 25%.

Michael Imison Playwrights Ltd
See **Alan Brodie Representation Ltd**

International Copyright Bureau Ltd
22A Aubrey House, Maida Avenue, London W2 1TQ
☎0171 724 8034   Fax 0171 724 7662
Contact *Joy Westendarp*
FOUNDED 1905. *Handles* scripts for TV, theatre, film and radio. No books. Preliminary letter for unsolicited material essential. *Commission* Home 10%; US & Translation 19%. *Overseas agents* in New York and most foreign countries.

International Scripts
1 Norland Square, London W11 4PX
☎0171 229 0736   Fax 0171 792 3287
Contact *Bob Tanner, Pat Hornsey, Jill Lawson*
FOUNDED 1979 by Bob Tanner. *Handles* most types of books and scripts for most media. No poetry, articles or short stories. Preliminary letter

plus s.a.e. required. CLIENTS include Masquerade (USA), Lifetime Books (USA), Barrons (USA), Simon Clark, Ed Gorman, Peter Haining, Julie Harris, Robert A. Heinlein, Anna Jacobs, Dean R. Koontz, Richard Laymon, Nick Oldham, Mary Ryan, John and Anne Spencer. *Commission* Home 15%; US & Translation 20–25%. *Overseas associates* include Ralph Vicinanza, USA; Thomas Schluck, Germany; Yanez, Spain; Eliane Benisti, France.

Heather Jeeves Literary Agency★
9 Kingsfield Crescent, Witney, Oxfordshire OX8 6JB
☎01993 700253   Fax 01993 700253
Contact *Heather Jeeves*

FOUNDED 1989. *Handles* general trade, specialising in crime and cookery. Scripts for TV, film, and theatre are handled through **Casarotto Ramsay Ltd**. Not interested in academic, fantasy, science fiction, romances, poetry, short stories, sports, military history or freelance journalism. No unsolicited mss. Approach in the first instance in writing describing the project and professional experience. Return postage essential. No reading fee. CLIENTS include Debbie Bliss, Lindsey Davis, estate of Elspeth Huxley, Susan Kay, Mark Timlin. *Commission* Home 10%; US 15–20%; Translation 20%. *Overseas associates* throughout Europe and in the US.

John Johnson (Authors' Agent) Limited★
Clerkenwell House, 45/47 Clerkenwell Green, London EC1R 0HT
☎0171 251 0125   Fax 0171 251 2172
Contact *Andrew Hewson, Margaret Hewson, Elizabeth Fairbairn*

FOUNDED 1956. *Handles* general fiction and non-fiction. No science fiction, technical or academic material. Scripts from existing clients only. No unsolicited mss; send preliminary letter and s.a.e. in the first instance. No reading fee. *Commission* Home 10%; USA 15–20%; Translation 20%.

Jane Judd Literary Agency★
18 Belitha Villas, London N1 1PD
☎0171 607 0273   Fax 0171 607 0623
Contact *Jane Judd*

FOUNDED 1986. *Handles* general fiction and non-fiction: women's fiction, crime, thrillers, literary fiction, cookery, humour, biography, investigative journalism, health, women's interests and travel. 'Looking for good contemporary women's fiction but not Mills & Boon-type.' No scripts, academic, gardening or DIY. Approach

with letter, including synopsis, first chapter and return postage. Initial telephone call helpful in the case of non-fiction. CLIENTS include Patrick Anthony, John Brunner, Jillie Collings, Andy Dougan, Jill Mansell, Lester Piggott, Jonathon Porritt, Rosie Rushton. *Commission* Home 10%; US & Translation 20%.

Juvenilia
Avington, Near Winchester, Hampshire SO21 1DB
☎01962 779656   Fax 01962 779656
Contact *Rosemary Bromley*

FOUNDED 1973. *Handles* young/teen fiction and picture books; non-fiction and scripts for TV and radio. No poetry or short stories unless part of a collection or picture book material. No unsolicited mss. Send preliminary letter with full details of work and biographical outline in first instance. Preliminary letters unaccompanied by return postage will not be answered. Phone calls not advised. CLIENTS include Paul Aston, Elisabeth Beresford, Linda Birch, Denis Bond, Nicola Davies, Linda Dearsley, Terry Deary, Steve Donald, Gaye Hicyilmaz, Tom Holt, Phil McMylor, Elizabeth Pewsey, Saviour Pirotta, Kelvin Reynolds, Peter Riley, Malcolm Rose, Cathy Simpson, Margaret Stuart Barry, Keith West, Jennifer Zabel. *Commission* Home 10%; US 15%; Translation 20%; Illustration 20%.

Michelle Kass Associates★
36–38 Glasshouse Street, London W1R 5RH
☎0171 439 1624   Fax 0171 734 3394
Contact *Michelle Kass, Tishna Molla*

FOUNDED 1991. *Handles* fiction, TV, film, radio and theatre scripts. Approach with telephone call/explanatory letter in the first instance. No reading fee. *Commission* Home 10%; US & Translation 15–20%.

Frances Kelly★
111 Clifton Road, Kingston upon Thames, Surrey KT2 6PL
☎0181 549 7830   Fax 0181 547 0051
Contact *Frances Kelly*

FOUNDED 1978. *Handles* non-fiction, including illustrated: biography, history, art, self-help, food & wine, complementary medicine and therapies, New Age; and academic non-fiction in all disciplines. No scripts except for existing clients. No unsolicited mss. Approach by letter with brief description of work or synopsis, together with c.v. and return postage. *Commission* Home 10%; US & Translation 20%.

Paul Kiernan

PO Box 120, London SW3 4LU
☎0171 352 5562   Fax 0171 351 5986
Contact *Paul Kiernan*

FOUNDED 1990. *Handles* fiction and non-fiction, including autobiography and biography, plus specialist writers like cookery or gardening. Also scripts for TV, film, radio and theatre (TV and film scripts from book-writing clients only). No unsolicited mss. Preferred approach is by letter or personal introduction. Letters should include synopsis and brief biography. No reading fee. CLIENTS include K. Banta, Lord Chalfont, Ambassador Walter J. P. Curley, Sir Paul Fox. *Commission* Home 15%; US 20%.

Knight Features

20 Crescent Grove, London SW4 7AH
☎0171 622 1467   Fax 0171 622 1522
Contact *Peter Knight, Gaby Martin, Ann King-Hall, Andrew Knight, Giovanna Farrell-Vinay*

FOUNDED 1985. *Handles* motor sports, cartoon books, puzzles, business, history, factual and biographical material. No poetry, science fiction or cookery. No unsolicited mss. Send letter accompanied by c.v. and s.a.e. with synopsis of proposed work. CLIENTS include Frank Dickens, Christopher Hilton, Barbara Minto, Frederic Mullally. *Commission* dependent upon authors and territories. *Overseas associates* United Media, US; Auspac Media, Australia.

Labour and Management Limited (tricia sumner – literary agency)

Milton House, Milton Street, Waltham Abbey, Essex EN9 1EZ
☎01992 711511   Fax 01992 711511
E-mail: TriciaSumner@classic.msn.com
Contact *Tricia Sumner*

FOUNDED 1995. *Specialises* in literary fiction, biography, general non-fiction, theatre, TV, radio and film. *Special interests* in multi-cultural, gay, feminist and anti-establishment writing. No unsolicited mss. Covering letter and brief synopsis and sample chapters essential, together with return postage. No reading fee. CLIENTS Marion Baraitser, Noel Currer-Briggs, John R. Gordon, Olusola Oyeleye. *Commission* Home 12½%; Overseas 20%.

Cat Ledger Literary Agency★

33 Percy Street, London W1P 9FG
☎0171 436 5030   Fax 0171 631 4273
Contact *Cat Ledger*

FOUNDED 1996. *Handles* non-fiction: popular culture – film, music, sport, travel, humour, biography, politics; investigative journalism; fiction (non-genre). No scripts. No children's, poetry, fantasy, science fiction, romance. No unsolicited mss; approach with preliminary letter, synopsis and s.a.e. No reading fee. *Commission* Home 10%; US & Translation 20%.

Barbara Levy Literary Agency★

64 Greenhill, Hampstead High Street, London NW3 5TZ
☎0171 435 9046   Fax 0171 431 2063
Contact *Barbara Levy, John Selby*

FOUNDED 1986. *Handles* general fiction, non-fiction and scripts for TV and radio. No unsolicited mss. Send detailed preliminary letter in the first instance. No reading fee. *Commission* Home 10%; US 20%; Translation by arrangement, in conjunction with **The Marsh Agency**. *US associate* Arcadia Ltd, New York.

Limelight Management★

33 Newman Street, London W1P 3PD
☎0171 637 2529   Fax 0171 637 2538
Contact *Fiona Lindsay, Linda Shanks*

FOUNDED 1991. *Handles* general non-fiction and fiction books; cookery, gardening, wine, art and crafts, health, historical and romantic. No TV, film, radio or theatre. Not interested in science fiction, short stories, plays, children's. *Specialises* in illustrated books. Unsolicited mss welcome; send preliminary letter (s.a.e. essential). No reading fee. *Commission* Home 12½%; USA & Translation 20%.

The Christopher Little Literary Agency (1979)★

10 Eel Brook Studios, 125 Moore Park Road, London SW6 4PS
☎0171 736 4455   Fax 0171 736 4490
Fiction/Non-fiction *Christopher Little, Patrick Walsh*
Office Manager *Emma Schlesinger*

FOUNDED 1979. *Handles* commercial and literary full-length fiction, non-fiction, and film/TV scripts. *Special interests* crime, thrillers, autobiography, popular science and narrative, and investigative non-fiction. Also makes a particular speciality out of packaging celebrities for the book market and representing book projects for journalists. Rights representative in the UK for six American literary agencies. No reading fee. Send detailed letter ('giving a summary of present and future intentions together with track record, if any'), synopsis and/or first two chapters and s.a.e. in first instance. CLIENTS include Felice Arena, Simon Beckett, Marcus Berkmann, Colin Cameron, Harriet Castor, Linford Christie, Michael Cordy, Mike Dash, John Gordon Davis, Frankie Dettori, Ginny Elliot, Simon Gandolfi, Janet Gleeson, Brian Hall, Paula Hamilton, Damon Hill, Tom Holland, Alastair MacNeill, Robert Mawson, Sanjida O'Connell, Samantha Phillips, A. J. Quinnell, Alvin Rakoff, Rebecca Ray, Candace Robb, Peter Rosenberg, J. K. Rowling, Simon Singh, Alan Smith, John Spurling, David Thomas, Laura Thompson, John Watson, James Whitaker, John Wilson. *Commission* Home 15%; US, Canada, Translation, Motion Picture 20%.

London Independent Books
26 Chalcot Crescent, London NW1 8YD
☎0171 706 0486   Fax 0171 724 3122
Proprietor *Carolyn Whitaker*

FOUNDED 1971. A self-styled 'small and idiosyncratic' agency. *Handles* fiction and non-fiction reflecting the tastes of the proprietors. All subjects considered (except computer books and young children's), providing the treatment is strong and saleable. Scripts handled only if by existing clients. *Special interests* boats, travel, travelogues, commercial fiction. No unsolicited mss; letter, synopsis and first two chapters with return postage the best approach. No reading fee. *Commission* Home 15%; US & Translation 20%.

Lucas Alexander Whitley★
(incorporating **Jacintha Alexander Associates**)
Elsinore House, 77 Fulham Palace Road, London W6 8JA
☎0181 600 3800   Fax 0181 600 3810

Contact *Mark Lucas, Julian Alexander, Araminta Whitley, Roger Houghton, Kirstan Romano, Sally Hughes, Tom Bancroft*

FOUNDED 1996. *Handles* full-length general and literary fiction and non-fiction. No plays, poetry, textbooks, children's books or fantasy. Film and TV scripts handled for established clients only. Preliminary letter with s.a.e. essential. *Commission* Home 15%; US & Translation 20%. *Overseas associates* worldwide.

Lutyens and Rubinstein★
231 Westbourne Park Road, London W11 1EB
☎0171 792 4855   Fax 0171 792 4833
Partners *Sarah Lutyens, Felicity Rubinstein*

Submissions *Susannah Godman*

FOUNDED 1993. *Handles* adult fiction and non-fiction books. No TV, film, radio or theatre scripts. Unsolicited mss accepted; send introductory letter, c.v., two chapters and return postage for all material submitted. No reading fee. *Commission* Home 10%; USA & Translation 20%.

Duncan McAra
28 Beresford Gardens, Edinburgh EH5 3ES
☎0131 552 1558   Fax 0131 552 1558
Contact *Duncan McAra*

FOUNDED 1988. *Handles* fiction (literary fiction) and non-fiction, including art, architecture, archaeology, biography, military, travel and books of Scottish interest. Preliminary letter, synopsis and sample chapter (including return postage) essential. No reading fee. *Commission* Home 10%; Overseas by arrangement.

Bill McLean
Personal Management
23B Deodar Road, London SW15 2NP
☎0181 789 8191
Contact *Bill McLean*

FOUNDED 1972. *Handles* scripts for all media. No books. No unsolicited mss. Phone call or introductory letter essential. No reading fee. CLIENTS include Dwynwen Berry, Jane Galletly, Lynn Robertson Hay, Tony Jordan, Bill Lyons, John Maynard, Michael McStay, Les Miller, Sharon Morgan, Ian Rowlands, Jeffrey Segal, Ronnie Smith, Frank Vickery, Mark Wheatley. *Commission* Home 10%.

McLean and Slora Agency
20A Eildon Street, Edinburgh EH3 5JU
☎0131 556 3368
25 Colinton Road, Edinburgh EH10 5DR
☎0131 447 8001
Contact *Barbara McLean, Annie Slora*

FOUNDED 1996. *Handles* literary fiction; some non-fiction including biography and cookery. *Specialises* in books of Scottish interest. No science fiction or scripts. No unsolicited mss. Send preliminary letter, synopsis, sample chapter(s); s.a.e. essential. No initial reading fee. CLIENTS Tom Bryan, John Herdman, Ruari McLean. *Commission* Home 15%; USA & Translation 25%.

Eunice McMullen Children's Literary Agent Ltd

38 Clewer Hill Road, Windsor, Berkshire
SL4 4BW
☎01753 830348   Fax 01753 833459

Contact *Eunice McMullen*

FOUNDED 1992. *Handles* all types of children's material from picture books to teenage fiction. Particularly interested in younger children's fiction and illustrated texts. Has 'an excellent' list of picture book illustrators. In need of strong picture book texts to pair with existing illustrators who don't write themselves. Authors with track record in this area preferred. No unsolicited scripts. CLIENTS include Wayne Anderson, Reg Cartwright, Richard Fowler, Charles Fuge, Adrian Henri, Simon James, Susie Jenkin-Pearce, Angela McAllister, Graham Oakley, Sue Porter, Susan Winter, David Wood. *Commission* Home 10%; US 15%; Translation 20%.

Andrew Mann Ltd★

1 Old Compton Street, London W1V 5PH
☎0171 734 4751   Fax 0171 287 9264

Contact *Anne Dewe, Tina Betts*

In association with **Jane Conway-Gordon**. FOUNDED 1975. *Handles* fiction, general non-fiction and film, TV, theatre, radio scripts. No unsolicited mss. Preliminary letter, synopsis and s.a.e. essential. No reading fee. *Commission* Home 15%; US & Translation 25%. *Overseas associates* various.

Manuscript ReSearch

PO Box 33, Bicester, Oxfordshire OX6 7PP
☎01869 323447   Fax 01869 324096

Contact *Graham Jenkins*

FOUNDED 1988. Principally *handles* scripts suitable for film/TV outlets. Will only consider book submissions from established clients. Preferred first approach from new contacts is by letter with brief outline and s.a.e. *Commission* Home 10%; Overseas 20%.

The Marsh Agency★

11/12 Dover Street, London W1X 3PH
☎0171 399 2800   Fax 0171 399 2801
E-mail: enquiries@marsh-agency.co.uk

Contact *Paul Marsh, Susanna Nicklin*

FOUNDED 1994. *Handles* translation rights only. No TV, film, radio or theatre. No unsolicited mss. CLIENTS include several British and American agencies and publishers. *Commission* 10%.

M. C. Martinez Literary Agency

60 Oakwood Avenue, Southgate, London
N14 6QL
☎0181 886 5829

Contact *Mary Caroline Martinez, Francoise Budd*

FOUNDED 1988. *Handles* high-quality fiction, children's books, arts and crafts, interior design, alternative health/complementary medicine, cookery, autobiography, biography, popular music, sport and business. Also scripts for films, TV and radio. *Specialises* in fiction, children's and alternative health. No unsolicited mss. Phone call in the first instance before sending letter with synopsis; s.a.e. essential. (Possible change of address; telephone first before sending submissions.) No reading fee but may charge an admin. fee where appropriate. DTP service available. *Commission* Home 15%; US, Overseas & Translation 20%; Performance Rights 20%. *Overseas associates* various.

MBA Literary Agents Ltd★

62 Grafton Way, London W1P 5LD
☎0171 387 2076   Fax 0171 387 2042
E-mail: agent@mbalit.co.uk

Contact *Diana Tyler, John Richard Parker, Meg Davis, Ruth Needham, Laura Longrigg*

FOUNDED 1971. *Handles* fiction and non-fiction. No poetry. Works in conjunction with agents in most countries. Also UK representative for **Writers House**, the Donald Maass Agency and the **Susan Schulman Agency**. No reading fee. No unsolicited mss. CLIENTS include Campbell Armstrong, A. L. Barker, Harry Bowling, Jeffrey Caine, Glenn Chandler, Andrew Cowan, Patricia Finney, Maggie Furey, Sue Gee, the estate of B. S. Johnson, Paul J. McAuley, Anne McCaffrey, Sir Roger Penrose, Susan Oudot, Anne Perry, Iain Sinclair, E. V. Thompson, Mark Wallington, Douglas Watkinson, Valerie Windsor, Zhang Xianliang. *Commission* Home 10%; Overseas 20%; Theatre/TV/Radio 10%; Film 10–15%.

Midland Exposure

4 Victoria Court, Oadby, Leicestershire
LE2 4AF
☎0116 271 8332   Fax 0116 281 2188

Partners *Cari Crook, Lesley Gleeson*

FOUNDED 1996. *Handles* short fiction for magazines only. *Specialises* in women's, teenage and children's magazine fiction. No books. 'Keen to encourage new writers.' Unsolicited mss welcome. No reading fee. *Commission* Home 15%; USA 20%.

Richard Milne Ltd

15 Summerlee Gardens, London N2 9QN
☎0181 883 3987   Fax 0181 883 0323
Contact *R. M. Sharples, K. N. Sharples*

FOUNDED 1956. *Specialises* in drama and comedy scripts for radio, film and television. Not presently in the market for new clients as 'fully committed handling work by authors we already represent'. No unsolicited mss. *Commission* Home 10%; US 15%; Translation 25%.

Jay Morris & Co., Authors' Agents

PO Box 2926, Brighton, East Sussex
BN1 3NR
☎01273 240070   Fax 01273 240072
Contact *Toby Tillyard-Burrows (Managing Director)*
Director *Dr Phillida Kanta*

FOUNDED 1994. *Handles* full-length mainstream commercial adult fiction, also racy sagas, gay erotica, horror, children's fantasy, women in power (not women's issues), thrillers and crime. No academic, articles, non-fiction, Aga sagas or romance. Approach by letter only, no faxes, enclosing synopsis and s.a.e. Reading fee may be requested. CLIENTS include Piers de Villias, Jonathan Douglas, Saxon Hollis, Hon. Joy Parker-Dixon, Elika Rise. *Commission* Home 10%; US & Translation 15%. *Overseas associates* in New York, San Francisco, Hawaii.

William Morris Agency UK Ltd★

1 Stratton Street, London W1X 6HB
☎0171 355 8500   Fax 0171 355 8600
Film/TV/Stage *Tanya Cohen, Jim Crabbe, Steve Kenis*
Books *Stephanie Cabot*

FOUNDED 1965. Worldwide theatrical and literary agency with offices in New York, Beverly Hills and Nashville and associates in Munich and Sydney. *Handles* film, TV, stage, radio scripts; fiction and general non-fiction. No unsolicited film, TV or stage material *at all*. Mss for books with preliminary letter. No reading fee. *Commission* Film/TV/Theatre/UK Books 10%; US Books & Translation 20%.

Michael Motley Ltd★

42 Craven Hill Gardens, London W2 3EA
☎0171 723 2973   Fax 0171 262 4566
Contact *Michael Motley*

FOUNDED 1973. *Handles* all subjects, except short mss (e.g. journalism), poetry and original dramatic material. *Special interest* literary fiction and crime novels. Mss will be considered but must be preceded by a preliminary letter with specimen chapters and s.a.e. No reading fee. CLIENTS include Simon Brett, Richard Denny, K. M. Peyton, Annette Roome, Barry Turner. *Commission* Home 10%; US 15%; Translation 20%. *Overseas associates* in all publishing centres.

William Neill-Hall Ltd

Flexbury End, Poughill Road, Bude,
Cornwall EX23 8NZ
☎01288 355335   Fax 01288 355335
E-mail: wneill-hall@msn.com
Contact *William Neill-Hall*

FOUNDED 1995. *Handles* general non-fiction, humour, religion. No TV, film, theatre or radio scripts; no fiction or poetry. *Specialises* in religion, sport, history, current affairs and humour. No unsolicited mss. Approach by phone or letter. Enclose return postage. No reading fee. CLIENTS Mary Batchelor, Mark Bryant, Archbishop of Canterbury (George Carey), Richard Foster, Jennifer Rees Larcombe, Heather Pinchen, David Pytches. *Commission* Home 10%; USA 15%; Translation 20%.

New Authors Showcase

See entry under **Editorial, Research and Other Services**

The Maggie Noach Literary Agency★

21 Redan Street, London W14 0AB
☎0171 602 2451   Fax 0171 603 4712
Contact *Maggie Noach*

FOUNDED 1982. Pronounced 'no-ack'. *Handles* a wide range of well-written books including general non-fiction, especially biography, commercial, fiction and non-illustrated children's books for ages 7–12. No scientific, academic or specialist non-fiction. No poetry, plays, short stories or books for the very young. Recommended for promising young writers but *very* few new clients taken on as it is considered vital to give individual attention to each author's work. Unsolicited mss not welcome. Approach by letter (*not by telephone*), giving a brief description of the book and enclosing a few sample pages. Return postage essential. No reading fee. *Commission* Home 15%; US & Translation 20%.

Northern Writes

4 Pilton Road, Pilton Park, Westerhope
Village, Tyne and Wear NE5 4PP
☎0191 214 5449   Fax 0191 243 4910
E-mail: N.Write@cableinet.co.uk
Contact *Carole Wilkinson* (Children's/humour),

Richard Brailey (Fiction/TV/Play Scripts)
FOUNDED 1997. *Handles* adult fiction (particularly reflecting contemporary life), children's fiction and humour (illustrated or otherwise; intelligent and satirical). TV, theatre, radio and film scripts also handled. No erotic, science fiction, technical, non-fiction or poetry. No unsolicited mss. Send synopsis and covering letter in the first instance. A reading fee of £25 is charged on acceptance of full manuscript. CLIENTS Tom Arto, Marie Pace, Harold Winter. *Commission* Home 10%; USA & Translation 20%.

Andrew Nurnberg Associates Ltd★
Clerkenwell House, 45–47 Clerkenwell Green, London EC1R 0HT
☎0171 417 8800   Fax 0171 417 8812
Directors *Andrew Nurnberg, Klaasje Mul, Sarah Nundy*
FOUNDED in the mid-1970s. *Specialises* in foreign rights, representing leading authors and agents. Branches in Moscow, Bucharest, Budapest, Prague, Sofia, Warsaw and Riga. *Commission* Home 15%; US & Translation 20%.

Alexandra Nye
44 Braemar Avenue, Dunblane, Perthshire FK15 9EB
☎01786 825114
Contact *Alexandra Nye*
FOUNDED 1991. *Handles* fiction and topical non-fiction. *Special interests* literary fiction, historicals, thrillers. No unsolicited mss. CLIENTS include Dr Tom Gallagher, Harry Mehta, Robin Jenkins. *Commission* Home 10%; US 20%; Translation 15%.

David O'Leary Literary Agents
10 Lansdowne Court, Lansdowne Rise, London W11 2NR
☎0171 229 1623   Fax 0171 727 9624
Contact *David O'Leary*
FOUNDED 1988. *Handles* fiction, both popular and literary, and non-fiction. Areas of interest include thrillers, history, popular science, Russia and Ireland (history and fiction). No poetry, science fiction or children's. No unsolicited mss but happy to discuss a proposal. Ring or write in the first instance. No reading fee. CLIENTS include James Barwick, David Crackanthorpe, Alexander Keegan, James Kennedy, Jim Lusby, Gretta Mulrooney. *Commission* Home 10%; US 10%. *Overseas associates* Lennart Sane, Scandinavia/Spain/South America; Tuttle Mori, Japan.

Deborah Owen Ltd★
78 Narrow Street, Limehouse, London E14 8BP
☎0171 987 5119/5441   Fax 0171 538 4004
Contact *Deborah Owen*
FOUNDED 1971. Small agency specialising in representing authors direct around the world. *Handles* international fiction and non-fiction (books which can be translated into a number of languages). No scripts, poetry, science fiction, children's or short stories. No unsolicited mss. No new authors at present. CLIENTS include Penelope Farmer, Amos Oz, Ellis Peters, Delia Smith. *Commission* Home 10%; US & Translation 15%.

Mark Paterson & Associates★
10 Brook Street, Wivenhoe, Colchester, Essex CO7 9DS
☎01206 825433   Fax 01206 822990
Contact *Mark Paterson, Mary Swinney, Penny Tyndale-Hardy*
FOUNDED 1961. World rights representatives of authors and publishers handling many subjects, with specialisation in psychoanalysis and psychotherapy. CLIENTS range from Balint, Bion, Casement and Ferenczi, through to Freud and Winnicott; plus Hugh Brogan, Peter Moss and the estates of Sir Arthur Evans, Hugh Schonfield and Dorothy Richardson. No scripts, poetry, children's, articles, short stories or 'unsaleable mediocrity'. No unsolicited mss, but preliminary letter and synopsis with s.a.e. welcome. *Commission* 20% (including sub-agent's commission).

John Pawsey
60 High Street, Tarring, Worthing, West Sussex BN14 7NR
☎01903 205167   Fax 01903 205167
Contact *John Pawsey*
FOUNDED 1981. Experience in the publishing business has helped to attract some top names here, but the door remains open for bright, new talent. *Handles* non-fiction: biography, politics, current affairs, show business, gardening, travel, sport, business and music; and fiction; will consider any well-written novel except science fiction, fantasy and horror. *Special interests* sport, current affairs and popular fiction. No drama scripts, poetry, short stories, journalism or academic. Preliminary letter with s.a.e. essential. No reading fee. CLIENTS include Jonathan Agnew, Emily Bell, Dr David Lewis, David Rayvern Allen, Caroline Fabre, Elwyn Hartley Edwards, Peter Hobday, Jon Silverman. *Commission*

Home 10–15%; US & Translation 19%. *Overseas associates* in the US, Japan, South America and throughout Europe.

Maggie Pearlstine Associates Ltd★
31 Ashley Gardens, Ambrosden Avenue, London SW1P 1QE
☎0171 828 4212   Fax 0171 834 5546
Contact *Maggie Pearlstine*

FOUNDED 1989. Small, selective agency. *Handles* commercial fiction, general and illustrated non-fiction: home and leisure, health, biography, history and politics. No children's or poetry. Deals only with scripts and short stories by existing clients. No unsolicited mss. Best approach first by letter with synopsis, sample material and s.a.e. for response. No reading fee. CLIENTS David Aaronovich, John Biffen, Matthew Baylis, Kate Bingham, Glorafilia, Prof Roger Gosden, Roy Hattersley, Prof Lisa Jardine, Charles Kennedy, Prof Nicholas Lowe, Simon Morris, Dr Raj Persaud, Prof Lesley Regan, Jackie Rowley, Chief Rabbi Jonathan Sacks, Polly Sellar, Lady Henrietta Spencer-Churchill, Jack Straw, Dr Thomas Stuttaford, Prof Robert Winston. Translation rights handled by **Aitken & Stone Ltd**. *Commission* Home 12½% (fiction), 10% (non-fiction); US & Translation 20%; TV, Film & Journalism 20%.

Pelican Literary Agency
17 Clare Hill, Huddersfield, West Yorkshire HD1 5BS
☎01484 469911   Fax 01484 469911
Contact *Mike Austin, Margo Whiteley*

FOUNDED 1998. *Handles* fiction and general non-fiction – memoirs, autobiography, biography, travel and children's stories; 'may consider some poetry'. No scripts, nor academic, manuals, cookery and crafts. No unsolicited mss. Send synopsis with one sample chapter with return postage. No reading fee. *Commission* Home 10%; USA & Translation 15%.

Peters Fraser & Dunlop Group Ltd★
503–504 The Chambers, Chelsea Harbour, Lots Road, London SW10 0XF
☎0171 344 1000
Fax 0171 352 7356/351 1756
E-mail: rscoular@pfd.co.uk
Website: http://www.pfd.co.uk
Managing Director *Anthony Baring*
Books *Michael Sissons, Pat Kavanagh, Caroline Dawnay, Charles Walker, Rosemary Canter, Sarah Leigh, Robert Kirby*

Serial *Pat Kavanagh*
Film/TV *Anthony Jones, Tim Corrie, Norman North, Charles Walker, Vanessa Jones, St. John Donald, Rosemary Scoular, Natasha Galloway*
Actors *Maureen Vincent, Ginette Chalmers, Dallas Smith, Lindy King*
Theatre *Kenneth Ewing, St John Donald, Nicki Stoddart*
Children's *Rosemary Canter*
Multimedia *Rosemary Scoular*

Europe's largest creative agency, with 70 years of international experience in all media. *Handles* all sorts of books including fiction and children's, plus scripts for film, theatre, radio and TV. Send a full outline for non-fiction and short synopsis for fiction with 2 or 3 sample chapters and autobiographical note. Return postage essential. No reading fee. E-mail submissions will not be read for the time being. Please say if you are submitting to other agencies at the same time. *Commission* Home 10%; US & Translation 20%.

Charles Pick Consultancy Ltd★
3/3 Bryanston Place, London W1H 7FN
☎0171 402 8043   Fax 0171 724 5990
E-mail: 100551.3554@compuserve.com
Contact *Martin Pick, Sandra Sljivic*

FOUNDED 1985. *Handles* Fiction and non-fiction general books. Deals only with scripts by existing clients. No unsolicited mss. Pefers an approach to be made on the recommendation of someone qualified in their field. Send letter with a short description/synopsis. CLIENTS include Wilbur Smith, Peter O'Toole, Deirdre Punch, Julie Parsons. *Commission* Home 15%; US & Translation 20%; Film 20%.

Laurence Pollinger Limited
18 Maddox Street, London W1R 0EU
☎0171 629 9761   Fax 0171 629 9765
E-mail: LaurencePollinger@compuserve.com
or 106225.3645@compuserve.com
Contacts *Gerald J. Pollinger, Heather Chalcroft*
Negotiating Editor *Juliet Burton*
Children's Books *Lesley Hadcroft*

FOUNDED 1958. A successor of Pearn, Pollinger & Higham. *Handles* all types of books including children's. No pure science, academic or technological. Good for crime and romantic fiction. CLIENTS include the estates of H. E. Bates, W. Heath Robinson, William Saroyan, John Cowper Powys, D. H. Lawrence and other notables. Unsolicited mss welcome if preceded by letter. A contribution of £20 is requested towards editorial costs. *Commission* Home & US 15%; Translation 20%.

Murray Pollinger*
See **David Higham Associates Ltd**

Shelley Power
Literary Agency Ltd*
Le Montaud, 24220 Berbiguières, France
☎00 33 55329 6252   Fax 00 33 55329 6254
Contact *Shelley Power*

FOUNDED 1976. Shelley Power works between London and France. This is an English agency with London-based administration/accounts office and the editorial office in France. *Handles* general commercial fiction, quality fiction, business books, self-help, true crime, investigative exposés, film and entertainment. No scripts, short stories, children's or poetry. Preliminary letter with brief outline of project (plus s.a.e.) essential. No reading fee. CLIENTS include Michael Beer, Paul Fifield, Sutherland Lyall, Shirley McLaughlin, Clive Reading, Richard Stern, Madge Swindells, Roger Wilkes. *Commission* Home 10%; US & Translation 19%.

PVA Management Limited
Hallow Park, Worcester WR2 6PG
☎01905 640663   Fax 01905 641842
E-mail: pvamanltd@aol.com
Managing Director *Paul Vaughan*

FOUNDED 1978. *Handles* mainly non-fiction. Please send synopsis and sample chapters together with return postage. *Commission* 15%.

Radala & Associates
17 Avenue Mansions, Finchley Road, London NW3 7AX
☎0171 794 4495   Fax 0171 431 7636
Contact *Richard Gollner, Neil Hornick, Anna Swan, Andy Marino*

FOUNDED 1970. *Handles* quality fiction, non-fiction, drama, performing and popular arts, psychotherapy, writing from Eastern Europe. Also provides editorial services, initiates in-house projects and can recommend independent professional readers if unable to read or comment on submissions. No poetry or screenplays. Prospective clients should send a shortish letter plus synopsis (maximum 2pp), first two chapters (double-spaced, numbered pages) and s.a.e. for return. *Commission* Home 10%; US 15–20%; Translation 20%. *Overseas associates* **Writers House, Inc.** (Al Zuckerman), New York; plus agents throughout Europe.

Rogers, Coleridge & White Ltd*
20 Powis Mews, London W11 1JN
☎0171 221 3717   Fax 0171 229 9084
Contacts *Deborah Rogers, Gill Coleridge, Patricia White, David Miller*
Foreign Rights *Ann Warnford-Davis*

FOUNDED 1967. *Handles* fiction, non-fiction and children's books. No poetry, plays or technical books. No unsolicited mss, please and no submissions by fax or e-mail. Rights representative in UK and translation for several New York agents. *Commission* Home 10%; US 15%; Translation 20%. *Overseas associates* ICM, New York.

Hilary Rubinstein Books
32 Ladbroke Grove, London W11 3BQ
☎0171 792 4282   Fax 0171 221 5291
Contact *Hilary Rubinstein*

FOUNDED 1992. *Handles* fiction and non-fiction. No poetry or drama. Approach in writing in the first instance. No reading fee but return postage, please. CLIENTS include Eric Lomax, Elisabeth Maxwell, Donna Williams. *Commission* Home 10%; US & Translation 20%. *Overseas associates* **Ellen Levine Literary Agency** New York; **Andrew Nurnberg Associates** (European rights).

Uli Rushby-Smith Literary Agency
72 Plimsoll Road, London N4 2EE
☎0171 354 2718   Fax 0171 354 2718
Contacts *Uli Rushby-Smith*

FOUNDED 1993. *Handles* fiction and non-fiction, commercial and literary, both adult and children's. Film and TV rights handled in conjunction with a sub-agent. No plays, poetry, science fiction or fantasy. Approach with an outline, two or three sample chapters and explanatory letter in the first instance (s.a.e. essential). No reading fee. *Commission* Home 10%; US & Translation 20%. Represents UK rights for **Curtis Brown**, New York (children's) and Henry Holt & Co. Inc. and 2.13.61 in the USA, and Penguin (Canada).

Rosemary Sandberg Ltd
6 Bayley Street, London WC1B 3HB
☎0171 304 4110   Fax 0171 304 4109
Contact *Rosemary Sandberg*

FOUNDED 1991. In association with **Ed Victor Ltd.** *Handles* children's picture books and novels; women's interests e.g. cookery. *Specialises* in children's writers and illustrators. No unsolicited mss as client list is currently full. *Commission* 10–15%.

Tessa Sayle Agency*

11 Jubilee Place, London SW3 3TE
☎0171 823 3883   Fax 0171 823 3363
Books *Rachel Calder*
Film/TV *Jane Villiers, Matthew Bates*

Handles fiction: literary novels rather than category fiction; non-fiction: current affairs, social issues, travel, biographies, historical; and drama (TV/film): contemporary social issues or drama with comedy, rather than broad comedy. No poetry, children's, textbooks, science fiction, fantasy, horror or musicals. No unsolicited mss. Preliminary letter essential, including a brief biographical note and a synopsis. No reading fee. CLIENTS Books: Stephen Amidon, Peter Benson, Pete Davies, Marele Day, Margaret Forster, Georgina Hammick, Paul Hogarth, Andy Kershaw, Phillip Knightley, Rory MacLean, Ann Oakley, Kate Pullinger, Ronald Searle, Gitta Sereny, William Styron, Mary Wesley. Drama: William Corlett, Shelagh Delaney, Marc Evans, John Forte, Stuart Hepburn, David Hilton, Chris Monger, Ken Russell, Dom Shaw, Sue Townsend. *Commission* Home 10%; US & Translation 20%. *Overseas associates* in the US, Japan and throughout Europe.

Seifert Dench Associates

24 D'Arblay Street, London W1V 3FH
☎0171 437 4551   Fax 0171 439 1355
Website: http://www.seifert-dench.co.uk
Contact *Linda Seifert, Elizabeth Dench, Michelle Arnold*

FOUNDED 1972. *Handles* scripts for TV and film. Unsolicited mss will be read, but a letter with sample of work and c.v. (plus s.a.e.) is preferred. CLIENTS include Peter Chelsom, Tony Grisoni, Stephen Volk. *Commission* Home 12½–15%. *Overseas associates* include: William Morris/Sanford Gross and C.A.A., Los Angeles.

The Sharland Organisation Ltd

9 Marlborough Crescent, London W4 1HE
☎0181 742 1919   Fax 0181 995 7688
Contact *Mike Sharland, Alice Sharland*

FOUNDED 1988. *Specialises* in national and international film and TV negotiations. Also negotiates multimedia, interactive TV deals and computer game contracts. *Handles* scripts for film, TV, radio and theatre; also non-fiction. Markets books for film and handles stage, radio, film and TV rights for authors. No scientific, technical or poetry. No unsolicited mss. Preliminary enquiry by letter or phone essential. *Commission* Home 15%; US & Translation 20%. *Overseas associates* various.

Vincent Shaw Associates

20 Jay Mews, Kensington Gore, London SW7 2EP
☎0171 581 8215   Fax 0171 225 1079
E-mail: vincentshaw@clara.net
Contact *Vincent Shaw*

FOUNDED 1954. *Handles* TV, radio, film and theatre scripts. Unsolicited mss welcome. Approach in writing enclosing s.a.e. No phone calls. *Commission* Home 10%; US & Translation by negotiation. *Overseas associates* Herman Chessid, New York.

Sheil Land Associates Ltd*

43 Doughty Street, London WC1N 2LF
☎0171 405 9351   Fax 0171 831 2127
Contact *Sonia Land, Anthony Sheil,*
Vivien Green, Simon Trewin, Luigi Bonomi,
John Rush (film/drama/TV)
Foreign & US *Laura Susijn, Susy Behr*

FOUNDED 1962. Incorporates the Richard Scott Simon Agency. *Handles* full-length general, commercial and literary fiction and non-fiction, including: biography, travel, cookery and humour, UK and foreign estates. Also theatre, film, radio and TV scripts. One of the UK's more dynamic agencies, Sheil Land represents over 270 established clients and welcomes approaches from new clients looking either to start or to develop their careers. Known to negotiate sophisticated contracts with publishers. Preliminary letter with s.a.e. essential. No reading fee. CLIENTS include Peter Ackroyd, Melvyn Bragg, John Banville, Catherine Cookson, Josephine Cox, Seamus Deane, John Fowles, Susan Hill, HRH The Prince of Wales, Michael Ignatieff, John Keegan, Bernard Kops, Charlotte Lamb, Richard Mabey, David Mellor, Andrew Miller, Van Morrison, Tom Sharpe, Alan Titchmarsh, Rose Tremain, John Wilsher. *Commission* Home 10–15%; US & Translation 20%. *Overseas associates* Georges Borchardt, Inc. (Richard Scott Simon). UK representatives for **Farrar, Straus & Giroux, Inc**. US Film and TV representation: CAA, **H.N. Swanson**, and others.

Caroline Sheldon Literary Agency*

London Farm, White Oaks Lane, Shalfleet, Isle of Wight PO30 4NU
☎01983 531205
Contact *Caroline Sheldon*

FOUNDED 1985. *Handles* adult fiction, in particular women's, both commercial and literary novels. Also full-length children's fiction. No

TV/film scripts unless by book-writing clients. Send letter with all relevant details of ambitions and four chapters of proposed book (enclose large s.a.e.). No reading fee. *Commission* Home 10%; US & Translation 20%.

The Shennan Agency
64 Ashton Lane, Glasgow G12 8SJ
☎0141 579 5040   Fax 0141 579 5041
Contact *Francis Shennan*
FOUNDED 1988. *Specialises* in journalism: strong features, business and finance, for newspapers and magazines, including *Daily Mail, The Express, The Scotsman, The Herald, Scotland on Sunday, Investors Chronicle*. Writers must be accurate, reliable, able to substantiate stories and have full rights to sell. No reading fee but a re-write fee if it is necessary. No unsolicited faxes. Keep copies as no mss returned. Disks preferred – 3.5in, stored as ASCII (Text Only) of Word for Windows files – with good photographs (and the rights to them) plus c.v. of writer. Associate company of Top Table Speakers Agency (other associates sought). *Commission* Home 25%; Foreign 40% plus translation costs.

Jeffrey Simmons
10 Lowndes Square, London SW1X 9HA
☎0171 235 8852   Fax 0171 235 9733
Contact *Jeffrey Simmons*
FOUNDED 1978. *Handles* biography and autobiography, cinema and theatre, fiction (both quality and commercial), history, law and crime, politics and world affairs, parapsychology and sport (but not exclusively). No science fiction/fantasy, children's books, cookery, crafts, hobbies or gardening. Film scripts handled only if by book-writing clients. *Special interests* personality books of all sorts and fiction from young writers (i.e. under 40) with a future. Writers become clients by personal introduction or by letter, enclosing a synopsis if possible, a brief biography, a note of any previously published books, plus a list of any publishers and agents who have already seen the mss. *Commission* Home 10–15%; US 15%; Translation 20%.

Simpson Fox Associates
52 Shaftesbury Avenue, London W1V 7DE
☎0171 434 9167   Fax 0171 494 2887
Contact *Georgina Capel*
ESTABLISHED 1973. *Handles* literary and commercial fiction, general non-fiction, and film/play scripts. No children's books. Approach with synopsis and sample chapter, with s.a.e., in the first instance. CLIENTS Julie Burchill, Henry

Porter, Andrew Roberts, Peter York. *Commission* Home, US & Translation 15%.

Carol Smith Literary Agency
22 Adam & Eve Mews, Kensington High Street, London W8 6UJ
☎0171 937 4874   Fax 0171 938 5323
Contact *Carol Smith, Petra Lewis, Zoë Waldie*
FOUNDED 1976. *Handles* full-length fiction and non-fiction. *Specialises* in commercial contemporary novels. Welcomes beginners. No telephone calls; send first three chapters and synopsis with preliminary letter. Return postage essential. No reading fee. Mss submissions by invitation only. *Commission* Home 10%; Overseas & Translation 20%.

Solo Literary Agency Ltd
49–53 Kensington High Street, London W8 5ED
☎0171 376 2166   Fax 0171 938 3165
Chairman *Don Short*
FOUNDED 1978. *Handles* non-fiction. *Special interests* celebrity autobiographies, unauthorised biographies, sports and adventure stories, wildlife, nature & ecology, crime, fashion, beauty & health. Also some fiction but only from established authors. No unsolicited mss. Preliminary letter essential. CLIENTS include Peter Essex, Rosemary Kingsland, Derek Shuff, Rick Sky. Also *specialises* in worldwide newspaper syndication of photos, features and cartoons. Professional contributors only. *Commission* Books: Home 15%; US 20%; Translation 20–30%; Journalism 50%.

Elaine Steel
110 Gloucester Avenue, London NW1 8HX
☎0181 348 0918/0171 483 2681
Fax 0181 341 9807
Contact *Elaine Steel*
FOUNDED 1986. *Handles* scripts and screenplays. No technical or academic. Initial phone call preferred. CLIENTS include Les Blair, Anna Campion, Michael Eaton, Brian Keenan, Troy Kennedy Martin, Rob Ritchie. *Commission* Home 10%; US & Translation 15–20%.

Abner Stein★
10 Roland Gardens, London SW7 3PH
☎0171 373 0456   Fax 0171 370 6316
Contact *Abner Stein*
FOUNDED 1971. Mainly represents US agents and authors but *handles* some full-length fiction

and general non-fiction. No scientific, technical, etc. No scripts. Send letter and outline in the first instance rather than unsolicited mss. *Commission* Home 10%; US & Translation 20%.

Micheline Steinberg Playwrights' Agent

409 Triumph House, 187–191 Regent Street, London W1R 7WF
☎0171 287 4383   Fax 0171 287 4384
Contact *Micheline Steinberg*

FOUNDED 1988. *Specialises* in plays for stage, TV, radio and film. Best approach by preliminary letter (with s.a.e.). Dramatic associate for **Laurence Pollinger Limited**. *Commission* Home 10%; Elsewhere 15%.

tricia sumner – literary agency
See **Labour and Management Limited**

The Susijn Agency

820 Harrow Road, London NW10 5 JU
☎0181 968 7435   Fax 0181 354 0415
E-mail: LSusijn@aol.com
Contact *Laura Susijn*

FOUNDED April 1998. *Specialises* in selling rights worldwide in literary fiction and non-fiction. Preliminary letter, synopsis and first two chapters preferred. No reading fee. Also represents non-English-language publishers for UK, US and translation rights worldwide. *Commission* Home 15%; US & Translation 15–20%.

J. M. Thurley Management

30 Cambridge Road, Teddington, Middlesex TW11 8DR
☎0181 977 3176   Fax 0181 943 2678
Contact *Jon Thurley*

FOUNDED 1976. *Handles* full-length fiction, non-fiction, TV and films. Particularly interested in strong commercial and literary fiction. Will provide creative and editorial assistance to promising writers. No unsolicited mss; approach by letter in the first instance with synopsis and first three chapters plus return postage. No reading fee. *Commission* Home 15%; US & Translation 15%.

Lavinia Trevor Agency★

7 The Glasshouse, 49A Goldhawk Road, London W12 8QP
☎0181 749 8481   Fax 0181 749 7377
Contact *Lavinia Trevor*

FOUNDED 1993. *Handles* general fiction and non-fiction, including popular science. No poetry, academic or technical work. No TV, film, radio, theatre scripts. Approach with a preliminary letter and first 50–100 typewritten pages, including s.a.e. No reading fee. *Commission* Rate by agreement with author.

Jane Turnbull★

13 Wendell Road, London W12 9RS
☎0181 743 9580   Fax 0181 749 6079
Contact *Jane Turnbull*

FOUNDED 1986. *Handles* fiction and non-fiction. No science fiction, sagas or romantic fiction. *Specialises* in literary fiction, history, current affairs, health and diet. No unsolicited mss. Approach with letter in the first instance. No reading fee. CLIENTS include Kirsty Gunn, Penny Junor, Kevin McCloud, Monty Roberts, Judith Wills. Translation rights handled by **Aitken & Stone Ltd**. *Commission* Home 10%; USA 15%; Translation 20%.

Ed Victor Ltd★

6 Bayley Street, Bedford Square, London WC1B 3HB
☎0171 304 4100   Fax 0171 304 4111
Contact *Ed Victor, Graham Greene, Maggie Phillips, Sophie Hicks*

FOUNDED 1976. *Handles* a broad range of material from Iris Murdoch to Jack Higgins, Erich Segal to Stephen Spender. Leans towards the more commercial ends of the fiction and non-fiction spectrums. No scripts, no academic. Takes on very few new writers. After trying his hand at book publishing and literary magazines, Ed Victor, an ebullient American, found his true vocation. Strong opinions, very pushy and works hard for those whose intelligence he respects. Loves nothing more than a good title auction. Please telephone in the first instance. No unsolicited mss. CLIENTS include Douglas Adams, Frederick Forsyth, Josephine Hart, Jack Higgins, Erica Jong, Kathy Lette, Iris Murdoch, Erich Segal, Will Self and the estates of Raymond Chandler, Sir Stephen Spender and Irving Wallace. *Commission* Home 15%; US 15%; Translation 20%.

Cecily Ware Literary Agents

19C John Spencer Square, London N1 2LZ
☎0171 359 3787   Fax 0171 226 9828
Contact *Cecily Ware, Gilly Schuster, Warren Sherman*

FOUNDED 1972. Primarily a film and TV script

agency representing work in all areas: drama, children's, series/serials, adaptations, comedies, etc. Also radio and occasional general fiction. No unsolicited mss or phone calls. Approach in writing only. No reading fee. *Commission* Home 10%; US 10–20% by arrangement.

Warner Chappell Plays Ltd

Griffin House, 161 Hammersmith Road, London W6 8BS
☎0181 563 5888   Fax 0171 563 5801
Contact *Michael Callahan*

Formerly the English Theatre Guild, Warner Chappell are now both agents and publishers of scripts for the theatre. No unsolicited mss; introductory letter essential. No reading fee. CLIENTS include Ray Cooney, John Godber, Peter Gordon, Debbie Isitt, Arthur Miller, Sam Shepard, John Steinbeck. *Overseas representatives* in the US, Canada, Australia, New Zealand, India, South Africa and Zimbabwe.

Watson, Little Ltd★

Capo Di Monte, Windmill Hill, London NW3 6RJ
☎0171 431 0770   Fax 0171 431 7225
Contact *Sheila Watson, Mandy Little, Sugra Zaman*

Handles fiction and non-fiction. *Special interests* history, popular science, psychology, self-help and business books. No scripts. Not interested in authors who wish to be purely academic writers. Send preliminary ('intelligent') letter with synopsis. *Commission* Home 10%; US 24%; Translation 19%. *Overseas associates* worldwide.

A. P. Watt Ltd★

20 John Street, London WC1N 2DR
☎0171 405 6774   Fax 0171 831 2154
Directors *Caradoc King, Linda Shaughnessy, Derek Johns, Joanna Frank, Sam North (Associate)*

FOUNDED 1875. The oldest-established literary agency in the world. *Handles* full-length typescripts, including children's books, screenplays for film and TV, and plays. No poetry, academic or specialist works. No unsolicited mss accepted. CLIENTS include Evelyn Anthony, Quentin Blake, Martin Gilbert, Nadine Gordimer, Michael Holroyd, Alison Lurie, Jan Morris, Graham Swift, and the estates of Wodehouse, Graves and Maugham. *Commission* Home 10%; US & Translation 20%.

John Welch,
Literary Consultant & Agent

Milton House, Milton, Cambridge CB4 6AD
☎01223 860641   Fax 01223 440575
Contact *John Welch*

FOUNDED 1992. *Handles* military history, aviation, history, biography and sport. No poetry, children's books or scripts for radio, TV, film or theatre. No unsolicited mss; already has a full hand of authors. Send letter with c.v., synopsis, two chapters and s.a.e. for return. Consultancy fees may apply for unpublished authors. CLIENTS include Alexander Baron, Michael Calvert, Paul Clifford, Norman Scarfe, Jason Woolgar, David Wragg. *Commission* Home 10%.

Dinah Wiener Ltd★

12 Cornwall Grove, Chiswick, London W4 2LB
☎0181 994 6011   Fax 0181 994 6044
E-mail: dinahwiener@enterprise.net
Contact *Dinah Wiener*

FOUNDED 1985. *Handles* fiction and general non-fiction: auto/biography, popular science, cookery. No scripts, children's or poetry. Approach with preliminary letter in first instance, giving full but brief c.v. of past work and future plans. Mss submitted must include s.a.e. and be typed in double-spacing. CLIENTS include Catherine Alliott, T. J. Armstrong, Christiaan Barnard, Joy Berthoud, Malcolm Billings, Alison Brodie, Hugh Brune, Guy Burt, David Deutsch, Robin Gardiner, Daemon Goodhope, Phillip Hall, Mark Jeffery, Tania Kindersley, Daniel Snowman, Peta Tayler, Scarlett Thomas, Marcia Willett. *Commission* Home 15%; US & Translation 20%.

Michael Woodward Creations Ltd

Parlington Hall, Aberford, West Yorkshire LS25 3EG
☎0113 2813913   Fax 0113 2813911
E-mail: art@mwc.uk.com
Contact *Michael Woodward, Janet Woodward*

FOUNDED 1979. International licensing company with own in-house studio. Worldwide representation for artists and illustrators. Current properties include *Rambling Ted, Teddy Tum Tum, Railway Children, Kit 'n' Kin, Bad Taste Bears, Robots in Big Boots*. New artists should forward full-concept synopses with sample illustrations. Scripts or stories not accepted without illustration/design or concept mock-ups. No standard commission rate; varies according to contract.

National Newspapers

Departmental e-mail addresses are too numerous to include in this listing. They can be obtained from the newspaper's main switchboard or the department in question.

Daily Mail

Northcliffe House, 2 Derry Street, Kensington, London W8 5TT
☎0171 938 6000   Fax 0171 937 4463

Owner *Associated Newspapers/Lord Rothermere*
Editor *Paul Dacre*
Circulation 2.33 million

In-house feature writers and regular columnists provide much of the material. Photo-stories and crusading features often appear; it's essential to hit the right note to be a successful *Mail* writer. Close scrutiny of the paper is strongly advised. Not a good bet for the unseasoned. Accepts news on savings, building societies, insurance, unit trusts, legal rights and tax.

News Editor *Ian MacGregor*
Features Editor *Veronica Wadley*
Business/Financial Editor *Michael Walters*
Political Editor *David Hughes*
Education Editor *Tony Halpin*
Environment Editor *David Derbyshire*
Diary Editor *Nigel Dempster*
Literary Editor *Jane Mays*
Sports Editor *Bryan Cooney*

Femail *Ted Verity*

Weekend: Saturday supplement **Editor** *Aileen Doherty*

Daily Record

Anderston Quay, Glasgow G3 8DA
☎0141 248 7000   Fax 0141 242 3340

Owner *Mirror Group Newspapers*
Editor *Martin Clarke*
Circulation 685,536

Mass-market Scottish tabloid. Freelance material is generally welcome.

News Editor *Murray Morse*
Features Editor *Alan Rennie*
Financial Editor *Colin Calder*
Education *Jamie McCaskill*
Political Editor *Tom Brown*
Women's Page *Lorna Frame*

Daily Star

Ludgate House, 245 Blackfriars Road, London SE1 9UX
☎0171 928 8000   Fax 0171 922 7960

Owner *United Media*

Editor *Philip Walker*
Circulation 579,845

In competition with *The Sun* for off-the-wall news and features. Freelance opportunities almost non-existent. Most material is written in-house or by regular outsiders.

News/Business Editor *Hugh Whittow*
Features Editor *Linda Duff*
Political Editor *Henry Macrory*
Sports Editor *Jim Mansell*
Women's Page *Dawn Neesom*

The Daily Telegraph

1 Canada Square, Canary Wharf, London E14 5DT
☎0171 538 5000   Fax 0171 538 6242

Owner *Conrad Black*
Editor *Charles Moore*
Circulation 1.08 million

Unsolicited mss not generally welcome – 'all are carefully read and considered, but only about one in a thousand is accepted for publication'. As they receive about 20 weekly, this means about one a year. Contenders should approach the paper in writing, making clear their authority for writing on that subject. No fiction.

News Editor *Neil Darbyshire* Tip-offs or news reports from *bona fide* journalists. Must phone the news desk in first instance. Maximum 200 words. *Payment* minimum £10 (tip).

Arts Editor *Sarah Crompton*
Business Editor *Roland Gribben*
Political Editor *George Jones*
Diary Editor *Simon Davis* Always interested in diary pieces; contact *Peterborough* (Diary column).

Education *John Clare*
Environment *Charles Clover*
Features Editor/Women's Page *Eleanor Mills* Most material supplied by commission from established contributors. New writers are tried out by arrangement with the features editor. Approach in writing. Maximum 1500 words.

Literary Editor *John Coldstream*
Sports Editor *Brian Oliver* Occasional opportunities for specialised items.
Payment by arrangement.

Telegraph Magazine: Saturday colour supplement. **Editor** *Emma Soames*. **Young Telegraph** (see entry under **Magazines**).

The European

200 Gray's Inn Road, London WC1X 8NE
☎0171 418 7777   Fax 0171 713 1840
Owner *The Barclay Brothers*
Editor-in-Chief *Andrew Neil*
Circulation 153,006
LAUNCHED May 1990. European news and current affairs, business, sport, society and politics, plus arts and lifestyle section, *The European Magazine*. Freelance contributions from recognised experts in their field will be considered. First approach in writing.
News/Features *David Meilton*
Business *Jonathan Miller*
Sports *Dominic O'Reilly*
The European Magazine *Nicola Davidson*
Payment by arrangement.

The Express/
The Express on Sunday

Ludgate House, 245 Blackfriars Road, London SE1 9UX
☎0171 928 8000   Fax 0171 620 1654
Owner *United News and Media*
Editor *Rosie Boycott*
Circulation 1.17 million(E.)/
  1.07 million (E.on S.)

Now being run as a seven-day publication with *The Express* published Monday to Friday, *The Express on Saturday* and *The Express on Sunday*, with all editors working for each publication. The general rule of thumb is to approach in writing with an idea; all departments are prepared to look at an outline without commitment. Ideas welcome but already receives many which are 'too numerous to count'.
News Editor *Simon Young*
Diary Editor *John McEntee (William Hickey)*
Features Editor *Sue Crawford*
Business Editor *Steven Day*
Political Editor *Roland Watson*
Financial Editor *Robert Miller*
Education Editor *Lewis Smith*
Literary Editor *Albert Read*
Sports Editor *Rob Shepherd*
Planning Editor (News Desk) should be circulated with copies of official reports, press releases, etc., to ensure news desk cover at all times.

Saturday magazine **Editor** *Catherine Ostler*

Express on Sunday Magazine: colour supplement. **Editor** *Katie Bowen-Bravery*. No unsolicited mss. All contributions are commissioned. Ideas in writing only.
Payment negotiable.

Financial Times

1 Southwark Bridge, London SE1 9HL
☎0171 873 3000   Fax 0171 873 3076
Owner *Pearson*
Acting Editor *Andrew Gowers*
Circulation 359,458
FOUNDED 1888. Business and finance-orientated certainly, but by no means as featureless as some suppose. All feature ideas must be discussed with the department's editor in advance. Not snowed under with unsolicited contributions – they get less than any other national newspaper. Approach in writing with ideas in the first instance.
News Editor *Julia Cuthbertson*
Features Editor *John Parker*
Arts/Literary Editor *Annalena McAfee*
Financial Editor *Ross Tieman*
Diary Editor *Michael Cassell*
Education *Simon Targett*
Environment *Leyla Boulton*
Political Editor *Robert Peston*
Small Businesses *Katherine Campbell*
Sports Editor *Peter Aspden*
Women's Page *Lucia van der Post*

The Guardian

119 Farringdon Road, London EC1R 3ER
☎0171 278 2332   Fax 0171 837 2114
Owner *The Scott Trust*
Editor *Alan Rusbridger*
Circulation 406,354

Of all the nationals *The Guardian* probably offers the greatest opportunities for freelance writers, if only because it has the greatest number of specialised pages which use freelance work. But mss must be directed at a specific slot.
News Editor *Harriet Sherwood* No opportunities except in those regions where there is presently no local contact for news stories.
Arts Editor *Claire Armitstead*
Financial Editor *Jonathan Confino*
Business Editor *Ben Clisset*
On Line *Bill O'Neill* Science, computing and technology. A major part of Thursday's paper, almost all written by freelancers. Expertise essential – but not a trade page; written for 'the interested man in the street' and from the user's point

of view. Computing/communications (Internet) articles should be addressed to *Jack Schofield*; science articles to *Tim Radford*. Mss on disk or by e-mail (online@guardian.co.uk).

Diary Editor *Matthew Norman*
Education Editor *John Carvel* Expert pieces on modern education welcome. Maximum 1000 words.
Environment *John Vidal*
Features Editor *Roger Alton* Receives up to 30 unsolicited mss a day; these are passed on to relevant page editors.
Guardian Society *Malcolm Dean* Focuses on social change in the 90s – the forces affecting us, from environment to government policies. Top journalists and outside commentators on nine editorial pages.
Literary Editor *Stephen Moss*
Media Editor *John Mulholland* Approximately six pieces a week, plus diary. Outside contributions are considered. All aspects of modern media, advertising, PR, consumer trends in arts/entertainments. Background insight important. Best approach is a note, followed by phone call.
Political Editor *Mike White*
Sports Editor *Mike Averis*
Women's Page *Sally Weale* Now runs three days a week. Unsolicited ideas used if they show an appreciation of the page in question. Maximum 800–1000 words.

The Guardian Weekend Saturday issue. **Editor** *Deborah Orr*. *The Guide* *Ben Olins*.

The Herald (Glasgow)

195 Albion Street, Glasgow G1 1QP
☎0141 552 6255   Fax 0141 552 2288
Owner *Scottish Television Plc*
Editor *Harry Reid*
Circulation 106,192

The oldest national newspaper in the English-speaking world, The Herald, which dropped its 'Glasgow' prefix in February 1992, was bought by Scottish Television in 1996. Lively, quality, national Scottish daily broadsheet. Approach with ideas in writing or by phone in first instance.
News Editor *Bill McDowall*
Arts Editor *Keith Bruce*
Business Editor *Robert Powell*
Diary *Tom Shields*
Education *Carlos Alba*
Environment *Liz Buie*
Sports Editor *Iain Scott*
Herald Magazine *Cate Devine*

The Independent

1 Canada Square, Canary Wharf, London E14 5DL
☎0171 293 2000   Fax 0171 293 2435
Owner *Independent Newspapers*
Editor *Simon Kelner*
Deputy Editor *Ian Birrell*
Circulation 215,676

FOUNDED October 1986. *The Independent* and *The Independent on Sunday* were acquired by Irish tycoon Tony O'Reilly's Independent Newspapers from Mirror Group Newspapers in March 1998. Particularly strong on its arts/media coverage, with a high proportion of feature material. Theoretically, opportunities for freelancers are good. However, unsolicited mss are not welcome; most pieces originate in-house or from known and trusted outsiders. Ideas should be submitted in writing.
News Editor *David Felton*
Features Editor *Catherine Pepinster*
Arts Editor *John Price*
Business Editor *Philip Thornton*
Financial Editor *Lea Paterson*
Education *Judith Judd*
Environment *Nicholas Schoon*
Literary Editor *Boyd Tonkin*
Political Editor *Donald Macintyre*
Sports Editor *Chris Maume*
Travel Editor *Simon Calder*

The Independent Magazine: Saturday supplement. **Editor** *Sue Matthias*

Independent on Sunday

1 Canada Square, Canary Wharf, London E14 5DL
☎0171 293 2000   Fax 0171 293 2435
Owner *Independent Newspapers*
Editor *Simon Kelner*
Deputy Editor *Ian Birrell*
Circulation 256,179

FOUNDED 1986. Regular columnists contribute most material but feature opportunites exist. Approach with ideas in first instance.
News Editor *Michael Streeter*
Features Editor *Ruth Metzstein*
Arts Editor *Rosanna de Lisle*
Commissioning Editor, Features *Caroline Roux*
Business/City Editor *Peter Koenig*
Education Editor *Judith Judd*
Literary Editor *Suzi Feay*
Environment *Geoffrey Lean*
Political Editor *Stephen Castle*
Sports Editor *Neil Morton*
Review supplement. **Editor** *Laurence Earle*.

International Herald Tribune
181 avenue Charles de Gaulle, 92200 Neuilly-sur-Seine, France
☎0033 1 4143 9300   Fax 0033 1 4143 9338
Editor *Michael Getler*
Circulation 207,000

Published in France, Monday to Saturday, and circulated in Europe, the Middle East, North Africa, the Far East and the USA. General news, business and financial, arts and leisure. Use regular freelance contributors. Query letter to features editor in first instance.
Features Editor *Katherine Knorr*
Managing Editor *Walter Wells*

The Mail on Sunday
Northcliffe House, 2 Derry Street, Kensington, London W8 5TS
☎0171 938 6000   Fax 0171 937 3829
Owner *Associated Newspapers/Lord Rothermere*
Editor *Jonathon Holborrow*
Circulation 2.20 million

Sunday paper with a high proportion of newsy features and articles. Experience and judgement required to break into its band of regular feature writers.
News Editor *Paul Henderson*
Financial Editor *Russell Hotton*
Business Editor *Ruth Sunderland*
Diary Editor *Nigel Dempster*
Features Editor/Women's Page *Sian James*
Literary Editor *Jane Adams*
Education Editor *Rosie Waterhouse*
Industrial/Environment Editor *Christopher Leake*
Political Editor *Joe Murphy*
Sports Editor *Daniel Evans*

Night & Day: review supplement. **Acting Editor** *Kate Carr*

You – The Mail on Sunday Magazine: colour supplement. Many feature articles, supplied entirely by freelance writers. **Editor** *Dee Nolan*
Features Editor *Helen Birch*
Arts Editor *Liz Galbraith*

The Mirror
1 Canada Square, Canary Wharf, London E14 5AP
☎0171 293 3000   Fax 0171 293 3409
Owner *Mirror Group Newspapers*
Editor *Piers Morgan*
Circulation 2.34 million

No freelance opportunities for the inexperi-enced, but strong writers who understand what the tabloid market demands are always needed.
News Editor *Eugene Duffy*
Features Editor *Mark Thomas*
Political Editor *Kevin Maguire*
Business Editor *Clinton Manning*
Education Editor *Richard Garner*
Showbusiness Diary Editor *Matthew Wright*
Sports Editor *Des Kelly*
Women's Page *Lisa Collins*

Morning Star
1–3 Ardleigh Road, London N1 4HS
☎0171 254 0033   Fax 0171 254 5950
Owner *Peoples Press Printing Society*
Editor *John Haylett*
Circulation 9,000

Not to be confused with the *Daily Star*, the *Morning Star* is the farthest left national daily. Those with a penchant for a Marxist reading of events and ideas can try their luck, though feature space is as competitive here as in the other nationals.
Business/City Editor *Brian Denny*
News/Features/Education/Women's Page *Paul Corry*
Literary Editor *Jeff Sawtell*
Political Editor *Mike Ambrose*
Sports Editor *Amanda Kendal*

The News of the World
1 Virginia Street, London E1 9XR
☎0171 782 4000
Fax 0171 782 4433 (Features)
Owner *News International plc/Rupert Murdoch*
Editor *Phil Hall*
Circulation 4.42 million

Highest circulation Sunday paper. Freelance contributions welcome. Features Department welcomes tips and ideas. Approach by fax in first instance with follow-up phone call.
Assistant Editor (News) *Greg Miskiw*
Features Editor *Gary Thompson*
Business/City Editor *Peter Predergast*
Political/Environment Editor *Eben Black*
Sports Editor *Mike Dunn*

Sunday Magazine: colour supplement. **Editor** *Judy McGuire*. Showbiz interviews and strong human-interest features make up most of the content, but there are no strict rules about what is 'interesting'. Unsolicited mss and ideas welcome.

The Observer
119 Farringdon Road, London EC1R 3ER
☎0171 278 2332   Fax 0171 713 4250
E-mail: editor@observer.co.uk
Owner *Guardian Newspapers Ltd*
Editor *Will Hutton*
Circulation 409,808

FOUNDED 1791. Acquired by Guardian Newspapers from Lonrho in May 1993. Occupies the middle ground of Sunday newspaper politics. Unsolicited material is not generally welcome, 'except from distinguished, established writers'. Receives far too many unsolicited offerings already. No news, fiction or special page opportunities. The newspaper runs annual competitions which change from year to year. Details are advertised in the newspaper.
   News Editor *Paul Dunn*
   Features Editor *Lisa O'Kelly*
   Arts Editor *Jane Ferguson*
   Political Editor *Patrick Wintour*
   Business News Editor *Sheila Fitzsimons*
   City Editor *Paul Farrelly*
   Education Correspondent *Martin Bright*
   Environment Editor *John Arlidge*
   Literary Editor *Robert McCrum*
   Sports Editor *Alan Hubbard*

Life: arts and lifestyle supplement. **Editor** *Justine Picardie*.

Scotland on Sunday
20 North Bridge, Edinburgh EH1 1YT
☎0131 225 2468   Fax 0131 220 2443
Owner *The Barclay Brothers*
Editor *John McGurk*
Circulation 118,649

Scotland's top-selling quality broadsheet. Welcomes ideas rather than finished articles.
   News Editor *William Paul*
   Political Editor *Kenneth Farquharson*

Scotland on Sunday Magazine: colour supplement. **Editor** *Margot Wilson*. Features on personalities, etc.

The Scotsman
20 North Bridge, Edinburgh EH1 1YT
☎0131 225 2468   Fax 0131 226 7420
Owner *The Barclay Brothers*
Editor *Alan Ruddock*
Circulation 79,930

Scotland's national newspaper. Many unsolicited mss come in, and stand a good chance of being read, although a small army of regulars supply much of the feature material not written in-house.

   News Editor *Richard Neville*
   City/Financial Editor *Martin Flanagan*
   Education *Tom Little*
   Environment *Christopher Cairn*
   Assistant Editor, Features *Jane Johnson*
   Literary Editor *Catherine Lockerbie*
   Weekend Editor *Alistair McKay*. Includes book reviews, travel articles, etc.

The Sport
19 Great Ancoats Street, Manchester M60 4BT
☎0161 236 4466   Fax 0161 236 4535
Owner *Sport Newspapers Ltd*
Editor *Jeff McGowan*
Circulation 235,000

Tabloid catering for young male readership. Unsolicited material welcome; send to News Editor.
   News Editor *Paul Carter*
   Sports Editor *Marc Smith*

The Sun
1 Virginia Street, London E1 9BD
☎0171 782 4000   Fax 0171 488 3253
Owner *News International plc/Rupert Murdoch*
Editor *Stuart Higgins*
Circulation 3.77 million

Highest circulation daily with a populist outlook; very keen on gossip, pop stars, TV soap, scandals and expose[aa]s of all kinds. No room for non-professional feature writers; 'investigative journalism' of a certain hue is always in demand, however.
   News Editor *Glenn Goodey*
   Features Editor *Jonathan Worsnop*
   Political Editor *Trevor Kavanagh*
   Education *David Wooding*
   Sports Editor *Paul Ridley*
   Literary Editor/Women's Page
      Sam Carlisle

Sunday Business
200 Gray's Inn Road, London WC1X 8XR
☎0171 418 9605   Fax 0171 418 9605
Owner *The Barclay Brothers*
Editor *Jeff Randall*
Circulation 80,000

LAUNCHED April 1996 and 'relaunched' March 1998. National newspaper dedicated entirely to business.
   News Editor *Frank Kane*
   Features Editor *Vivien Goldsmith*
   City Editor *Nils Pratley*
   Political Editor *Steve Bevan*

Sunday Life
124–144 Royal Avenue, Belfast BT1 1EB
☎01232 264300   Fax 01232 554507
Owner *Trinity International Holdings plc*
Editor *Martin Lindsay*
Circulation 101,120
Deputy Editor *Dave Culbert*
  Sports Editor *Jim Gracey*

Sunday Mail
Anderston Quay, Glasgow G3 8DA
☎0141 248 7000   Fax 0141 242 3587
Owner *Mirror Group Newspapers*
Editor *Jim Cassidy*
Circulation 847,776

Popular Scottish Sunday tabloid.
  News Editor *Brian Steel*
  Features Editor *Rob Bruce*
  Political Editor *Angus McLeod*
  Women's Page *Melanie Reid*

XS: weekly supplement. **Editor** *Janette Harkess*.

Sunday Mirror
1 Canada Square, Canary Wharf, London
E14 5AP
☎0171 293 3000   Fax 0171 293 3939
Owner *Mirror Group Newspapers*
Editor *Colin Myler*
Circulation 2.01 million

Receives anything up to 100 unsolicited mss weekly. In general terms, these are welcome, though the paper patiently points out it has more time for contributors who have taken the trouble to study the market. Initial contact in writing preferred, except for live news situations. No fiction.
  News Editor *John McShane* The news desk is very much in the market for tip-offs and inside information. Contributors would be expected to work with staff writers on news stories.
  City/Financial Editor *Diane Boliver*
  Features Editor *Teena Lyons* 'Anyone who has obviously studied the market will be dealt with constructively and courteously.' Cherishes its record as a breeding ground for new talent.
  Sports Editor *To be appointed*
Personal: colour supplement. **Editor** *Teena Lyons*.

Sunday People
1 Canada Square, Canary Wharf, London
E14 5AP
☎0171 293 3000   Fax 0171 293 3810
Owner *Mirror Group Newspapers*
Editor *Neil Wallis*

Circulation 1.77 million
Slightly up-market version of *The News of the World*. Keen on exposés and big-name gossip. Interested in ideas for investigative articles. Phone in first instance.
  News Editor *Alan Qualtrough*
  City Editor *Cathy Gunn*
  Features Editor *Nick Brownlee*
  Political Editor *Nigel Nelson*
  Sports Editor *Ed Barry*
  Travel Editor/Women's Page *Linda Udall*
The People Magazine. **Editor** *Amanda Cable*. Approach by phone with ideas in first instance.

Sunday Post
2 Albert Square, Dundee DD1 9QJ
☎01382 223131   Fax 01382 201064
Owner *D. C. Thomson & Co. Ltd*
Editor *Russell Reid*
Circulation 791,400

The highest circulation Scottish Sunday paper. Contributions should be addressed to the editor.
  News Editor *Iain MacKinnon*

Sunday Post Magazine: monthly colour supplement. **Editor** *Maggie Dun*.

Sunday Sport
19 Great Ancoats Street, Manchester
M60 4BT
☎0161 236 4466   Fax 0161 236 4535
Owner *David Sullivan*
Editor *Mark Harris*
Circulation 263,791

FOUNDED 1986. Sunday tabloid catering for a particular sector of the male 15–35 readership. As concerned with 'glamour' (for which, read: 'page 3') as with human interest, news, features and sport. Regular short story competition (maximum 1000 words). Unsolicited mss are welcome; receives about 90 a week. Approach should be made by phone in the case of news and sports items, by letter for features. All material should be addressed to the news editor.
  News Editor *Paul Carter* Off-beat news, human interest, preferably with photographs.
  Features Editor *Paul Carter* Regular items: glamour, showbiz and television, as well as general interest.
  Sports Editor *Marc Smith* Hard-hitting sports stories on major soccer clubs and their personalities, plus leading clubs/people in other sports. Strong quotations to back up the news angle essential.
Payment negotiable and on publication.

Sunday Telegraph

1 Canada Square, Canary Wharf, London
E14 5DT
☎0171 538 5000   Fax 0171 513 2504

Owner *Conrad Black*
Editor *Charles Moore*
Circulation 842,880

Right-of-centre quality Sunday paper which, although traditionally formal, has pepped up its image to attract a younger readership. Unsolicited material from untried writers is rarely ever used. Contact with idea and details of track record.

News Editor *Chris Anderson*
Features Editor *Rebecca Nicolson*
City Editor *Neil Bennett*
Political Editor *David Wastell*
Education Editor *Jonathan Petre*
Arts Editor *John Preston*
Environment Editor *Greg Neale*
Literary Editor *Miriam Gross*
Diary Editor *Mark Inglefield*
Sports Editor *Colin Gibson*
Women's Page *Rebecca Nicolson*
Sunday Telegraph Magazine *Rebecca Tyrrel*

The Sunday Times

1 Pennington Street, London E1 9XW
☎0171 782 5000   Fax 0171 782 5658

Owner *News International plc/Rupert Murdoch*
Editor *John Witherow*
Circulation 1.36 million

FOUNDED 1820. Tendency to be anti-establishment, with a strong crusading investigative tradition. Approach the relevant editor with an idea in writing. Close scrutiny of the style of each section of the paper is strongly advised before sending mss. No fiction. All fees by negotiation.

News Editor *Charles Hymas* Opportunities are very rare.
News Review Editor *Sarah Baxter* Submissions are always welcome, but the paper commissions its own, uses staff writers or works with literary agents, by and large. The features sections where most opportunities exist are *Style* and *The Culture*.

Arts Editor *Helen Hawkins*
Business Editor *Andrew Lorenz*
City Editor *Kirstie Hamilton*

Education *Judith O'Reilly*
Environment *Jonathan Leake*
Literary Editor *Geordie Greig*
Sports Editor *Alex Butler*
Style Editor *Jeremy Langmead*

Sunday Times Magazine: colour supplement.
Editor *Robin Morgan*. No unsolicited material. Write with ideas in first instance.

The Times

1 Pennington Street, London E1 9XN
☎0171 782 5000   Fax 0171 488 3242

Owner *News International plc/Rupert Murdoch*
Editor *Peter Stothard*
Circulation 783,852

Generally right (though features can range in tone from diehard to libertarian). *The Times* receives a great many unsolicited offerings. Writers with feature ideas should approach by letter in the first instance. No fiction.

News Editor *John Wellman*
Features Editor *Sandra Parsons*
Associate Editor *Brian MacArthur*
City/Financial Editor *Patience Wheatcroft*
Business Editor *Jason Nisse*
Diary Editor *Jasper Gerrard*
Arts Editor *Richard Morrison*
Education *John O'Leary*
Environment *Nick Nuttall*
Literary Editor *Erica Wagner*
Political Editor *Phil Webster*
Sports Editor *David Chappell*
Weekend Times **Editor** *Gill Morgan*
The Times Magazine: Saturday supplement.
Editor *Nicholas Wapshott*
Features Editor *Sandra Parsons*

Wales on Sunday

Thomson House, Havelock Street, Cardiff
CF1 1WR
☎01222 223333   Fax 01222 583725

Owner *Trinity International Holdings plc*
Editor *Alan Edmunds*
Circulation 61,541

LAUNCHED 1989. Tabloid with sports supplement. Does not welcome unsolicited mss.

News Editor *Alistair Milburn*
Features/Women's Page *Mike Smith*
Sports Editor *Richard Morgans*

Freelance Rates – Newspapers

Freelance rates vary enormously. The following minimum rates, negotiated by the **National Union of Journalists**, should be treated as guidelines. Most work can command higher fees from employers whether or not they have NUJ agreements. It is up to freelancers to negotiate the best deal they can.

National Newspapers
(including *The European, The Herald, Daily Record, Sunday Mail, The Scotsman, Scotland on Sunday, Evening Standard*)

Features (including reviews, obituaries, etc)
Broadsheet rates start at under £200 per 1000 words but sums of over £300 are common. Payment of less than £200 is not acceptable. Tabloids often pay considerably more than broadsheets though items are usually shorter.

News
News may be paid for per 1000 words or by the day. When payment is by the word, the absolute minimum should be £200 per 1000 words or pro rata. (Applies to all areas of news reporting, including sport.)

Day Rates
£100 lowest minimum, but preferably £120 or more. Accept day rates only if required to be in the office for the day.

Exclusives
These can command very high fees, depending on how much the newspaper wants the story. A prominent position for the piece should command £500 or more. A guaranteed minimum of at least £250 should be negotiated in case it appears further down the page in a shorter form.

Colour Supplements
Seek payment of double all the rates given above.

Cartoons
Cartoon size: 1 column b&w £100, thereafter subject to individual negotiation. For a colour cartoon charge double the above rate. (All rates quoted are for one British use.)

Crosswords
15x15 squares and under: at least £105; 15x15 squares and over: at least £130.

Regional & Provincial Newspapers (England & Wales)

News

Minimum Lineage (usually 4 words) Rate Weekly newspapers: £1.70 for up to and including 10 lines; 17p per line thereafter. Daily, evening and Sunday newspapers: £2.90 for up to and including 10 lines; 29p per line thereafter.

Features

Minimum Rate (for features submitted on spec) Weekly newspapers: £1.85 for up to and including 10 lines; 19p per line thereafter. Daily, evening and Sunday newspapers: £3.24 for up to and including 10 lines; 32p per line thereafter.

Cartoons

Single Frame: at least £52
Feature Strip (up to 4 frames): £96

Crosswords

At least £60.

Regional Newspapers

Regional newspapers are listed in alphabetical order under town. Thus the *Evening Standard* appears under 'L' for London; the *Lancashire Evening Post* under 'P' for Preston.

Aberdeen

Evening Express (Aberdeen)
PO Box 43, Lang Stracht, Mastrick, Aberdeen
AB15 6DF
☎01224 690222   Fax 01224 699575
Owner *Northcliffe Newspapers Group Ltd*
Editor *Donald Martin*
Circulation 67,441

Circulates in Aberdeen and the Grampian region. Local, national and international news and pictures, family finance and property news. Unsolicited mss welcome 'if on a controlled basis'.

News Editor *Yvonne Flynn* Freelance news contributors welcome.
Payment £30–60.

The Press and Journal
PO Box 43, Lang Stracht, Mastrick, Aberdeen
AB9 8AF
☎01224 690222   Fax 01224 663575
Owner *Northcliffe Newspapers Group Ltd*
Editor *Derek Tucker*
Circulation 107,138

Circulates in Aberdeen, Grampians, Highlands, Tayside, Orkney, Shetland and the Western Isles. A well-established regional daily which is said to receive more unsolicited mss a week than the *Sunday Mirror*. Unsolicited mss are nevertheless welcome; approach in writing with ideas. No fiction.

News Editor *David Knight* Wide variety of hard or off-beat news and features relating especially, but not exclusively, to the North of Scotland.
Sports Editor *Jim Dolan*
Women's Page *Kate Yuill*
Payment by arrangement.

Barrow in Furness

North West Evening Mail
Abbey Road, Barrow in Furness, Cumbria
LA14 5QS
☎01229 821835   Fax 01229 840164
Owner *CN Group Ltd*

Editor *Sara Hadwin*
Circulation 20,673

All editorial material should be addressed to the editor.

Assistant Editor (Production) *Bill Myers*
Assistant Editor (Mail) *R. A. Herbert*
Sports Editor *Leo Clarke*

Basildon

Evening Echo
Newspaper House, Chester Hall Lane, Basildon, Essex SS14 3BL
☎01268 522792   Fax 01268 282884
Owner *Newsquest Media Group*
Editor *Martin McNeill*
Circulation 47,000

Relies almost entirely on staff and regular outside contributors, but will very occasionally consider material sent on spec. Approach the editor in writing with ideas. Although the paper is Basildon-based, its largest circulation is in the Southend area.

Bath

The Bath Chronicle
Windsor House, Windsor Bridge Road, Bath
BA2 3AU
☎01225 322322   Fax 01225 322291
Owner *Newsquest (Wessex) Ltd*
Editor *David Gledhill*
Circulation 17,720

Local news and features especially welcomed.
Deputy Editor *John McCready*
News Editor *Paul Wiltshire*
Features Editor *Andrew Knight*
Sports Editor *Neville Smith*

Belfast

Belfast Telegraph
Royal Avenue, Belfast BT1 1EB
☎01232 264000   Fax 01232 554506/554540
Owner *Trinity International Holdings Plc*
Editor *Edmund Curran*

Circulation 131,829

Weekly business supplement.
Deputy Editor *Jim Flanagan*
News Editor *Janet Devlin*
Features Editor *John Caruth*
Sports Editor *John Laverty*
Business Editor *Rosie Cowan*

The Irish News

113/117 Donegall Street, Belfast BT1 2GE
☎01232 322226   Fax 01232 337505
Owner *Irish News Ltd*
Editor *Tom Collins*
Circulation 44,500

All material to appropriate editor (phone to check), or to the news desk.
Deputy Editor *Noel Doran*
Head of Content *Fiona McGarry*
Arts Editor *Colin McAlpin*
Sports Editor *Stephen O'Reilly*
Women's Page *Ann Molloy*

Ulster News Letter

46–56 Boucher Crescent, Belfast BT12 6QY
☎01232 680000   Fax 01232 664412
Owner *Century Newspapers Ltd*
Editor *Geoff Martin*
Circulation 33,753

Supplements: *Farming Life* (weekly); *Shopping News; Belfast Newsletter, North Down News.*
Deputy Editor *Mike Chapman*
Assistant Editor *Billy Kennedy*
News Editor *Ric Clark/Steven Moore*
Features Editor *Geoff Hill*
Sports Editor *Brian Millar*
Fashion & Lifestyle/Property Editor
Sandra Chapman
Business Editor *David Kirk*
Agricultural Editor *David McCoy*

Birmingham

Birmingham Evening Mail

28 Colmore Circus, Queensway, Birmingham
B4 6AX
☎0121 236 3366   Fax 0121 233 0271
Owner *Midland Independent Newspapers Plc*
Editor *Ian Dowell*
Circulation 197,532

Freelance contributions are welcome, particularly topics of interest to the West Midlands and Women's Page pieces offering original and lively comment.
News Editor *Norman Stinchcombe*
Features Editor *Steve Dyson*
Women's Page *Bryony Jones*

Birmingham Post

28 Colmore Circus, Queensway, Birmingham
B4 6AX
☎0121 236 3366Fax 0121 233 0271/625 1105
Owner *Midland Independent Newspapers Plc*
Editor *Nigel Hastilow*
Circulation 28,000

One of the country's leading regional newspapers. Freelance contributions are welcome. Topics of interest to the West Midlands and pieces offering lively, original comment are particularly welcome.
News Editor *Chris Russon*
Features Editor *Peter Bacon*
Women's Page *Ros Dodd*

Sunday Mercury (Birmingham)

28 Colmore Circus, Queensway, Birmingham
B4 6AZ
☎0121 236 3366   Fax 0121 234 5877
Owner *Birmingham Post & Mail Ltd*
Editor *Fiona Alexander*
Circulation 145,472
Assistant Editor (News & Features)
James Windle
Assistant Editor (Sport) *Lee Gibson*

Blackburn

Lancashire Evening Telegraph

Newspaper House, High Street, Blackburn,
Lancashire BB1 1HT
☎01254 678678   Fax 01254 680429
Owner *Newsquest Media Group Ltd*
Editor *Peter Butterfield*
Circulation 44,919

News stories and feature material with an East Lancashire flavour (a local angle, or written by local people) welcome. Approach in writing with an idea in the first instance. No fiction.
News/Features/Women's Page Editor
Nick Nunn

Blackpool

Evening Gazette (Blackpool)

PO Box 20, Preston New Road, Blackpool,
Lancashire FY4 4AU
☎01253 839999   Fax 01253 831070
Owner *United Newspapers*
Managing Editor *Philip Welsh*
Editor *Gerrard Henderson*
Circulation 44,578

Unsolicited mss welcome in theory. Approach in

writing with an idea. Supplements: *Eve* (women, Tuesday); *Wheels* (motoring, Wednesday); *Property* (Thursday); *Sevendays* (entertainment & leisure, Saturday).

Sports Editor *Jonathan Lee*

Bolton

Bolton Evening News

Newspaper House, Churchgate, Bolton, Lancashire BL1 1DE

☎01204 522345   Fax 01204 365068

Owner *Newsquest Media Group Ltd*
Editor *Mark Rossiter*
Circulation 43,837

Business, children's page, travel, local services, motoring, fashion and cookery.

News Editor *Melvyn Horrocks*
Features Editor/Women's Page
  Angela Kelly

Bournemouth

Daily Echo

Richmond Hill, Bournemouth, Dorset BH2 6HH

☎01202 554601   Fax 01202 292115

Owner *Southern Newspapers Plc*
Managing Editor *Ian Murray*
Circulation 46,808

FOUNDED 1900. Has a strong features content and invites specialist articles, particularly on unusual and contemporary subjects but only with a local angle. Supplements: business, education, homes and gardens, motoring, what's on, *Weekender*. Regular features on weddings, property, books, local history, green issues, the Channel coast. All editorial material should be addressed to the **News Editor** *Andy Martin*.

Payment on publication.

Bradford

Telegraph & Argus (Bradford)

Hall Ings, Bradford, West Yorkshire BD1 1JR

☎01274 729511   Fax 01274 723634

Owner *Newsquest Media Group Ltd*
Editor *Perry Austin-Clarke*
Circulation 57,213

No unsolicited mss – approach in writing with samples of work. No fiction.

News Editor *Jan Brierley* Local features and general interest. Showbiz pieces. 600–1000 words (maximum 1500).

Sports Editor *Alan Birkinshaw*
Features Editor *Lynn Ashwell*

Brighton

Evening Argus

Argus House, Crowhurst Road, Hollingbury, Brighton, East Sussex BN1 8AR

☎01273 544544   Fax 01273 505703

Owner *Newsquest (Sussex) Ltd*
Editor *Adrian Faber*
Circulation 64,264

News Editor *Claire Byrd*
Sports Editor *Chris Giles*
Women's Page *Winifred Blackmore*

Bristol

Evening Post

Temple Way, Bristol BS99 7HD

☎0117 9343000   Fax 0117 9343575

Owner *Bristol United Press plc*
Editor *Mike Lowe*
Circulation 84,939

News Editor *Kevan Blackadder*
Features Editor *Matthew Shelley*
Sports Editor *Chris Bartlett*

Western Daily Press

Temple Way, Bristol BS99 7HD

☎0117 9343000   Fax 0117 9343574

Owner *Bristol Evening Post & Press Ltd*
Editor *Ian Beales*
Circulation 60,000

Contents Editor *Roger Tavener*
Features Editor *Jane Riddiford*
Sports Editor *Bill Beckett*
Women's Page *Lynda Cleasby*

Burton upon Trent

Burton Mail

65–68 High Street, Burton upon Trent, Staffordshire DE14 1LE

☎01283 512345   Fax 01283 515351

Owner *Burton Daily Mail Ltd*
Editor *Brian Vertigen*
Circulation 20,030

Fashion, health, wildlife, environment, nostalgia, financial/money (Monday); consumer, motoring (Tuesday); women's world, rock (Wednesday); property (Thursday); motoring, farming, what's on (Friday); what's on, leisure (Saturday).

News/Features Editor *Andrew Parker*
Sports Editor *Rex Page*
Women's Page *Bill Pritchard*

Cambridge

Cambridge Evening News
Winship Road, Milton, Cambridge CB4 6PP
☎01223 434434   Fax 01223 434415

Owner *Cambridge Newspapers Ltd*
Editor *Robert Satchwell*
Circulation 41,906

News Editor *John Conlon*
Business Editor *Phil Davis*
Sports Editor *Alex Martin*
Women's Page *Angela Singer*

Cardiff

South Wales Echo
Thomson House, Havelock Street, Cardiff
CF1 1XR
☎01222 223333   Fax 01222 583624

Owner *Trinity International Holdings Plc*
Editor *Robin Fletcher*
Circulation 77,618

Circulates in South and Mid Glamorgan and
Gwent.

Head of News *Mark Walden*
Features *John Scantlebury*
Sports Editor *Richard Williams*

The Western Mail
Thomson House, Havelock Street, Cardiff
CF1 1WR
☎01222 223333   Fax 01222 583652

Owner *Trinity International Holdings Plc*
Editor *Neil Fowler*
Circulation 64,172

Circulates in Cardiff, Merthyr Tydfil, Newport,
Swansea and towns and villages throughout
Wales. Mss welcome if of a topical nature, and
preferably of Welsh interest. No short stories or
travel. Approach in writing to the editor. 'Usual
subjects already well covered, e.g. motoring,
travel, books, gardening. We look for the unusual.' Maximum 1000 words. Opportunities
also on women's page. Supplements: Television
Wales; Arena; Welsh Homes; Country and
Farming; Business; Sport.

Assistant Editor *Simon Irwin*
Sports Editor *Mark Tattersall*

Carlisle

News & Star
Newspaper House, Dalston Road, Carlisle,
Cumbria CA2 5UA
☎01228 523488   Fax 01228 512828

Owner *Cumbrian Newspaper Group Ltd*

Editor *Keith Sutton*
Circulation 26,795

News Editor *Nick Turner*
Head of Content *Steve Johnston*
Sports Editor *John Reynolds*
Women's Page *Jane Loughran*

Chatham

Kent Today
395 High Street, Chatham, Kent ME4 4PQ
☎01634 830600   Fax 01634 829484

Owner *Kent Messenger Group*
Editor *C. Stewart*
Circulation 24,148

Assistant Editor (Production) *Neil Webber*
Community Editor *David Jones*
Sports Editor *Mike Rees*
Women's Page *Helen Daly*
Business Editor *Trevor Sturgess*

Cheltenham

Gloucestershire Echo
1 Clarence Parade, Cheltenham,
Gloucestershire GL50 3NZ
☎01242 271900   Fax 01242 271803

Owner *Northcliffe Newspapers Group Ltd*
Editor *Anita Syvret*
Circulation 26,387

All material, other than news, should be
addressed to the editor.

News Editor *Rachel Broderick*

Chester

Chronicle Newspapers (Chester & North Wales)
Chronicle House, Commonhall Street,
Chester CH1 2BJ
☎01244 340151   Fax 01244 340165

Owner *Trinity International Holdings Plc*
Editor-in-Chief *Bob Adams*

All unsolicited feature material will be considered.

Colchester

Evening Gazette (Colchester)
Oriel House, 43–44 North Hill, Colchester,
Essex CO1 1TZ
☎01206 506000   Fax 01206 508274

Owner *Essex County Newspapers*
Editor *Irene Kettle*
Circulation 29,525

Unsolicited mss not generally used. Relies heavily on regular contributors.

Features Editor *Iris Clapp*

Coventry

Coventry Evening Telegraph

Corporation Street, Coventry CV1 1FP
☎01203 633633   Fax 01203 550869

Owner *Mirror Group*
Editor *Dan Mason*
Circulation 83,838

Unsolicited mss are read, but few are published. Approach in writing with an idea. No fiction. All unsolicited material should be addressed to the editor. Maximum 600 words for features.

News Editor *Peter Mitchell*
Features Editor *Paul Simoniti*
Sports Editor *Roger Draper*
Women's Page *Barbara Argument*
Payment negotiable.

Darlington

The Northern Echo

Priestgate, Darlington, Co. Durham DL1 1NF
☎01325 381313   Fax 01325 380539

Owner *North of England Newspapers*
Editor *Andrew Smith*
Circulation 72,499

FOUNDED 1870. Freelance pieces welcome but telephone first to discuss submission.

News Editor *Sarah Andrews* Interested in reports involving the North-east or North Yorkshire. Preferably phoned in.

Features Editor *Chris Lloyd* Background pieces to topical news stories relevant to the area. Must be arranged with the features editor before submission of any material.

Business Editor *Colin Tapping*
Sports Editor *Kevin Dinsdale*
Payment and length by arrangement.

Derby

Derby Evening Telegraph

Northcliffe House, Meadow Road, Derby DE1 2DW
☎01332 291111   Fax 01332 253027

Owner *Northcliffe Newspapers Group Ltd*
Editor *Keith Perch*
Circulation 63,478

Weekly business supplement.

News Editor *Robert Irvine*

Features Editor/Women's Page *Nigel Poulson*
Sports Editor *Steve Nicholson*
Motoring Editor *Bob Maddox*

Doncaster

The Doncaster Star

40 Duke Street, Doncaster, South Yorkshire DN1 3EA
☎01302 344001   Fax 01302 329072

Owner *Sheffield Newspapers Ltd*
Editor/News Editor *Graham Walker*
Circulation 10,000

All editorial material to be addressed to the editor.

Deputy News Editor *Jane Cartledge*
Sports Editor *Steve Hossack*
Women's Page *Jane Stapleton*

Dundee

The Courier and Advertiser

80 Kingsway East, Dundee DD4 8SL
☎01382 223131   Fax 01382 454590

Owner *D. C. Thomson & Co. Ltd*
Editor *Adrian Arthur*
Circulation 99,820

Circulates in East Central Scotland. Features occasionally accepted on a wide range of subjects, particularly local/Scottish interest – including finance, insurance, agriculture, motoring, modern homes, lifestyle and fitness. Maximum length, 500 words.

News Editor *Steve Bargeton*
Features Editor/Women's Page *Shona Lorimer*
Sports Editor *Graham Dey*

Evening Telegraph & Post

80 Kingsway East, Dundee DD4 8SL
☎01382 223131   Fax 01382 454590

Owner *D. C. Thomson & Co. Ltd*
Editor *Alan Proctor*
Circulation 34,505

Circulates in Tayside, Dundee and Fife. All material should be addressed to the editor.

East Anglia

East Anglian Daily Times

See under **Ipswich**

Eastern Daily Press
See under *Norwich*

Edinburgh

Evening News
20 North Bridge, Edinburgh EH1 1YT
☎0131 225 2468   Fax 0131 225 7302

Owner *European Press Holdings Ltd*
Editor *John C. McLellan*
Circulation 85,502

FOUNDED 1873. Circulates in Edinburgh, Fife, Central and Lothian. Coverage includes: lifestyle (Tuesday) and entertainment (Thursday); motoring (Friday); gardening, book reviews, historical memories, shopping, fashion, nature, show business, and health. Occasional platform pieces, features of topical interest and/or local interest. Unsolicited feature material welcome. Approach the appropriate editor by telephone.
   Associate Editor (News) *David Lee*
   Associate Editor (Features) *Helen Martin*
   Sports Editor *Paul Greaves*
   Payment NUJ/house rates.

Exeter

Express & Echo
Heron Road, Sowton, Exeter, Devon EX2 7NF
☎01392 442211
Fax 01392 442294/442287 (editorial)

Owner *Express & Echo Publications Ltd*
Editor *Steve Hall*
Circulation 30,812

Weekly supplements: *Business Week; Property Echo; Wheels; Weekend Echo.*
   News Editor *Chris Styles*
   Features Editor/Women's Page *Sue Kemp*
   Sports Editor *Jerry Charge*

Glasgow

Evening Times
195 Albion Street, Glasgow G1 1QP
☎0141 552 6255   Fax 0141 553 1355

Owner *Scottish Media Group*
Editor *John D. Scott*
Circulation 138,066

Circulates in the Strathclyde region. Supplements: *Job Search; Home Front; Woman; Time Out* (leisure); *TGIF* (weekend preview).
   News Editor *Ally McLaws*
   Features Editor *Russell Kyle*
   Sports Editor *David Stirling*
   Women's Editor *Lesley Roberts*

The Herald (Glasgow)
See **National Newspapers**

Gloucester

The Citizen
St John's Lane, Gloucester GL1 2AY
☎01452 424442   Fax 01452 307238

Owner *Northcliffe Newspapers Group Ltd*
Editor *Spencer Feeney*
Circulation 37,087

All editorial material to be addressed to the **News Editor** *Chris Hill.*

Gloucestershire Echo
See under *Cheltenham*

Greenock

Greenock Telegraph
2 Crawfurd Street, Greenock PA15 1LH
☎01475 726511   Fax 01475 783734

Owner *Clyde & Forth Press Ltd*
Editor *Ian Wilson*
Circulation 20,618

Circulates in Greenock, Port Glasgow, Gourock, Kilmacolm, Langbank, Bridge of Weir, Inverkip, Wemyss Bay, Skelmorlie, Largs. Unsolicited mss considered 'if they relate to the newspaper's general interests'. No fiction. All material to be addressed to the editor.

Grimsby

Grimsby Evening Telegraph
80 Cleethorpe Road, Grimsby, N. E. Lincs DN31 3EH
☎01472 360360   Fax 01472 372257

Owner *Northcliffe Newspapers Group Ltd*
Editor *Peter Moore*
Circulation 71,167

Sister paper of the *Scunthorpe Evening Telegraph*. Unsolicited mss generally welcome. Approach in writing. No fiction. Monthly supplement: *Business Telegraph*. All material to be addressed to the **News Editor** *S. P. Richards*. Particularly welcome hard news stories – approach in haste by telephone.
   Special Publications Editor *B. Farnsworth*

Guernsey

Guernsey Evening Press & Star
Braye Road, Vale, Guernsey, Channel Islands GY1 3BW
☎01481 45866   Fax 01481 48972

Owner *Guernsey Press Co. Ltd*
Editor *Nick Machon*
Circulation 15,891

Special pages include children's and women's interest, gardening and fashion.
  News Editor *Dave Edmonds*
  Sports Editor *Rob Batiste*
  Women's Page *Kay Leslie*

Halifax
Evening Courier
PO Box 19, Halifax, West Yorkshire HX1 2SF
☎01422 365711   Fax 01422 330021

Owner *Johnston Press Plc*
Editor *Edward Riley*
Circulation 31,937

News Editor *John Kenealy*
  Features Editor *William Marshall*
  Sports Editor *Ian Rushworth*
  Women's Page *Diane Crabtree*

Hartlepool
Mail (Hartlepool)
New Clarence House, Wesley Square,
Hartlepool TS24 8BX
☎01429 274441   Fax 01429 869024

Owner *Northeast Press Ltd*
Editor *Peter Barron*
Circulation 25,705

Deputy Editor *Harry Blackwood*
  News Editor *Neil Hunter*
  Features Editor *Bernice Saltzer*
  Sports Editor *Roy Kelly*
  Women's Page *Margaret O'Rourke*

Huddersfield
Huddersfield Daily Examiner
Queen Street South, Huddersfield, West Yorkshire HD1 2TD
☎01484 430000   Fax 01484 423722

Owner *Trinity International Holdings plc*
Editor *John Williams*
Circulation 37,694

Home improvement, home heating, weddings, dining out, motoring, fashion, services to trade and industry.
  Deputy Editor *Melvyn Briggs*
  Assistant Editor *John Bird*
  News Editor *Neil Atkinson*
  Features Editor *Andrew Flynn*
  Sports Editor *John Gledhill*
  Women's Page *Hilarie Stelfox*

Hull
Hull Daily Mail
Blundell's Corner, Beverley Road, Hull,
North Humberside HU3 1XS
☎01482 327111   Fax 01482 584353

Owner *Northcliffe Newspapers Group Ltd*
Editor *John Meehan*
Circulation 90,036

Head of News *Marc Astley*
  Production Editor *Chris Harvey*
  Sports Editor *Andy Whitaker*
  Women's Page *Jo Davison*

Ipswich
East Anglian Daily Times
30 Lower Brook Street, Ipswich, Suffolk
IP4 1AN
☎01473 230023   Fax 01473 211391

Owner *Eastern Counties Newspaper Group*
Editor *Terry Hunt*
Circulation 52,289

FOUNDED 1874. Unsolicited mss generally not welcome; three or four received a week and almost none are used. Approach in writing in the first instance. No fiction. Supplements: Sport (Monday); Community News (Tuesday); Job Quest (Wednesday); Business (Wednesday); Property (Thursday); Motoring (Friday); Leisure Guide (Saturday).
  News Editor *Mark Hindle* Hard news stories involving East Anglia (Suffolk, Essex particularly) or individuals resident in the area are always of interest.
  Features Editor *Robyn Bechelet* Mostly in-house, but will occasionally buy in when the subject is of strong Suffolk/East Anglian interest. Photo features preferred (extra payment). Special advertisement features are regularly run. Some opportunities here. Maximum 1000 words.
  Sports Editor *Nick Garnham*
  Women's Page *Victoria Hawkins*

Evening Star
30 Lower Brook Street, Ipswich, Suffolk
IP4 1AN
☎01473 282290   Fax 01473 255622

Owner *Eastern Counties Newspaper Group*
Editor *Nigel Pickover*
Circulation 30,391

Deputy Editor (News) *Russell Cook*
  Sports Editor *Mike Horne*

Jersey

Jersey Evening Post
PO Box 582, Jersey, Channel Islands JE4 8XQ
☎01534 611611   Fax 01534 611622
Owner *Jersey Evening Post Ltd*
Editor *Chris Bright*
Circulation 23,249

Special pages: gardening, motoring, farmers and growers, property, boating, computer and office, young person's (16–25), women, food and drink, personal finance, rock and classical reviews.
    News Editor *Sue Le Ruez*
    Features Editor *Richard Pedley*
    Sports Editor *Ron Felton*

Kent

Kent Messenger
See under *Maidstone*

Kent Today
See under *Chatham*

Kettering

Evening Telegraph
Northfield Avenue, Kettering,
Northamptonshire NN16 9TT
☎01536 481111   Fax 01536 485983
Owner *Johnston Press Plc*
Editor-in-Chief *David Rowell*
Circulation 36,118

Northamptonshire Business Guide (weekly); *Guide* supplement (Thursday/Saturday), featuring TV, gardening, videos, films, eating out; and a monthly supplement, *Home & Garden*.
    News Editor *Helen O'Neill*
    Business Editor *Chris Pritchard*
    Sports Editor *Ian Davidson*

Lancashire

Lancashire Evening Post
See under *Preston*

Lancashire Evening Telegraph
See under *Blackburn*

Leamington Spa

Leamington Spa Courier
32 Hamilton Terrace, Leamington Spa,
Warwickshire CV32 4LY
☎01926 888222   Fax 01926 451690

Owner *Central Counties Newspapers*
Editor *Martin Lawson*
Circulation 13,410

One of the Leamington Spa Courier Series which also includes the *Warwick Courier* and *Kenilworth Weekly News*. Unsolicited feature articles considered, particularly matter with a local angle. Telephone with idea first.
    News Editor *Joan Hewitt*

Leeds

Yorkshire Evening Post
Wellington Street, Leeds, West Yorkshire
LS1 1RF
☎0113 2432701   Fax 0113 2388536
Owner *United Provincial Newspapers Ltd*
Editor *Christopher Bye*
Circulation 101,810

Evening sister of the *Yorkshire Post*.
    News Editor *David Helliwell*
    Features Editor *Anne Pickles*
    Sports Editor *Stephen White*
    Women's Page *Carmen Bruegmann*

Yorkshire Post
Wellington Street, Leeds, West Yorkshire
LS1 1RF
☎0113 2432701   Fax 0113 2388537
Owner *United Provincial Newspapers Ltd*
Editor *Tony Watson*
Circulation 76,771

A serious-minded, quality regional daily with a generally conservative outlook. Three or four unsolicited mss arrive each day; all will be considered but initial approach in writing preferred. All submissions should be addressed to the editor. No fiction.
    Head of Content *John Furbisher*
    Features Editor *Mick Hickling* Open to suggestions in all fields (though ordinarily commissioned from specialist writers).
    Sports Editor *Bill Bridge*
    Women's Page *Jill Armstrong*

Leicester

Leicester Mercury
St George Street, Leicester LE1 9FQ
☎0116 2512512   Fax 0116 2530645
Owner *Northcliffe Newspapers Group Ltd*
Editor *Nick Carter*
Circulation 117,416

News Editor *Simon Orrell*
    Features Editor *Mark Clayton*

Lincoln

Lincolnshire Echo

Brayford Wharf East, Lincoln LN5 7AT
☎01522 525252   Fax 01522 545759
Owner *Northcliffe Newspapers Group Ltd*
Editor *Brian Aitken*
Circulation 30,124

Best buys, holidays, motoring, dial-a-service, restaurants, sport, leisure, home improvement, record review, gardening corner, stars. All editorial material to be addressed to the **Assistant Editor** *Mike Gubbins.*

Liverpool

Daily Post

PO Box 48, Old Hall Street, Liverpool L69 3EB
☎0151 227 2000   Fax 0151 236 4682
Owner *Liverpool Daily Post & Echo Ltd*
Editor *Alastair Machray*
Circulation 72,776

Unsolicited mss welcome. Receives about six a day. Approach in writing with an idea. No fiction. Local, national/international news, current affairs, profiles – with pictures. Maximum 800–1000 words.

   Features Editor *Claire Stocks*
   News Editor *Mark Davies*
   Sports Editor *Len Capeling*
   Women's Page *Margaret Kitchen*

Liverpool Echo

PO Box 48, Old Hall Street, Liverpool L69 3EB
☎0151 227 2000   Fax 0151 236 4682
Owner *Liverpool Daily Post & Echo Ltd*
Editor *John Griffith*
Circulation 160,861

One of the country's major regional dailies. Unsolicited mss welcome; initial approach with ideas in writing preferred.

   News Editor *John Thompson*
   Features Editor *Fiona Ennys*
   Sports Editor *Ken Rogers*
   Women's Editor *Caroline Storah*

London

Evening Standard

Northcliffe House, 2 Derry Street, London W8 5EE
☎0171 938 6000   Fax 0171 937 2648
Owner *Associated Newspapers/Lord Rothermere*
Editor *Max Hastings*

Circulation 450,000

Long-established evening paper, serving Londoners with both news and feature material. Genuine opportunities for London-based features. Produces a weekly colour supplement, *ES The Evening Standard Magazine*, a weekly listings magazine *Hot Tickets* and regular weekly supplements: *Just the Job* (Monday) and *Homes & Property* (Wednesday).

   Deputy Editor *Peter Boyer*
   Associate Editor (Features) *Nicola Jeal*
   News Editor *Stephen Clackson*
   Features Editor *Bernice Davison*
   Sports Editor *Simon Greenberg*
   Editor, *ES Adam Edwards*
   Editor, *Hot Tickets Miles Chapman*

Maidstone

Kent Messenger

6 & 7 Middle Row, Maidstone, Kent ME14 1TG
☎01622 695666   Fax 01622 757227
Owner *Kent Messenger Group*
Editor *Ron Green*
Circulation 43,300

Very little freelance work is commissioned.

Manchester

Manchester Evening News

164 Deansgate, Manchester M60 2RD
☎0161 832 7200   Fax 0161 834 3814
Owner *Manchester Evening News Ltd*
Editor *Paul Horrocks*
Circulation 183,543

One of the country's major regional dailies. Initial approach in writing preferred. No fiction. Property (Tuesday); holiday feature (Saturday); Lifestyle (Friday/Saturday).

   News Editor *Lisa Roland*
   Features Editor *Maggie Henfield* Regional news features, personality pieces and showbiz profiles considered. Maximum 1200 words.
   Sports Editor *Peter Spencer*
   Women's Page *Diane Cooke*
   Payment based on house agreement rates.

Middlesbrough

Evening Gazette

Borough Road, Middlesbrough, Cleveland TS1 3AZ
☎01642 234242   Fax 01642 249843
Owner *Trinity International Holdings plc*

Editor *Ranald Allan*
Circulation 69,000

Special pages: business, motoring, home, computing.

> **News Editor** *Tony Beck*
> **Features Editor** *Alan Sims*
> **Sports Editor** *Allan Boughey*
> **Women's Page** *Kathryn Armstrong*
> **Environment** *Iain Laing*
> **Consumer** *Karen Bell*
> **Health** *Amanda Todd*
> **Councils** *Sandy McKenzie*

Mold
Evening Leader
Mold Business Park, Wrexham Road, Mold, Clwyd CH7 1XY
☎01352 707707   Fax 01352 752180

Owner *North Wales Newspapers*
Editor *Reg Herbert*
Circulation 30,976

Circulates in Wrexham, Flintshire, Rhyl, Deeside and Chester. Special pages/features: motoring, travel, arts, women's, children's, photography, local housing, information and news for the disabled, music and entertainment.

> **Features Page** *Debra Greenhouse*
> **News Editor** *Joanne Shone (Welsh edition); Nick Bourne (Chester); Steve Rogers (Rhyl)*
> **Women's Page** *Gail Cooper*
> **Sports Editor** *Allister Syme*

Newcastle upon Tyne
Evening Chronicle
Thomson House, Groat Market, Newcastle upon Tyne, Tyne & Wear NE1 1ED
☎0191 232 7500   Fax 0191 232 2256

Owner *Trinity International Holdings Plc*
Editor *Alison Hastings*
Circulation 118,360

Receives a lot of unsolicited material, much of which is not used. Family issues, gardening, pop, fashion, cooking, consumer, films and entertainment guide, home improvements, motoring, property, angling, sport and holidays. Approach in writing with ideas.

> **News Editor** *Mick Smith*
> **Features Editor** *Richard Ord* Limited opportunities due to full-time feature staff. Maximum 1000 words.
> **Sports Editor** *Paul New*
> **Women's Interests** *Kay Jordan*

The Journal
Thomson House, Groat Market, Newcastle upon Tyne, Tyne & Wear NE1 1ED
☎0191 232 7500   Fax 0191 232 2256

Owner *Trinity International Holdings Plc*
Editor *Mark Dickinson*
Circulation 53,086

Daily platforms include farming and business. Monthly full-colour business supplement: *The Journal Northern Business Magazine*.

> **Deputy Editor** *Paul Robertson*
> **Sports Editor** *Nick Crockford*
> **Arts & Entertainment Editor** *David Whetstone*
> **Environmental Editor** *Tony Henderson*

Sunday Sun
Thomson House, Groat Market, Newcastle upon Tyne, Tyne & Wear NE1 1ED
☎0191 201 6330   Fax 0191 230 0238

Owner *Trinity International Holdings Plc*
Editor *Peter Montellier*
Circulation 123,962

All material should be addressed to the appropriate editor (phone to check), or to the editor.

> **Associate Editor** *Carole Watson*
> **Sports Editor** *Dylan Younger*

Newport
South Wales Argus
Cardiff Road, Maesglas, Newport, Gwent NP9 1QW
☎01633 810000   Fax 01633 462202

Owner *Southern Newspapers plc*
Editor *Gerry Keighley*
Circulation 33,524

Circulates in Newport, Gwent and surrounding areas.

> **News Editor** *Nicole Garnon*
> **Features Editor/Women's Page** *Lesley Williams*
> **Sports Editor** *Carl Difford*

Northampton
Chronicle and Echo
Upper Mounts, Northampton NN1 3HR
☎01604 231122   Fax 01604 233000

Owner *Northampton Mercury Co. Ltd*
Editor *Mark Edwards*
Circulation 29,672

Unsolicited mss are 'not necessarily unwelcome but opportunities to use them are rare'.

Some three or four arrive weekly. Approach in writing with an idea. No fiction. Supplements: *Sports Chronicle* (Monday); *Property Week* (Wednesday); *What's On Guide* (Thursday); *Weekend Motors* (Friday).

News Editor *Steve Scoles*
Features Editor/Women's Page *Jessica Pilkington*
Sports Editor *Steve Pitts*

Northern Ireland

Belfast Telegraph
See under *Belfast*

The Irish News
See under *Belfast*

Sunday Life (Belfast)
See **National Newspapers**

Norwich

Eastern Daily Press
Prospect House, Rouen Road, Norwich, Norfolk NR1 1RE
☎01603 628311   Fax 01603 612930
Owner *Eastern Counties Newspapers*
Editor *Peter Franzen*
Circulation 79,880

Most pieces by commission only. Supplements: what's on (daily); motoring, business, property pages, women's interests, agriculture (all weekly); employment (twice-weekly); arts focus (monthly); plus horse and rider, boating, golf and wildlife.

News Editor *Paul Durrant*
Features Editor *Colin Chinery*
Sports Editor *David Thorpe*
Women's Page *Sarah Hardy*

Evening News
Prospect House, Rouen Road, Norwich, Norfolk NR1 1RE
☎01603 628311   Fax 01603 612930
Owner *Eastern Counties Newspapers*
Editor *Bob Crawley*
Circulation 39,891

Includes special pages on local property, motoring, children's page, pop, fashion, arts, entertainments and TV, gardening, local music scene, home and family.

Assistant Editor *Roy Strowger*
Deputy Editor *Celia Sutton*
Features Editor *Derek James*

Nottingham

Evening Post Nottingham
Forman Street, Nottingham NG1 4AB
☎0115 9482000   Fax 0115 9644027
Owner *Northcliffe Newspapers Group Ltd*
Editor *Graham Glen*
Circulation 100,000

Unsolicited mss welcome. Good local interest only. Maximum 800 words. No fiction. Send ideas in writing. Supplements: motoring, business, holidays and travel supplements; financial, employment and consumer pages.

News Editor *Neil White*
Deputy Editor *Jon Grubb*
Sports Editor *Mick Holland*

Oldham

Evening Chronicle
PO Box 47, Union Street, Oldham, Lancashire OL1 1EQ
☎0161 633 2121   Fax 0161 652 2111
Owner *Hirst Kidd & Rennie Ltd*
Editor *Philip Hirst*
Circulation 34,672

Motoring, food and wine, women's page, business page.

News Editor *Mike Attenborough*
Women's Page *Ralph Badham*

Oxford

Oxford Mail
Osney Mead, Oxford OX2 0EJ
☎01865 244988   Fax 01865 243382
Owner *Oxford & County Newspapers*
Editor *Chris Cowley*
Circulation 35,000

Unsolicited mss are considered but a great many unsuitable offerings are received. Approach in writing with an idea, rather than by phone. No fiction. All fees negotiable.

Head of Content *Anne Harrison*

Paisley

Paisley Daily Express
14 New Street, Paisley PA1 1YA
☎0141 887 7911   Fax 0141 887 6254
Owner *Scottish & Universal Newspapers Ltd*
Editor *Norman Macdonald*
Circulation 8,270

Circulates in Paisley, Linwood, Renfrew, Johnstone, Elderslie, Neilston and Barrhead. Unsolicited mss welcome only if of genuine local (Paisley) interest. The paper does not commission work, and will consider submitted material. Maximum 1000–1500 words. All submissions to the editor.

Newss Editor *Anne Dalrymple*
Sports Editor *Matthew Vallance*

Plymouth

Evening Herald
17 Brest Road, Derriford Business Park, Derriford, Plymouth, Devon PL6 5AA
☎01752 765500   Fax 01752 765527

Owner *Northcliffe Newspapers Group Ltd*
Editor *Rachael Campey*
Circulation 55,036

All editorial material to be addressed to the editor or the **News Editor** *Bill Martin*.

Sunday Independent
Burrington Way, Plymouth, Devon PL5 3LN
☎01752 206600   Fax 01752 206164

Owner *Southern Newspapers Plc*
Editor *Anna Jenkins*
Circulation 40,000

Tabloid Sunday covering the whole of the West Country from Bristol to Weymouth and Land's End. News stories/tips, news features. All editorial should be addressed to the editor. Payment by arrangement.

Western Morning News
17 Brest Road, Derriford Business Park, Derriford, Plymouth, Devon PL6 5AA
☎01752 765500   Fax 01752 765535

Owner *Northcliffe Newspapers Group Ltd*
Editor *Barrie Williams*
Circulation 50,556

Unsolicited mss welcome, but must be of topical and local interest. Special pages include a motoring supplement, West Country matters, books, antiques, lifestyle and arts. All other editorial material to be addressed to the editor.

News Editor *Jason Clark*
Sports Editor *Rick Cowdery*

Portsmouth

The News
The News Centre, Hilsea, Portsmouth, Hampshire PO2 9SX
☎01705 664488   Fax 01705 673363

Owner *Portsmouth Printing & Publishing Ltd*
Editor *Geoffrey Elliott*
Circulation 72,000

Unsolicited mss not generally accepted.

Approach by letter.
News Editor *Mark Acheson*
Features Editor *Rachel Hughes* General subjects of S.E. Hants interest. Maximum 600 words. No fiction.
Sports Editor *Dave King* Sports background features. Maximum 600 words.
Women's Page *Seren Boyd*

Preston

Lancashire Evening Post
Olivers Place, Eastway, Fulwood, Preston, Lancashire PR2 9ZA
☎01772 254841   Fax 01772 880173

Owner *United News & Media*
Editor *Neil Hodgkinson*
Circulation 65,000

Unsolicited mss are not generally welcome; many are received and not used. All ideas in writing to the editor.

Reading

Reading Evening Post
8 Tessa Road, Reading, Berkshire RG1 8NS
☎0118 9575833   Fax 0118 9599363

Owner *Guardian Media Group*
Editor *Kim Chapman*
Circulation 24,000

Unsolicited mss welcome; one or two received every day. Fiction rarely used. Interested in local news features, human interest, well-researched investigations. Special sections include holidays & travel (Monday); food page (Tuesday); children's page (Tuesday); style page (Wednesday); business (Wednesday & Friday); motoring and motorcycling; gardening; rock music (Friday).

Scarborough

Scarborough Evening News
17–23 Aberdeen Walk, Scarborough, North Yorkshire YO11 1BB
☎01723 363636   Fax 01723 354092

Owner *Yorkshire Regional Newspapers Ltd*
Editor *David Penman*
Circulation 17,052

Special pages include property (Monday); motoring (Tuesday/Friday).

News Editor *Damian Holmes*
Motoring *Dennis Sissons*
Sports Editor *Charles Place*
All other material should be addressed to the editor.

Scotland
Daily Record (Glasgow)
See **National Newspapers**

Scotland on Sunday (Edinburgh)
See **National Newspapers**

The Scotsman (Edinburgh)
See **National Newspapers**

Sunday Mail (Glasgow)
See **National Newspapers**

Sunday Post (Dundee)
See **National Newspapers**

Scunthorpe
Scunthorpe Evening Telegraph
Doncaster Road, Scunthorpe, N. E. Lincs
DN15 7RQ
☎01724 273273   Fax 01724 273101
Owner *Northcliffe Newspapers Group Ltd*
Editor *P. L. Moore*
Circulation 24,810

All correspondence should go to the news editor.
Assistant Editor *D. H. Stephens*
News Editor *Jane Manning*

Sheffield
The Star
York Street, Sheffield, South Yorkshire
S1 1PU
☎0114 2767676   Fax 0114 2725978
Owner *Sheffield Newspapers Ltd*
Editor *Peter Charlton*
Circulation 102,749

Unsolicited mss not welcome, unless topical
and local.
News Editor *Bob Westerdale* Contributions
only accepted from freelance news reporters if
they relate to the area.
Features Editor *Jim Collins* Very rarely
require outside features, unless on specialised
subject.
Sports Editor *Martin Smith*
Women's Page *Fiona Firth*
Payment negotiable.

Shropshire
Shropshire Star
See under **Telford**

South Shields
Gazette
Chapter Row, South Shields, Tyne & Wear
NE33 1BL
☎0191 455 4661   Fax 0191 456 8270
Owner *Northeast Press Ltd*
Editor *Rob Lawson*
Circulation 24,177
  News Editor *Julie Stewart*
  Sports Editor *John Cornforth*
  Women's Page *Joy Yates*

Southampton
The Southern Daily Echo
Newspaper House, Test Lane, Redbridge,
Southampton, Hampshire SO16 9JX
☎01703 424777   Fax 01703 424770
Owner *Southern Newspapers Ltd*
Editor *Mike Woods*
Circulation 64,101

Unsolicited mss 'tolerated'. Approach the editor in writing with strong ideas; staff supply
almost all the material.

Stoke on Trent
The Sentinel
Sentinel House, Etruria, Stoke on Trent,
Staffordshire ST1 5SS
☎01782 602525   Fax 01782 280781
Owner *Staffordshire Sentinel Newspapers Ltd*
Editor *Sean Dooley*
Circulation 95,334

Weekly sports final supplement. All material
should be sent to the **Head of Content** *Michael
Wood.*

Sunderland
Sunderland Echo
Echo House, Pennywell, Sunderland, Tyne &
Wear SR4 9ER
☎0191 534 3011   Fax 0191 534 5975
Owner *North East Press Ltd*
Editor *Ian Holland*
Circulation 59,177

All editorial material to be addressed to the
News Editor *Patrick Lavell.*

Swansea
South Wales Evening Post
Adelaide Street, Swansea, West Glamorgan
SA1 1QT
☎01792 510000   Fax 01792 514697

Owner *Northcliffe Newspapers Group Ltd*
Editor *George Edwards*
Circulation 66,566

Circulates throughout south west Wales.
News Editor *Jonathan Isaacs*
Features Editor *Andy Pearson*
Sports Editor *David Evans*

Swindon
Evening Advertiser
100 Victoria Road, Swindon, Wiltshire
SN1 3BE
☎01793 528144   Fax 01793 542434
Owner *Newsquest (Wiltshire) Ltd*
Editor *Simon O'Neill*
Circulation 25,168

Copy and ideas invited. 'All material must be strongly related or relevant to the town of Swindon or the county of Wiltshire.' Little scope for freelance work. Fees vary depending on material.
Deputy Editor *Pauline Leighton*
Sports Editor *Alan Johnson*

Telford
Shropshire Star
Ketley, Telford, Shropshire TF1 4HU
☎01952 242424   Fax 01952 254605
Owner *Shropshire Newspapers Ltd*
Editor *Andy Wright*
Circulation 94,160

No unsolicited mss; approach the editor with ideas in writing in the first instance. No news or fiction.
News Editor *Sarah-Jane Smith*
Features Editor *Alun Owen* Limited opportunities; uses mostly in-house or syndicated material. Maximum 1200 words.
Sports Editor *Peter Byram*
Women's Page *Sharon Walters*

Torquay
Herald Express
Harmsworth House, Barton Hill Road, Torquay, Devon TQ2 8JN
☎01803 676000   Fax 01803 676299/676228
Owner *Northcliffe Newspapers Group Ltd*
Editor *J. C. Mitchell*
Circulation 29,899

Drive scene, property guide, Monday sports, special pages, rail trail, Saturday surgery, nature and conservation column. Supplements: *Garden-*

ing, Healthcare News (all quarterly); *Visitors Guide* and *Antiques & Collectables* (fortnightly); *Devon Days Out* (every Saturday in summer and at Easter and May Bank Holidays). Unsolicited mss generally not welcome. All editorial material should be addressed to the editor in writing.

Wales
South Wales Argus
See under *Newport*

South Wales Echo
See under *Cardiff*

South Wales Evening Post
See under *Swansea*

Wales on Sunday
See **National Newspapers**

Western Mail
See under *Cardiff*

West of England
Express & Echo
See under *Exeter*

Western Daily Press
See under *Bristol*

Western Morning News
See under *Plymouth*

Weymouth
Dorset Evening Echo
57 St Thomas Street, Weymouth, Dorset
DT4 8EU
☎01305 784804   Fax 01305 760387
Owner *Southern Newspapers plc*
Editor *David Lee*
Circulation 21,386

Farming, by-gone days, films, arts, showbiz, brides, children's page, motoring, property, weekend leisure and entertainment including computers and gardening.
News Editor *Paul Thomas*
Sports Editor *Jack Wyllie*

Wolverhampton
Express & Star
Queen Street, Wolverhampton, West Midlands
WV1 3BU
☎01902 313131   Fax 01902 319721
Owner *Midlands News Association*

Editor *Warren Wilson*
Circulation 204,231
  Deputy Editor *Richard Ewels*
  News Editor *David Evans*
  Features Editor *Garry Copeland*
  Sports Editor *Steve Gordos*
  Women's Page *Shirley Tart*

Worcester
Evening News
Berrow's House, Hylton Road, Worcester
WR2 5JX
☎01905 748200   Fax 01905 748009
Owner *Newsquest (Midlands South) Ltd*
Editor *Andrew Martin*
Circulation 23,588

Local events (Tuesday); property (Thursday);
showbiz/what's on, motoring/Pulse pop page
(Friday); holidays/what's on (Saturday).
  News Editor *Nick Watson*
  Features Editor/Women's Page *Mark
    Higgitt*
  Sports Editor *Paul Ricketts*

York
Evening Press
PO Box 29, 76–86 Walmgate, York YO1 1YN
☎01904 653051   Fax 01904 612853
Owner *Newsquest Media Group*
Editor *Elizabeth Page*
Circulation 41,704

Unsolicited mss not generally welcome, unless
submitted by journalists of proven ability.
Business Press Pages (Wednesday); *Women's
Press Extra* (monthly section); *Property Press*
(Thursday); *8 Days* leisure and entertainments
supplement (Saturday).
  News Editor *Bill Hearld*
  Picture Editor *Martin Oates*
  Sports Editor *Martin Jarred*
  Payment negotiable.

Yorkshire
Yorkshire Evening Post
See under *Leeds*

Yorkshire Post
See under *Leeds*

Price Right Copyright

Forty years ago the satirist Tom Lehrer revealed the one word secret of literary success. Plagiarism. How true that is. Academic authors do it all the time. An original idea may occupy a thousand words in a learned journal. But to give it the substance that earns the writer promotion to professorial rank, the concept has to be expanded to book length. This is done by quoting extensively from every related source, however marginal.

Biographers do it. Those who are commercially sharp choose a subject already visited by other biographers. Not having to do the spadework on too many original sources saves time and money. Even novelists do it. The best advice to an aspiring prize winner is to read books that are out of print. It is amazing how the same ideas, in slightly amended form, come round time and time again.

All of which goes to show that copyright is a hazy notion, to say the least. It is thus difficult and, on occasion, almost impossible to enforce. Just think what can be done with the new technology.

Nicholas Negroponte, the media guru at Massachusetts Institute of Technology, predicts the end to all constraints on the copying of material.

> 'Most people worry about copyright in terms of the ease of making copies. In the digital world, not only the ease is at issue, but also the fact that the digital copy is as perfect as the original and, with some fancy computing, even better. In the same way that bit strings can be error-corrected, a copy can be cleaned up, enhanced, and have noise removed. The copy is perfect ...'

Moreover,

> 'We see a new a new kind of fraud, which may not be fraud at all. When I read something on the Internet and, like a clipping from a newspaper, wish to send a copy of it to somebody else or to a mailing list of people, this seems harmless. But, with less than a dozen keystrokes, I could redeliver that material to literally thousands of people all over the world.'

Duplication is not only efficient, it is incredibly cheap which is why, after initial enthusiasm, few publishers are making money from the Internet. Even if this changes in the future and some rational economic model is laid on top of the Internet, it may cost a penny or two to distribute a million bits to a million people. It certainly will not cost anything like postage. Negroponte concludes: 'Copyright law is totally out of date. It is a Gutenberg artefact. Since it is a reactive process, it will probably have to break down completely before it is corrected.'

There is no shortage of statistics to underline his message. In the Far East it is reckoned that over 90 per cent of all videocassettes sold are pirated. Unauthorised printing of books in China, Russia and a motley of smaller nations is said to be depriving British publishers and their authors of £200 million a year. As for the dear old photocopier, a luxury product just ten years ago, it is now responsible for some 300 billion pages of illegally reproduced material.

What is to be done? On one side are those who argue for abandoning traditional ideas of copyright. Rather than try to tighten up the current law a more liberal regime would best serve the interests of education, economic growth and civilisation. Their case is illustrated by the long running dispute between America and China. It may be galling for the US to have its finest brains picked clean by a repressive regime but if we want to bring the Chinese into the family of democracies, should we not be delighted by their enthusiasm for Western technology and, by extension, Western culture?

So what that they lift ideas that should be making money for their originators. Owners of intellectual property could look to other sources of income. This is how publishers reacted to the photocopying threat, by hiking up the price of academic and reference books and journals. In this way, the cost of illicit copying was built into the overheads.

Owners of electronic rights are beginning to think the same way.

> 'Maybe the price of software will reduce and the price of manuals increase,' says Francis Pritchard, an academic specialising in computer law. 'People who create works must find other ways of earning money from their creations than simply by charging for copies. Take the "shareware" business as an example; software developers make their products freely available, and ask people who use it regularly to send them a small fee. Shareware might not make developers multi-billionaires, like Bill Gates, the Microsoft founder. Yet some earn comfortable livings, even when only five per cent of users pay up.'

Naturally this is not a strategy that appeals to writers who want to hold their market value. After all, it is only lately that the potential for making money from copyright has taken off. As Michael Sissons, writing in *The Author* points out, 'A generation ago the main constraint on the earnings of writers was in fact the inhibition on the transmission of the written word to the consumer. Paperbacks were in their infancy, bookshops were still, in the main, Dickensian shambles, the processes of production, distribution, reprinting and marketing were antique. Today the book is a more attractive and desirable object for the consumer, it can be produced and reprinted far quicker, and the computer has revolutionised the distributive and retail processes.'

But that is only part of the story. The time has long since gone when authors had to rely exclusively on royalties from their books in print. Nowadays there is a kaleidoscope of potential revenue-earning opportunities - translation rights, serial rights, rights of quotation, anthology, merchandising, bookclub rights, film and TV adaptation rights, dramatisation rights, and, not least, electronic publishing and copying.

In endeavouring to enforce their rights copyright holders have the legislation on their side. Until recently, British copyright lasted for 50 years beyond the author's death. Now, courtesy of the European Community, it is 70 years. There is support too for efforts to secure a decent return from those who would readily exploit an author's work without paying for it. Photocopying used to be a licence to save money. Hardly anyone thought twice before reproducing articles, chapters from books or even a whole book without reference to the copyright holder. Today, the Authors' Licensing and Collecting Society (ALCS) has forged agreements with education and commerce on a licensing scheme for reprographic rights which now brings in over £14 million a year. Whether or not a similar scheme can be applied to electronic rights depends largely on developing an effective policing system. If Negroponte is right in believing that the superhighway is also a freeway, then a large area of copyright will be unenforceable. But reports are already filtering through the technological grapevine of new metering systems which will allow publishers to monitor and record the use of its information on the Internet and other networks. In early 1997, WIPO (the World Intellectual Property Organisation, the UN's agency responsible for administering copyright conventions) required member states to outlaw devices aimed at bypassing technical measures to prevent unauthorised copying.

Meanwhile, there is much that the individual writer can do to guard against the free use of what is, or what might turn out to be, a valuable property. Start with a resolution always to check the small print of a contract.

Any publisher who offers a deal that is dependent on exclusive rights must be regarded with suspicion. The chances are that he has in mind a nice little earner that does not require him to pay the author a single penny beyond a basic fee or royalty. This is what happens to contributors to academic and specialist journals who are invariably asked to assign their copyright as a condition of publication. The reasons given are wildly imaginative, ranging from conditions in the US where a publisher must assert copyright over a whole journal to prevent pirating (not true) to the need to regularise applications to reproduce.

Even those who make a living out of writing and are skilled in the devious ways of publishing can lose out simply by ignoring the subsidiary clauses of a contract or, if reading them, by not realising the long term implications. In 1984, Random House of New York announced a revised standard contract demanding all electronic publishing rights from authors *including rights for technologies not yet invented*. The sad litany of rights carelessly discarded would make a sizeable volume in itself.

Once surrendered, there is no going back. As Nicola Solomon, a lawyer specialising in copyright law, warns, 'an assignment of copyright is binding ... it is not contingent on an agreed fee or royalties being paid. If a publisher fails to pay, your only remedy ... is to sue for the unpaid debt but you will not be able to regain copyright.'

Never say never. There must be occasions when the surrender of copyright is justified. A writer who works to order, adapting material provided for a company training course, say, or a sponsored history to be used as a promotional tool, would be pushing his luck to argue for more than a set fee.

Another moot point arises when it is not altogether clear who it is that has first claim to copyright. The most obvious example is the journalist - say, a columnist whose by-line appears twice weekly in a national newspaper. If he is on the payroll, with all the rights and responsibilities of an employee, then copyright on his articles is assumed to belong to his employer - 'unless otherwise agreed'. In other words, if the journalist is a self-assertive type who is ready to bargain with his editor he may well emerge with a contract which secures his copyright beyond the first printing. A scribe with less muscle might prefer to rely on his editor's sense of decency in handing over a share of any supplementary fees. It does happen on most national papers but over the rest of the printed media those who commission work invariably demand exclusive copyright, including syndication rights. This applies to free-lancers who, technically speaking, are entitled to copyright, as well as to regular employees. The journalists' unions urge members to resist but the need to make a living in a highly competitive market weakens the resolve of all but the star turns.

Film and television

In late 1992 the European Commission's Rental and Lending Directive declared the 'author' of a film to have the right to sanction (or stop) rental and to be paid ' "equitable" remuneration'. But who is the 'author'? Under British law, he is generally assumed to be the producer, an interpretation which naturally offends writers and directors. The European Community, on the other hand, takes its lead from France where the primary author of a film is the director while others, including the scriptwriter, can be named as co-authors. Producers have done their worst to frustrate the change, threatening expensive legal action and claiming that equitable remuneration should be deemed to have been paid under whatever financial arrangements have been made to set up a project. But in late 1996, Parliament gave the go-ahead for scriptwriters and authors whose work has been filmed or broadcast to receive payments for the rental of their works even when they have assigned all rights to a third party. Checking who owes what to whom is made easier by signing up with the ALCS which acts as a collecting agency on behalf of its members.

Problems remain, however. Lending is horrendously difficult to control. It has been known for years that the loss of income attributed to domestic sound and video recorders runs into billions. With the advance of technology, the problem is bound to worsen. Before long we will have video on demand, an almost limitless choice of programming available to any home at a push of the remote control. Imagine what that will do to undermine copyright.

Extent of copyright

Copyright applies to all written work, unpublished as well as published. For works not published during the author's lifetime, the period of copyright runs from the date of publication. For a published work of joint authorship, protection extends from the end of the year of the death of the author who dies last.

In most books a copyright notice appears on one of the front pages. In its simplest form this is the symbol © followed by the name of the copyright owner and the year of first publication. The assertion of copyright may be emphasised by the phrase 'All rights reserved', and in case there are any lingering doubts the reader may be warned that 'No part of this publication may be reproduced or transmitted in any form or by any means without permission'.

But this is to overstate the case. In principle, a quotation of a 'substantial' extract from a copyright work or for any quotation of copyright material, however short, for an anthology must be approved by the publishers of the original work.

But there is no fixed rule on what constitutes a substantial extract. In any case, even a lengthy quotation from a copyright work may not be an infringement if it is 'fair dealing ... for purposes of criticism or review'. Much depends on the standing of the writer being quoted. If he is a world famous author he or his heirs are liable to take a tougher line than, say, the copyright holder of an esoteric work on relative density. The families of literary giants are notoriously stingy. In granting permission to quote they are liable to charge hefty fees or, if the applicant is at all suspect, a biographer who is liable to do the dirt on a revered memory, for example, to refuse to cooperate in any way. For this, if for no other reason, an author who needs permission to quote should deal with the matter at an early stage in his work. Last minute requests just before a book goes to press can lead to crisis if fees are too high or if permission is refused.

A contract must specify the territory permissions will cover. The difference between British Commonwealth and the World can be a yawning gap in costs. Some publishers have a standard letter for clearing permissions which may help to speed up negotiations. But rights departments are notoriously slow in responding to requests from individuals who are unclear as to what they want or who give the impression of writing in on spec.

Difficulties can arise when the identity of a copyright holder is unclear. The publisher of the relevant book may have gone out of business or been absorbed into a conglomerate, leaving no records of the original imprint. Detective work can be yet more convoluted when it comes to unpublished works. When copyright holders are hard to trace, the likeliest source of help is the Writers and their Copyright Holders project, otherwise known as W.A.T.C.H. A joint enterprise of the universities of Texas and Reading, W.A.T.C.H. has created a database of English language authors whose papers are housed in archives and manuscript repositories. The database is available free of charge on the Internet.

If, despite best efforts, a copyright owner cannot be found, there are two options; either to cut the extract or to press ahead with publication in the hope that if the copyright holder does find out he will not object or will not demand an outrageous fee. The risk can be minimised by open acknowledgement that every effort to satisfy the law has been made.

Moral rights

With the 1988 Copyright Designs and Patents Act, the European concept of 'moral rights' was introduced into British law. The most basic is the right of paternity which entitles authors to be credited as the creators of their work. However, paternity must be asserted in writing and is not retrospective. No right of paternity attaches to authors of computer programs or to writers who create works as part of their employment or journalists or as contributors to a 'collective work' such as an encyclopedia, dictionary or year book.

A second moral right is that of integrity. In theory, this opens the way to forceful objections to any 'derogatory treatment' if derogatory amounts to 'distortion or mutilation ... or is otherwise prejudicial to the honour or reputation of the author'. Mis-correction of grammar by an illiterate editor does not qualify. In the absence of test cases, all things are possible, but relying on lawyers' gossip it seems that a book would have to be savaged beyond recognition for an injunction to be granted.

Those most likely to have their right of integrity infringed are film directors (specifically mentioned in the 1988 Act) and visual artists who might, for example, suffer the attentions of an airbrusher. For those in the writing trade, the Society of Authors urges 'locking the stable door before the horse bolts by ensuring that your contract does not permit the publishers to make significant editorial changes without your agreement' though with the virtual abandonment of hard copy in favour of disks, changes can be introduced without the author noticing - until it is too late.

Moral rights may 'be waived by written agreement or with the consent of the author'. There are cases where the concession is justified. For example, a ghost writer who has chosen to be anonymous may reasonably be expected to waive moral rights.

Titles and trademarks

Technically, there is no copyright in a title. But where a title is inseparable from the work of a particular author, proceedings for 'passing off' are likely to be successful. Everything depends on the nature of the rival works, the methods by which they are exploited and the extent to which the title is essentially distinctive.

The risks of causing offence multiply when a unique image is involved. In a full-page advertisement promoting the services of The Patent Office the *Mr Men* characters created by Roger Hargreaves (60 million books sold to date) are offered as an example of a registered trademark that protects the author against literary and other predators. The interesting feature of trademarks is that unlike copyright, they go on for ever. The Coca-Cola and Kodak marks, for example, are well over 100 years old. Neither of these have close literary associations but what about Thomas the Tank Engine, who now has his own trademark, or

Mickey Mouse? The official British artist of the Gulf war, John Keene, has faced legal threats from the Disney Corporation for having painted a picture of the devastation of a Kuwait beach which included a Mickey Mouse doll.

In theory it should be easier to preserve copyright in fictional characters than on titles. But in broadcasting, a frequent source of dispute is the lifting of characters from one series to another when there are two or more writers involved. Sometimes royalties are paid; other times, not. Production companies are liable to take possession of fictional characters unless their originators make a fuss.

The singularity of letters

The copyright status of a letter is something of a curiosity. The actual document belongs to the recipient, but the copyright remains with the writer and after his or her death, to the writer's estate. This has caused difficulty for some biographers who have assumed that it is the owners of letters who are empowered to give permission to quote from them. This only applies if the writer has assigned copyright. Even then, the way may not be smooth. Witness the frustration of Eric Jacobs, the biographer of Sir Kingsley Amis, who found himself unable to quote from letters written by the novelist because the Bodleian Library, which has the bulk of the Amis papers, would not concede any part of the copyright Sir Kingsley has invested in them. The matter was resolved only when the letter writer himself requested permission to quote from his own correspondence.

It is dangerous to assume that letters which are not in themselves of great intrinsic value are fair game for a biographer. Copyright owners do not have to look far for reasons to assert their rights and may not be swayed by appeals for liberality. The author Diana Souhami spent five years researching a book detailing the 'strange romance' of Greta Garbo and Cecil Beaton which fell victim to a failure to gain permission to use letters Garbo wrote to her friend Mimi Pollak. Cape had to pulp the entire hardback edition.

Copyright in lectures and speeches

Even if a speaker talks without notes, copyright exists in a lecture as soon as it is recorded (in writing or otherwise) but not until then. The copyright belongs to the person who spoke the words, whether or not the recording was made by, or with the permission of, the speaker.

This means that nobody may make substantial use of a transcript of a lecture without permission. There is one important exception: Where a record of spoken words is made to report current events, it is not an infringement of copyright to use or copy the record for that purpose provided that the record is a direct record of the spoken words and the making of the record was not prohibited by the speaker.

Copyright on ideas

Writers trying to sell ideas should start on the assumption that it is almost impossible to stake an exclusive claim. So much unsolicited material comes the way of publishers and script departments, the duplication of ideas is inevitable.

Frequent complaints of plagiarism have led publishers and production companies to point out the risks whenever they acknowledge an unsolicited synopsis or script, warning correspondents, 'it is often the case that we are currently considering or have already considered ideas that may be similar to your own'. Having something in print to wave at the judge helps to assert a charge of plagiarism. Recently, Guy Lyon Playfair scored a triumph with a little help from Willesden County Court. His case related to a BBC programme called *Ghostwatch* which, he argued, was inspired by and, to a significant extent, based on his book *This House is Haunted*. He listed 20 close similarities between book and film. The BBC offered an out of court settlement. Another BBC settlement was with the writer Tony Collins, who said an episode of the award-winning police series *Between the Lines* took its storyline from *Open Verdict*, his non-fiction book about deaths among defence scientists. Collins had sent a dramatisation to the BBC in 1992. Two years later the episode called *The Lone Soldier* appeared under the name of another writer. 'It has taken two years of fighting a completely intransigent BBC before it made one offer, then another and finally a fourth, which I accepted,' said Collins.

In America, the columnist Art Buchwald finally won his case against Paramount Pictures after a seven-year fight. The studio, he claimed, had taken his synopsis and turned it into the Eddie Murphy film *Coming to America*. 'In America they are now so worried about being sued that any writer offering an idea or script must sign a document waiving rights and simply accept the risk of not being able to sue,' says Mark Le Fanu, general secretary of the Society of Authors. 'I haven't heard of that in Britain yet, but it might happen.'

A writer who is nervous of the attention of rivals is best advised to maintain a certain reticence in dealings with the media. He should, for example, resist the urge to give out all his best ideas at an expensive lunch or in a brain-storming session with an ever so friendly producer who just might be able to slot your programme into his overcrowded schedule. It is flattering to be invited to hold forth but the experience can be costly unless there is an up front fee.

At the same time, remember that there is no such thing as an entirely original plot. To succeed in an action for infringement of copyright on an idea or on the bare bones of a plot, the copying of 'a combination or series of dramatic events' must be very close indeed. Proceedings have failed because incidents common to two works have been stock incidents or revolving around stock characters common to many works. Recently, The Patent Office has been collecting views on possible amendments to copyright law to give specific protection to programme formats. But so far there is not even a consensus on whether there is a problem to be overcome.

Anthology and quotation rates

Prose

The rate suggested by the Society of Authors and the Publishers Association is £95–115 per 1,000 words for world rights. The rate for the UK and Commonwealth or the USA alone is usually half of the world rate. For an individual country: one quarter of the world rate. Where an extract is complete in itself (e.g. a chapter or short story) publishers sometimes charge an additional fee at half the rate applicable for 1,000 words. This scale generally covers one edition only. An additional fee may be payable if the material is used in a reset or offset edition or in a new format or new binding (e.g. a paperback edition) and will certainly be required if the publisher of an anthology sub-licenses publication rights to another publisher.

Fees vary according to the importance of the author quoted, the proportion of the original work that the user intends to quote and its value to the author/publisher requesting permission. The expected size of the print-run should also be taken into consideration. Fees for quotations in scholarly works with print-runs of under 1,000 copies are usually charged at half the normal rate.

Poetry

For anthology publication in the UK and Commonwealth a minimum fee of £36 should be charged for the first 10 lines; thereafter £1.80 per line for the next 20 lines and £1.20 a line subsequently but the rates for established poets may well be significantly higher.

US copyright

The US Copyright Act of 1909 provided for two separate terms of copyright, a period of twenty-eight years from publication followed by a renewal period of a further twenty-eight years. A new copyright act, which came into force in January 1978, made changes in the duration of copyright protection and set out rules for the transition of existing works.

Copyrights registered before 1950 and renewed before 1978 were automatically extended by the new act until December of the seventy-fifth year of the original date of registration. This meant that all copyrights in their second term were extended for nineteen years. But copyrights registered after 1950 and before December 1977 had to be renewed. Strictly speaking, this should no longer be necessary. Following a 1992 Congressional amendment, if copyright has already been secured, the period of protection is extended automatically. But there may still be advantages in renewing copyright protection in a work's twenty-eighth year (i.e. by 31 December 1998 for works published in this country in 1970). For example, the legal costs of bringing an action for copyright infringement will not be met (even if you win the action) unless copyright has been formally registered. For unregistered works that have gone out of print an expensive Copyright Office search will be necessary to acquire rights. Copyright renewal, along with registration (if the work was not registered with the Library of Congress in the first place) costs $20. Further information and the appropriate forms are available from the Copyright Office, Library of Congress, Washington DC 20559, USA.

For any queries on British copyright contact: The Intellectual Property Policy Directorate, Copyright Enquiries, Room 4/5, Hazlitt House, 45 Southampton Buildings, London WC2A 1AR (☎0171 438 4778).

Magazines

Abraxas

57 Eastbourne Road, St Austell, Cornwall
PL25 4SU
☎01726 64975   Fax 01726 64975
Owner *Paul Newman*
Editors *Paul Newman, Pamela Smith-Rawnsley*

FOUNDED 1991. QUARTERLY incorporating the *Colin Wilson Newsletter*. Aims at being a periodical, but sometimes turns out to be a spasmodical. Unsolicited mss welcome after a study of the magazine – initial approach by phone or letter preferred.

Features Essays, translations and reviews. Issues have had Colin Wilson remembering R.D. Laing and appraising the work of Jacques Derrida and Michel Foucault; Paul Newman on *Little Grey Gropers from Mars* or 'Close Encounters of a Fourth Kind', and Ted Brown appraising 'Frozen Atlantis'. *Abraxas* welcomes provocative, lively articles on little-known literary figures (e.g. David Lindsay/E.H. Visiak/Laura Del Rivo/P.D. Ouspensky/Brocard Sewell) and new slants on psychology, existentialism and ideas. Maximum length 2000 words. *Payment* nominal if at all.

Fiction One story per issue. Favours compact, obsessional stories – think of writers like Kafka, Borges or Wolfgang Borchert – of not more than 2000 words.

Poetry Double-page spread – slight penchant for the surreal but open to most styles – has published D. M. Thomas, Zofia Ilinksa, Kenneth Steven and John Ellison.
Payment free copy of magazine.

Acclaim

See **The New Writer**

Accountancy

40 Bernard Street, London WC1N 1LD
☎0171 833 3291   Fax 0171 833 2085
Owner *Institute of Chartered Accountants in England and Wales*
Editor *Brian Singleton-Green*
Circulation 69,081

FOUNDED 1889. MONTHLY. Written ideas welcome. **Features** *Brian Singleton-Green* Accounting/tax/business-related articles of high technical content aimed at professional/managerial readers. Maximum 2000 words.
Payment by arrangement.

Accountancy Age

32–34 Broadwick Street, London W1A 2HG
☎0171 316 9000   Fax 0171 316 9250
Owner *VNU Business Publications*
Editor *Douglas Broom*
Circulation 76,650

FOUNDED 1969. WEEKLY. Unsolicited mss welcome. Ideas may be suggested in writing provided they are clearly thought out.

Features Topics right across the accountancy, business and financial world. Max. 2000 words.
Payment negotiable.

Active Life

Aspen Specialist Media, Christ Church, Cosway Street, London NW1 5NJ
☎0171 262 2622   Fax 0171 706 4811
Owner *Aspen Publishing*
Editor *Helene Hodge*

FOUNDED 1990. BI-MONTHLY magazine aimed at over 50s. General consumer interests including travel, finance, property and leisure. Opportunities for freelancers in all departments, including fiction. Approach in writing with synopsis of ideas. Authors' notes available on receipt of s.a.e.

Acumen

See under **Poetry Magazines**

African Affairs

Dept of Historical & Cultural Studies, Goldsmiths College, University of London, New Cross, London SE14 6NW
☎0171 919 7486   Fax 0171 919 7398
E-mail: hsa02dk@gold.ac.uk
Owner *Royal African Society*
Editors *David Killingray, Stephen Ellis*
Circulation 2250

FOUNDED 1901. QUARTERLY learned journal publishing articles on recent political, social and economic developments in sub-Saharan countries. Also included are historical studies that illuminate current events in the continent. Unsolicited mss welcome. Maximum 8000 words.
No payment.

Air International

PO Box 100, Stamford, Lincolnshire PE9 1XQ
☎01780 755131   Fax 01780 757261
Owner *Key Publishing Ltd*

Editor *Malcolm English*

FOUNDED 1971. MONTHLY. Civil and military aircraft magazine. Unsolicited mss welcome but initial approach by phone or in writing preferred.

Airforces Monthly

PO Box 100, Stamford, Lincolnshire PE9 1XQ
☎01780 55131   Fax 01780 57261
Owner *Key Publishing Ltd*
Editor *David Oliver*
Circulation 24,749

FOUNDED 1988. MONTHLY. Modern military aircraft magazine. Unsolicited mss welcome but initial approach by phone or in writing preferred.

Amateur Gardening

Westover House, West Quay Road, Poole, Dorset BH15 1JG
☎01202 680586   Fax 01202 674335
Owner *IPC Magazines Ltd*
Editor *Graham Clarke*
Circulation 50,823

FOUNDED 1884. WEEKLY. New contributions are welcome provided that they have a professional approach. Of the 20 unsolicited mss received each week, 90% are returned as unsuitable. All articles/news items are supported by colour pictures (which may or may not be supplied by the author).

Features Topical and practical gardening articles. Maximum 800 words.

News Compiled and edited in-house generally.

Payment negotiable.

Amateur Photographer

King's Reach Tower, Stamford Street, London SE1 9LS
☎0171 261 5100   Fax 0171 261 5404
Owner *IPC Magazines Ltd*
Group Editor *Keith Wilson*
Circulation 29,008

WEEKLY. For the competent amateur with a technical interest. Freelancers are used but writers should be aware that there is ordinarily no use for words without pictures.

Amateur Stage

Hampden House, 2 Weymouth Street, London W1N 3FD
☎0171 636 4343   Fax 0171 636 2323
E-mail: cvtheatre@aol.com
Owner *Platform Publications Ltd*

Editor *Charles Vance*

Some opportunity here for outside contributions. Topics of interest include amateur premières, technical developments within the amateur forum and items relating to landmarks or anniversaries in the history of amateur societies. Approach in writing only (include s.a.e. for return of mss).

No payment.

Ambit

See under **Poetry Magazines**

The American

114–115 West Street, Farnham, Surrey GU9 7HL
☎01252 713366/721267/0171 242 4033
Fax 01252 737938/0171 242 4034
Owner *British American Newspapers Ltd*
Editor *Molly Touger*
Circulation 15,000

FOUNDED 1976. FORTNIGHTLY community newspaper for US citizens resident in the UK. 'We are on the look-out for items on business and commerce, diplomacy, defence and "people" stories.' Maximum length 'five minutes read'. First approach in writing with samples of previous work.

Payment 'modest but negotiable'.

Amiga Format

30 Monmouth Street, Bath BA1 2AP
☎01225 442244   Fax 01225 732341
Owner *Future Publishing*
Editor *Nick Veitch*
Circulation 22,175

FOUNDED 1988. MONTHLY. Specialist computer magazine dedicated to Commodore Amiga home computers, offering reviews, features and product information of specific interest to Amiga users. Unsolicited material welcome. Contact by phone with ideas.

News *Ben Vost* Amiga-specific exclusives and product information. Length 500–1000 words.

Features *Nick Veitch* Computer-related features (i.e. CD-ROMs, games, virtual reality) with Amiga-specific value. Max. 10,000 words.

Special Pages *Ben Vost* Hardware and software reviews. Maximum 3000 words.

Payment £100 per 1000 words.

Animal Action

Causeway, Horsham, West Sussex RH12 1HG
☎01403 264181   Fax 01403 241048
Owner *RSPCA*
Editor *Michaela Miller*

Circulation 80,000

BI-MONTHLY. RSPCA youth membership magazine. Articles (pet care, etc.) are written in-house. Good-quality animal photographs welcome.

The Antique Dealer and Collectors' Guide

PO Box 805, Greenwich, London SE10 8TD
☎0181 691 4820   Fax 0181 691 2489
Owner *Statuscourt Ltd*
Publisher *Philip Bartlam*
Circulation 12,500

FOUNDED 1946. MONTHLY. Covers all aspects of the antiques and fine art worlds. Unsolicited mss welcome.

Features Practical but readable articles on the history, design, authenticity, restoration and market aspects of antiques and fine art. Maximum 2000 words. *Payment* £76 per 1000 words.

News *Philip Bartlam* Items on events, sales, museums, exhibitions, antique fairs and markets. Maximum 300 words.

Antique Interiors International

162 Parkington Street, Islington, London
N1 8RA
☎0171 359 6011   Fax 0171 359 6025
Owner *Antique Publications*
Editor-in-Chief *Alistair Hicks*
Managing Editor *Christopher Gower*
Circulation 22,000

FOUNDED 1986. QUARTERLY. Amusing coverage of antiques, art and interiors. Unsolicited mss not welcome. Approach by phone or in writing in the first instance. Interested in freelance contributions on international art news items.

Antiques & Art Independent

PO Box 1945, Comely Bank, Edinburgh
EH4 1AB
☎07000 765263   Fax 07000 268408
Owner *Antiques & Art Independent Ltd*
Publisher/Editor *Tony Keniston*
Circulation 20,000

FOUNDED 1997. BI-MONTHLY. Up-to-date information for the British antiques and art trade, circulated to dealers and collectors throughout the UK. News, photographs, gossip and controversial views on all aspects of the fine art and antiques world welcome. Articles on antiques and fine arts themselves are not featured. Approach in writing with ideas.

Apollo Magazine

1 Castle Lane, London SW1E 6DR
☎0171 233 6640   Fax 0171 630 7791
Owner *Paul Z. Josefowitz*
Editor *David Ekserdjian*

FOUNDED 1925. MONTHLY. Specialist articles on art and antiques, exhibition and book reviews, exhibition diary, information on dealers and auction houses. Unsolicited mss welcome. Interested in specialist, usually new research in fine arts, architecture and antiques. Approach in writing. Not interested in crafts or practical art or photography.

Aquarist & Pondkeeper

20 High Street, Charing, Kent TN27 0HX
☎01233 713188   Fax 01233 714288
Owner *M. J. Publications Ltd*
Editor *Dick Mills*
Circulation 20,000

FOUNDED 1924. MONTHLY. Covers all aspects of aquarium and pondkeeping: conservation, herpetology (study of reptiles and amphibians), news, reviews and aquatic plant culture. Unsolicited mss welcome. Ideas should be submitted in writing first.

Features Good opportunities for writers on any of the above topics or related areas. 1500 words (maximum 2500), plus illustrations. 'We have stocks in hand for up to two years, but new material and commissioned features will be published as and when relevant.' Average lead-in 4–6 months.

News Very few opportunities.

Architects' Journal

151 Rosebery Avenue, London EC1R 4QX
☎0171 505 6700   Fax 0171 505 6701
Owner *EMAP Construct*
Editor *Paul Finch*
Circulation 18,000

WEEKLY trade magazine dealing with all aspects of the industry. No unsolicited mss. Approach in writing with ideas.

Architectural Design

42 Leinster Gardens, London W2 3AN
☎0171 262 5097   Fax 0171 262 5093
Owner *Academy Group Ltd*
Editor *Maggie Toy*
Circulation 12,000

FOUNDED 1930. BI-MONTHLY. Theoretical architectural magazine. Unsolicited mss not generally welcome. Copy tends to come from experts in the field.

The Architectural Review

151 Rosebery Avenue, London EC1R 4QX
☎0171 505 6725   Fax 0171 505 6701
Owner *EMAP Construct*
Editor *Peter Davey*
Circulation 23,000

MONTHLY professional magazine dealing with architecture and all aspects of design. No unsolicited mss. Approach in writing with ideas.

Arena

Block A, Exmouth House, Pine Street,
London EC1R 0JL
☎0171 689 9999   Fax 0171 698 0901
Owner *Wagadon Ltd/Condé Nast Publications*
Editor *Ekow Eshun*
Circulation 86,922

Style and general interest magazine for men. Intelligent feature articles and profiles, plus occasional fiction.

Features Fashion, lifestyle, film, television, politics, business, music, media, design, art, architecture and theatre.

Payment £200–250 per 1000 words.

Art & Craft

Villiers House, Clarendon Avenue,
Leamington Spa, Warwickshire CV32 5PR
☎01926 887799   Fax 01926 883331
Owner *Scholastic Ltd*
Editor *Sian Morgan*
Circulation 17,000

FOUNDED 1936. MONTHLY aimed at a specialist market – the needs of primary school teachers, art coordinators and pupils. Ideas and synopses considered for commission.

Features The majority of contributors are primary school teachers with good art and craft skills and familiar with the curriculum.

News Handled by in-house staff. No opportunities.

Art Monthly

Suite 17, 26 Charing Cross Road, London
WC2H 0DG
☎0171 240 0389   Fax 0171 497 0726
E-mail: artmonthly@compuserve.com
Owner *Brittania Art Publications*
Editor *Patricia Bickers*
Circulation 5000

FOUNDED 1976. TEN ISSUES YEARLY. News and features of relevance to those interested in modern and contemporary visual art. Unsolicited mss welcome. Contributions should be addressed to the editor, accompanied by an s.a.e.

Features Alongside exhibition reviews: usually 750–1000 words and almost always commissioned. Interviews and articles of up to 1500 words on art theory, individual artists, contemporary art history and issues affecting the arts (e.g. funding and arts education). Book reviews of 750–1000 words.

News Brief reports (250–300 words) on art issues.

Payment negotiable.

The Art Newspaper

27–29 Vauxhall Grove, London SW8 1SY
☎0171 735 3331   Fax 0171 735 3332
Owner *Umberto Allemandi & Co. Publishing*
Editor *Anna Somers Cocks*
Circulation 30,000

FOUNDED 1990. MONTHLY. Tabloid format with up-to-date information on the international art market, news, museums, exhibitions, archaeology, conservation, books and current debate topics. Length 250–2000 words. No unsolicited mss. Approach with ideas in writing. Commissions only.

Payment £120 per 1000 words.

The Artist

Caxton House, 63–65 High Street,
Tenterden, Kent TN30 6BD
☎0158076 3673   Fax 0158076 5411
Owner *Irene Briers*
Editor *Sally Bulgin*
Circulation 17,500

FOUNDED 1931. MONTHLY.

Features *Sally Bulgin* Art journalists, artists, art tutors and writers with a good knowledge of art materials are invited to write to the editor with ideas for practical and informative features about art, materials, techniques and artists.

Artscene

Dean Clough Industrial Park, Halifax,
West Yorkshire HX3 5AX
☎01422 322527   Fax 01422 322518
Owner *Yorkshire and Humberside Arts*
Editor *Victor Allen*
Circulation 25,000

FOUNDED 1973. MONTHLY. Listings magazine for Yorkshire and Humberside. No unsolicited mss. Approach by phone with ideas.

Features Profiles of artists (all media) and associated venues/organisers of events of interest. Topical relevance vital. Maximum length 1500 words. *Payment* £100 per 1000 words.

News Artscene strives to bring journalistic

values to arts coverage – all arts 'scoops' in the region are of interest. Maximum length 500 words. *Payment* £100 per 1000 words.

Asian Times
148 Cambridge Heath Road,
London E1 5QJ
☎0171 702 8012   Fax 0171 702 7937
Owner *Ethnic Media Group*
Editor *Sanjay Gohil*
Circulation 33,000

FOUNDED 1983. WEEKLY community paper for the Asian community in Britain. Interested in relevant general, local and international issues. Approach in writing with ideas for submission.

Attitude
Northern & Shell Tower, City Harbour,
London E14 9GL
☎0171 308 5090   Fax 0171 308 5075
Owner *Northern & Shell plc*
Editor *Paul Hunwick*
Circulation 50,000

FOUNDED 1994. MONTHLY. Style magazine aimed primarily, but not exclusively, at gay men. Fashion and cultural coverage. Unsolicited mss not welcome. No phone calls. Brief summaries of proposed features, together with details of previously published work, should be sent by post or fax only. 'It sounds obvious, but anyone wanting to contribute to the magazine should read it first.'

Audit
19 Rutland Street, Cork,
Republic of Ireland
☎00 353 21313855   Fax 00 353 21313496
Editor *Ken Ebbage* (01707 373355)
Circulation 1000

BI-MONTHLY with a specialist, professional readership and world-wide circulation. Features tend to be commissioned. Approach in writing with ideas. Maximum 3000 words. No unsolicited mss. *Payment* £250.

The Author
84 Drayton Gardens, London SW10 9SB
☎0171 373 6642
Owner *The Society of Authors*
Editor *Derek Parker*
Manager *Kate Pool*
Circulation 7000

FOUNDED 1890. QUARTERLY journal of **The Society of Authors**. Most articles are commissioned.

Autocar
60 Waldegrave Road, Teddington, Middlesex
TW11 8LG
☎0181 943 5630   Fax 0181 943 5759
Owner *Haymarket Magazines Ltd*
Editor *Patrick Fuller*
Circulation 77,403

FOUNDED 1895. WEEKLY. All news stories, features, interviews, scoops, ideas, tip-offs and photographs welcome.
   Features *Gavin Conway*
   News *Chris Rosamond*
   Payment from £200 per 1000 words/negotiable.

Baby Magazine
WV Publications, 57–59 Rochester Place,
London N1 9JY
☎0171 226 2222   Fax 0171 359 5225
Owner *Highbury House Communications*
Editor *Dan Bromage*
Circulation 79,000

MONTHLY. For parents-to-be and parents of children up to two years old. No unsolicited mss.
   Features Send synopsis of feature with covering letter in the first instance. Unsolicited material is not returned.

Back Brain Recluse (BBR)
PO Box 625, Sheffield S1 3GY
Owner/Editor *Chris Reed*
Circulation 3000

International speculative fiction magazine providing opportunity for new writers. 'We strongly recommend familiarity with our guidelines for contributors, and with recent issues of *BBR*, before any material is submitted.' All correspondence must be accompanied by s.a.e. or international reply coupons.
   Payment £10 per 1000 words.

Badminton
Connect Sports, 14 Woking Road, Cheadle
Hulme, Cheshire SK8 6NZ
☎0161 486 6159   Fax 0161 488 4505
Owner *Mrs S. Ashton*
Editor *William Kings*

BI-MONTHLY. Specialist badminton magazine, with news, views, product information, equipment reviews, etc. Unsolicited material will be considered. Approach the editor by phone with an idea.
   Features *William Kings/Sue Ashton* Open to approaches and likes to discuss ideas in the first

instance. Interested in badminton-related articles on health, fitness, psychology, clothing, accessories, etc.
Payment £60.

The Badminton Times
PO Box 3443, London SE8 5BG
☎0181 692 6302   Fax 0181 692 6302
Editor *Mr R. Richardson*
FOUNDED 1980. QUARTERLY. Events, players, fashion and footwear, rackets, facilities, technique and tactics.

Balance
British Diabetic Association, 10 Queen Anne Street, London W1M 0BD
☎0171 323 1531   Fax 0171 637 3644
E-mail: balance@diabetes.org.uk
Owner *British Diabetic Association*
Editor *John Isitt*
Circulation 170,000
FOUNDED 1935. BI-MONTHLY. Unsolicited mss are not accepted. Writers may submit a brief proposal in writing. Only topics relevant to diabetes will be considered.
   Features *John Isitt* Medical, diet and lifestyle features written by people with diabetes or with an interest and expert knowledge in the field. General features are mostly based on experience or personal observation. Maximum 1500 words. *Payment* NUJ rates.
   News *John Isitt* Short pieces about activities relating to diabetes and the lifestyle of diabetics. Maximum 150 words.
   Young Balance *Jackie Mace* Any kind of article written by those under 18 and with personal experience of diabetes.
   Payment varies.

The Banker
149 Tottenham Court Road, London W1P 9LL
☎0171 896 2507   Fax 0171 896 2586
Owner *Financial Times Business*
Editor *Stephen Timewell*
Circulation 14,520
FOUNDED 1926. MONTHLY. News and features on banking, finance and capital markets worldwide and technology.

BBC Gardeners' World Magazine
Woodlands, 80 Wood Lane, London W12 0TT
☎0181 576 3959   Fax 0181 576 3986
Owner *BBC Worldwide Publishing*

Editor *Adam Pasco*
Circulation 303,385
FOUNDED 1991. MONTHLY. Gardening advice, ideas and inspiration. No unsolicited mss. Approach by phone or in writing with ideas.

BBC Good Food
Woodlands, 80 Wood Lane, London W12 0TT
☎0181 576 2000   Fax 0181 576 3931
Owner *BBC Worldwide Publishing*
Editor *Orlando Murrin*
Circulation 323,837
FOUNDED 1989. MONTHLY food and drink magazine with television and radio links. No unsolicited mss.

BBC Homes & Antiques
Woodlands, 80 Wood Lane, London W12 0TT
☎0181 576 3490   Fax 0181 576 3867
Owner *BBC Worldwide Publishing*
Editor *Judith Hall*
Circulation 201,582
FOUNDED 1993. MONTHLY traditional home interest magazine with a strong bias towards antiques and collectables. Opportunities for freelancers are limited; most features are commissioned from regular stable of contributors. No fiction, health and beauty, fashion or general showbusiness. Approach with ideas by phone or in writing.
   Features *Caroline Wheater* At-home features: inspirational houses – people-led items. Pieces commissioned on recce shots and cuttings. Guidelines available on request. Celebrity features: 'at homes or favourite things' – send cuttings of relevant work published. Maximum 1500 words.
   Special Pages Regular feature on memories of childhood homes. Maximum 800 words.
   Payment negotiable.

BBC Music Magazine
Room A1004, Woodlands, 80 Wood Lane, London W12 0TT
☎0181 576 3283   Fax 0181 576 3292
Owner *BBC Worldwide Publishing*
Editor *Graeme Kay*
Circulation 68,104 (UK edition)
FOUNDED 1992. MONTHLY. All areas of classical music. Not interested in unsolicited material. Approach with ideas only, by fax or in writing.

BBC Vegetarian Good Food
Room AG175, Woodlands, 80 Wood Lane,
London W12 0TT
☎0181 576 3767   Fax 0181 576 3825

Owner *BBC Worldwide Publishing*
Editor *Gilly Cubitt*
Circulation 80,720

FOUNDED 1992. MONTHLY magazine containing recipes, health and environment features. Unsolicited mss not welcome. Approach in writing with ideas.

BBC Wildlife Magazine
Broadcasting House, Whiteladies Road,
Bristol BS8 2LR
☎0117 973 8402   Fax 0117 946 7075

Owner *BBC Worldwide Publishing*
Editor *Rosamund Kidman Cox*
Circulation 116,537

FOUNDED 1963 (formerly *Wildlife*, née *Animals*). MONTHLY. Unsolicited mss generally not welcome.

    Features Most features commissioned from writers with expert knowledge of wildlife or conservation subjects. Maximum 3500 words. *Payment* £120–350.

    News Most news stories commissioned from known freelancers. Maximum 800 words. *Payment* £40–100.

Bedfordshire Magazine
Simla House, 34 Spring Road, Kempston,
Bedfordshire MK42 8LP
☎01234 266839

Owner *White Crescent Press*
Editor *Ann Collett-White*
Circulation 2400

FOUNDED 1947. QUARTERLY. Unsolicited material welcome on Bedfordshire. No general interest articles. Approach by phone or in writing in the first instance.

    Features History, biography, natural history and arts. Nothing in the way of consumer features.

    News Very little. Long-term county interest only.

    Fiction Occasional stories and poems of county interest only.

    Special Pages Primarily historical material on Bedfordshire. Maximum 1500 words. *Payment* nominal.

Bee World
18 North Road, Cardiff CF1 3DY
☎01222 372409   Fax 01222 665522
E-mail: ibra@cf.ac.uk

☎Website: http://www.cf.ack.uk/ibra/
Owner *International Bee Research Association*
Editor *Dr P. A. Munn*
Circulation 1700

FOUNDED 1919. QUARTERLY. High-quality factual journal, including peer-reviewed articles, with international readership. Features on apicultural science and technology. Unsolicited mss welcome, but authors should write to the Editor for guidelines before submitting mss.

Bella
H. Bauer Publishing, Shirley House,
25–27 Camden Road, London NW1 9LL
☎0171 284 0909   Fax 0171 485 3774

Owner *H. Bauer Publishing*
Editor-in-Chief *Jackie Highe*
Circulation 661,807

FOUNDED 1987. WEEKLY. Women's magazine specialising in real-life, human interest stories.

    Features *Sue Ricketts* Contributions welcome for some sections of the magazine: readers' letters, 'Precious Moments', 'Blush with Bella', 'Bella Fella' and 'Bella Rat'.

    Fiction *Linda O'Byrne* Maximum 1200–2000 words. Send s.a.e. for guidelines. *Payment* about £300 per 1000 words/varies.

Best
197 Marsh Wall, London E14 9SG
☎0171 519 5500   Fax 0171 519 5516

Owner *G & J (UK)*
Editor *Louise Court*
Circulation 511,841

FOUNDED 1987. WEEKLY women's magazine and stablemate of the magazine *Prima*. Multiple features, news, short stories on all topics of interest to women. Important for would-be contributors to study the magazine's style which differs from many other women's weeklies. Approach in writing with s.a.e.

    Features Maximum 1500 words. No unsolicited mss.

    Fiction 'Five-Minute Story' slot; unsolicited mss accepted. Maximum 1200 words. *Payment* £100.

Best of British
CMS Publishing, Rock House, Scotgate,
Stamford, Lincolnshire PE9 2YQ
☎01780 763063   Fax 01780 765788

Owner *CMS Publishing*
Editor *Ian Beacham*

FOUNDED 1994. MONTHLY magazine celebrating all things British, both past and present.

Study of the magazine is advised in the first instance. All preliminary approaches should be made in writing. No telephone calls, please.

Best Solutions
38 Broad Street, Earls Barton, Northamptonshire NN6 0ND
☎01635 522488   Fax 01635 522212
Owner *Grahame White*
Editor *Geoff Ellis*
Circulation 380,000
FOUNDED 1996. QUARTERLY business to business consultancy magazine. No unsolicited mss. 'Interested in articles (1000 words) for heads of substantial consultancy practices.' Approach in writing.

The Big Issue
Fleet House, 57–61 Clerkenwell Road, London EC1M 5NP
☎0171 418 0418   Fax 0171 418 0427
Editor-in-Chief *A. John Bird*
Editor *Becky Gardiner*
Assistant Editor *Simon Rogers*
Circulation 139,066
FOUNDED 1991. WEEKLY. An award-winning campaigning and street-wise general interest magazine sold in London and the south of England. Separate regional editions sold in Manchester, Scotland, Wales and Ireland.
Features *Simon Rogers* Interviews, campaigns, comment, opinion and social issues reflecting a twenty-something informed audience. Balance includes social issues but mixed with arts and cultural features. Freelance writers used each week – commissioned from a variety of writers. Best approach is to fax or post synopses to features editor with examples of work in the first instance. Maximum 1200 words. *Payment* £150 for 1000 words.
News *Jane Cassidy* Hard-hitting exclusive stories with emphasis on social injustice. Not interested in re-runs of other people's stories. Emphasis on magazine's publication area.
Arts *Tina Jackson* Interested in comment, interviews and analysis ideas. Reviews written in-house. Send synopses to arts editor.
Fiction Annual short story season covering variety of subjects – not only homelessness. Send stories/synopses to arts editor.

BIG!
Mappin House, 4 Winsley Street, London W1N 7AR
☎0171 436 1515   Fax 0171 312 8246
Owner *EMAP Metro*

Editor *Richard Galpin*
Circulation 206,116
FOUNDED 1990. FORTNIGHTLY celebrity/entertainment magazine for teenage girls. Interested in interviews with celebrities from the worlds of pop, film and television. 1500 words maximum; approach by phone in the first instance.

Bird Life Magazine
RSPB, The Lodge, Sandy, Bedfordshire SG19 2DL
☎01767 680551   Fax 01767 683262
Owner *Royal Society for the Protection of Birds*
Editor *Mark Boyd*
Circulation 90,000
FOUNDED 1965. BI-MONTHLY. Bird, wildlife and nature conservation for 8–12-year-olds (Young Ornithologist Club members). No unsolicited mss. No 'captive/animal welfare' articles.
Features *Mark Boyd* Unsolicited material rarely used. 'Good transparencies to accompany articles help success.'
News *Mark Boyd* News releases welcome but news stories must relate to YOC members. Approach in writing in the first instance.

Birds
The Lodge, Sandy, Bedfordshire SG19 2DL
☎01767 680551   Fax 01767 683262
Owner *Royal Society for the Protection of Birds*
Editor *R. A. Hume*
Circulation 549,188
QUARTERLY magazine which covers not only wild birds but also wildlife and related conservation topics. No interest in features on pet birds or 'rescued' sick/injured/orphaned ones. Mss or ideas welcome. 'No captive birds, please.'

Birdwatch
310 Bow House, 153–159 Bow Road, London E3 2SE
☎0181 983 1855   Fax 0181 983 0246
Owner *Solo Publishing*
Editor *Dominic Mitchell*
Circulation 16,500
FOUNDED 1992. MONTHLY high-quality magazine featuring illustrated articles on all aspects of birds and birdwatching, especially in Britain. No unsolicited mss. Approach in writing with synopsis of 100 words maximum. Annual **Birdwatch Bird Book of the Year** award (see entry under **Prizes**).
Features *Dominic Mitchell* Unusual angles/personal accounts, if well-written. Articles of an educative or practical nature suited to the readership. Maximum 2000–3000 words.

Fiction *Dominic Mitchell* Very little opportunity although occasional short story published. Maximum 1500 words.

News *Tim Harris* Rarely uses external material.

Payment £40 per 1000 words.

Bizarre

John Brown Publishing, The New Boathouse, 136–142 Bramley Road, London W10 6SR
☎0171 565 3000   Fax 0171 565 3053
E-mail: bizarre@johnbrown.co.uk

Owner *John Brown Publishing*
Editor *Fiona Jerome*
Circulation 71,782

FOUNDED 1997. MONTHLY magazine featuring amazing stories and images from around the world. No fiction, poetry, illustrations, short snippets.

Features *Fiona Jerome* 'Particularly interested in global stories and celebrity interviews.' Maximum 2,500 words. Approach in writing

Payment £120 per 1000 words.

Black Beauty & Hair

Hawker Consumer Publications Ltd, 13 Park House, 140 Battersea Park Road, London SW11 4NB
☎0171 720 2108   Fax 0171 498 3023

Owner *Hawker Consumer Publications Ltd*
Editor *Irene Shelley*
Circulation 22,017

QUARTERLY with one annual special: The Hairstyle Book in October; and a Bridal Supplement in the April/May issue. Black hair and beauty magazine with emphasis on authoritative articles relating to hair, beauty, fashion, health and lifestyle. Unsolicited contributions welcome.

Features Beauty and fashion pieces welcome from writers with a sound knowledge of the Afro-Caribbean beauty scene plus bridal features. Minimum 1000 words.

Payment £95 per 1000 words.

Boat International

5–7 Kingston Hill, Kingston upon Thames, Surrey KT2 7PW
☎0181 547 2662   Fax 0181 547 2890

Owner *Edisea Ltd*
Editor *Amanda McCracken*
Circulation 30,000

FOUNDED 1983. MONTHLY. Unsolicited mss welcome. Approach with ideas in writing and s.a.e.

Features Maximum 2000 words.
News Maximum 300 words.
Payment £100 per 1000 words.

Book and Magazine Collector

43–45 St. Mary's Road, London W5 5RQ
☎0181 579 1082   Fax 0181 566 2024

Owner *John Dean*
Editor *Crispin Jackson*
Circulation 12,000

FOUNDED 1984. MONTHLY. Contains articles about collectable authors/publications/subjects. Unsolicited mss welcome – but write first. Must be bibliographical and include a full bibliography and price guide. Not interested in purely biographical features. Approach in writing with ideas.

Features Maximum length 4000 words.
Payment £30 per 1000 words.

The Book Collector

PO Box 12426, London W11 3GW
☎0171 792 3492   Fax 0171 792 3492

Owner *The Collector Ltd*
Editor *Nicolas J. Barker*

FOUNDED 1950. QUARTERLY magazine on bibliography and the history of books, book-collecting, libraries and the book trade.

Book World Magazine

2 Caversham Street, London SW3 4AH
☎0171 351 4995   Fax 0171 351 4995

Owner *Christchurch Publishers Ltd*
Editor *James Hughes*
Circulation 5,500

FOUNDED 1980. MONTHLY news and reviews for serious book collectors, librarians, antiquarian and other booksellers. No unsolicited mss. Interested in material relevant to literature, art and book collecting. Send letter in the first instance.

Bookdealer

Suite 34, 26 Charing Cross Road, London WC2H 0DH
☎0171 240 5890   Fax 0171 379 5770

Editor *Barry Shaw*

WEEKLY trade paper which acts almost exclusively as a platform for people wishing to buy or sell rare/out-of-print books. Twelve-page editorial only; occasional articles and book reviews by regular freelance writers.

Books

43 Museum Street, London WC1A 1LY
☎0171 404 0304   Fax 0171 242 0762

Editor *Liz Thomson*
Circulation 115,000

Formerly *Books and Bookmen*. Consumer magazine dealing chiefly with features about authors and reviews of books. Carries few commissioned pieces.

Payment negotiable.

Books in Wales

See **Llais Llyfrau**

The Bookseller

12 Dyott Street, London WC1A 1DF
☎0171 420 6000
Fax 0171 420 6103 (Editorial)
Website: http://www.theBookseller.com

Owner *J. Whitaker & Sons Ltd*
Editor *Louis Baum*

Trade journal of the publishing and book trade – the essential guide to what is being done to whom. Trade news and features, including special features, company news, publishing trends, etc. Unsolicited mss rarely used as most writing is either done in-house or commissioned from experts within the trade. Approach in writing first.

Features *Jenny Bell*
News *Ms Danuta Kean*

Boxing Monthly

40 Morpeth Road, London E9 7LD
☎0181 986 4141   Fax 0181 986 4145
E-mail: bm@boxing-monthly.demon.co.uk

Owner *Topwave Ltd*
Editor *Glyn Leach*
Circulation 30,000

FOUNDED 1989. MONTHLY. International coverage of professional boxing; previews, reports and interviews. Unsolicited material welcome. Interested in small hall shows and grass-roots knowledge. No big fight reports. Approach in writing in the first instance.

Brides and Setting Up Home

Vogue House, Hanover Square, London W1R 0AD
☎0171 499 9080   Fax 0171 460 6369

Owner *Condé Nast Publications Ltd*
Editor *Sandra Boler*
Circulation 63,543

BI-MONTHLY. Much of the magazine is produced in-house, but a good, relevant feature on cakes, jewellery, music, flowers, etc. is always welcome. Maximum 1000 words. Prospective contributors should telephone with an idea in the first instance.

British Birds

Fountains, Park Lane, Blunham, Bedford MK44 3NJ
☎01767 640025   Fax 01767 640025

Owner *British Birds Ltd*
Editor *Dr J. T. R. Sharrock*
Circulation 10,000

FOUNDED 1907. MONTHLY ornithological magazine published by non-profit-making company. Features annual *Reports on Rare Birds in Great Britain*, bird news from official national correspondents throughout Europe and sponsored competitions for Bird Photograph of the Year, Bird Illustrator of the Year and Young Ornithologists of the Year. Unsolicited mss welcome from ornithologists only.

Features Well-researched, original material relating to Western Palearctic birds welcome. Maximum 6000 words.

News *Bob Scott/Wendy Dickson* Items ranging from conservation to humour. Maximum 200 words.

Payment only for photographs, drawings and paintings.

British Chess Magazine

The Chess Shop, 69 Masbro Road, London W14 OLS
☎0171 603 2877   Fax 0171 371 1477

Owner/Editor *Murray Chandler*

FOUNDED 1881. MONTHLY. Emphasis on tournaments, the history of chess and chess-related literature. Approach in writing with ideas. Unsolicited mss not welcome unless from qualified chess experts and players.

British Medical Journal

BMA House, Tavistock Square, London WC1H 9JR
☎0171 387 4499   Fax 0171 383 6418

Owner *British Medical Association*
Editor *Professor Richard Smith*

British Philatelic Bulletin

Royal Mail National, Royal London House, 22 Finsbury Square, London EC2A 1NL
☎0171 614 7064/7029   Fax 0171 614 7209

Owner *Royal Mail*
Editor *John Holman*
Circulation 30,000

FOUNDED 1963. MONTHLY bulletin giving details of forthcoming British stamps, features on older stamps and postal history, and book reviews. Welcome photographs of interesting, unusual or historic letter boxes.

Features Articles on all aspects of British philately. Maximum 1500 words.

News Reports on exhibitions and philatelic events. Maximum 500 words. Approach in writing in the first instance.

Payment £45 per 1000 words.

British Railway Modelling
The Maltings, West Street, Bourne, Lincolnshire PE10 9PH
☎01778 391167   Fax 01778 394748
Owner *Warners Group Publications Plc*
Editor *David Brown*
Assistant Editor *Jarrod Cotter*
Circulation 17,594

FOUNDED 1993. MONTHLY. A general magazine for the practising modeller. No unsolicited mss but ideas are welcome. Interested in features on quality models, from individual items to complete layouts. Approach in writing.

Features Articles on practical elements of the hobby, e.g. locomotive construction, kit conversions etc. Layout features and articles on individual items which represent high standards of the railway modelling art. Maximum length 6000 words (single feature). *Payment* up to £50 per published page.

News News and reviews containing the model railway trade, new products etc. Maximum length 1000 words. *Payment* up to £50 per published page.

Broadcast
33-39 Bowling Green Lane, London EC1R 0DA
☎0171 505 8014   Fax 0171 505 8050
Owner *EMAP Business Communications*
Editor *Steve Clarke*
Circulation 13,556

FOUNDED 1960. WEEKLY. Opportunities for freelance contributions. Write to the relevant editor in the first instance.

Features *Mark McNulty* Any broadcasting issue. Maximum 1500 words.

News *Tabitha Cole* Broadcasting news. Maximum 350 words.

Payment £180 per 1000 words.

Brownie
17–19 Buckingham Palace Road, London SW1W 0PT
☎0171 834 6242   Fax 0171 828 8317
Owner *The Guide Association*
Editor *Marion Thompson*
Circulation 30,000

FOUNDED 1962. MONTHLY. Aimed at Brownie members aged 7–10. **Articles** Crafts and simple make-it-yourself items using inexpensive or scrap materials.

Fiction Brownie content an advantage. No adventures involving unaccompanied children in dangerous situations – day or night. Maximum 600 words.

Payment £50 per 1000 words pro rata.

Building
Exchange Tower, 2 Harbour Exchange Square, London E14 9GE
☎0171 560 4141   Fax 0171 560 4004
Owner *The Builder Group*
Editor *Adrian Barrick*
Circulation 23,000

FOUNDED 1842. WEEKLY. Features articles on aspects of the modern building industry. Unsolicited mss are not welcome but freelancers with specialist knowledge of the industry are often used.

Features Focus on the modern industry. No building history required. Maximum 1000 words.

News Maximum 300 words.

Payment by arrangement.

The Burlington Magazine
14–16 Duke's Road, London WC1H 9AD
☎0171 388 1228   Fax 0171 388 1230
Owner *The Burlington Magazine Publications Ltd*
Editor *Caroline Elam*

FOUNDED 1903. MONTHLY. Unsolicited contributions welcome on the subject of art history provided they are previously unpublished. All preliminary approaches should be made in writing.

Exhibition Reviews Usually commissioned, but occasionally unsolicited reviews are published if appropriate. Maximum 1000 words.

Articles Maximum 4500 words. *Payment* £100 (maximum).

Shorter Notices Maximum 2000 words. *Payment* £50 (maximum).

Business Brief
PO Box 582, Five Oaks, St Saviour, Jersey JE4 8XQ
☎01534 611600   Fax 01534 611610
Owner *MSP Publishing*
Editor *Alex Mallinson*
Circulation 5,000

FOUNDED 1989. MONTHLY magazine covering business developments in the Channel Islands and how they affect the local market. Interested

in business-orientated articles only – 800 words maximum.
Payment £8 per 100 words.

Business Life
Haymarket House, 1 Oxendon Street, London SW1Y 4EE
☎0171 925 2544   Fax 0171 839 4508
Owner *Premier Magazines*
Editor *Sandra Harris*
Assistant Editor *Catherine Flanagan*
Circulation 193,000

TEN ISSUES YEARLY plus two double issues. Glossy business travel magazine with few opportunities for freelancers. Distributed on BA European routes, TAT and Deutsche BA only. Unsolicited mss not welcome. Approach with ideas in writing only.

Business Traveller
Russell Square House, 10–12 Russell Square, London WC1B 5ED
☎0171 580 9898   Fax 0171 580 6676
Owner *Perry Publications*
Editor *Julia Brookes*
Circulation 35,652

MONTHLY. Consumer publication. Opportunities exist for freelance writers but unsolicited contributions tend to be 'irrelevant to our market'. Would-be contributors are advised to study the magazine first. Approach in writing with ideas.
Payment varies.

Camcorder User
57–59 Rochester Place, London NW1 9JU
☎0171 331 1000   Fax 0171 331 1242
Owner *W. V. Publications*
Editor *Christine Morgan*
Circulation 21,797

FOUNDED 1988. MONTHLY magazine dedicated to camcorders, with features on creative technique, shooting advice, new equipment, accessory round-ups and interesting applications on location. Unsolicited mss, illustrations and pictures welcome. *Payment* negotiable.

Campaign
174 Hammersmith Road, London W6 7JP
☎0171 413 4036   Fax 0171 413 4507
Owner *Haymarket Publishing Ltd*
Editor *Stefano Hatfield*
Circulation 17,700

FOUNDED 1968. WEEKLY. Lively magazine serving the advertising and related industries.

Freelance contributors are best advised to write in the first instance.
Features Articles of 1500–2000 words.
News Relevant news stories of up to 300 words.
Payment negotiable.

Camping and Caravanning
Greenfields House, Westwood Way, Coventry, Warwickshire CV4 8JH
☎01203 694995   Fax 01203 694886
Owner *Camping and Caravanning Club*
Editor *Peter Frost*
Circulation 139,159

FOUNDED 1901. MONTHLY. Interested in journalists with camping and caravanning knowledge. Write with ideas for features in the first instance.
Features Outdoor pieces in general, plus items on specific regions of Britain. Maximum 1200 words. Illustrations to support text essential.

Camping Magazine
Star Brewery, Castle Ditch Lane, Lewes, East Sussex BN7 1YJ
☎01273 477421   Fax 01273 477421
Owner *Garnett Dickinson Publishing*
Editor *John Lloyd*

FOUNDED 1961. MONTHLY magazine with features on camping. Aims to reflect this enjoyment by encouraging readers to appreciate the outdoors and to pursue an active camping holiday, whether as a family in a frame tent or as a lightweight backpacker. Articles that have the flavour of the camping lifestyle without being necessarily expeditionary or arduous are always welcome. Study of the magazine is advised in the first instance. Ideas welcome. Contact editor by phone before sending mss.
Payment negotiable.

Canal and Riverboat
c/o Burrows Design Works, Jonathan Scott Hall, Thorpe Road, Norwich, Norfolk NR1 1UH
☎01603 623856   Fax 01603 623856
Owner *A. E. Morgan Publications Ltd*
Editor *Chris Cattrall*
Circulation 26,000

Covers all aspects of waterways, narrow boats and cruisers. Contributions welcome. Make initial approach in writing.
Features *Chris Cattrall* Waterways, narrow boats and motor cruisers, cruising reports, practical advice, etc. Unusual ideas and personal com-

ments are particularly welcome. Maximum 2000 words. Articles should be supplied in PC Windows format disk. *Payment* around £50 per page.

News *Chris Cattrall* Items of up to 300 words welcome on the Inland Waterways System, plus photographs if possible. *Payment* £15.

Car Mechanics

Kelsey Publishing, Cudham Tithe Barn, Bottom Burn Farm, Cudham, Kent TN16 3AG
☎01959 541444   Fax 01959 541400

Owner *Kelsey Publishing*
Editor *Peter Simpson*
Circulation 35,000

MONTHLY. Practical guide to maintenance and repair of post–1978 cars for DIY and the motor trade. Unsolicited mss, with good-quality colour prints or transparencies, 'at sender's risk'. Ideas preferred. Initial approach by letter or phone welcome and strongly recommended, 'but please read a recent copy first for style'.

Features Good, technical, entertaining and well-researched material welcome, especially anything presenting complex matters clearly and simply.

Payment by arrangement ('but generous for the right material').

Caravan Life

Warners Group Publications plc, The Maltings, West Street, Bourne, Lincolnshire PH10 9PH
☎01778 391027   Fax 01778 425437

Editor *Nick Harding*
Circulation 15,809

FOUNDED 1987. Magazine for experienced caravanners and enthusiasts providing practical and useful information and product evaluation. Opportunities for caravanning, relevant touring and travel material with good-quality colour photographs.

Caravan Magazine

Link House, Dingwall Avenue, Croydon, Surrey CR9 2TA
☎0181 686 2599   Fax 0181 781 6044

Owner *Link House Magazines Ltd*
Editor *Paul Carter*
Circulation 24,285

FOUNDED 1933. MONTHLY. Unsolicited mss welcome. Approach in writing with ideas. All correspondence should go direct to the editor.

Features Touring with strong caravan bias, technical/DIY features and how-to section. Maximum 1500 words.

Payment by arrangement.

Caribbean Times

148 Cambridge Heath Road, London E1 5QJ
☎0171 702 8012   Fax 0171 702 7937

Owner *Ethnic Media Group*
Editor *Clive Morgan*
Circulation 22,500

FOUNDED 1981. WEEKLY community paper for the African and Caribbean communities in Britain. Interested in general, local and international issues relevant to these communities. Approach in writing with ideas for submission.

Carmarthenshire Life

The Old Butter Factory, Station Road, St Clears, Carmarthenshire SA33 4BL
☎01994 231689/231691

Owner *Swan House Publishing*
Editor *David Fielding*

FOUNDED 1995. MONTHLY county magazine with articles on local history, issues, characters, off-beat stories with good colour or b&w photographs. No country diaries, short stories or poems. Most articles are commissioned from known freelancers but 'always prepared to consider ideas from new writers'. No mss. Send cuttings of previous work (published or not) and synopsis to the editor.

Cars and Car Conversions Magazine

Link House, Dingwall Avenue, Croydon, Surrey CR9 2TA
☎0181 686 2599   Fax 0181 781 6042

Owner *Link House Magazines Ltd*
Editor *Steve Bennett*
Circulation 46,537

FOUNDED 1965. MONTHLY. Unsolicited mss welcome but prospective contributors are advised to make initial contact by telephone.

Features Technical articles on current motorsport and unusual sport-orientated road cars. Length by arrangement.

Payment negotiable.

Cat World

Avalon Court, Star Road, Partridge Green, West Sussex RH13 8RY
☎01403 711511   Fax 01403 711521

Owner *Ashdown Publishing*
Editor *Joan Moore*
Circulation 19,000

FOUNDED 1981. MONTHLY. Unsolicited mss welcome but initial approach in writing preferred.

Features Lively, first-hand experience features on every aspect of the cat. Breeding features and veterinary articles by acknowledged experts only. Maximum 1800 words.

News Short, concise, factual or humorous items concerning cats. Maximum 100 words.

Catholic Herald

Lamb's Passage, Bunhill Row, London EC1Y 8TQ
☎0171 588 3101   Fax 0171 256 9728
E-mail: catholic@atlas.co.uk

Editor Deborah Jones
News Editor Joe Jenkins
Literary Editor Damian Thompson
Circulation 22,000

WEEKLY. Interested mainly in straight Catholic issues but also in general humanitarian matters, social policies, the Third World, the arts and books. 'No poetry, please.'

Payment by arrangement.

The Celtic Field

Celtic Publications, Glendoo Cottage, Glen Road, Ballaugh, Isle of Man IM7 5JB
☎01624 897263   Fax 01624 897263

Owner/Editor Robert Watson
Circulation 5000

FOUNDED 1996. QUARTERLY Celtic magazine featuring anything to do with Scotland, Ireland, Wales, Cornwall, Isle of Man, Brittany and other Celtic countries. Unsolicited mss welcome on Celtic/Gaelic subjects; ancient or modern history; fiction and book reviews welcome if on a Celtic theme – maximum 2000 words for fiction.

Payment negotiable/free magazine for news items.

Challenge

PO Box 300, Kingstown Broadway, Carlisle, Cumbria CA3 0QS
☎01228 512512 (ext. 2305)Fax 01228 593388
E-mail: donald.banks@stl.org

Owner Challenge Publishing
Editor Donald Banks
Circulation 80,000

FOUNDED 1958. MONTHLY Christian newspaper which welcomes contributions. Send for sample copy of writers' guidelines in the first instance.

Fiction Short children's stories. Maximum 600 words.

News Items of up to 500 words (preferably with pictures) 'showing God at work', and human interest photo stories. 'Churchy' items not wanted. Stories of professional sportsmen and musicians who are Christians always wanted but check first to see if their story has already been used.

Women's Page Relevant items of interest welcome.

Payment negotiable.

Champs-Elysées

119 Altenburg Gardens, The Conservatory, Bakery Place, London SW11 1JQ
☎0171 738 9316   Fax 0171 738 0707

Owner Wes Green
European Editor David Ralston

FOUNDED 1984. MONTHLY audio magazine for advanced speakers of French, German, Italian and Spanish issued in two parts: Part One is an hour-long programme (original stories, interviews and songs) in one of the above languages on cassette; Part Two is a booklet comprising a complete transcript with a glossary of difficult words plus features in English relating to topics covered on the tape. Interested in receiving ideas for unusual, well-researched features (for online use) for a sophisticated and well-educated readership.

Features European culture and travel. 1500 words maximum. *Payment* £200 per 1000 words. Approach in writing in the first instance.

Chapman

4 Broughton Place, Edinburgh EH1 3RX
☎0131 557 2207   Fax 0131 556 9565

Owner/Editor Joy M. Hendry
Circulation 2000

FOUNDED 1970. QUARTERLY. Scotland's quality literary magazine. Features poetry, short works of fiction, criticism, reviews and articles on theatre, politics, language and the arts. Unsolicited material welcome if accompanied by s.a.e. Approach in writing unless discussion is needed. Priority is given to full-time writers.

Features Topics of literary interest, especially Scottish literature, theatre, culture or politics. Maximum 5000 words.

Fiction Short stories, occasionally novel extracts if self-contained. Maximum 6000 words. *Payment* £15 per 1000 words.

Special Pages Poetry, both UK and non-UK in translation (mainly, but not necessarily, European). *Payment* by negotiation.

Chapter One

See **Alliance of Literary Societies** under **Professional Associations**

Chat
King's Reach Tower, Stamford Street,
London SE1 9LS
☎0171 261 6565   Fax 0171 261 6534

Owner *IPC Magazines Ltd*
Editor-in-Chief *Iris Burton*
Editor *Keith Kendrick*
Circulation 494,671

FOUNDED 1985. WEEKLY general interest
women's magazine. Unsolicited mss considered;
approach in writing with ideas. Not interested in
contributors 'who have never bothered to read
Chat and don't therefore know what type of
magazine it is'.

Features *Paul Merrill* Human interest and
humour. Maximum 1000 words. *Payment* up
to £600 maximum.

Fiction *Shelley Silas* Maximum 1000 words.

Cheshire Life
2nd Floor, Oyston Mill, Strand Road,
Preston, Lancashire PR1 8UR
☎01772 722022   Fax 01772 760905

Owner *Life Magazines*
Editor *Patrick O'Neill*
Circulation 11,000

FOUNDED 1934. MONTHLY. Homes, gardens,
personalities, business, farming, conservation,
heritage, books, fashion, arts, science – anything which has a Cheshire connection somewhere.

Child Education
Villiers House, Clarendon Avenue,
Leamington Spa, Warwickshire CV32 5PR
☎01926 887799   Fax 01926 883331

Owner *Scholastic Ltd*
Editor *Gill Moore*
Circulation 56,791

FOUNDED 1923. MONTHLY magazine aimed at
nursery, pre-school playgroup, infant and first
teachers. Articles from teachers, relating to education for 4–7-year age group, are welcome.
Maximum 1200 words. Approach in writing
with synopsis. No unsolicited mss.

Choice
Apex House, Oundle Road, Peterborough,
Cambridgeshire PE2 9NP
☎01733 555123   Fax 01733 898487

Owner *EMAP/Bayard Presse*
Editor *Sue Dobson*
Circulation 98,015

MONTHLY full-colour, lively and informative
magazine for people aged 50 plus which helps
them get the most out of their lives, time and
money after full-time work.

Features Real-life stories, hobbies, interesting
(older) people, British heritage and countryside,
involving activities for active bodies and minds,
health, competitions. Unsolicited mss read (s.a.e.
for return of material); write with ideas and
copies of cuttings if new contributor. No phone
calls, please.

Rights/News All items affecting the magazine's readership are written by experts. Areas of
interest include pensions, state benefits, health,
money, property, legal, and caring for elderly
relatives.

Payment by arrangement.

Church Music Quarterly
151 Mount View Road, London N4 4JT
☎0181 341 6408   Fax 0181 340 0021
E-mail: cmqeditor@aol.com

Owner *Royal School of Church Music*
Editor *Trevor Ford*
Associate Editor *Marianne Barton*
Circulation 13,700

QUARTERLY. Contributions welcome. Tele-
phone in the first instance. **Features** *Trevor Ford*
Articles on church music or related subjects considered. Maximum 2000 words.

Payment £60 per page.

Church of England Newspaper
10 Little College Street, London SW1P 3SH
☎0171 878 1545   Fax 0171 976 0783

Owner *Parliamentary Communications Ltd*
Editor *Colin Blakely*
Circulation 11,600

FOUNDED 1828. WEEKLY. Almost all material is
commissioned but unsolicited mss are considered. **Features** *Emma Watkins* Preliminary
enquiry essential. Maximum 1200 words.

News *Andrew Carey* Items must be sent
promptly and should have a church/Christian
relevance. Maximum 200–400 words.

Payment negotiable.

Church Times
33 Upper Street, London N1 0PN
☎0171 359 4570   Fax 0171 226 3073

Owner *Hymns Ancient & Modern*
Editor *Paul Handley*
Circulation 38,000

FOUNDED 1863. WEEKLY. Unsolicited mss
considered.

Features *Paul Handley* Articles and pictures
(any format) on religious topics. Maximum
1600 words. *Payment* £100 per 1000 words.

News *Paul Handley* Occasional reports (commissions only) and up-to-date photographs.
Payment by arrangement.

Circa21
55 Merches Gardens, Cardiff CF1 7RF
☎01222 377694

Owner *Totem*
Editor *Ishmael Fiifi Annobil*
Circulation 500

FOUNDED in 1996 as the first broadsheet international arts newspaper for Wales. Now evolved into magazine format supported by editorial volunteers. Relies on press-releases and illustrations from arts organisations. Features some off-the-beaten-track travelogues of cultural value, also interviews. Unsolicited mss welcome. 'Circa21 respects intellect, originality of style and sensitivity. No destructive critiques.'
Payment two copies of issue featuring writers' contribution.

Classic Boat
Link House, Dingwall Avenue, Croydon, Surrey CR9 2TA
☎0181 686 2599   Fax 0181 781 6535
E-mail: cb@lhm.co.uk
Website: http://www.marinedata.co.uk/classic

Owner *Link House Magazines*
Editor *Nic Compton*
Circulation 15,500

FOUNDED 1987. MONTHLY. Traditional boats and classic yachts old and new; maritime history. Unsolicited mss, particularly if supported by good photos, are welcome. Sail and power boat pieces considered. Approach in writing with ideas. Interested in well-researched stories on all nautical matters. News reports welcome. Contributor's notes available (s.a.e.).

Features Boatbuilding, boat history and design, events, yachts and working boats. Material must be well-informed and supported where possible by good-quality or historic photos. Maximum 3000 words. Classic is defined by excellence of design and construction – the boat need not be old and wooden! *Payment* £75-100 per published page.

News New boats, restorations, events, boatbuilders, etc. Maximum 500 words. *Payment* according to merit.

Classic Cars
Abbots Court, 34 Farringdon Lane, London EC1R 3AU
☎0171 216 6240   Fax 0171 216 6270

Owner *EMAP National Publications*

Editor *Robert Coucher*
Circulation 86,177

FOUNDED 1973. MONTHLY international classic car magazine containing entertaining and informative articles about classic cars and associated personalities.

Classical Guitar
Olsover House, 43 Sackville Road, Newcastle upon Tyne NE6 5TA
☎0191 276 0448   Fax 0191 276 1623

Owner *Ashley Mark Publishing Co.*
Editor *Colin Cooper*

FOUNDED 1982. MONTHLY.

Features *Colin Cooper* Usually written by staff writers. Maximum 1500 words. *Payment* by arrangement.

News *Thérèse Wassily Saba* Small paragraphs and festival concert reports welcome. *No payment.*

Reviews *Chris Kilvington* Concert reviews of up to 250 words are usually written by staff reviewers.

Classical Music
241 Shaftesbury Avenue, London WC2H 8EH
☎0171 333 1742   Fax 0171 333 1769
E-mail: classical.music@rhinegold.co.uk

Owner *Rhinegold Publishing Ltd*
Editor *Keith Clarke*

FOUNDED 1976. FORTNIGHTLY. A specialist magazine using precisely targeted news and feature articles aimed at the music business. Most material is commissioned but professionally written unsolicited mss are occasionally published. Freelance contributors may approach in writing with an idea but should familiarise themselves beforehand with the style and market of the magazine.
Payment negotiable.

Climber
PO Box 28, Altrincham, Cheshire WA14 2FG
☎0161 928 3480   Fax 0161 941 6897

Owner *Myatt McFarlane plc*
Editor *Bernard Newman*

FOUNDED 1962. MONTHLY. Unsolicited mss welcome (they receive about ten a day). Ideas welcome.

Features Freelance features (accompanied by photographs) are accepted on climbing and mountaineering in the UK and abroad, but the standard of writing must be extremely high. Maximum 2000 words. *Payment* negotiable.

News No freelance opportunities as all items are handled in-house.

Club Guide
PO Box 6160, Birmingham B16 8XA
☎0121 643 1575   Fax 0121 643 4450
Managing Editor *Sam Allen*
Editor *Kim Gould*
Circulation 30,000

FOUNDED 1990. QUARTERLY. Club features and listings. Interested in receiving items for club listings; approach in writing. No unsolicited mss.

Club International
2 Archer Street, London W1V 8JJ
☎0171 734 9191   Fax 0171 734 5030
Owner *Paul Raymond*
Editor *Robert Swift*
Circulation 180,000

FOUNDED 1972. MONTHLY. Features and short humorous items aimed at young male readership aged 18–30.
Features Maximum 1000 words.
Shorts 200–750 words.
Payment negotiable.

Coin News
Token Publishing Ltd, PO Box 14, Honiton, Devon EX14 9YP
☎01404 46972   Fax 01404 831895
Owner *J. W. Mussell and Carol Hartman*
Editor *J. W. Mussell*
Circulation 10,000

FOUNDED 1964. MONTHLY. Contributions welcome. Approach by phone in the first instance.
Features Opportunity exists for well-informed authors 'who know the subject and do their homework'. Maximum 2500 words.
Payment £20 per 1000 words.

Comhairle
See **ignotus press** under **Small Presses**

Commerce Magazine
Station House, Station Road, Newport Pagnell, Milton Keynes MK16 0AG
☎01908 614477   Fax 01908 616441
Owner *Holcot Press Group*
Group Editor *Steve Brennan*
Circulation 25,000

MONTHLY. Ideas welcome. Approach by phone or in writing first.
Features *Isabelle Morgan* By-lined articles frequently used. Generally 750–800 words with photos.
News Handled in-house.
Special Pages Throughout the year – media

and marketing; building and construction; finance and professional; office update.
No payment.

Company
National Magazine House, 72 Broadwick Street, London W1V 2BP
☎0171 439 5000   Fax 0171 439 5117
Owner *National Magazine Co. Ltd*
Editor *Fiona McIntosh*
Circulation 284,092

MONTHLY. Glossy women's magazine appealing to the independent and intelligent young woman. A good market for freelancers: 'We look for great newsy features relevant to young British women'. Keen to encourage bright, new, young talent, but uncommissioned material is rarely accepted. Feature outlines are the only sensible approach in the first instance. Maximum 1500–2000 words. Features to *Rachel Loos*.
Payment £250 per 1000 words.

Company Clothing Magazine
7 Holbrook Road, Leicester LE2 3LG
☎0116 270 4075   Fax 0116 270 4075
Owner *Company Clothing Information Services Ltd*
Editor *Leonie Barrie*
Circulation 13,000

Only UK magazine dedicated to the corporate clothing industry. Unsolicited mss welcome on any aspect of business clothing and workwear.

Computer Weekly
Quadrant House, The Quadrant, Sutton, Surrey SM2 5AS
☎0181 652 3122   Fax 0181 652 8979
Owner *Reed Business Information*
Editor *Helena Sturridge*
Circulation 120,000

FOUNDED 1966. Freelance contributions welcome.
Features *Ian Mitchell* Always looking for good new writers with specialised industry knowledge. Previews and show features on industry events welcome. Maximum 1500 words.
News *Karl Schneider* Some openings for regional or foreign news items. Maximum 300 words.
Payment Up to £50 for stories/tips.

Computing, The IT Newspaper
32–34 Broadwick Street, London W1A 2HG
☎0171 316 9158   Fax 0171 316 9160
Owner *VNU Business Publications Ltd*
Editor *Peter Kirwan*

Circulation 114,000

FOUNDED 1973. WEEKLY newspaper for IT professionals.

Associate Editor *Colin Barker*
Features *Dave Evans*
News *Louisa Bryan*

Unsolicited technical articles welcome. Please enclose s.a.e. for return.

Payment negotiable.

Condé Nast Traveller

Vogue House, Hanover Square, London W1R 0AD
☎0171 499 9080   Fax 0171 493 3758
E-mail: traveller@msmail.condenast.co.uk

Owner *Condé Nast publications*
Editor *Sarah Miller*
Circulation 70,000

FOUNDED 1997. Monthly travel magazine. Proposals rather than completed mss preferred. Approach in writing in the first instance.

Contemporary Review

Cheam Business Centre, 14 Upper Mulgrave Road, Cheam, Surrey SM2 7AZ
☎0181 643 4846   Fax 0181 241 7507

Owner *Contemporary Review Co. Ltd*
Editor *Dr Richard Mullen*

FOUNDED 1866. MONTHLY. One of the first periodicals to devote considerable space to the arts. Covers a wide spectrum of interests, including home affairs and politics, literature and the arts, history, travel and religion. No fiction. Maximum 3000 words.

Literary Editor *Dr James Munson* Monthly book section with reviews which are always commissioned.

Payment £5 per page.

Cosmopolitan

National Magazine House, 72 Broadwick Street, London W1V 2BP
☎0171 439 5000   Fax 0171 439 5016

Owner *National Magazine Co. Ltd*
Editor *Mandi Norwood*
Circulation 461,116

MONTHLY. Designed to appeal to the mid-twenties, modern-minded female. Popular mix of articles, with emphasis on relationships and careers, and hard news. Known to have a policy of not considering unsolicited mss but always on the look-out for 'new writers with original and relevant ideas and a strong voice'. Send short synopsis of idea. All would-be writers should be familiar with the magazine.

Payment about £250 per 1000 words.

Cotswold Life

Beshara House, Northway Trading Estate, Northway Lane, Tewkesbury, Gloucestershire GL20 8JH
☎01684 854410   Fax 01684 854458

Owner *Beshara Press*
Managing Editor *David MacDonald*
Circulation 10,000

FOUNDED 1968. MONTHLY. News and features on life in the Cotswolds. Contributions welcome.

Features Interesting places and people, reminiscences of Cotswold life in years gone by, and historical features on any aspect of Cotswold life. Approach in writing in the first instance. Maximum 1500–2000 words.

Payment by negotiation after publication.

Country

Shuttleworth, Old Warden Park, Biggleswade, Bedfordshire SG18 9EA
☎01767 626242   Fax 01767 627158

Owner *The Country Gentlemen's Association*
Publisher *Tim New*
Circulation 25,000

FOUNDED 1893. SUBSCRIPTION MONTHLY. News and features covering rural events, countryside, leisure, heritage, homes and gardens. Some outside contributors. Approach in writing in the first instance.

Payment by arrangement.

Country Garden & Smallholding

Broad Leys Publishing Company, Buriton House, Station Road, Newport, Saffron Walden, Essex CB11 3PL
☎01799 540922   Fax 01799 541367

Owner *D. and K. Thear*
Editor *Helen Sears*
Circulation 21,000

FOUNDED 1975. MONTHLY journal dealing with practical country living. Unsolicited mss welcome; around 30 are received each week. Articles should be detailed and practical, based on first-hand knowledge and experience of smallholding.

Country Homes and Interiors

King's Reach Tower, Stamford Street, London SE1 9LS
☎0171 261 6451   Fax 0171 261 6895

Owner *IPC Magazines Ltd*
Editor *Katherine Hadley*
Circulation 110,071

FOUNDED 1986. MONTHLY. The best approach

for prospective contributors is with an idea in writing as unsolicited mss are not welcome.

Features *Jean Carr* Monthly personality interviews of interest to an intelligent, affluent readership (women and men), aged 25–44. Maximum 1200 words. Also hotel reviews, leisure pursuits and weekending pieces in England and abroad. Length 750 words.

Houses *Sarah Whelan* Country-style homes with excellent design ideas. Length 1000 words.

Payment negotiable.

Country Life

King's Reach Tower, Stamford Street, London SE1 9LS
☎0171 261 7058   Fax 0171 261 5139

Owner *IPC Magazines Ltd*
Editor *Clive Aslet*
Circulation 46,414

ESTABLISHED 1897, *Country Life* features articles which relate to the countryside, wildlife, rural events, sports and pursuits, and are of interest to country dwellers. Arts, exhibitions and current events are featured weekly. Strong informed material rather than amateur enthusiasm. 'No responsibility can be taken for transparencies/artwork submitted.'

Payment from £120 per 1000 words.

Country Living

National Magazine House, 72 Broadwick Street, London W1V 2BP
☎0171 439 5000   Fax 0171 439 5093

Owner *National Magazine Co. Ltd*
Editor *Susy Smith*
Circulation 178,119

Magazine aimed at country dwellers and town dwellers who love the countryside. Covers people, conservation, wildlife, houses (gardens and interiors) and country businesses. No unsolicited mss.

Payment negotiable.

Country Sports

The Old Town Hall 367 Kennington Road, London SE1 4PT
☎0171 582 5432   Fax 0171 793 8484

Owner *British Field Sports Society*
Editor *Graham Downing*
Circulation 84,000

FOUNDED 1996. QUARTERLY magazine on country sports and conservation issues. No unsolicited mss.

Country Walking

Bretton Court, Bretton, Peterborough, Cambridgeshire PE3 8DZ
☎01733 264666   Fax 01733 465939

Owner *EMAP Plc*
Editor *Lynne Maxwell*
Circulation 50,027

FOUNDED 1987. MONTHLY magazine containing walks, features related to walking and things you see, country crafts, history, nature, photography etc, plus pull-out walks guide containing 25+ routes every month. Very few unsolicited mss accepted. An original approach to subjects welcomed. Not interested in book or gear reviews, news cuttings or poor-quality pictures. Approach by phone with ideas.

Features *Vincent Crump* Reader's story (maximum 800 words). Health-related features (500–1000 words).

Special Pages *Guy Procter* 'Down your way' section walks. Accurately and recently researched walk and fact file. Points of interest along the way and pictures to illustrate. Please contact for guidelines (unsolicited submissions not often accepted for this section).

Payment not negotiable.

Country-Side

BNA, 48 Russell Way, Higham Ferrers, Northamptonshire NN10 8EJ
☎01933 314672   Fax 01933 314672

Owner *British Naturalists' Association*
Editor *Dr D. Applin*
Circulation *c.* 20,000

FOUNDED 1905. BI-MONTHLY. Conservation and natural history magazine. Unsolicited mss and ideas for features welcome on conservation, environmental and natural history topics. Approach in writing with ideas. Maximum 1400 words.

Payment £50 (with pictures).

The Countryman

Sheep Street, Burford, Oxon OX18 4LH
☎01993 822258   Fax 01993 822703

Owner *Link House Magazines Limited*
Editor *Tom Quinn*
Circulation 50,000

FOUNDED 1927. SIX ISSUES YEARLY. Unsolicited mss with s.a.e. welcome; about 120 received each week. Contributors are strongly advised to study the magazine's content and character in the first instance. Approach in writing with ideas. Articles supplied with top quality illustrations (colour transparencies, archive b&w prints and line drawings) are far more likely to be used.

The Countryman's Weekly
(incorporating **Gamekeeper and Sporting Dog**)
Yelverton, Devon PL20 7PE
☎01822 855281   Fax 01822 855372
Publisher *Vic Gardner*
Editor *Jayne Willcocks*

FOUNDED 1895. WEEKLY. Unsolicited material welcome.
  Features On any country sports topic. Maximum 1000 words.
  Payment rates available on request.

County
PO Box 2486, Sonning, Reading, Berkshire
RG4 6YA
☎0118 969 8884   Fax 0118 969 8885
Owner *Mr and Mrs Watts*
Editor *Mrs Ashlyn Watts*
Circulation 50,000

FOUNDED 1986. QUARTERLY lifestyle magazine featuring homes, interiors, gardening, fashion and beauty, motoring, leisure and dining. Welcomes unsolicited mss. All initial approaches should be made in writing.

The Cricketer International
Third Street, Langton Green, Tunbridge Wells, Kent TN3 0EN
☎01892 862551   Fax 01892 863755
Owner *Ben G. Brocklehurst*
Editor *Peter Perchard*
Circulation 40,000

FOUNDED 1921. MONTHLY. Unsolicited mss considered. Ideas in writing only. No initial discussions by phone. All correspondence should be addressed to the editor.

Cumbria and Lake District Magazine
Dalesman Publishing Co. Ltd, Stable Courtyard, Broughton Hall, Skipton, North Yorkshire BD23 3AE
☎01756 701381   Fax 01756 701326
Owner *Dalesman Publishing Co. Ltd*
Editor *Terry Fletcher*
Circulation 16,100

FOUNDED 1951. MONTHLY. County magazine of strong regional and countryside interest, focusing on the Lake District. Unsolicited mss welcome. Maximum 1500 words. Approach in writing or by phone with feature ideas.

Cycle Sport
King's Reach Tower, Stamford Street, London SE1 9LS
☎0171 261 5588   Fax 0171 261 5758
Owner *IPC Magazines Ltd*
Editor *Andrew Sutcliffe*
Circulation 26,108

MONTHLY magazine dedicated to professional cycle racing. Unsolicited ideas for features welcome.

Cycling Today
24 Beauval Road, Dulwich, London SE22 8UQ
☎0181 693 6463   Fax 0181 299 0719
Owner *Yachting Press*
Editor *Roger St Pierre*
Circulation 20,800

Previously *New Cyclist*. MONTHLY general interest cycling magazine. Unsolicited feature proposals welcome. Not interested in personal accounts such as how you began cycling.
  Features Almost any cycling subject. Touring pieces on Mac-compatible (Word for Windows) disk with hard copy and high-quality transparencies. Submissions welcomed from writers and illustrators with specialist knowledge: e.g. sports medicine, bike mechanics. NB It may take some time to reply. Maximum 2000 words.

Cycling Weekly
King's Reach Tower, Stamford Street, London SE1 9LS
☎0171 261 5588   Fax 0171 261 5758
Owner *IPC Magazines Ltd*
Editor *Andrew Sutcliffe*
Circulation 33,179

FOUNDED 1891. WEEKLY. All aspects of cycle sport covered. Unsolicited mss and ideas for features welcome. Approach in writing with ideas. Fiction rarely used.
  Features Cycle racing, technical material and related areas. Maximum 2000 words. Most work commissioned but interested in seeing new work. *Payment* £60–100 per 1000 words (quality permitting).
  News Short news pieces, local news, etc. Maximum 300 words. *Payment* £15 per story.

The Dalesman
Stable Courtyard, Broughton Hall, Skipton, North Yorkshire BD23 3AE
☎01756 701381   Fax 01756 701326
Owner *Dalesman Publishing Co. Ltd*
Editor *Terry Fletcher*

Circulation 51,000

FOUNDED 1939. Now the biggest-selling regional publication of its kind in the country. MONTHLY magazine with articles of specific Yorkshire interest. Unsolicited mss welcome; receive approximately ten per day. Initial approach in writing or by phone. Maximum 1500 words.

Payment negotiable.

Dance & Dancers
83 Clerkenwell Road, London EC1R 5AR
☎0171 813 1049   Fax 0171 813 1049
Owner *Dance & Dancers Ltd*
Editor *John Percival*

FOUNDED 1950. MONTHLY magazine covering ballet and modern dance throughout the world. Some opportunity here for 'good writers with good knowledge of dance', but preliminary discussion is strongly advised.

Payment nominal.

Dance Theatre Journal
Laban Centre for Movement & Dance, Laurie Grove, London SE14 6NH
☎0181 692 4070   Fax 0181 694 8749
Owner *Laban Centre for Movement & Dance*
Editor *Ian Bramley*
Circulation 2000

FOUNDED 1982. THRICE-YEARLY. Interested in features on every aspect of the contemporary dance scene, particularly issues such as the funding policy for dance, critical assessments of choreographers' work and the latest developments in the various schools of contemporary dance. Unsolicited mss welcome. Length 1000–3000 words.

Payment varies 'according to age and experience'.

The Dancing Times
Clerkenwell House, 45–47 Clerkenwell Green, London EC1R 0EB
☎0171 250 3006   Fax 0171 253 6679
E-mail: dancing_times@compuserve.com
Owner *The Dancing Times Ltd*
Editor *Mary Clarke*

FOUNDED 1910. MONTHLY. Freelance suggestions welcome from specialist dance writers and photographers only. Approach in writing.

Darts World
28 Arrol Road, Beckenham, Kent BR3 4PA
☎0181 650 6580   Fax 0181 654 4343
Owner *World Magazines Ltd*

Editor *A. J. Wood*
Circulation 24,500

Features Single articles or series on technique and instruction. Maximum 1200 words.

Fiction Short stories with darts theme of no more than 1000 words.

News Tournament reports and general or personality news required. Maximum 800 words.

Payment negotiable.

Dateline Magazine
25 Abingdon Road, London W8 6AL
☎01869 324100   Fax 01869 324529
Owner *Jonathan Patterson*
Editors *Peter Bennett, Nicky Boult*
Circulation 15,000

FOUNDED 1976. MONTHLY magazine for single people. Unsolicited mss welcome.

Features Anything of interest to, or directly concerning, single people. Max. 2500 words.

News Items required at least six weeks ahead. Max. 2500 words.

Payment from £45 per 1000 words; £10 per illustration/picture used.

Day by Day
Woolacombe House, 141 Woolacombe Road, Blackheath, London SE3 8QP
☎0181 856 6249
Owner *Loverseed Press*
Editor *Patrick Richards*
Circulation 24,000

FOUNDED 1963. MONTHLY. News commentary and digest of national and international affairs, with reviews of the arts (books, plays, art exhibitions, films, opera, musicals) and county cricket reports among regular slots. Unsolicited mss welcome (s.a.e. essential). Approach in writing with ideas. Contributors are advised to study the magazine in the first instance.

News *Ronald Mallone* Interested in themes connected with non-violence and social justice only. Maximum 600 words.

Features No scope for freelance contributions here.

Fiction *Michael Gibson* Very rarely published.

Poems *Michael Gibson* Short poems in line with editorial principles considered. Maximum 20 lines.

Payment negotiable.

Decanter
583 Fulham Road, London SW6 5UA
☎0171 610 3929   Fax 0171 381 5282
Editor *Susan Keevil*

Circulation 35,000

FOUNDED 1975. Glossy wines and spirits magazine. Unsolicited material welcome but an advance telephone call is appreciated. No fiction.

News/Features All items and articles should concern wines, spirits, food and related subjects.

Derbyshire Life and Countryside
Heritage House, Lodge Lane, Derby DE1 3HE
☎01332 347087   Fax 01332 290688
Owner *B. C. Wood*
Editor *Vivienne Irish*
Circulation 12,007

FOUNDED 1931. MONTHLY county magazine for Derbyshire. Unsolicited mss and photographs of Derbyshire welcome, but written approach with ideas preferred.

Descent
51 Timbers Square, Roath, Cardiff CF2 3SH
☎01222 486557   Fax 01222 486557
Owner *Gloster Publications*
Editor *Chris Howes*
Assistant Editor *Judith Calford*

FOUNDED 1969. BI-MONTHLY magazine for cavers and mine enthusiasts. Submissions welcome from freelance contributors who can write accurately and knowledgeably on any aspect of caves, mines or underground structures.

Features General interest articles of under 1000 words welcome, as well as short foreign news reports, especially if supported by photographs/illustrations. Suitable topics include exploration (particularly British, both historical and modern), expeditions, equipment, techniques and regional British news. Maximum 2000 words.

Payment on publication according to page area filled.

Desire Direct
192 Clapham High Street, London SW4 7UD
☎0171 627 5155   Fax 0171 627 5808
Owner *Moondance Media Ltd*
Editor *Ian Jackson*

FOUNDED 1994. SIX ISSUES YEARLY. Britain's first erotic magazine for both women and men, celebrating sex and sensuality with a mix of articles, columns, features, reviews, interviews, fantasy and poetry (1000–2500 words).

For sample copy of magazine plus contributors' guidelines and rates, please enclose 2x first class stamps.

Director
Mountbarrow House, Elizabeth Street, London SW1W 9RB
☎0171 730 8320   Fax 0171 235 5627
Editor *Tom Nash*
Deputy Editor *Ian Fraser*
Circulation 42,000

1991 Business Magazine of the Year. Published by The Director Publications Ltd. for the members of the Institute of Directors. Wide range of features from political and business profiles and management thinking to employment and financial issues. Also book reviews. Regular contributors used. Send letter with synopsis/published samples rather than unsolicited mss. Strictly no 'lifestyle' writing.

Payment negotiable.

Dirt Bike Rider (DBR)
PO Box 100, Stamford, Lincolnshire PE9 1XQ
☎01780 755131   Fax 01780 757261
E-mail: dbr@keymags.demon.co.uk
Owner *Key Publishing Ltd*
Editor *Roddy Brooks*
Circulation 19,836

FOUNDED 1981. MONTHLY. Off-road dirt bikes (motocross, enduro and trials).

Disability Now
6 Market Road, London N7 9PW
☎0171 619 7323   Fax 0171 619 7331
Publisher *SCOPE* (Formerly The Spastics Society)
Editor *Mary Wilkinson*
Circulation 30,000

FOUNDED 1984. MONTHLY. Leading publication for disabled people in the UK, reaching people with a wide range of physical disabilities, as well as their families, carers and relevant professionals. No unsolicited material but freelance contributions welcome. Approach in writing.

Features Covering new initiatives and services, personal experiences and general issues of interest to a wide national readership. Maximum 1200 words. Disabled contributors welcome.

News Maximum 300 words.

Special Pages Possible openings for cartoonists.

Payment by arrangement.

Disabled Driver
DDMC, Cottingham Way, Thrapston, Northamptonshire NN14 4PL
☎01832 734724   Fax 01832 733816
Owner *Disabled Drivers' Motor Club*
Editor *Lesley Browne*

Circulation 14,500 plus

BI-MONTHLY publication of the Disabled Drivers' Motor Club. Includes information for members, members' letters. Approach in writing with ideas. Unsolicited mss welcome.

Diva, Lesbian Life and Style
Worldwide House, 116–134 Bayham Street, London NW1 0BA
☎0171 482 2576   Fax 0171 284 0329
E-mail: diva@gaytimes.co.uk
Owner *Millivres Ltd*
Editor *Gillian Rodgerson*

FOUNDED 1994. MONTHLY journal of lesbian news and culture. Welcomes news, features, short fiction and photographs. No poetry. Contact *Vicky Powell* with news items and *Gillian Rodgerson* with features, fiction and photographs. Approach in writing in the first instance.

Dog World
Somerfield House, Wotton Road, Ashford, Kent TN23 6LW
☎01233 621877   Fax 01233 645669
Owner *Dog World Ltd*
Editor *Simon Parsons*
Circulation 28,365

FOUNDED 1902. WEEKLY newspaper for people who are seriously interested in pedigree dogs. Unsolicited mss occasionally considered but initial approach in writing preferred.

Features Well-researched historical items or items of unusual interest concerning dogs. Maximum 1000 words. Photographs of unusual 'doggy' situations occasionally of interest. *Payment* up to £50; photos £15.

News Freelance reports welcome on court cases and local government issues involving dogs.

Eastern Eye
148 Cambridge Heath Road, London E1 5QJ
☎0171 702 8012   Fax 0171 702 7937
Owner *Ethnic Media Group*
Editor *Sarwar Ahmed*
Circulation 40,000

WEEKLY community paper for the Asian community in Britain. Interested in relevant general, local and international issues. Approach in writing with ideas for submission.

The Ecologist
Agriculture House, Bath Road, Sturminster Newton, Dorset DT10 1DU
☎01258 473476   Fax 01258 473476
Owner *Ecosystems Ltd*

Co-Editors *Edward Goldsmith, Zac Goldsmith*
Circulation 9000

FOUNDED 1970. BI-MONTHLY. Unsolicited mss welcome but initial approach in writing preferred.

Features Contents tend to be academic, but accessible to the general reader, looking at the social, political, economic and environmental aspects of development. Writers are advised to study the magazine for style. Max. 5000 words. *Payment* £20 per 1000 words.

The Economist
25 St James's Street, London SW1A 1HG
☎0171 830 7000   Fax 0171 839 2968
Owner *Pearson/individual shareholders*
Editor *Bill Emmott*
Circulation 650,000

FOUNDED 1843. WEEKLY. Worldwide circulation. Approaches should be made in writing to the editor. No unsolicited mss.

The Edge
111 Guinness Buildings, Fulham Palace Road, London W6 8BQ
☎0181 741 7757
Editor *Graham Evans*

BI-MONTHLY magazine. Looking for articles on film (non-Hollywood/mainstream), modern fiction, TV, popular culture. Film reviewers wanted. Contact the editor (enclose s.a.e.). 'Always reading for modern science fiction/horror and imaginative fiction.' Sample copy £2.50, cheques payable to The Edge. Writers' guidelines available on request. Send s.a.e.
Payment £20 per 1000 words, fiction; £20–50, articles; £150+, interviews.

Edinburgh Review
22 George Square, Edinburgh EH8 9LF
☎0131 650 4218   Fax 0131 662 0053
Owner *Edinburgh University Press*
Editor *Robert Alan Jamieson*
Circulation 750

FOUNDED 1969. BI-ANNUAL. Articles and fiction on Scottish and international literary, cultural and philosophical themes. Unsolicited contributions are welcome (1600 are received each year), but prospective contributors are strongly advised to study the magazine first. Allow up to six months for a reply.

Features Interest will be shown in accessible articles on philosophy and its relationship to literature or visual art.

Fiction Scottish and international. Maximum 6000 words.

Electrical Times

Quadrant House, The Quadrant, Sutton,
Surrey SM2 5AS
☎0181 652 3115   Fax 0181 652 8972
Owner *Reed Business Information*
Editor *Christopher Bennett*
Circulation 13,000

FOUNDED 1891. MONTHLY. Aimed at electrical
contractors, designers and installers. Unsolicited
mss welcome but initial approach preferred.

Elle

Endeavour House, 189 Shaftesbury Avenue,
London WC2H 8JG
☎0171 437 9011   Fax 0171 208 3599
Owner *EMAP Elan Publications*
Editor *Marie O'Riordan*
Circulation 218,077

FOUNDED 1985. MONTHLY fashion glossy.
Prospective contributors should approach the
relevant editor in writing in the first instance,
including cuttings.
 Features Maximum 2000 words.
 News/Insight Short articles on
current/cultural events with an emphasis on
national, not London-based, readership.
Maximum 500 words.
 Payment about £250 per 1000 words.

Embroidery

PO Box 42B, East Molesley, Surrey KT8 9BB
☎0181 943 1229   Fax 0181 977 9882
Owner *Embroiderers' Guild*
Editor *Maggie Grey*
Circulation 14,500

FOUNDED 1933. QUARTERLY. Features articles
on embroidery techniques, historical and foreign
embroidery, and specific artists' work with illustrations. Also reviews. Unsolicited mss welcome.
Maximum 1000 words.
 Payment negotiable.

Empire

Mappin House, 4 Winsley Street, London
W1N 7AR
☎0171 436 1515   Fax 0171 312 8249
Owner *EMAP Metro Publications*
Editor *Ian Nathan*
Circulation 165,778

FOUNDED 1989. Launched at the Cannes Film
Festival. MONTHLY guide to the movies which
aims to cover the world of films in a 'comprehensive, adult, intelligent and witty package'.
Although most of *Empire* is devoted to films and
the people behind them, it also looks at the

developments and technology behind television
and video plus music, multimedia and books.
Wide selection of in-depth features and stories
on all the main releases of the month, and
reviews of over 100 films and videos. Contributions welcome but must approach in writing
first.
 Features Short, behind-the-scenes features
on films.
 Payment by agreement.

The Engineer

30 Calderwood Street, London SE18 6QH
☎0181 855 7777   Fax 0181 316 3040
Owner *Miller Freeman*
Editor *Paul Carslake*
Circulation 38,000

FOUNDED 1856. News magazine for the UK
manufacturing industry.
 Features Most outside contributions are
commissioned but good ideas are always welcome. Maximum 2000 words.
 News Scope for specialist regional freelancers, and for tip-offs. Maximum 500 words.
 Techscan Technology news from specialists, and tip-offs. Maximum 500 words.
 Payment by arrangement.

The English Garden

Romsey Publishing Ltd, Glen House,
Stag Place, London SW1E 5AQ
☎0171 233 9191   Fax 0171 630 8084
Owner *Romsey Publishing Ltd*
Editor *Vanessa Berridge*
Circulation 55,656

FOUNDED 1996. MONTHLY. Features on beautiful gardens with practical ideas on design and
planting. No unsolicited mss.
 Features *Julia Watson/Caroline Jowett* Maximum 1000–1200 words. Approach in writing in
the first instance; send synopsis of 150 words
with strong design and planting ideas, or sets of
photographs of interesting gardens. 'No stately
home or estate gardens with teams of gardeners.'

English Nature

English Nature, Northminster House,
Peterborough, Cambridgeshire PE1 1UA
☎01733 455193   Fax 01733 455188
Owner *English Nature*
Editor *Martin Tither*
Circulation 13,500

FOUNDED 1992. BI-MONTHLY magazine which
explains the work of English Nature, the government adviser on wildlife policies. No unsolicited material.

ES (Evening Standard magazine)
See entry under **Regional Newspapers**

Esquire
National Magazine House, 72 Broadwick
Street, London W1V 2BP
☎0171 439 5000   Fax 0171 312 3920
Owner *National Magazine Co. Ltd*
Editor *Peter Howarth*
Circulation 106,203

FOUNDED 1991. MONTHLY. Quality men's
general interest magazine. No unsolicited mss
or short stories.

Essentials
King's Reach Tower, Stamford Street,
London SE1 9LS
☎0171 261 6970   Fax 0171 261 5262
Owner *IPC Magazines*
Editor *Karen Livermore*
Circulation 272,685

FOUNDED 1988. MONTHLY women's interest
magazine. Unsolicited mss (not originals) welcome if accompanied by s.a.e. Initial approach
in writing preferred. Prospective contributors
should study the magazine thoroughly before
submitting anything. No fiction.
Features Maximum 2000 words (double-
spaced on A4).
Payment negotiable, but minimum £100 per
1000 words.

Essex Countryside
Griggs Farm, West Street, Coggeshall, Essex
CO6 1NT
☎01376 563994   Fax 01376 562581
Owner *Market Link Publishing Ltd*
Editor *Sue Corner*
Circulation 15,000

FOUNDED 1952. MONTHLY. Unsolicited mate-
rial of Essex interest welcome. No general
interest material.
Features Countryside, culture and crafts in
Essex. Maximum 1500 words.
Payment £40.

European Medical Journal
Publishing House, Trinity Place, Barnstaple,
Devon EX32 9HJ
☎01271 328892   Fax 01271 328768
Owner/Editor *Dr Vernon Coleman*
Circulation 21,000

FOUNDED 1991. MONTHLY critical medical
review. Unsolicited ideas and synopses welcome.

Eventing
See **Horse and Hound**

Evergreen
PO Box 52, Cheltenham, Gloucestershire
GL50 1YQ
☎01242 577775   Fax 01242 222034
Editor *R. Faiers*
Circulation 75,000

FOUNDED 1985. QUARTERLY magazine featuring articles and poems about Britain. Unsolicited contributions welcome.
Features Britain's natural beauty, towns and
villages, nostalgia, wildlife, traditions, odd customs, legends, folklore, crafts, etc. Length 250–
2000 words.
Payment £15 per 1000 words; poems £4.

Executive Travel
Church Street, Dunstable, Bedfordshire
LU5 4HB
☎01582 695097   Fax 01582 695095
Owner *Reed Travel Group*
Editor *Mike Toynbee*
Circulation 43,079

FOUNDED 1979. MONTHLY. Aimed specifically
at frequent corporate travellers.

Executive Woman
2 Chantry Place, Harrow, Middlesex HA3 6NY
☎0181 420 1210   Fax 0181 420 1691
Owner *Saleworld*
Editor *Angela Giveon*
Circulation 75,000

FOUNDED 1987. BI-MONTHLY magazine for
female executives in the corporate field and
female entrepreneurs. Unsolicited material welcome. Initial approach by phone or in writing.
Features New and interesting business issues
and 'Women to Watch'. Health and fitness,
beauty, fashion, training and arts items. Maximum 850–1600 words.
Legal/Financial Opportunities for lawyers/
accountants to write on issues in their field.
Maximum 850 words.
Payment negotiable.

Express on Sunday Magazine
See under **National Newspapers (Express
on Sunday)**

The Face
3rd Floor, Block A, Exmouth House,
Pine Street, London EC1R 0JL
☎0171 689 9999   Fax 0171 689 0300
Owner *Wagadon Ltd*

Editor *Adam Higginbotham*
Fashion Editor *Karina Givargisoff*
Circulation 100,744

FOUNDED 1980. Magazine of the style generation, concerned with who's what and what's cool. Profiles, interviews and stories. No fiction. Acquaintance with the 'voice' of *The Face* is essential before sending mss on spec.

Features *Craig McLean* New contributors should write to the features editor with their ideas. Maximum 3000 words. *Payment* £150 per 1000 words.

Diary No news stories.

Family Circle

King's Reach Tower, Stamford Street, London SE1 9LS
☎0171 261 5000   Fax 0171 261 5929
Owner *IPC Magazines Ltd*
Editor-in-Chief *Sue James*
Circulation 280,295

FOUNDED 1964. THIRTEEN ISSUES YEARLY. Little scope for freelancers as most material is produced in-house. Unsolicited material is rarely used, but it is considered. Prospective contributors are best advised to send written ideas to the relevant editor.

Style *Amanda Cooke*
Food and Wine *Jane Curran*
Features *Gillian Drummond* Very little outside work commissioned.
Fiction *Dee Remmington* Short stories of 1000–1500 words.
Home *Lucy Searle*
Payment not less than £100 per 1000 words.

Family Tree Magazine

61 Great Whyte, Ramsey, Huntingdon, Cambridgeshire PE17 1HL
☎01487 814050   Fax 01487 711361
Owner *Armstrong Boon & Marriott (Publishing)*
Editorial Director *J.M. Armstrong*
Circulation 39,000

FOUNDED 1984. MONTHLY. News and features on matters of genealogy. Unsolicited mss considered. Keen to receive articles about unusual sources of genealogical research. Not interested in own family histories. Approach in writing with ideas. All material should be addressed to *Avril Cross*.

Features Any genealogically related subject. Maximum 2500 words. No puzzles or fictional articles.
Payment £35 per 1000 words (news and features).

Farmers Weekly

Quadrant House, Sutton, Surrey SM2 5AS
☎0181 652 4911   Fax 0181 652 4005
Owner *Reed Business Information*
Editor *Stephen Howe*
Circulation 98,268

WEEKLY. 1996 Business Magazine of the Year. For practising farmers. Unsolicited mss considered.

Features A wide range of material relating to farmers' problems and interests: specific sections on arable and livestock farming, farm life, practical and general interest, machinery and business.
News General farming news.
Payment negotiable.

Farming News

Miller Freeman House, Sovereign Way, Tonbridge, Kent TN9 1RW
☎01732 364422   Fax 01732 377675
Owner *Miller Freeman plc*
Editor *Donald Taylor*
Circulation 74,000

News of direct concern to farmers and the agricultural supply trade.

Fast Car

Berwick House, 8–10 Knoll Rise, Orpington, Kent BR6 0PS
☎01689 874025   Fax 01689 896847
Owner *SPL*
Editor *Ian Strachan*
Circulation 85,000

FOUNDED 1987. FOUR-WEEKLY. Concerned with the modification of road vehicles, with technical data and testing results. No kit-car features, race reports or road-test reports of standard cars.

Features Innovative ideas in line with the magazine's title, generally four pages long.
News Any item in line with magazine's title. Copy should be as concise as possible.
Payment negotiable.

Festival Guide

PO Box 6160, Birmingham B16 8XA
☎0121 643 1575   Fax 0121 643 4450
Managing Editor *Sam Allen*
Editor *Kim Gould*
Circulation 30–50,000

FOUNDED 1990. ANNUAL publication of festival listings and features. Interested in receiving items for festival listings; approach in writing. No unsolicited mss.

The Field

King's Reach Tower, Stamford Street,
London SE1 9LS
☎0171 261 5198   Fax 0171 261 5358

Owner *IPC Magazines*
Editor *J. Young*
Circulation 32,111

FOUNDED 1853. MONTHLY magazine for those who are serious about the British countryside and its pleasures. Unsolicited mss (and transparencies) welcome but initial approach should be made in writing.

Features Exceptional work on any subject concerning the countryside. Most work tends to be commissioned.
Payment varies.

Film and Video Maker

Church House, 1st Floor, 102 Pendlebury Road, Swinton, Manchester M27 4BF
☎0161 794 8282   Fax 0161 793 9696

Owner *Film Maker Publications*
Editor *Mrs Liz Donlan*
Circulation 2600

FOUNDED in the 1930s. BI-MONTHLY magazine of the Institute of Amateur Cinematographers. Reports news and views of the Institute. Unsolicited mss welcome but all contributions are unpaid.

Film Review

Visual Imagination Ltd, 9 Blades Court,
Deodar Road, London SW15 2NU
☎0181 875 1520   Fax 0181 875 1588

Owner *Visual Imagination Ltd*
Editor *Neil Corry*
Circulation 50,000

MONTHLY. Reviews, profiles, interviews and special reports on films. Unsolicited material considered.

First Down

7–9 Rathbone Street, London W1P 1AF
☎0171 323 1988   Fax 0171 637 0862

Owner *Independent Magazines (UK)Ltd*
Editor *Keith Webster*
Circulation 15,000

FOUNDED 1986. WEEKLY American football tabloid paper. Features and news. Welcomes contributions; approach in writing.

The First Word Bulletin

Calle Domingo Fernandez 5, Box 500, 28036
Madrid Spain
☎00 34 1 359 6418   Fax 00 34 1 320 8961
E-mail: gw83@correo.interlink.es

Website: http://www.interlink.es/peraso/first

Owner *The First Word Bulletin Associates*
Publisher/Editor *G. W. Amick*
Circulation 5000

FOUNDED 1995. QUARTERLY international magazine, printed in Madrid and distributed to the English speaking community worldwide. Welcomes articles on self-improvement, both mental and physical, also environmental problems and cures. Human interest, alternative medicine, fiction and non-fiction, nature stories, young adult and senior citizen retirement articles. 'No smut, pornography, love stories, detective stories, science fiction or horror.' 400 words maximum. Approach in writing with s.a.e. and IRCs. Disk submissions accepted; no submissions by e-mail. Contributors' guidelines not sent by e-mail.
Payment £30 maximum.

Fishkeeping Answers

See **Practical Fishkeeping**

Flight International

Quadrant House, The Quadrant, Sutton,
Surrey SM2 5AS
☎0181 652 3882   Fax 0181 652 3840
E-mail: flight.international@rbi.co.uk

Owner *Reed Business Information*
Editor *Carole Reed*
Circulation 60,000

FOUNDED 1909. WEEKLY. International trade magazine for the aerospace industry, including civil, military and space. Unsolicited mss considered. Commissions preferred - phone with ideas and follow up with letter. E-mail, modem and disk submissions encouraged.

Features *Carole Reed* Technically informed articles and pieces on specific geographical areas with international appeal. Analytical, in-depth coverage required, preferably supported by interviews. Maximum 1800 words.

News *Andrew Chuter* Opportunities exist for news pieces from particular geographical areas on specific technical developments. Maximum 350 words.
Payment NUJ rates.

Flora International

The Fishing Lodge Studio, 77 Bulbridge Road, Wilton, Salisbury, Wiltshire SP2 0LE
☎01722 743207   Fax 01722 743207

Owner/Publisher *Maureen Foster*
Editor *Judith Blacklock*
Circulation 16,000

FOUNDED 1974. BI-MONTHLY magazine for

flower arrangers and florists. Unsolicited mss welcome. Approach in writing with ideas. Not interested in general gardening articles.

Features Fully illustrated, preferably with b&w photos or illustrations/colour transparencies. Flower arranging, flower gardens and flowers. Floristry items written with practical knowledge and well illustrated are particularly welcome. Maximum 2000 words.

Profiles/Reviews Personality profiles and book reviews.

Payment £40 per 1000 words.

FlyPast
PO Box 100, Stamford, Lincolnshire PE9 1XQ
☎01780 755131   Fax 01780 757261
Owner *Key Publishing Ltd*
Editor *Ken Delve*
Circulation 47,000

FOUNDED 1981. MONTHLY. Historic aviation, mainly military, Second World War period up to c.1970. Unsolicited mss welcome.

Focus
See **British Science Fiction Association** under **Professional Associations**

Folk Roots
PO Box 337, London N4 1TW
☎0181 340 9651   Fax 0181 348 5626
Owner *Southern Rag Ltd*
Editor *Ian A. Anderson*
Circulation 14,000

FOUNDED 1979. MONTHLY. Features on folk and roots music, and musicians. Maximum 3000 words.

For Women
Fantasy Publications, 4 Selsdon Way, London E14 9EL
☎0171 308 5090   Fax 0171 308 5075
Editor *Zak Jane Keir*
Circulation 60,000

FOUNDED 1992. MONTHLY magazine of erotic and sex interest for women - celebrity interviews, beauty, health and sex, erotic fiction and erotic photography. No homes and gardens articles. Approach in writing in the first instance.

Features Relationships and sex. Maximum 2500 words. *Payment* £150 per 1000 words.

Fiction Erotic short stories. Maximum 2000 words. *Payment* £125 total.

Fortean Times: The Journal of Strange Phenomena
PO Box 2409, London NW5 4NP
☎0171 485 5002   Fax 0171 485 5002
Owners/Editors *Bob Rickard/Paul Sieveking*
Circulation 50,000

FOUNDED 1973. MONTHLY. Accounts of strange phenomena and experiences, curiosities, mysteries, prodigies and portents. Unsolicited mss welcome. Approach in writing with ideas. No fiction, poetry, rehashes or politics.

Features Well-researched and referenced material on current or historical mysteries, or first-hand accounts of oddities. Maximum 3000 words, preferably with good relevant photos/illustrations.

News Concise copy with full source references essential.

Payment negotiable.

Foundation: The International Review of Science Fiction
c/o Dept. of History, University of Reading, Whiteknights, Reading, Berkshire RG6 6AA
☎0118 9263047   Fax 0118 9316440
Owner *Science Fiction Foundation*
Editor *Professor Edward James*

THRICE-YEARLY publication devoted to the critical study of science fiction.

Payment None.

France Magazine
Dormer House, Digbeth Street, Stow-on-the-Wold, Gloucestershire GL54 1BN
☎01451 833210   Fax 01451 833234
Owner *Centralhaven*
Editor *Philip Faiers*
Circulation 61,000

FOUNDED 1989. QUARTERLY magazine containing all things of interest to Francophiles – in English. Approach in writing in the first instance.

Freelance Market News
Sevendale House, 7 Dale Street, Manchester M1 1JB
☎0161 228 2362   Fax 0161 228 3533
Editor *Angela Cox*
Circulation 3000

MONTHLY. News and information on the freelance writers' market, both inland and overseas. Includes market information on competitions, seminars, courses, overseas openings, etc. Short articles (700 words maximum). Unsolicited contributions welcome.

Payment £35 per 1000 words.

The Freelance

NUJ, Acorn House, 314 Gray's Inn Road, London WC1X 8DP
☎0171 278 7916   Fax 0171 278 1812

BI-MONTHLY published by the **National Union of Journalists**. Contributions welcome.

Freudian Variant

68 Bellevue Road, Ramsgate, Kent CT11 8DN
☎01843 590502

Publisher *Call Times Publications*
Editor *David L. Stone*

FOUNDED 1996. Fantasy/horror short stories and genre-related press review. Incorporates Darkhaven small press review. Contributor's guidelines available. Send s.a.e. Welcomes unsolicited ideas.

Payment £2 per 1000 words for fiction; non-fiction payment by arrangement.

Garden Answers (incorporating Practical Gardening)

Apex House, Oundle Road, Peterborough, Cambridgeshire PE2 9NP
☎01733 898100   Fax 01733 898433

Owner *EMAP Apex Publications Ltd*
Editor *Jim Ward*
Circulation 125,636

FOUNDED 1982. MONTHLY. 'It is unlikely that unsolicited manuscripts will be used, as articles are usually commissioned and must be in the magazine style.' Prospective contributors should approach the editor in writing. Interested in hearing from gardening writers on any subject, whether flowers, fruit, vegetables, houseplants or greenhouse gardening.

Garden News

Apex House, Oundle Road, Peterborough, Cambridgeshire PE2 9NP
☎01733 898100   Fax 01733 898433

Owner *EMAP Apex Publications Ltd*
Editor *Geoff Hodge*
Circulation 86,967

FOUNDED 1958. Britain's biggest-selling, full-colour gardening WEEKLY. News and advice on growing flowers, fruit and vegetables, plus colourful features on all aspects of gardening especially for the committed gardener. News and features welcome, especially if accompanied by top-quality photos or illustrations. Contact the editor before submitting any material.

The Garden, Journal of the Royal Horticultural Society

Apex House, Oundle Road, Peterborough, Cambridgeshire PE2 9NP
☎01733 898100   Fax 01733 341895

Owner *The Royal Horticultural Society*
Editor *Ian Hodgson*
Circulation 239,041

FOUNDED 1866. MONTHLY journal of the Royal Horticultural Society. Covers all aspects of the art, science and practice of horticulture and garden making. 'Articles must have depth and substance'; approach by letter with a synopsis in the first instance. Maximum 2500 words.

Gardens Illustrated

John Brown Publishing Ltd, The New Boathouse, 136–142 Bramley Road, London W10 6SR
☎0171 565 3000   Fax 0171 565 3056

Owner *John Brown Publishing Ltd*
Editor *Rosie Atkins*
Circulation 48,070

FOUNDED 1993. BI-MONTHLY. 'Britain's fastest growing garden magazine' with a world-wide readership. The focus is on garden design, with a strong international flavour. Unsolicited mss are rarely used and it is best that prospective contributors approach the editor with ideas in writing, supported by photographs.

Gargoyle Magazine

152 Harringay Road, London N15 3HL
☎0181 292 7350   Fax 0171 401 2055

Owner *Paycock Press*
London Editor *Maja Prausnitz*
US Editors *Richard Peabody, Lucinda Ebersole*
Circulation 5000

FOUNDED 1976. BI-ANNUAL literary magazine dedicated to championing work by new poets and fiction writers alongside the more established, and aiming to bridge the American and European literary worlds. Unsolicited mss welcome, though some knowledge of *Gargoyle* is recommended before submission.

Payment one copy of relevant issue.

Gay Times

Worldwide House, 116–134 Bayham Street, London NW1 0BA
☎0171 482 2576   Fax 0171 284 0329

Owner *Millivres Ltd*
Editor *David Smith*
Circulation 57,000

Covers all aspects of gay life, plus general inter-

est likely to appeal to the gay community, art reviews and news. Regular freelance writers used. Unsolicited contributions welcome.
Payment negotiable.

Gibbons Stamp Monthly
Stanley Gibbons, 5 Parkside, Ringwood, Hampshire BH24 3SH
☎01425 472363   Fax 01425 470247
Owner *Stanley Gibbons Holdings plc*
Editor *Hugh Jefferies*
Circulation 22,000
FOUNDED 1890. MONTHLY. News and features. Unsolicited mss welcome. Make initial approach in writing or by telephone to avoid disappointment.
Features *Hugh Jefferies* Unsolicited material of specialised nature and general stamp features welcome. Maximum 3000 words but longer pieces can be serialised. *Payment* £20–50 per 1000 words.
News *Michael Briggs* Any philatelic news item. Maximum 500 words. *No payment.*

Girl About Town
9 Rathbone Street, London W1P 1AF
☎0171 636 6651   Fax 0171 255 2352
Owner *Independent Magazines*
Editor-in-Chief *Bill Williamson*
News/Style Pages *Dee Pilgrim*
Circulation 100,000
FOUNDED 1972. Free WEEKLY magazine for women aged 16 to 26. Unsolicited mss may be considered. No fiction.
Features Standards are 'exacting'. Commissions only. Some chance of unknown writers being commissioned and unsolicited material is considered. Maximum 1500 words.
Payment negotiable.

Golf Monthly
King's Reach Tower, Stamford Street, London SE1 9LS
☎0171 261 7237   Fax 0171 261 7240
Owner *IPC Magazines Ltd*
Editor *Colin Callander*
Circulation 67,501
FOUNDED 1911. MONTHLY. Player profiles, golf instruction, general golf features and columns. Not interested in instruction material from outside contributors. Unsolicited mss welcome. Approach in writing with ideas.
Features Maximum 1500–2000 words.
Payment by arrangement.

Golf Weekly
Bretton Court, Bretton, Peterborough, Cambridgeshire PE3 8DZ
☎01733 264666   Fax 01733 465221
Owner *EMAP Pursuit Ltd*
Managing Editor *Bob Warters*
Circulation 20,000
FOUNDED 1890. WEEKLY. Unsolicited material welcome from full-time journalists only. For features, approach in writing in first instance; for news, fax or phone.
Features Maximum 1500 words.
News Maximum 300 words.
Payment negotiable.

Golf World
Angel House, 338–346 Goswell Road, London EC1V 7QP
☎01733 264666   Fax 0171 477 7274
Owner *EMAP Pursuit Ltd*
Editor *David Clarke*
Circulation 85,181
FOUNDED 1962. MONTHLY. No unsolicited mss. Approach in writing with ideas.

Good Food Retailing
PO Box 1525, Gillingham, Dorset SP8 5TA
☎01963 371271   Fax 01963 371270
Owner/Editor *Robert Farrand*
Circulation 4200
FOUNDED 1980. TEN ISSUES YEARLY. Serves the speciality food retail trade. Small budget for freelance material.

Good Health Magazine
Shadwell House, 65 Lower Green Road, Rusthall, Tunbridge Wells, Kent TN4 8TW
☎01892 535300   Fax 01892 535311
Owner *Pantile Publications Ltd*
Editor *Jack Hay*
FOUNDED 1997. MONTHLY. Aimed primarily at women and their families, covering all aspects of maintaining a healthy lifestyle, featuring health expert writers and professional practitioners. The magazine gives advice on all aspects of family health, including allergies, diet, emotions, fitness, hair, skin and body care, with emphasis on real-life experiences. Features and casebooks: variable length – average article 1200 words.
Payment negotiable.

Good Holiday Magazine
3A High Street, Esher, Surrey KT10 9RP
☎01372 468140   Fax 01372 470765
E-mail: goodskiguide@btinternet.com   •

Editor *John Hill*
Circulation 100,000

FOUNDED 1985. QUARTERLY aimed at better-off holiday-makers rather than travellers. World-wide destinations including Europe and domestic. Any queries regarding work/commissioning must be in writing. Copy must be precise and well-researched – the price of everything from coffee and tea to major purchases are included along with exchange rates, etc.
Payment negotiable.

Good Housekeeping

National Magazine House, 72 Broadwick Street, London W1V 2BP
☎0171 439 5000   Fax 0171 439 5591

Owner *National Magazine Co. Ltd*
Editor-in-Chief *Pat Roberts Cairns*
Circulation 450,183

FOUNDED 1922. MONTHLY glossy. No unsolicited mss. Write with ideas in the first instance to the appropriate editor.
    Features *Hilary Robinson* Most work is commissioned but original ideas are always welcome. Send short synopsis, plus relevant cuttings, showing previous examples of work published. No unsolicited mss.
    Fiction *Hilary Robinson* No unsolicited mss.
    Entertainment *Alison Packer* Reviews and previews on film, television, theatre and art.

Good Motoring

Station Road, Forest Row, East Sussex RH18 5EN
☎01342 825676 •   Fax 01342 824847

Owner *Guild of Experienced Motorists*
Editor *Derek Hainge*
Circulation 53,000

FOUNDED 1932. QUARTERLY motoring, road safety and travel magazine. Occasional general features. 1500 words maximum. Prospective contributors should approach in writing only.

Good Ski Guide

3A High Street, Esher, Surrey KT10 9RP
☎01372 468140   Fax 01372 470765
E-mail: goodskiguide@btinternet.com

Editor *John Hill*
Circulation 40,000

FOUNDED 1976. QUARTERLY. Unsolicited mss welcome from writers with a knowledge of skiing and ski resorts. Prospective contributors are best advised to make initial contact in writing as ideas and work need to be seen before any discussion can take place.
Payment negotiable.

Good Taste

PO Box 5, Fleet Street, Ashton–under–Lyne OL6 7FA
☎0161 339 2228   Fax 0161 339 4271

Owner/Editor *Sinclair Newton*
Circulation 5,000

FOUNDED 1996. MONTHLY north west of England lifestyle magazine.
    Features *Sinclair Newton* Travel, food and drink. 500–1000 words.
    Promotional features with potential advertisers also welcome. 1000 words maximum. Approach in writing or by fax in the first instance.
Payment by arrangement.

GQ

Vogue House, Hanover Square, London W1R 0AD
☎0171 499 9080   Fax 0171 495 1679

Owner *Condé Nast Publications Ltd*
Editor *James Brown*
Deputy Editor *Bill Prince*
Circulation 129,294

FOUNDED 1988. MONTHLY. Men's style magazine. No unsolicited material. Write or fax with an idea in the first instance.

Granta

2–3 Hanover Yard, Noel Road, London N1 8BE
☎0171 704 9776   Fax 0171 704 0474

Editor *Ian Jack*
Deputy Editor *Robert Winder*

QUARTERLY magazine of new writing, including fiction, autobiography, politics, history and reportage published in paperback book form. Highbrow, diverse and contemporary, with a thematic approach. Unsolicited mss (including fiction) considered. A lot of material is commissioned. Important to read the magazine first to appreciate its very particular fusion of cultural and political interests. No reviews. No poetry.
Payment negotiable.

The Great Outdoors

See **TGO**

Guardian Weekend

See under **National Newspapers (The Guardian)**

Guiding

17–19 Buckingham Palace Road, London SW1W 0PT
☎0171 834 6242   Fax 0171 828 8317

Owner *The Guide Association*

Editor *Nora Warner*
Circulation 30,000

FOUNDED 1914. MONTHLY. Unsolicited mss welcome provided topics relate to the Movement and/or women's role in society. Ideas in writing appreciated in first instance.

Features Topics that can be useful in the Guide programme, or special interest features with Guide link. Max. 1200 words.
News Guide activities. Max. 100–150 words.
Special Pages Outdoor activity, information pieces, Green issues. Max. 1200 words.
Payment £70 per 1000 words.

Hair

King's Reach Tower, Stamford Street,
London SE1 9LS
☎0171 261 6975   Fax 0171 261 7382

Owner *IPC Magazines Ltd*
Editor *Annette Dennis*
Circulation 165,274

FOUNDED 1980. BI-MONTHLY hair and beauty magazine. No unsolicited mss, but always interested in good photographs. Approach with ideas in writing.

Features *Sharon Christal* Fashion pieces on hair trends and styling advice. Maximum 1000 words.
Payment negotiable.

Hairflair

2 Coral Row, Plantation Wharf, London
SW11 3UF
☎0171 738 9911   Fax 0171 738 9922

Owner *James Kimber Management Ltd*
Editor *Rebecca Barnes*
Circulation 100,000

FOUNDED 1982. BI-MONTHLY. Original and interesting hair and beauty-related features written in a young, lively style to appeal to a readership aged 16–35 years. Unsolicited mss not welcome, but as the magazine is expanding new ideas are encouraged. Write to the editor.

Features Hair and beauty. Max. 1500 words.
Payment negotiable.

Harpers & Queen

National Magazine House, 72 Broadwick Street, London W1V 2BP
☎0171 439 5000   Fax 0171 439 5506

Owner *National Magazine Co. Ltd*
Editor *Fiona Macpherson*
Circulation 93,545

MONTHLY. Up-market glossy combining the stylish and the streetwise. Approach in writing (not phone) with ideas.

Features *Anthony Gardner/Susanna Gross* Ideas only in the first instance.
News Snippets welcome if very original.
Payment negotiable.

Health & Fitness Magazine

Nexus Media, Nexus House, Azalea Drive, Swanley, Kent BR8 8HY
☎01322 660070   Fax 01322 615636

Owner *Nexus Media*
Editor *Sharon Walker*
Circulation 65,000

FOUNDED 1983. MONTHLY. Will consider ideas; approach in writing in the first instance.

Health Education

MCB University Press, 60–62 Toller Lane, Bradford, West Yorkshire BD8 9BY
☎01274 777700   Fax 01274 785200/785201

Owner *MCB University Press*
Editor *Sharon Kingman*
Circulation 2000

FOUNDED 1992. SIX ISSUES YEARLY. Health education magazine with an emphasis on schools and young people. Professional readership. Most work is commissioned but ideas are welcome.

Hello!

Wellington House, 69–71 Upper Ground, London SE1 9PQ
☎0171 667 8700   Fax 0171 667 8716

Owner *Hola!* (Spain)
Editor *Maggie Koumi*
Circulation 574,585

WEEKLY. Owned by a Madrid-based publishing family, *Hello!* has grown faster than any other British magazine since its launch here in 1988 and continues to grow despite the recession. The magazine is printed in Madrid, with editorial offices both there and in London. Major colour features plus regular news pages. Although much of the material is provided by regulars, good proposals do stand a chance. Approach with ideas in the first instance. No unsolicited mss.

Features Interested in celebrity-based features, with a newsy angle, and exclusive interviews from generally unapproachable personalities.
Payment by arrangement.

Here's Health

Endeavour House, 189 Shaftesbury Avenue, London WC2H 8JG
☎0171 437 9011   Fax 0171 2-8 3583

Owner *EMAP Elan Publications*

Editor *Sheena Miller*
Circulation 38,468

FOUNDED 1956. MONTHLY. Full-colour magazine dealing with alternative medicine, nutrition, natural health, wholefoods, supplements, organics and the environment. Prospective contributors should bear in mind that this is a specialist magazine with a pronounced bias towards alternative/complementary medicine, using expert contributors on the whole.
Features Length varies.
Payment negotiable.

Heritage
4 The Courtyard, Denmark Street,
Wokingham, Berkshire RG40 2AZ
☎01189 771677   Fax 01189 772903
Owner *Bulldog Magazines*
Editor *Sian Ellis*
Circulation 77,000

FOUNDED 1984. BI-MONTHLY. Interested in complete packages of written features with high-quality transparencies – words or pictures on their own also accepted. Not interested in poetry, fiction or non-British themes. Approach in writing with ideas.
Features British villages, tours, towns, castles, gardens, traditions, crafts, historical themes and people. Maximum length 1200 words. *Payment* approx. £100 per 1000 words.
News Small pieces – usually picture stories in Diary section. Limited use. Maximum length 100–150 words. *Payment* £20.

Heritage Scotland
5 Charlotte Square, Edinburgh EH2 4DU
☎0131 243 9387   Fax 0131 243 9309
Owner *National Trust for Scotland*
Editor *Myra Sanderson*
Circulation 137,373

FOUNDED 1983. QUARTERLY magazine containing heritage/conservation features. No unsolicited mss.

Hi-Fi News & Record Review
Link House, Dingwall Avenue, Croydon,
Surrey CR9 2TA
☎0181 686 2599   Fax 0181 781 6046
Owner *Link House Magazines Ltd*
Editor *Steve Harris*
Circulation 34,000

FOUNDED 1956. MONTHLY. Write in the first instance with suggestions based on knowledge of the magazine's style and subject. All articles must be written from an informed technical or enthusiast viewpoint.

Payment negotiable, according to technical content.

High Life
Haymarket House, 1 Oxendon Street,
London SW1Y 4EE
☎0171 925 2544   Fax 0171 839 4508
Owner *Premier Magazines*
Editor *Mark Jones*
Circulation 295,000

FOUNDED 1973. MONTHLY glossy. British Airways in-flight magazine. Almost all the content is commissioned. No unsolicited mss. Few opportunities for freelancers.

Home & Country
104 New Kings Road, London SW6 4LY
☎0171 731 5777   Fax 0171 736 4061
Owner *National Federation of Women's Institutes*
Editor *Amber Tokeley*
Circulation 68,000

FOUNDED 1919. MONTHLY. Official full-colour journal of the Federation of Women's Institutes, containing articles on a wide range of subjects of interest to women. Strong environmental country slant with crafts and cookery plus gardening appearing every month. Unsolicited mss, photos and illustrations welcome.
Payment by arrangement.

Home & Family
Mary Sumner House, 24 Tufton Street,
London SW1P 3RB
☎0171 222 5533   Fax 0171 222 1591
Owner *MU Enterprises Ltd*
Editor *Jill Worth*
Circulation 85,000

FOUNDED 1976. QUARTERLY. Unsolicited mss considered. No fiction or poetry.
Features Family life, social problems, marriage, Christian faith, etc. Maximum 1000 words.
Payment 'modest'.

Home Wine and Beer Maker
304 Northridge Way, Hemel Hempstead,
Hertfordshire HP1 2AB
☎01442 267228   Fax 01442 267228
Owner *Homebrew Publications*
Editor *Evelyn Barrett*
Circulation 150,000

FOUNDED 1986. QUARTERLY. Articles on all aspects of home wine and beer making and the use of homemade wine in cooking, etc. Unsolicited mss welcome.

Homes & Gardens

King's Reach Tower, Stamford Street,
London SE1 9LS
☎0171 261 5000   Fax 0171 261 6247
Owner *IPC Magazines Ltd*
Editor *Matthew Line*
Circulation 171,142

FOUNDED 1919. MONTHLY. Almost all published articles are specially commissioned. No fiction or poetry. Best to approach in writing with an idea.

Horse & Pony Magazine

Bretton Court, Bretton, Peterborough,
Cambridgeshire PE3 8DZ
☎01733 264666   Fax 01733 465939
Owner *EMAP Pursuit Publications*
Editor *Andrea Oakes*
Circulation 54,260

Magazine for young (aged 10–16) owners and 'addicts' of the horse. Features include pony care, riding articles and celebrity pieces. Some interest in freelancers but most feature material is produced by staff writers.

Horse and Hound

King's Reach Tower, Stamford Street,
London SE1 9LS
☎0171 261 6315   Fax 0171 261 5429
Owner *IPC Magazines Ltd*
Editor *Arnold Garvey*
Circulation 66,850

WEEKLY. The oldest equestrian magazine on the market, now relaunched with modern make-up and colour pictures throughout. Contains regular veterinary advice and instructional articles, as well as authoritative news and comment on fox hunting, international showjumping, horse trials, dressage, driving and cross-country riding. Also weekly racing and point-to-points, breeding reports and articles. Includes junior sections for the Pony Club. Regular books and art reviews, and humorous articles and cartoons are frequently published. Plenty of opportunities for freelancers. Unsolicited contributions welcome.

Also publishes a sister monthly publication, *Eventing*, which covers the sport of horse trials comprehensively.

Payment NUJ rates.

Horse and Rider

Haslemere House, Lower Street, Haslemere,
Surrey GU27 2PE
☎01428 651551   Fax 01428 653888
Owner *D. J. Murphy (Publishers) Ltd*
Editor *Alison Bridge*

Assistant Editor *Sarah Muir*
Circulation 46,000

FOUNDED 1949. MONTHLY. Adult readership, largely horse-owning. News and instructional features, which make up the bulk of the magazine, are almost all commissioned. New contributors and unsolicited mss are occasionally used. Approach the editor in writing with ideas.

Horticulture Week

174 Hammersmith Road, London W6 7JP
☎0171 413 4595   Fax 0171 413 4518
Owner *Haymarket Magazines Ltd*
Editor *Vicky Browning*
Circulation 11,200

FOUNDED 1841. WEEKLY. Specialist magazine involved in the supply of business-type information. No unsolicited mss. Approach in writing in first instance.

Features No submissions without prior discussion. *Payment* negotiable.

News *Maja Pawinska* Information about horticultural businesses – nurseries, garden centres, landscapers and parks departments in the various regions of the UK. No gardening stories.

House & Garden

Vogue House, Hanover Square, London
W1R 0AD
☎0171 499 9080   Fax 0171 629 2907
Owner *Condé Nast Publications Ltd*
Editor *Susan Crewe*
Circulation 163,330

FOUNDED 1947. MONTHLY. Most feature material is produced in-house but occasional specialist features are commissioned from qualified freelancers, mainly for the interiors, wine and food sections and travel.

Features *Liz Elliot* Suggestions for features, preferably in the form of brief outlines of proposed subjects, will be considered.

House Beautiful

National Magazine House, 72 Broadwick
Street, London W1V 2BP
☎0171 439 5000   Fax 0171 439 5595
Owner *National Magazine Co. Ltd*
Editor *Caroline Atkins*
Circulation 305,067

FOUNDED 1989. MONTHLY. Lively magazine offering sound, practical information and plenty of inspiration for those who want to make the most of where they live. Over 100 pages of easy-reading editorial. Regular features about decoration, DIY and home finance.

Approach in writing with synopses or ideas in the first instance.

House Buyer
302 Ewell Road, Surbiton, Surrey KT6 7AQ
☎0181 390 8980   Fax 0181 399 5921
Owner *Dalton's Weekly Plc*
Editor *Con Crowley*
Circulation 14,000

FOUNDED 1955. MONTHLY magazine with features and articles for house buyers, including retirement homes, mortgage information, etc. A 32-page section includes details of over 200,000 new homes throughout the UK. Unsolicited mss will neither be read nor returned.

i-D Magazine
Universal House, 251–255 Tottenham Court Road, London W1P 0AE
☎0171 813 6170   Fax 0171 813 6179
Owner *Levelprint*
Editor *Avril Mair*
Circulation 45,000

FOUNDED 1980. MONTHLY lifestyle magazine for both sexes aged 16–24. Very hip. 'We are always looking for freelance non-fiction writers with new or unusual ideas.' A different theme each issue – past themes include Green politics, taste, films, sex, love and loud dance music – means it is advisable to discuss feature ideas in the first instance.

Ideal Home
King's Reach Tower, Stamford Street, London SE1 9LS
☎0171 261 6474   Fax 0171 261 6697
Owner *IPC Magazines Ltd*
Editor-in-chief *Sally O'Sullivan*
Circulation 208,016

FOUNDED 1920. MONTHLY glossy. Unsolicited feature articles are welcome if appropriate to the magazine. Prospective contributors wishing to submit ideas should do so in writing to the editor. No fiction.
   Features Furnishing and decoration of houses, kitchens or bathrooms; interior design, soft furnishings, furniture and home improvements, lifestyle, travel, etc. Length to be discussed with editor.
   Payment negotiable.

The Illustrated London News
20 Upper Ground, London SE1 9PF
☎0171 805 5562   Fax 0171 805 5911
Owner *James Sherwood*

Editor *Alison Booth*
Circulation 47,547

FOUNDED 1842. BI-ANNUAL: the Christmas and Summer issues, plus the occasional special issue to coincide with particular events. Although the *ILN* covers issues concerning the whole of the UK, its emphasis remains on the capital and its life. Travel, wine, restaurants, events, cultural and current affairs are all covered. There are few opportunities for freelancers but all unsolicited mss are read (receives about 20 a week). The best approach is with an idea in writing. Particularly interested in articles relating to events and developments in contemporary London, and about people working in the capital. All features are illustrated, so ideas with picture opportunities are particularly welcome.

Image Magazine
Upper Mounts, Northampton NN1 3HR
☎01604 231122   Fax 01604 233000
Owner *Northamptonshire Newspapers Ltd*
Editor *Ruth Supple*
Circulation 12,000

FOUNDED 1905. MONTHLY general interest regional magazine. No unsolicited mss. Approach by phone or in writing with ideas. No fiction.
   Features Local issues, personalities, businesses, etc., of Northamptonshire, Bedfordshire, Buckinghamshire interest. Maximum 500 words. *Payment* £60.
   News No hard news as such, just monthly diary column.
   Other Regulars on motoring, fashion, beauty, lifestyle, travel and horoscopes. Maximum 500 words. *Payment* £60.

In Britain
Haymarket House, 1 Oxendon Street, London SW1Y 4EE
☎0171 925 2544   Fax 0171 976 1088
Owner *Premier Magazines*
Editor *Andrea Spain*
Circulation 40,000

MONTHLY. Travel magazine of the British Tourist Authority. Articles vary from 1000 to 1500 words. Approach in writing with ideas and samples – not much opportunity for unsolicited work.

Independent Magazine
See under **National Newspapers (The Independent)**

Infusion
16 Trinity Churchyard, Guildford, Surrey
GU1 3RR
☎01483 562888   Fax 01483 302732
Publisher *Bond Clarkson Russell*
Editor *Lorna Swainson*
Circulation 1.5 million

FOUNDED 1986. ISSUED ANNUALLY. Sponsored
by the Tea Council. Features all subjects related to tea. All editorial features are commissioned. Approach with ideas only in writing.

Interzone: Science Fiction & Fantasy
217 Preston Drove, Brighton, East Sussex
BN1 6FL
☎01273 504710
Owner/Editor *David Pringle*
Circulation 10,000

FOUNDED 1982. MONTHLY magazine of science
fiction and fantasy. Unsolicited mss welcome
'from writers who have a knowledge of the magazine and its contents'. S.a.e. essential for return.
  Fiction 2000–6000 words. *Payment* £30 per
1000 words.
  Features Book/film reviews, interviews with
writers and occasional short articles. Length by
arrangement. *Payment* negotiable.

Investors Chronicle
Greystoke Place, Fetter Lane, London
EC4A 1ND
☎0171 405 6969   Fax 0171 405 5276
Owner *Pearson*
Editor *Ceri Jones*
Surveys Editor *Faith Glasgow*
Circulation 61,246

FOUNDED 1860. WEEKLY. Opportunities for
freelance contributors in the survey section
only. All approaches should be made in writing. Over forty surveys are published each year
on a wide variety of subjects, generally with a
financial, business or investment emphasis.
Copies of survey list and synopses of individual
surveys are obtainable from the surveys editor.
  Payment negotiable.

J17
Endeavour House, 189 Shaftesbury Avenue,
London WC2H 8JG
☎0171 208 3408   Fax 0171 208 3590
Owner *EMAP Elan Publications*
Editor *Ally Oliver*
Circulation 242,590

FOUNDED 1983. MONTHLY. News, articles and
quizzes of interest to girls aged 13–17. Ideas are
sought in all areas. Prospective contributors
should send ideas to the features editor.
  Beauty *Lara Williamson*
  Features *Sarah Pyper*
  Music/News *Sarra Manning*
  Payment by arrangement.

Jane's Defence Weekly
Sentinel House, 163 Brighton Road,
Coulsdon, Surrey CR5 2NH
☎0181 700 3700   Fax 0181 763 1007
Owner *Jane's Information Group*
Publishing Director *Alan Condron*
Editor *Clifford Beale*
Circulation 21,016

FOUNDED 1984. WEEKLY. No unsolicited mss.
Approach in writing with ideas in the first
instance.
  Features Current defence topics (politics,
strategy, equipment, industry) of worldwide
interest. No history pieces. Maximum 2000
words.

Jazz Journal International
1–5 Clerkenwell Road, London EC1M 5PA
☎0171 608 1348   Fax 0171 608 1292
Owner *Jazz Journal Ltd*
Editor-in-Chief *Eddie Cook*
Circulation 10,000+

FOUNDED 1948. MONTHLY. A specialised jazz
magazine, mainly for record collectors, principally using expert contributors whose work is
known to the editor. Unsolicited mss not welcome, with the exception of news material (for
which no payment is made). It is not a gig
guide, nor a free reference source for students.

Jersey Now
PO Box 582, Five Oaks, St Saviour, Jersey,
Channel Islands JE4 8XQ
☎01534 611600   Fax 01534 611610
Owner *MSP Publishing*
Production Manager *Simon Petulla*
Circulation 10,000

FOUNDED 1984. SEASONAL lifestyle magazine
with features on homes, leisure, motoring,
fashion, beauty, health, local issues and travel.
No fiction. No unsolicited mss. Approach
by phone in the first instance.

Jewish Chronicle
25 Furnival Street, London EC4A 1JT
☎0171 415 1500   Fax 0171 405 9040
Owner *Kessler Foundation*
Editor *Edward J. Temko*

Circulation 50,000

WEEKLY. Unsolicited mss welcome if 'the specific interests of our readership are borne in mind by writers'. Approach in writing, except for urgent current news items. No fiction. Maximum 1500 words for all material.
   Features *Gerald Jacobs*
   Leisure/Lifestyle *Alan Montague*
   Home News *Barry Toberman*
   Foreign News *Joseph Millis*
   Supplements *Angela Kiverstein*
   Payment negotiable.

Jewish Quarterly
PO Box 2078, London W1A 1JR
☎0171 629 5004   Fax 0171 629 5110
Publisher *Jewish Literary Trust Ltd*
Editor *Matthew Reisz*

FOUNDED 1953. QUARTERLY illustrated magazine featuring Jewish literature and fiction, politics, art, music, film, poetry, history, dance, community, autobiography, Hebrew, Yiddish, Israel and the Middle East, Judaism, interviews, Zionism, philosophy and holocaust studies. Features a major books and arts section. Unsolicited mss welcome but letter or phone call preferred in first instance.

Jewish Telegraph
Jewish Telegraph Group of Newspapers, 11 Park Hill, Bury Old Road, Prestwich, Manchester M25 0HH
☎0161 740 9321   Fax 0161 740 9325
Editor *Paul Harris*
Circulation 16,000

FOUNDED 1950. WEEKLY publication with local, national and international news and features. (Separate editions published for Manchester, Leeds, Liverpool and Glasgow.) Unsolicited features on Jewish humour and history welcome.

The Journal Magazines (Norfolk, Suffolk, Cambridgeshire)
The Old Eagle, Market Place, Dereham, Norfolk NR19 2AP
☎01362 699699   Fax 01362 699606
Owner *Hawksmere plc*
Editor *Pippa Bastin*
Circulation 9000 each

FOUNDED 1990. MONTHLY magazines covering items of local interest – history, people, conservation, business, places, food and wine, fashion, homes and sport.
   Features 750 words maximum, plus pictures. Approach the editor by phone with ideas in the first instance.

Just Seventeen
See **J17**

Kennel Gazette
Kennel Club, 1–5 Clarges Street, Piccadilly, London W1Y 8AB
☎0171 493 6651   Fax 0171 495 6162
Owner *Kennel Club*
Editor *Charles Colborn*
Circulation 10,000

FOUNDED 1873. MONTHLY concerning dogs and their breeding. Unsolicited mss welcome.
   Features Maximum 2500 words.
   News Maximum 500 words.
   Payment £70 per 1000 words.

Kent Life
Dateam Publishing, Fairmeadow, Maidstone, Kent ME14 1NG
☎01622 687031   Fax 01622 757646
Publisher *Datateam Publishing*
Editor *Roderick Cooper*
Circulation 10,000

FOUNDED 1962. MONTHLY. Strong Kent interest plus fashion, food, books, wildlife, motoring, property, sport, interiors with local links. Unsolicited mss welcome. Interested in anything with a genuine Kent connection. No fiction or non-Kentish subjects. Approach in writing with ideas. Maximum length 1500 words.
   Payment negotiable.

The Lady
39–40 Bedford Street, Strand, London WC2E 9ER
☎0171 379 4717   Fax 0171 497 2137
Owner *T. G. A. Bowles*
Editor *Arline Usden*
Circulation 50,130

FOUNDED 1885. WEEKLY. Unsolicited mss are accepted provided they are not on the subject of politics or religion, or on topics covered by staff writers, i.e. fashion and beauty, health, cookery, household, gardening, finance and shopping.
   Features Well-researched pieces on British and foreign travel, historical subjects or events; interviews and profiles and other general interest topics. Maximum 1000 words for illustrated articles; 900 words for one-page features; 450 words for first-person 'Viewpoint' pieces. All material should be addressed to the editor. Photographs supporting features may be supplied as colour transparencies or b&w prints.

Lakeland Walker
8 Faircroft, 37 St Andrews Grove, London
N16 5NJ
☎0181 809 2338

Owner *Raven Marketing Group*
Editors *Les Douglas, David Sharp*

FOUNDED 1996. QUARTERLY. News and features relating to the Lake District and walking in the area – wildlife, local history, places to visit, local transport. Maximum 1000–1500 words. Unsolicited material welcome.

Land Rover World
Link House, Dingwall Road, Croydon, Surrey
CR9 2TA
☎0181 686 2599   Fax 0181 781 6042

Owner *Link House Magazines Ltd*
Editor *John Carroll*
Circulation 30,000

FOUNDED 1993. MONTHLY. Incorporates *Practical Land Rover World*. Unsolicited material welcome, especially if supported by high-quality illustrations. 'Editorial policy is to encourage and support unknown writers and beginners wherever possible.'
  Features All articles with a Land Rover theme of interest. Potential contributors are strongly advised to examine previous issues before starting work.
  Payment negotiable.

Learning Resources Journal/ Learning Resources News
5 White Hart Lane, Wistaston, Crewe,
Cheshire CW2 8EX
☎01270 568550   Fax 0161 247 6370

Owner *Learning Resources Development Group*
Editor *David Scott*

THRICE-YEARLY publications. The Journal publishes articles by those involved in the management of resources in modern academic libraries and custom-built learning resource centres. The problems of identifying the resources needed to maintain the curriculum in higher, further and school level education are discussed. The main aim of the News is to provide information on the availability of resource management tools, products and services. Resource managers and providers are encouraged to send information about their work/products to the editor.

Leisure Vehicle Times
Golden Boot Chambers, 27 Gabriels Hill,
Maidstone, Kent ME15 6HX
☎01622 670377   Fax 01622 670377

Owner *Déésse Media*

Editor *Dave Randle*
Circulation 85,000

FOUNDED 1997. Colour magazine for leisure motorists. 'More scope for freelancers as title becomes established.' Approach by 'phone or letter/fax with ideas.

Let's Go Coarse Fishing Magazine
Temple Building, Railway Terrace, Rugby,
Warwickshire CV21 3EJ
☎01788 535218   Fax 01788 541845

Owner *David Hall Publishing Ltd*
Editor *John Hunter*
Circulation 50,000

FOUNDED 1985. MONTHLY. Unsolicited mss welcome but initial approach by phone or in writing preferred.
  Features Any general coarse angling interest accepted. Length 1000–2000 words plus photos.
  Reviews Product reviews welcome (include photos).
  Payment variable.

Lexikon
PO Box 754, Stoke-on-Trent, Staffordshire
ST1 4BU
☎01782 205060   Fax 01782 285331
E-mail: lexikon@anderson.karoo.co.uk

Editors *Francis Anderson, Alan Barrett,*
  Roger Bradley, Rosemary Munden

'Sharp, discerning prose, giving writers in the UK and abroad the opportunity to share their work and exchange new ideas.' Poetry, short stories, critical articles, book reviews plus regular competitions with cash prizes. Maximum of 2000 words for short stories; maximum of 60 lines for poetry. Please enclose s.a.e. with all submissions. Subscription: £8 for 4 issues available in print, disk (ASCII/WP), e-mail and on audiocassette. *Payment* complimentary copies.

Liberal Democrat News
4 Cowley Street, London SW1P 3NB
☎0171 222 7999   Fax 0171 222 7904

Owner *Liberal Democrats*
Editor *David Boyle*

FOUNDED 1988. WEEKLY. As with the political parties, this is the result of the merger of *Liberal News* (1946) and *The Social Democrat* (1981). Political and social topics of interest to party members and their supporters. Unsolicited contributions welcome.
  Features Maximum 800 words.
  News Maximum 350 words.
  No payment.

Lincolnshire Life

County Life Ltd, PO Box 81, Lincoln
LN1 1HD
☎01522 527127   Fax 01522 560035

Publisher *A.L. Robinson*
Executive Editor *Jez Ashberry*
Circulation 10,000

FOUNDED 1961. MONTHLY county magazine
featuring geographically relevant articles. Max.
1000–1500 words. Contributions supported by
three or four good-quality photographs are
always welcome. Approach in writing.
Payment varies.

The List

14 High Street, Edinburgh EH1 1TE
☎0131 558 1191   Fax 0131 557 8500

Owner *The List Ltd*
Publisher *Robin Hodge*
Editor *Kathleen Morgan*
Circulation 15,000

FOUNDED 1985. FORTNIGHTLY. Events guide
covering Glasgow and Edinburgh. Interviews
and profiles of people working in film, theatre,
music and the arts. Maximum 1200 words. No
unsolicited mss. Phone with ideas. News material tends to be handled in-house.
Payment £100.

Literary Review

44 Lexington Street, London W1R 3LH
☎0171 437 9392   Fax 0171 734 1844

Owner *Namara Group*
Editor *Auberon Waugh*
Circulation 15,000

FOUNDED 1979. MONTHLY. Publishes book
reviews (commissioned), features and articles on
literary subjects. Prospective contributors are
best advised to contact the editor in writing.
Unsolicited mss not welcome. Runs a monthly
competition, the Literary Review Grand Poetry
Competition, on a given theme. Open to subscribers only. Details published in the magazine.
Payment varies.

Living France

The Picture House, 79 High Street, Olney,
Buckinghamshire MK46 4EF
☎01234 713203   Fax 01234 711507

Editor *Trevor Yorke*

FOUNDED 1989. TEN ISSUES YEARLY. A Franco-
phile magazine catering for those with a passion
for France, French culture and lifestyle.
Editorial covers all aspects of holidaying, living
and working in France. Property section for

those owning or wishing to buy a property in
France. No unsolicited mss; approach in writing with an idea.

Llais Llyfrau/Books in Wales

Cyngor Llyfrau Cymru/Welsh Books
Council, Castell Brychan, Aberystwyth,
Ceredigion SY23 2JB
☎01970 624151   Fax 01970 625385

Owner *Cyngor Llyfrau Cymru/*
    Welsh Books Council
Editors *Katie Gramich, Hedd ap Emlyn, Lorna
Herbert-Egan*

FOUNDED 1961. QUARTERLY bilingual magazine containing articles of relevance to the
book trade in Wales plus reviews of new books
and comprehensive lists of recent titles. A complete section devoted to children's books
appears every quarter. No unsolicited mss. All
initial approaches should be made in writing.

Features *Hedd ap Emlyn* (Welsh)/*Katie
Gramich* (English) Each edition features a
writer's diary in Welsh and English, plus articles on books, publishing, the media etc. Most
items commissioned. Articles on the literature
of Wales are welcome, in either language.

Special pages *Lorna Herbert-Egan* Children's
Books section – latest Welsh-language and
Welsh-interest books reviewed.
Payment £30 maximum.

Loaded

King's Reach Tower, Stamford Street,
London SE1 9LS
☎0171 261 5562   Fax 0171 261 5557
E-mail: kate-jacobs@ipc.co.uk

Owner *IPC Magazines*
Editor *Derek Harbison*
Circulation 441,567

FOUNDED 1994. MONTHLY men's lifestyle
magazine featuring music, sport, sex, humour,
travel, fashion, hard news and popular culture.
Will consider material which comes into these
categories; approach in writing in the first
instance. No fiction, poetry or articles on relationships.

Logos

5 Beechwood Drive, Marlow,
Buckinghamshire SL7 2DH
☎01628 477577   Fax 01628 477577

Owner *Whurr Publishers Ltd*
Editor *Gordon Graham*
Associate Editor *Betty Graham*

FOUNDED 1990. QUARTERLY. Aims to 'deal in
depth with issues which unite, divide, excite

and concern the world of books,' with an international perspective. Each issue contains 6–8 articles of between 3500–7000 words. Hopes to establish itself as a forum for contrasting views. Suggestions and ideas for contributions are welcome, and should be addressed to the editor. 'Guidelines for Contributors' available. Contributors write from their experience as authors, publishers, booksellers, librarians, etc.

No payment.

London Magazine
30 Thurloe Place, London SW7 2HQ
☎0171 589 0618

Owner/Editor *Alan Ross*
Deputy Editor *Jane Rye*
Circulation 4500

FOUNDED 1954. BI-MONTHLY paperback journal providing an eclectic forum for literary talent, thanks to the dedication of Alan Ross. *The Times* once said that '*London Magazine* is far and away the most readable and level-headed, not to mention best value for money, of the literary magazines'. Today it boasts the publication of early works by the likes of William Boyd, Graham Swift and Ben Okri among others. The broad spectrum of interests includes art, memoirs, travel, poetry, criticism, theatre, music, cinema, short stories and essays, and book reviews. Unsolicited mss welcome; s.a.e. essential. About 150–200 unsolicited mss are received weekly.

Fiction Maximum 5000 words.
Payment £100 maximum.
Annual Subscription £28.50 or $67.

London Review of Books
28 Little Russell Street, London WC1A 2HN
☎0171 209 1101   Fax 0171 209 1102

Owner *LRB Ltd*
Editor *Mary-Kay Wilmers*
Circulation 25,585

FOUNDED 1979. FORTNIGHTLY. Reviews, essays and articles on political, literary, cultural and scientific subjects. Also poetry. Unsolicited contributions welcome (approximately 50 received each week). No pieces under 2000 words. Contact the editor in writing. Please include s.a.e.

Payment £100 per 1000 words; poems £50.

Looking Good
Upper Mounts, Northampton NN1 3HR
☎01604 231122   Fax 01604 233000

Owner *Northamptonshire Newspapers Ltd*
Editor *Ruth Supple*

Circulation 6000

FOUNDED 1984. QUARTERLY county lifestyle magazine of Northamptonshire. Contributions are not required as all work is done in-house.

Looks
Endeavour House, 189 Shaftesbury Avenue, London WC2H 8JG
☎0171 437 9011   Fax 0171 208 3586

Owner *EMAP Elan*
Editor *Eleni Kyriacou*
Circulation 115,479

MONTHLY celebrity-led magazine for young women aged 16–24, with fashion, beauty and hair, as well as general interest features, interviews, giveaways, etc. Freelance writers are occasionally used in all areas of the magazine. Contact the editor with ideas.

Payment varies.

Loving Holiday Special
PO Box 435A, Surbiton, Surrey KT6 6YT

Owner *Perfectly Formed Publishing Ltd*
Editor *Jo Pink*
Circulation 40,000

ANNUAL. Uncliched summer love stories for women under 30. Story lengths 1000–4000 words. Write with an s.a.e. for a style guide (January/February only) before putting pen to paper.

M & E Design
Quadrant House, The Quadrant, Sutton, Surrey SM2 5AS
☎0181 652 3115   Fax 0181 652 8972

Owner *Reed Business Information*
Editor *Steve Hobson*
Circulation 8,000

FOUNDED 1996. MONTHLY. Aimed at mechanical and electrical consulting engineers and designers.

Machine Knitting Monthly
PO Box 1479, Maidenhead, Berkshire SL6 8YX
☎01628 783080   Fax 01628 633250

Owner *Machine Knitting Monthly Ltd*
Editor *Anne Smith*

FOUNDED 1986. MONTHLY. Unsolicited mss considered 'as long as they are applicable to this specialist publication. We have our own regular contributors each month but we're always willing to look at new ideas from other writers.' Approach in writing in first instance.

Management Today
174 Hammersmith Road, London W6 7JP
☎0171 413 4566
E-mail: management.today@haynet.com
Owner *Haymarket Business Publications Ltd*
Acting Editor *Dominic Mills*
Circulation 89,414

General business topics and features. Ideas welcome. Send brief synopsis to the editor.
Payment about £300 per 1000 words.

marie claire
2 Hatfields, London SE1 9PG
☎0171 261 5240   Fax 0171 261 5277
Owner *European Magazines Ltd*
Editor *Juliet Warkentin*
Circulation 415,550

FOUNDED 1988. MONTHLY. An intelligent glossy magazine for women, with strong international features and fashion. No unsolicited mss. Approach with ideas in writing. No fiction.
Features *Fiona Neill* Detailed proposals for feature ideas should be accompanied by samples of previous work.

Market Newsletter
Focus House, 497 Green Lanes, London N13 4BP
☎0181 882 3315   Fax 0181 886 5174
Owner *Bureau of Freelance Photographers*
Editor *John Tracy*
Deputy Editor *Stewart Gibson*
Circulation 7,000

FOUNDED 1965. MONTHLY. News of current markets – magazines, books, cards, calendars etc – and the type of submissions (mainly photographs) they are currently looking for. Includes details of new magazine launches, publication revamps etc. Also profiles of particular markets and photographers. Circulated to members of the Bureau of Freelance Photographers (annual membership fee: £40 UK; £50 Overseas). Limited scope for non-members to contribute.

Marketing Week
St Giles House, 50 Poland Street, London W1V 4AX
☎0171 970 4000   Fax 0171 970 4298
Owner *Centaur Communications*
Editor *Stuart Smith*
Circulation 39,000

WEEKLY trade magazine of the marketing industry. Features on all aspects of the business,
written in a newsy and up-to-the-minute style. Approach with ideas in the first instance.
Features *Tom O'Sullivan*
Payment negotiable.

Match
Bretton Court, Bretton, Peterborough, Cambridgeshire PE3 8DZ
☎01733 260333   Fax 01733 465206
Owner *EMAP Pursuit Publications*
Editor *Chris Hunt*
Circulation 145,749

FOUNDED 1979. Popular WEEKLY football magazine aimed at 10–15-year-olds. Most material is generated in-house by a strong news and features team. Some freelance material used if suitable, apart from photographs. No submissions without prior consultation with editor, either by phone or in writing.
Features/News Good and original material is always considered. Maximum 500 words.
Payment negotiable.

Matrix
See **British Science Fiction Association** under **Professional Associations**

Maxim
19 Bolsover Street, London W1P 7HJ
☎0171 631 1433   Fax 0171 917 7663
Owner *Dennis Publishing*
Editor *Nigel Ambrose*
Circulation 249,096

ESTABLISHED 1995. MONTHLY glossy men's lifestyle magazine featuring sex, travel, health, finance, motoring and fashion. No fiction or poetry. Approach in writing in the first instance, sending outlines of ideas only together with examples of published work. Some scope for first-person accounts.

Mayfair
2 Archer Street, Piccadilly Circus, London W1V 8JJ
☎0171 292 8000   Fax 0171 734 5030
Owner *Paul Raymond Publications*
Editor *Steve Shields*
Circulation 331,760

FOUNDED 1966. THIRTEEN ISSUES YEARLY. Unsolicited material accepted if suitable to the magazine. Interested in features and humour aimed at men aged 20–30. For style, length, etc., writers are advised to study the magazine. 'No more romantic fiction, we beseech you!'

Mayfair Times

102 Mount Street, London W1X 5HF
☎0171 629 3378　　　Fax 0171 629 9303
Owner *Mayfair Times Ltd*
Editor *Stephen Goringe*
Circulation 20,000

FOUNDED 1985. MONTHLY. Features on Mayfair of interest to both residential and commercial readers. Unsolicited mss welcome.

Medal News

Token Publishing Ltd, PO Box 14, Honiton, Devon EX14 9YP
☎01404 46972　　　Fax 01404 831895
Owners *J. W. Mussell, Carol Hartman*
Editor *Diana Birch*
Circulation 4500

FOUNDED 1989. MONTHLY. Unsolicited material welcome but initial approach by phone or in writing preferred.

Features Only interested in articles from well-informed authors 'who know the subject and do their homework'. Maximum 2500 words.
Payment £20 per 1000 words.

Media Week

Quantum House, 19 Scarbrook Road, Croydon, Surrey CR9 1LX
☎0181 565 4200　　　Fax 0181 565 4394
Owner *Quantam*
Editor *Conor Dignam*
Circulation 13,944

FOUNDED 1986. WEEKLY trade magazine. UK and international coverage on all aspects of commercial media. No unsolicited mss. Approach in writing with ideas.

Melody Maker

26th Floor, King's Reach Tower, Stamford Street, London SE1 9LS
☎0171 261 6229　　　Fax 0171 261 6706
Owner *IPC Magazines Ltd*
Editor *Mark Sutherland*
Circulation 42,105

WEEKLY. Freelance contributors used on this tabloid magazine competitor of the *NME*. Opportunities exist in reviewing and features.

Features *Ian Watson* A large in-house team, plus around six regulars, produce most feature material.

Reviews *Sharon O'Connell* (Live), *Neil Mason* (Albums) Sample reviews, whether published or not, welcome on pop, rock, soul, funk, etc.
Payment negotiable.

Mensa Quest

Pageant Publishing Ltd, 105 Ladbroke Grove, London W11 1PG
☎0171 606 8480　　　Fax 0171 616 8481
Owner *Pageant Publishing Ltd*
Publisher/Managing Director *Barry Goodman*
Editor *Charlotte Eagar*
Production *Sonia Hunt*
Circulation 40,000

FOUNDED March 1998. MONTHLY mind-bending magazine that invites people to assess their own intelligence. 'Informative and fun with mind-games and features.'

MiniWorld Magazine

Link House, Dingwall Road, Croydon, Surrey CR9 2TA
☎0181 686 2599　　　Fax 0181 781 1158
Owner *Link House Magazines Ltd*
Editor *Monty Watkins*
Circulation 50,000

FOUNDED 1991. MONTHLY car magazine devoted to the Mini. Unsolicited material welcome but prospective contributors are advised to make initial contact by phone.

Features Restoration, tuning tips, technical advice and sporting events. Readers' cars and product news. Length by arrangement.
Payment negotiable.

Minx

Endeavour House, 189 Shaftesbury Avenue, London WC2H 8JG
☎0171 208 3428　　　Fax 0171 208 3323
Owner *EMAP*
Editor *Sam Baker*
Circulation 160,088

FOUNDED 1996. MONTHLY lifestyle magazine for young women. Interested in receiving ideas for features; approach in writing in the first instance. No fiction.

Mizz

King's Reach Tower, Stamford Street, London SE1 9LS
☎0171 261 6319　　　Fax 0171 261 6032
Owner *IPC Magazines Ltd*
Editor *Lucy Tobin*
Circulation 110,441

FOUNDED 1985. FORTNIGHTLY magazine for the 12–17-year-old girl. Freelance articles welcome on real life, human interest stories and emotional issues. Also quizzes. All material should be addressed to the features editor.

Features *Julie Burniston* Approach in writing,

with synopsis, for feature copy; send sample writing with letter for general approach.

Fiction Maximum 1000 words.

Model Railway Enthusiast
8 Cornelian Drive, Scarborough, North Yorkshire YO11 3AJ
☎01723 506326   Fax 01723 506326

Owner *Garnett Dickinson Publishing*
Editor *Pat Hammond*
Circulation 20,000

FOUNDED 1993. MONTHLY magazine which is the only national model railway magazine in the UK catering specifically for model railway collectors as well as average railway modellers. Articles with good photographs (prints or drawings preferred) on the subject of collecting or modelling are welcome but ideas should be discussed first with the editor.

Payment £40 per 1000 words; £5 per picture published.

Mojo
Mappin House, 4 Winsley Street, London W1N 7AR
☎0171 436 1515   Fax 0171 312 8926

Owner *EMAP-Metro*
Editor *Mat Snow*
Circulation 70,428

FOUNDED 1993. MONTHLY magazine containing features, reviews and news stories about rock music and its influences. Receives about five mss per day.

Features Amateur writers discouraged except as providers of source material, contacts, etc. *Payment* negotiable.

News All verifiable, relevant stories considered. *Payment* approx. £150 per 1000 words.

Reviews Write to Reviews Editor with relevant specimen material. *Payment* approx. £150 per 1000 words.

Moneywise
RD Publications Ltd, 11 Westferry Circus, Canary Wharf, London E14 4HE
☎0171 715 8469   Fax 0171 715 8725

Owner *Reader's Digest Association*
Editor *Matthew Vincent*
Circulation 105,000

FOUNDED 1990. MONTHLY. Unsolicited mss with s.a.e. welcome but initial approach in writing preferred.

More!
Endeavour House, 189 Shaftesbury Avenue, London WC2H 8JG
☎0171 437 9011   Fax 0171 285 3595

Owner *EMAP Elan Publications*
Editor *Tammy Butt*
Features Editor *Nigel May*
Circulation 343,150

FOUNDED 1988. FORTNIGHTLY women's magazine aimed at the working woman aged 18–24. Features on sex and relationships plus news. Most items are commissioned; approach features editor with idea. Prospective contributors are strongly advised to study the magazine's style before submitting anything.

Mother and Baby
Endeavour House, 189 Shaftesbury Avenue, London WC2H 8JG
☎0171 437 9011   Fax 0171 208 3584

Owner *EMAP Elan Publications*
Acting Editor *Melanie Deeprose*
Circulation 100,632

FOUNDED 1956. MONTHLY. Unsolicited mss welcome, about practical baby and childcare. Personal 'viewpoint' pieces are considered. Approach by phone or in writing.

Motor Boat and Yachting
King's Reach Tower, Stamford Street, London SE1 9LS
☎0171 261 5333   Fax 0171 261 5419

Owner *IPC Magazines Ltd*
Editor *Alan Harper*
Circulation 19,625

FOUNDED 1904. MONTHLY for those interested in motor boats and motor cruising.

Features *Alan Harper* Cruising features and practical features especially welcome. Illustrations (mostly colour) are just as important as text. Maximum 3000 words. *Payment* £100 per 1000 words or by arrangement.

News *Dennis O'Neill* Factual pieces. Maximum 200 words. *Payment* up to £50 per item.

Motorcaravan Motorhome Monthly (MMM)
14 Eastfield Close, Andover, Hampshire SP10 2QP
Fax 01264 324794

Owner *Sanglier Publications Ltd*
Editor *Mike Jago*
Circulation 24,468

FOUNDED 1966. MONTHLY. 'There's no money in motorcaravan journalism but for those wishing to cut their first teeth...' Unsolicited mss welcome if relevant, but ideas in writing preferred in first instance.

Features Caravan site reports. Maximum 500 words.

Travel Motorcaravanning trips (home and overseas). Maximum 2000 words.

News Short news items for miscellaneous pages. Maximum 200 words.

Fiction Must be motorcaravan-related and include artwork/photos. Max. 2000 words.

Special pages DIY – modifications to motorcaravans. Maximum 1500 words.

Owner Reports Contributions welcome from motorcaravan owners. Contact the Editor for requirements. Maximum 2000 words.

Payment varies.

Ms London

7–9 Rathbone Street, London W1P 1AF
☎0171 636 6651   Fax 0171 255 2352

Owner *Independent Magazines*
Editor-in-Chief *Bill Williamson*
Editor *Cathy Howes*
Circulation 85,000

FOUNDED 1968. WEEKLY. Aimed at working women in London, aged 18–35. Unsolicited mss must be accompanied by s.a.e.

Features Content is varied and ambitious, ranging from stage and film interviews to issues, fashion, careers, relationships, homebuying and furnishing. Approach in writing only with ideas in the first instance and enclose sample of published writing. Material should be London-angled, sharp and fairly sophisticated in content. Maximum 1500 words. *Payment* about £130 per 1000 words.

News Handled in-house but follow-up feature ideas welcome.

Music Week

8 Montague Close, London SE1 9UR
☎0171 620 3636   Fax 0171 401 8035

Owner *Miller Freeman Entertainment*
Editor-in-Chief *Steve Redmond*
Editor *Selina Webb*
Circulation 13,900

Britain's only WEEKLY music business magazine also includes dance industry title *Record Mirror*. No unsolicited mss; approach in writing with ideas.

Features *Selina Webb* Analysis of specific music business events and trends. Max. 2000 words.

News Music industry news only. Maximum 350 words.

Musical Option

2 Princes Road, St Leonards on Sea, East Sussex TN37 6EL
☎01424 715167   Fax 01424 712214

Owner *Musical Option Ltd*

Editor *Denby Richards*
Circulation 5000

FOUNDED 1877. QUARTERLY with free supplement in intervening months. Classical music content, with topical features on music, musicians, festivals, etc., and reviews (concerts, festivals, opera, ballet, jazz, CDs, CD-Roms, videos, books and printed music). International readership. No unsolicited mss; commissions only. Ideas always welcome though; approach by phone or fax, giving telephone number. It should be noted that topical material has to be submitted six months prior to events. Not interested in review material, which is already handled by the magazine's own regular team of contributors.

Payment Negotiable.

Musical Times

☎0171 482 5697   Fax 0171 482 5697

Owner *The Musical Times Publications Ltd*
Editor *Antony Bye*

FOUNDED 1844. Scholarly journal with a practical approach to its subject. All material is commissioned.

My Weekly

80 Kingsway East, Dundee DD4 8SL
☎01382 223131   Fax 01382 452491

Owner *D. C. Thomson & Co. Ltd*
Editor *Harrison Watson*
Circulation 376,146

A traditional women's WEEKLY. D. C. Thomson has long had a policy of encouragement and help to new writers of promise. Ideas welcome. Approach in writing.

Features Particularly interested in human interest pieces (1000–1500 words) which by their very nature appeal to all age groups.

Fiction Three stories a week, ranging in content from the emotional to the off-beat and unexpected. 1500–4000 words. Also serials.

Payment negotiable.

The National Trust Magazine

36 Queen Anne's Gate, London SW1H 9AS
☎0171 222 9251   Fax 0171 222 5097

Owner *The National Trust*
Editor *Gina Guarnieri*
Circulation 2.3 million

FOUNDED 1968. THRICE-YEARLY. Conservation of historic houses, coast and countryside in England, Northern Ireland and Wales. No unsolicited mss. Approach in writing with ideas.

Natural World

Victory House, 14 Leicester Place, London
WC2H 7QH
☎0171 306 0304   Fax 0171 306 0314
Owner *River Publishing Ltd*
Editor *Sarah-Jane Forder*
Circulation 178,000

FOUNDED 1981. THRICE-YEARLY. Unsolicited
mss welcome if of high quality and relevant to
ideals of the magazine. Ideas in writing preferred. No poetry.

Features Popular but accurate articles on
British wildlife and the countryside, particularly projects associated with the local wildlife
trusts. Maximum 1500 words.

News Interested in national wildlife conservation issues, particularly those involving local
nature conservation or wildlife trusts.
Maximum 300 words.
Payment negotiable.

The Naturalist

c/o University of Bradford, Bradford,
West Yorkshire BD7 1DP
☎01274 384212   Fax 01274 384231
E-mail: m.r.d.seaward@bradford.ac.uk
Owner *Yorkshire Naturalists' Union*
Editor *Prof. M. R. D. Seaward*
Circulation 5000

FOUNDED 1875. QUARTERLY. Natural history,
biological and environmental sciences for a
professional and amateur readership. Unsolicited mss and b&w illustrations welcome. Particularly interested in material – scientific
papers – relating to the north of England.
No payment.

Nature

Porters South, 4–6 Crinan Street, London
N1 9XW
☎0171 833 4000
Owner *Macmillan Magazines Ltd*
Editor *Philip Campbell*
Circulation 57,762

Covers all fields of science, with articles and
news on science policy only. No features. Little
scope for freelance writers.

Needlecraft

30 Monmouth Street, Bath BA1 2BW
☎01225 442244   Fax 01225 732398
Owner *Future Publishing*
Editor *Sue Grant*
Circulation 57,011

FOUNDED 1991. MONTHLY. Needlework projects with full instructions covering cross-stitch,
needlepoint, embroidery, patchwork quilting
and lace. Will consider ideas or sketches for
projects covering any of the magazine's topics.
Initial approaches should be made in writing.

Features on the needlecraft theme. Discuss
ideas before sending complete mss. Maximum
1000 words.

Technical pages on 'how to' stitch, use
different threads, etc. Only suitable for experienced writers.
Payment negotiable.

New Beacon

224 Great Portland Street,
London W1N 6AA
☎0171 388 1266   Fax 0171 388 0945
Owner *Royal National Institute for the Blind*
Editor *Ann Lee*
Circulation 6000

FOUNDED 1917. MONTHLY (except August).
Published in print, braille and on tape and disk.
Unsolicited mss welcome. Approach with ideas
in writing. Personal experiences by writers who
have a visual impairment (partial sight or blind-
ness), and authoritative items by professionals or
volunteers working in the field of visual impairment welcome. Maximum 1500 words.
Payment negotiable.

New Christian Herald

Herald House, 96 Dominion Road,
Worthing, West Sussex BN14 8JP
☎01903 821082   Fax 01903 821081
Owner *Herald House Ltd*
Editor *Russ Bravo*
Circulation 20,000

WEEKLY. Evangelical, inter-denominational
Christian newspaper aimed at committed
Christians. News, bible-based comment and
incisive features. No poetry. Contributors'
guidelines available.
Payment Herald House rates.

New Humanist

Bradlaugh House, 47 Theobald's Road,
London WC1X 8SP
☎0171 430 1371   Fax 0171 430 1271
E-mail: jim.rpa@humanism.org.uk
Owner *Rationalist Press Association*
Editor *Jim Herrick*
Circulation 1500

FOUNDED 1885. QUARTERLY. Unsolicited mss
welcome. No fiction.

Features Articles with a humanist perspective welcome in the following fields: religion

(critical), humanism, human rights, philosophy, current events, literature, history and science. 2000–4000 words. *Payment* nominal, but negotiable.

Book reviews 750–1000 words, by arrangement with the editor.

New Impact
Anser House, Courtyard Offices, 3 High Street, Marlow, Bucks SL7 1AX
☎01628 475570   Fax 01628 475570
Owner *D. E. Sihera*
Editor *Elaine Sihera*
Features Editor *Karen Kennedy*
Circulation 10,000

FOUNDED 1993. BI-MONTHLY. Celebrates diversity, enterprise and achievement from a minority ethnic perspective. Unsolicited mss welcome. Interested in training, arts, features, personal achievement, small business features, profiles or personalities especially for a multicultural audience. Not interested in anything unconnected to training or business. Approach in writing with ideas. Promotes the British Diversity Awards each November and the Diversity Associates Register (DIVAS) among employers.

News Local training/business features – some opportunities. Maximum length 250 words. *Payment* negotiable.

Features Original, interesting pieces with a deliberate multicultural/diversity focus. Personal/professional successes and achievements welcome. Maximum length 1500 words. *Payment* negotiable.

Fiction Short stories, poems – especially from minority writers. Not interested in romantic/sexual narratives. Maximum length 1500 words. *Payment* negotiable.

Special Pages Interviews with personalities – especially Asian, African Caribbean. Maximum length 1200 words. *Payment* negotiable.

New Internationalist
55 Rectory Road, Oxford OX4 1BW
☎01865 728181   Fax 01865 793152
Owner *New Internationalist Trust*
Co-Editors *Vanessa Baird, Chris Brazier, David Ransom, Nikki van der Gaag*
Circulation 70,000

Radical and broadly leftist in approach, but unaligned. Concerned with world poverty and global issues of peace and politics, feminism and environmentalism, with emphasis on the Third World. Difficult to use unsolicited material as they work to a theme each month and

features are commissioned by the editor on that basis. The way in is to send examples of published or unpublished work; writers of interest are taken up. Unsolicited material for shorter articles could be used in the magazine's regular *Update* section.

New Musical Express
King's Reach Tower, Stamford Street, London SE1 9LS
☎0171 261 6472   Fax 0171 261 5185
Owner *IPC Magazines Ltd*
Editor *Steve Sutherland*
Circulation 100,093

Britain's best-selling musical WEEKLY. Freelancers used, but always for reviews in the first instance. Specialisation in areas of music (or film, which is also covered) is a help.

Reviews: Books *Stephen Dalton* **Film** *Stephen Dalton* **LPs** *John Robinson* **Live** *James Oldham*. Send in examples of work, either published or specially written samples.

New Nation
148 Cambridge Heath Road, London E1 5QJ
☎0171 702 8012   Fax 0171 702 7937
Owner *Ethnic Media Group*
Editor *Michael Eboda*
Circulation 30,000

FOUNDED 1996. WEEKLY community paper for the Black community in Britain. Interested in relevant general, local and international issues. Approach in writing with ideas for submission.

New Scientist
1st Floor, 151 Wardour Street, London W1V 4BN
☎0171 331 2701   Fax 0171 331 2777
Owner *Reed Business Information Ltd*
Editor *Dr Alun Anderson*
Circulation 127,030

FOUNDED 1956. WEEKLY. No unsolicited mss. Approach with ideas – one A4-page synopsis – by fax.

Features *Jeremy Webb* Commissions only, but good ideas welcome. Maximum 3500 words.

News *Peter Aldhous* Mostly commissions, but ideas for specialist news welcome. Maximum 1000 words.

Reviews *Maggie McDonald* Reviews are commissioned.

Forum *Richard Fifield* Unsolicited material welcome if of general/humorous interest and related to science. Maximum 1000 words.

Payment £200+ per 1000 words.

New Statesman

Victoria Station House, 191 Victoria Street, London SW1E 5NE
☎0171 828 1232   Fax 0171 828 1881
Publisher *Spence Neal*
Editor *Peter Wilby*
Deputy Editor *Jane Taylor*
Circulation 26,000

WEEKLY magazine, the result of a merger (May 1988) of *New Statesman* and *New Society*. Coverage of news, book reviews, arts, current affairs, politics and social reportage. Unsolicited contributions with s.a.e. will be considered. No short stories.
  Books *Peter Wilby*
  Arts *Laura Cummings*

New Welsh Review

Chapter Arts Centre, Market Road, Cardiff CF5 1QE
☎01222 665529   Fax 01222 665529
Owner *New Welsh Review Ltd*
Editor *Robin Reeves*
Circulation 1000

FOUNDED 1988. QUARTERLY Welsh literary magazine in the English language. Welcomes material of literary and cultural interest to Welsh readers and those with an interest in Wales. Approach in writing in the first instance.
  Features Max. 3000 words. *Payment* £20 per 1000 words.
  Fiction Max. 5000 words. *Payment* £40–80 average.
  News Max. 400 words. *Payment* £5–15.

New Woman

Endeavour House, 189 Shaftesbury Avenue, London WC2H 8JG
☎0171 957 8383   Fax 0171 930 7246
Owner *Hachette/EMAP Magazines Ltd*
Editor *Dawn Bébe*
Circulation 268,449

MONTHLY women's interest magazine. Re-launched and redesigned under new editor. Aimed at women aged 25–35. An 'entertaining, informative and intelligent' read. Main topics of interest include men, sex, love, health, careers, beauty and fashion. Uses mainly established freelancers but unsolicited ideas submitted in synopsis form will be considered. Welcomes ideas from male writers for humorous 'men's opinion' pieces.
  Features/News *Emma Marlin* Articles must be original and look at subjects or issues from a new or unusual perspective.
  Fashion *Corinna Kitchen*

The New Writer

PO Box 60, Cranbrook, Kent TN17 2ZR
☎01580 212626   Fax 01580 212041
Publisher *Merric Davidson*
Editor *Suzanne Ruthven*
Poetry Editor *Abi Hughes-Edwards*

FOUNDED 1996. Published MONTHLY following the merger between *Acclaim* and *Quartos* magazines. TNW continues to offer practical 'nuts and bolts' advice on poetry and prose but with the emphasis on *forward-looking* articles and features on all aspects of the written word that demonstrate the writer's grasp of contemporary writing and current editorial/publishing policies. Plenty of news, views, competitions, reviews and regional gossip in the Newsletter section; writers' guidelines available with s.a.e.
  Features Unsolicited mss welcome. Interested in lively, original articles on writing in its broadest sense. Approach in writing with ideas. Material is not returned unless accompanied by s.a.e. *Payment* £20 per 1000 words.
  Fiction Publishes short-listed entries from the **Ian St James Awards** and subscriber-only submissions. *Payment* £10 per story.
  Poetry Unsolicited poetry welcome. Both short and long unpublished poems, providing they are original and interesting. *Payment* £3 per poem.

Newcastle Life

See **North East Times**

19

King's Reach Tower, Stamford Street, London SE1 9LS
☎0171 261 6410   Fax 0171 261 7634
Owner *IPC Magazines Ltd*
Editor *Lee Kynaston*
Circulation 170,716

MONTHLY women's magazine aimed at 16–20-year-olds. A little different from the usual teen magazine mix: *19* are now aiming for a 50/50 balance between fashion/lifestyle aspects and newsier, meatier material, e.g. women in prison, boys, abortion, etc. 40% of the magazine's feature material is commissioned, ordinarily from established freelancers. 'But we're always keen to see bold, original, vigorous writing from people just starting out.'
  Features Approach in writing with ideas.

North East Times

Tattler House, Beech Avenue, Fawdon, Newcastle upon Tyne NE3 4LA
☎0191 284 4495   Fax 0191 285 9606

Owner *Chris Robinson (Publishing) Ltd*
Editor *Chris Robinson*
Circulation 10,000

MONTHLY county magazine incorporating *Newcastle Life*. No unsolicited mss. Approach with ideas in writing. Not interested in any material that is not applicable to ABC1 readers.

The North
See **Poetry Magazines**

Nursing Times
Porters South, Crinan Street,
London N1 9XW
☎0171 843 4600   Fax 0171 843 4633
Owner *EMAP Healthcare*
Editor *Tricia Reid*
Circulation 80,670

A large proportion of *Nursing Times*' feature content is from unsolicited contributions sent on spec. Pieces on all aspects of nursing and health care, both practical and theoretical, written in a lively and contemporary way, are welcome. Commissions also.

Payment varies/NUJ rates apply to commissioned material from union members only.

Office Secretary
Brookmead House, Thorney Leys Business Park, Witney, Oxfordshire OX8 7GE
☎01993 775545   Fax 01993 778884
Owner *Peebles Publishing Group*
Editor *Elizabeth Topping*
Circulation 60,000

FOUNDED 1986. QUARTERLY. Features articles of interest to secretaries and personal assistants aged 25–60. No unsolicited mss.

Features Informative pieces on current affairs, health, food, fashion, hotel, travel, motoring, office and employment-related topics. Length 1000 words.
Payment by negotiation.

OK! Magazine
The Northern & Shell Tower, City Harbour,
London E14 9GL
☎0171 308 5391   Fax 0171 301 5082
Owner *Richard Desmond*
Editor *Sharon Ring*
Circulation 226,504

FOUNDED 1996. WEEKLY celebrity-based magazine. Welcomes interviews and pictures on well known personalities, and ideas for general features. Approach by phone or fax in the first instance.

The Oldie
45–46 Poland Street, London W1V 4AU
☎0171 734 2225   Fax 0171 734 2226
E-mail: theoldie@theoldie.demon.co.uk
Owner *Oldie Publications Ltd*
Editor *Richard Ingrams*
Circulation 45,000

FOUNDED 1992. MONTHLY general interest magazine with a strong humorous slant for the older person. Submissions welcome; enclose s.a.e.

OLS (Open Learning Systems) News
11 Malford Grove, Gilwern, Abergavenny,
Gwent NP7 0RN
☎01873 830872   Fax 01873 830872
E-mail: GSSE@zoo.co.uk
Owner/Editor *David P. Bosworth*
Circulation 800

FOUNDED 1980. QUARTERLY dealing with the application of open, flexible, distance learning and supported self-study at all educational/training levels. Interested in open-access learning and the application of educational technology to learning situations. Case studies particularly welcome. Not interested in theory of education alone, the emphasis is strictly on applied policies and trends.

Features Learning programmes (how they are organised); student/learner-eye views of educational and training programmes with an open-access approach. Approach the editor by phone or in writing.
No payment for 'news' items. Focus items will negotiate.

On the Ball
Moondance Publications, The Design Works,
William Street, Gateshead, Tyne and Wear
NE10 0JP
☎0191 420 8383   Fax 0191 420 4950
Owner *Moondance Publications Ltd*
Editor *Pippa Turnbull*
Circulation 30,000

FOUNDED 1996. MONTHLY. The only magazine for women football players. Contributions welcome.

Features *Andrew Mullen* International reports, player and team profiles, diet, health and fitness, tactics, training advice, fund-raising, play improvement. 1500 words maximum.

News *Wilf Frith* Match reports, team news, transfers, injuries, results and fixtures. 600 words maximum.
Payment negotiable.

Opera

1A Mountgrove Road, London N5 2LU
☎0171 359 1037   Fax 0171 354 2700
E-mail: operamag@classic.msn.com
Website: http://www.opera.co.uk

Owner *Opera Magazine Ltd*
Editor *Rodney Milnes*
Circulation 11,500

FOUNDED 1950. MONTHLY review of the current opera scene. Almost all articles are commissioned and unsolicited mss are not welcome. All approaches should be made in writing.

Opera Now

241 Shaftesbury Avenue, London WC2H 8EH
☎0171 333 1740   Fax 0171 333 1769

Publisher *Rhinegold Publishing Ltd*
Editor-in-Chief *Ashutosh Khandekar*
Deputy Editor *Antonia Carling*
Assistant Editor *Matthew Peacock*

FOUNDED 1989. BI-MONTHLY. News, features and reviews for those interested in opera. No unsolicited mss. All work is commissioned. Approach with ideas in writing.

Options

King's Reach Tower, Stamford Street,
London SE1 9LS
☎0171 261 5000   Fax 0171 261 7344

Owner *IPC Magazines Ltd*
Editor *Lesley Johnston*
Circulation 127,772

'Invest in yourself' is the motto of this women's magazine with an emphasis on practical and self-help articles but a planned relaunch in mid-1998 may result in a new format. Almost all material is written by a regular team of freelancers, but new writers are encouraged.
    Payment about £250 per 1000 words.

Orbis

See under **Poetry, Little Magazines**

Organic Gardening

PO Box 4, Wiveliscombe, Taunton, Somerset
TA4 2QY
☎01984 623998   Fax 01984 623998

Owner *Wardnest Ltd*
Editor *Basil Caplan*
Circulation 20,000

FOUNDED 1988. MONTHLY. Articles and features on all aspects of gardening based on organic methods, with special emphasis on old varieties and conservation. Unsolicited material welcome, maximum 600–2000 words for features and 100–

300 for news items. Prefer 'hands-on' accounts of projects, problems, challenges and how they are dealt with. Approach by phone or in writing.
    Payment by arrangement.

Palmtop Magazine

Palmtop Publishing, 25 Avocet Way, Bicester,
Oxfordshire OX6 0YN
☎01869 249287   Fax 01869 246043

Owner *Mr S. Clack/Miss R. A. Rolfe*
Editor *Mr S. Clack*
Circulation 5000

FOUNDED 1994. BI-MONTHLY users' magazine for Psion hand-held computers. No unsolicited mss; approach by 'phone in the first instance.

Parents

Endeavour House, 189 Shaftesbury Avenue,
London WC2H 8JG
☎0171 437 9011   Fax 0171 208 3584

Owner *EMAP Elan Publications*
Associate Editor *Ruth Beattie*
Circulation 46,628

FOUNDED 1976. MONTHLY. Features commissioned from outside contributors. No unsolicited mss. Approach with ideas in the first instance. Age span: from pregnancy to four years.

PC Week

32–34 Broadwick Street, London W1A 2HG
☎0171 316 9000   Fax 0171 316 9355
E-mail: pcweek@vnu.co.uk

Owner *VNU Business Publications*
Editor *Martin Lynch*
Circulation 50,000

FOUNDED 1986. WEEKLY news, analysis and opinion on the corporate desktop market. Welcomes reviews of PC software and hardware products; brief synopsis in the first instance. Approach by e-mail, fax or in writing.
    Features *Cliff Saran* Most articles are commissioned. Maximum 2000 words.
    News *Fiona Harvey* Maximum 800 words.

Peak and Pennine

33 Park Road, Bakewell, Derbyshire
DE45 1AX
☎01629 812034   Fax 01629 812034

Owner *Dalesman Publishing Co. Ltd*
Editor *Roly Smith*

FOUNDED 1997. MONTHLY. Predominantly outdoors, natural history and heritage, serving the Peak District National Park and South Pennines. Unsolicited material considered. Maximum 1500 words.

Pembrokeshire Life
Swan House Publishing, The Old Butter
Factory, Station Road, St Clears,
Carmarthenshire SA33 4BL
☎01994 231689/231691
Owner *Swan House Publishing*
Editor *David Fielding*

FOUNDED 1989. MONTHLY county magazine
with articles on local history, issues, characters,
off-beat stories with good colour or b&w photographs. No country diaries, short stories,
poems. Most articles are commissioned from
known freelancers but 'always prepared to consider ideas from new writers'. No mss. Send
cuttings of previous work (published or not)
and synopsis to the editor.

The People's Friend
80 Kingsway East, Dundee DD4 8SL
☎01382 462276/223131   Fax 01382 452491
Owner *D. C. Thomson & Co. Ltd*
Editor *Sinclair Matheson*
Circulation 449,595

The *Friend* is basically a fiction magazine, with
two serials and several short stories each week.
FOUNDED in 1869, it has always prided itself on
providing 'a good read for all the family'. All
stories should be about ordinary, identifiable
characters with the kind of problems the average
reader can understand and sympathise with. 'We
look for the romantic and emotional developments of characters, rather than an over-compli-
cated or contrived plot. We regularly use period
serials and, occasionally, mystery/adventure.'
Guidelines on request with s.a.e.
Short Stories Can vary in length from 1000
words or less to as many as 4000.
Serials Long-run serials of 10–15 instalments or more preferred. Occasionally shorter.
Articles Short fillers welcome.
Payment on acceptance.

Period Living &
Traditional Homes
Endeavour House, 189 Shaftesbury Avenue,
London WC2H 8JG
☎0171 208 3507   Fax 0171 208 3597
Owner *EMAP Elan*
Editor *Clare Weatherall*
Circulation 105,878

FOUNDED 1992. Formed from the merger of
Period Living and *Traditional Homes*. Covers
interior decoration in a period style, period
house profiles, traditional crafts, renovation of
period properties.

Features *Pamela Shipkey*
Payment varies according to length/type of
article.

Personal
See under **National Newspapers**
(Sunday Mirror)

Personal Finance
4 Tabernacle Street, London EC2A 4LU
☎0171 638 1916   Fax 0171 638 3128
Owner *Charterhouse Communications plc*
Editor *Juliet Oxborrow*
Circulation 50,000

ESTABLISHED 1994. MONTHLY finance magazine.
Features All issues relating to personal
finance, particularly investment, insurance,
banking, mortgages, savings, borrowing, health
care and pensions. No corporate articles or personnel issues. Write to the editor with ideas in
the first instance. No unsolicited mss.
Payment £150–175.
News All items written in-house.

The Philosopher
4 Wellington Road, Ilkley, West Yorkshire
LS29 8HR
Owner *The Philosophical Society*
Editor *Martin Cohen*
Website:
    http://www.rmplc.co.uk/eduweb/sites/cite
    /staff/philosopher/

FOUNDED 1913. BI-ANNUAL journal of the
Philosophical Society of Great Britain with an
international readership made up of members,
libraries and specialist booksellers. Wide range
of interests, but leaning towards articles that
present philosophical investigation which is
relevant to the individual and to society in our
modern era. Accessible to the non-specialist.
Will consider articles and book reviews. Notes
for Contributors available; send s.a.e. or see
website.
As well as short philosophical papers, will
accept:
News about lectures, conventions, philosophy groups. Ethical issues in the news. Maximum 1000 words.
Reviews of philosophy books (maximum
600 words); discussion articles of individual
philosophers and their published works (maximum 2000 words)
Miscellaneous items, including graphics, of
philosophical interest and/or merit.
Payment free copies.

Piano

241 Shaftesbury Avenue, London WC2H 8EH
☎0171 333 1724   Fax 0171 333 1769
Owner *Rhinegold Publishing*
Editor *Jeremy Siepmann*
Circulation 11,000

FOUNDED 1993. BI-MONTHLY magazine containing features, profiles, technical information, news, reviews of interest to those with a serious amateur or professional concern with pianos or their playing. No unsolicited material. Approach with ideas in writing only.

Picture Postcard Monthly

15 Debdale Lane, Keyworth, Nottingham
NG12 5HT
☎0115 9374079   Fax 0115 9376197
Owners *Brian & Mary Lund*
Editor *Brian Lund*
Circulation 4300

FOUNDED 1978. MONTHLY. News, views, clubs, diary of fairs, sales, auctions, and well-researched postcard-related articles. Might be interested in general articles supported by postcards. Unsolicited mss welcome. Approach by phone or in writing with ideas.

Pilot

The Clock House, 28 Old Town, Clapham, London SW4 0LB
☎0171 498 2506   Fax 0171 498 6920
E-mail: pilotmagazine@compuserve.com
Owner/Editor *James Gilbert*
Circulation 30,669

FOUNDED 1968. MONTHLY magazine for private plane pilots. No staff writers; the entire magazine is written by freelancers – mostly regulars. Unsolicited mss welcome but ideas in writing preferred. Perusal of any issue of the magazine will reveal the type of material bought. 700 words of 'Advice to would-be contributors' sent on receipt of s.a.e. (mark envelope 'Advice').

Features *James Gilbert* Many articles are unsolicited personal experiences/travel accounts from pilots of private planes; good photo coverage is very important. Maximum 5000 words. *Payment* £100–700 (first rights). Photos £26 each.

News *Mike Jerram* Contributions need to be as short as possible. See *Pilot Notes* in the magazine.

The Pink Paper

72 Holloway Road, London N7 8NZ
☎0171 296 6210   Fax 0171 957 0046
Owner *Chronos Group*
Editor *Tim Teeman*
Circulation 55,000

FOUNDED 1987. WEEKLY. Only national newspaper for lesbians and gay men covering politics, social issues, health, the arts and all areas of concern to lesbian/gay people. Unsolicited mss welcome. Initial approach by phone with an idea preferred. Interested in profiles, reviews, in-depth features and short news pieces.

News Maximum 300 words.

Listings/Arts & Reviews *Tim Teeman* Maximum 200 words/**Books** *Tim Teeman Payment* by arrangement.

Planet: The Welsh Internationalist

See **Planet** under **Small Presses**

Plays and Players Applause

Northway House, 1379 High Road, London N20 9LP
☎0181 343 9977   Fax 0181 343 7831
Owner *Mineco Designs*
Editor *Sandra Rennie*
Circulation 10,000

Theatre MONTHLY which publishes a mixture of news, reviews, reports and features on all the performing arts. Rarely uses unsolicited material but writers of talent are taken up. Almost all material is commissioned.

PN Review

See under **Poetry, Magazines**

Poetry Ireland Review

See under **Poetry Magazines**

Poetry Review

See under **Poetry Magazines**

Poetry Scotland

See under **Poetry Magazines**

Poetry Wales

See under **Poetry Magazines**

The Polish Gazette (Gazeta)

PO Box 1945, Edinburgh EH4 1AB
☎0131 315 2002
Owner *Gazeta Ltd*
Editor *Maria Rayska*

FOUNDED 1995. QUARTERLY. The only English language publication in the UK for the Polish community, friends of Poland, and businesses dealing with Poland. Approach in writing with ideas for articles.

Features *Tony Keniston* Travel, business, autobiography. 600 words maximum.

News *Maria Rayska* General, local and inter-

national news of interest to the Polish community in Britain, Poland, exhibitions and events, etc.
Payment by arrangement.

Pony
D.J. Murphy (Publishers) Ltd, Haslemere House, Lower Street, Haslemere, Surrey GU27 2PE
☎01428 651551 Fax 01428 653888
Owner *D. J. Murphy (Publishers) Ltd*
Editor *Janet Rising*
Circulation 38,000

FOUNDED 1948. Lively MONTHLY aimed at 10–16-year-olds. News, instruction on riding, stable management, veterinary care, interviews. Approach in writing with an idea.
Features welcome. Maximum 900 words.
News Written in-house. Photographs and illustrations (serious/cartoon) welcome.
Payment £65 per 1000 words.

Popular Crafts
Nexus House, Boundary Way, Hemel Hempstead, Hertfordshire HP2 7ST
☎01442 66551 Fax 01442 66998
Owner *Nexus Special Interests*
Editor *Lisa Leonard*
Circulation 32,000

FOUNDED 1980. MONTHLY. Covers crafts of all kinds. Freelance contributions welcome – copy needs to be lively and interesting. Approach in writing with an outline of idea.
Features Project-based under the following headings: Homecraft; Needlecraft; Popular Craft; Kidscraft; News and Columns. Any craft-related material including projects to make, with full instructions/patterns supplied in all cases; profiles of crafts people and news of craft group activities or successes by individual persons; articles on collecting crafts; personal experiences and anecdotes.
Payment on publication.

PR Week
174 Hammersmith Road, London W6 7JP
☎0171 413 4520 Fax 0171 413 4509
Owner *Haymarket Business Publications Ltd*
Editor *Stephen Farish*
Circulation 17,000

FOUNDED 1984. WEEKLY. Contributions accepted from experienced journalists. Approach in writing with an idea.
Features *Stephanie France*
News *Juliette Garside*
Payment £185 per 1000 words.

Practical Boat Owner
Westover House, West Quay Road, Poole, Dorset BH15 1JG
☎01202 680593 Fax 01202 674335
Owner *IPC Magazines*
Editor *Rodger Witt*
Circulation 54,789

FOUNDED 1967. MONTHLY magazine of practical information for cruising boat owners. Receives about 1500 mss per year. Interested in hard facts about gear, equipment, pilotage from experienced yachtsmen.
Features Technical articles about maintenance, restoration, modifications to cruising boats, power and sail up to 45ft, or reader reports on gear and equipment. European pilotage articles and cruising guides. Approach in writing with synopsis in the first instance.
Payment negotiable.

Practical Caravan
60 Waldegrave Road, Teddington, Middlesex TW11 8LG
☎0181 943 5664 Fax 0181 943 5777
Owner *Haymarket Magazines Ltd*
Editor *Rob McCabe*
Deputy Editor *John Rawlings*
Circulation 47,037

FOUNDED 1967. MONTHLY. Contains caravan reviews, travel features, investigations, products, park reviews. Unsolicited mss welcome on travel relevant only to caravanning/touring vans. No motorcaravan or static van stories. Approach with ideas by phone or letter.
Features *John Rawlings* Must refer to caravanning, towing. Written in friendly, chatty manner. Features with pictures/transparencies preferred (to include caravans where possible). Maximum length 2000 words. *Payment* negotiable (usually £120 per 1000 words).

Practical Fishkeeping (incorporating Fishkeeping Answers)
Apex House, Oundle Road, Peterborough, Cambridgeshire PE2 9NP
☎01733 898100 Fax 01733 898487
Owner *EMAP Apex Publications Ltd*
Managing Editor *Steve Windsor*
Circulation 31,000

MONTHLY. Practical articles on all aspects of fishkeeping. Unsolicited mss welcome. Approach in writing with ideas. Quality photographs of fish always welcome. No fiction or verse.

Practical Gardening
See **Garden Answers**

Practical Parenting

King's Reach Tower, Stamford Street,
London SE1 9LS
☎0171 261 5058   Fax 0171 261 6542
Owner *IPC Magazines Ltd*
Editor-in-Chief *Jayne Marsden*
Circulation 82,069

FOUNDED 1987. MONTHLY. Practical advice
on pregnancy, birth, babycare and childcare up
to five years. Submit ideas in writing with synopsis or send mss on spec. Interested in feature
articles of up to 3000 words in length, and in
readers' experiences/personal viewpoint pieces
of between 750–1000 words. Humorous articles on some aspect of parenthood may also
stand a chance. All material must be written for
the magazine's specifically targeted audience
and in-house style.

Payment negotiable.

Practical Photography

Apex House, Oundle Road, Peterborough,
Cambridgeshire PE2 9NP
☎01733 898100   Fax 01733 894472
Owner *EMAP Apex Publications Ltd*
Editor *David Ogle*
Circulation 77,654

MONTHLY. All types of photography, particularly technique-orientated pictures. No unsolicited mss. Preliminary approach may be made
by telephone. Always interested in new ideas.

Features Anything relevant to the world of
photography, but not 'the sort of feature produced by staff writers'. Features on technology
and humour are two areas worth exploring.
Bear in mind that there is a three-month lead-
in time. Maximum 2000 words.

News Only 'hot' news applicable to a
monthly magazine. Maximum 400 words.

Payment varies.

Practical Wireless

Arrowsmith Court, Station Approach,
Broadstone, Dorset BH18 8PW
☎01202 659910   Fax 01202 659950
Owner *P.W. Publishing*
Editor *Rob Mannion*
Circulation 27,000

FOUNDED 1932. MONTHLY. News and features
relating to amateur radio, radio construction and
radio communications. Unsolicited mss welcome. Guidelines available (send s.a.e.).
Approach by phone with ideas in the first
instance. Copy should be supported where pos-

sible by artwork, either illustrations, diagrams or
photographs.

Payment £54–70 per page.

Practical Woodworking

Boundary Way, Hemel Hempstead,
Hertfordshire HP2 7ST
☎01442 266551   Fax 01442 266998
Owner *Nexus Special Interests Ltd*
Editor *Mark Chisholm*
Circulation 41,000

FOUNDED 1965. MONTHLY. Contains articles
relating to woodworking – projects, techniques,
new products, tips, letters etc. Unsolicited mss
welcome. No fiction. Approach with ideas in
writing or by phone.

News Anything related to woodworking.
Payment £60 per published page.

Features Projects, techniques etc. *Payment*
£60 per published page.

Prediction

Link House, Dingwall Avenue, Croydon,
Surrey CR9 2TA
☎0181 686 2599   Fax 0181 781 1159
Owner *Link House Magazines Ltd*
Editor *Jo Logan*
Circulation 35,000

FOUNDED 1936. MONTHLY. Covering astrology and occult-related topics. Unsolicited
material in these areas welcome (about
200–300 mss received every year). Writers'
guidelines available on request.

Astrology Pieces, of either 750 words or
1500–2000 words, depending on number of
charts, should be practical and of general interest. Charts and astro data should accompany
them, especially if profiles.

Features *Jo Logan* Articles on mysteries of
the   earth,   alternative   medicine,
psychical/occult experiences and phenomena
are considered. 800–2000 words. *Payment*
£25–100 and over.

News & Views Items of interest to readership welcome. Maximum 300 words. *No payment.*

Press Gazette

Quantum House, 19 Scarbrook Road,
Croydon, Surrey CR9 1LX
☎0181 565 4200   Fax 0181 565 4395
Owner *Quantum*
Editor *Adam Leyland*
Deputy Editor *Jon Slattery*
Circulation 9,500

WEEKLY magazine for all journalists – in

regional and national newspapers, magazines, broadcasting, and on-line – containing news, features and analysis of all areas of journalism, print and broadcasting. Unsolicited mss welcome; interested in profiles of magazines, broadcasting companies and news agencies, personality profiles, technical and current affairs relating to the world of journalism. Approach with ideas by phone, fax or in writing.

Prima
197 Marsh Wall, London E14 9SG
☎0171 519 5500   Fax 0171 519 5514
Owner *Gruner & Jahr (UK)*
Editor *Lindsay Nicholson*
Circulation 540,727

FOUNDED 1986. MONTHLY women's magazine.
   Features Coordinator *Verity Watkins* Mostly practical and written by specialists, or commissioned from known freelancers. Unsolicited mss not welcome.

Private Eye
6 Carlisle Street, London W1V 5RG
☎0171 437 4017   Fax 0171 437 0705
Owner *Pressdram*
Editor *Ian Hislop*
Circulation 190,000

FOUNDED 1961. FORTNIGHTLY satirical and investigative magazine. Prospective contributors are best advised to approach the editor in writing. News stories and feature ideas are always welcome, as are cartoons. All jokes written in-house.
   Payment in all cases is 'not great', and length of piece varies as appropriate.

Prospect
4 Bedford Square, London WC1B 3RA
☎0171 255 1281   Fax 0171 255 1279
Owner *Prospect Publishing Limited*
Editor *David Goodhart*
Circulation 20,000

FOUNDED1995. MONTHLY. Essays, reviews and research on current/international affairs and cultural issues. No news features. No unsolicited mss. Approach in writing with ideas in the first instance.

Psychic News
Clock Cottage, Stansted Hall, Stansted, Essex CM24 8UD
☎01279 817050   Fax 01279 817051
Owner *Psychic Press 1995 Ltd*
Editor *Lyn Guest de Swarte*

Circulation 40,000

FOUNDED 1932. *Psychic News* is the world's only WEEKLY spiritualist newspaper. It covers subjects such as psychic research, hauntings, ghosts, poltergeists, spiritual healing, survival after death, and paranormal gifts. Unsolicited material considered.

Publishing News
43 Museum Street, London WC1A 1LY
☎0171 404 0304   Fax 0171 242 0762
Editor *Rodney Burbeck*

WEEKLY newspaper of the book trade. Hardback and paperback reviews and extensive listings of new paperbacks and hardbacks. Interviews with leading personalities in the trade, authors, agents and features on specialist book areas.

Punch
Trevor House, 100 Brompton Road, London SW3 1ER
☎0171 225 6716   Fax 0171 225 6766
Owner *Liberty Publishing*
Editor *James Steen*

FOUNDED in 1841, this WEEKLY humorous magazine was RELAUNCHED in 1996. Ideas are welcome; approach in writing in the first instance.
   Payment negotiable.

Q
Mappin House, 4 Winsley Street, London W1N 7AR
☎0171 436 1515   Fax 0171 312 8247
Owner *EMAP Metro Publications*
Editor *David Davies*
Circulation 201,979

FOUNDED 1986. MONTHLY. Glossy aimed at educated rock music enthusiasts of all ages. Few opportunities for freelance writers. Unsolicited mss are strongly discouraged. Prospective contributors should approach in writing only.

Quartos Magazine
See **The New Writer**

QWF (Quality Women's Fiction)
80 Main Street, Linton, Nr Swadlincote, Derbyshire DE12 6QA
☎01283 761042
Editor *Jo Good*

BI-MONTHLY small press magazine. FOUNDED in 1994 as a show-case for the best in women's short story writing – original and thought-provoking. Will only consider stories that are previously unpublished and of less than 4000 words; articles must be less than 1000 words and of interest to the writer. Include covering letter and brief biography with mss. Also runs a script appraisal service and regular short story competitions. For further information and detailed guidelines for contributors, contact the editor at the above address (enclose s.a.e.).

Racing Post (incorporating The Sporting Life)

1 Canada Square, Canary Wharf, London E14 5AP
☎0171 293 3000
E-mail: info@racingpost.co.uk
Owner *Mirror Group Newspapers Ltd*
Editor *Alan Byrne*

FOUNDED 1986. DAILY horse racing paper with some general sport. In April 1998, following an agreement between the owners of *The Sporting Life* and the *Racing Post*, the two papers merged with the latter becoming the senior partner.

Radio Times

80 Wood Lane, London W12 0TT
☎0181 576 3066   Fax 0181 576 3160
E-mail: radio.times@bbc.co.uk
Owner *BBC Worldwide Limited*
Editor *Sue Robinson*
Deputy Editor *Liz Vercoe*
Circulation 1,406,152

WEEKLY. UK's leading broadcast listings magazine. The majority of material is provided by freelance and retained writers, but the topicality of the pieces means close consultation with editors is essential. Very unlikely to use unsolicited material. Detailed BBC, ITV, Channel 4, Channel 5 and satellite television and radio listings are accompanied by feature material relevant to the week's output.
Payment by arrangement.

RAIL

Apex House, Oundle Road, Peterborough, Cambridgeshire PE2 9NP
☎01733 898100   Fax 01733 894472
Owner *EMAP Apex Publications*
Managing Editor *Nigel Harris*
Circulation 32,634

FOUNDED 1981. FORTNIGHTLY magazine dedicated to modern railway. News and features, and topical newsworthy events. Unsolicited mss welcome. Approach by phone with ideas. Not interested in personal journey reminiscences. No fiction.

Features By arrangement with the editor. Traction-related subjects of interest. Maximum 2000 words. *Payment* varies/negotiable.

News Any news item welcomed. Maximum 500 words. *Payment* varies (up to £100 per 1000 words).

The Railway Magazine

King's Reach Tower, Stamford Street, London SE1 9LS
☎0171 261 5533/5821   Fax 0171 261 5269
E-mail: railway@ipc.co.uk
Owner *IPC Magazines Ltd*
Editor *Nick Pigott*
Circulation 33,115

FOUNDED 1897. MONTHLY. Articles, photos and short news stories of a topical nature, covering modern railways, steam preservation and railway history, welcome. Maximum 2000 words, with sketch maps of routes, etc., where appropriate. Unsolicited mss welcome.
Payment negotiable.

Rambling Today

1–5 Wandsworth Road, London SW8 2XX
☎0171 339 8500   Fax 0171 339 8501
Owner *Ramblers' Association*
Editor *Annabelle Birchall*
Circulation 122,000

QUARTERLY. Official magazine of the Ramblers' Association, available to members only. Unsolicited mss welcome. S.a.e. required for return.

Features Freelance features are invited on any aspect of walking in Britain and abroad. Length 800–1300 words, preferably with good photographs. No general travel articles.

Reader's Digest

11 Westferry Circus, Canary Wharf, London E14 4HE
☎0171 715 8000   Fax 0171 715 8716
Owner *Reader's Digest Association Ltd*
Editor-in-Chief *Russell Twisk*
Circulation 1.5 million

In theory, a good market for general interest features of around 2500 words. However, 'a tiny proportion' comes from freelance writers, all of which are specially commissioned. Toughening up its image with a move into investigative journalism. Opportunities exist for short humorous contributions to regular features – 'Life's Like That', 'Humour in Uniform'. Issues a helpful booklet called 'Writing for Reader's Digest' available by post at £2.50.
Payment up to £200.

Record Collector
43–45 St Mary's Road, Ealing, London
W5 5RQ
☎0181 579 1082   Fax 0181 566 2024
Owner *Johnny Dean*
Editor *Peter Doggett*
FOUNDED 1979. MONTHLY. Detailed, well-researched articles welcome on any aspect of record collecting or any collectable artist in the field of popular music (1950s–1990s), with complete discographies where appropriate. Unsolicited mss welcome. Approach with ideas by phone.
Payment negotiable.

Record Mirror
See **Music Week**

Reincarnation International
Phoenix Research Publications, PO Box 10839, London SW13 0ZG
☎0181 241 2184   Fax 0181 241 2184
Publisher *Reincarnation International Ltd*
Editor *Roy Stemman*
Circulation 3000
QUARTERLY. The only publication in the world dealing with all aspects of reincarnation – from people who claim to recall their past lives spontaneously to the many thousands who have done so through hypnotic regressions. It also examines reincarnation in the light of various religious beliefs and the latest discoveries about the mind and how it works.

Report
ATL, 7 Northumberland Street, London WC2N 5DA
☎0171 930 6441   Fax 0171 930 1359
Owner *Association of Teachers and Lecturers*
Editor *Nick Tester*
Circulation 160,000
FOUNDED 1978. EIGHT ISSUES YEARLY during academic terms. Contributions welcome. All submissions should go directly to the editor. Articles should be no more than 800 words and must be of practical interest to the classroom teacher and F. E. lecturers.

Resident Abroad
Greystoke Place, Fetter Lane, London EC4A 1ND
☎0171 463 3000   Fax 0171 463 3152
Owner *Financial Times*
Editor *Cristina Nordenstahl*
Circulation 16,577
FOUNDED 1979. MONTHLY magazine aimed at British expatriates. Unsolicited mss considered, if suitable to the interests of the readership.
Features Up to 1200 words on finance, property, employment opportunities and other topics likely to appeal to readership, such as living conditions in countries with substantial British expatriate populations. No 'lighthearted looks' at anything.
Fiction Rarely published, but exceptional, relevant stories (no longer than 1000 words) might be considered.
Payment negotiable.

Riding
Suite B, Barber House, Storeys Bar Road, Fengate, Peterborough, Cambridgeshire PE1 5YS
☎01733 555830   Fax 01733 555831
Owner *GreenShires Creative Colour Ltd*
Editor *Steve Moore*
Aimed at an adult, horse-owning audience. Most of the writers on *Riding* are freelance with the emphasis on non-practical and lifestyle-orientated features. New and authoritative writers always welcome.
Payment negotiable.

Right Now!
BCM Right, London WC1N 3XX
☎0181 692 7099   Fax 0181 692 7099
E-mail: rightnow@compuserve.com
Owner *Right Now!*
Editor *Derek Turner*
Circulation 2000
FOUNDED 1993. QUARTERLY right-wing conservative commentary. Welcomes well-documented disputations, news stories and elegiac features about British heritage ('the more politically incorrect, the better!'). No fiction and poems, although exceptions may be made. Approach in writing in the first instance.
No payment.

Rugby News & Monthly
7–9 Rathbone Street, London W1P 1AF
☎0171 323 1944   Fax 0171 323 1943
Owner *Independent Magazines Ltd*
Editor *Graeme Gillespie*
Circulation 44,000
FOUNDED 1987 and incorporated *Rugby Monthly* magazine in July 1994. Contains news, views and features on the UK and the world rugby scene, with special emphasis on clubs, schools, fitness and coaching. Welcomes unsolicited material.

Rugby World

23rd Floor, King's Reach Tower, Stamford
Street, London SE1 9LS
☎0171 261 6830   Fax 0171 261 5419
Owner *IPC Magazines Ltd*
Editor *Alison Kervin*
Circulation 36,872

MONTHLY. Features of special rugby interest
only. Unsolicited contributions welcome but
s.a.e. essential for return of material. Prior
approach by phone or in writing preferred.

Runner's World

7–10 Chandos Street, London W1M 0AD
☎0171 291 6000   Fax 0171 291 6080
Owner *Rodale Press*
Editor *Steven Seaton*
Circulation 44,604

FOUNDED 1979. MONTHLY magazine giving
practical advice on all areas of distance running
including product and training, travel features,
up-to-date athletics profiles and news. Personal
running-related articles, famous people who
run or off-beat travel articles are welcome. No
elite athletics or training articles. Approach in
writing in the first instance.

Saga Magazine

The Saga Building, Middelburg Square,
Folkestone, Kent CT20 1AZ
☎01303 711523   Fax 01303 712699
Owner *Saga Publishing Ltd*
Editor *Paul Bach*
Circulation 879,860

FOUNDED 1984. MONTHLY. '*Saga Magazine* sets
out to celebrate the role of older people in society. It reflects their achievements, promotes their
skills, protects their interests, and campaigns on
their behalf. A warm personal approach, addressing the readership in an up-beat and positive
manner, required.' It has a hard core of celebrated commentators/writers (e.g. Clement
Freud, Keith Waterhouse) as regular contributors. Articles mostly commissioned or written in-
house but exclusive celebrity interviews welcome if appropriate/relevant. Length 1000–1200
words (maximum 1600).

Sailing Today

30 Monmouth Street, Bath BA1 2BW
☎01225 442244   Fax 01225 732248
Owner *Future Publishing*
Editor-at-large *Philip Dunn*

FOUNDED 1997. MONTHLY magazine featuring
family cruising under sail with an emphasis on
enjoyment and practical aspects. Most articles are
commissioned but will consider practical features
and cruise stories with photos. Approach by telephone or in writing in the first instance.

Features/News *Colin Jarman*. **Payment** by
agreement.

Sailplane and Gliding

281 Queen Edith's Way,
Cambridge CB1 4NH
☎01223 247725   Fax 01223 413793
E-mail: bgs.sandg@virgin.net
Owner *British Gliding Association*
Editor *Gillian Bryce-Smith*
Circulation 8400

FOUNDED 1930. BI-MONTHLY for gliding
enthusiasts. A specialist magazine with very few
opportunities for freelancers.
No payment.

Sainsbury's The Magazine

20 Upper Ground, London SE1 9PD
☎0171 633 0266   Fax 0171 401 9423
Owner *New Crane Publishing*
Editor *Michael Wynn Jones*
Consultant Food Editor *Delia Smith*
Circulation 422,718

FOUNDED 1993. MONTHLY featuring a main
core of food and cookery, features, health,
beauty, fashion, home, gardening and news.
No unsolicited mss. Approach in writing with
ideas only in the first instance.

The Salisbury Review

33 Canonbury Park South, London N1 2JW
☎0171 226 7791   Fax 0171 354 0383
E-mail: salisbury-review@easynet.co.uk
Website: http://www.easyweb.easynet.
co.uk/~salisbury-review
Owner *Claridge Press*
Editor *Roger Scruton*
Managing Editor *Merrie Cave*
Circulation 1700

FOUNDED 1982. QUARTERLY magazine of
conservative thought. Editorials and features
from a right-wing viewpoint. Unsolicited
material welcome.
Features Maximum 4000 words.
Reviews Maximum 1000 words.
No payment.

Scene Update

22 Stephenson Way, London NW1 2HD
☎0171 388 6689   Fax 0171 388 6649
Owner *Virtual Universe Ltd*
Editor *Cary James*

Circulation 30,000

FOUNDED 1996. BI-MONTHLY. Gay arts and entertainment: film, video, theatre, celebrity interviews, lifestyle, fitness, alternative medicine, HIV/AIDS concern. Will consider mss which come into the above category. Maximum 1200 words. *Payment* 5–6p. per word.

Scotland on Sunday Magazine

See under **National Newspapers (Scotland on Sunday)**

The Scots Magazine

2 Albert Square, Dundee DD1 9QJ
☎01382 223131   Fax 01382 322214

Owner *D. C. Thomson & Co. Ltd*
Editor *John Methven*
Circulation 65,000

FOUNDED 1739. MONTHLY. Covers a wide field of Scottish interests ranging from personalities to wildlife, climbing, reminiscence, history and folklore. Outside contributions welcome; 'staff delighted to discuss in advance by letter'.

The Scottish Farmer

Caledonian Magazines Ltd, 6th Floor, 195 Albion Street, Glasgow G1 1QQ
☎0141 302 7700   Fax 0141 302 7799
E-mail: info@calmags.co.uk

Owner *Caledonian Magazines Ltd*
Editor *Alasdair Fletcher*
Circulation 25,00

FOUNDED 1893. WEEKLY. Farmer's magazine covering most aspects of Scottish agriculture. Unsolicited mss welcome. Approach with ideas in writing.

Features *Alasdair Fletcher* Technical articles on agriculture or farming units. 1000–2000 words.

News *John Duckworth* Factual news about farming developments, political, personal and technological. Maximum 800 words.

Weekend Family Pages Rural and craft topics.

Scottish Field

Special Publications, Royston House, Caroline Park, Edinburgh EH5 1QJ
☎0131 551 2942   Fax 0131 551 2938

Owner *Oban Times*
Editor *Archie Mackenzie*

FOUNDED 1903. MONTHLY. Scotland's quality lifestyle magazine. Unsolicited mss welcome but writers should study the magazine first.

Features Articles of general interest on Scotland and Scots abroad with good photo-graphs or, preferably, colour slides. Approx 1000 words.
Payment negotiable.

Scottish Golfer

c/o The Scottish Golf Union, Drumoig, Leuchars, St Andrews, Fife KY16 0BE
☎01382 549500   Fax 01382 549510

Owner *Scottish Golf Union*
Editor *Martin Dempster*
Circulation 30,000

FOUNDED mid-1980s. MONTHLY. Features and results, in particular the men's events. No unsolicited mss. Approach in writing with ideas.

Scottish Home & Country

42A Heriot Row, Edinburgh EH3 6ES
☎0131 225 1934   Fax 0131 225 8129

Owner *Scottish Women's Rural Institutes*
Editor *Stella Roberts*
Circulation 14,000

FOUNDED 1924. MONTHLY. Scottish or rural-related issues. Unsolicited mss welcome but reading time may be from 2–3 months. Commissions are rare and tend to go to established contributors only.

Scottish Rugby Magazine

11 Dock Place, Leith, Edinburgh EH6 6LU
☎0131 554 0540   Fax 0131 554 0482

Editor *Kevin Ferrie*
Circulation 19,200

FOUNDED 1990. MONTHLY. Features, club profiles, etc. Approach in writing with ideas.

Scouting Magazine

Baden Powell House, Queen's Gate, London SW7 5JS
☎0171 584 7030   Fax 0171 590 5124

Owner *The Scout Association*
Editor *David Easton*
Circulation 30,000

MONTHLY magazine for adults connected to or interested in the Scouting movement. Interested in Scouting-related features only. No fiction.
Payment by negotiation.

Screen

Gilmorehill Centre for Theatre, Film and Television, University of Glasgow, Glasgow G12 8QQ
☎0141 330 5035   Fax 0141 330 3515
E-mail: screen:arts.gla.ac.uk

Owner *The John Logie Baird Centre*
Editors *Annette Kuhn, John Caughie, Simon Frith, Norman King, Karen Lury, Jackie Stacey*

Editorial Assistant *Caroline Beven*
Circulation 1500

QUARTERLY refereed academic journal of film and television studies for a readership ranging from undergraduates to screen studies academics and media professionals. There are no specific qualifications for acceptance of articles. Straightforward film reviews are not normally published. Check the magazine's style and market in the first instance.

Screen International

33–39 Bowling Green Lane, London
EC1R 0DA
☎0171 505 8080   Fax 0171 505 8117
Owner *EMAP Business Communications*
Editor *Boyd Farrow*

International trade paper of the film, video and television industries. Expert freelance writers are occasionally used in all areas. No unsolicited mss. Approach with ideas in writing.
  Features *Denis Seguin*
  Payment negotiable on NUJ basis.

Sea Breezes

Units 28–30, Spring Valley Industrial Estate, Braddan, Isle of Man IM2 2QS
☎01624 626018   Fax 01624 661655
Owner *Print Centres*
Editor *Captain A. C. Douglas*
Circulation 14,500

FOUNDED 1919. MONTHLY. Covers virtually everything relating to ships and seamen. Unsolicited mss welcome; they should be thoroughly researched and accompanied by relevant photographs. No fiction, poetry, or anything which 'smacks of the romance of the sea'.
  Features Factual tales of ships, seamen and the sea, Royal or Merchant Navy, sail or power, nautical history, shipping company histories, epic voyages, etc. Length 1000–4000 words. 'The most readily acceptable work will be that which shows it is clearly the result of first-hand experience or the product of extensive and accurate research.'
  Payment £7 per page (about 500 words).

She Magazine

National Magazine House, 72 Broadwick Street, London W1V 2BP
☎0171 439 5000   Fax 0171 439 5350
Owner *National Magazine Co. Ltd*
Editor *Alison Pylkkanen*
Circulation 241,460

Glossy MONTHLY for the thirtysomething woman, addressing her needs as an individual, a partner and a parent. Talks to its readers in an intelligent, humorous and sympathetic way. Features should be about 1500 words long. Approach with ideas in writing. No unsolicited material.
  Payment NUJ rates.

Shoot Magazine

King's Reach Tower, Stamford Street, London SE1 9LS
☎0171 261 6287   Fax 0171 261 6019
Owner *IPC Magazines Ltd*
Editor *Andy Winter*
Circulation 94,722

FOUNDED 1969. WEEKLY football magazine. No unsolicited mss. Present ideas for news, features or colour photo-features to the editor by telephone.
  Features Hard-hitting, topical and off-beat.
  News Items welcome, especially exclusive gossip and transfer speculation.
  Payment negotiable.

Shooting and Conservation (BASC)

Marford Mill, Rossett, Wrexham, Clwyd LL12 0HL
☎01244 573000   Fax 01244 571678
Owner *The British Association for Shooting and Conservation (BASC)*
Editor *Lesley Ferguson*
Circulation 120,000

FIVE ISSUES PER YEAR. Good articles and stories on shooting, conservation and related areas are always sought although most material used is commissioned. Maximum 1500 words.
  Payment negotiable.

Shooting Times & Country Magazine

King's Reach Tower, Stamford Street, London SE1 9LS
☎0171 261 6180   Fax 0171 261 7179
Owner *IPC Magazines*
Editor *John Gregson*
Circulation 27,356

FOUNDED 1882. WEEKLY. Covers shooting, fishing and related countryside topics. Unsolicited mss considered.
  Payment negotiable.

Shropshire Magazine

77 Wyle Cop, Shrewsbury, Shropshire SY1 1UT
☎01743 362175
Owner *Shropshire Newspapers Ltd*
Editor *Keith Parker*

FOUNDED 1950. MONTHLY. Unsolicited mss welcome but ideas in writing preferred.

Features Personalities, topical items, historical (e.g. family) of Shropshire; also general interest: homes, weddings, antiques, etc. Maximum 1000 words.

Payment negotiable 'but modest'.

Sight & Sound
British Film Institute, 21 Stephen Street, London W1P 1PL
☎0171 255 1444   Fax 0171 436 2327
Owner *British Film Institute*
Editor *Nick James*

FOUNDED 1932. MONTHLY. Topical and critical articles on international cinema, with regular columns from the USA and Europe. Length 1000–5000 words. Relevant photographs appreciated. Also book, film and video release reviews. Unsolicited material welcome. Approach in writing with ideas.

Payment by arrangement.

The Sign
See **Hymns Ancient & Modern Ltd** under **UK Publishers**

Ski and Board
The White House, 57–63 Church Road, Wimbledon, London SW19 5SB
☎0181 410 2000   Fax 0181 410 2001
Owner *Ski Club of Great Britain*
Editor *Gill Williams*
Circulation 19,675

FOUNDED 1903. FIVE ISSUES YEARLY. Features from established ski writers only.

The Skier and
The Snowboarder Magazine
48 London Road, Sevenoaks, Kent TN13 1AP
☎01732 743644   Fax 01732 743647
Owner *Mountain Marketing Ltd*
Editor *Frank Baldwin*
Circulation 20,000

Official magazine to the World Ski and Snowboard Association, UK. SEASONAL. From September to May. FIVE ISSUES YEARLY. Outside contributions welcome.

Features Various topics covered, including race reports, resort reports, fashion, equipment update, dry slope, school news, new products, health and safety. Crisp, tight, informative copy of 1000 words or less preferred.

News All aspects of skiing news covered.

Payment negotiable.

Slimming
Endeavour House, 189 Shaftesbury Avenue, London WC2H 8JG
☎0171 437 9011   Fax 0171 434 0656
Owner *EMAP Elan Publications*
Editor *Christine Michael*
Circulation 121,552

FOUNDED 1969. ELEVEN ISSUES YEARLY. Leading magazine about slimming, diet and health. Opportunities for freelance contributions on general health (diet-related); psychology related to health and fitness; celebrity interviews. It is best to approach with an idea in writing.

Payment negotiable.

Smallholder
Hook House, Wimblington March, Cambridgeshire PE15 0QL
☎01354 741182   Fax 01354 741182
Owner *Southern Bailey Newspaper Group Dursley Glos.*
Editor *Liz Wright*
Circulation 20,000

FOUNDED 1982. MONTHLY. Outside contributions welcome. Send for sample magazine and editorial schedule before submitting anything. Follow up with samples of work to the editor so that style can be assessed for suitability. No poetry or humorous but unfocused personal tales.

Features New writers always welcome, but must have high level of technical expertise – 'not textbook stuff'. Length 750–1500 words.

News All agricultural and rural news welcome. Length 200–500 words.

Payment negotiable ('but modest').

Smash Hits
Mappin House, Winsley Street, London W1N 7AR
☎0171 436 1515   Fax 0171 636 5792
Owner *EMAP Metro Publications*
Editor *Gavin Reeve*
Circulation 434,525

FOUNDED 1979. FORTNIGHTLY. Top of the mid-teen market. Unsolicited mss are not accepted, but prospective contributors may approach in writing with ideas.

Snooker Scene
Cavalier House, 202 Hagley Road, Edgbaston, Birmingham B16 9PQ
☎0121 454 2931   Fax 0121 452 1822
Owner *Everton's News Agency*
Editor *Clive Everton*
Circulation 16,000

FOUNDED 1971. MONTHLY. No unsolicited mss. Approach in writing with an idea.

Somerset Magazine
23 Market Street, Crewkerne, Somerset
TA18 7JU
☎01460 78000   Fax 01460 76718
Owner *Smart Print Publications Ltd*
Editor *Roy Smart*
Circulation 6000

FOUNDED 1990. MONTHLY magazine with features on any subject of interest (historical, geographical, arts, crafts) to people living in Somerset. Length 1000–1500 words, preferably with illustrations. Unsolicited mss welcome but initial approach in writing preferred.
    Payment negotiable.

The Spectator
56 Doughty Street, London WC1N 2LL
☎0171 405 1706   Fax 0171 242 0603
Owner *The Spectator (1828) Ltd*
Editor *Frank Johnson*
Circulation 56,313

FOUNDED 1828. WEEKLY political and literary magazine. Prospective contributors should write in the first instance to the relevant editor. Unsolicited mss welcome, but no 'follow up' phone calls, please.
    Deputy Editor *Petronella Wyatt*
    Assistant Editor *Edward Heathcoat Amory*
    Books *Mark Amory*
    Payment nominal.

Spirit Magazine
Trojan Horse Publishing, 2/4 Vestry Street, London N1 7RE
☎0171 251 3457   Fax 0171 250 4024
Owner *David O'Sullivan*
Editor *Susan Kamil*
Circulation 35,000

FOUNDED 1996. BI-MONTHLY new edge, lifestyle magazine. 'Mind, body and spirit with style. Interested in articles on travel, health, holistic, big ideas, positive profiles.' Maximum 400–500 words for news; 1500–2000, features. Send synopsis in the first instance.

The Sporting Life
See **Racing Post**

Sports in the Sky
Freestyle Publications, Alexander House, Ling Road, Tower Park, Poole, Dorset BH12 4NZ
☎01202 735090   Fax 01202 733969
Owner *Mark Nuttall*

Editor *Gethin James*

FOUNDED 1996. MONTHLY magazine highlighting the excitement of aerial sports such as skydiving, paragliding, hang-gliding, ballooning and microlighting. Features, equipment reviews, profiles and flight guides. Unsolicited material welcome; approach in writing in the first instance. Not interested in 'my first parachute jump' stories.

Springboard – Writing To Succeed
30 Orange Hill Road, Prestwich, Manchester M25 1LS
☎0161 773 5911
E-mail: LeoBrooks@compuserve.com
Owner/Editor *Leo Brooks*
Circulation 200

FOUNDED 1990. QUARTERLY. *Springboard* is not a market for writers but a forum from which they can find encouragement and help. Provides articles, news, market information, competition/folio news directed at helping writers to achieve success. Free to subscribers: a copy of *The Curate's Egg* – a collection of poetry submitted.

The Squash Times
PO Box 3443, London SE8 5BG
☎0181 692 6302   Fax 0181 692 6302
Editor *Mr R. Richardson*

FOUNDED 1980. QUARTERLY. Events, players, fashion and footwear, rackets, facilities, technique and tactics.

Staffordshire Life
The Publishing Centre, Derby Street, Stafford ST16 2DT
☎01785 257700   Fax 01785 253287
Owner *The Staffordshire Newsletter*
Editor *Philip Thurlow-Craig*
Circulation 20,000

FOUNDED 1982. NINE ISSUES YEARLY. Full-colour county magazine devoted to Staffordshire, its surroundings and people. Contributions welcome. Approach in writing with ideas.
    Features Maximum 1200 words.
    Fashion Copy must be supported by photographs.
    Payment NUJ rates.

The Stage (incorporating Television Today)
47 Bermondsey Street, London SE1 3XT
☎0171 403 1818   Fax 0171 357 9287
Owner *The Stage Newspaper Ltd*

Editor *Brian Attwood*
Circulation 42,000

FOUNDED 1880. WEEKLY. No unsolicited mss. Prospective contributors should write with ideas in the first instance.

Features Preference for middle-market, tabloid-style articles. 'Puff pieces', PR plugs and extended production notes will not be considered. Maximum 800 words.

News News stories from outside London are always welcome. Maximum 300 words.

Payment £100 per 1000 words.

Stand Magazine
See under **Poetry Magazines**

Staple Magazine
See under **Poetry Magazines**

Stone Soup
37 Chesterfield Road, London W4 3HQ
☎0181 742 7554   Fax 0181 742 7554

Editors *Igor Klikovac, Ken Smith*
Associate Editors *Srdja Pavlovic, Vesna Domany-Hardy*
Circulation 3000

THRICE-YEARLY international magazine for new writing – mainly poetry and theory, combined with some fiction and criticism. Edited by English poet Ken Smith and Bosnian poet Igor Klikovac, the magazine is printed bilingually, in English and languages of former Yugoslavia but it also attracts a broad audience across Europe. It tends to bring the most interesting work from Eastern Europe and combines it with well-established authors from the West. Contributors for the first three issues include Edward W. Said, Umberto Eco, Jean Baudrillard, Noam Chomsky, Hanif Kureishi, Adam Zagajewski and Alain Bosquet. Most work is commissioned. Approach in writing, mss should be sent in duplicate, preferably on disk, with s.a.e. supplied.

The Strad
7 St. John's Road, Harrow, Middlesex HA1 2EE
☎0181 863 2020   Fax 0181 863 2444

Owner *Orpheus Publications Ltd*
Editor *Joanna Pieters*
Circulation 16,000

FOUNDED 1890. MONTHLY for classical string musicians, makers and enthusiasts. Unsolicited mss welcome 'though acknowledgement/return not guaranteed'.

Features Profiles of string players, teachers,

luthiers and musical instruments, also relevant research. Maximum 2000 words.

Reviews *Juliette Barber.*
Payment £100 per 1000 words.

Student Guide
PO Box 6160, Birmingham B16 8XA
☎0121 643 1575   Fax 0121 643 4450

Managing Editor *Sam Allen*
Editor *Kim Gould*
Circulation 30,000

FOUNDED 1990. Published each semester. Sudent listings and lifestyle. Interested in receiving features and listings items; approach in writing. No unsolicited mss.

Suffolk and Norfolk Life
Barn Acre House, Saxtead Green, Suffolk IP13 9QJ
☎01728 685832   Fax 01728 685842

Owner *Today Magazines Ltd*
Editor *Kevin Davis*
Circulation 17,000

FOUNDED 1989. MONTHLY. General interest, local stories, historical, personalities, wine, travel, food. Unsolicited mss welcome. Approach by phone or in writing with ideas. Not interested in anything which does not relate specifically to East Anglia.

Features *Kevin Davis* Maximum 1500 words, with photos.

News *Kevin Davis* Maximum 1000 words, with photos.

Special Pages *William Locks* Study the magazine for guidelines. Maximum 1500 words.

Payment £25 (news); £30 (other).

Sunday Magazine
See under **National Newspapers (The News of the World)**

Sunday Post Magazine
See under **National Newspapers (Sunday Post, Glasgow)**

Sunday Times Magazine
See under **National Newspapers (The Sunday Times)**

Superbike Magazine
Link House, Dingwall Avenue, Croydon, Surrey CR9 2TA
☎0181 686 2599   Fax 0181 781 1164

Publisher *Alan Morgan*
Editor *Grant Leonard*
Circulation 54,000

FOUNDED 1977. MONTHLY. Dedicated to all

that is best and most exciting in the world of high-performance motorcycling. Unsolicited mss, synopses and ideas welcome.

Surrey Life
Datateam Publishing, Fairmeadow, Maidstone, Kent ME14 1NG
☎01622 687031   Fax 01622 757646
Owner *Datateam Publishing*
Editor *Roderick Cooper*
Circulation 10,000

FOUNDED 1970. MONTHLY. Strong Surrey interest plus fashion, food, books, wildlife, motoring, property, sport, interiors with local links. Unsolicited mss welcome. Interested in anything with a genuine Surrey connection. No fiction or non-Surrey subjects. Approach in writing with ideas. Maximum length 1500 words.
  Payment negotiable.

Sussex Life
30–32 Teville Road, Worthing, West Sussex BN11 1UG
☎01903 218719   Fax 01903 820193
Owner *Sussex Life Ltd*
Editor *Trudi Linscer*
Circulation 35,000

FOUNDED 1965. MONTHLY. Sussex and general interest magazine. Regular supplements on education, fashion, homes and gardens. Interested in investigative, journalistic pieces relevant to the area and celebrity profiles. No historical pieces. Unsolicited mss, synopses and ideas in writing welcome. Minimum 500 words.
  Payment £15 per 500 words and picture.

Swimming Times
18 Derby Square, Loughborough, Leicestershire LE11 5AL
☎01509 618743   Fax 01509 618746
Owner *Amateur Swimming Association*
Editor *P. Hassall*
Circulation 20,000

FOUNDED 1923. MONTHLY about competitive swimming and associated subjects. Unsolicited mss welcome.
  Features Technical articles on swimming, water polo, diving or synchronised swimming. Length and payment negotiable.

The Tablet
1 King Street Cloisters, Clifton Walk, London W6 0QZ
☎0181 748 8484   Fax 0181 748 1550
E-mail: TheTablet@compuserve.com
Owner *The Tablet Publishing Co Ltd*

Editor *John Wilkins*
Circulation 20,000

FOUNDED 1840. WEEKLY. Quality international Roman Catholic magazine featuring articles – political, social, cultural, theological or spiritual – of interest to concerned Christian laity and clergy. Unsolicited material welcome (1500 words) if relevant to magazine's style and market. All approaches should be made in writing.
  Payment from about £50.

Take a Break
Shirley House, 25–27 Camden Road, London NW1 9LL
☎0171 284 0909
Owner *H. Bauer*
Editor *John Dale*
Circulation 1.3 million

FOUNDED 1990. WEEKLY. True-life feature magazine. Approach with ideas in writing.
  News/Features Always on the look-out for good, true-life stories. Maximum 1200 words. *Payment* negotiable.
  Fiction Sharp, succinct stories which are well told and often with a twist at the end. All categories, provided it is relevant to the magazine's style and market. Maximum 1000 words. *Payment* negotiable.

Talking Business
9/10 Barnard Mews, London SW11 1QU
☎0171 801 0104   Fax 0171 801 0105
Owner *Square One Publishing Ltd*
Editor *Peter Dean*
Circulation 6,500

FOUNDED 1994. MONTHLY. News, reviews, features and charts covering the expanding audiobooks market. Interested in considering business-oriented material and personality profiles. Approach in writing in the first instance.

Taste of Wales
The Food Hall, Royal Welsh Showground, Builth Wells LD2 3SY
☎01982 552952   Fax 01982 553474
Owner *Welsh Food Promotions Ltd*
Editor *Sandra Williams*
Circulation 30,000

FOUNDED 1991. QUARTERLY Welsh national food magazine. Features on Welsh food and drink, food-related tourist attractions and events, interesting people in the food and hospitality industries, new product reviews and recipes. Articles on Welsh food welcome. Max. 1000 words. Contact the editor by phone.
  Payment negotiable.

The Tatler
Vogue House, Hanover Square, London
W1R 0AD
☎0171 499 9080   Fax 0171 409 0451
Owner *Condé Nast Publications Ltd*
Editor *Jane Procter*
Circulation 90,346

Up-market glossy from the Condé Nast stable. New writers should send in copies of either published work or unpublished material; writers of promise will be taken up. The magazine works largely on a commission basis: they are unlikely to publish unsolicited features, but will ask writers to work to specific projects.
　Features *Wendy Holden*

The Tea Club Magazine
PO Box 221, Guildford, Surrey GU1 3YT
☎01483 562888   Fax 01483 302732
Publisher *Bond Clarkson Russell*
Editor *Lorna Swainson*

FOUNDED 1992 by The Tea Council. SIX ISSUES PER YEAR. Specialist focus on tea and tea-related topics. All editorial features are commissioned. Approach with ideas only.

Telegraph Magazine
See under **National Newspapers**
(**The Daily Telegraph**)

The Tennis Times
PO Box 3443, London SE8 5BG
☎0181 692 6302   Fax 0181 692 6302
Editor *Mr R. Richardson*

FOUNDED 1980. QUARTERLY. Events, players, fashion and footwear, rackets, facilities, technique and tactics.

TGO (The Great Outdoors)
195 Albion Street, Glasgow G1 1QP
☎0141 302 7700   Fax 0141 302 7799
Owner *Caledonian Magazines Ltd*
Editor *Cameron McNeish*
Circulation 22,000

FOUNDED 1978. MONTHLY. Deals with walking, backpacking and countryside topics. Unsolicited mss are welcome.
　Features Well-written and illustrated items on relevant topics. Maximum 2000 words. Colour photographs only please.
　News Short topical items (or photographs). Maximum 300 words.
　Payment £100–200 for features; £10–20 for news.

that's life!
2nd Floor, 1–5 Maple Place, London W1P 5FX
☎0171 462 4700   Fax 0171 636 1824
Owner *H. Bauer Publishing Ltd*
Editor *Janice Turner*
Circulation 499,439

FOUNDED 1995. WEEKLY. True-life stories, puzzles, fashion, cookery and fun. Interested in considering true-life stories. Approach by phone or in writing in the first instance.
　Features *Karen Jones* Maximum 1600 words. *Payment* £650.
　Fiction *Emma Fabian* 1200. *Payment* £200–300.

Theologia Cambrensis
Church in Wales Centre, Woodland Place, Penarth, Cardiff CF64 2EX
☎01222 705278   Fax 01222 712413
Owner *The Church in Wales*
Editor *Rev. Nigel John*

FOUNDED 1988. THRICE YEARLY. Concerned exclusively with theology and news of theological interest. Includes religious poetry, letters and book reviews (provided they have a scholarly bias). No secular material. Unsolicited mss welcome. Approach in writing with ideas.

The Third Alternative
5 Martins Lane, Witcham, Ely, Cambridgeshire CB6 2LB
☎01353 777931
Owner *TTA Press*
Editor *Andy Cox*

FOUNDED 1993. Quarterly A4 colour magazine of horror, fantasy, science fiction and slipstream fiction, plus varied features and artwork. Publishes talented newcomers alongside famous authors. Unsolicited mss welcome if accompanied by s.a.e. or International Reply Coupons (no length restriction, but no novels or serialisations). Potential contributors are advised to study the magazine. Contracts are exchanged upon acceptance; payment is upon publication. Winner of British Fantasy Awards. The magazine is supported by **Eastern Arts**.

This England
PO Box 52, Cheltenham, Gloucestershire GL50 1YQ
☎01242 577775   Fax 01242 222034
Owner *This England Ltd*
Editor *Roy Faiers*
Circulation 180,000

FOUNDED 1968. QUARTERLY, with a strong

overseas readership. Celebration of England and all things English: famous people, natural beauty, towns and villages, history, traditions, customs and legends, crafts, etc. Generally a rural basis, with the 'Forgetmenots' section publishing readers' recollections and nostalgia. Up to one hundred unsolicited pieces received each week. Unsolicited mss/ideas welcome. Length 250–2000 words.

Payment £25 per 1000 words.

Time

Brettenham House, Lancaster Place, London WC2E 7TL
☎0171 499 4080   Fax 0171 322 1230

Owner *Time Warner, Inc.*
Editor *Christopher Redman*
Circulation 5.46 million

FOUNDED 1923. WEEKLY current affairs and news magazine. There are few opportunities for freelancers on *Time* as almost all the magazine's content is written by staff members from various bureaux around the world. No unsolicited mss.

Time Out

Universal House, 251 Tottenham Court Road, London W1P 0AB
☎0171 813 3000   Fax 0171 813 6001

Publisher *Tony Elliott*
Editor *Dominic Wells*
Circulation 99,250

FOUNDED 1968. WEEKLY magazine of news and entertainment in London.

Features *Elaine Paterson* 'Usually written by staff writers or commissioned, but it's always worth submitting an idea by phone if particularly apt to the magazine.' Maximum 2500 words.

News *Tony Thompson* Despite having a permanent team of staff news writers, sometimes willing to accept contributions from new journalists 'should their material be relevant to the issue'.

Payment £164 per 1000 words.

The Times Educational Supplement

Admiral House, 66–68 East Smithfield, London E1 9XY
☎0171 782 3000   Fax 0171 782 3200

Owner *News International*
Editor *Caroline St John-Brooks*
Circulation 143,238

FOUNDED 1910. WEEKLY. New contributors are welcome and should fax ideas on one sheet of A4 for news, features or reviews.

Opinion *Caroline St John-Brooks* 'Platform': a weekly slot for a well-informed and cogently argued viewpoint. Max. 1200 words. 'Another Voice': a shorter comment on an issue of the day by non-education professionals. Max. 700 words.

School Management *Bob Doe* Weekly pages on practical issues for school governors and managers. Max. 800 words.

Further Education *Ian Nash* Includes training, college management and lifelong learning.

Friday A weekly magazine with *The TES* which includes:

Features *Sarah Bayliss* Unsolicited features are rarely accepted but ideas are welcome accompanied by cuttings and/or c.v. Length from 1000–2000 words.

Arts and Books *Heather Neill*
Curriculum Materials *Mary Cruickshank*
Resources, TV and Health *Janette Wolf*
Primary *Diane Hofkins*
Secondary *Brendan O'Malley*
Subject of the Week *Joyce Arnold* Subjects covered include: science, music, modern languages, history, geography, mathematics, environmental education, design and technology (includes food, textiles, graphics), special needs. Articles should relate to current educational practice. Age range covered is primary to sixth form. Maximum 1000–1300 words.

Talkback *Jill Craven* Short, first-person pieces, maximum 650 words, are welcome for consideration. Humour from teachers is encouraged, especially for the 'Thank God it's Friday' column.

Primary *Diane Hofkins* A monthly glossy magazine with *The TES*.

Online Education *Merlin John* A magazine devoted to information technology appearing with *The TES* six times a year.

Special Issues Occasional pull-outs on topics including school management (*Bob Doe*), first appointments (*Joyce Arnold*), business links (*Ian Nash*), school visits – *Going Places* – (*Joyce Arnold*).

The Times Educational Supplement Scotland

37 George Street, Edinburgh EH2 2HN
☎0131 220 1100   Fax 0131 220 1616

Owner *Times Supplements Ltd*
Editor *Willis Pickard*
Circulation 9000

FOUNDED 1965. WEEKLY. Unsolicited mss welcome.

Features Articles on education in Scotland. Maximum 1200 words.

News Items on education in Scotland. Maximum 600 words.

The Times Higher Education Supplement

Admiral House, 66–68 East Smithfield,
London E1 9XY
☎0171 782 3000   Fax 0171 782 3300
Owner *News International*
Editor *Auriol Stevens*
Circulation 33,000

FOUNDED 1971. WEEKLY. Unsolicited mss are welcome but most articles and *all* book reviews are commissioned. 'In most cases it is better to write, but in the case of news stories it is all right to phone.'

Books *Andrew Robinson*
Features *Sian Griffiths* Most articles are commissioned from academics in higher education.
News *Clare Sanders-Smith* Freelance opportunities very occasionally.
Science *Kam Patel*
Science Books *Andrew Robinson*
Foreign *David Jobbins*
Payment NUJ rates.

The Times Literary Supplement

Admiral House, 66–68 East Smithfield,
London E1 9XY
☎0171 782 3000   Fax 0171 782 3100
Owner *Times Supplements*
Editor *Ferdinand Mount*
Circulation 34,500

FOUNDED 1902. WEEKLY review of literature. Contributors should approach in writing and be familiar with the general level of writing in the *TLS*.

Literary Discoveries *Alan Jenkins*
Poems *Mick Imlah*
News *Ferdinand Mount* News stories and general articles concerned with literature, publishing and new intellectual developments anywhere in the world. Length by arrangement.
Payment by arrangement.

Titbits

2 Caversham Street, London SW3 4AH
☎0171 351 4995   Fax 0171 351 4995
Owner *Sport Newspapers Ltd*
Editor *James Hughes*
Circulation 150,000

FOUNDED 1895. MONTHLY. Consumer magazine for men covering show business and general interests. Unsolicited mss and ideas in writing welcome. Max. 3000 words. News, features, particularly photofeatures (colour), and fiction.
Payment negotiable.

To & Fro

PO Box 1479, Maidenhead, Berkshire
SL6 8YX
☎01628 783080   Fax 01628 633250
Owner *RPA Publishing Ltd*
Editor *Anne Smith*

FOUNDED 1978. BI-MONTHLY specialist machine knitting magazine. Interested in material related to machine knitting only. Unsolicited mss and ideas welcome. Contact the editor in writing in the first instance.

Today's Golfer

Bretton Court, Bretton, Peterborough,
Cambridgeshire PE3 8DZ
☎01733 264666   Fax 01733 465221
Owner *EMAP Pursuit Publishing*
Editor *Neil Pope*
Deputy Editor *David Ayres*
Circulation 60,081

FOUNDED 1988. MONTHLY. Golf instruction, features, player profiles and news. Most features written in-house but unsolicited mss will be considered. Approach in writing with ideas. Not interested in instruction material from outside contributors.

Features/News *Kevin Brown* Opinion, player profiles and general golf-related features.

Today's Runner

Bretton Court, Bretton, Peterborough,
Cambridgeshire PE3 8DZ
☎01733 465924   Fax 01733 465939
Owner *EMAP Pursuit Publishing Ltd*
Editor *Paul Larkins*
Circulation 26,075

FOUNDED 1985. MONTHLY. Instructional articles on running, fitness, and lifestyle, plus running-related activities and health.

Features Specialist knowledge an advantage. Opportunities are wide, but approach with ideas in first instance.
News Opportunities for people stories, especially if backed up by photographs.

Top of the Pops Magazine

Room A1047, Woodlands, 80 Wood Lane,
London W12 0TT
☎0181 576 3910   Fax 0181 576 2694
Owner *BBC Worldwide Publishing*
Editor *Peter Loraine*
Circulation 500,963

FOUNDED 1995. MONTHLY teenage pop music magazine with a lighthearted and humorous approach. No unsolicited material apart from pop star interviews.

Total Football
30 Monmouth Street, Bath BA1 2BW
☎01225 442244   Fax 01225 732248
Owner *Future Publishing*
Editor *Richard Jones*
Circulation 34,791

FOUNDED 1995. MONTHLY. News, features and reviews covering all aspects of domestic and international football. Contributions welcome.
Features *Richard Jones/Alex Murphy* New and interesting angles; particularly funny pieces and fan-based articles. 2000 words maximum. *Payment* negotiable.
News *Richard Jones/Alex Murphy* Unusual stories from all areas of the game – tabloid style. 500 words maximum. *Payment* £75 per 500 words.
Special Pages Celebrity interviews. 500 words maximum. *Payment* £75 per 500 words.

Totem
55 Merches Gardens, Cardiff CF1 7RF
☎01222 377694
Owner *Totem*
Editor *Ishmael Fiifi Annobil*
Circulation 500

FOUNDED 1998. QUARTERLY Welsh-based international short story magazine, specialising in English language work from all over the world. No poetry or non-fiction. Aims to capture the diverse approaches to global story-telling traditions and provides a vital forum often denied the short story writer. Length: 2000–3500 words. Original items only. No translations. A brief biography required (150 words maximum), and a photo of the author. Send s.a.e. or IRCs.
Payment two copies of the issue featuring the author's work.

Tourer
Warners Group Publications plc, The Maltings, West Street, Bourne, Lincolnshire PH10 9PH
☎01778 391027   Fax 01778 425437
Editor *Nick Harding*
Circulation 45,000

FOUNDED 1998. Travel/lifestyle MONTHLY aimed at the owners of the estimated 500,000 touring caravans and 100,000 motorcaravans in the UK.

Tourism Times
MSP Publishing, PO Box 582, Jersey JE4 8XQ
☎01534 611600   Fax 01534 611610
Owner *The Guiton Group*
Editor *Alex Mallinson*

Circulation 5000

FOUNDED 1993. BI-ANNUAL travel trade newspaper of the Jersey tourist industry. Contributions from travel experts welcome; interesting tourism stories which relate to the Channel Islands – 1000 words maximum. Approach by phone in the first instance.

Town and Country Post
Bridge House, Blackden Lane, Goostrey, Cheshire CW4 8PZ
☎01477 534440   Fax 01477 535756
E-mail: post2001@aol.com
Owner *Town and Country Post Ltd*
Editor *John Williams*
Circulation 28,000

FOUNDED 1981. MONTHLY. Local news and features on mid-Cheshire. Very little freelance material is used. No unsolicited mss. Approach by telephone in the first instance.

Townswoman
Media Associates, 8 Capitol House, Heigham Street, Norwich, Norfolk NR2 4TE
☎01603 616005   Fax 01603 767397
Owner *Townswomen's Guilds*
Editor *Moira Eagling*
Circulation 30,000

FOUNDED 1933. QUARTERLY. No unsolicited mss. Few opportunities as in-house editorial staff are strong.

Traditional Woodworking
The Well House, High Street, Burton on Trent, Staffordshire DE14 1JQ
☎01283 742950   Fax 01283 561077
Owner *Waterways World*
Editor *Helen Adkins*

FOUNDED 1988. MONTHLY. Features workshop projects, techniques, reviews of the latest woodworking tools and equipment, general articles on woodworking and furniture making.
Features Technique features and furniture projects welcome. The latter must include drawings and cutting lists. A photograph of the piece is required before commissioning. *Payment* negotiable. Approach in writing in the first instance.

Trail
Bretton Court, Bretton, Peterborough, Cambridgeshire PE3 8DZ
☎01733 264666   Fax 01733 465939
Owner *EMAP Pursuit Publishing Ltd*
Editor *Victoria Tebbs*
Circulation 30,653

FOUNDED 1990. MONTHLY. Gear reports, where

to walk and practical advice for the hillwalker and long distance walker. Inspirational reads on people and outdoor/walking issues. Health, fitness and injury prevention for high level walkers and outdoor lovers. Approach by phone or in writing in the first instance.

Features *Victoria Tebbs* Very limited requirement for overseas articles, 'written to our style'. Ask for guidelines. Maximum 2000 words.

Big requirement for guided walks articles. Specialist writers only. Ask for guidelines. Maximum 750–2000 words (depending on subject). *Payment* £80 per 1000 words.

Traveller

45–49 Brompton Road, London SW3 1DE
☎0171 581 4130   Fax 0171 581 1357
Owner *I. M. Wilson*
Editor *Miranda Haines*
Circulation 35,359

FOUNDED 1970. QUARTERLY. **Features** Six colour features per issue. Copy must be accompanied by good-quality colour transparencies. Articles welcome on off-beat cultural or anthropological subjects. Western Europe rarely covered. No general travel accounts. Max. 2000 words. *Payment* £150 per 1000 words.

Trout Fisherman

Bretton Court, Bretton, Peterborough, Cambridgeshire PE3 8DZ
☎01733 264666   Fax 01733 465436
Owner *EMAP Pursuit Publications*
Editor *Chris Dawn*
Circulation 42,220

FOUNDED 1977. MONTHLY instructive magazine on trout fishing. Most of the articles are commissioned, but unsolicited mss and quality colour transparencies welcome.

Features Maximum 2500 words.
Payment varies.

Turkeys

PO Box 18, Bishopsdale, Leyburn DL8 3YY
☎01969 663764   Fax 01969 663764
Owner *Fancy Fowl Publications Ltd*
Editor *Shirley Murdoch*
Circulation 3000

BI-MONTHLY publication aiming to deal with all aspects of turkey breeding, growing, processing and marketing at an international level. Specialist technical information from qualified contributors will always be considered. Length by arrangement. No unsolicited mss. Approach in writing with ideas, or by phone. *Payment* £70 per 1000 words.

TV Times

King's Reach Tower, Stamford Street, London SE1 9LS
☎0171 261 5000   Fax 0171 261 7777
Owner *IPC Magazines*
Editor *Liz Murphy*
Circulation 883,281

FOUNDED 1955. WEEKLY magazine of listings and features serving the viewers of independent television, BBC, satellite and radio. Almost no freelance contributions used, except where the writer is known and trusted by the magazine. No unsolicited contributions.

Twinkle

2 Albert Square, Dundee DD1 2QJ
☎01382 223131 ext. 4149 Fax 01382 322214
Owner *D. C. Thomson & Co. Ltd*
Editor *Bill Moodie*
Circulation 65,000

FOUNDED 1968. WEEKLY magazine for 5–7-year-olds. Mainly picture stories but some text-based pieces. Will consider unsolicited material but would-be contributors are advised to study the magazine first. 500-600 words maximum for text-based stories.

Ulster Tatler

39 Boucher Road, Belfast BT12 6UT
☎01232 681371   Fax 01232 381915
E-mail: ulstertat@aol.com
Website: http://www.ulstertatler.com
Owner/Editor *Richard Sherry*
Circulation 15,000

FOUNDED 1965. MONTHLY. Articles of local interest and social functions appealing to Northern Ireland's ABC1 population. Welcomes unsolicited material; approach by phone or in writing in the first instance.

Features *Noreen Dorman* Max. 1500 words. *Payment* £50.
Fiction *Richard Sherry* Max. 3000 words. *Payment* £150.

The Universe

St James's Buildings, Oxford Street, Manchester M1 6FP
☎0161 236 8856   Fax 0161 236 8892
Owner *Gabriel Communications Ltd*
Editor *Joe Kelly*
Circulation 80,000

Occasional use of new writers, but a substantial network of regular contributors already exists. Interested in a very wide range of material: all subjects which might bear on Christian life. Fiction not normally accepted.

Payment negotiable.

Vector

See **British Science Fiction Association** under **Professional Associations**

The Vegan

Donald Watson House, 7 Battle Road, St Leonards on Sea, East Sussex TN37 7AA
☎01424 427393   Fax 01424 717064

Owner *Vegan Society*
Editor *Richard Farhall*
Circulation 5000

FOUNDED 1944. QUARTERLY. Deals with the ecological, ethical and health aspects of veganism. Unsolicited mss welcome. Maximum 2000 words.

Payment negotiable.

Veteran Car

Jessamine Court, 15 High Street, Ashwell, Hertfordshire SG7 5NL
☎01462 742818   Fax 01462 742997

Owner *The Veteran Car Club of Great Britain*
Editor *Elizabeth Bennett*
Circulation 1600

FOUNDED 1938. BI-MONTHLY magazine which exists primarily for the benefit of members of The Veteran Car Club of Great Britain. It is concerned with all aspects of the old vehicle hobby – events, restoration, history, current world news, legislation, etc., relating to pre-1919 motor cars. Most professional writers who contribute to the magazine are Club members. No budget for paid contributions.

Vintage Times

PhD Publishing, Navestock Hall, Navestock, Essex RM4 1HA
☎01708 370053

Owner *PhD Publishing*
Editor *David Hoppit*
Circulation 60,000

FOUNDED 1994. QUARTERLY lifestyle magazine 'for over-40s who have not quite given up hope of winning Wimbledon'. Preliminary approach by phone or in writing with ideas.

Vogue

Vogue House, Hanover Square, London W1R 0AD
☎0171 499 9080   Fax 0171 408 0559

Owner *Condé Nast Publications Ltd*
Editor *Alexandra Shulman*
Circulation 202,028

Condé Nast Magazines tend to use known writers and commission what's needed, rather than using unsolicited mss. Contacts are useful.

Features *Louise Chunn* Upmarket general interest rather than 'women's'. Good proportion of highbrow art and literary articles, as well as travel, gardens, food, home interest and reviews. No fiction.

The Voice

370 Coldharbour Lane, London SW9 8PL
☎0171 737 7377   Fax 0171 274 8994
E-mail: veeteeay@gn.apc.org

Owner *Vee Tee Ay Media Resources*
Editor *Annie Stewart*
Circulation 50,060

FOUNDED 1982. WEEKLY newspaper, particularly aimed at the Black British community. Copy for consideration welcome but 'publication is not guaranteed'. Initial approach in writing preferred. Opportunities in both features and news – especially from the regions.

Payment from £100 per 1000 words/negotiable.

Voyager

Mediamark Publishing International, 35 Gresse Street, Rathbone Place, London W1P 1PN
☎0171 580 3105   Fax 0171 580 1695
E-mail: info@mediamark.co.uk

Owner *Mediamark/British Midland Airways*
Editor *Bill Hagerty*
Circulation 40,000

TEN ISSUES PER YEAR. In-flight magazine of British Midland Airways. European lifestyle features and profiles, plus British Midland information. No unsolicited mss. Approach in writing with ideas in the first instance. No destination travel articles.

The War Cry

101 Queen Victoria Street, London EC4P 4EP
☎0171 332 0022   Fax 0171 236 3491

Owner *The Salvation Army*
Editor *Captain Charles King*
Circulation 80,000

FOUNDED 1879. WEEKLY magazine containing Christian comments on current issues. Unsolicited mss welcome if appropriate to contents. No fiction or poetry. Approach by phone with ideas.

News relating to Christian Church or social issues. Maximum length 500 words. *Payment* £20 per article.

Features Magazine-style articles of interest to the 'man/woman-in-the-street'. Maximum length 500 words. *Payment* £20 per article.

The Water Gardener
Somerfield House, Wotton Road, Ashford, Kent TN23 6LW
☎01233 621877   Fax 01233 645669
Owner *Dog World Publishing*
Editor *Yvonne Rees*
Circulation 23,568

FOUNDED 1994. NINE ISSUES PER YEAR. Everything relevant to water gardening. Will consider in-depth features on aspects of the subject; write with idea in the first instance. Maximum 2000 words.
Payment by negotiation.

Waterways World
The Well House, High Street, Burton on Trent, Staffordshire DE14 1JQ
☎01283 742950   Fax 01283 742957
E-mail: ww@wellhouse.easynet.co.uk
Owner *Waterways World Ltd*
Editor *Hugh Potter*
Circulation 22,408

FOUNDED 1972. MONTHLY magazine for inland waterway enthusiasts. Unsolicited mss welcome, provided the writer has a good knowledge of the subject. No fiction.
Features *Hugh Potter* Articles (preferably illustrated) are published on all aspects of inland waterways in Britain and abroad, including recreational and commercial boating on rivers and canals.
News *Regan Milnes* Maximum 500 words.
Payment £37 per 1000 words.

Waymark
Woodlands, West Lane, Sutton in Craven, Keighley, West Yorkshire BD20 7AS
☎01535 637957   Fax 01535 637576
Editor *Stephen Jenkinson*
Circulation 800

FOUNDED 1986. QUARTERLY journal of the Institute of Public Rights of Way Officers. Glossy, spot colour magazine for countryside access managers in England and Wales, employed throughout the public and private sectors. Also available to non-members by subscription.
News Most produced in-house but some opportunities for original/off-beat items. Maximum 500 words.
Features Ideas welcome on any topic broadly relating to the British countryside and public access to it. Controversial, thought pro-voking pieces readily considered. Maximum 1500 words.
Special Pages Cartoons or brief humorous items on an access or countryside/environmental theme welcome. Send ideas in writing with s.a.e. initially.
Payment negotiable, up to £25.

Wedding and Home
King's Reach Tower, Stamford Street, London SE1 9LS
☎0171 261 7471   Fax 0171 261 7459
Owner *IPC Magazines Ltd*
Editor *Christine Prunty*
Circulation 47,427

BI-MONTHLY offering ideas and inspiration for women planning their wedding. Most features are written in-house or commissioned from known freelancers. Unsolicited mss are not welcome, but approaches may be made in writing.

Weekly News
Albert Square, Dundee DD1 9QJ
☎01382 223131   Fax 01382 201390
Owner *D. C. Thomson & Co. Ltd*
Editor *David Hishmurgh*
Circulation 206,302

FOUNDED 1855. WEEKLY. Newsy, family-orientated magazine designed to appeal to the busy housewife. 'We get a lot of unsolicited stuff and there is great loss of life among them.' Usually commissions, but writers of promise will be taken up. Series include showbiz, royals and television. No fiction.
Payment negotiable.

West Lothian Life
Ballencrieff Cottage, Ballencrieff Toll, Bathgate, West Lothian EH48 4LD
☎01506 632728   Fax 01506 635444
E-mail: Suse.Coon@pages.clara.net
Owner *Pages Editorial & Publishing Services*
Editor *Susan Coon*

QUARTERLY county magazine for people who live, work or have an interest in West Lothian. Includes three or four major features (1500 words) on successful people, businesses or initiatives. A local walk takes up the centre spread. Regular articles by experts on collectables, property, interior design, cookery and local gardening, plus news items, letters and a competition. Freelance writers used exclusively for main features. Phone first to discuss content and timing.
Payment by arrangement.

What Car?

60 Waldegrave Road, Teddington, Middlesex
TW11 8LG
☎0181 943 5000   Fax 0181 943 5750

Owner *Haymarket Motoring Publications Ltd*
Editor *Mark Payton*
Circulation 153,164

MONTHLY. The car buyer's bible, *What Car?*
concentrates on road test comparisons of new
cars, news and buying advice on used cars, as
well as a strong consumer section. Some scope
for freelancers. Testing is only offered to the
few, and general articles on aspects of driving
are only accepted from writers known and
trusted by the magazine. No unsolicited mss.
Payment negotiable.

What Hi-Fi?

38–42 Hampton Road, Teddington,
Middlesex TW11 0JE
☎0181 943 5000   Fax 0181 943 5019

Owner *Haymarket Magazines Ltd*
Editor *Jez Ford*
Publishing Editor *Rahiel Nasir*
Circulation 74,087

FOUNDED 1976. MONTHLY. Features on hi-fi
and new technology. No unsolicited contributions. Prior consultation with the editor essential.
   Features General or more specific on hi-fi
and new technology pertinent to the consumer
electronics market.
   Reviews Specific product reviews. All
material is now generated by in-house staff.
Freelance writing no longer accepted.

What Investment

3rd Floor, 4–8 Tabernacle Street, London
EC2A 4LU
☎0171 638 1916   Fax 0171 638 3128

Owner *Charterhouse Communications*
Editor *Sarah Barnett*
Circulation 37,000

FOUNDED 1983. MONTHLY. Features articles
on a variety of savings and investment matters.
All approaches should be made in writing.
   Features Length 1200–1500 words (maximum 2000). *Payment* NUJ rates minimum.

What Mortgage

4–8 Tabernacle Street, London EC2A 4LU
☎0171 638 1916   Fax 0171 638 3128

Owner *Charterhouse Communications*
Editor *Nia Williams*
Circulation 35,000

FOUNDED 1982. MONTHLY magazine on property purchase, choice and finance. No unso-

licited material; prospective contributors may
make initial contact with ideas either by telephone or in writing.
   Features Up to 1500 words on related topics
are considered. Particularly welcome are new
angles, ideas or specialities relevant to mortgages.
Payment £150 per 1000 words.

What Satellite TV

WV Publications, 57–59 Rochester Place,
London NW1 9JU
☎0171 331 1000   Fax 0171 331 1241

Owner *WV Publications*
Editor *Geoff Bains*
Circulation 65,000

FOUNDED 1986. MONTHLY including news,
technical information, equipment tests, programme background, listings. Contributions
welcome – phone first.
   Features *Geoff Bains* Unusual installations
and users. In-depth guides to popular/cult
shows. Technical tutorials.
   News *Mark Newman* Industry and programming. 250 words maximum.

What's New in Building

Miller Freeman House, 30 Calderwood Street,
London SE18 6QH
☎0181 855 7777   Fax 0181 854 8058

Owner *Miller Freeman plc*
Editor *Mark Pennington*
Circulation 31,496

MONTHLY. Specialist magazine covering new
products for building. Unsolicited mss not generally welcome. The only freelance work available is rewriting press release material. This is
offered on a monthly basis of 25–50 items of
about 150 words each.
   Payment £5.25 per item.

What's On in London

180–182 Pentonville Road, London N1 9LB
☎0171 278 4393   Fax 0171 837 5838

Owner *E. G. Shaw*
Editor *Michael Darvell*
Circulation 40,000

FOUNDED 1935. WEEKLY entertainment-based
guide and information magazine. Features, listings and reviews. Always interested in well-
thought-out and well-presented mss. Articles
should have London/Home Counties connection, except during the summer when they can
be of a wider tourist/historic interest, relating
to unusual traditions and events. Approach the
editor by telephone in the first instance.
   Features *Graham Hassell*

Art *Ria Higgins*
Cinema *David Clark*
Pop Music *Danny Scott*
Classical Music *Michael Darvell*
Theatre *Neil Smith*
Events *Roger Foss*
Payment by arrangement.

Whatson UK

PO Box 6160, Birmingham B16 8XA
☎0121 643 1575   Fax 0121 643 4450
Managing Editor *Sam Allen*
Editor *Kim Gould*
Circulation 30–50,000

FOUNDED 1990. MONTHLY music-orientated magazine aimed at 18–30-year-olds. Interested in youth entertainment items; approach in writing. No unsolicited mss.

Wine

Quest Magazines Ltd., 652 Victoria Road, South Ruislip, Middlesex HA4 0SX
☎0181 842 1010   Fax 0181 841 2557
Owner *Wilmington Publishing*
Editor *Susan Vumback Low*
Circulation 35,000

FOUNDED 1983. MONTHLY. No unsolicited mss. **News/Features** Wine, food and food/wine-related travel stories. Prospective contributors should approach in writing.

Wisden Cricket Monthly

25 Down Road, Merrow, Guildford, Surrey GU1 2PY
☎01483 570358   Fax 01483 533153
Owner *Wisden Cricket Magazines Ltd*
Editor *Tim de Lisle*
Circulation 25,000

FOUNDED 1979. MONTHLY. Very few uncommissioned articles are used, but would-be contributors are not discouraged. Approach in writing. *Payment* varies.

Woman

King's Reach Tower, Stamford Street, London SE1 9LS
☎0171 261 5000   Fax 0171 261 5997
Owner *IPC Magazines Ltd*
Editor *Carole Russell*
Circulation 731,754

Long-running, popular women's magazine which boasts a readership of over 2.5 million. No unsolicited mss. Most work commissioned. Approach with ideas in writing.
    Features *Kate Corr* Maximum 1250 words.
    Books *Gillian Carter*

Woman and Home

King's Reach Tower, Stamford Street, London SE1 9LS
☎0171 261 5000   Fax 0171 261 7346
Owner *IPC Magazines Ltd*
Editor *Jan Henderson*
Circulation 344,041

FOUNDED 1926. MONTHLY. No unsolicited mss. Prospective contributors are advised to write with ideas, including photocopies of other published work or details of magazines to which they have contributed. S.a.e. essential for return of material. Most freelance work is specially commissioned.

Woman's Journal

King's Reach Tower, Stamford Street, London SE1 9LS
☎0171 261 6220   Fax 0171 261 7061
Owner *IPC Magazines Ltd*
Editor *Marcelle d'Argy Smith*
Circulation 121,546

MONTHLY. Original feature ideas on 35+ women and their lives welcome, with samples of previous work. Major features are generally commissioned.
    Payment negotiable.

Woman's Own

King's Reach Tower, Stamford Street, London SE1 9LS
☎0171 261 5474   Fax 0171 261 5346
Owner *IPC Magazines Ltd*
Editor *Keith McNeill*
Circulation 702,765

WEEKLY. Prospective contributors should contact the features editor *in writing* in the first instance before making a submission.
    Features *Keith Richmond*
    Fiction No unsolicited fiction.

Woman's Realm

King's Reach Tower, Stamford Street, London SE1 9LS
☎0171 261 5000
Fax 0171 261 5326/261 7678 (Features)
Owner *IPC Magazines Ltd*
Editor *Kathy Watson*
Deputy Editor *Linda Belcher*
Circulation 230,373

FOUNDED 1958. WEEKLY. Some scope here for freelancers. Write to the appropriate editor.
    Features *Ktima Heathcote* General, real-life and human interest. No unsolicited mss.
    Fiction Two short stories used every week, a

one-pager (up to 1200 words), plus a longer one (2500 words). Unsolicited mss not accepted.

Woman's Weekly

King's Reach Tower, Stamford Street,
London SE1 9LS
☎0171 261 5000   Fax 0171 261 6322
Owner *IPC Magazines Ltd*
Editor *Olwen Rice*
Deputy Editor *Frances Quinn*
Circulation 638,306

Mass-market women's WEEKLY.

Features Inspiring, positive human interest stories, especially first-hand experiences, of up to 1200 words. Freelancers used regularly but tend to be experienced magazine journalists. Synopses and ideas should be submitted in writing.

Fiction *Gaynor Davies* Short stories 1000–2500 words; serials 12,000–30,000 words. Guidelines for serials: 'a strong emotional theme with a conflict not resolved until the end'; short stories should have warmth and originality.

Wonderland

See **Kent Fantasy Society** under **Literary Societies**

Woodworker

Nexus House, Boundary Way, Hemel Hempstead, Hertfordshire HP2 7ST
☎01442 266551   Fax 01442 266998
Owner *Nexus Special Interests*
Editor *Mark Ramuz*
Circulation 45,000

FOUNDED 1901. MONTHLY. Contributions welcome; approach with ideas in writing.

Features Articles on woodworking with good photo support appreciated. Max. 2000 words. *Payment* £40–60 per page.

News Stories and photos (b&w) welcome. Max. 300 words. *Payment* £10–25 per story.

World Fishing

Nexus House, Swanley, Kent BR8 8HY
☎01322 660070   Fax 01322 666408
Owner *Nexus Media Ltd*
Editor *Mark Say*
Circulation 6,700

FOUNDED 1952. MONTHLY. Unsolicited mss welcome; approach by phone or in writing with an idea.

News/Features of a technical or commercial nature relating to the commercial fishing and fish processing industries worldwide. Maximum 1000 words.
Payment by arrangement.

World of Bowls

2 Scotgate Mews, Stamford, Lincolnshire PE9 2FX
☎01780 480977   Fax 01780 480988
Owner *HBP Ltd*
Editor *Chris Mills*
Circulation 10,000

MONTHLY on all aspects of flat green bowling. Welcomes personality pieces. Approach in writing in the first instance.

Features Unusual, off-the-wall bowling features. Maximum 1000 words.

News Hard news stories. Maximum 200 words. *Payment* by negotiation.

The World of Interiors

Vogue House, Hanover Square, London W1R 0AD
☎0171 499 9080   Fax 0171 493 4013
Owner *Condé Nast Publications Ltd*
Editor *Min Hogg*
Circulation 69,766

FOUNDED 1981. MONTHLY. Best approach by phone, fax or letter with an idea, preferably with reference snaps or guidebooks.

Features *Sarah Howell* Most feature material is commissioned. 'Subjects tend to be found by us, but we are delighted to receive suggestions of interiors, archives, little-known museums, collections, etc. unpublished elsewhere, and would love to find new writers.'

World Soccer

King's Reach Tower, Stamford Street,
London SE1 9LS
☎0171 261 5737   Fax 0171 261 7474
Owner *IPC Magazines Ltd*
Editor *Gavin Hamilton*
Circulation 54,554

FOUNDED 1960. MONTHLY. Unsolicited material welcome but initial approach by phone or in writing preferred. News and features on world soccer.

Writers News/Writing Magazine

PO Box 4, Nairn IV12 4HU
☎01667 455050   Fax 01667 454401
Owner *David St John Thomas*
Editor *Richard Bell*
Circulation 18,500(WN)/35,000(WM)

FOUNDED 1989. MONTHLY/BI-MONTHLY magazines containing news and advice for writers. *Writers News* is exclusive to mail-order members who also receive *Writing Magazine* which is available on newsstands. No poetry or general items

---

on 'how to become a writer'. Receive 1000 mss each year. Approach in writing.

News *Carolyn Stowe* Exclusive news stories of interest to writers. Max. 350 words.

Features *Richard Bell* How-to articles of interest to professional writers. Max. 2000 words.

Xenos
22 Poplar Street, Haslingden, Rossendale BB4 5LY
☎01706 211590
E-mail: xenos@xenos.demon.co.uk
Website: http://www.xenos.demon.co.uk
Editor *Stephen Copestake*

FOUNDED 1990. BI-MONTHLY. Science fiction, fantasy, horror, occult, humour, mystery and suspense short story digest. Devoted to a very wide definition of 'fantasy'. 'We favour an optimistic emphasis and demand real plots/characterisation. No mood pieces; purely romantic stories, blood and gore, navel-gazing angst or pornographic/experimental material.' No bad language. No poetry or plays. Length 2000–10,000 words – anything outside this range will not be read. All stories printed are evaluated by readers and their comments printed in the subsequent issue. All submissions receive free and prompt analysis by the editor, plus suggestions for revision if appropriate. All submissions *must* be accompanied by s.a.e. or IRCs and be well presented. No submissions by e-mail. Annual competition with cash prizes (see entry under **Prizes**). Single issue £3.45; annual subscription £16.50. Special services: novel evaluation (s.a.e. for details) and 'Writers' Tips', a bi-monthly listing of writing markets; £15 per annum.

Yachting Monthly
King's Reach Tower, Stamford Street, London SE1 9LS
☎0171 261 6040   Fax 0171 261 7555
Owner *IPC Magazines Ltd*
Editor *James Jerman*
Circulation 38,018

FOUNDED 1906. MONTHLY magazine for yachting enthusiasts. Unsolicited mss welcome, but many are received and not used. Prospective contributors should make initial contact in writing.

Features *Paul Gelder* A wide range of features concerned with maritime subjects and cruising under sail; well-researched and innovative material always welcome, especially if accompanied by colour transparencies. Maximum 2750 words.

Payment £90–£110 per 1000 words.

Yachting World
King's Reach Tower, Stamford Street, London SE1 9LS
☎0171 261 6800   Fax 0171 261 6818
Owner *IPC Magazines Ltd*
Editor *Andrew Bray*
Circulation 34,197

FOUNDED 1894. MONTHLY with international coverage of yacht racing, cruising and yachting events. Will consider well researched and written sailing stories. Preliminary approaches should be by phone for news stories and in writing for features.

Payment by arrangement.

You – The Mail on Sunday Magazine
See under **National Newspapers (The Mail on Sunday)**

You and Your Wedding
Silver House, 31–35 Beak Street, London W1R 3LD
☎0171 437 2998 (editorial)Fax 0171 287 8655
Owner *AIM Publications Ltd*
Editor *Carole Hamilton*
Circulation 58,000

FOUNDED 1985. BI-MONTHLY. Anything relating to weddings, setting up home, and honeymoons. No unsolicited mss. Ideas may be submitted in writing only, especially travel features. No phone calls.

Young Telegraph
346 Old Street, London EC1V 9NQ
☎0171 684 4000   Fax 0171 613 3372
Editor *Kitty Melrose*
Circulation 1.25 million

FOUNDED 1990. WEEKLY colour supplement for 8–12-year-olds. Unsolicited mss and ideas in writing welcome.

Features *Richard Mead* Usually commissioned. Any youth-orientated material. Maximum 500 words.

News *Victoria Stanley* Short, picture-led articles always welcome. Maximum 80 words.

Payment by arrangement.

Young Writer
Glebe House, Weobley, Hereford HR4 8SD
☎01544 318901   Fax 01544 318901
Editor *Kate Jones*

Describing itself as 'The Magazine for Children with Something to Say', *Young Writer* is issued three times a year, at the back-to-school times of

September, January and April. A forum for young people's writing – fiction and non-fiction, prose and poetry – the magazine is an introduction to independent writing for young writers.

Payment from £20 to £100 for freelance commissioned articles.

Your Cat Magazine

Apex House, Oundle Road, Peterborough, Cambridgeshire PE2 9NP
☎01733 898100   Fax 01733 898487
Owner *EMAP Apex*
Editor *Sue Parslow*

FOUNDED 1994. MONTHLY magazine giving practical information on the care of cats and kittens, pedigree and non-pedigree, plus a wide range of general interest items on cats. Will consider 'true life' cat stories (maximum 900 words) and quality fiction. Send synopsis in the first instance. 'No articles written as though by a cat.'

Your Garden Magazine

IPC Magazines Ltd., Westover House, West Quay Road, Poole, Dorset BH15 1JG
☎01202 680603   Fax 01202 674335
Owner *IPC Magazines Ltd*
Editor *Michael Pilcher*
Circulation 55,191

FOUNDED 1993. MONTHLY full colour glossy for all gardeners. Welcomes good, solid gardening advice that is well written. Receives approx 50 mss per month but only five per cent are accepted. Always approach in writing in the first instance.

Features *Michael Pilcher* Good gardening features, preferably with a new slant. Small gardens only. Maximum 1000 words. Photographs welcome.

Payment negotiable – all rights preferred.

Yours Magazine

Apex House, Oundle Road, Peterborough, Cambridgeshire PE2 9NP
☎01733 555123   Fax 01733 898487
Owner *Choice Publications - Bayard Presse*
Editor *Neil Patrick*
Circulation 266,570

FOUNDED 1973. MONTHLY plus four seasonal specials. Aimed at a readership aged 55 and over.

Features Best approach by letter with outline in first instance. Maximum 1000 words.

News Short, newsy items of interest to readership welcome. Length 300–500 words.

Fiction One or two short stories used in each issue.

Payment negotiable.

ZENE

5 Martins Lane, Witcham, Ely, Cambridgeshire CB6 2LB
☎01353 777931
Owner *TTA Press*
Editor *Andy Cox*

FOUNDED 1994. Features detailed contributors' guidelines of international small press and semi-professional publications, plus varied articles, news, views, reviews and interviews.

Features Unsolicited articles welcome on any aspect of small press publishing: market information, writing, editing, illustrating, interviews and reviews. All genres. Submissions should include adequate return postage. 'Please study the magazine: this will greatly enhance your chances of acceptance.'

The Zone

13 Hazely Combe, Arreton, Isle of Wight PO30 3AJ
☎01983 865668
Publisher *Pigasus Press*
Editor *Tony Lee*

FOUNDED 1994. BI-ANNUAL science fiction magazine. Unsolicited mss welcome but writers are advised to study recent issues and be familiar with the content before sending material. Contributors' guidelines and mail order details available. (All correspondence must be accompanied by an s.a.e. or IRC.)

Fiction Original, imaginative science fiction and fantasy (no supernatural horror), 1000–5000 words. Prose-poems, 60–70 lines; genre verse also appears in the SF poetry showcase, but by invitation only.

Features Interviews with prominent SF authors. Critical articles and essays on any aspect or theme related to SF/fantasy scene, whether topical or retrospective, will be considered. Length 1000–10,000 words. Approach in writing with ideas in the first instance.

Reviews Books, cinema, video and TV. Reviews are usually commissioned but will consider reviews of new SF and non-fiction books. Length 300–500 words.

Payment Token £5 for stories and non-fiction of over 2000 words; otherwise payment in copy only.

Freelance Rates – Magazines

Freelance rates vary enormously. The following minimum rates, negotiated by the **National Union of Journalists**, should be treated as guidelines. Most work can command higher fees from employers whether or not they have NUJ agreements. It is up to freelancers to negotiate the best deal they can.

Examples of NUJ categories for magazines:

Group A (over £10,000 per page of advertising)
Cosmopolitan, Hello!, Radio Times, TV Times, Woman, Woman's Own.

Group B (between £4000 and £10,000 per page of advertising)
The Economist, GQ, Loaded, marie claire, Q, Vanity Fair.

Group C (between £2000 and £4000 per page of advertising)
Architect's Journal, The British Medical Journal, Music Week, The Spectator, Time Out.

Group D (less than £2000 per page of advertising)
Accountancy Age, Nursing Times.

The following figures are the minimum rates which should be paid by magazines in the above groups for first use only:

Features (per 1000 words)

Group A	£350
Group B	£250
Group C	£180
Group D	£130

Cartoons (b&w)

	Group A	Group B&C	Group D
Minimum fee	£94	£76	£60
Feature strip (up to 4 frames)	£116	£101	£94

For colour, charge at least double these rates.

Crosswords

	Group A	Group B&C	Group D
15x15 squares and under	£150	£80	£60
Over 15x15 squares	£200	£120	£80

News Agencies

AP–Dow Jones News Service
10 Fleet Place, London EC4M 7RB
☎0171 832 9105   Fax 0171 832 9101

A real-time financial and business newswire operated by The Associated Press, the US news agency, and Dow Jones & Co., publishers of *The Wall Street Journal*. No unsolicited material.

Associated Press News Agency
12 Norwich Street, London EC4A 1BP
☎0171 353 1515
Fax 0171 353 8118 (Newsdesk)

Material is either generated in-house or by regulars. Hires the occasional stringer. No unsolicited mss.

National News Press and Photo Agency
109 Clifton Street, London EC2A 4LD
☎0171 684 3000   Fax 0171 684 3030

All press releases welcome. Most work is ordered or commissioned. Coverage includes courts, tribunals, conferences, general news, etc. – words and pictures – as well as PR.

PA News Ltd
292 Vauxhall Bridge Road, London SW1V 1AE
☎0171 963 7000
Fax 0171 963 7192 (24-hr Newsdesk)

No unsolicited material. Most items are produced in-house though occasional outsiders may be used. A phone call to discuss specific material may lead somewhere 'but this is rare'.

Reuters Ltd
85 Fleet Street, London EC4P 4AJ
☎0171 250 1122

No unsolicited mss.

Solo Syndication Ltd
49-53 Kensington High Street, London W8 5ED
☎0171 376 2166   Fax 0171 938 3165

FOUNDED 1978. *Specialises* in world-wide newspaper syndication of photos, features and cartoons. Professional contributors only.

Worldwide Media Limited
PO Box 3821, London NW2 4DQ
☎0181 452 6241   Fax 0181 452 7258

FOUNDED 1995. Supplies magazines around the world with well-written feature articles, most of which focus on women's interests and health topics. Commissions a large proportion of the features it syndicates. 'Often looking for freelance writers to research and write specific pieces.'

Television and Radio

BBC TV and Radio

The BBC's major restructuring resulted in two directorates: BBC Production and BBC Broadcast under which both network television and radio were brought together as bi-media departments. The Broadcast Directorate is responsible for the commissioning, scheduling and broadcasting of programmes on television and radio. BBC Production includes all the BBC drama producers (television, radio and World Service) in England, as well as education, entertainment, music, arts and factual areas. The bi-media divisions within BBC Production are BBC Arts, BBC Children's Programmes, BBC Documentaries and History, BBC Drama Production, BBC Education Production, BBC Entertainment, BBC Light Entertainment, BBC Features and Events, BBC Classical Music, BBC Music Entertainment, BBC Religion, BBC Science, BBC Sport and BBC Topical Features.

Television

Director of Television *Alan Yentob*
Chief Executive, BBC Broadcast *Will Wyatt*
Chief Executive, BBC Production *Ronald Neil*
Controller, BBC1 *Peter Salmon*
Controller, BBC2 *Mark Thompson*

Radio

Director of Radio/Controller, Radio 1 *Matthew Bannister*
Controller, Radio 2 *James Moir*
Controller, Radio 3 *Nicholas Keynon*
Controller, Radio 4 *James Boyle*

Radio 1 is the popular music-based station; Radio 2 broadcasts popular light entertainment with celebrity presenters; Radio 3 is devoted to classical and contemporary music; Radio 4 is the main news and current affairs station while broadcasting a wide range of other programmes such as consumer matters, wildlife, science, gardening, etc. It also produces the bulk of drama, comedy, serials and readings. Radio 5 Live is the 24-hour news and sport station.

BBC News and Current Affairs

BBC Television Centre, Wood Lane, London W12 7RJ
☎0181 743 8000

Chief Executive, BBC News and Current Affairs *Tony Hall*
Head of Current Affairs *Mark Damazer*
Head of News Programmes *Richard Clemmow*
Head of News Gathering *Richard Sambrook*
Director, Continuous News *Jenny Abramsky*
Head of Political Programmes *Samir Shah*
Head of Business Programmes *Helen Boaden*
Managing Editor, World News *Peter Knowles*

News and current affairs broadcasting across television and radio were unified as a bi-media directorate in 1987. BBC World is the new 24-hour international television news channel.

PROGRAMME EDITORS
Editor, Breakfast News *Andrew Thompson*
Editor, One O'Clock News/Six O'Clock News *Gary Rogers*
Editor, Nine O'Clock News *Jonathan Baker*
Editor, Newsnight *Sian Kevill*
Editor, Today *Rod Liddle*
Editor, The World at One/PM *Kevin Marsh*
Editor, Ceefax *Peter Clifton*
Head of Subtitling *Ruth Griffiths*

Ceefax

Room 7013, BBC Television Centre, Wood Lane, London W12 7RJ
☎0181 576 1801

The BBC's main news and information service, broadcasting hundreds of pages on both BBC1, BBC2 and the 24 hour news channel. It is on the air at all times when transmitters are broadcasting.

Subtitling

Room 1468, BBC White City, Wood Lane, London W12 7RJ
☎0181 752 7054/0141 339 8844 ext. 2128

A rapidly expanding service available via Ceefax page 888. Units based in both London and Glasgow.

BBC Arts

EM07 East Tower, BBC Television Centre, Wood Lane, London W12 9RJ
☎0181 895 6770/6500   Fax 0181 895 6586

Head of BBC Arts *Kim Evans*
Editor, Arts Features *Keith Alexander*
Series Editor, Omnibus *Gillian Greenwood*
Series Editor, Arena *Anthony Wall*

Editor, Arts Features *Keith Alexander*
Editor, Radio *John Boundy*
Editor, World Service *Jenny Bowen*

Television, radio and World Service production of Arts programmes such as *Omnibus, Arena, Late Review, Night Waves* and *Meridian.*

BBC Children's Programes
BBC Television Centre, Wood Lane, London W12 7RJ
☎0181 743 8000

Head of BBC Children's Programmes
Lorraine Heggessey
Executive Producer, Children's Drama
Richard Langridge
Executive Producer, Light Entertainment
Christopher Pilkington
Executive Producer, Factual Programmes
Eric Rowan
Editor, Blue Peter *Oliver MacFarlane*
Producer, Grange Hill *Stephen Andrew*
Editor, Live & Kicking *Christopher Bellinger*
Editor, Newsround *Susie Staples*

BBC Documentaries and History
BBC White City: 201 Wood Lane, London W12 7TS
☎0181 752 5252   Fax 0181 752 6060

Head of BBC Documentaries and History, Television *Paul Hamann*
Editor, Inside Story *Olivia Lichtenstein*
Editor, Modern Times *Stephen Lambert*
Editor, Reputations *Janice Hadlow*
Editor, Timewatch *Laurence Rees*

BBC Drama Production
TV
BBC Television Centre, Wood Lane, London W12 7RJ
☎0181 743 8000

Controller, BBC Drama *Colin Adams*
Head of Serials *Michael Wearing*
Head of Series *Mal Young*
Head of Single Drama & Films *David Thompson*
Head of TV Drama (Birmingham) *Tony Virgo*

Radio
Broadcasting House, London W1A 1AA
☎0171 580 4468

Head of Radio Drama *Kate Rowland*

Executive Producer *Jeremy Mortimer*
Executive Producer *Eoin O'Callaghan*
Executive Producer *David Hunter*
Executive Producer (Manchester) *Sue Roberts*
Executive Producer (Birmingham)/ Editor, The Archers *Vanessa Whitburn*
Executive Producer (World Service Drama) *Gordon House*

BBC Radio Drama is produced by the Radio Drama Department (with Production Centres in London, Birmingham and Manchester) and by production teams in Edinburgh, Belfast and Cardiff. The Department is divided into six production teams and produces drama and readings for broadcast on Radios 2, 3, 4, 5-Live and the World Service. Writers interested in proposing dramatisations of extant work should check with the Department to ensure that the work has not already been dramatised for radio. All mss should be accompanied by s.a.e. Response time is approx. 3–4 months. Commissioning cycles for Radio Drama are set by the Network commissioners, who are also responsible for all Independent commissioning. For further information and copies of Radio 4's Drama Commissioning Guidelines, contact BBC Radio Drama, Room 6058 at the Broadcasting House address above (enclose an A4 s.a.e.).

BBC Education Production
BBC White City, 201 Wood Lane, London W12 7TS
☎0181 752 5252

Head of BBC Education Production
Marilyn Wheatcroft
Executive Producers, Schools *Clare Elstow, Geoff Marshall-Taylor*

BBC Open University Production Centre
Walton Hall, Milton Keynes, MK7 6BH
☎01908 655544   Fax 01908 376324

Head of Production *Ian Rosenbloom*;

Television and radio production of schools and college programmes, language courses, education for adults, plus multimedia and audiovisual material in partnership with the Open University. The Learning Zone broadcasts education, training and information programmes on BBC2 from midnight during the week.

BBC Entertainment
BBC Television Centre, Wood Lane, London W12 7RJ
☎0181 743 8000

Head of BBC Entertainment *Paul Jackson*

Head of Light Entertainment, Television
  Michael Leggo
Head of Light Entertainment, Radio
  Jonathan James-Moore (at Broadcasting
  House, London W1A 1AA)
Head of Comedy *Geoffrey Perkins*
Script Executive *Bill Dare*
Head of Comedy Entertainment
  Jon Plowman
Head of Factual Entertainment *Tony Moss*

Programmes produced by BBC Entertainment
range from *Only Fools and Horses* and *Jonathan
Creek* on television to *Just a Minute, I'm Sorry I
Haven't a Clue* and *The News Quiz* on Radio 4.
Virtually every comic talent in Britain got their
first break writing one-liners for topical comedy weeklies like Radio 4's *The News Huddlines*
(currently paying about £9 for a 'quickie' –
one- or two-liners). Ideas welcome.

BBC Features and Events
Room 4357, BBC White City Wood Lane,
London W12 7TS
☎0181 752 6945   Fax 0181 752 5915
Head of BBC Features and Events
  Anne Morrison
Editor, Holiday *Jane Lush*
Editor, Crimewatch *Seetha Kumar*

Covers consumer affairs, major national events
and informal education, producing television
and radio progammes such as *Crimewatch, Points
of View* and *Holiday*.

BBC Classical Music
TV
Room EG09, BBC Television Centre,
Wood Lane, London W12 7RJ
☎0181 895 2636

Radio
Room 4105, Broadcasting House,
London W1A 1AA
☎0171 7651810

Head of BBC Classical Music *Roger Wright*
Head of TV Classical Music *Avril MacRory*
Head of Radio Classical Music *Dr John Evans*

Regular programmes include *Composer of the
Week, Record Review* and *Music Matters*.

BBC Music Entertainment
Room 213, Western House, 99 Great
Portland Street, London W1A 1AA
☎0171 765 5407

Head of BBC Music Entertainment
  Trevor Dann

Pop music production for television, radio and
video with programmes such as *Top of the Pops,
Later with Jools* and coverage of the Glastonbury
Festival.

BBC Religion
New Broadcasting House, Oxford Road,
Manchester M60 1SJ
☎0161 200 2020   Fax 0161 244 3183
Head of BBC Religious Broadcasting
  Rev. Ernest Rea
Editor, Religious Programmes
  Helen Alexander

Regular programmes for television include *Songs
of Praise; Everyman; Heart of the Matter*. Radio
output includes *Good Morning Sunday; Sunday
Half Hour; Choral Evensong; Seeds of Faith*.

BBC Science
BBC White City, 201 Wood Lane,
London W12 7TS
☎0181 752 5252

Head of BBC Science *Glenwyn Benson*
Editor, Tomorrow's World *Saul Nasse*
Editor, Horizon *John Lynch*
Editor, QED *Michael Mosley*

Produces programmes such as *Animal Hospital*
and *Tomorrow's World* for television and radio.

BBC Sport
Broadcasting House, London W1A 1AA
☎0171 765 5050
Controller, TV Sport *Jonathan Martin*
Head of Radio Sport Production *Bob
  Shennan*
Editor, Match of the Day/Sportsnight
  Niall Sloane
Editor, Grandstand *David Gordon*

Sports news and commentaries across television
and Radios 1, 4 and 5 Live, with the majority of
output on Radio 5 Live. Regular programmes
include *Sportsnight; Match of the Day; Sports on
Five* and *6-0-6* (presented by David Mellor).

BBC Topical Features
Broadcasting House, London W1A 1AA
☎0171 765 4809

Head of BBC Topical Features *Anne Winder*

Regular programmes include *Woman's Hour;
Desert Island Discs; Loose Ends; Any Questions?*
on Radio 4 and *Pick of the World* on the World
Service.

BBC Birmingham

Broadcasting Centre, Pebble Mill Road,
Birmingham B5 7QQ
☎0121 414 8888   Fax 0121 414 8634

Controller, English Regions *Nigel Chapman*
Head of Network Production *Rod Natkiel*
Head of Regional and Local Programmes
   Laura Dalgleish
Head of Newsgathering *Roger Clark*

Home of the Pebble Mill Studio. Regular programmes include *Midlands Today* and *The Midlands Report*. Output for the network includes: *The Clothes Show; Telly Addicts; Top Gear; The Really Useful Show; Style Challenge; Call My Bluff; Gardener's World; Kilroy*. Openings exist for well-researched topical or local material.

BBC Birmingham serves opt-out stations in Nottingham and Norwich:

BBC East Midlands (Nottingham)

East Midlands Broadcasting Centre,
York House, Mansfield Road, Nottingham
NG1 3JA
☎0115 9550500

Head of Regional and Local Programmes
   Richard Lucas
Head of Newsgathering *Emma Agnew*

Local news programmes such as *East Midlands Today*.

BBC East (Norwich)

St Catherine's Close, All Saint's Green,
Norwich, Norfolk NR1 3ND
☎01603 619331

Head of Regional and Local Programmes
   David Holdsworth
Head of Newsgathering *Tim Bishop*

Regular slots include *Look East* (regional magazine) and *Matter of Fact*.

BBC Bristol

Broadcasting House, Whiteladies Road,
Bristol BS8 2LR
☎0117 9732211

Head of Features *Jeremy Gibson* (bi-media)
Head of Natural History Unit *Alastair Fothergill* (bi-media)

BBC Bristol is the home of the BBC's Natural History Unit, producing programmes such as *Wildlife on One; The Natural World; Land of the Tiger; Animal People*; and *The Really Wild Show* for BBC1 and BBC2. It also produces natural history programmes for Radio 4 and Radio 5

Live. The Features department produces a wide range of television programmes, including *999; Antiques Roadshow; Superstore; Holiday Reps; 10x10; Picture This; Vets in Practice; Driving School; War Walks* and *Under the Sun* in addition to radio programmes specialising in history, travel, literature and human interest features for Radio 4.

BBC Northern Ireland

Broadcasting House, Ormeau Avenue, Belfast
BT2 8HQ
☎01232 338000

Controller *Patrick Loughrey*
Head of Broadcasting *Anna Carragher*
Head of Production *Paul Evans*
Head of News & Current Affairs
   Tony Maddox
Head of Drama *Robert Cooper*
Chief Producer, Features *Charlie Warmington*
Chief Producer, Sport *Terry Smyth*
Chief Producer, Agriculture *Veronica Hughes*
Chief Producer, Music & Arts *Ian Kirk-Smith*
Chief Producer, Youth & Community
   Fedelma Harkin
Chief Producer, Education *Michael McGowan*
Chief Producer, Topical Programmes
   Bruce Batten
Chief Producer, Religion *Bert Tosh*

Regular television programmes include *Newsline 6.30; Hearts and Minds* and *Country Times*. Radio stations: BBC Radio Foyle and BBC Radio Ulster (see entries).

BBC Scotland

Broadcasting House, Queen Margaret Drive,
Glasgow G12 8DG
☎0141 339 8844

Controller *John McCormick*
Head of Production *Colin Cameron*
Head of Broadcast *Ken MacQuarrie*
Head of Drama *To be appointed*
Head of News and Current Affairs
   Kenneth Cargill
Head of Arts & Entertainment *Mike Bolland*
Head of Education & Religious
   Broadcasting *Andrew Barr*

Headquarters of BBC Scotland with centres in Aberdeen, Dundee, Edinburgh and Inverness. Regular programmes include *Reporting Scotland* and *Sportscene* on television and *Good Morning Scotland; People and Power* and *Storyline* on radio.

Aberdeen
Broadcasting House, Beechgrove Terrace,
Aberdeen AB9 2ZT
☎01224 625233

News, plus some features, but most programmes are made in Glasgow. Second TV
centre, also with regular radio broadcasting.

Dundee
Nethergate Centre, 66 Nethergate, Dundee
DD1 4ER
☎01382 202481

News base only; contributors' studio.

Edinburgh
Broadcasting House, Queen Street, Edinburgh
EH2 1JF
☎0131 225 3131

Religious, arts and science programming base.
Bi-media news operation.

Inverness
7 Culduthel Road, Inverness 1V2 4AD
☎01463 720720

News features for Radio Scotland. HQ for Radio
Nan Gaidheal, the Gaelic radio service serving
most of Scotland (**Editor** *Ishbel MacLennan*).

BBC North/BBC North West/BBC North East

The regional centres at Leeds, Manchester and
Newcastle make their own programmes on a
bi-media approach, each centre having its own
head of regional and local programmes.

BBC North (Leeds)
Broadcasting Centre, Woodhouse Lane,
Leeds, West Yorkshire LS2 9PX
☎0113 2441188
Head of Regional and Local Programmes
Colin Philpott
Editor, Newsgathering *Paul Greenan*
**Regional Political Editor/Producer,
North of Westminster** *Geoff Talbott*
Series Producer, Close Up North *Ian Cundall*

BBC North West (Manchester)
New Broadcasting House, Oxford Road,
Manchester M60 1SJ
☎0161 200 2020
Head of Regional and Local Programmes
Martin Brooks
Editor, Newsgathering *Mike Briscoe*
Producers, Northwest Tonight *Tamsin*
O'Brien, Jim Clark

Producer, Close Up North *Deborah van
Bishop*
Producer, Northwestminster *Liam Fogarty*

BBC North East (Newcastle upon Tyne)
Broadcasting Centre, Barrack Road,
Newcastle Upon Tyne NE99 2NE
☎0191 232 1313
Head of Regional and Local Programmes
Olwyn Hocking
Editor, Newsgathering *Andrew Hartley*
Producers, Look North *Iain Williams,
Andrew Lambert*
Producer, North of Westminster
Michael Wild
Series Producer, Close Up North
Jacqui Hodgson
Producers, Close Up North *Dave Morrison,
Barry Wood*

BBC Wales
Broadcasting House, Llandaff, Cardiff
CF5 2YQ
☎01222 322000   Fax 01222 552973
Controller *Geraint Talfan Davies*
Head of Production *John Geraint*
Head of Programmes (Welsh Language)
Gwynn Pritchard
Head of Programmes (English Language)
Dai Smith
Head of News & Current Affairs *Aled Eurig*
Head of Drama *Pedr James*
Series Editor, Pobol y Cwm *William Gwyn*

Headquarters of BBC Wales, with regional
centres in Bangor and Swansea. All Welsh language television programmes are transmitted
by **S4C** and produced in Cardiff or Swansea.
Regular programmes include *Wales Today;
Wales on Saturday;* and *Pobol y Cwm* (Welsh-
language drama series) on television and *Good
Morning Wales; Meet for Lunch; Bore Newydd* and
Post Prynhawn on radio.

Bangor
Broadcasting House, Meirion Road, Bangor,
Gwynedd LL57 2BY
☎01248 370880   Fax 01248 351443
Head of Centre *Marian Wyn Jones*
News only.

Swansea
Broadcasting House, 32 Alexandra Road,
Swansea, West Glamorgan SA1 5DZ
☎01792 654986   Fax 01792 468194
Senior Producer *Geraint Davies*

BBC West/BBC South/BBC South West/BBC South East

The four regional television stations, BBC West, BBC South, BBC South West and BBC South East produce more than 1,100 hours of television each year, including the nightly news magazine programmes, as well as regular 30-minute local current affairs programmes and parliamentary programmes. The leisure programme *Out + About* is also produced regionally. The region operates a comprehensive local radio service. The four stations all have a 'bi-media' approach – which means that both radio and television share their resources – as well as a range of correspondents specialising in health, education, business, local government, home affairs and the environment.

BBC West (Bristol)
Broadcasting House, Whiteladies Road, Bristol BS8 2LR
☎0117 9732211

Head of Regional and Local Programmes
John Conway (Responsible for BBC West, BBC Radio Bristol, BBC Somerset Sound, BBC Radio Gloucestershire and BBC Wiltshire Sound)
Editor, Newsgathering *Ian Cameron*
Series Producer, Close Up West
James Macalpine

BBC South (Southampton)
Broadcasting House, Havelock Road, Southampton, Hampshire SO14 7PU
☎01703 226201

Head of Regional and Local Programmes
Andy Griffee (Responsible for BBC South, BBC Solent and BBC Southern Counties Radio)
Editors, Newsgathering *Mia Costello, Lee Desty*
Series Producer, Southern Eye *Peter Pitt*

BBC South West (Plymouth)
Broadcasting House, Seymour Road, Mannamead, Plymouth, Devon PL3 5BD
☎01752 229201

Head of Regional and Local Programmes
Eve Turner (Responsible for BBC South West, BBC Radio Devon, BBC Radio Cornwall, BBC Radio Guernsey and BBC Radio Jersey)
Editor, Newsgathering *Simon Read*
Editor, Current Affairs *Simon Willis*

BBC South East (Elstree)
Elstree Centre, Clarendon Road, Borehamwood, Hertfordshire WD6 1JF
☎0181 953 6100

Head of Regional and Local Programmes
Jane Mote (Responsible for BBC South East, BBC Radio Kent, BBC Thames Valley FM and BBC GLR)
Editor, Newsgathering *Peter Solomons*
Executive Producer, First Sight *John Samson*

BBC World Service
PO Box 76, Bush House, Strand, London WC2B 4PH
☎0171 240 3456   Fax 0171 379 6729

Managing Director *Sam Younger*
Director, World Service News & Programme Commissioning *Bob Jobbins*

The World Service broadcasts in English and 43 other languages. The English service is round-the-clock, with news and current affairs as the main component. With around 140 million Listeners, excluding countries where research is not possible, it reaches a bigger audience than its five closest competitors combined. The World Service is increasingly available throughout the world on local FM stations, via satellite and on-line as well as through short-wave frequencies. Coverage includes world business, politics, people/events/opinions, development issues, the international scene, developments in science and technology, sport, religion, music, drama, the arts. BBC World Service broadcasting is financed by a grant-in-aid voted by Parliament amounting to £160.9 million for 1998/99.

If you have an idea for a feature programme or series, please direct your enquiry to: Radio News Features 0171 257 2203.

BBC Regional Broadcasting
Room 715, Henry Wood House, 3 & 6 Langham Place, London W1A 1AA
☎0171 580 4468

There are 39 local BBC radio stations in England transmitting on FM and medium wave. These present local news, information and entertainment to local audiences and reflect the life of the communities they serve. They have their own newsroom which supplies local bulletins and national news service. Many have specialist producers. A comprehensive list of programmes for each is unavailable and would soon be out of date. For general information on programming, contact the relevant station direct.

BBC Asian Network

BBC Pebble Mill, Birmingham B5 7SH
☎0121 414 8558   Fax 0121 472 3174

Also at: Epic House, Charles Street, Leicester
LE1 3SH
☎0116 2516688   Fax 0116 2511463

Managing Editor *Vijay Sharma*

Commenced broadcasting in November 1996 to a Midlands audience with programmes in English, Bengali, Gujerati, Hindi, Punjabi and Urdu.

BBC Radio Berkshire

See **Thames Valley FM**

BBC Radio Bristol

PO Box 194, Bristol BS99 7QT
☎0117 9741111   Fax 0117 9732549

Managing Editor *Jenny Lacey*

Wide range of feature material used.

BBC Radio Cambridgeshire

PO Box 96, 104 Hills Road, Cambridge
CB2 1LD
☎01223 259696   Fax 01223 460832

Editor, Local Services *Leo Devine*

Short stories are broadcast occasionally.

BBC Radio Cleveland

Broadcasting House, PO Box 95FM,
Middlesbrough, Cleveland TS1 5DG
☎01642 225211   Fax 01642 211356

Managing Editor *David Peel*
Assistant Editor *John Allard*

Material used is almost exclusively local to Cleveland, Co. Durham and North Yorkshire, and written by local writers. Contributions welcome for *House Call* (Sundays 5–6 pm, presented by Bill Hunter). Poetry and the occasional short story are included.

BBC Radio Cornwall

Phoenix Wharf, Truro, Cornwall TR1 1UA
☎01872 275421   Fax 01872 275045

Senior Broadcast Journalists *Pauline
Causey, Chris Lyddon, Lidia Rapecki*

On air from 1983 serving Cornwall and the Isles of Scilly. The station broadcasts a news/talk format 18 hours a day on 103.9/95.2 FM. Chris Blount's afternoon programme includes interviews with local authors and arts-related features on Cornish themes.

BBC Coventry & Warwickshire

Holt Court, Greyfriars Road, Coventry
CV1 2WR
☎01203 860086   Fax 01203 570100

Managing Editor *David Robey*
Senior Editor *Conal O'Donnell*

News, current affairs, public service information and community involvement, relevant to its broadcast area: Coventry and Warwickshire. Occasionally uses the work of local writers, though cannot handle large volumes of unsolicited material. Any material commissioned will need to be strong in local interest and properly geared to broadcasting.

BBC Radio Cumbria

Annetwell Street, Carlisle, Cumbria
CA3 8BB
☎01228 592444   Fax 01228 511195

Editor, Local Services *Nigel Dyson*

Few opportunities for writers apart from *Write Now*, a weekly half-hour regional local writing programme, shared with BBC Radio Merseyside, BBC GMR and BBC Radio Lancashire (see BBC Radio Merseyside).

BBC Radio Derby

PO Box 269, Derby DE1 3HL
☎01332 361111   Fax 01332 290794

Managing Editor *Mike Bettison*

News and information (the backbone of the station's output), local sports coverage, daily magazine and phone-ins, minority interest, Asian and West Indian weekly programmes.

BBC Radio Devon

PO Box 5, Broadcasting House, Seymour Road, Plymouth, Devon PL3 5YQ
☎01752 260323   Fax 01752 234599

Managing Editor *John Lilley*

Short stories – up to 1000 words from local authors only – used weekly on the Sunday afternoon show (2.05–3.30 pm) and on Friday's *Late Night Sou' West* (10.05pm–midnight). Contact *Debbie Peers/Becky Newell*.

BBC Essex

198 New London Road, Chelmsford, Essex
CM2 9XB
☎01245 262393   Fax 01245 492983

Editor *Margaret Hyde*

Provides no regular outlets for writers but mounts special projects from time to time; these are well publicised on the air.

BBC Radio Foyle

8 Northland Road, Londonderry BT48 7JT
☎01504 378600   Fax 01504 378666
Editor *Ana Leddy*
News Producers *Jim Lindsay, Felicity McCall,
Paul McFadden*
Arts/Book Reviews *Frank Galligan,
Colum Arbuckle*
Features *Michael Bradley, Marie Louise Kerr,
Danny Kelly*

Radio Foyle broadcasts about seven hours of
original material a day, seven days a week to the
north west of Northern Ireland. Other programmes are transmitted simultaneously with
Radio Ulster. The output ranges from news,
sport, and current affairs to live music recordings
and arts reviews. Provides programmes as
required for Radio Ulster and the national networks and also provides television input to
nightly BBC NI News Magazine programme.

BBC Radio Gloucestershire

London Road, Gloucester GL1 1SW
☎01452 308585   Fax 01452 306541
Managing Editor *Bob Lloyd-Smith*

News and information covering the large variety
of interests and concerns in Gloucestershire.
Leisure, sport and music, plus African-Caribbean
and Asian interests. Regular book reviews and
interviews with local authors.

BBC GLR

PO Box 94.9, 35c Marylebone High Street,
London W1A 4LG
☎0171 224 2424   Fax 0171 935 0821
Managing Editor *Steve Panton*
Assistant Editor (News) *Martin Shaw*
Assistant Editor (General Programmes)
Jude Howells

Greater London Radio was launched in 1988. It
broadcasts news, information, travel bulletins,
sport and rock music to Greater London and the
Home Counties.

BBC GMR

PO Box 951, Manchester M60 1SD
☎0161 244 3002 Fax 0161 228 6110 (admin)
Editor *Karen Hannah*
Contacts *Sally Wheatman*

Programmes of interest to writers are: *GM Arts*,
a weekly arts and events programme on a
Thursday evening, 6.30–7.30pm; and James H.
Reeve's afternoon programme, Monday to
Friday 12 midday to 4.00pm, includes coverage
of leisure, entertainment and arts. *Write Now*, a

weekly half-hour regional local writing programme is shared with BBC Radio Merseyside,
BBC Radio Cumbria and BBC Radio
Lancashire (see BBC Radio Merseyside). GMR
is predominately a talk station and often carries
interviews with new, as well as established, local
writers.

BBC Radio Guernsey

Commerce House, Les Banques, St Peter
Port, Guernsey, Channel Islands GY1 2HS
☎01481 728977   Fax 01481 713557
Managing Editor *Denzil Dudley*

BBC Hereford & Worcester

Hylton Road, Worcester WR2 5WW
☎01905 748485   Fax 01905 748006
Also at: 43 Broad Street, Hereford HR4 9HH
☎01432 355252   Fax 01432 356446
Managing Editor *James Coghill*

Holds competitions on an occasional basis for
short stories, plays or dramatised documentaries
with a local flavour.

BBC Radio Humberside

9 Chapel Street, Hull, North Humberside
HU1 3NU
☎01482 323232   Fax 01482 326038
Acting Editor *Barrie Stephenson*

Occasionally broadcasts short stories by local
writers and holds competitions for local amateur authors and playwrights.

BBC Radio Jersey

18 Parade Road, St Helier, Jersey, Channel
Islands JE2 3PL
☎01534 870000   Fax 01534 32569
Managing Editor *Denzil Dudley*
Senior Producer *Claire Stanley*

Local news, current affairs and community items.

BBC Radio Kent

Sun Pier, Chatham, Kent ME4 4EZ
☎01634 830505   Fax 01634 830573
Editor, Local Services *David Farwig*

Occasional commissions are made for local
interest documentaries and other one-off programmes.

BBC Radio Lancashire

Darwen Street, Blackburn, Lancashire BB2 2EA
☎01254 262411   Fax 01254 680821
Editor *Steve Taylor*

Journalism-based radio station, interested in
interviews with local writers. Also *Write Now*, a

weekly half-hour regional local writing pro-gramme, shared with BBC Radio Cumbria, BBC Radio Merseyside and BBC GMR (see BBC Radio Merseyside).

BBC Radio Leeds
Broadcasting House, Woodhouse Lane, Leeds, West Yorkshire LS2 9PN
☎0113 2442131   Fax 0113 2420652
Managing Editor *Ashley Peatfield*

One of the country's biggest local radio stations, BBC Radio Leeds was also one of the first, coming on air in the 1960s as something of an experimental venture. The station is 'all talk', with a comprehensive news, sport and informa-tion service as the backbone of its daily output. BBC Radio Leeds has been a regular finalist for the title of Sony Regional Station of the Year. Has also won two Gold Sonys for best presenta-tion. For the past five years, it has won the National Award for best speech-based religious affairs programmes.

BBC Radio Leicester
Epic House, Charles Street, Leicester, LE1 3SH
☎0116 2516688   Fax 0116 2513632(Manage-ment)/2511463 (News)
Managing Editor *Liam McCarthy*

The first local station in Britain. Concentrates on speech-based programmes in the morning and on a music/speech mix in the afternoon.

BBC Radio Lincolnshire
PO Box 219, Newport, Lincoln LN1 3XY
☎01522 511411   Fax 01522 511726
Managing Editor *David Wilkinson*
Assistant Editor *Mike Curtis*

Unsolicited material considered only if locally relevant. Maximum 1000 words: straight narra-tive preferred, ideally with a topical content.

BBC Radio Manchester
See **BBC GMR**

BBC Radio Merseyside
55 Paradise Street, Liverpool L1 3BP
☎0151 708 5500   Fax 0151 794 0988
Editor *Mick Ord*

Write Now, a weekly 25-minute regional writers' programme, is produced at Radio Merseyside and also broadcast on BBC Radio Cumbria, BBC GMR and BBC Radio Lancashire. Short stories (maximum 1200 words), plus poetry and features on writing. Contact *Jenny Collins* by post at the address above.

BBC Radio Newcastle
Broadcasting Centre, Newcastle upon Tyne NE99 1RN
☎0191 232 4141
Editor *Tony Fish*
Senior Producer (Programmes) *Jon Harte*

'We welcome short stories of about 10 minutes duration for consideration for broadcast in our afternoon programme. We are *only* interested in stories by local writers or those set within the Newcastle area.' Afternoon programme producer: *Sarah Miller.*

BBC Radio Norfolk
Norfolk Tower, Surrey Street, Norwich, Norfolk NR1 3PA
☎01603 617411   Fax 01603 633692
Editor *David Clayton*

Good local material welcome for features/doc-umentaries, but must relate directly to Norfolk.

BBC Radio Northampton
Broadcasting House, Abington Street, Northampton NN1 2BH
☎01604 239100   Fax 01604 230709
Managing Editor *Claire Paul*
Senior Broadcast Journalists *Mike Day, Sarah Foster, Jim Hawkins, Matthew Price*

No literary outlets although books of local interest are reviewed on air occasionally.

BBC Radio Nottingham
PO Box 222, Nottingham NG1 3HZ
☎0115 9550500   Fax 0115 9550501
Editor, News & Programmes *Kevin Hill*
Editor, Local Services *Antony Bellekom*

Rarely broadcasts scripted pieces of any kind but interviews with authors form a regular part of the station's output.

BBC Radio Oxford
See **Thames Valley FM**

BBC Radio Scotland (Dumfries)
Elmbank, Lover's Walk, Dumfries DG1 1NZ
☎01387 268008   Fax 01387 252568
Senior Producer *Glenn Cooksley*
News Editor *Willie Johnston*

Previously Radio Solway. The station mainly outputs news bulletins (four daily). Changes have seen the station become more of a production centre with programmes being made for Radio Scotland as well as BBC Radio 2 and 5 Live. Freelancers of a high standard, familiar with Radio Scotland, should contact the producer.

BBC Radio Scotland (Orkney)
Castle Street, Kirkwall, Orkney KW15 1DF
☎01856 873939   Fax 01856 872908

Senior Producer *John Fergusson*

Regular programmes include *Around Orkney* (weekday news programme); *Bruck* (magazine programme); *Yesterday's Yarns* (local archive material).

BBC Radio Scotland (Selkirk)
Municipal Buildings, High Street, Selkirk TD7 4BU
☎01750 21884   Fax 01750 22400

Senior Producer *Carol Wightman*

Formerly BBC Radio Tweed. Produces weekly international travel and holiday programme, *The Case for Packing*.

BBC Radio Scotland (Shetland)
Brentham House, Lerwick, Shetland ZE1 0LR
☎01595 694747   Fax 01595 694307

Senior Producer *Mary Blance*

Regular programmes include *Good Evening Shetland*. An occasional books programme highlights the activities of local writers and writers' groups.

BBC Radio Sheffield
60 Westbourne Road, Sheffield S10 2QU
☎0114 2686185   Fax 0114 2664375

Editor *Barry Stockdale*

BBC Radio Shropshire
2–4 Boscobel Drive, Shrewsbury, Shropshire SY1 3TT
☎01743 248484   Fax 01743 271702

Managing Editor *Barbara Taylor*
Assistant Editor *Bob Calver*

Unsolicited literary material very rarely used, and then only if locally relevant.

BBC Radio Solent
Broadcasting House, Havelock Road, Southampton, Hampshire SO14 7PW
☎01703 631311   Fax 01703 339648

Managing Editor *Chris van Schaick*

BBC Somerset Sound
14 Paul Street, Taunton, Somerset TA1 3PF
☎01823 252437   Fax 01823 332539

Senior Producer *Richard Greenaway*

Informal, speech-based programming, with strong news and current affairs output and regular local-interest features, including local writing.

Poetry and short stories on the *Adam Thomas Programme*.

BBC Southern Counties Radio
Broadcasting Centre, Guildford, Surrey GU2 5AP
☎01483 306306   Fax 01483 304952

Managing Editor *Mike Hapgood*

Formerly known as BBC Radio Sussex and Surrey. Regular programmes include three individual breakfast shows: *Breakfast Live in Brighton with Jo Anne Good*/*in Surrey with Adrian Love*/*in Sussex with John Radford*.

BBC Radio Stoke
Cheapside, Hanley, Stoke on Trent, Staffordshire ST1 1JJ
☎01782 208080   Fax 01782 289115

Managing Editor *Phil Ashworth*

Emphasis on news, current affairs and local topics. Music represents one fifth of total output. Unsolicited material of local interest is welcome – send to managing editor.

BBC Radio Suffolk
Broadcasting House, St Matthews Street, Ipswich, Suffolk IP1 3EP
☎01473 250000   Fax 01473 210887

Managing Editor *Ivan Howlett*
Assistant Editor *Kevin Burch*

Strongly speech-based, dealing with news, current affairs, community issues, the arts, agriculture, commerce, travel, sport and leisure. Programmes frequently carry interviews with writers.

BBC Thames Valley FM
269 Banbury Road, Oxford OX2 7DW
☎0645 311444   Fax 0645 311555

Acting Editor *David Clargo*

Formed from a merger of BBC Radio Berkshire and BBC Radio Oxford. No opportunities at present as the outlet for short stories has been discontinued for the time being though the station frequently carries interviews with authors and offers books as prizes.

BBC Three Counties Radio
PO Box 3CR, Hastings Street, Luton, Bedfordshire LU1 5XL
☎01582 441000   Fax 01582 401467

Managing Editor *Andrew Wilson*
Senior Broadcast Journalists *Natalie Christian, Mark Norman*

Encourages freelance contributions from the community across a wide range of radio output, including interview and feature material. The station *very* occasionally broadcasts drama. Stringent local criteria are applied in selection. Particularly interested in historical topics (five minutes maximum).

BBC Radio Ulster

Broadcasting House, Ormeau Avenue, Belfast BT2 8HQ
☎01232 338000   Fax 01232 338800
Head of Broadcasting *Anna Carragher*
Head of Production *Paul Evans*

Programmes broadcast from 6.30 am–midnight weekdays and from 7.55 am–midnight at weekends. Radio Ulster has won seven Sony awards in recent years. Programmes include: *Good Morning Ulster, John Bennett, Gerry Anderson, Talkback, Newsbreak, Afternoon Spin, Just Jones, Evening Extra* and *Across the Line.*

BBC Radio Wales

The Old School House, Glanrafon Road, Mold, Clwyd CH7 1PA
☎01352 700367   Fax 01352 759821/750919
Senior Broadcast Journalist *Tracy Cardwell*
Producers, Factual Programmes *Gavin McCarthy, Jane Morris*

Broadcasts regular news bulletins Monday to Friday and until lunchtime on Saturday; *The Big Idea* and *Gravel's Travels* network programmes Friday (6–7.30 pm); *Adam Walton* on Saturday evening.

BBC Wiltshire Sound

Broadcasting House, Prospect Place, Swindon, Wiltshire SN1 3RW
☎01793 513626   Fax 01793 513650
Managing Editor *Sandy Milne*

Regular programmes include: *Wake Up Wiltshire; Wiltshire Today; Wiltshire at One.*

BBC Radio WM

PO Box 206, Birmingham B5 7SD
☎0121 432 8484   Fax 0121 432 8510
Managing Editor *David Robey*

News and current affairs station.

BBC Radio York

20 Bootham Row, York YO3 7BR
☎01904 641351   Fax 01904 610937
Editor *Jane Sampson*
Senior Broadcast Journalist *Alan Greyeson*

A regular outlet for short stories of up to 10 minutes' duration. They must be locally written or based (i.e. North Yorkshire).

Independent television

Anglia Television

Anglia House, Norwich, Norfolk NR1 3JG
☎01603 615151   Fax 01603 631032

London office: 48 Leicester Square, London WC2H 7FB
☎0171 389 8555   Fax 0171 930 8499
Managing Director/Director of Programmes *Graham Creelman*
Controller of News *Guy Adams*

Anglia Television is a major producer of programmes for the ITV network and Channel 4. These include *The Time ... The Place* and the *Survival* wildlife documentaries, Britain's best-selling programme export. Network dramas for 1997 included: *Pale Horse; The Man Who Made Husbands Jealous* and *Touching Evil.*

Border Television plc

Television Centre, Durranhill, Carlisle, Cumbria CA1 3NT
☎01228 25101   Fax 01228 41384
Chairman & Chief Executive *James Graham OBE*
Head of Programmes *Neil Robinson*

Border's programming concentrates on documentaries rather than drama. Most scripts are supplied in-house but occasionally there are commissions. Apart from notes, writers should not submit written work until their ideas have been fully discussed.

Carlton Television

101 St Martin's Lane, London WC2N 4AZ
☎0171 240 4000   Fax 0171 240 4171
Chairman *Nigel Walmsley*
Chief Executive *Clive Jones*
Director of Programmes *Andy Allan*

Carlton Television comprises: Carlton Broadcasting, which is responsible for the ITV licence for London and the South East, **Central Broadcasting** and **Westcountry** (see entries); **Carlton Productions** (see under **Film, TV and Video Production Companies**); Carlton Sales which sells airtime and sponsorship. Also runs two facilities operations: Carlton Studios in Nottingham, supplying studios and related services and Carlton 021, the largest commercial operator of Outside Broadcast Services in Europe.

Central Television

Central Court, Gas Street, Birmingham B1 2JT
☎0121 643 9898
Chairman *Nigel Walmsley*
Managing Director *Ian Squires*

Part of **Carlton Television**. Responsible for the ITV licence for East, West and South Midlands. Ideas for programmes should be addressed to **Carlton Productions** (see entry under **Film, TV and Video Production Companies**). Regular programmes include *Central Weekend Live; Asian Eye; Heart of the Country; Crime Stalker; 24 Hours;*.

Channel 4
124 Horseferry Road, London SW1P 2TX
☎0171 396 4444   Fax 0171 306 8356
Deputy Director of Programmes
 Karen Brown
Head of Film *Paul Webster*
Head of Entertainment *Kevin Lygo*
COMMISSIONING EDITORS
Independent Film & Video (Acting Editor) *Robin Gutch*
Arts *Janey Walker*
Head of Drama and Animation *Gub Neal*
Entertainment *Graham K. Smith*
Documentaries *Peter Moore*
News & Current Affairs *David Lloyd*
Comedy *Seamus Cassidy*
Sport *Mike Miller*
Multicultural Programmes *Yasmin Anwar*
Religion & Features *Peter Grimsdale*
Head of Purchased Programmes
 Mairi MacDonald

When Channel 4 started broadcasting as a national channel in November 1982, it was the first new TV service to be launched in Britain for 18 years. Under the 1981 Broadcasting Act it was required to cater for tastes and audiences not previously served by the other broadcast channels, and to provide a suitable proportion of educational programmes. Channel 4 does not make any of its own programmes; they are commissioned from the independent production companies, from the ITV sector, or co-produced with other organisations. The role of the commissioning editors is to sift through proposals for programmes and see interesting projects through to broadcast. Regulated by the ITC.

Channel 5
22 Long Acre, London WC2E 9LY
☎0171 550 5555   Fax 0171 497 5222
Chief Executive *David Elstein*
Director of Programmes *Dawn Airey*
Controller of Children's Programmes
 Nick Wilson
Controller of Features & Arts *Michael Attwell*
Controller of News, Current Affairs & Documentaries *Tim Gardam*

Controller of Drama *Corinne Hollingworth*
Channel 5 Broadcasting Ltd, led by Greg Dyke of Pearson TV, won the franchise for Britain's third commercial terrestrial television station in 1995 and came on air at the end of March 1997. Regular programmes include *Family Affairs* (Monday to Friday soap opera) and *The Jack Docherty Show* (late-night chat show), plus mainstream drama, films, sport and entertainment.

Channel Television
The Television Centre, La Pouquelaye, St Helier, Jersey, Channel Islands JE1 3ZD
☎01534 816816   Fax 01534 816817
Also at: Television House, Bulwer Avenue, St Sampsons, Guernsey GY2 4LA
☎01481 41888   Fax 01481 41889
Chief Executive *John Henwood*
Managing Director *Michael Lucas*
Head of Programmes *Karen Rankine*

After its successful debut on ITV, *Island*, Channel's 'teen drama' went to a second series. Also, a broadcast pilot, *Escape From the Black Hole*, was recorded in the Jersey studio. The series is a new entertainment format for children shot 'in the dark' using the unique BVS technology. Two comedies in development. Previous commissions for ITV and Ch4 include one-off documentaries, factual series and animation programmes.

GMTV
The London Television Centre, Upper Ground, London SE1 9TT
☎0171 827 7000   Fax 0171 827 7001
Managing Director *Christopher Stoddart*
Director of Programmes *Peter McHugh*
Managing Editor *John Scammell*

Winner of the national breakfast television franchise. Jointly owned by Scottish Television, Carlton, Granada, The Guardian and Disney. GMTV took over from TV-AM on 1 January 1993, with live programming from 6 am to 9.25 am. Regular news headlines, current affairs, topical features, showbiz and lifestyle, sports and business, quizzes and competitions, travel and weather reports.

Grampian Television plc
Queen's Cross, Aberdeen AB15 4XJ
☎01224 846846   Fax 01224 846800
Controller *Alistair Gracie*
Head of News & Current Affairs
 Bert Ovenstone
Head of Gaelic *Robert Kenyon*
Extensive regional news and reports including

farming, fishing and sports, interviews and leisure features, various light entertainment, Gaelic and religious programmes, and live coverage of the Scottish political, economic and industrial scene. Serves the area stretching from Fife to Shetland. Regular programmes include *Gaelic News; North Tonight; Scotland's Larder* and *Reflections.*

Granada Television

Quay Street, Manchester M60 9EA
☎0161 832 7211   Fax 0161 953 0283

Director of Programmes *Simon Shaps*
Director of Production *Max Graesser*
Controller GSB and Lifestyle
  Programmes *James Hunt*
Controller of Drama *Simon Lewis*
Controller of Factual Programmes
  Charles Tremayme
Controller of Comedy *Andy Harries*

Opportunities for freelance writers are not great but mss from professional writers will be considered. All mss should be addressed to the head of scripts. Regular programmes include *Coronation Street; World in Action* and *This Morning.*

HTV Wales

Television Centre, Culverhouse Cross,
Cardiff CF5 6XJ
☎01222 590590   Fax 01222 597183

Managing Director *Menna Richards*

HTV (West)

Television Centre, Bath Road, Bristol BS4 3HG
☎0117 9722722   Fax 0117 9722400

Managing Director *Jeremy Payne*
Controller of Children's Programmes
  Dan Maddicott
Controller of Factual Programmes
  Tom Archer
Director of Programmes, Partridge Films
  Michael Rosenberg

Drama, children's, factual and natural history programming is produced for national and international markets. Programmes include *Wycliffe, The Famous Five* and *The Slow Norris.* Now part of the UNM Group (United News and Media).

ITN (Independent Television News Ltd)

200 Gray's Inn Road, London WC1X 8XZ
☎0171 833 3000

Chief Executive *Stewart Purvis*
Editor-in-Chief *Richard Tait*

Editor, ITN Programmes for ITV
  Nigel Dacre
Editor, ITN Programmes on Channel 4
  Jim Gray
Editor, ITN Programmes on Channel 5
  Chris Shaw

Provider of the main national and international news for ITV, Channels 4 and 5 and radio news for IRN. Programmes on ITV: *Lunchtime News; Early Evening News; News at Ten; ITN Morning News,* plus regular news summaries, and three programmes a day at weekends. Programmes on Channel 4: in-depth news analysis programmes, including *Channel 4 News* and *The Big Breakfast.* Programmes on Channel 5: *5 News Early; 5 News at Noon; 5 News* plus regular updates. ITN also provides World News, the first international English-language news programme, and has operating control of Euronews, Europe's only pan-European broadcaster.

LWT (London Weekend Television)

The London Television Centre, Upper Ground, London SE1 9LT
☎0171 620 1620

Chief Operating Officer *Charles Allen*
Managing Director *Eileen Gallagher*
Director of Programmes *Marcus Plantin*
Controller of Entertainment *Nigel Lythgoe*
Controller of Drama *Jo Wright*
Controller of Arts *Melvyn Bragg*
Controller of Factual Programmes *Jim Allen*

Makers of current affairs, entertainment and drama series such as *Blind Date; Surprise Surprise; The Knock; London's Burning;* also *The South Bank Show* and *Jonathan Dimbleby.* Provides a large proportion of ITV's drama and light entertainment, and also BSkyB and Channel 4.

Meridian Broadcasting

Television Centre, Southampton, Hampshire SO14 0PZ
☎01703 222555   Fax 01703 335050
London office: Ludgate House, 245 Blackfriars Road, London SE1 9UY
☎0171 921 5000

Managing Director *Mary McAnally*
Director of Broadcasting *Richard Platt*
Controller of Programmes *Richard Simons*
Director of News Strategy *Jim Raven*
Controller of Drama *Michele Buck*
Controller of Children's Programmes
  Richard Morss

Meridian's newly refurbished studios in Southampton provide a base for network and regional productions. Regular regional programmes include the award-winning news service, *Meridian Tonight; Countryways* and *The Pier.*

S4C
Parc Ty Glas, Llanishen, Cardiff CF4 5DU
☎01222 747444   Fax 01222 754444
Chief Executive *Huw Jones*
Director of Broadcasting *Dafydd Rhys*
Director of Production *Huw Eirug*

The Welsh 4th Channel, established by the Broadcasting Act 1980, is responsible for a schedule of Welsh and English programmes on the Fourth Channel in Wales. Known as S4C, the service is made up of about 30 hours per week of Welsh language programmes and more than 85 hours of English language output from Channel 4. Ten hours a week of the Welsh programmes are provided by the BBC; the remainder are purchased from HTV and independent producers. Drama, comedy and documentary are all part of S4C's programming.

Scottish Television
Cowcaddens, Glasgow G2 3PR
☎0141 300 3000   Fax 0141 300 3030
London office: 20 Lincoln's Inn Field, London WC2A 3ED
☎0171 446 7000   Fax 0171 446 7010
Chairman *Gus MacDonald*
Managing Director, Broadcasting
    Donald Emslie
Controller, Regional Programming
    Sandy Ross
Controller, Scottish Television *Scott Ferguson*
Controller of Drama *Philip Hinchcliffe*
Head of Features *Agnes Wilkie*
Head of Current Affairs *Alan Smart*
Head of News *Mark Smith*
Head of General Factual Programmes (Social action, Arts, Religion)
    Denis Mooney
Head of Sport *Ian Crawford*

An increasing number of STV programmes such as *Taggart* and *McCallum* are now networked nationally. Programme coverage includes drama, religion, news, sport, outside broadcasts, special features, entertainment and the arts, education and Gaelic programmes. Produces many one-offs for ITV and Channel 4.

Teletext Ltd
101 Farm Lane, Fulham, London SW6 1QJ
☎0171 386 5000   Fax 0171 386 5002
Managing Director *Peter van Gelder*

Editor *Graham Lovelace*

On 1 January 1993 Teletext Ltd took over the electronic publishing service, previously the domain of Oracle, servicing both ITV and Channel 4. Transmits a wide range of news pages and features, including current affairs, sport, TV listings, weather, travel, holidays, finance, games, competitions, etc. Provides a regional service to each of the ITV regions.

Tyne Tees Television
Television Centre, Newcastle upon Tyne NE1 2AL
☎0191 261 0181   Fax 0191 261 2302
Managing Director *Margaret Fry*
Director of Broadcasting and Controller of News & Current Affairs *Graeme Thompson*
Head of Young People's Programmes
    Lesley Oakden
Head of Entertainment *Christine Williams*
Head of Training & Community Affairs
    Annie Wood
Head of Sport *Roger Tames*
Head of Features *Malcolm Wright*

Programming covers religion, politics, news and current affairs, regional documentaries, business, entertainment, sport and arts. Regular programmes include *North East Tonight with Mike Neville* and *Around the House* (politics).

UTV (Ulster Television)
Havelock House, Ormeau Road, Belfast BT7 1EB
☎01232 328122   Fax 01232 246695
Controller of Programming *Alan Bremner*
Head of News & Current Affairs
    Rob Morrison
Head of General Programmes *Philip Morrow*

Regular programmes on news and current affairs, politics, sport, education, music, light entertainment, arts, health and local culture.

Westcountry
Langage Science Park, Western Wood Way, Plymouth, Devon PL7 5BG
☎01752 333333   Fax 01752 333444
Managing Director *Mark Haskell*
Director of Programmes *Jane McCloskey*
Director of News & Current Affairs
    Brad Higgins

Part of **Carlton Television**. Came on air in January 1993. News, current affairs, documentary and religious programming. Regular programmes include *Westcountry Live; Westcountry Focus; Westcountry Showcase.*

September 1992. It plays accessible classical music 24 hours a day and broadcasts news, weather, travel, business information, charts, music and book event guides, political/celebrity/general interest talks, features and interviews. Classic has gone well beyond its expectations, attracting 4.7 million listeners a week.

Talk Radio UK
76 Oxford Street, London W1N 0TR
☎0171 636 1089   Fax 0171 636 1053
Managing Director *Paul Robinson*
Programme Director *John Simons*

LAUNCHED in February 1995, Talk Radio is the third national commercial radio station. Broadcasts 24 hours a day with a mix of news, opinions, entertainment, weather, traffic and sport based on studio interviews, celebrity chat and 'the views of the Great British listening audience'.

Virgin Radio
1 Golden Square, London W1R 4DJ
☎0171 434 1215   Fax 0171 434 1197

Chief Executive *John Pearson*
Programme Director *Geoff Holland*

Classic tracks and the best of today's music aimed at an audience of 25–45 year-olds. Acquired by Chris Evans' Ginger Media Group in December 1997, Virgin has seen its audience figures rocket to around 7 million, making it the most successful commercial radio station in the UK.

Independent local radio

96.3 Aire FM/Magic 828
PO Box 2000, 51 Burley Road, Leeds, West Yorkshire LS3 1LR
☎0113 2835500   Fax 0113 2835501
Programme Director *John O'Hara*

Music-based programming. 96.3 Aire FM caters for the 15–34-year-old listener while Magic 828 aims at the 25–44 age group with classic oldies.

Amber Radio
47–49 Colegate, Norwich, Norfolk NR3 1DB
☎01603 630621   Fax 01603 666252
Programme Controller *Dave Brown*

Part of the GWR Group plc. Broadcasts classic hits of the '60s and '70s and easy listening; national and local news.

Beacon FM/WABC
267 Tettenhall Road, Wolverhampton, West Midlands WV6 0DQ
☎01902 757211   Fax 01902 838266
Programme Director, Beacon Radio
   Tim Lawrence
Programme Director, WABC *Dave Myatt*

Part of the GWR Group plc. No outlets for unsolicited literary material at present.

Radio Borders
Tweedside Park, Tweedbank, Galashiels TD1 3TD
☎01896 759444   Fax 01896 759494
Programme Controller *Danny Gallagher*
Head of News *David Marsland*

Music-based station with local and national news.

The Breeze
See **Essex FM**

BRMB-FM 96.4/1152 XTRA-AM
Radio House, Aston Road North, Birmingham B6 4BX
☎0121 359 4481   Fax 0121 359 1117
Programme Controller, BRMB/XTRA
   Paul Jackson
News Editor *Robyn Dangerfield*

Music-based stations; no outlets for writers.

Broadland 102
St Georges Plain, 47–49 Colegate, Norwich, Norfolk NR3 1DB
☎01603 630621   Fax 01603 666252
Programme Controller *Dave Brown*

Part of GWR Group plc. Popular music programmes only.

Capital Radio
30 Leicester Square, London WC2H 7LA
☎0171 766 6000   Fax 0171 766 6100
Group Programme Director *Richard Park*

Britain's largest commercial radio station. Main outlet is news and showbiz programme each weekday evening at 7 pm called *Drivetime Showtime*. This covers current affairs, showbiz, features and pop news, aimed at a young audience. The vast majority of material is generated in-house.

Central FM Ltd
201–203 High Street, Falkirk FK1 1DU
☎01324 611164   Fax 01324 611168
Managing Director *Sheena Borthwick*

Programme Controller *David Bain*

Broadcasts music, sport and local news to Central Scotland 24 hours a day.

Century Radio

Century House, PO Box 100, Church Street, Gateshead NE8 2YY
☎0191 477 6666   Fax 0191 477 5660

Programme Controller *To be appointed*

Music, talk, news and interviews, 24 hours a day.

CFM

PO Box 964, Carlisle, Cumbria CA1 3NG
☎01228 818964   Fax 01228 819444

Head of Programming *Simon Grundy*
Head of Production *Simon Monk*
News Editor *Gill Garston*

Music, news and information station.

Channel 103 FM

6 Tunnell Street, St Helier, Jersey, Channel Islands JE2 4LU
☎01534 888103   Fax 01534 887799

Station Manager *Richard Johnson*

Music programmes, 24 hours a day.

Cheltenham Radio

Regent Arcade, Cheltenham, Gloucestershire GL50 1JZ
☎01242 699555   Fax 01242 699666

Programme Controller *Peter MacFarlane*

Music-based programmes, broadcasting 24 hours a day.

Classic Gold 1260/GWR FM (West)

Classic Gold: PO Box 2020, Bristol BS99 7SN
☎0117 9843200   Fax 0117 9843202

GWR FM (West): PO Box 2000, Bristol BS99 7SN
☎0117 9843200   Fax 0117 9843202

Programme Controller, Classic Gold 1260
Paul Robey
Programme Controller, GWR FM (West)
Vaughan Hobbs

Very few opportunities. Almost all material originates in-house. Part of the GWR Group plc.

Classic Gold 1557

19–21 St Edmunds Road, Northampton NN1 5DY
☎01604 795600   Fax 01604 795601

Programme Controller *Terry Doyle*

Music and news, 24 hours a day.

Radio Clyde/Clyde 1 FM/Clyde 2

Clydebank Business Park, Clydebank G81 2RX
☎0141 565 2272   Fax 0141 565 2265

Director *Alex Dickson, OBE,AE,FRSA,FIMgt*

Programmes usually originate in-house or by commission. All documentary material is made in-house. Good local news items always considered.

Cool FM

See **Downtown Radio**

Downtown Radio/Cool FM

Newtownards, Co. Down, Northern Ireland BT23 4ES
☎01247 815555   Fax 01247 815252

Programme Head *John Rosborough*

Downtown Radio first ran a highly successful short story competition in 1988, attracting over 400 stories. The competition is now an annual event and writers living within the station's transmission area are asked to submit material during the winter and early spring. The competition is promoted in association with Eason Shops. For further information, write to *Derek Ray* at the station.

Essex FM/The Breeze

Radio House, Clifftown Road, Southend on Sea, Essex SS1 1SX
☎01702 333711   Fax 01702 345224

Programme Controller *Paul Chantler*

Music-based stations. No real opportunities for writers' work as such, but will occasionally interview local authors of published books. Contact *Sarah Burke* (Programming Secretary) in the first instance.

Fame 1521 AM

See **Mercury FM 102.7/Fame 1521 AM**

FM 103 Horizon

Broadcast Centre, Crownhill, Milton Keynes, Buckinghamshire MK8 0AB
☎01908 269111   Fax 01908 564893

Programme Controller *Paul Kenton*

Part of the GWR Group plc. Music and news.

Forth AM/Forth FM

Forth House, Forth Street, Edinburgh EH1 3LF
☎0131 556 9255   Fax 0131 558 3277

Director of Programming *Tom Steele*
News Editor *David Johnston*

News stories welcome from freelancers. Music-based programming.

FOX FM
Brush House, Pony Road, Cowley, Oxford
OX4 2XR
☎01865 871000 Fax 01865 871037 (news)
Managing Director *Lyn Long*
Head of News *Karen Thorpe*

Backed by an impressive list of shareholders
including the Blackwell Group of Companies
and Capital Radio Plc. No outlet for creative
writing.

Galaxy 101
Millennium House, 26 Baldwin Street, Bristol
BS1 1SE
☎0117 9010101 Fax 0117 9014666
Programme Controller *John Dash*

Dance music, 24 hours a day. Occasionally
interviews local authors and features books
about local places. Contact the Programme
Controller in the first instance.

GEM AM
29–31 Castle Gate, Nottingham NG1 7AP
☎0115 9527000 Fax 0115 9129302
Managing Director *Chris Hughes*

Part of the GWR Group plc. Music and news.

Gemini Radio FM/AM
Hawthorn House, Exeter Business Park,
Exeter, Devon EX1 3QS
☎01392 444444 Fax 01392 444433
Programme Controller (FM) *Kevin Kane*
Programme Controller (AM) *Colin Slade*

Took over the franchise previously held by
DevonAir Radio in January 1995. Part of
Orchard Media Group. Occasional outlets for
poetry and short stories on the AM wavelength.
Contact *Colin Slade.*

Great North Radio (GNR)
See **Metro FM**

GWR FM (West)
See **Classic Gold 1260**

Hallam FM
Radio House, 900 Herries Road, Sheffield
S6 1RH
☎0114 2853333 Fax 0114 2853159
Programme Director *Tony McKenzie*

Heart FM
1 The Square, 111 Broad Street, Birmingham
B15 1AS
☎0121 626 1007 Fax 0121 696 1007
Managing Director *Phil Riley*

Programme Director *Paul Fairburn*

Commenced broadcasting in September 1994.
Music, regional news and information.

Heartbeat 1521 AM
Carn Business Park, Craigavon, Co Armagh
BT63 5RH
☎01762 330033 Fax 01762 391896
Managing Director *Kenny James*

Commenced broadcasting in April 1996 as
Radio 1521 AM and was relaunched as Heart-
beat in November 1997. Predominantly music-
based programmes.

102.7 Hereward FM/ Classic Gold 1332 AM
PO Box 225, Queensgate Centre,
Peterborough, Cambridgeshire PE1 1XJ
☎01733 460460 Fax 01733 281445
Programme Controller *Chris Pegg*

Part of GWR Group plc. Not usually any
openings offered to writers as all material is
compiled and presented by in-house staff.

Invicta FM/Invicta Supergold
PO Box 100, Whitstable, Kent CT5 3QX
☎01227 772004 Fax 01227 771558
Programme Controller *Andrew Phillips*

Music-based station, serving listeners in Kent.

Island FM
12 Westerbrook, St Sampsons, Guernsey,
Channel Islands GY2 4QQ
☎01481 42000 Fax 01481 49676
Managing Director *Kevin Stewart*

Music-based programming.

Isle of Wight Radio
Dodnor Park, Newport, Isle of Wight
PO30 5XE
☎01983 822557 Fax 01983 821690
Programme Director *Andy Shier*

Part of the Local Radio Company, Isle of Wight
Radio is the island's only radio station broadcasting local news, music and general entertainment.

Key 103
See **Piccadilly 1152**

LBC 1152 AM
See **News Direct 97.3 FM**

105.4 FM Leicester Sound
Granville House, Granville Road, Leicester
LE1 7RW
☎0116 2561300 Fax 0116 2561305

Station Director *Carlton Dale*
Programme Controller *Steve Marsh*
News Editor *Peter Bearne*

Part of GWR Group plc. Predominantly a music station. Very occasionally, unsolicited material of local interest – 'targeted at our particular audience' – may be broadcast.

1458 Lite AM

PO Box 1458, Quay West, Trafford Park, Manchester M17 1FL
☎0161 872 1458   Fax 0161 872 0206
Head of Programming *Simon Wynne*

Music-based programmes, 24 hours a day.

Magic 1161
See **Viking FM**

Magic 1548
See **Radio City Ltd**

Magic 828
See **96.3 Aire FM**

Magic AM

Radio House, 900 Herries Road, Sheffield S6 1RH
☎0114 2852121   Fax 0114 2853159
Programme Director *Tony McKenzie*

Music, news and features, 24 hours a day.

Marcher Coast FM

41 Conwy Road, Colwyn Bay, Conwy LL28 5AB
☎01492 534555   Fax 01492 535248
Programme Controller *Kevin Howard*

Programmes include an hour of Welsh language items each weekday. Broadcasts 24 hours a day.

Marcher Gold

Marcher Sound Ltd., The Studios, Mold Road, Wrexham LL11 4AF
☎01978 752202   Fax 01978 759701
Programme Controller *Kevin Howard*

Occasional features and advisory programmes. Hour-long Welsh language broadcasts are aired weekdays at 6.00 pm.

Medway FM

Berkeley House, 186 High Street, Rochester, Kent ME1 1EY
☎01634 841111   Fax 01634 841122
Managing Director *Nick Jenkins*
Programme Director *Bob Le-Roi*

A wide range of music programming plus news, views and local interest.

Mercia FM/Mercia Classic Gold

Mercia Sound Ltd., Hertford Place, Coventry CV1 3TT
☎01203 868200   Fax 01203 868202
Station Director *Ian Rufus*
Programme Controller *Alex Roland*
Music-based station.

Mercury FM 102.7/Fame 1521 AM

The Stanley Centre, Kelvin Way, Manor Royal, Crawley, West Sussex RH10 2SE
☎01293 519161   Fax 01293 560927
Programme Director *Carole Straker*

Mercury FM plays contemporary music targeting 25–44 years. Fame 1521 plays hits from the '60s to '90s, targeting 35 years-plus. Both services carry local, national and international news.

Metro FM/Great North Radio (GNR)

Swalwell, Newcastle upon Tyne NE99 1BB
☎0191 420 0971 (Metro)/420 3040 (GNR)
Fax 0191 488 0933
Programme Controller, Metro *Sean Marley*
Programme Director, GNR *John O'Hara*

Very few opportunities for writers, but phone-in programmes may interview relevant authors.

Minster FM

PO Box 123, Dunnington, York YO1 5ZX
☎01904 488888   Fax 01904 488811
Managing Director *Lynn Bell*

Music, local news and sport.

Moray Firth Radio

PO Box 271, Scorguie Place, Inverness IV3 6SF
☎01463 224433   Fax 01463 243224
Managing Director/Programme Controller *Thomas Prag*
Programme Organiser *Ray Atkinson*
Book Reviews *May Marshall*

Book reviews every Monday afternoon at 2.20 pm. Also fortnightly arts programme called *The North Bank Show* which features interviews with authors, etc.

New Chiltern FM/Classic Gold

Chiltern Road, Dunstable, Bedfordshire LU6 1HQ
☎01582 676200   Fax 01582 676251
Programme Controller, FM *Trevor James*
Programme Controller, Classic Gold *Paul Robey*

Part of the GWR Group plc. Music-based programmes, broadcasting 24 hours a day.

New Wyvern FM/Classic Gold 954/1530 AM

5–6 Barbourne Terrace, Worcester
WR1 3JZ
☎01905 612212

Managing Director *Rhian Garbett-Edwards*
Programme Controller (New Wyvern FM) *Liz Rhodes*
Programme Controller (Classic Gold) *Sammy Southall*

Part of the GWR Group plc since spring 1997.

News Direct 97.3 FM/ LBC 1152 AM

200 Gray's Inn Road, London WC1X 8XZ
☎0171 973 1152
Fax 0171 312 8470 (FM)/8565 (AM)

Editor (FM) *Chris Mann*
Programme Controller (AM) *Charles Golding*

News Direct 97.3 FM – 24-hour rolling news station; LBC 1152 AM – news, views and entertainment for London.

Northants 96 FM

19–21 St Edmunds Road, Northampton
NN1 5DY
☎01604 795600   Fax 01604 795601

Programme Controller *Mark Jeeves*

Music and news, 24 hours a day.

NorthSound Radio

45 King's Gate, Aberdeen AB15 4EL
☎01224 632234   Fax 01224 633282

Programme Controller *Rod Webster*

Features and music programmes 24 hours a day.

Ocean FM

See **Power FM**

Orchard FM

Haygrove House, Shoreditch, Taunton, Somerset TA3 7BT
☎01823 338448   Fax 01823 321044

Programme Director *Bob McCreadie*
News Editor *Alan Jennings*.
Music-based programming only.

Piccadilly 1152/Key 103

Castlequay, Castlefield, Manchester M15 4NJ
☎0161 288 5000   Fax 0161 288 5001

Programme Director *John Dash*

Music-based programming with some opportunities for comedy writers.

Plymouth Sound FM/AM

Earl's Acre, Alma Road, Plymouth, Devon
PL3 4HX
☎01752 227272   Fax 01752 670730

Programme Controller *Peter Greig*

Music-based station. No outlets for writers.

Power FM/Ocean FM/ South Coast Radio

Whittle Avenue, Segensworth West, Fareham, Hampshire PO15 5PA
☎01489 589911   Fax 01489 589453

Programme Controller *Steve Power*
News Editor *Karen Woods*
Music-based programming only.

Premier Radio

Glen House, Stag Place, London
SW1E 5AG
☎0171 233 6705   Fax 0171 233 6706

Managing Director *Peter Kerridge*

Broadcasts programmes that reflect the beliefs and values of the Christian faith, 24 hours a day.

Q103.FM

PO Box 103, Vision Park, Chivers Way, Histon, Cambridge CB4 4WW
☎01223 235255   Fax 01223 235161

Station Director *Alistair Wayne*

Part of GWR Group plc. Music and news.

96.3 QFM

PO Box 96.3, Paisley PA1 2NS
☎0141 887 9630   Fax 0141 887 0963

Programme Director *John Collins*

Music-based programming plus local information and news.

Radio City Ltd/Magic 1548

8–10 Stanley Street, Liverpool L1 6AF
☎0151 227 5100   Fax 0151 471 0330

Managing Director *Tom Humter*
Programme Director *Paul Jordan*

Opportunities for writers are very few and far between as this is predominantly a music station.

RAM FM

Market Place, Derby DE1 3AA
☎01332 292945   Fax 01332 292229

Programme Controller *Rob Wagstaff*

Part of the GWR Group plc. Music-based programming only.

Red Dragon FM/Touch Radio

Radio House, West Canal Wharf, Cardiff
CF1 5XJ
☎01222 384041   Fax 01222 384014

Programme Controller *Mark Franklin*
News Editor *Andrew Jones*

Music-based programming only.

Red Rose 999 AM/Rock FM

PO Box 301, St Paul's Square, Preston,
Lancashire PR1 1YE
☎01772 556301   Fax 01772 201917

Programme Director *Paul Jordan*

Music-based stations. No outlets for writers.

Sabras Sound

Radio House, 63 Melton Road, Leicester
LE4 6PN
☎0116 2610666   Fax 0116 2667776

Programme Controller *Don Kotak*

Programmes for the Asian community, broadcasting 24 hours a day.

SCOT FM

Number 1 Albert Quay, Leith, Edinburgh
EH6 7DN
☎0131 554 6677   Fax 0131 554 2266

Managing Director *David Forbes*
Programme Controller *John Collins*

Commenced broadcasting in September 1994
to the central Scottish region. Music and conversation.

Severn Sound FM/
Severn Sound Classic Gold

Old Talbot House, Southgate Street,
Gloucester GL1 2DQ
☎01452 423791
Fax 01452 529446/423008 (news)

Managing Director *Penny Holton*

Part of the GWR Group plc. Music and news.

SGR FM 97.1/96.4

Alpha Business Park, Whitehouse Road,
Ipswich, Suffolk IP1 5LT
☎01473 461000   Fax 01473 741200

Managing Director *Mike Stewart*
Programme Controller *Mark Pryke*
Features Producer *Nigel Rennie*

Music-based programming.

Signal FM

Regent House, 1st Floor, Heaton Lane,
Stockport, Cheshire SK4 1BX
☎0161 285 4545   Fax 0161 285 1010

Programme Controller *Mark Chivers*

Strong local flavour to programmes. Part of the
Signal Network.

Signal One/Signal Two/
Signal Stafford

Stoke Road, Stoke on Trent, Staffordshire
ST4 2SR
☎01782 747047   Fax 01782 744110

Programme Director *John Evington*
Head of News *Paul Sheldon*

Music-based station. No outlets for writers.
Part of the Radio Partnership.

South Coast Radio

See **Power FM**

Southern FM

PO Box 2000, Brighton, East Sussex BN41 2SS
☎01273 430111   Fax 01273 430098

Programme Controller *Danny Pike*
News Manager *Phil Bell*

Music, news, entertainment and competitions.

Spectrum Radio

204–206 Queenstown Road, Battersea,
London SW8 3NR
☎0171 627 4433   Fax 0171 627 3409

Managing Director *Wolfgang Bucci*

Programmes for a broad spectrum of ethnic
groups in London.

Spire FM

City Hall Studios, Malthouse Lane, Salisbury,
Wiltshire SP2 7QQ
☎01722 416644   Fax 01722 415102

Station Director *Gary Haberfield*

Music, news current affairs, quizzes and sport.
Won the Sony Award for the best local radio
station in 1994.

Sun FM 103.4

PO Box 1034, Sunderland, Tyne & Wear
SR1 3YZ
☎0191 567 3333   Fax 0191 567 0888

General Manager *Jon Hewson*

Music-based programmes only.

Sunrise FM

Sunrise House, 30 Chapel Street, Bradford,
West Yorkshire BD1 5DN
☎01274 735043   Fax 01274 728534

**Programme Controller, Chief Executive
& Chairman** *Usha Parmar*

Programmes for the Asian community in
Bradford. Part of the Sunrise Radio Group.

Sunshine 855
South Shropshire Communications Ltd.,
Sunshine House, Waterside, Ludlow,
Shropshire SY8 1GS
☎01584 873795   Fax 01584 875900
Station Manager & Programme
   Controller *Tony Simon*
Music, news and information broadcast 24 hours
a day.

Swansea Sound 1170 M/Wave
Victoria Road, Gowerton, Swansea SA4 3AB
☎01792 511170   Fax 01792 511171
Managing Director *Terry Mann*
Head of News *Lynn Courtney*
Interested in a wide variety of material, though
news items must be of local relevance. An ex-
planatory letter, in the first instance, is advisable.

Tay FM/Radio Tay AM
Radio Tay Ltd., PO Box 123, Dundee
DD1 9UF
☎01382 200800   Fax 01382 593252
Managing Director *Sandy Wilkie*
Programme Director *Ally Ballingall*
Wholly-owned subsidiary of Scottish Radio
Holdings. Unsolicited material is assessed.
Short stories and book reviews of local interest
are welcome. Send to the programme director.

Thames FM
Brentham House, 45c High Street, Hampton
Wick, Kingston upon Thames, Surrey
KT1 4DG
☎0181 288 1300   Fax 0181 288 1330
Station Manager *Martin Mumford*
Music-based programmes of current hits and
classic pop.

Touch Radio
See **Red Dragon FM**

TRENT FM
29–31 Castlegate, Nottingham NG1 7AP
☎0115 9527000   Fax 0115 9129302
Managing Director *Chris Hughes*
Part of the GWR Group plc.

2CR-FM (Two Counties Radio)
5–7 Southcote Road, Bournemouth, Dorset
BH1 3LR
☎01202 259259   Fax 01202 255244
Programme Controller *Tom Hardy*
Wholly-owned subsidiary of the GWR Group
Plc. Serves Dorset and Hampshire. All reviews/
topicality/press releases to The Programme
Controller, 2CRFM at the above address.

2-Ten FM/Classic Gold 1431
PO Box 2020, Reading, Berkshire RG31 7FG
☎0118 9454400   Fax 0118 9288456
Programme Controller *Jana Rangooni*
A subsidiary of the GWR Group plc. Music-
based programming.

Viking FM/Magic 1161
Commercial Road, Hull, North Humberside
HU1 2SA
☎01482 325141   Fax 01482 587067
Managing Director *Dee Ford*
Programme Controller *Paul Saunders*
News Co-ordinator *Shirley Renwick*
Features Producer *Paul Bromley*
Music-based programming.

WABC
See **Beacon Radio**

Wessex FM
Radio House, Trinity Street, Dorchester,
Dorset DT1 1DJ
☎01305 250333   Fax 01305 250052
Programme Manager *Phil Miles*
Music, local news, information and features.
These include motoring, cooking, reviews of
theatre, cinema, books, videos, local music.
Expert phone-ins on gardening, antiques, pets,
legal matters, DIY and medical issues.

West Sound FM/West FM
Radio House, 54 Holmston Road, Ayr
KA7 3BE
☎01292 283662
Fax 01292 283665/262607 (news)
Programme Controller *Gordon McArthur*
Music-based broadcasting.

102.4 Wish FM
Orrell Road, Wigan WN5 8HJ
☎01942 761024   Fax 01942 777694
Programme Controller *Steve Collins*
Music-based programming plus news and sport.

Radio XL 1296 AM
KMS House, Bradford Street, Birmingham
B12 0JD
☎0121 753 5353   Fax 0121 753 3111
Station Manager *Barry Curtis*
Asian broadcasting for the West Midlands, 24
hours a day.

1152 XTRA-AM
See **BRMB-FM 96.4**

Freelance Rates – Broadcasting

Freelance rates vary enormously. The following minimum rates, negotiated by the **National Union of Journalists,** should be treated as guidelines. Most work can command higher fees from employers whether or not they have NUJ agreements. It is up to freelancers to negotiate the best deal they can.

BBC Guidelines for Freelance Minimum Rates

BBC – Published Material
Domestic Radio

Plays/prose (per minute)	£12.04
Prose for dramatisation (per minute)	£9.39
Poems (per half-minute)	£12.04

World Service Radio (English)

Plays/prose (per minute)	£6.03
Prose for dramatisation (per minute)	£4.70
Poems (per half-minute)	£6.03

Television

Prose (per minute)	£18.24
Poems (per half-minute)	£21.17

BBC Radio Drama
A beginner in radio drama should receive at least £39.89 per minute for a 60-minute script. For an established writer – one who has three or more plays to his credit – the minimum rate per minute is £60.73.
An attendance payment of £35.72 per production is paid to established writers.
The rate per script for *The Archers* is £558.83.

BBC News Reports
National Regional Radio and Television (Radio Scotland, Ulster and Wales): £70 for up to 2 minutes; £14.75 per minute thereafter.
Local Radio and Regional Television within a cluster (group of local stations): £55 for up to 2 minutes; £12.50 per minute thereafter.
Regional Television: £46.75 for up to 2 minutes; £11.50 per minute thereafter.

Interviews and Talks
Interviews of up to 5 minutes: £48 (professional broadcaster); £29 (non-professional); *5 to 10 minutes:* negotiable but not less than above fees; *over 10 minutes:* £64.

Linked interviews: 1 interview £79; 2 interviews £103
Illustrated talks: £14.80 per minute.

Features/documentaries
Up to 7 minutes: £171.50; £24.50 per minute thereafter.

Independent Radio

News reports: £20.69 for the first 2 minutes; £6.89 per minute thereafter (CRCA agreement).
News copy: £7.67 per item.

Research
TV organisations which hire freelancers to research programme items should pay on a day rate which reflects the value of the work and the importance of the programme concerned.

Presentation
In all broadcast media, presenters command higher fees than news journalists. There is considerable variation in what is paid for presenting programmes and videos, according to their audience and importance. Day rates with television companies are usually about £140 – £160 a day.

Television Drama

For a 60-minute teleplay, the BBC will pay an established writer £7170 and a beginner £4551. The corresponding figures for ITV are £9245 for the established writer and £6568 for a writer new to television but with a solid reputation in other literary areas. ITV also has a 'beginner' category with a payment of £6296 for a 60-minute teleplay.

Day rates for attendance at read-throughs and rehearsals is £65 for the BBC and £74.40 for ITV.

Feature Films

An agreement between **The Writer's Guild** and **PACT** allows for a minimum guaranteed payment to the writer of £31,200 on a feature film with a budget in excess of £2 million; £19,000 on a budget from £750,000 to £2 million; £14,000 on a budget below £750,000.

Film, TV and Video Production Companies

Absolutely Productions Ltd
8th Floor, Alhambra House, 27–31 Charing
Cross Road, London WC2H 0AU
☎0171 930 3113   Fax 0171 930 4114
Executive Producer *Miles Bullough*
Development Executive *Alex Jackson-Long*

TV and radio production company specialising
in comedy and entertainment. OUTPUT
Absolutely series 1–4 (Ch4); *mr don and mr george*
(Ch4); *Squawkietalkie* (comedy wildlife pro-
gramme for Ch4); *The Preventers* (ITV);
Scotland v England (Ch4); *Barry Welsh is Coming*
(HTV); *The Jack Docherty Show* (Ch5); *The
Morwenna Banks Show* (Ch5); *Stressed Eric*
(BBC2); *Armstrong & Miller* (Paramount/Ch4).

Action Time Ltd
Wrendal House, 2 Whitworth Street West,
Manchester M1 5WX
☎0161 236 8999   Fax 0161 236 8845
Chairman *Stephen Leahy*
Director of Programming *Trish Kinane*

Major producers and licensers of TV quiz and
game entertainment shows such as *Catchphrase;
Here's One I Made Earlier; Crazy Cottage;
Backdate; Body Heat; A Game of War; Jeopardy;
Spellbound.* Action Time has co-production
partners in Spain, Sweden, Denmark, Norway,
Ireland and India.

Alomo Productions
1 Stephen Street, London W1P 1PJ
☎0171 691 6000   Fax 0171 691 6081

Bought by Pearson in 1996. Major producers
of television drama and comedy. OUTPUT
*Goodnight Sweetheart; Birds of a Feather; Love
Hurts; The New Statesman; Grown Ups.* Scripts
not welcome unless via agents but new writing
is encouraged.

Antelope (UK) Ltd
29b Montague Street, London WC1B 5BH
☎0171 209 0099   Fax 0171 209 0098
Managing Director *Mick Csáky*
Head of Non-Fiction *Krishan Arora*

Film, television and video productions for
drama, documentary and corporate material.
OUTPUT *Cyberspace* (ITV); *Brunch* (Ch5); *The*

Pier (weekly arts and entertainment programme);
Placido Domingo (ITV); *Baden Powell – The Boy
Man; Howard Hughes – The Naked Emperor* (Ch4
'Secret Lives' series); *Hiroshima.* No unsolicited
mss – 'we are not reading any new material at
present'.

**Apex Television Production &
Facilities Ltd**
Button End Studios, Harston, Cambridge
CB2 5NX
☎01223 872900   Fax 01223 873092
Contact *Bernard Mulhern*

Video producer: drama, documentary, commercials and corporate. Largely corporate production
for a wide range of international companies.
Many drama-based training programmes and
current-affairs orientated TV work. No scripts.
All work is commissioned against a particular
project.

Arena Films Ltd
2 Pelham Road, London SW19 1SX
☎0181 543 3990   Fax 0181 540 3992
Producer *David Conroy*

Film and TV drama. Scripts with some sort of
European connection or tie-in particularly
welcome. Open-minded with regard to new
writing.

Arlington Productions Limited
Pinewood Studios, Iver Heath,
Buckinghamshire SL0 0NH
☎01753 651700   Fax 01753 656050
Contact *Kevin Francis, Gillian Garrow*

Television drama. OUTPUT *The Masks of Death*
(TVM); *Murder Elite* (TVM); *A One-Way Ticket
to Hollywood* (entertainment documentary).
Prefers to see synopsis in the first instance. 'We
try to encourage new writers.'

**The Ashford Entertainment
Corporation Ltd**
20 The Chase, Coulsdon, Surrey CR5 2EG
☎0181 763 2558   Fax 0181 763 2558
E-mail: frazer_ashford@compuserve.com
Managing Director *Frazer Ashford*

FOUNDED in 1996 by award-winning film and

TV producer Frazer Ashford whose credits include *Great Little Trains* (Mainline Television for Westcountry/Ch4, starring the late Willie Rushton); *Street Life* and *Make Yourself at Home* (both for WTV). Produces theatrical films and television – drama, lifestyle and documentaries. Happy to receive ideas for dramas and documentaries but submit a one-page synopsis only in the first instance, enclosing s.a.e. 'Be patient, allow up to four weeks for a reply. Be precise with the idea; specific details rather than vague thoughts. Attach a back-up sheet with credentials and supporting evidence, ie, can you ensure that your idea is feasible?'

Steve Barron

30 Oval Road, Camden, London NW1 7DE
E-mail: steveba@bago.co.uk

Film and TV drama. Director of *Teenage Mutant Ninja Turtles; Coneheads; The Adventures of Pinocchio* and executive producer on *While You Were Sleeping* and *The Specialist*. Welcomes unsolicited scripts.

Bazal Productions

See **Broadcast Communications**

Beckmann Productions Ltd

Meadow Court, West Street, Ramsey, Isle of Man IM8 1AE
☎01624 816585   Fax 01624 816589
E-mail: beckmann@enterprise.net

Contact *Stuart Semark*

Isle of Man-based company. Video and television documentary. OUTPUT *Practical Guide to Europe* (travel series); *Maestro* (12-part series on classical composers); *Elephant Orphans*. One-page proposals considered. No scripts.

Behr Cinematography

22 Redington Road, London NW3 7RG
☎0171 794 2535   Fax 0171 794 2535
Contact *Arnold Behr, Betty Burghes*

Documentary, educational, corporate film and/or video, often for voluntary organisations. No actors, except for voice-overs. No unsolicited mss. S.a.e. appreciated from applicants needing a reply.

Paul Berriff Productions Ltd

Cedar House, 53 Heads Lane, Hessle, East Yorkshire HU13 0JH
☎01482 641158   Fax 01482 649692
E-mail: kba98@dial.pipex.com
Contact *Paul Berriff*

Television documentary. OUTPUT *Rescue* (13-part documentary for ITV); *M25: The Magic Roundabout* ('First Tuesday'); *Animal Squad Undercover* (Ch4); *Evidence of Abuse* (BBC1 'Inside Story'); *Lessons of Darkness* (BBC2 'Fine Cut'); *The Nick* (Ch4 series); *Confrontation on E Wing* (BBC 'Everyman'); *Astronauts* (Ch4 series); *Streets of Fire* (Ch4 series); *Passport Control* ('Cutting Edge').

BFI Production

29 Rathbone Street, London W1P 1AG
☎0171 636 5587   Fax 0171 580 9456
Head of Production *Roger Shannon*

Part of the **British Film Institute**. Produces a range of projects from short films and videos to feature-length films, acting as executive producer and co-investor. Feature treatments or screenplays are accepted for consideration, generally low-budget and innovative. Unsolicited mss have a two-month turnaround period. OUTPUT includes *Gallivant; Stella Does Tricks; Smalltime; Under the Skin; Love Is the Devil*. Runs a New Directors Scheme (advertised annually).

Black Coral Productions Ltd

PO Box 333, Woodford Green, Essex IG9 6DB
☎0181 880 4860   Fax 0181 504 3338
Contacts *Lazell Daley, Isabelle Tracy*

Producers of drama and documentary film and television. Committed to the development of new writing. Offers a script evaluation service for which a fee is payable, with a particular interest in short and feature-length dramas. Runs courses – see **Black Coral Training** under **Writers' Courses, Circles and Workshops**.

Blue Heaven Productions Ltd

45 Leather Lane, London EC1N 7TJ
☎0171 404 4222   Fax 0171 404 4266
Contact *Graham Benson, Christine Benson*

Film and television drama and occasional documentary. OUTPUT *The Ruth Rendell Mysteries; Crime Story: Dear Roy, Love Gillian; Ready When You Are/Screen Challenge* (three series for Meridian Regional); *The Man who Made Husbands Jealous* (Anglia Television Entertainment/Blue Heaven). Scripts considered but treatments or ideas preferred in the first instance. New writing encouraged.

Bond Clarkson Russell Ltd

16 Trinity Churchyard, Guildford, Surrey GU1 3RR
☎01483 562888   Fax 01483 302732
E-mail: bcr@bcr-marketing.demon.co.uk
Contact *Peter Bond, Simon Kozak*

Corporate literature, film, video and multi-media producer of a wide variety of material, including conference videos, for blue-chip companies in the main. No scripts. All work is commissioned.

Matt Boney Associates
Woodside, Holdfast Lane, Grayswood, Haslemere, Surrey GU27 2EU
☎01428 656178

Contact *Matt Boney*

Writer/director for video and television: commercials, documentaries, skiing and travel. No unsolicited mss.

Box Clever Productions
The Maples Centre, 144 Liverpool Road, London N1 1LA
☎0171 619 0606   Fax 0171 700 2248
Contact *Claire Walmsley*

Broadcast TV, film and video documentaries, specialising in social and current affairs. Sister company of Boxclever Communication Training, specialising in media interview skills, presentation and communication skills. OUTPUT documentaries for BBC and Ch4; corporate videos for the European Commission, public sector and voluntary organisations. No unsolicited scripts; outlines and proposals only.

British Lion
Screen Entertainment Ltd
Pinewood Studios, Iver, Buckinghamshire SL0 0NH
☎01753 651700   Fax 01753 656391
Chief Executive *Peter R. E. Snell*

Film production. OUTPUT has included *A Man for All Seasons; Treasure Island; A Prayer for the Dying; Lady Jane; The Crucifer of Blood; Death Train*. No unsolicited mss. Send synopses only.

Broadcast Communications
46/47 Bedford Square, London WC1B 3DP
☎0171 462 9000   Fax 0171 462 9001
Chief Executive *Tom Barnicoat*
Director of Factual Programming
  Peter Bazalgette
Director of Music and Entertainment
  Malcolm Gerrie

Television division of *The Guardian Media Group*. One of Britain's largest independent producers, responsible for nearly 1000 hours of programming for all the UK's terrestrial networks as well as cable and satellite. It has two production companies, wholly owned. These

are: Bazal Productions, specialising in leisure, including cooking and gardening, and Initial Film and Television, specialising in music and entertainment.

Caravel Film Techniques Ltd
The Great Barn Studios, Cippenham Lane, Slough, Berkshire SL1 5AU
☎01753 534828   Fax 01753 571383
Contact *Denis Statham*

Film, video and TV: documentary, commercials and corporate. OUTPUT Promos for commercial TV, documentaries for BBC & ITV, sales and training material for corporate blue chip companies. No unsolicited scripts. Prepared to review mostly serious new writing.

Carlton Productions
35–38 Portman Square, London W1H 9FH
☎0171 486 6688   Fax 0171 486 1132
Director of Programmes *Andy Allan*
Director of Drama & Co-production
  Jonathan Powell
Controller of Entertainment and Comedy
  John Bishop
Controller of Factual Programmes
  Steve Clark

Makers of independently produced TV drama for ITV. OUTPUT *She's Out; Kavanagh QC; Morse; Boon; Gone to the Dogs; The Guilty; Tanamera; Soldier, Soldier; Seekers; Sharpe; Peak Practice; Cadfael; Faith*. 'We try to use new writers on established long-running series.' Scripts welcome from experienced writers and agents only.

Carnival (Films & Theatre) Ltd
12 Raddington Road, Ladbroke Grove, London W10 5TG
☎0181 968 0968/1818/1717
Fax 0181 968 0155/0177
Contact *Brian Eastman*

Film, TV and theatre producers. OUTPUT Film: *The Mill on the Floss* (BBC); *Firelight* (Hollywood Pictures/Wind Dancer Productions); *Shadowlands* (Savoy/Spelling); *In Hitler's Shadow* (Home Box Office); *Under Suspicion* (Columbia/Rank/LWT); *Wilt* (Rank/LWT); *Whoops Apocalypse* (ITC). Television: *Oktober* (ITV Network Centre); *The Fragile Heart* (Ch4); *Crime Traveller* (BBC); *Poirot* (LWT); *Bugs* (BBC); *Anna Lee* (LWT); *All or Nothing At All* (LWT); *Head Over Heels* (Carlton); *The Big Battalions* (Ch4); *Jeeves & Wooster* I–IV (Granada); *Traffik* (Ch4); *Forever Green* (LWT); *Porterhouse Blue* (Ch4); *Blott on the Landscape* (BBC). Theatre:

What a Performance; Juno & the Paycock; Murder is Easy; Misery; Ghost Train; Map of the Heart; Shadowlands; Up on the Roof.

Cartwn Cymru

Screen Centre, Llantrisant Road, Cardiff
CF5 2PU
☎01222 575999   Fax 01222 575919
Contact *Naomi Jones*
Animation production company. OUTPUT *Toucan 'Tecs* (YTV/S4C); *Funnybones* (S4C/BBC); *Funnybones* (S4C/BBC); *Testament: The Bible in Animation* (BBC2/S4C); *Turandot: Operavox* (S4C/BBC). In production: *The Jesus Story* (S4C)

CCC Wadlow

3rd Floor South, Harling House, 47–51 Great Suffolk Street, London SE1 0BL
☎0171 450 4720   Fax 0171 450 4734
Head of Productions *Sarah Dent*
Film and video, multimedia and graphic design: corporate and commercials. CLIENTS include Bovis; Camelot; De La Rue plc; Del Monte Foods International; East Midlands Electricity; Hill & Norton; Knowlton; Lloyds of London; Nationwide Building Society; P&O; M&C Saatchi; Samaritans. 'We are very keen to hear from new writers, but please send c.v.s rather than scripts.'

Central Office of Information Film & Video

Hercules Road, London SE1 7DU
☎0171 261 8667   Fax 0171 261 8776
Contact *Geoff Raison*
Film, video and TV: drama, documentary, commercials, corporate and public information films. OUTPUT includes government commercials and corporate information. No scripts. New writing commissioned as required.

Channel X Communications Ltd

22 Stephenson Way, London NW1 2HD
☎0171 387 3874   Fax 0171 387 0738
Contact *Alan Marke*
FOUNDED 1986 by Jonathan Ross and Alan Marke to develop Ross's first series *The Last Resort.* Now producing comedy series and documentary. Actively developing narrative comedy and game shows. OUTPUT *Unpleasant World of Penn & Teller; XYZ; Jo Brand – Through The Cakehole; Sean's Show; The Smell of Reeves & Mortimer; Fantastic Facts; One for the Road; Funny Business; Shooting Stars; Barking; Food Fight.*

Chatsworth Television Ltd

97–99 Dean Street, London W1V 5RA
☎0171 734 4302   Fax 0171 437 3301
Head of Drama Development
  Stephen Jeffery-Poulter
Drama and light entertainment TV producers. All unsolicited drama scripts will be considered. Mainly interested in contemporary, factually based or comedy drama material, but *not* sitcoms. S.a.e. must accompany *all* submissions.

Childsplay Productions Ltd

8 Lonsdale Road, London NW6 6RD
☎0171 328 1429   Fax 0171 328 1416
Contact *Kim Burke*
Television: drama, children's and family. OUTPUT includes *Eye of the Storm; Pirates; Children of the New Forest.*

Circus Films

See **Elstree (Production) Co. Ltd.**

Claverdon Films Ltd

28 Narrow Street, London E14 8DQ
☎0171 702 8700   Fax 0171 702 8701
Contact *Mike Bluett, Tony Palmer*
Film and TV: drama and documentary. OUTPUT *Menuhin; Maria Callas; Testimony; In From the Cold; Pushkin; England, My England* (by John Osborne); *Kipling.* Unsolicited material is read, but please send a written outline first.

The Clear Picture Co.

PO Box 12, Bakewell, Derbyshire
DE45 1ZP
☎01246 583005
Contact *Shaun Gilmartin, Judy Laybourn*
Television documentaries, sport and corporate programmes. OUTPUT includes programmes for Carlton Television, Central Television, YTV and Sky Sports. No drama. 'We use inhouse writers on most projects. However, we do occasionally use freelance talent from across a range of skills.'

Cleveland Productions

5 Rainbow Court, Oxhey, Near Watford, Hertfordshire WD1 4RP
☎01923 254000   Fax 01923 254000
Contact *Michael Gosling*
Communications in sound and vision A/V production and still photography specialists in education and sport.

Collingwood & Convergence Productions Ltd

10–14 Crown Street, Acton, London W3 8SB
☎0181 993 3666   Fax 0181 993 9595
E-mail: info@crownstreet.co.uk

Producers *Christopher O'Hare, Terence Clegg, Tony Collingwood*
Development Director *Helen Stroud*

Film and TV. Convergence Productions produces live action, drama documentaries; Tony Collingwood Productions specialises in children's animation. OUTPUT Convergence: *Coral Browne: Caviar to the General* (Ch4 documentary); *On the Road Again* (8-part documentary series for BBC and Discovery Channel UK); *Pierrepoint* (6-part film drama series); 60-minute programme for Ch4's 'Witness', *Better Dead Than Gay* and a half-hour documentary for Ch4's 'Without Walls', *Marco Polo: Not*. Recent credits include 13x[oh]hrs *Plastic Fantastic* (UK cosmetic surgery techniques, Ch5) and *David Starkey's Henry VIII* (Ch4 historical documentary). Collingwood: *RARG* (award-winning animated film); two series of *Captain Zed and the Zee Zone* (ITV); *Daisy-Head Mayzie* (Dr Seuss animated series for Turner Network and Hanna-Barbera); *Oscar's Orchestra* (52-part animated series for BBC and Time Warner); *Dennis and Gnasher* (26-episode animated series for HIT Entertainment and D. C. Thomson); *Animal Stories* (26x5 minute animated poems, ITV network).

Complete Communications

Communications House, Garsington Road, Cowley, Oxford OX4 2NG
☎01865 384004/383073   Fax 01865 749854

Contact *A. M. Black, Ms C. Richman, Mrs V. Andrews-Semple*

Video production for corporate, commercial and documentary work, plus satellite/business production. No unsolicited mss. Samples of work are kept on file. Freelancers used.

Creative Channel Ltd

Channel TV, Television Centre, La Pouquelaye, St Helier, Jersey, Channel Islands JE1 3ZD
☎01534 816873   Fax 01534 816889

Production Manager *David Evans*

Part of the Channel Television Group. Producers of TV commercials and corporate material: information, promotional, sales, training and events coverage. OUTPUT *Exploring Guernsey* and *This is Jersey* (video souvenir travel guides); promotional videos for all types of businesses in the Channel Islands and throughout Europe; plus over 300 commercials a year. No unsolicited mss; new writing/scripts commissioned as required. Interested in hearing from local writers resident in the Channel Islands.

Creative Film Makers Ltd

Pottery Lane House, 34A Pottery Lane, London W11 4LZ
☎0171 229 5131   Fax 0171 229 4999

Contact *Michael Seligman, Nicholas Seligman*

Corporate and sports documentaries, commercials and television programmes. OUTPUT *The World's Greatest Golfers*, plus various corporate and sports programmes for clients like Nestlé, Benson & Hedges, Wimpey, Bouygues. 'Always open to suggestions but have hardly ever received unsolicited material of any value.' Keen nevertheless to encourage new writers.

Creative Film Productions

68 Conway Road, London N14 7BE
☎0181 447 8187   Fax 0181 886 3054

Contact *Phil Davies*

Producers of animation shorts, documentary and corporate.

The Creative Partnership

13 Bateman Street, London W1V 5TB
☎0171 439 7762   Fax 0171 437 1467

Contact *Christopher Fowler, Jim Sturgeon*

Producers of commercials and marketing campaigns for feature films. OUTPUT includes campaigns for *Tomorrow Never Dies; Starship Troopers; Velvet Goldmine; Trainspotting*. No scripts. 'We train new writers in-house, and find them from submitted c.v.s. All applicants must have previous commercial writing experience.' Freelance writers employed for special projects.

Cricket Ltd

Ganton House, 14–22 Ganton Street, London W1V 1LB
☎0171 287 4848   Fax 0171 413 0654
E-mail: john@cricket-ltd.co.uk

Creative Director *Andrew Davies*
Head of Production (Film & Video) *Jonathan Freer*

Film and video, live events and conferences, print and design, and business television. 'Communications solutions for business clients wishing to influence targeted external and internal audiences.'

Croft Television and Graphics Ltd

Croft House, Progress Business Centre, Whittle Parkway, Slough SL1 6DQ
☎01628 668735   Fax 01628 668791
Contact *Keith Jones, Terry Adlam*

Producers of video and TV for drama, documentary, commercials, corporate, training and children's educational programmes. Also any form of visual communication and entertainment. Fresh and creative new writing encouraged.

Cromdale Films Ltd

12 St Paul's Road, London N1 2QN
☎0171 226 0178
Contact *Ian Lloyd*

Film, video and TV: drama and documentary. OUTPUT *The Face of Darkness* (feature film); *Drift to Dawn* (rock music drama); *The Overdue Treatment* (documentary); *Russia, The Last Red Summer* (documentary). Initial phone call advised before submission of scripts.

Crown Business Communications Ltd

United House, 9 Pembridge Road, London W11 3JY
☎0171 727 7272   Fax 0171 727 9940
E-mail: samowens@crownbc.com
Contact *Sam Owens*

Leading producers of video, live events, digital and internet communication for business. Interested in talented scriptwriters with experience in any of these areas, especially internet.

Dareks Production House

58 Wickham Road, Beckenham, Kent BR3 6RQ
☎0181 658 2012   Fax 0181 325 0629
E-mail: dareks@dircon.co.uk
Contact *David Crossman*

Independent producers of corporate and broadcast television. 'We are interested in *short* (10–15 minute) narrative scripts.'

Delphic IVP Ltd

16 York Place, Edinburgh EH1 3EP
☎0131 557 2151   Fax 0131 557 5465
Contact *Catherine Ann G. Reid*

Film, video and TV production for documentary, commercials, corporate and title sequences material. Unsolicited scripts welcome.

Diverse Production Limited

Gorleston Street, London W14 8XS
☎0171 603 4567   Fax 0171 603 2148
Contact *Roy Ackerman, Narinder Minhas*

Broadcast television production with experience in popular prime-time formats, strong documentaries (one-offs and series), investigative journalism, science, business and history films, travel series, arts and music, talk shows, schools and education. 'We have always been committed to editorial and visual originality.' Recent OUTPUT includes *Secret Lives; Omnibus; Cutting Edge; Equinox; Modern Times; Dispatches; Without Walls; Panorama; The Big Idea; Empires and Emperors* and the *Little Picture Show*.

Drake A-V Video Ltd

89 St Fagans Road, Fairwater, Cardiff CF5 3AE
☎01222 560333   Fax 01222 554909
Contact *Ian Lewis*

Corporate A-V film and video, mostly promotional, training or educational. Scripts in these fields welcome. Other work includes interactive multimedia and CD-ROM production.

The Drama House Ltd

1 Hertford Place, London W1P 5RS
☎0171 388 9140   Fax 0171 388 3511
Contact *Jack Emery*

Film and television producers. OUTPUT *Little White Lies* (BBC1); *Witness Against Hitler* (BBC1); *Suffer the Little Children* (BBC2 'Stages'). Scripts (synopses preferred) welcome but only read and returned if accompanied by full postage. Interested in developing contacts with new and established writers.

Charles Dunstan Communications Ltd

42 Wolseley Gardens, London W4 3LS
☎0181 994 2328   Fax 0181 994 2328
Contact *Charles Dunstan*

Producers of film, video and TV for documentary and corporate material. OUTPUT *Renewable Energy* for broadcast worldwide in *Inside Britain* series; National Power Annual Report video *The Electric Environment*. No unsolicited scripts.

Eagle and Eagle Ltd

15 Marlborough Road, London W4 4EU
☎0181 995 1884   Fax 0181 995 5648
Contact *Robert Eagle, Catharine Alen-Buckley*

Film, video and TV: drama, documentary and children's programmes. No unsolicited scripts.

East Anglian Productions

Studio House, 21–23 Walton Road, Frinton on Sea, Essex CO13 0AA
☎01255 676252   Fax 01255 850528

Contact *Ray Anderson*

Film, video and TV: drama and documentary, children's television, comedy, commercials and corporate.

Eclipse Presentations Ltd

Walters Farm Road, Tonbridge, Kent TN9 1QT
☎01732 365107   Fax 01732 362600

Contact *Brian Adams*

Practitioners in audio and visual communications. *Specialises* in corporate videos, conferences, PR events and award ceremonies, safety, sales and marketing, and training.

Edinburgh Film & Video Productions

Nine Mile Burn, by Penicuik, Midlothian EH26 9LT
☎01968 672131   Fax 01968 672685

Contact *R. Crichton*

Film, TV drama and documentary. OUTPUT *Sara; Moonacre; Torch; Silent Mouse; The Curious Case of Santa Claus; The Stamp of Greatness.* No unsolicited scripts at present.

Elstree (Production) Co. Ltd

Shepperton Studios, Studios Road, Shepperton, Middlesex TW17 0QD
☎01932 572680/1   Fax 01932 572682

Contact *Greg Smith*

Produces feature films and TV drama. OUTPUT *Othello* (BBC); *Great Expectations* (Disney Channel); *Porgy & Bess* (with Trevor Nunn); *Old Curiosity Shop* (Disney Channel/RHI); *London Suite* (NBC/Hallmark). Co-owner of Circus Films with Trevor Nunn for feature film projects.

Enigma Productions Ltd

13–15 Queen's Gate Place Mews, London SW7 5BG
☎0171 581 0238   Fax 0171 584 1799

Chairman *Lord Puttnam of Queensgate*

Backed by Warner Bros. OUTPUT *Memphis Belle* ; *Meeting Venus; Being Human; War of the Buttons; Le Confessional* by Robert Lepage. Enigma has no plans for production in the near future. 'Lord Puttnam is currently concentrating on his role as a working Peer. We are not accepting *any* submissions.'

Excalibur Productions

13–15 Northgate, Heptonstall, West Yorkshire HX7 7ND
☎01422 844595   Fax 01422 843871

Contact *Jay Jones*

Most recent productions are medical documentaries such as an investigation into diabetes control sponsored by Bayer Diagnostics, collaborative literary and cultural projects such as *The Boys From Savoy* with David Glass, and corporates for clients such as South Yorkshire Supertram and Datacolor International. Interested in ideas, scripts and possible joint development for broadcast, sell-through and experimental arts.

Farnham Film Company Ltd

34 Burnt Hill Road, Lower Bourne, Farnham, Surrey GU10 3LZ
☎01252 710313   Fax 01252 725855
Website: www.farnfilm.demon.co.uk

Contact *Ian Lewis*

Television and film: children's drama and documentaries. Unsolicited mss welcome. No unsolicited mss. Check website for current needs.

Farrant Partnership

91 Knatchbull Road, London SE5 9QU
☎0171 733 0711   Fax 0171 738 5224

Contact *James Farrant*

Corporate video productions.

Feelgood Fiction

49 Goldhawk Road, London W12 8QP
☎0181 746 2535   Fax 0181 740 6177

Contact *Laurence Bowen*

Producer of film and TV drama. Recent OUTPUT includes: *The Hello Girls; Stone, Scissors, Paper; Dual Balls* and *Painted Angels.*

Filmit Productions

2 Tunstall Road, London SW9 8BN
☎0171 738 4175   Fax 0171 738 3787

Contact *John Samson*

Television documentaries and corporate work. OUTPUT *A Polite Enquiry; The Gulf Between Us; Loyalty on the Line; Who Let Our Children Die* (all documentaries for Ch4); *Free for All; Speak Out* (Ch4 series). Unsolicited scripts welcome. Keen to discover and nurture new writing talent.

First Creative Group Ltd

Belgrave Court, Caxton Road, Fulwood, Preston, Lancashire PR2 9PL
☎01772 651555   Fax 01772 651777
E-mail: mail@firstcreative.com

Contact *M. Mulvihill*

Film, video and TV productions for documentary, corporate and multimedia material. Unsolicited scripts welcome. Open to new writing.

First Information Group

Knightsbridge House, 197 Knightsbridge, London SW7 1RB
☎0171 393 3000   Fax 0171 393 3033
Contact *Michael Rodd*

Multi-media for business and industry including video, computer and on-line services. No unsolicited material but always interested in c.v.s and personal profiles.

Fitting Images Ltd

Alfred House, 127A Oatlands Drive, Weybridge, Surrey KT13 9LB
☎01932 840056   Fax 01932 858075
E-mail: fitting_image@compuserve.com
Managing Director *Sue Fleetwood*

Promotional, training, medical/pharmaceutical; contacts from experienced writers of drama and comedy welcome. We are also interested in broadcast projects.

Flashback Communication Ltd

25 Greenhead Street, Glasgow G40 1ES
☎0141 554 6868   Fax 0141 554 6869
Contact *Chris Attkins*

Video and TV producers: drama, documentary, corporate, training and education, and sellthroughs. OUTPUT includes dramatised training videos and TV programmes or inserts for the ITV network, BBC and stations worldwide. Proposals considered; no scripts. New talent encouraged. Interested in fresh ideas and effective style.

Flicks Films Ltd

101 Wardour Street, London W1V 3TD
☎0171 734 4892   Fax 0171 287 2307
Managing Director/Producer *Terry Ward*

Film and video: children's animated series and specials. OUTPUT *The Mr Men; Little Miss; Bananaman; The Pondles; Nellie the Elephant; See How They Work With Dig and Dug; Timbuctoo.* Scripts specific to their needs will be considered. 'Always willing to read relevant material.'

Focus Films Ltd

The Rotunda Studios, Rear of 116–118 Finchley Road, London NW3 5HT
☎0171 435 9004/5   Fax 0171 431 3562
E-mail: focus@pupix.demon.co.uk

Contact *David Pupkewitz, Lisa Disler, Malcolm Kohill (Head of Development)*

Film and TV producers. Drama OUTPUT *CrimeTime* (medium-budget feature thriller); *Diary of a Sane Man* (experimental feature for Ch4); *Othello* (Ch4 drama). Projects in development include *The 51st State; Spindrift; Camden Girls; Secret Society; The Turn; The Complete History of the Breast.* No unsolicited scripts.

Mark Forstater Productions Ltd

27 Lonsdale Road, London NW6 6RA
☎0171 624 1123   Fax 0171 624 1124
Production *Mark Forstater, Rosie Homan*

Active in the selection, development and production of material for film and TV. OUTPUT *Monty Python and the Holy Grail; The Odd Job; The Grass is Singing; Xtro; Forbidden; Separation; The Fantasist; Shalom Joan Collins; The Silent Touch; Grushko; The Wolves of Willoughby Chase; Between the Devil and the Deep Blue Sea; Doing Rude Things.* No unsolicited mss.

Friday Productions Ltd

23a St. Leonards Terrace, London SW3 4QG
☎0171 730 0608   Fax 0171 730 0608
Contact *Georgina Abrahams*

Film and TV productions for drama material. OUTPUT *Goggle Eyes; Harnessing Peacocks; The December Rose.* No unsolicited scripts. New writing encouraged especially from under-represented groups.

Gaia Communications

Sanctuary House, 35 Harding Avenue, Eastbourne, East Sussex BN22 8PL
☎01323 734809/727183   Fax 01323 734809
Producer *Robert Armstrong*
Script Editor *Loni Webb*

Video and TV corporate and documentary. OUTPUT *Discovering* (tourist and local knowledge series); *Holistic* (therapies & general information). 'Open to new ideas'; synopsis only on first contact.

Gala International Ltd

25 Stamford Brook Road, London W6 0XJ
☎0181 741 4200   Fax 0181 741 2323
Producer *David Lindsay*

TV commercials, promos, film and TV documentaries.

John Gau Productions
Burston House, 1 Burston Road, Putney,
London SW15 6AR
☎0181 788 8811   Fax 0181 789 0903
Contact *John Gau*

Documentaries and series for TV, plus corporate video. OUTPUT includes *The Great Sell-Off* (BBC2); *Korea* series (BBC1); *Reaching for the Skies* (BBC2); *Voyager* (Central); *The Power and The Glory* (BBC2); *The Team – A Season With McLaren* (BBC2); *The Great Outdoors* (Ch4); *Lights, Camera, Action!: A Century of the Cinema* (ITV network); *The Triumph of the Nerds* (Ch4). Open to ideas from writers.

Noel Gay Television
1 Albion Court, Albion Place, Hammersmith,
London W6 0QT
☎0181 600 5200   Fax 0181 600 5222
Contact *Anne Mensah*

The association with Noel Gay (agency/management and music publishing) makes this one of the most securely financed independents in the business. OUTPUT: *Hububb – Series 2 & 3* (BBC); *I-Camcorder* (Ch4); *10%ers – Series 2* (Carlton/ITV); *Call Up the Stars* (BBC1); *Smeg Outs* (BBC video); *Les Bubb* (BBC Scotland); *Red Dwarf – Series 8; Making of Red Dwarf* (BBC video); *Dave Allen* (ITV); *Windrush* (BBC documentary). Joint ventures and companies include a partnership with Odyssey, a leading Indian commercials, film and TV producer, and international networks; a joint venture with Reed Consumer Books to develop book and magazine ideas for film, video and television, and the Noel Gay Motion Picture Company, whose credits include *Virtual Sexuality*; *Trainspotting* (with Ch4 and Figment Films), and *Killer Tongue*, a co-production with Iberoamericana. Other associate NGTV companies are Grant Naylor Productions, Rose Bay Film Productions, Pepper Productions and Jane Davies Casting.

Geofilms Ltd
Larkhill House, PO Box 400, Abingdon,
Oxford OX14 1FD
☎01235 537400
E-mail: network@geofilms.co.uk
Contact *Ms Martine Benoit*

An independent production company FOUNDED in 1982 to produce high-quality factual programming, including science, current affairs, series, authored documentaries for television, as well as for corporates and heritage markets.

OUTPUT Ch4's *Equinox, Dispatches* and *Short Stories*, plus BBC2's *Horizon*.

Goldcrest Films International Ltd
65–66 Dean Street, London W1V 6PL
☎0171 437 8696   Fax 0171 437 4448
Chairman *John Quested*
Contact *Ekatarina Mosesson*

FOUNDED in the late '70s. Formerly part of the Brent Walker Leisure Group but independent since 1990 following management buy-out led by John Quested. The company's core activities are film production and worldwide distribution. Scripts via agents only.

The Good Film Company
2nd Floor, 14–15 D'Arblay Street, London W1V 3FP
☎0171 734 1331   Fax 0171 734 2997
Contact *Yanina Barry*

Commercials and pop videos. CLIENTS include Hugo Boss, Cadbury's, Wella, National Express Coaches, Camel Cigarettes, Tunisian Tourist Board. No unsolicited mss.

Granada Film
The London Television Centre, Upper Ground, South Bank, London SE1 9LT
☎0171 737 8681   Fax 0171 737 8682
Contact *Pippa Cross, Janette Day, Tessa Gibbs*

Films and TV films. OUTPUT *My Left Foot; Jack & Sarah; Misadventures of Margaret; Girls Night*. No unsolicited scripts. Supportive of new writing but often hard to offer real help as Granada are developing mainstream commercial projects which usually requires some status in talent areas.

Grasshopper Enterprises Ltd
50 Peel Street, London W8 7PD
☎0171 229 1181   Fax 0171 229 2070
Contact *Joy Whitby*

Children's programmes and adult drama. No unsolicited mss.

Green Umbrella Ltd
The Production House, 147a St Michael's Hill, Bristol BS2 8DB
☎0117 9731729   Fax 0117 9467432
Website: www.umbrella.co.uk

Television documentary makers and children's drama producers. OUTPUT includes episodes for *The Natural World, Wildlife on One* and original series such as *Living Europe* and *Triumph of Life*. Unsolicited treatments relating to natural history and science subjects are welcome.

Howard Hall

6 Foster Road, Abingdon, Oxfordshire
OX14 1YN
☎01235 533981/0860 775438
Fax 01235 533981

Contact *Howard Hall*

Film, video and TV: drama, documentary, commercials and corporate programmes. OUTPUT includes drama training programmes, satellite programmes, commercials, and programmes for broadcast channels. Scripts welcome. 'Always looking for new writers. We need a store of good writers in different fields of work.' Howard Hall has written two books: *Corporate Video Directing* (Focal Press) and *Careers in Film and Video* (**Kogan Page**).

Hammer Film Productions Ltd

Millennium Studios, Elstree Way,
Borehamwood, Hertfordshire WD6 1SF
☎0181 207 4011   Fax 0181 905 1127

Contact *Roy Skeggs, Graham Skeggs*

Feature films. No unsolicited scripts.

Hammerwood Film Productions

110 Trafalgar Road, Portslade, East Sussex
BN41 1GS
☎01273 277333   Fax 01273 705451

Contact *Ralph Harvey, Karen King,*
   Petra Ginman

Film, video and TV drama. OUTPUT *Sacre Bleu*; *Operation Pandora* (on-going TV series, episodes are invited); *Boadicea – Queen of the Iceni* (co-production with Pan-European Film Productions). 1998 projects: *Maison D'Amour* and *Hobgoblin Hill*. Most material is written in-house. 'We do not have the time to read scripts but will always read 2–3-page synopses/plot outlines. Anything of interest will be followed up and then script requested.' Hammerwood are also distributors with a stock of 5000 movies and TV programmes.

Hand Pict Productions Ltd

4 Picardy Place, Edinburgh EH1 3JT
☎0131 558 1543   Fax 0131 556 0792

Contact *George Cathro*

Television production for drama and documentary material. OUTPUT *The Ken Fine Show* (6-part series for Scottish Television); *Face Value* (Ch4); *Et in Stadia Ego* ('Without Walls', Ch4); *Blood Ties* (arts documentary for BBC Wales); *Blackfish* (current affairs for Ch4); *The Boat Band* (BBC). Unsolicited scripts welcome but pressure of work and programmes in pro-

duction can lead to delays in response. Encourages new writing.

HandMade Films Ltd

19 Beak Street, London W1R 3LB
☎0171 434 3132   Fax 0171 434 3143

Feature films. OUTPUT has included *The Life of Brian; Withnail and I; Mona Lisa; The Missionary; Time Bandits; The Lonely Passion of Judith Hearne; The Raggedy Rawney; Long Good Friday; A Private Function; How To Get Ahead in Advertising; Nuns on the Run; Intimate Relations; Sweet Angel Mine; The Wrong Guy; The Assistant; The James Gang; Dinner at Fred's.* Films in post-production/completed: *The Man With Rain in His Shoes; The Secret Laughter of Women; Lock, Stock and Two Smoking Barrels.* No unsolicited mss at present.

Hartswood Films Ltd

Twickenham Studios, The Barons,
St Margarets, Middlesex TW1 2AW
☎0181 607 8736   Fax 0181 607 8744

Contact *Elaine Cameron*

Film and TV production for drama and light entertainment. OUTPUT *Men Behaving Badly* (BBC, previously Thames); *Is It Legal?* (Ch4); *The English Wife* (Meridian); *A Woman's Guide to Adultery* (Carlton); *My Good Friend* (ITV); *Code Name Kyril* (HTV). No unsolicited scripts. New writing read if recommended by agents.

Hat Trick Productions Ltd

10 Livonia Street, London W1V 3PH
☎0171 434 2451   Fax 0171 287 9791

Contact *Denise O'Donoghue*

Television programmes. OUTPUT includes *Father Ted; Drop the Dead Donkey; Have I Got News For You; Confessions; Game On; Whatever You Want; The Peter Principle; Clive Anderson All Talk; Room 101; The Best Show in the World...Probably; Whose Line is it Anyway?* The company's drama output includes: *A Very Open Prison; Eleven Men Against Eleven; Lord of Misrule; Crossing the Floor; Gobble; Underworld; Mr White Goes to Westminster.*

Hawthornden Films

Now **Silent/Sound Films Ltd** (see entry).

Head to Head Communication Ltd

The Hook, Plane Tree Crescent, Feltham,
Middlesex TW13 7AQ
☎0181 893 7766   Fax 0181 893 2777
E-mail: hth.co.uk

Contact *Bob Carson*

Producers of business and corporate communication programmes and events.

Jim Henson Productions Ltd
30 Oval Road, Camden, London NW1 7DE
☎0171 428 4000   Fax 0171 428 4001
Contact *Angus Fletcher*

Feature films and TV: family entertainment and children's. OUTPUT *Gulliver's Travels; Buddy; Muppet Treasure Island; The Muppet Christmas Carol; Labyrinth; The Witches* (films); *Dinosaurs* (ABC); *Muppet Tonight* (BBC/Sky); *The Muppet Show* (ITV); *The Storyteller* (Ch4); *Dr Seuss; The Secret Life of Toys* (BBC); *The Animal Show* (BBC); *Bear in the Big Blue House* (Disney Channel). Scripts via agents only.

Hightimes Productions Ltd
7 Anglers Lane, London NW5 3DG
☎0171 482 5202   Fax 0171 485 4254
Contact *A. C. Mitchell*

Television comedies. OUTPUT *Trouble in Mind* (sitcom, 9 episodes, LWT); *Me & My Girl* (sitcom, 5 series, LWT package); *The Zodiac Game* (game show, 2 series, Anglia package); *Guys 'n' Dolls* (light entertainment, 13 episodes, BSkyB). Unsolicited scripts welcome.

Philip Hindin
66 Melbourne Way, Bush Hill Park, Enfield, Middlesex EN1 1XQ
☎0181 366 2978   Fax 0181 366 2978
Contact *P. Hindin*

Producers of quiz-panel game shows for TV and theatre. No unsolicited material but always interested in new ideas/writing, e.g. *Call My Bluff; Password*.

Holmes Associates
38–42 Whitfield Street, London W1P 5RF
☎0171 813 4333   Fax 0171 637 9024
Contact *Andrew Holmes, Ian Benson*

Prolific originators, producers and packagers of documentary, drama and music television and films. OUTPUT has included *Prometheus* (Ch4 'Film on 4'); *The Shadow of Hiroshima* (Ch4 'Witness'); *The House of Bernarda Alba* (Ch4/ WNET/Amaya); *Piece of Cake* (drama miniseries for LWT); *The Cormorant* (BBC/Screen 2); *John Gielgud Looks Back; Rock Steady; Well Being* and *Signals* (all Ch4); *Timeline* (with MPT, TVE Spain & TRT Turkey). Now concentrating on TV drama and feature films through development company Devco (in production: *The*

Weekend). Unsolicited drama/film scripts will be considered but may take some time for response.

Hourglass Pictures Ltd
117 Merton Road, Wimbledon, London SW19 1ED
☎0181 540 8786   Fax 0181 542 6598
Director *Martin Chilcott*

Film and video: documentary, drama and commercials. OUTPUT includes television science documentaries; public relations material for government and industrial bodies; health and social issues for the World Health Organisation; product promotion for pharmaceutical companies. Open to new writing.

Hourglass Productions Limited
4 The Heights, London SE7 8JH
☎0181 858 6870   Fax 0181 858 6870
Producer/Director *John Walsh, MD*
Producer/Head of Finance
  David Walsh, ACA
Producer/Head of Development
  Maura Walsh

Award-winning producers of drama, documentaries. OUTPUT *Monarch* (major feature film marking the 450th anniversary of the death of King Henry VIII); *Ray Harryhausen: Movement Into Life; The Comedy Store; Spiritual World; Sceptic & The Psychic; The Sleeper*. We prefer to receive mss through agents but do consider unsolicited material. Currently in development with feature film and documentary projects including *The Frozen Four, a.k.a. Otto Palindrome; Part Time Love*. Co-production enquiries welcome.

Hubner Video & Film Ltd
79 Dean Street, London W1V 5MA
☎0171 439 4060   Fax 0171 287 1072
Contact *Martin Hubner, Christine Fontaine*

Film commercials, corporate videos and documentaries, and feature film scripts. CLIENTS Associated Newspapers, Gateway Supermarkets, De Beers Diamonds, Bentalls, British Gas, IBM, Nat West, Audi, Parkfield/Ford (USA). Unsolicited scripts or outlines for feature films and documentaries welcome. Material is read and discussed before being forwarded if promising to TV/film companies or agents for production packaging.

Alan Hydes Associates
East Royd House, Woodlands Drive, Apperley Bridge, West Yorkshire BD10 0PA
☎0113 2503467   Fax 0113 2503467

Contact *Alan Hydes*

Film, video and TV: drama and corporate work, including children's TV programmes, promotional, recruitment and security films for the Halifax Building Society. Also news agency facilities for national press and television. No unsolicited scripts. Interested in new ideas for conversion to drama.

Icon Films

4 West End, Somerset Street, Bristol BS2 8NE
☎0117 9248535   Fax 0117 9420386

Contact *Harry Marshall*

Film and TV documentaries. OUTPUT *The Elephant Men* (WNET/Ch4); *The Living Edens – Bhutan, The Last Shangri La* (ABC/Kane); *Joanna Lumley in the Kingdom of the Thunder Dragon* (BBC); *Lost Civilisations – Tibet* (Time Life for NBC). Specialises in documentaries. Open-minded to new filmmakers. Proposals welcome.

Ideal Image Ltd

Cherrywood House, Crawley Down Road, Felbridge, Surrey RH19 2PP
☎01342 300566   Fax 01342 312566

Contact *Alan Frost*

Producers of documentary and drama for film, video, TV and corporate clients. OUTPUT *Just Another Friday* (corporate drama); *Living in a Box; The Future for Rupert.*

Illuminations Films

19–20 Rheidol Mews, Rheidol Terrace, London N1 8NU
☎0171 226 0266   Fax 0171 359 1151

Contact *Keith Griffiths*

Film and TV drama. OUTPUT includes projects with directors like Jan Svankmajer, the Brothers Quay, G. F. Newman, Chris Petit and Patrick Keiller. 'We try to promote new talent and develop work by young writers new to the screen and experienced writers looking for new and imaginative ways to express their ideas.'

Initial Film and Television

See **Broadcast Communications**

Interesting Television Ltd

Oakslade Studios, Station Road, Hatton, Warwickshire CV35 7LH
☎01926 844044

Senior Producer *John Pluck*

Producers of broadcast television documen-

taries and feature series on film and video for ITV and BBC TV. Currently looking towards cable, satellite and home video to broaden its output. Ideas for television documentaries particularly welcome. Send a treatment in the first instance, particularly if the subject is 'outside our area of current interest'. OUTPUT has included television programmes on heritage, antiques, gardening, science and industry; also projects on heritage, health and sports for the home video front.

Isis Productions

106 Hammersmith Grove, London W6 7HB
☎0181 748 3042   Fax 0181 748 3046

Director *Nick de Grunwald*
Director *Jamie Rugge-Price*
Production coordinator *Catriona Lawless*

Formed in 1991 and maintaining an earlier link with **Oxford University Press**, Isis Productions focuses on the production of music and documentary programmes, and co-produces children's programmes under its Rocking Horse banner. Current: *Classic Albums* (major international series on the making of the greatest records in rock history, including films on Grateful Dead, Stevie Wonder, Jimi Hendrix, Paul Simon, The Band. Co-produced with Daniel Television, BBC, NCRV, VH-1 and Castle Communications). *Energize!* – kids-in-sport magazine series for Westcountry TV (Rocking Horse). OUTPUT *Behind the Reporting Line* (behind-the-scenes look at foreign news gathering with Foreign Editor John Simpson for BBC2); *Dido and Aeneas* (film of Purcell's opera for BBC2/Thirteen WNET/ZDF-Arte/NVC Arts); *The Score* (classical music magazine series, co-produced with After Image for BBC2); *The Making of Sgt Pepper* (60-min film for Buena Vista International/LWT – winner of Grand Prix at MIDEM); *Mine Eyes Have Seen the Glory* (3-part documentary series for Ch4, co-produced with Cutting Edge/WTTW Chicago).

Kay Communications Ltd

Now **Octopus Multimedia Ltd** (see entry).

King Rollo Films Ltd

Dolphin Court, High Street, Honiton, Devon EX14 8LS
☎01404 45218   Fax 01404 45328

Contact *Clive Juster*

Film, video and TV: children's animated series. OUTPUT *Surprise, Surprise; It's My Birthday; Badger's Bring Something Party; How Many Days to My Birthday?; The Trouble With Jack; Bear's*

Birthday; Elephant Pie; Good Night, Sleep Tight; Go to Sleep; Get into Bed; I'm not Sleepy; Good Night Everyone; Little Princess Bedtime; Bedtime Story; Dad, I Can't Sleep; Spot and His Grandparents Visit the Carnival; Spot's Magical Christmas; Fred; Philipp; Jakob. Generally works from existing published material 'although there will always be the odd exception'. Proposals or phone calls in the first instance. No scripts.

Kingfisher Television Productions Ltd

Carlton Studios, Lenton Lane, Nottingham NG7 2NA
☎0115 9645262   Fax 0115 9645263
Contact *Tony Francis*

Broadcast television production.

Lagan Pictures Ltd

7 Rugby Court, Agincourt Avenue, Belfast BT7 1PN
☎01232 326125
Producer/Director *Stephen Butcher*
Producer *Alison Grundle*

Film, video and TV: drama, documentary and corporate. OUTPUT *A Force Under Fire* (Ulster TV). In development: *Smallholdings* (one-off drama); *Into the Bright Light of Day* (drama-doc). 'We are always interested in hearing from writers originating from or based in Northern Ireland or anyone with, preferably unstereo-typical, projects relevant to Northern Ireland. We do not have the resources to deal with unsolicited mss, so please phone or write with a brief treatment/synopsis in the first instance.'

Landseer Film and Television Productions Ltd

140 Royal College Street,
London NW1 0TA
☎0171 485 7333   Fax 0171 485 7573
Contact *Claire Mills*

Film and video production: documentary, drama, music and arts, children's and current affairs. OUTPUT *Sunny Stories – Enid Blyton* (Bookmark); *J. R. R. Tolkien* (Tolkien Partnership); *Should Accidentally Fall* (BBC/Arts Council); *Nobody's Fool* ('South Bank Show' on Danny Kaye for LWT); *Gounod's Faust* (Ch4); *Swinger* (BBC2/Arts Council); *Auld Lang Syne* (BBC Scotland); *Nureyev Unzipped* (Ch4); *Retying the Knot – The Incredible String Band* (BBC Scotland); *Benjamin Zander* ('The Works', BBC2); *Zeffirelli* ('The South Bank Show', LWT).

Helen Langridge Associates

30 Percy Street, London W1P 9EE
☎0171 299 1000   Fax 0171 299 1001
Managing Directors *Helen Langridge, Mike Wells*

Film, video and TV: drama, music videos and commercials.

Lawson Productions Ltd

Newton Park, Wicklow, Co Wicklow
Republic of Ireland
☎00 353 404 69497   Fax 00 353 404 69092
Contact *Sarah Lawson*

Film and TV: drama and comedy. OUTPUT has included *That's Love* (UK and US); *Home to Roost* (US version); *The Dawning* with Anthony Hopkins; *Life After Life* (ITV) with George Cole; *Natural Lies* (BBC); *Seekers* (ITV). Interested in new talent but no unsolicited mss unless via agents.

Lightarama Ltd

12a Wellfield Avenue, London N10 2EA
☎0181 444 8315   Fax 0181 444 8315
Contact *Alexis Key*

Video and TV production for commercials and corporate material and also special effects (lighting). OUTPUT Mercedes Benz training programme; Renault UK training programme; British Gas special effects; Discovery Channel, new idents, lighting effects; Video London Sound Studios Ltd; French to English transla-tion of French Natural History series; IPSEN International Ltd, brochure and communi-cation consultancy. No unsolicited scripts but c.v.s welcome. Interested in new and creative ideas.

Lilyville Productions Ltd

7 Lilyville Road, London SW6 5DP
☎0171 371 5940   Fax 0171 736 9431
E-mail: tonycash@msn.com
Contact *Tony Cash*

Drama and documentaries for TV. OUTPUT *Poetry in Motion* (series for Ch4); *South Bank Show: Ben Elton & Vanessa Redgrave; Musique Enquête* (drama-based French language series, Ch4); *Landscape and Memory* (arts documentary series for the BBC); Jonathan Miller's production of the *St Matthew Passion* for the BBC; major documentary on the BeeGees for the *South Bank Show*. Scripts with an obvious application to TV may be considered. Interested in new writing for documentary programmes.

Little Dancer Ltd
Avonway, Naseby Road, London SE19 3JJ
☎0181 653 9343   Fax 0181 653 9343

Contact *Robert Smith, Sue Townsend*

Television and cinema, both shorts and full-length features.

Living Tape Productions
See **Videotel Productions**

Lucida Productions
Studio 1A, 14 Havelock Walk, London
SE23 3HG
☎0181 699 5070   Fax 0181 693 8002

Contact *Paul Joyce*

Television and cinema: arts, adventure, current affairs, documentary, drama and music. OUTPUT has included *Motion and Emotion: The Films of Wim Wenders; Dirk Bogarde – By Myself; Sam Peckinpah – Man of Iron; Kris Kristofferson – Pilgrim; Wild One: Marlon Brando; Stanley Kubrick: 'The Invisible Man'*. Currently in development for documentary and drama projects.

Main Communications
City House, 16 City Road, Winchester,
Hampshire SO23 8SD
☎01962 870680   Fax 01962 870699

Contact *Eben Wilson*

Multimedia marketing, communications, electronic and publishing company for film, video and TV: drama, documentary and commercials. OUTPUT includes marketing communications, educational, professional and managerial distance learning, documentary programmes for broadcast TV and children's material. Interested in proposals for television programmes, and in ideas for video sell-throughs, interactive multimedia and business information texts and programming.

Malone Gill Productions Ltd
3 Neal Street, London WC2H 9PU
☎0171 460 4683/4   Fax 0171 460 4747
E-mail: ikonic@compuserve.com

Contact *Georgina Denison*

Mainly documentary but also some drama. OUTPUT includes *The Face of Russia* (PBS); *Vermeer* ('South Bank Show'); *Highlanders* (ITV); *Storm Chasers* (Ch4); *Nature Perfected* (Ch4); *The Feast of Christmas* (Ch4); *The Buried Mirror: Reflections on Spain and the New World* by Carlos Fuentes (BBC2/Discovery Channel). Approach by letter with proposal in the first instance.

Mike Mansfield Television Ltd
41–42 Berners Street, London W1P 3AA
☎0171 580 2581   Fax 0171 580 2582

Contact *Mr Hilary McLaren*

Television for BBC, ITV network, Ch4 and Ch5. OUTPUT includes *Animal Country; Just a Minute; The James Whale Show; The Exchange; The Entertainers; HRH the Princess of Wales Concert of Hope; Cue the Music; Helter Skelter; Funky Bunker.*

Bill Mason Films Ltd
Orchard House, Dell Quay, Chichester,
West Sussex PO20 7EE
☎01243   783558
E-mail: bill.mason@argonet.co.uk

Contact *Bill Mason*

Film and video: documentaries only. OUTPUT *Racing Mercedes; The History of Motor Racing; The History of the Motor Car.* No need for outside writing; all material is written in-house. The emphasis is on automotive history.

Maverick Television
The Custard Factory, Gibb Street,
Birmingham B9 4AA
☎0121 771 1812   Fax 0121 771 1550

Contact *Jonnie Turpie*

FOUNDED 1994. High quality and innovative DVC programming in both documentary and drama. Expanding into light entertainment and more popular drama. OUTPUT includes *Trade Secrets* and *Picture This: Accidental Hero* (BBC2); *Motherless Daughters, Highland Bollywood: Black Bag* and *Health Alert: My Teenage Menopause* (all for Ch4).

Maya Vision Ltd
43 New Oxford Street, London WC1A 1BH
☎0171 836 1113   Fax 0171 836 5169

Contact *John Cranmer*

Film and TV: drama and documentary. OUTPUT *Saddam's Killing Fields* (for 'Viewpoint', Central TV); *3 Steps to Heaven* and *A Bit of Scarlet* (feature films for BFI/Ch4); *A Place in the Sun* and *North of Vortex* (drama for Ch4/Arts Council); *Barcelona* (for 'Omnibus', BBC1); *In the Footsteps of Alexander the Great* (BBC1 documentary); *Out* (several pieces for Ch4's lesbian and gay series). No unsolicited material; commissions only.

MBP
Saucelands Barn, Coolham, Horsham,
West Sussex RH13 8QG
☎01403 741620   Fax 01403 741647

Contact *Alastair Martin-Bird*

Makers of film and video specialising in programmes covering equestrianism and the countryside. No unsolicited scripts, but always looking for new writers who are fully acquainted with the subject.

MediSci Healthcare Communications

Stoke Grange, Fir Tree Avenue, Stoke Poges, Buckinghamshire SL2 4NN
☎01753 516644   Fax 01753 516965
Contact *Peter Fogarty, Kerry Williams*

Corporate: medical programmes and training packages for health care professionals. Health care ideas welcome. No unsolicited mss.

Melendez Films

1–17 Shaftesbury Avenue, London W1V 7RL
☎0171 434 0220   Fax 0171 434 3131
Contact *Steven Melendez, Graeme Spurway*

Independent producers working with TV stations. Animated films aimed mainly at a family audience, produced largely for the American market, and prime-time network broadcasting. Also develops and produces feature films (eight so far). OUTPUT has included *Peanuts* (half-hour TV specials); *The Lion, the Witch and the Wardrobe; Babar the Elephant* (TV specials); *Dick Deadeye or Duty Done*, a rock musical based on Gilbert & Sullivan operettas; and a video of fairytales *Happily Ever After, Jules Feiffer Series.* 'Three of the above walked in through the door and we have taken an option recently on an idea received in 1997.' Synopses only, please. Enclose s.a.e. for return.

Melrose Film Productions

Dumbarton House, 68 Oxford Street, London W1N 0LH
☎0171 627 8404   Fax 0171 622 0421

Producers of generic management and staff training films, and interactive programmes.

Mentorn Films

138–140 Wardour Street, London W1V 3AV
☎0171 287 4545   Fax 0171 287 3728
Contact *Tom Gutteridge, John Needham*

FOUNDED in 1985 by ex-BBC arts producer Tom Gutteridge. Producer of successful peaktime show *Challenge Anneka* and Emmy award-winning drama *The Bullion Boys.* Co-producer of Gerry Anderson's *Space Precinct.* Film, video and television: cinema, documentary, drama, music and arts.

Mersey Television Company Ltd

Campus Manor, Childwall Abbey Road, Liverpool L16 0JP
☎0151 722 9122   Fax 0151 722 1969
Chairman *Prof. Phil Redmond*

The best known of the independents in the North of England. Makers of television drama. OUTPUT *Brookside; Hollyoaks* (both for Ch4).

Alan More Films

Suite 205–206, Pinewood Studios, Pinewood Road, Iver, Buckinghamshire SL0 0NH
☎01753 656789   Fax 01753 656844
Contact *Alan More, Judith More*

Film, video and TV: documentary, commercials and corporate. No scripts. No need of outside writers.

Max Morgan-Witts Productions Ltd

26 Woodsford Square, London W14 8DP
☎0171 602 0657   Fax 0171 602 8556
Contact *Max Morgan-Witts*

Film, video and TV: drama, documentary, corporate and sell-through videos. Literary: joint-author 10 non-fiction books including re-published *Voyage of the Damned; Enola Gay; Guernica.* Scandinavian publishers' representative.

The Morrison Company

302 Clive Court, Maida Vale, London W9 1SF
☎0171 289 7976   Fax 0171 681 1031
Contact *Don Morrison*

Film and video: drama, documentary and commercials. Unsolicited mss welcome.

MW Entertainments Ltd

48 Dean Street, London W1V 5HL
☎0171 734 7707   Fax 0171 734 7727
Contact *Michael White*

High-output company whose credits include *Widow's Peak; White Mischief; Nuns on the Run* (co-production with **HandMade Films Ltd**); *The Comic Strip Series.* Also theatre projects, including *Fame; Me and Mamie O'Rourke; She Loves Me; Crazy for You.* Contributions are passed by Michael White to a script reader for consideration.

Newgate Company

13 Dafford Street, Larkhall, Bath, Somerset BA1 6SW
☎01225 318335
Contact *Jo Anderson*

A commonwealth of established actors, directors and playwrights, Newgate originally concerned itself solely with theatre writing (at the Bush, Stratford, Roundhouse, etc.) However, in the course of development, several productions fed into a list of ongoing drama for BBC TV/Ch4. Now looking to develop this co-production strand for film, television and radio projects with other 'Indies'.

Northlight Productions Ltd
The Media Village, Grampian Television, Queen's Cross, Aberdeen AB15 4XJ
☎01224 646460   Fax 01224 646450
Contact *Robert Sproul-Cran*

Film, video and TV: drama, documentary and corporate work. OUTPUT ranges from high-end corporate fund-raising videos for the National Museum of Scotland to *Anything But Temptation*, a feature film currently in development; *Calcutta Chronicles* (5-part documentary series for Ch4) and two schools series for Ch4. Scripts welcome. Has links with EAVE (European Audio-Visual Entrepreneurs) and Media.

Nova Productions
11a Winholme, Armthorpe, Doncaster DN3 3AF
☎01302 833422   Fax 01302 833422
Contact *Andrew White, Maurice White, Gareth Atherton*

Film and TV production company, specialising in documentary, entertainment, special event and music promo production. Producers of programmes released on sell-through video country-wide. Also, game show and drama developments a speciality. 'We always welcome unsolicited mss, either fiction or non-fiction ideas. Please allow time for us to read them and respond. We always acknowledge receipt of mss instantly.'

Octopus Multimedia Ltd
Gauntley Court Studios, Gauntley Court, Nottingham NG7 5HD
☎0115 9172222   Fax 0115 9172211
Contact *John Alexander*

Makers of industrial video programmes and training programmes. Scripts written in-house. No unsolicited mss.

Open Media
Ground Floor, 9 Leamington Road Villas, London W11 1HS
☎0171 229 5416   Fax 0171 221 4842
Contact *Alice Kramers Pawsey, Sebastian Cody*

Broadcast television: OUTPUT *After Dark; The Secret Cabaret; James Randi Psychic Investigator; Opinions; Is This Your Life?; Don't Quote Me; Brave New World; The Talking Show; Natural Causes; Equinox; Dispatches.*

Open Mind Productions
6 Newburgh Street, London W1V 1LH
☎0171 437 0624   Fax 0171 434 9256
Directors *Chris Ellis, Roland Tongue*

Video and TV production, including documentary and educational. OUTPUT *Investigating Britain* (BBC); *Living Proof* (Ch4); *The Geography Programme: Images of the Earth* (for BBC Schools TV); *Eureka: The Earth in Space; Geography, Start Here: The Local Network; Rat-a-tat-tat; One Last Lie* (for Ch4 Schools). No unsolicited material. Currently developing children's drama series. 'We are a small company interested in programmes that reflect our name. We want to produce more drama and multi-media resources.' Chris Ellis, a writer himself, is a guest lecturer on scriptwriting with BBC TV Training and the London Media Workshop.

Orlando TV Productions
Up-the-Steps, Little Tew, Chipping Norton, Oxfordshire OX7 4JB
☎01608 683218   Fax 01608 683364
E-mail: 100564.561@compuserve.com
Contact *Mike Tomlinson*

Producers of TV documentaries, with science subjects as a specialisation. OUTPUT includes programmes for *Horizon* and *QED* (BBC). Approaches by established writers/journalists to discuss proposals for collaboration are welcome.

Orpheus Productions
6 Amyand Park Gardens, Twickenham, Middlesex TW1 3HS
☎0181 892 3172   Fax 0181 892 4821
Contact *Richard Taylor*

Television documentaries and corporate work. OUTPUT has included programmes for BBC Current Affairs, Music and Arts, and the African-Caribbean Unit as well as documentaries for the Shell Film Unit and Video Arts. Unsolicited scripts are welcomed with caution. 'We have a preference for visually stirring documentaries with quality writing of the more personal and idiosyncratic kind, not straight reportage.'

Ovation Productions

One Prince of Wales Passage, 117 Hampstead
Road, London NW1 3EF
☎0171 387 2342   Fax 0171 380 0404
Contact *John Plews*

Corporate video and conference scripts. Unsolicited mss not welcome. 'We talk to new writers
from time to time.' Ovation also runs the fringe
theatre, 'Upstairs at the Gatehouse' in Highgate,
north London, and welcomes new plays.

Oxford Scientific Films Ltd

Lower Road, Long Hanborough, Oxfordshire
OX8 8LL
☎01993 881881   Fax 01993 882808
Commercials Division: 45–49 Mortimer
Street, London W1N 7TD
☎0171 323 0061   Fax 0171 323 0161
Managing Director *Karen Goldie-Morrison*

Established media company with specialist
knowledge and expertise in award-winning natural history films and science-based programmes.
Film, video and TV: documentaries, TV commercials, multimedia, and educational films.
Scripts welcome. Operates an extensive stills and
film footage library specialising in wildlife and
special effects (see **Picture Libraries**).

Pace Productions Ltd

12 The Green, Newport Pagnell,
Buckinghamshire MK16 0JW
☎01908 618767   Fax 01908 617641
Contact *Chris Pettit*

Film and video: drama, documentary, corporate and commercials.

Pacesetter Productions Ltd

The Gardener's Lodge, Cloisters Business
Centre, 8 Battersea Park Road, London
SW8 4BH
☎0171 720 4545   Fax 0171 720 4949
Contact *Timothy Spencer*

Film and video producers of drama, documen-
tary and corporate work. OUTPUT *History of the
Telephone; Pictures from the Past; The Wheatfield;
Merchant of Wood Street; Mr Nobody's Eyes* (the
latter three are feature films in development).
CLIENTS include BT, British Gas, Midland Bank,
Lloyds Bank. No unsolicited scripts.

Barry Palin Associates Ltd

143 Charing Cross Road, London WC2H 0EE
☎0171 478 4680   Fax 0171 494 1305
Contact *Barry Palin*

Film, video and TV production for drama,

documentary, commercials and corporate
material. OUTPUT *Harmfulness of Tobacco* Anton
Chekhov short story – BAFTA Best Short Film
Award-winner (Ch4); Corporate: Kraft Jacobs
Suchard. Unsolicited scripts welcome. New
writing encouraged.

Paper Moon Productions

Wychwood House, Burchetts Green Lane,
Littlewick Green, Nr. Maidenhead, Berkshire
SL6 3QW
☎01628 829819   Fax 01628 825949
Contact *David Haggas*

Television and video: medical and health education documentaries. OUTPUT includes *Shamans
and Science*, a medical documentary examining
the balance between drugs discovered in nature
and those synthesised in laboratories. Unsolicited scripts welcome. Interested in new writing
'from people who really understand television
programme-making'.

Parallax Pictures Ltd

7 Denmark Street, London WC2H 8LS
☎0171 836 1478   Fax 0171 497 8062
Contact *Sally Hibbin*

Feature films/television drama. OUTPUT *Riff-
Raff; Bad Behaviour; Raining Stones; Ladybird,
Ladybird; I.D.; Land and Freedom; The Englishman
Who Went up a Hill But Came Down a Mountain;
Bliss; Jump the Gun; Carla's Song; The Governess;
My Name Is Joe; Stand and Deliver.*

Philip Partridge Productions Ltd

The High Street, South Woodchester, Near
Stroud, Gloucestershire GL5 5EL
☎01453 872743   Fax 01453 872743
Contact *Phil Partridge*

Film and TV producers for drama and comedy
material. OUTPUT *Once Upon a Time in the
North* Tim Firth six 30-minute comedies on
film (BBC1). Special interest in new comedy
feature films and situation comedy. Unsolicited
scripts considered 'providing writers are patient
while they're read'.

PBF Motion Pictures

The Little Pickenhanger, Tuckey Grove,
Ripley, Surrey GU23 6JG
☎01483 225179   Fax 01483 224118
Contact *Peter B. Fairbrass*

Film, video and TV: drama, documentary,
commercials and corporate. Also televised chess
series and chess videos. OUTPUT *Grandmaster
Chess* (in association with Thames TV); *Glue*

Sniffing; RN Special Services; Nightfrights (nighttime TV chiller series). CLIENTS include GEC-Marconi, Coca Cola, MoD, Marks & Spencer, various government departments, British Consulate. No scripts; send one-page synopsis only in the first instance. 'Good scripts which relate to current projects will be followed up, otherwise not, as PBF do not have the time to reply to proposals which do not interest them. Only good writing stands a chance.'

Pearson Television Ltd

1 Stephen Street, London W1P 1PJ
☎0171 691 6000
Chief Executive *Greg Dyke*
Chief Executive, UK Production *Alan Boyd*
Head of Entertainment *Richard Holloway*
Head of Comedy *Tony Charles*

UK's largest independent production and distribution company. OUTPUT includes *The Bill; Birds Of A Feather; Goodnight Sweetheart; This is Your Life; Strike it Lucky; Mosley; Neighbours; Wish You Were Here ...?*

Pelicula Films

59 Holland Street, Glasgow G2 4NJ
☎0141 287 9522   Fax 0141 287 9504
E-mail: pelicula.films@btinternet.com
Contact *Mike Alexander*

Television producers. Makers of drama documentaries and music programmes for the BBC and Ch4. OUTPUT *As an Eilean (From the Island); The Highland Sessions; The Trans-Atlantic Sessions; Songroads; Follow the Moonstone.*

Penumbra Productions Ltd

Flat 3, 80 Brondesbury Road, London NW6 6RX
☎0171 328 4550   Fax 0171 328 3844
Contact *H. O. Nazareth*

Film, video, TV and radio: drama, documentary and information videos on health, housing, arts and political documentaries. OUTPUT includes *Will It Be a Likeness?* (Radio 3 play); *Repomen* ('Cutting Edge', Ch4); *Doctors and Torture* ('Inside Story', BBC); *Bombay & Jazz* (BBC2); *Awaaz* (information video in eight languages for Kings Fund/Manchester Council for Community Relations). In development: *Slave Brides* (for TV/cinema). Film treatments, drama proposals and documentary synopses welcome. Keen to assist in the development of new writing but only interested in social issue-based material.

Picture Palace Films Ltd

19 Edis Street, London NW1 8LE
☎0171 586 8763   Fax 0171 586 9048
E-mail: 100444.2737@compuserve.com
Contact *Malcolm Craddock*

FOUNDED 1971. Leading independent producer of TV drama. OUTPUT *Sharpe's Rifles* (14 x 2-hour films for Carlton TV); *Little Napoleons* (4-part comedy drama for Ch4); *The Orchid House* (4-part drama serial for Ch4); plus episodes of *Eurocops; Tandoori Nights; 4 Minutes; When Love Dies; Ping Pong* (feature film). Material will only be considered if submitted through an agent.

Phil Pilley Productions

Ferryside, Felix Lane, Shepperton, Middlesex TW17 8NG
☎01932 246455   Fax 01932 246455
Contact *Phil Pilley*

Programmes for TV and video, mainly sports, including documentaries for the BBC, ITV, Ch4 and the US. Also books, newspapers and magazine features, mainly sports. Unsolicited ideas and synopses welcome.

Planet 24 Ltd

The Planet Building, Thames Quay, 195 Marsh Wall, London E14 9SG
☎0171 345 2424   Fax 0171 345 9400
Executive Producer/Managing Director *Charles Parsons*

Television and radio producers of light entertainment, comedy, music and features. OUTPUT TV: *The Big Breakfast; The Word; The Messiah* (live recording); *Hotel Babylon; Gaytime TV; Delicious; Extra Time, Nothing But the Truth; Extra Time, Rock Parties.* Radio: *Entertainment Superhighway; Straight Up; Rock Wives; Pulp; Planet A-List; Arthur Smith's Amusing Bits.*

Platinum Film & TV Production Ltd

1B Murray Street, London NW1 9RE
☎0171 916 9091   Fax 0171 916 5238
Contact *Terry Kelleher*

Television documentaries, including drama-documentary. OUTPUT *South Africa's Black Economy* (Ch4); *Murder at the Farm* (Thames TV); *The Biggest Robbery in the World* (major investigative true-crime drama-documentary for Carlton TV). Scripts and format treatments welcome.

Portman Productions
167 Wardour Street, London W1V 3TA
☎0171 468 3400   Fax 0171 468 3499
Head of Development *Katherine Butler*

Television drama. OUTPUT includes: *Gravy Train* and *Gravy Train Goes East*; *Downwardly Mobile*; *Famous Five Series*; *Rebecca*. Synopses in the first instance, please.

Premiere Productions Ltd
3 Colville Place, London W1P 1HN
☎0171 255 1650
Contact *Henrietta Williams*

Film and video: drama and corporate, including dramatised training videos. Currently looking for feature film scripts, with Anglo/American/East European themes. Preference for stories with humour. No horror or sci-fi. Please enclose a list of previous submissions and return postage.

Primetime plc
Seymour Mews House, Seymour Mews, Wigmore Street, London W1H 9PE
☎0171 935 9000   Fax 0171 935 1992
Contact *Richard Price, Simon Willock*

Television distribution and packaging, plus international co-productions. OUTPUT *An Evening with Sir Peter Ustinov*; *Porgy and Bess* (BBC, Homevale, Greg Smith); *Re:Joyce* (BBC); *The CIA* (BBC/A&E/NRK); *José Carreras – A Life* (LWT); *Othello* (BBC); *Ustinov on the Orient Express* (A&E/CBC/ NOB/ JMP); *Ethan Frome* (American Playhouse). Works closely with associated US company, Primetime Entertainment and in the music and arts area through Anglo-German company Euro-Arts-Primetime. OUTPUT *Who could ask for anything more?* (Ira Gershwin tribute); *The Gold and Silver Gala* (a celebration of Placido Domingo's 25th anniversary and 50th anniversary of the Royal Opera House company); *Neville's Island 90* (comedy, ITV). No unsolicited scripts.

Prospect Pictures
Prospect House, 150 Great Portland Street, London W1N 6BB
☎0171 636 1234   Fax 0171 636 1236
Contact *Kirsten Parker*

Drama, documentary and corporate video and TV. Actively looking for projects from new writers; 'using our development fund for new drama'. Welcomes treatments and synopses of scripts.

Red Lion Communications
1–5 Poland Street, London W1V 3DG
☎0171 734 5364   Fax 0171 734 0322
Contact *Mike Kilcooley*

Video producers: commercials, training and corporate work, including product launch videos, in-house training, open learning, multimedia programmes, etc. 'We are always on the look-out for new, well thought through ideas for broadcast.'

Red Rooster Film and Television Entertainment
14/15 D'Arblay Street, London W1V 3FP
☎0171 439 6969   Fax 0171 439 6767
Contact *Joanna Anderson (Development Executive), Linda James, Jill Green*

Film and TV drama. OUTPUT *Deadly Summer; Beyond Fear; The Sculptress; Wilderness; Crocodile Shoes; Body & Soul*. No unsolicited scripts. Encourages new writers; 'recommend that they find an agent'.

Renaissance Vision
15 Capitol House, Heigham Street, Norwich, Norfolk NR2 4TE
☎01603 767272   Fax 01603 768163
Contact *B. Gardner*

Video: full range of corporate work (training, sales, promotional, etc.). Producers of educational and special-interest video publications. Willing to consider good ideas and proposals.

Richmond Films & Television Ltd
5 Dean Street, London W1V 5RN
☎0171 734 9313   Fax 0171 287 2058
Contact *Sandra Hastie*

Film and TV: drama and comedy. OUTPUT *Press Gang; The Lodge; The Office; Wavelength.* 'We will accept *two pages only* consisting of a brief treatment of your project (either screenplay or TV series) which includes its genre and its demographics. Please tell us also where the project has been submitted previously and what response you have had. If we are interested in reading a longer treatment or the script you will then be contacted. Only projects/scripts with s.a.e. will be returned.'

Roberts & Wykeham Films
7 Barb Mews, Hammersmith, London W6 7PA
☎0171 602 4897   Fax 0171 602 3016
Contact *S. Wykeham*

Television documentaries and packaging.

OUTPUT Ch4 'Dispatches': *The Saudi Tapes; Trail of Red Mercury; Mandela's Nuclear Nightmare;* BBC 'Everyman': *The Road Back to Hell.* No unsolicited scripts.

Rocking Horse
See **Isis Productions**

Rose Bay Film Productions
1 Albion Court, Albion Place, London W6 0QT
☎0181 600 5200   Fax 0181 600 5222
Contact *Matthew Steiner, Simon Usiskin*

Associate company of **Noel Gay Television**. Film and TV production for drama, entertainment and documentary. Unsolicited scripts welcome.

Sands Films
119 Rotherhithe Street, London SE16 4NF
☎0171 231 2209   Fax 0171 231 2119
Contact *Richard Goodwin, Christine Edzard, Olivier Stockman*

Film and TV drama. OUTPUT *Little Dorrit; The Fool; As You Like It; A Dangerous Man; The Long Day Closes; A Passage to India; The Kiss; Swan Princess; Berlioz; The Nutcracker; Seven Years in Tibet.* In development: *Buddenbrooks.* No unsolicited scripts.

Scala Productions
39–43 Brewer Street, London W1R 3FD
☎0171 734 7060   Fax 0171 437 3248
Contact *Stephen Woolley, Nik Powell, Rachel Wood*

Production company set up by ex-Palace Productions Nik Powell and Stephen Woolley, who have an impressive list of credits including *Company of Wolves; Absolute Beginners; Mona Lisa; Scandal; Crying Game; Backbeat; Hollow Reed; Neon Bible.* Productions include: *B. Monkey; 24:7; Little Voice; Divorcing Jack; Dead Heart* (now known as *Welcome to Woop Woop*). In development: *St Agnes' Stand; Skintight; Jonathan Wild; Mort; Wise Children; Money; Dwarves of Death;* in production: *The Lost Son.*

Schwops Productions
34 Ashton Road, Luton, Bedfordshire LU1 3QE
☎01582 412622   Fax 01582 412095
Contact *Maureen Brown*

Video producer of drama, documentary and corporate material. Areas of interest include music, travel, ballet, medical and training

material. Also distribution, facilities, duplication, and sell-through videos. Open-minded to new writing. Scripts welcome.

Scope Productions Ltd
Keppie House, 147 Blythswood Street, Glasgow G2 4EN
☎0141 332 7720   Fax 0141 332 1049
TV Commercials *Sharon Fullarton*
Corporate *Bill Gordon*

Corporate film and video; broadcast documentaries and sport; TV commercials. Unsolicited, realistic scripts/ideas welcome.

Screen First Ltd
The Studios, Funnells Farm, Down Street, Nutley, East Sussex TN22 3LG
☎01825 712034   Fax 01825 713511
Contact *M. Thomas, P. Madden*

Television dramas, documentaries, arts and animation programmes. OUTPUT *Secret Passions* series I, II, III, IV (presenting new animation for Ch4). Developing major drama series and feature films. No unsolicited scripts.

Screen Ventures Ltd
49 Goodge Street, London W1P 1FB
☎0171 580 7448   Fax 0171 631 1265
Contact *Christopher Mould, Caroline Furness*

Film and TV sales and production: documentary, music videos and drama. OUTPUT *Woodstock Diary; Vanessa Redgrave* (LWT 'South Bank Show'); *Mojo Working: Burma: Dying for Democracy* (Ch4); *Genet* (LWT 'South Bank Show'); *Dani Dares* (Ch4 series on strong women); *Amandla* (HBO).

Securicor Media Services
Sutton Park House, 15 Carshalton Road, Sutton, Surrey SM1 4LE
☎0181 770 7000   Fax 0181 722 2672
Contact *Paul Fahey, Gill Arney*

Television producers of drama, documentary and corporate material. OUTPUT includes promotional, information and training videos for the Securicor Group and selected clients. Also audio, print design and production.

Seventh House Films
1 Hall Farm Place, Bawburgh, Norwich, Norfolk NR9 3LW
☎01603 749068   Fax 01603 749069
Contact *Clive Dunn, Angela Rule*

Documentary for film, video and TV on subjects ranging from arts to history and science to social.

affairs. OUTPUT *Dark Miracle* (an investigation into a near nuclear disaster in East Anglia); *A Pleasant Terror* (life and ghosts of M. R. James); *Piano Pieces* (musical excursion exploring different aspects of the piano); *Rockin' the Boat* (memories of pirate radio); *White Knuckles* (on the road with a travelling funfair); *King Romance* (life of Henry Rider Haggard); *A Drift of Angels* (three women and the price of art); *Bare Heaven* (the life and fiction of L. P. Hartley); *A Swell of the Soil* (life of Alfred Munnings); *Light Out of the Sky* (the art and life of Edward Seago). 'We welcome programme proposals with a view to collaborative co-production. Always interested in original and refreshing expressions for visual media.'

Sianco Cyf
7 Ffordd Segontiwm, Caernarfon, Gwynedd LL55 2LL
☎01286 673436   Fax 01286 673436
Contact *Siân Teifi*

Children's, youth and education programmes. Children's drama.

Signals, Essex Media Centre
21 St Peter's Street, Colchester, Essex CO1 1EW
☎01206 560255   Fax 01206 369086
Coordinator *Rebecca Maguire*

Promotion and documentary work for the voluntary and arts sectors. Specialists in media education projects. No unsolicited mss.

Silent/Sound Films Ltd
Cambridge Court, Cambridge Road, Frinton on Sea, Essex CO13 9HN
☎01255 676381   Fax 01255 676381
Contact *Timothy Foster*

Active in European film co-production with mainstream connections in the USA. Special interest in developing new projects for live orchestral accompaniment. Also film musicals and documentaries on the arts. No unsolicited material.

Siriol Productions
3 Mount Stuart Square, Butetown, Cardiff CF1 6RW
☎01222 488400   Fax 01222 485962
Contact *Andrew Offiler*

Animated series, mainly for children. OUTPUT includes *The Hurricanes; Tales of the Toothfairies; Billy the Cat*, as well as the feature films, *Under Milkwood* and *The Princess and the Goblin*. Write with ideas and sample script in the first instance.

Sleeping Giant Films
56-58 Clerkenwell Road, London EC1M 5PX
☎0171 490 5060   Fax 0171 490 5060
Contact *Harriet Pacaud*

Documentary film producer. OUTPUT includes *Kirkby's Kingdom*, the story of a Yorkshire smallholder whose land is threatened by property developers. Interested in original ideas with strong visual potential on environmental, natural history, arts and cultural themes. No fiction-based material. Happy to look at documentary ideas. Commentary writers used.

Smith & Watson Productions
The Gothic House, Fore Street, Totnes, South Devon TQ9 5EH
☎01803 863033   Fax 01803 864219
Contact *Chris Watson, Nick Smith*

Film, video and TV: documentaries, drama, party political broadcasts (for the Liberal Democrats), and commercials. In production: *The Lads* (ITV series).

Solo Vision Ltd
49–53 Kensington High Street, London W8 5ED
☎0171 376 2166   Fax 0171 938 3165
Contact *Don Short*

Video and TV: documentary, game shows, and corporate work. OUTPUT *Starmate* (the astrology game); *Surrogate Grandmother* (documentary, LWT/Cable USA); plus video packaging.

Specific Films
25 Rathbone Street, London W1P 1AG
☎0171 580 7476   Fax 0171 494 2676
Contact *Michael Hamlyn, Christian Routh*

FOUNDED 1976. OUTPUT includes *Mr Reliable* (feature film co-produced by PolyGram and the AFFC); *The Adventures of Priscilla, Queen of the Desert*, full-length feature film co-produced with Latent Image (Australia) and financed by PolyGram and AFFC; *U2 Rattle and Hum* (full-length feature – part concert film/part cinema verité documentary); *Pause* (executive producer); *The Last Seduction 2* (Polygram); and numerous pop promos for major international artists. First-Look deal with PolyGram Filmed Entertainment.

Spectel Productions Ltd
1 Trethorns Court, Ludgvan, Penzance, Cornwall TR20 8HE
☎01736 740989   Fax 01736 740989
E-mail: Davidwebster@msn.com

Contact *David Webster*

Film and video: documentary and corporate; also video publishing. No unsolicited scripts.

Spellbound Productions Ltd

90 Cowdenbeath Path, Islington, London N1 0LG
☎0171 278 0052   Fax 0171 278 0052
Contact *Paul Harris*

Film and television drama. OUTPUT includes *Leave to Remain* for 'Film on 4'. Unsolicited scripts welcome. Please enclose s.a.e. for return of material. Keen to support and encourage new writing.

SPI 1980 Ltd

27 Old Gloucester Street, London WC1N 3XX
☎0171 435 1007
Contact *Victor Schonfeld*

Drama, arts, current affairs, documentary, films for TV and cinema. OUTPUT includes *It's a Boy!; MoneyLove; Shattered Dreams, Picking Up the Pieces; The Animals Film; Courage Along the Divide; And I Don't Have to Do the Dishes*. Send a brief letter prior to submission of unsolicited material.

'Spoken' Image Ltd

The Design Centre, 44 Canal Street, Manchester M1 3WD
☎0161 236 7522   Fax 0161 236 0020
Contact *Geoff Allman, Steve Foster, Phil Griffin*

Film, video and TV production for documentary and corporate material. Specialising in high-quality brochures and reports, CD-ROMs, exhibitions, conferences, film and video production for broadcast, industry and commerce. Unsolicited scripts welcome. Interested in educational, and historical new writing, mainly for broadcast programmes.

Straight Forward Film & Television Productions Ltd

Ground Floor, Crescent House, 14 High Street, Holywood, Co. Down BT18 9AZ
☎01232 426298   Fax 01232 423384
Contact *Clarissa Neill, John Nicholson, Ian Kennedy*

Northern Ireland-based production company specialising in documentary, feature and lifestyle series. Unsolicited mss welcome. New work in drama and documentary fields welcome, particularly those with a strong Irish theme, contemporary or historical. OUTPUT

Close to Home (Ch4 documentary on abortion laws in N. Ireland); *Greenfingers* (BBC/RTE gardening series); *Places Apart* (BBC Northern Ireland series); *The Last Colony* (Ch4 documentary on the Troubles); *Adventure Ireland* (BBC N. Ireland holiday series). In production: *Just Jones* (BBC Radio Ulster daily show); *Missing* (BBC N. Ireland documentary); *Awash With Colour* (10-part painting series, BBC N. Ireland/BBC Daytime).

Strawberry Productions Ltd

36 Priory Avenue, London W4 1TY
☎0181 994 4494   Fax 0181 742 7675
Contact *John Black*

Film, video and TV: drama and documentary; corporate and video publishing.

Swanlind Communication

The Wharf, Bridge Street, Birmingham B1 2JR
☎0121 616 1701   Fax 0121 616 1520
E-mail: comms@swanlind.co.uk
Website: www.swanlind.co.uk
Chief Executive *Peter Stack*

Producer of business television, internal communication strategies, multimedia and conferences. 'Culture measurement and communication audits.'

Table Top Productions

1 The Orchard, Chiswick, London W4 1JZ
☎0181 742 0507   Fax 0181 742 0507
Contact *Alvin Rakoff*

TV and film. OUTPUT *Paradise Postponed* (TV mini-series); *A Voyage Round My Father; The First Olympics 1896; Dirty Tricks; A Dance to the Music of Time*. No unsolicited mss. Also Dancetime Ltd.

Talisman Films Ltd

5 Addison Place, London W11 4RJ
☎0171 603 7474   Fax 0171 602 7422
Contact *Richard Jackson*

Drama for film and TV: developing the full range of drama – TV series, serials and single films, as well as theatric features. 'We will only consider material submitted via literary agents.' Interested in supporting and encouraging new writing.

TalkBack Productions

36 Percy Street, London W1P 0LN
☎0171 323 9777   Fax 0171 637 5105
Managing Director *Peter Fincham*

Independent TV production company set up

in 1981 by comedians Mel Smith and Griff Rhys Jones. Specialises in comedy, comedy drama and drama; also corporate and training films. OUTPUT *Smith and Jones; Murder Most Horrid; Bonjour la Classe; Demob; The Day Today; Paris; Knowing Me Knowing You with Alan Patridge; Milner; Loose Talk; In Search of Happiness; They Think It's All Over; Never Mind the Buzzcocks; Brass Eye.*

Teamwork Productions

Gate House, Walderton, Chichester,
West Sussex PO18 9ED
☎01705 631384/0410 483149

Contact *Rob Widdows*

Video and TV producer of documentary, corporate and commercial work. OUTPUT includes motor racing coverage, motor sport productions and corporate motor sport videos. Good ideas will always be considered. No scripts.

Telemagination Ltd

41 Buckingham Palace Road, London
SW1W 0PP
☎0171 828 5331   Fax 0171 828 7631
E-mail: mail@tmation.co.uk
Website: www.telemagination.co.uk

Contact *John M. Mills*

Producers of television animation. OUTPUT includes *The Animals of Farthing Wood; Noah's Island; Wiggly Park.* 'New writing welcome although please ask for a submissions letter before presenting any work.'

Televideo Productions

The Riverside, Furnival Road, Sheffield,
South Yorkshire S4 7YH
☎0114 2491500   Fax 0114 2491505

Contact *Graham King*

Video and television: TV news and sports coverage, documentary and corporate work; sell-through videos (distributed on own label). OUTPUT includes *The Premier Collection* (football club videos); varied sports coverage for cable, satellite and terrestrial broadcasters plus a wide range of corporate work from drama-based material to documentary.

Teliesyn

Helwick House, 19 David Street, Cardiff
CF1 2EH
☎01222 667556   Fax 01222 667546

Chief Executive *Deryk Williams*

Film and video: produces drama, documentary,

music and social action in English and Welsh. Celtic Film Festival, BAFTA Cymru, Grierson and Indie award winner. OUTPUT *Branwen* (90 minute feature film for S4C); *Reel Truth* (drama doc series on the history of early film for S4C and Ch4); *Subway Cops and the Mole Kings* (Ch4); *Dragon's Song* (music series for schools, Ch4); *Codi Clawr Hanes II* (a second drama-documentary series on women's history for S4C). Will consider unsolicited mss only if accompanied by synopsis and c.v.. Encourages new writing wherever possible, in close association with a producer.

Tern Television Productions Ltd

73 Crown Street, Aberdeen AB11 6EX
☎01224 211123   Fax 01224 211199

Contact *David Strachan, Gwyneth Hardy, Nick Ibbotson*

Broadcast, video, corporate and training. Specialises in factual entertainment. Currently developing drama. Unsolicited mss welcome.

Theatre of Comedy Co.

See **Theatre Producers**

Huw Thomas & Associates

17 Brunswick Gardens, London W8 4AS
☎0171 727 9953   Fax 0171 727 9931

Contact *Anne E. Thomas*

Video and TV: documentary and corporate; also media training. CLIENTS include Lloyd's of London, Nestlé, Morgan Crucible. No unsolicited scripts.

Tiger Aspect Productions

5 Soho Square, London W1V 5DE
☎0171 434 0672   Fax 0171 287 1448

Contact *Charles Brand*

Television producers for documentary programmes, drama, light entertainment and comedy – variety, sitcom and comedy drama. OUTPUT *Mr Bean; The Thin Blue Line; The Vicar of Dibley; Howard Goodall's Organ Works; Deacon Brodie; Hospital; Harry Enfield & Chums.* Only considers material submitted via an agent or from writers with a known track record.

Tonfedd

Uned 33, Cibyn, Caernarfon, Gwynedd
LL55 2BD
☎01286 676800   Fax 01286 676466

Contact *Hefin Elis*

Light entertainment and music.

Alan Torjussen Productions Ltd

17 Heol Wen, Cardiff CF4 6EG
☎01222 624669   Fax 01222 624669
Contact *Alan Torjussen*

Film, video and TV production for drama, documentary, commercials and corporate material. Particularly interested in all types of documentary, education, schools and drama. Background includes work in the Welsh language. Unsolicited scripts welcome, particularly if about Wales by Welsh writers (includes Welsh language scripts). Also original ideas for comedy and documentary/dramas.

Transatlantic Films Production and Distribution Company

Studio One, 3 Brackbury Road,
London W6 0BE
☎0181 735 0505   Fax 0181 735 0605
Executive Producer *Revel Guest*

Producers of TV documentaries. OUTPUT *Horse Tales* (Discovery Channel); *History's Turning Points* 26x30-mins programmes on decisive moments in world history (The Learning Channel); *Greek Fire* 10x30 mins on Greek culture (Ch4); *Four American Composers* 4x1 hour (Ch4); *The Horse in Sport* 8x1 hour (Ch4); *A Year in the Life of Placido Domingo*. No unsolicited scripts. Interested in new writers to write 'the book of the series', e.g. for *Greek Fire* and *The Horse in Sport*, but not usually drama script writers.

Turning Point Productions

Pinewood Studios, Pinewood Road, Iver Heath, Buckinghamshire SL0 0NH
☎01753 630666   Fax 01753 650855
Contact *Adrian Bate*

Television drama producers. OUTPUT includes *Red Fox* (mini-series for LWT); *Cider With Rosie* (Carlton TV film). No unsolicited scripts. Very keen to nurture new writing talent though.

Twentieth Century Fox Film Co

Twentieth Century House, 31–32 Soho Square, London W1V 6AP
☎0171 437 7766   Fax 0171 434 2170

London office of the American giant.

Two Four Productions Limited

Quay West Studios, Old Newnham,
Plymouth, Devon PL7 5BH
☎01752 345424   Fax 01752 344224
Managing Director *Charles Wace*

Broadcast Director *Jill Lourie*

Video and television: drama, documentary, commercials and corporate. OUTPUT includes current productions: *Collectors' Lot* (120 x 30min, Ch4); *What Would You Do?* (65 x 30 min, BBC1)and the RTS award-winning *Christmas With the Royal Navy*. *Treasures* (6-part series for Westcountry Television/ LWT); *On the Moor* (a 6-part documentary filmed inside Dartmoor Prison); and *The West At Work* (business magazine for Westcountry Television). Corporate clients include British Heart Foundation and Audi(UK).

Two Sides TV Ltd

53A Brewer Street, London W1R 3FD
☎0171 439 9882   Fax 0171 287 2289
Managing Director *Catherine Robins*

Broadcast TV including children's programmes such as *The Adventures of Captain Zeelig; Bug Alert!* for ITV. Also documentaries ('Equinox', 'Under the Sun') for Ch4 and BBC.

UBA Ltd

21 Alderville Road, London SW6 2EE
☎01984 623619   Fax 01984 623733
Contact *Peter Shaw*

Quality feature films and TV for an international market. OUTPUT *Windprints; The Lonely Passion of Judith Hearne* (co-production with **Hand-Made Films Ltd**); *Taffin; Castaway; Turtle Diary; Sweeney Todd; Keep the Aspidistra Flying*. In development: *Hunting the Devil; A Witch in New York; Kinder Garden; Paul Robeson; Rebel Magic; No Man's Land; Murdering Shakespeare*. Prepared to commission new writing whether adapted from another medium or based on a short outline/treatment. Concerned with the quality of the script (*Turtle Diary* was written by Harold Pinter) and breadth of appeal. 'Exploitation material' not welcome.

United Film and Television Productions

48 Leicester Square, London WC2H 7FB
☎0171 389 8555   Fax 0171 930 8499
Managing Director *Vernon Lawrence*
Controller of Drama *Simon Lewis*
Head of Drama Development *Sue Hogg*

Television drama. RECENT OUTPUT Jane Austen's *Emma*; *No Child of Mine* by Peter Kosminsky (drama-doc); *Where the Heart Is* by Ashley Pharoah (6x60min series); *Touching Evil* by Paul Abbott (6x60min series).

United International Pictures (UK)

Mortimer House, 37–41 Mortimer Street,
London W1A 2JL
☎0171 636 1655   Fax 0171 636 4118

UK office of American giant; distributes for
MGM/UA, Paramount, SKG DreamWorks
and Universal.

United Media Ltd

68 Berwick Street, London W1V 3PE
☎0171 287 2396   Fax 0171 287 2398

Contact L. Patterson

Film, video and TV: drama. OUTPUT To the
Lighthouse (TV movie with BBC); Jamaica Inn
(HTV mini-series); The Krays (feature film
with Fugitive/Rank). Unsolicited scripts welcome but synopses preferred in the first
instance. 'We encourage new writing if we see
commercially orientated talent.'

Vanson Productions

PO Box 16926, London SW18 3ZP
☎0181 874 4241   Fax 0181 874 4241

Contact Yvette Vanson

OUTPUT The Stephen Lawrence Story and Violence
and the Censors(both for Ch4); Cock o' the North
(Granada arts documentary). Vanson Productions are currently working in production with a
science fiction series with Channel 5. Also in
production: a sequel to The Stephen Lawrence
Story for Ch4 and a drama/documentary for
LWT. In development: various feature film projects and a children's adventure series for television.

Video Arts (Production) Ltd

Dumbarton House, 68 Oxford Street, London
W1N 0LH
☎0171 637 7288   Fax 0171 580 8103

Contact Margaret Tree

Film and video, CDi and CD-ROM: training,
corporate and educational.

Video Enterprises

12 Barbers Wood Road, High Wycombe,
Buckinghamshire HP12 4EP
☎01494 534144 (mobile: 0831 875216)
Fax 01494 534144
E-mail: maurice@vident.u-net.com
Website: http://www.vident.u-net.com

Contact Maurice R. Fleisher

Video and TV, mainly corporate: business and
industrial training, promotional material and
conferences. No unsolicited material 'but
always ready to try out good new writers'.

Video Newsreels

Church Cottage, Ruscombe, Nr Twyford,
Berkshire RG10 9UB
☎0118 9321123   Fax 0118 9321333

Contact Gerry Clarke

Corporate video production: sales and training.
OUTPUT has included staff-training videos for
British Airways and Midland Bank. Unsolicited
mss welcome.

Video Presentations

PO Box 281, Wimbledon, London SW19 3DD
☎0181 542 7721   Fax 0181 543 0855

Contact John Holloway

Corporate video. CLIENTS include the Post
Office, IBM, British Gas, Freemans, Eastern
Electricity.

Videotel Productions/ Living Tape Productions

84 Newman Street, London W1P 3LD
☎0171 299 1800   Fax 0171 299 1818

Contact Robin Jackson

Film, video and TV mostly for education and
training. OUTPUT has included Oceans of
Wealth (British Gas, DTI & Ch4); Response to
Marine Chemical Spills (for industrial consor-
tium); Dealing with Violence and Aggression at
Work (NHS, THF); Defence against Drug
Traffickers (SKULD); Alcohol, Beware! (Mobil);
Responsible Chemical Manufacturing (consortium
of chemical companies); Hospital Security
(NAHAT); The Office (BBC/EBS Trust); More
than Meets the Eye (DOH, EBS Trust).

Brian Waddell Productions Ltd

Strand Studios, 5/7 Shore Road, Holywood,
Co. Down BT18 9HX
☎01232 427646   Fax 01232 427922

Contacts Brian Waddell, Maureen Gallagher

Producers of a wide range of television programmes in leisure activities, the arts, music,
children's, comedy, travel/adventure and documentaries. Currently developing several
drama projects. Interested in encouraging new
writers, particularly within Ireland.

Wall to Wall Television

8–9 Spring Place, London NW5 3ER
☎0171 485 7424   Fax 0171 267 5292

Contact Alex Graham

Documentary, features and drama. OUTPUT
includes Plotlands; It's Not Unusual; Nightmare:
The Birth of Horror (BBC); Baby It's You; A
Taste of the Times; Weekly Planet (Ch4).

Material is produced in-house; occasional outside ideas accepted. Continued expansion of drama production means more opportunities for writers.

The Walnut Partnership
Crown House, Armley Road, Leeds,
West Yorkshire LS12 2EJ
☎0113 2456913   Fax 0113 2439614
E-mail: info@walnut.co.uk
Contact *Geoff Penn*

A film and video production company specialising in business communication.

Warner Sisters Film & TV Ltd
Canalot Studios, 222 Kensal Road, London
W10 5BN
☎0181 960 3550   Fax 0181 960 3880
Chief Executives *Lavinia Warner, Jane Wellesley, Anne-Marie Casey, Dorothy Viljoen*

FOUNDED 1984. Drama and comedy. TV and feature films. OUTPUT includes *Selling Hitler; Rides; Life's a Gas; She-Play; A Village Affair; Dangerous Lady; Dressing for Breakfast; The Spy that Caught a Cold; The Bite; Jilting Joe; The Jump.* Developing a wide range of projects including *Mad Mary* (feature film).

Western Eye Business Television
Easton Business Centre, Felix Road, Easton,
Bristol BS5 0HE
☎0117 9415854   Fax 0117 9415851
Contact *Steve Spencer*

Corporate video production for Royal Mail, Re-Solv, NACAB, Water Aid, BT. Looking for experienced writers in the above field.

Michael White Productions Ltd
See **MW Entertainments Ltd**

WitzEnd Productions
1 Stephen Street, London W1P 1PJ
☎0171 691 6000   Fax 0171 691 6088

Bought by Pearson in 1996. Producers of television drama and comedy. OUTPUT *Pie in the Sky; Lovejoy; Tracey Ullman: A Class Act; We Know Where You Live.* Scripts not welcome unless via agents but new writing is encouraged.

Workhouse Television
Granville House, St Peter Street, Winchester,
Hampshire SO23 8BP
☎01962 626400   Fax 01962 626401
Television Manager *Carol Wade*

Video and TV: documentary, light entertainment, magazine programmes and corporate work. OUTPUT *Dear Nick* (ITV); *Lifeschool A–Z* (BBC); *Big Day Out* (BBC); *Parents Talking; DIY; Cash in Hand* (The Learning Channel); *Time Off; Tale of Three Seaside Towns* (Meridian); *Mastercraft* (Westcountry TV); *Wizadora* (network). Corporate clients include BZW, Barclays, Price Waterhouse, Nuclear Electric.

Working Title Films Ltd
Oxford House, 76 Oxford Street, London
W1N 9FD
☎0171 307 3000   Fax 0171 307 3001/2/3
Co-Chairmen (Films) *Tim Bevan, Eric Fellner*
Head of Development (Films)
   Debra Hayward
Development Executive (Films)
   Natascha Wharton
Television *Simon Wright*

Affiliated to PolyGram Filmed Entertainment. Feature films, TV drama; also family/children's entertainment and TV comedy. OUTPUT Films: *Elizabeth; Hi Lo Country; Plunkett & Macleane; Notting Hill; Bean; The Borrowers; The Matchmaker; Fargo; Dead Man Walking; French Kiss; Four Weddings and a Funeral; The Hudsucker Proxy; The Tall Guy; A World Apart; Wish You Were Here; My Beautiful Laundrette.* Television: *More Tales of the City; Lano and Woodley; The Borrowers I & II; Armisted Maupin's Tales of the City; News Hounds; Echoes.* No unsolicited mss at present, but keen to encourage new writing nevertheless via New Writers Scheme - contact Natascha Wharton.

Worldview Pictures
10 Cameron House, 12 Castlehaven Road,
London NW1 8QW
☎0171 916 4696   Fax 0171 916 1091
Contact *Stephen Trombley, Bruce Eadie*

Documentaries and series for television, plus theatrical. OUTPUT *Nuremberg* (Discovery/Ch4); *Raising Hell: The Life of A. J. Bannister; The Execution Protocol* (both for Discovery/BBC/France 2); *Drancy: A Concentration Camp in Paris; The Lynchburg Story* (both for Discovery/Ch4/France 2).

Worldwide Television News
The Interchange, Oval Road, London
NW1 7DZ
☎0171 410 5200   Fax 0171 413 8302
Contact *Tim Sparke*

Video and TV: documentary, news, features,

sport and entertainment. OUTPUT *Flightline* (aviation magazine series); *Animal Tracks* (children's wildlife series); *Top Secret* (3 x 1 hour documentary series); *Animal X* (animal mysteries); plus many one-off specials. Unsolicited material welcome.

Wortman Productions UK
48 Chiswick Staithe, London W4 3TP
☎0181 994 8886

Producer *Neville Wortman*

Film, video and TV production for drama, documentary, commercials and corporate material. OUTPUT *House in the Country* John Julius Norwich (ITV series); *Ellington* (Jazz series); *'C'm on to My House* (TV feature series); *Theatre* (CD-ROM); *Celebration Theatre Company for the Young – The Winter's Tale*; *Lost Ships* (major maritime archeology series, Discovery Channel,

US). Send outline treatments 2–3 pages and s.a.e. and a couple of pages of dialogue if appropriate. Open to new writing but preferably from agents.

Zenith Productions Ltd
43–45 Dorset Street, London W1H 4AB
☎0171 224 2440   Fax 0171 224 3194

Script Executive *Ming Ho*

Feature films and TV drama. OUTPUT Films: Todd Haynes' *Velvet Goldmine; Wisdom of Crocodiles*; Nicole Holofcener's *Walking and Talking*. Television: *Hamish Macbeth; Rhodes; Bodyguards; The Uninvited*. No unsolicited scripts.

The Zoom Production Company
3rd Floor South, Harling House, 47–51 Great Suffolk Street, London SE1 0BL

Now part of **CCC Wadlow** (see entry).

Theatre Producers

Actors Touring Company

Alford House, Aveline Street, London
SE11 5DQ
☎0171 735 8311Fax 0171 735 1031 attn ATC
Artistic Director *Nick Philippou*

'Actors Touring Company takes old stories and works with living writers to produce new theatre.' Collaborations with writers are based on adaptation and/or translation work and unsolicited mss will only be considered in this category. 'We endeavour to read mss but do not have the resources to do so quickly.' As a small-scale company, all plays must have a cast of six or less.

Almeida Theatre Company

Almeida Street, Islington, London N1 1TA
☎0171 226 7432   Fax 0171 704 9581
Artistic Directors *Ian McDiarmid,
Jonathan Kent*

FOUNDED 1980. Now in its tenth year as a full-time producing theatre, presenting a year-round theatre and music programme in which international writers, composers, performers, directors and designers are invited to work with British artists on challenging new and classical works. Previous productions: *Butterfly Kiss; The Rules of the Game; Medea; No Man's Land; The Rehearsal; Bajazet; Galileo; Moonlight; The School for Wives; Hamlet; Tartuffe; Who's Afraid of Virginia Woolf; Ivanov; The Government Inspector; Naked; The Judas Kiss; The Iceman Cometh*. No unsolicited mss: 'our producing programme is very limited and linked to individual directors and actors'.

Alternative Theatre Company Ltd

Bush Theatre, Shepherds Bush Green,
London W12 8QD
☎0171 602 3703   Fax 0171 602 7614
Literary Manager *Tim Fountain*

FOUNDED 1972. Trading as The Bush Theatre. Produces about six new plays a year (principally British) and hosts up to four visiting companies also producing new work: 'we are a writer's theatre'. Previous productions: *Kiss of the Spiderwoman* Manuel Puig; *Raping the Gold* Lucy Gannon; *The Wexford Trilogy* Billy Roche; *Love and Understanding* Joe Penhall; *This Limetree Bower* Conor McPherson; *Discopigs* Enda Walsh;

The Pitchfork Disney Philip Ridley; *Phoenix* Roy MacGregor; *Beautiful Thing* Jonathan Harvey; *Killer Joe* Tracy Letts. Scripts are read by a team of associates, then discussed with the management, a process which takes about three months. The theatre offers a small number of commissions, recommissions to ensure further drafts on promising plays, and a guarantee against royalties so writers are not financially penalised even though the plays are produced in a small house. Writers should send scripts with small s.a.e. for acknowledgement and large s.a.e. for return of script.

Annexe Theatre Company Ltd

The Bishops House, Porterfield Road,
Kilmacolm PA13 4PD
☎01505 874111   Fax 01505 874111
Artistic Director *Wendy Seager*
Literary Manager *Noel McMonagle*

FOUNDED 1986. Touring productions, play readings and workshops for writers. Interested in considering new work from Scottish writers. Writers' pack available. All scripts are read and reports given; writers are encouraged through re-writes, one-to-one meetings; playwrights with potential are invited to join the company's Development Programme. In 1997/98, Annexe staged a production of a new play at the Cottesloe Theatre at the Royal National Theatre, a community production in Coatbridge and held a series of play readings.

Yvonne Arnaud Theatre

Millbrook, Guildford, Surrey GU1 3UX
☎01483 440077   Fax 01483 564071
Contact *James Barber*

Credits include: *Things We Do For Love* Alan Ayckbourn; *Laughter on the 23rd Floor* Neil Simon; *A Passionate Woman* Kay Mellor; *The Weekend* Michael Palin; *Indian Ink* Tom Stoppard; *Home* David Storey; *Cellmates* Simon Gray; *Letter of Resignation* Hugh Whitemore.

Birmingham Repertory Theatre

Broad Street, Birmingham B1 2EP
☎0121 236 6771   Fax 0121 236 7883
Artistic Director *Bill Alexander*
Associate Director *Tony Clark*
Literary Manager *Ben Payne*

The Birmingham Repertory Theatre aims to provide a platform for the best work from new writers from both within and beyond the West Midlands region along with a programme which also includes classics and 'discovery' plays. The Rep is committed to a policy of integrated casting and to the production of new work which reflects the diversity of contemporary experience. The commissioning of new plays takes place across the full range of the theatre's activities: in the Main House, the Studio (which is a dedicated new writing space) and the touring work of the Youth, Community and Education Department. 'Writers are advised that the Rep is very unlikely to produce an unsolicited script. We usually assess unsolicited submissions on the basis of whether it indicates a writer with whom the theatre may be interested in working. The theatre runs a programme of writers' attachments every year in addition to its commissioning policy and maintains close links with *Stagecoach* (the regional writers' training agency) and the **MA in Playwriting Studies** at the University of Birmingham.' For more information contact the Literary Manager.

Black Theatre Co-op
Unit 3P Leroy House, 436 Essex Road, London N1 3QP
☎0171 226 1225   Fax 0171 226 0223
Artistic Director *Felix Cross*
FOUNDED 1978. Plays to a mixed audience, approximately 65% female. Usually tours nationally twice a year. 'Committed in the first instance to new writing by Black British writers and work which relates to the Black culture and experience throughout the Diaspora, although anything considered.' Unsolicited mss welcome.

Bootleg Theatre Company
23 Burgess Green, Bishopdown, Salisbury, Wiltshire SP1 3El
☎01722 421476
Contact *Colin Burden*
FOUNDED 1984. Tries to encompass as wide an audience as possible and has a tendency towards plays with socially relevant themes. A good bet for new writing since unsolicited mss are very welcome. 'Our policy is to produce new and/or rarely seen plays and anything received is given the most serious consideration.' Actively seeks to obtain grants to commission new writers for the company. *Hanging Hanratty* by Michael Burnham toured throughout 1996/97 and may have a London run followed by a film version. Future productions include *The Boys Are Back in Town* by Trevor Suthers and *Fighting for Breath* by Michelle Harris.

Borderline Theatre Company
Darlington New Church, North Harbour Street, Ayr KA8 8AA
☎01292 281010   Fax 01292 263825
Artistic Director *Leslie Finlay*
Chief Executive *Eddie Jackson*
FOUNDED 1974. Borderline is one of Scotland's leading touring companies. Committed to new writing, it tours a programme of new plays and radical adaptations/translations of classic texts in an accessible and entertaining style. Tours to main-house theatres across Scotland and small venues in outlying districts. Shows are premièred at the Edinburgh Festival and in London. Recently toured *Sabina!*, a revival of the award-winning romantic comedy by Chris Dolan and *The Misanthrope*, a new version by Martin Crimp. Under commission: *The Angels' Share* by Chris Dolan. 'We are committed to touring new writing for young people' – *Broken Angel* by Lin Coghlan and *The Prince and the Pilot* by Anita Sullivan (under commission). Past tours have included works by Dario Fo, A. L. Kennedy, Liz Lochhead, Roald Dahl and Carl MacDougal. Synopsis with cast size preferred in the first instance.

Bristol Express Theatre Company
24 Well's House Road, East Acton, London NW10 6EE
☎0181 838 4482   Fax 0181 838 4482
Director *Andy Jordan*
A non-funded, professional, sometimes middle-scale national touring company which has a continuing commitment to the discovery, development and encouragement of new writing, principally through its research and development programme *The Play's The Thing!* This consists of public/private staged and rehearsed readings; workshops and full-scale productions. Previous productions: *Child's Play* Jonathan Wolfman; *Winter Darkness* Allan Cubitt; *Prophets in the Black Sky* John Matshikiza; *Lunatic & Lover* Michael Meyer; *Heaven* Sarah Aicher; *Syme* Michael Bourdages; *Gangster Apparel* Richard Vetere. 'We look for plays that are socially/emotionally/theatrically/politically significant, analytical and challenging. The company is keen to produce work which attempts to mix genres (and create new ones!), is eloquent and honest, while remaining accessible and entertaining.'

Bristol Old Vic Company
Theatre Royal, King Street, Bristol BS1 4ED
☎0117 9493993   Fax 0117 9493996

Bristol Old Vic is committed to the commissioning and production of new writing in both the Theatre Royal (650 seats) and the New Vic Studio (150 seats). Plays must have the potential to attract an audience of significant size in either auditorium. 'We are eager to discover plays which possess genuine theatricality, are assured in characterisation and dramatic structure, recognise the power of emotion, and display a sense of humour.' The theatre will read and report on unsolicited scripts, and asks for a fee of £10 per script to cover the payments to readers.

Bush Theatre
See **Alternative Theatre Company Ltd**

Carnival (Films & Theatre) Ltd
See entry under **Film, TV and Video Production Companies**

Cheek By Jowl
From autumn 1998, the company is taking a sabbatical with no plans to produce anything for an indefinite period.

Chester Gateway Theatre Trust Ltd
Hamilton Place, Chester, Cheshire
CH1 2BH
☎01244 344238   Fax 01244 317277
Artistic Director *Deborah Shaw*

FOUNDED 1968. Plays to a broad audience across a wide range of work, classical to contemporary, including Shakespeare, John Godber, Tennessee Williams, Alan Ayckbourn, Arthur Miller, Pinter, etc. An emphasis on new writing with 14 world premières in the last four years. Small-cast material, children's and young people, large-scale youth theatre, people with learning difficulties, plays by women and adaptations of novels. We budget on 70% capacity in a 440-seat theatre. Anything with a cast of over eight is unlikely to reach production. The smaller the cast the better. Scripts welcome but reading will take some time. Please send synopsis first. Winner of *The Stage* Award for Special Achievement in Regional Theatre in 1996.

Churchill Theatre
High Street, Bromley, Kent BR1 1HA
☎0181 464 7131   Fax 0181 290 6968

Produces a broad variety of popular plays, both new and revivals. Previous productions: *Of Mice and Men; The Goodbye Girl; South Pacific; Wallace and Gromit; Brief Lives; Stepping Out; To Kill a Mockingbird; Boogie Nights; Singular Women; Sweet Charity*. Most productions go on either to tour or into the West End.

Citizens Theatre
Gorbals, Glasgow G5 9DS
☎0141 429 5561   Fax 0141 429 7374
Artistic Director *Giles Havergal*

No formal new play policy. The theatre has a play reader but opportunities to do new work are limited.

Michael Codron Plays Ltd
Aldwych Theatre Offices, Aldwych, London WC2B 4DF
☎0171 240 8291   Fax 0171 240 8467
General Manager *Stephen Langstaff*

Michael Codron Plays Ltd manages the Aldwych Theatre in London's West End. The plays it produces don't necessarily go into the Aldwych, but always tend to be big-time West End fare. Previous productions: *Hapgood; Uncle Vanya; The Sneeze; Rise and Fall of Little Voice; Arcadia; Dead Funny*. No particular rule of thumb on subject matter or treatment. The acid test is whether 'something appeals to Michael'. Straight plays rather than musicals.

Colchester Mercury Theatre Limited
Balkerne Gate, Colchester, Essex CO1 1PT
☎01206 577006   Fax 01206 769607
Administrator *David Fairclough*

Producing theatre with a wide-ranging audience. Unsolicited scripts not welcome as there is a lack of appropriate staff to process them correctly. The theatre has a Writer in Residence, shared with the University of Essex MA in Theatre Studies Course.

The Coliseum, Oldham
Fairbottom Street, Oldham, Lancashire
OL1 3SW
☎0161 624 1731   Fax 0161 624 5318
Chief Executive *Kenneth Alan Taylor*

The policy of the Coliseum is to present high quality work that is unashamedly 'popular'. Has a special interest in new work that has a Northern flavour, however this does not rule out other plays. Unsolicited scripts are all read but will only be returned if a s.a.e. is included.

Communicado Theatre Company

2 Hill Street, Edinburgh EH2 3JZ
☎0131 624 4040　　　Fax 0131 624 4041
Artistic Director *Gerard Mulgrew*

FOUNDED 1982. Scottish touring company which aims to present dynamic and challenging theatre to the widest range of audience in Scotland and internationally. 'We encourage new writing, especially, but not exclusively, of Scots origin. Unfortunately there are no facilities for dealing with unsolicited scripts.' Productions have included: *The House with the Green Shutters* adapt. Gerard Mulgrew; *Carmen 1936* Stephen Jeffreys; *The Hunchback of Notre Dame* adapt. Andrew Dallmeyer; *Mary Queen of Scots Got Her Head Chopped Off* Liz Lochhead; *Blood Wedding* trans. David Johnston; *Cyrano de Bergerac* trans. Edwin Morgan; *Crying Wolf* Gerald Mangan; *Sacred Hearts* Sue Glover; *Tall Tales for Cold Dark Nights; Tales of the Arabian Nights* both by Gerard Mulgrew.

Contact Theatre Company

Oxford Road, Manchester M15 6JA
☎0161 274 3434　　　Fax 0161 273 6286
Artistic Director *Benjamin Twist*

FOUNDED 1972. Plays to a young audience (up to 25). Limited opportunities for new plays without a specific marketing 'hook' for young people. Send s.a.e. for writers' guidelines before submitting script. Recent new productions: *Rupert Street Lonely Hearts Club* Jonathan Harvey; *Tell Me* Matthew Dunster (both world premières). Work by black, female and young writers, and work which creates opportunities for black and female performers, is particularly welcome. Commissions work and runs an annual **Young Playwrights Festival** (see entry under **Festivals**).

Crucible Theatre

55 Norfolk Street, Sheffield S1 1DA
☎0114 2760621　　　Fax 0114 2701532
Artistic Director *Deborah Paige*

'Our priorities are towards new emerging writers and established writers from whom *we* seek ideas for development. However, all unsolicited scripts are seen by a reader and will be returned if accompanied by s.a.e.'

Cwmni Theatr Gwynedd

Deiniol Road, Bangor, Gwynedd LL57 2TL
☎01248 351707　　　Fax 01248 351915
Artistic Director *Siân Summers*

FOUNDED 1984. A mainstream company, performing in major theatres on the Welsh circuit. Welsh-language work only at present. Classic Welsh plays, translations of European repertoire and new work, including adaptations from novels. New Welsh work always welcome; work in English considered if appropriate for translation (i.e. dealing with issues relevant to Wales). 'We are keen to discuss projects with established writers and offer commissions where possible.'

Derby Playhouse

Eagle Centre, Derby DE1 2NF
☎01332 363271　　　Fax 01332 294412
Artistic Director *Mark Clements*

FOUNDED 1948. Plays to a mixed audience. Previous productions include *Zips Together, Teeth Apart* Terence McNally; *Our Boys* Jonathan Lewis; *Three Viewings* Jeffrey Hatcher; *A Passionate Woman* Kay Mellor; *Gym and Tonic* John Godber. 'We have a discreet commissioning budget and hold several readings a season. Productions of unsolicited scripts are rare and initially we prefer treatments to mss. Writers are welcome to send details of rehearsed readings and productions as an alternative means of introducing the theatre to their work. Scripts from East Midlands writers are also submitted to a separate regional reading panel.'

Druid Theatre Company

Druid Lane, Galway, Republic of Ireland
☎00 353 91 568660　　Fax 00 353 91 563109
Contact *Literary Manager*

FOUNDED 1975. Plays to a wide-ranging audience, urban and rural, from young adults to the elderly. National and international theatre with an emphasis on new Irish work, though contemporary European theatre is commonplace in the repertoire. Currently has six writers under commission and is commissioning more. Enclose s.a.e. for return of scripts.

The Dukes

Moor Lane, Lancaster LA1 1QE
☎01524 67461　　　Fax 01524 846817
Artistic Director *Ewan Marshall*

FOUNDED 1971. The only producing house in Lancashire. Wide target market. Plays in 322-seater end-on auditorium plus 198-seater in-the-round studio. Promenade performances in the summer months in Williamson Park. No unsolicited mss.

Dundee Repertory Theatre
Tay Square, Dundee DD1 1PB
☎01382 227684   Fax 01382 228609
Artistic Director *Hamish Glen*

FOUNDED 1939. Plays to a varied audience. Translations and adaptations of classics, and new local plays. Most new work is commissioned. Interested in contemporary plays in translation and in new Scottish writing. No scripts except by prior arrangement.

Eastern Angles Theatre Company
Sir John Mills Theatre, Gatacre Road, Ipswich, Suffolk IP1 2LQ
☎01473 218202   Fax 01473 250954
Contact *Ivan Cutting*

FOUNDED 1982. Plays to a rural audience for the most part. New work only: some commissioned, some devised by the company, some researched documentaries. Unsolicited mss welcome from regional writers. 'We are always keen to develop and produce new writing, especially that which is germane to a rural area.'

Edinburgh Royal Lyceum Theatre
See **Royal Lyceum Theatre Company**

English Stage Company Ltd
See **Royal Court Theatre**

English Touring Theatre
New Century Building, Hill Street, Crewe CW1 1BX
☎01270 501800   Fax 01270 501888
Artistic Director *Stephen Unwin*

FOUNDED 1993. National touring company visiting middle-scale receiving houses and arts centres throughout England. Mostly mainstream. Largely classical programme, but with increasing interest to tour one modern English play per year. Strong commitment to Education and Community Outreach work. No unsolicited mss.

Everyman Theatre
5–9 Hope Street, Liverpool L1 9BH
☎0151 708 0338   Fax 0151 709 0398
Contact *Literary Manager*

Currently offers a script-reading service and commissions new work.

Robert Fox Ltd
6 Beauchamp Place, London SW3 1NG
☎0171 584 6855   Fax 0171 225 1638
Contact *Robert Fox*

Producers and co-producers of work suitable for West End production. Previous productions: *Another Country; Chess; Lettice and Lovage; Madhouse in Goa; Burn This; When She Danced; The Ride Down Mount Morgan; Me & Mamie O'Rouke; The Importance of Being Earnest; The Seagull; Goosepimples; Vita & Virginia; The Weekend; Three Tall Women; Skylight; Who's Afraid of Virginia Woolf; Masterclass; A Delicate Balance; Amy's View.* Scripts, while usually by established playwrights, are always read.

Gate Theatre Company Ltd
11 Pembridge Road, London W11 3HQ
☎0171 229 5387   Fax 0171 221 6055
Literary Manager *Pete Staves*

FOUNDED 1979. Plays to a mixed, London-wide audience, depending on production. Aims to produce British premières of plays which originate from abroad and translations of neglected classics. Most work is with translators. Recent productions: *Shakuntala; Candide; Woyzeck; Leonce and Lena* adapt. by Lee Hall; *Epitaph for the Whales* by Voji Sakate. Positively encourages writers from abroad to send in scripts or translations. All unsolicited scripts are read but it is unlikely that new British, Irish or North American plays will have any future at the theatre due to emphasis on plays originating from abroad. Always enclose s.a.e. if play needs returning.

Gay Sweatshop
FOUNDED 1975. The Company has temporarily suspended operations due to funding withdrawal.

Geese Theatre Company
See **MAC - The Centre for Birmingham**

Graeae Theatre Company
Interchange Studios, Dalby Street, London NW5 3NQ
☎0171 267 1959   Fax 0171 267 2703
Minicom 0171 267 3164
Artistic Director *Jenny Sealey*
Administrative Director *Kevin Dunn*

Europe's premier theatre company of disabled people, the company tours nationally and internationally with innovative theatre productions highlighting both historical and contemporary disabled experience. Graeae also runs T.I.E. and educational programmes available to schools, youth clubs and day centres nationally, provides vocational training in theatre arts (including playwriting) and runs London's only fully accessible Young People's Theatre Programme (called 'The Works') for the disabled community. Unsolicited scripts – particularly from disabled writers - welcome. New work examining disability issues is commissioned.

Greenwich Theatre Ltd
Crooms Hill, London SE10 8ES
☎0181 858 4447   Fax 0181 858 8042

Due to a withdrawal of funding, Greenwich Theatre is unlikely to stage in-house productions in future but may remain open as a receiving house.

Hampstead Theatre
Swiss Cottage Centre, Avenue Road, London NW3 3EX
☎0171 722 9224   Fax 0171 722 3860
Literary Manager *Ben Jancovich*

Produces new plays and the occasional modern classic. Scripts are initially assessed by a team of script readers and their responses are shared with management in monthly script meetings. The literary manager and/or artistic director then read and consider many submissions in more detail. It can therefore take 2–3 months to reach a decision. Writers produced in the past ten years include Marguerite Duras, Terry Eagleton, Brad Fraser, Michael Frayn, Brian Friel, William Gaminara, Beth Henley, Stephen Jeffreys, Terry Johnson, Tony Kushner, Doug Lucie, Frank McGuinness, Rona Munro, Jennifer Phillips, Stephen Poliakoff, Philip Ridley, Martin Sherman, Shelagh Stephenson and Timberlake Wertenbaker.

Harrogate Theatre Company
Oxford Street, Harrogate, North Yorkshire HG1 1QF
☎01423 502710   Fax 01423 563205
Contact *Artistic Director/Executive Director*

FOUNDED 1950. Describes its audience as 'eclectic, all ages and looking for innovation'. Previous productions: *The Marriage of Figaro* (commissioned adaptation of Beaumarchais, Mozart, Da Ponte); *Barber of Seville* (commissioned translation and adaptation of Beaumarchais, Rossini and Sterbini); *School for Wives*; *The Baltimore Waltz* Paula Vogel (European première); *Hot 'n' Throbbing* Paula Vogel (European première); *My Children! My Africa!*; *Wings* (Kopit, Lunden & Perlman European première); new adaptations of *The Government Inspector* and *The Turn of the Screw*; European premières of adaptations/trans-

lations by David Mamet of *The Cherry Orchard, Uncle Vanya* and *Three Sisters*; *Marisol* Jose Rivera; *Lulu* Angela Carter world première. Always struggling to produce new work. The studio theatre is being reopened in 1998 for small-scale productions including *White Lies* and *Mercy Killing* by Robert Shearman.

The Hiss & Boo Company
1 Nyes Hill, Wineham Lane, Bolney, West Sussex RH17 5SD Fax 01444 882057
Contact *Ian Liston*

Particularly interested in new thrillers, comedy thrillers, comedy and melodrama – must be commercial full-length plays. Also interested in plays/plays with music for children. No one-acts. Previous productions: *Sleighrider; Beauty and the Beast; An Ideal Husband; Mr Men's Magical Island; Mr Men and the Space Pirates; Nunsense; Corpse!; Groucho: A Life in Revue; See How They Run; Christmas Cat and the Pudding Pirates; Pinocchio*. No unsolicited scripts; no telephone calls. Send synopsis and introductory letter in the first instance.

Hull Truck Theatre Company
Spring Street, Hull HU2 8RW
☎01482 224800   Fax 01482 581182
General Manager *Simon Stallworthy*

John Godber, of *Teechers, Bouncers, Up 'n' Under* fame, the artistic director of this high-profile Northern company since 1984, has very much dominated the scene in the past with his own successful plays. The emphasis is still on new writing but Godber's work continues to be toured extensively. Most new plays are commissioned. Previous productions: *Dead Fish* Gordon Steel; *Off Out* Gill Adams; *Fish and Leather* Gill Adams; *Happy Families* John Godber. The company now reads all unsolicited scripts and aims to respond within three months. Bear in mind the artistic policy of Hull Truck, which is 'accessibility and popularity'. In general they are not interested in musicals, or in plays with casts of more than eight.

Humberside Theatre in Education
See **Making Space Theatre Company**

Pola Jones Associates Ltd
14 Dean Street, London W1V 5AH
☎0171 439 1165   Fax 0171 437 3994
Contact *André Ptaszynski*

FOUNDED 1982. Comedy, musicals and sitcoms preferred. Previous productions have included: *Neville's Island*; *The Nerd*; *Tommy*; *Crazy For*

You; Me and My Girl; Return To The Forbidden Planet. Current productions include: Chicago; West Side Story; From A Jack To A King. Also produces comedy for TV: Tygo Road; Joking Apart; Chalk. Unsolicited scripts welcome.

Stephen Joseph Theatre

Westborough, Scarborough, North Yorkshire YO11 1JW
☎01723 370540   Fax 01723 360506
Artistic Director Alan Ayckbourn
Director/Literary Manager Connal Orton

A two-auditoria complex housing a 165-seat end stage theatre/cinema (the McCarthy) and a 400-seat theatre-in-the-round (the Round). Positive policy on new work. For obvious reasons, Alan Ayckbourn's work features quite strongly but with a new writing programme now in place, plays from other sources are actively encouraged. Previous première productions include: Woman in Black (adapt. Stephen Mallatratt); The Ballroom Peter King; Neville's Island and The End of the Food Chain Tim Firth; Penny Blue Vanessa Brooks; Fool To Yourself Robert Shearman; All Things Considered Ben Brown. Plays should have a strong narrative and be accessible. Submit to Connal Orton enclosing an s.a.e. for return of mss.

Bill Kenwright Ltd

55–59 Shaftesbury Avenue, London W1V 8JA
☎0171 439 4466   Fax 0171 437 8370
Contact Bill Kenwright

Presents both revivals and new shows for West End and touring theatres. Although new work tends to be by established playwrights, this does not preclude or prejudice new plays from new playwrights. Scripts should be addressed to Bill Kenwright with a covering letter and s.a.e. 'We have enormous amounts of scripts sent to us although we very rarely produce unsolicited work. Scripts are read systematically. Please do not phone; the return of your script or contact with you will take place in time.'

King's Head Theatre

115 Upper Street, London N1 1QN
☎0171 226 8561   Fax 0171 226 8507

The first pub theatre since Shakespearean times and the first venue in the UK for dinner theatre, the King's Head produces some strong work, including previously neglected work by playwrights such as Terence Rattigan and Vivian Ellis. Noël Coward's work also has a strong presence; the company is committed to its contribution to the reappraisal of his work

and in 1995 toured Cavalcade. Previous productions: Noël and Gertie; The Famous Five; Philadelphia, Here I Come!; Accapulco; Elegies for Angels, Punks and Raging Queens; A Day in the Death of Joe Egg; Journey's End. Recent productions which have transferred to the West End include The Boys in the Band and Burning Blue. Unsolicited submissions are not encouraged.

Knightsbridge Theatrical Productions Ltd

21 New Fetter Lane, London EC4A 1JJ
☎0171 583 8687   Fax 0171 583 1040
Contact Mrs S. H. Gray

Straight plays and musicals suitable for production in the West End only. No unsolicited scripts.

Komedia

14–17 Manchester Street, Brighton, East Sussex BN2 1TF
☎01273 277070   Fax 01273 277010
Contact David Lavender

FOUNDED in 1994, Komedia promotes, produces and presents new work. Mss of new plays welcome.

Leeds Playhouse

See **West Yorkshire Playhouse**

Leicester Haymarket Theatre

Belgrave Gate, Leicester LE1 3YQ
☎0116 2530021   Fax 0116 2513310
Artistic Director Paul Kerryson

'We aim for a balanced programme of original and established works.' Recent productions include: Edward II with Eddie Izzard; King Lear with Kathryn Hunter as Lear; Sondheim's Sweeney Todd. A script-reading panel has been established, and new writing is welcome. An Asian initiative has been set up to promote Asian work and Asian practitioners. Future productions include a new commission for Clare McIntyre, a new play by David Greer and Strindberg's rarely performed There Are Crimes and Crimes. There is also a full studio season and programme of activity for the outreach and education department, including youth theatre and community tours.

Library Theatre Company

St Peter's Square, Manchester M2 5PD
☎0161 234 1913   Fax 0161 228 6481
Artistic Director Christopher Honer

Produces new and contemporary work, as well

as occasional classics. No unsolicited mss. Send outline of the nature of the script first. Encourages new writing through the commissioning of new plays and through a programme of rehearsed readings to help writers' development.

Live Theatre Company

7–8 Trinity Chare, Newcastle upon Tyne
NE1 3DF
☎0191 261 2694   Fax 0191 232 2224

Artistic Director *Max Roberts*
General Manager *Jane Tarr*

FOUNDED 1973. Produces shows at its newly refurbished 200-seat venue, The Live Theatre, and also tours regionally and nationally. Company policy is to produce work that is rooted in the culture of the region, particularly for those who do not normally get involved in the arts. The company is particularly interested in promoting new writing. As well as full-scale productions the company organises workshops, rehearsed readings and other new writing activities. The company also enjoys a close relationship with New Writing North. Productions include: *Close the Coalhouse Door* Alan Plater; *Only Joking* Steve Chambers; *Blow Your House Down* Sarah Daniels; *The Grass House* Pauline Hadaway; *Your Home in the West* Rod Wooden; *Seafarers* Tom Hadaway; *Up and Running* Phil Woods; *Buffalo Girls* by Karin Young; *Two* Jim Cartwright; *Cabaret*, and an ambitious cycle of plays – *Twelve Tales of Tyneside* – which involved 12 writers.

Liverpool Everyman

See **Everyman Theatre**

Liverpool Playhouse

Williamson Square, Liverpool L1 1EL
☎0151 709 8478   Fax 0151 709 7113

The theatre is closed for an indefinite period while administrators seek new owners to undertake refurbishment of the building.

London Bubble Theatre Company

3–5 Elephant Lane, London SE16 4JD
☎0171 237 4434   Fax 0171 231 2366
E-mail: peth@londonbubble.org.uk

Artistic Director *Jonathan Petherbridge*

Produces workshops, plays and events for a mixed audience of theatregoers and non-theatregoers, wide-ranging in terms of age, culture and class. Previous productions: *Dealing With Feelings; The Lower Depths; Ali Baba and the Forty Thieves.* Unsolicited mss welcome but

'our reading service is extremely limited and there can be a considerable wait before we can give a response'. Produces at least one new show a year which is invariably commissioned.

Lyric Theatre Hammersmith

King Street, London W6 0QL
☎0181 741 0824   Fax 0181 741 7694

Chief Executive *Sue Storr*
Artistic Director *Neil Bartlett*
Administrative Producer *Simon Mellor*

The main theatre stages an eclectic programme of new and revived classics with a particular interest in music theatre. Interested in developing projects with writers, translators and adaptors. Treatments, synopses and c.v.s only. No longer able to produce in its 110-seat studio owing to reduced funding but the venue continues to host work, including new, by some of the best touring companies in the country.

MAC – The Centre for Birmingham

Cannon Hill Park, Birmingham B12 9QH
☎0121 440 4221   Fax 0121 446 4372

Programme Director *Dorothy Wilson*

Home of the Geese Theatre Company and a host of other arts/performance-related organisations based in Birmingham. Details on Geese available from the Centre.

Cameron Mackintosh

1 Bedford Square, London WC1B 3RA
☎0171 637 8866   Fax 0171 436 2683

Musical producer. His productions include *Oliver!; Little Shop of Horrors; Side by Side by Sondheim; Cats; Les Misérables; Phantom of the Opera; Miss Saigon.* Unsolicited scripts are read and considered (there is no literary manager, however) but new projects are rarely taken on.

Made In Wales

Chapter, Market Road, Canton, Cardiff
CF5 1QE
☎01222 344737   Fax 01222 344738

Artistic Director *Jeff Teare*

Varied audience. Works with Welsh and Wales-based writers and actors to create new and exciting plays which reflect the authentic Anglo-Welsh voice, whilst not being parochially Welsh. Formed in 1982, since when it has premièred 40 new plays. The company also runs a programme of development work for playwrights at different levels of experience throughout the year. This includes workshops, rehearsed readings and a free script-reading service.

Making Space Theatre Company

Cultural Enterprise Centre, Middleton Street, Springbank, Hull HU3 1NB
☎01482 324256   Fax 01482 326190
Artistic Director *John Hazlett*

FOUNDED 1983. Formerly Humberside Theatre in Education. Full-time company playing to Humberside schools, with a strong tradition of devising its own work. Previous productions: *Natural Forces* (for 13–14-year-olds); *The Wrong Side of the River* by Mary Cooper (for 15–18-year-olds); *Whose Voices?* by John Hazlett, Linda Taylor and Carol Bush (for 10–12-year-olds); *Festival* devised by the company for rural schools and communities; Shakespeare's *A Midsummer Night's Dream*; *Bellies* by Linda Taylor, Carol Bush and Janet Gordon; *Beauty and the Gaze* Linda Taylor; *Our Bodies* devised by the company; *Stoneface* by Linda Taylor.

Man in the Moon Theatre Ltd

392 Kings Road, Chelsea, London SW3 5UZ
☎0171 351 5701   Fax 0171 351 1873
Executive Director *Leigh Shine*
Administrator *Pete Staves*

FOUNDED 1982. Fringe theatre. In 1996, awarded the Guinness Ingenuity Award for creativity and innovation. Often tries to fit new plays into seasons such as 'Nationalism' and 'Family Values' and very keen to do rehearsed readings. Unsolicited scripts welcome; 'interested in submissions from first-time writers or writers in the initial stages of their career'. No unfinished scripts or treatments.

Manchester Library Theatre

See **Library Theatre Company**

Method & Madness

25 Short Street, London SE1 8LJ
☎0171 450 1990   Fax 0171 450 1991
Artistic Director *Mike Alfreds*

Method & Madness tends to form long-term relationships with authors and is 'unlikely to be in a position to produce another writer's new work until the year 2000'. Limited script-reading facilities. Unsolicited mss will not be read. Letters welcome; scripts only returned with s.a.e.

Midland Arts Centre

See **MAC – The Centre for Birmingham**

N.T.C. Touring Theatre Company

The Playhouse, Bondgate Without, Alnwick, Northumberland NE66 1PQ
☎01665 602586   Fax 01665 605837
Contact *Gillian Hambleton*
Administrator *Anna Flood*

FOUNDED 1978. Formerly Northumberland Theatre Company. Winner of one of only two drama production franchises in the Northern region. Predominantly rural, small-scale touring company, playing to village halls and community centres throughout the Northern region, the Scottish Borders and countrywide. Productions range from established classics to new work and popular comedies, but must be appropriate to their audience. Unsolicited scripts welcome but are unlikely to be produced. All scripts are read and returned with constructive criticism within six months. Writers whose style is of interest may then be commissioned. The company encourages new writing and commissions when possible. Financial constraints restrict casting to a *maximum* of five.

New Victoria Theatre

Etruria Road, Newcastle under Lyme, Staffordshire ST5 0JG
☎01782 717954   Fax 01782 712885
Theatre Director *Gwenda Hughes*

FOUNDED 1962. Plays to a fairly broad-based audience which tends to vary from one production to another. A high proportion are not regular theatre-goers and new writing has been one of the main ways of contacting new audiences. Synopses preferred to unsolicited scripts.

Newpalm Productions

26 Cavendish Avenue, London N3 3QN
☎0181 349 0802   Fax 0181 346 8257
Contact *Phil Compton*

Rarely produces new plays (*As Is* by William M. Hoffman, which came from Broadway to the Half Moon Theatre, was an exception to this). National tours of productions such as *Peter Pan (The Musical); Noises Off, Seven Brides for Seven Brothers* and *Rebecca*, at regional repertory theatres, are more typical examples of Newpalm's work. Unsolicited mss, both plays and musicals, are, however, welcome; scripts are preferable to synopses.

Northampton Royal Theatre

See **Royal Theatre**

Northcott Theatre

Stocker Road, Exeter, Devon EX4 4QB
☎01392 256182   Fax 01392 499641
Artistic Director *Ben Crocker*

FOUNDED 1967. The Northcott is the South-west's principal subsidised repertory theatre, situated on the University of Exeter campus. Describes its audience as 'geographically diverse, conservative in taste, with a core audience of AB1s (40–60 age range)'. Continually looking to broaden the base of its audience profile, targeting younger and/or non-mainstream theatregoers in the 16–35 age range. Aims to develop, promote and produce quality new writing which reflects the life of the region and addresses the audience it serves. Generally works on a commission basis but occasionally options existing new work. Unsolicited mss welcome – current turnaround on script reading service approximately three months and no mss can be returned unless a correct value s.a.e. is included with the original submission. Primarily interested in larger scale work with a strong story line that avoids TV naturalism (both original work and adaptation/translation welcome). Recently produced new work includes *Breaking Bread Together* Rob Shearman; *A Curlew's Cry* Paul McClure; *Northanger Abbey* Cathy Turner.

Northern Stage

Newcastle Playhouse, Barras Bridge,
Newcastle upon Tyne NE1 7RH
☎0191 232 3366   Fax 0191 261 8093
Artistic Director *Alan Lyddiard*

A young company whose trademarks are a strongly visual and physical style, international influences, appeal to young people and strongly linked programmes of community work. As likely to produce devised work as conventional new writing. Before submitting unsolicited scripts, please contact Rosie Hunter, Programme and Planning Coordinator.

Norwich Puppet Theatre

St James, Whitefriars, Norwich, Norfolk
NR3 1TN
☎01603 615564   Fax 01603 617578
Artistic Director *Luis Boy*
General Manager *Tim Smith*

Plays to a young audience (aged 3–12) but developing shows for adult audiences interested in puppetry. All year round programme plus tours to school. Unsolicited mss welcome if relevant.

Nottingham Playhouse

Nottingham Theatre Trust, Wellington
Circus, Nottingham NG1 5AF
☎0115 9474361   Fax 0115 9475759
Artistic Director *Martin Duncan*

Aims to make innovation popular, and present the best of world theatre, working closely with the communities of Nottingham and Nottinghamshire. Unsolicited mss will be read. It normally takes about six months, however, and 'we have never yet produced an unsolicited script. All our plays have to achieve a minimum of 60 per cent audiences in a 732-seat theatre. We have no studio.' Also see **Roundabout** - the Nottingham Playhouse's theatre-in-education company.

Nuffield Theatre

University Road, Southampton, Hampshire
SO17 1TR
☎01703 315500   Fax 01703 315511
Artistic Director *Patrick Sandford*
Script Executive *Penny Gold*

Well-known as a good bet for new playwrights, the Nuffield gets an awful lot of scripts. They do a couple of new main stage plays every season. Previous productions: *Exchange* by Yri Trifonov (trans. Michael Frayn) which transferred to the Vaudeville Theatre; *The Floating Light Bulb* Woody Allen (British première); new plays by Claire Luckham: *Dogspot; The Dramatic Attitudes of Miss Fanny Kemble;* and by Claire Tomalin: *The Winter Wife.* Open-minded about subject and style, producing musicals as well as straight plays. Also opportunities for some small-scale fringe work. Scripts preferred to synopses in the case of writers new to theatre. All will, eventually, be read 'but please be patient. We do not have a large team of paid readers. We read everything ourselves.'

Octagon Theatre Trust Ltd

Howell Croft South, Bolton, Lancashire
BL1 1SB
☎01204 529407   Fax 01204 380110
Artistic Director *Lawrence Till*
Administrative Director *Amanda Belcham*

FOUNDED 1967. Audience is made up of a wide age range. Productions include Shakespeare, 'Northern' plays, European plays, new plays, 1960s plays. Unsolicited mss considered, but may take up to six months for reply. Interested in good theatrical pieces that connect with the audience – socially, politically, emotionally and often geographically, with casts of about six. No thin comedies or epic plays with casts over eight.

The Old Vic
Waterloo Road, London SE1 8NB
☎0171 928 2651   Fax 0171 261 9161

At the time of going to press the theatre was for sale at an asking price of £7.5 million.

Orange Tree Theatre
1 Clarence Street, Richmond, Surrey
TW9 2SA
☎0181 940 0141   Fax 0181 332 0369
Artistic Director *Sam Walters*

One of those theatre venues just out of London which are good for new writing, both full-scale productions and rehearsed readings (although these usually take place in The Room, above the Orange Tree pub). Productions, from August 1997: *Family Circles* Alan Ayckbourn; *Overboard* and *The Neighbours* Michael Vinaver (part of the London French Theatre Season); *All In the Wrong* Arthur Murphy; *Macbeth* Shakespeare; *Silas Marner* George Eliot, adapt. Geoffrey Beevers; *The Rink* Kander and Ebb. The Room: *The Outside* Susan Glaspell; *A Glass of Water* Ludmila Petrushevskaya; *On the Couch With Chrissie* Vanessa Brooks; *She'll Be Wearing Silk Pyjamas* Kate O'Riordan. Unsolicited mss are read, but patience (and s.a.e.) required.

Orchard Theatre
108 Newport Road, Barnstaple, Devon
EX32 9BA
☎01271 371475   Fax 01271 371825
Artistic Director *Bill Buffery*

FOUNDED 1969. Plays appealing to a wide age range, which tour some 60 or 70 cities, towns and villages throughout Devon, Cornwall, Dorset, Somerset and Gloucestershire. Programme includes classics, new adaptations, outstanding modern work and newly commissioned plays. OUTPUT *A Doll's House; East o' the Sun and West o' the Moon; Halfway to Paradise; La Ronde; An Enemy of the People*. Due to a major cut in funding, Orchard Theatre is unable to commission new work for the foreseeable future.

Oxford Stage Company
3rd Floor, 15–19 George Street, Oxford
OX1 2AU
☎01865 723238   Fax 01865 790625
Contact *Artistic Director*

A middle-scale touring company producing established and new plays. At least one new

play or new adaptation a year. Special interest in new writing for young people aged 13–18. Due to forthcoming projects not considering new scripts at present.

Paines Plough – New Writing New Theatre
4th Floor, 43 Aldwych, London WC2B 4DA
☎0171 240 4533   Fax 0171 240 4534
E-mail: paines.plough@dial.pipex.com
Artistic Director *Vicky Featherstone*
Literary Director *Mark Ravenhill*
Literary Manager *Jessica Dromgoole*

Tours new plays nationally. Works with writers to develop their skills and voices through courses, workshops, free script-reading service and surgeries. Encourages writers to bridge the gap between arthouse and commercial plays with entertaining and provocative work for audiences beyond the London fringe and West End. Welcomes new scripts from writers. For script-reading service send two s.a.e.s for acknowledgement and return of script.

Palace Theatre, Watford
Clarendon Road, Watford, Hertfordshire
WD1 1JZ
☎01923 235455   Fax 01923 819664
Artistic Director *Giles Croft*

An important point of policy is the active commissioning of new plays. Previous productions: *Woman Overboard* Adrian Mitchell; *Diplomatic Wives* Louise Page; *Over A Barrel* Stephen Bill; *The Marriage of Figaro; The Barber of Seville* (adapt. Ranjit Bolt); Jon Canter's *The Baby*; Lou Stein's musical adaptation of *La Celestina* by Fernando de Rojas, entitled *Salsa Celestina; Borders of Paradise* by Sharman Macdonald; *Elton John's Glasses* by David Farr (winner of the 1997 **Writers' Guild** Best Regional Play award). Also supports local writers via Education Department (☎01923 810307).

Perth Repertory Theatre Ltd
185 High Street, Perth PH1 5UW
☎01738 472700   Fax 01738 624576
Artistic Director *Michael Winter*
General Manager *Paul McLennan*

FOUNDED 1935. A wide range of productions, including musicals, classics, new plays, comedy, etc. for a loyal audience. Unsolicited mss are read when time permits, but the timetable for return of scripts is lengthy. New plays staged by the company are invariably commissioned under the SAC scheme.

Plymouth Theatre Royal
See **Theatre Royal**

Polka Theatre for Children
240 The Broadway, Wimbledon, London
SW19 1SB
☎0181 542 4258   Fax 0181 542 7723
E-mail: polkatheatre@dial.pipex.com
Artistic Director *Vicky Ireland*
Administrator *Stephen Midlane*

FOUNDED in 1967 and moved into its
Wimbledon base in 1979. Leading children's
theatre committed to commissioning and producing new plays. Programmes are planned
two years ahead and at least three new plays are
commissioned each year. 'Because of our specialist needs and fixed budgets, all our scripts
are commissioned from established writers with
whom we work very closely. Writers are
selected via recommendation and previous
work. We do not perform unsolicited scripts.
Potential new writers' work is read and discussed on a regular basis; thus we constantly
add to our pool of interesting and interested
writers.'

Q20 Theatre Company
Ivy Lea, Fyfe Lane, Baildon, Shipley,
West Yorkshire BD17 6DP
☎01274 591417   Fax 01274 591417
Director *John Lambert*

Produces shows mainly for school and community venues. Particularly interested in plays for
children. Q20 writes a lot of its own material
and rarely has the resources to pay outside professional contributors. Write initially with
ideas.

Queen's Theatre, Hornchurch
Billet Lane, Hornchurch, Essex RM11 1QT
☎01708 456118   Fax 01708 452348
Artistic Director *Bob Carlton*

The Queen's Theatre is a 500-seat producing
theatre in the London Borough of Havering,
within the M25. Established in 1953, the
theatre has been located in its present building
since 1975 and produces up to nine in-house
productions per year, including pantomime.
The Queen's has re-established a permanent
core company of actor/musicians under the
new artistic leadership of Bob Carlton. Aims to
produce distinctive and accessible performances in an identifiable house style focused
upon actor/musician shows but, in addition,
embraces straight plays, classics and comedies.

'New play/musical submissions are welcome
and will be read and given a report.' Each year
there is a large-scale community play commissioned from a local writer, culminating in a
summer event beside the theatre.

The Questors Theatre
12 Mattock Lane, Ealing, London W5 5BQ
☎0181 567 0011   Fax 0181 567 8736
Artistic Director *Spencer Butler*
Theatre Manager *Kris Collier*
Production Secretary *Christine Greening*

FOUNDED 1929. Attracts an intelligent, dis-
cerning, wide age range audience looking for
something different, innovative, daring.
Recent productions include: *A Doll's House*
Ibsen; *The Rose Tattoo* Tennessee Williams;
Accidental Death of an Anarchist Dario Fo;
Andromache Racine. Unsolicited mss welcome.
All new plays are carefully assessed. Scripts
received are acknowledged and all writers
receive a written response to their work.
Occasionally, unsolicited plays receive produc-
tions, others rehearsed readings.

The Really Useful Group Ltd
20 Tower Street, London WC2H 9NS
☎0171 240 0880   Fax 0171 240 1204

Commercial/West End theatre producers whose
output has included *Jesus Christ Superstar; Sunset
Boulevard; Joseph and the Amazing Technicolor
Dreamcoat; Cats; Phantom of the Opera; Starlight
Express; Daisy Pulls It Off; Lend Me a Tenor;
Arturo Ui* and *Aspects of Love*.

Red Ladder Theatre Company
3 St Peter's Buildings, York Street, Leeds,
West Yorkshire LS9 8AJ
☎0113 2455311   Fax 0113 2455351
E-mail: red-ladder@geo2.poptel.org.uk
Artistic Director/Literary Manager *Kully
Thiarai*
Administrator *Ann Cross*

FOUNDED 1968. Commissioning company touring 2–3 shows a year with a strong commitment
to new work and new writers. Aimed at an audience of young people aged between 14–25 years
who have little or no access to theatre. Performances held in youth clubs and similar venues (not
schools) where young people choose to meet.
Recent productions: 1996: *End of Season* Noël
Greig, an international collaboration with
Theatre Direct of Canada; 1997: *Kaahini* a new
play by Asian writer Maya Chowdhry. 'The
company is currently developing its writing pol-

icy which will be available to writers interested in working for the company. Whilst unsolicited scripts are not discouraged, the company is particularly keen to enter into a dialogue with writers with regard to creating new work for young people.'

Red Shift Theatre Company

9 The Leathermarket, Weston Street, London SE1 3ER

☎0171 378 9787   Fax 0171 378 9789

Contact *Jonathan Holloway, Artistic Director*
General Manager *Sophie Elliott*

FOUNDED 1982. Small-scale touring company which plays to a theatre-literate audience. Unlikely to produce an unsolicited script as most work is commissioned. Welcomes contact with writers – 'we try to see their work ... and welcomes receipt of c.v.s and treatments'. Occasionally runs workshops bringing new scripts, writers and actors together. These can develop links with a reservoir of writers who may feed the company. Interested in new plays with subject matter which is accessible to a broad audience and concerns issues of importance; also new translations and adaptations. 1998 production: *The Aspern Papers* by Henry James.

Ridiculusmus

The Playhouse, 5–7 Artillery Street, Londonderry BT48 6RG

☎01504 373800   Fax 01504 261884

Artistic Directors *Jon Hough, David Woods*

FOUNDED 1992. Touring company which plays to a wide range of audiences. Productions have included adaptations of *Three Men In a Boat; The Third Policeman; At Swim Two Birds* and two new works: *All About H. Hatterr* and *The Exhibitionists*. Unsolicited scripts welcome but not political drama.

Roundabout Theatre in Education

College Street Centre for Performing Arts, College Street, Nottingham NG1 5AQ

☎0115 9476202   Fax 0115 9539055

Contact *Kitty Parker*

FOUNDED 1973. Theatre-in-Education company of the Nottingham Playhouse. Plays to a young audience aged 5–18 years of age. Some programmes are devised or adapted in-house, many are commissioned. Unable to resource the adequate response required for unsolicited scripts. 'We are committed to the encouragement of new writing as and when resources permit.'

Royal Court Theatre/ English Stage Company Ltd

St Martin's Lane, London WC2N 4BG

☎0171 565 5050   Fax 0171 565 5002

Literary Manager *Graham Whybrow*

The English Stage Company was founded by George Devine in 1956 to put on new plays. John Osborne, John Arden, Arnold Wesker, Edward Bond, Caryl Churchill, Howard Barker and Michael Hastings are all writers this theatre has discovered. Christopher Hampton and David Hare have worked here in the literary department. 'The aim of the Royal Court is to develop and perform the best in new writing for the theatre, encouraging writers from all sections of society to address the problems and possibilities of our times.'

Royal Exchange Theatre Company

St Ann's Square, Manchester M2 7DH

☎0161 833 9333   Fax 0161 832 0881

Literary Manager *Sarah Frankcom*

FOUNDED 1976. The Royal Exchange has developed a new writing policy which it finds is attracting a younger audience to the theatre. The company has produced new plays by Shelagh Stephenson, Brad Fraser, Simon Burke, Michael Wall, Rod Wooden, and Alex Finlayson. Also English and foreign classics, modern classics, adaptations and new musicals. The Royal Exchange receives 500–2000 scripts a year. These are read by Sarah Frankcom and a team of experienced readers. Only a tiny percentage is suitable, but a number of plays are commissioned each year.

Royal Lyceum Theatre Company

Grindlay Street, Edinburgh EH3 9AX

☎0131 229 7404   Fax 0131 228 3955

Artistic Director *Kenny Ireland*
General Manager *Nikki Axford*

FOUNDED 1965. Repertory theatre which plays to a mixed urban Scottish audience. Produces classic, contemporary and new plays. Would like to stage more new plays, especially Scottish. No full-time literary staff to provide reports on submitted scripts.

Royal National Theatre

South Bank, London SE1 9PX

☎0171 452 3333   Fax 0171 452 3344

Literary Manager *Jack Bradley*

The majority of the National's new plays come about as a result of direct commission or from existing contacts with playwrights. There is no quota for new work, though so far more than a third of plays presented have been the work of living playwrights. Writers new to the theatre would need to be of exceptional talent to be successful with a script here, though the Royal National Theatre Studio acts as a bridge between the theatre and helps a limited number of playwrights, through readings, workshops and discussions. In some cases a new play is presented for a shorter-than-usual run in the Cottesloe Theatre. Scripts considered (send s.a.e).

Royal Shakespeare Company

Literary Office, Barbican Centre, London EC2Y 8BQ
☎0171 628 3351   Fax 0171 374 0818
Artistic Director *Adrian Noble*
Literary Manager *Simon Reade*

The RSC is a classical theatre company based in Stratford upon Avon, bringing its repertoire into London at the Barbican Theatre for six months of the year, and with residencies in Newcastle and Plymouth. It also tours extensively – nationally and internationally. As well as Shakespeare, English classics and foreign classics in translation, new plays counterpoint the RSC's repertory, especially those which celebrate language. 'The literary department is proactive rather than reactive and seeks out the plays and playwrights it wishes to commission. It will read all translations of classic foreign works submitted, or of contemporary works where the original writer and/or translator is known. It is unable to read unsolicited work from less established writers. It can only return scripts if an s.a.e. is enclosed with submission.'

Royal Theatre

15 Guildhall Road, Northampton NN1 1EA
☎01604 638343   Fax 01604 602408
Artistic Director *Michael Napier Brown*

Describes its audience as 'wide-ranging in terms of taste, with a growing population which is encouraging a more adventurous and innovative programme'. Produces at least three new works each year. The studio theatre, theatre-in-education, community touring and youth theatre tend to produce the majority of new work, but there are normally two mainhouse premières each year. Previous productions: *Oleanna; An Old Man's Love; Mail Order Bride; Keely and Du; The Winter's Tale; Top Girls; Shaken not Stirred*. Unsolicited scripts welcome and always read, 'but be patient!'.

7:84 Theatre Company Scotland

333 Woodlands Road, Glasgow G3 6NG
☎0141 334 6686   Fax 0141 334 3369
E-mail: 7.84-theatre@btinternet.com
Artistic Director *Iain Reekie*
Administrator *Tessa Rennie*
Literary Manager *Robert Thomson*

FOUNDED 1973. One of Scotland's foremost touring theatre companies committed to producing work that addresses current social, cultural and political issues. Recent productions include commissions by Scottish playwrights such as David Greig and Stephen Greenhorm, and the Scottish premières of Tony Kushner's *Angels in America* and Athol Fugard's *Valley Song*. 'The company is committed to a new writing policy that encourages and develops writers at every level of experience, to get new voices and strong messages on to the stage.' Although happy to read unsolicited mss, 'it would be impossible to respond in detail to everything that we receive... we simply do not have the resources to make this possible'. For the last nine years 7:84 has run a Summer School for beginners, led by playwright Iain Heggie, and has started a Writers Group for more experienced writers (membership by invitation).

Shared Experience Theatre

The Soho Laundry, 9 Dufours Place, London W1V 1FE
☎0171 434 9248   Fax 0171 287 8763
Artistic Director *Nancy Meckler*
Associate Director *Polly Teale*

FOUNDED 1975. Varied audience depending on venue, since this is a touring company. Recent productions have included: *The Birthday Party* Harold Pinter; *Sweet Sessions* Paul Godfrey; *Anna Karenina* (adapt. Helen Edmundson); *Trilby & Svengali* (adapt. David Fielder); *Mill on the Floss* (adapt. Helen Edmundson); *The Danube* Maria Irene Fornes; *Desire Under the Elms* Eugene O'Neill; *War and Peace* (adapt. Helen Edmundson); *The Tempest* William Shakespeare; *Jane Eyre* (adapt. Polly Teale); *I Am Yours* Judith Thompson. No unsolicited mss. Primarily not a new writing company but 'we are interested in innovative new scripts'.

Sherman Theatre Company

Senghennydd Road, Cardiff CF2 4YE
☎01222 396844   Fax 01222 665581
Artistic Director *Phil Clark*

FOUNDED 1973. Theatre for Young People,

with main house and studio. Encourages new writing; has produced 70 new plays in the last six years. Previous productions: *Erogenous Zones, Roots & Wings* Frank Vickery; *Fern Hill, A Long Time Ago* Mike Kenny; *A Spell of Cold Weather* Charles Way; *101 Dalmations* adapt. Glyn Robbins; *Under the Bed* Brendan Murray; *Break, My Heart* Arnold Wesker. In 1997, the company presented six new plays live on stage and broadcast on BBC Radio Wales, and a new series of one-act lunchtime plays on stage and then filmed for HTV Wales. Priority will be given to Wales-based writers.

Show of Strength
Hebron House, Sion Road, Bedminster, Bristol BS3 3BD
☎0117 9537735   Fax 0117 9631770
Artistic Directors *Alan Coveney,*
   Sheila Hannon
Contact *Sheila Hannon*

FOUNDED 1986. Plays to an informal, younger than average audience. Aims to stage at least one new play each season with a preference for work from Bristol and the South West. Will read unsolicited scripts but a lack of funding means they are unable to provide written reports. Interested in full-length stage plays; 'we are undeterred by large casts'. OUTPUT *A Busy Day* Fanny Burney; *A Man and Some Women* Githa Sowerby; *Blue Murder* Peter Nichols and *Rough Music* James Wilson (both world premières). Also, three rehearsed readings of new work each season.

Snap People's Theatre Trust
Unit A, Causeway Business Centre, Bishop's Stortford, Hertfordshire CM23 2UB
☎01279 504095/503066   Fax 01279 501472
Contact *Andy Graham, Mike Wood*

FOUNDED 1979. Plays to young people in four age groups (5–7; 7–11; 11–14; 15–21), and to the thirty-something age group. Classic adaptations and new writing. Writers should make an appointment to discuss possibilities rather than submit unsolicited material. New writing encouraged. 'Projects should reflect the writer's own beliefs, be thought-provoking, challenging and accessible.'

Soho Theatre Company
21 Dean Street, London W1V 6NE
☎0171 493 8050   Fax 0171 493 8051
Artistic Director *Abigail Morris*
Literary Manager *Paul Sirett*
Soho Theatre Company is dedicated to new

writing. Having bought 21 Dean Street in 1997 with the help of Lottery money, work is underway to transform it into a new theatre and writers centre, due to open in 1999. The company has an extensive research and development programme consisting of a free script reading service, workshops and readings. The company produces around four plays a year. Previous productions include: *Gabriel* Moira Buffini, winner of the 1996 LWT Award; *Brothers of the Brush* Jimmy Murphy; *Kindertransporte* Diane Samuels. Runs the **Verity Bargate Award**, a biennial competition (see entry under **Prizes**).

The Sphinx
25 Short Street, London SE1 8LJ
☎0171 401 9993   Fax 0171 501 9995
Artistic Director *Sue Parrish*
General Manager *Alison Gagen*

FOUNDED 1973. Tours new plays by women nationally to studio theatres and arts centres. Synopses and ideas are welcome.

Barrie Stacey Productions
9 Denmark Street, London WC2
☎0171 836 4128/6220   Fax 0171 836 2949
Contact *Barrie Stacey*

Touring company, much of the work being Barrie Stacey's own but not exclusively so. Previous productions: *Adventures of Pinocchio; Snow White and the Seven Dwarfs; West End to Broadway Songbook; Tales From the Jungle Book* Barrie Stacey. Always interested in two/three-handers for production, and in film synopses. Fast, experienced scriptwriters in-house.

The Steam Industry
Finborough Theatre, 118 Finborough Road, London SW10 9ED
☎0171 244 7439   Fax 0171 835 1853
Artistic Director *Phil Willmott*
Contact *The Literary Manager*

Since June 1994, the Finborough Theatre has been a base for The Steam Industry who produce in and out of the building. Their output is diverse and prolific and includes a high percentage of new writing alongside radical adaptations of classics and musicals. The space is also available for a number of hires per year and the hire fee is sometimes negotiable to encourage innovative work. Unsolicited scripts are welcome but due to minimal resources it can take up to six months to respond. Send s.a.e. with material. The company regularly workshops new scripts at Monday–night play-readings and has developed new work by writers such as

Anthony Neilson, Naomi Wallace, Tony Marchant, Diane Samuels and Mark Ravenhill's *Shopping and Fucking*.

Stoll Moss Theatres Ltd

Manor House, 21 Soho Square, London W1V 5FD
☎0171 494 5200   Fax 0171 434 1217
Contact *Nica Burns*

Influential theatrical empire, with ten theatres under its umbrella: Apollo; Cambridge; Duchess; Garrick; Gielgud; Her Majesty's; London Palladium; Lyric Shaftesbury Avenue; Queen's and Theatre Royal Drury Lane.

Swan Theatre

The Moors, Worcester WR1 3EF
☎01905 726969   Fax 01905 723738
Artistic Director *Jenny Stephens*

Repertory company producing a wide range of plays to a mixed audience coming largely from the City of Worcester and the county of Hereford and Worcester. A writing group meets at the theatre. Unsolicited scripts are discouraged.

Swansea Little Theatre Ltd

Dylan Thomas Theatre, Maritime Quarter, Gloucester Place, Swansea, West Glamorgan SA1 1TY
☎01792 473238
Contact *The Secretary*

A wide variety of plays, from pantomime to the classics. New writing encouraged. New plays considered by the Artistic Committee.

Talawa Theatre Company Ltd

23/25 Great Sutton Street, London EC1V 0DN
☎0171 251 6644   Fax 0171 251 5969
Artistic Director *Yvonne Brewster*
General Manager *Anthony Corriette*

FOUNDED 1985. Plays to an ABC audience of 60% black, 40% white across a wide age range depending upon the nature of productions and targeting. Previous productions include all-black performances of *The Importance of Being Earnest* and *Antony and Cleopatra*; plus Jamaican pantomime *Arawak Gold; The Gods Are Not to Blame; The Road* Wole Soyinka; *Beef, No Chicken* Derek Walcott; *Flying West* Pearl Cleage; *Othello* William Shakespeare. Restricted to new work from Black writers only. Occasional commissions, though these tend to go to established writers. 'Interested in the innovative, the modern classic with special reference to the African diasporic experience.' Runs a Black Women's Writers' project funded by **London Arts Board** (for three years).

Theatr Clwyd

Mold, Clwyd CH7 1YA
☎01352 756331   Fax 01352 758323
Literary Manager *William James*

Lively repertory company producing a season of plays each year performed in repertoire by a resident company, along with tours throughout Wales (in English and Welsh). Plays are a healthy mix of classics, revivals, contemporary drama and new writing. Previous productions: *Barnaby and the Old Boys* Keith Baxter; *Self Portrait* Sheila Yeger; *HRH* Snoo Wilson; *Full Moon* by Caradog Prichard, adapt. Helena Kaut-Howson and John Owen; *Rape of the Fair Country* Alexander Cordell, adapt. Manon Eames; *The Journey of Mary Kelly* Sian Evans; *The Changelings* Greg Cullen. Unsolicited plays by Welsh writers or with Welsh themes will be considered.

Theatre Absolute

16 St Thomas Road, Longford, Coventry CV6 7AR
☎01203 680125
Artistic Director *Chris O'Connell*
Producer *Julia Negus*

FOUNDED 1992. Commissions and tours one new play per year, for performance in studio theatres. The plays are between one-and-a-half and two hours in length, with a maximum of six characters. Previous productions have included: *She's Electric; Big Burger Chronicles; Between; Violent Times, The Turn; Contenders*. 'Happy to advise and talk to new writers' but, due to financial and staffing restrictions, unable to accept unsolicited scripts. Launched 'The Writing House' in March 1998; a new writing initiative to serve the writer and to establish a firm relationship with them, Theatre Absolute and associates, the Belgrade Theatre in Coventry.

Theatre of Comedy Company

210 Shaftesbury Avenue, London WC2H 8DP
☎0171 379 3345   Fax 0171 836 8181
Contact *Andrew Leigh (Chief Executive)*

FOUNDED 1983 to produce new work as well as classics and revivals. Interested in strong comedy in the widest sense – Chekhov comes under the definition as does farce. Also has a light entertainment division, developing new scripts for television, namely situation comedy and series. A good bet for new work.

Theatre Royal, Plymouth

Royal Parade, Plymouth, Devon
PL1 2TR
☎01752 668282   Fax 01752 671179
Contact *Liz Turgeon, Simon Stokes*

Stages small-, middle- and large-scale drama including musicals and music theatre. Commissions and produces new plays. Unsolicited scripts are read and reported on.

Theatre Royal Stratford East

Gerry Raffles Square, London E15 1BN
☎0181 534 7374   Fax 0181 534 8381
Associate Director *Kerry Michael*

Lively East London theatre, catering for a very mixed audience, both local and London-wide. Produces plays, musicals, youth theatre and local community plays/events, all of which is new work. Special interest in Asian and Black British work. Unsolicited scripts which are fully complete are welcome.

Theatre Royal Windsor

Windsor, Berkshire SL4 1PS
☎01753 863444   Fax 01753 831673
Executive Producer *Bill Kenwright*
Executive Director *Mark Piper*

Plays to a middle-class, West End-type audience. Produces thirteen plays a year and 'would be disappointed to do fewer than two new plays in a year; always hope to do half a dozen'. Modern classics, thrillers, comedy and farce. Only interested in scripts along these lines.

Theatre Workshop Edinburgh

34 Hamilton Place, Edinburgh EH3 5AX
☎0131 225 7942   Fax 0131 220 0112
Artistic Director *Robert Rae*

Plays to a young, broad-based audience with much of the work targeted towards particular groups or communities. OUTPUT has included adaptations of Gogol's *The Nose* and Aharon Appelfeld's *Badenheim 1939* – two community performance projects. Particularly interested in new work for children and young people. Frequently engages writers for collaborative/ devised projects. Commissions a significant amount of new writing for a wide range of contexts, from large-cast community plays to small-scale professional tours. Favours writers based in Scotland, producing material relevant to a contemporary Scottish audience. Member of Scottish Script Centre to whom it refers senders of unsolicited scripts.

Tiebreak Touring Theatre

Heartsease High School, Marryat Road,
Norwich, Norfolk NR7 9DF
☎01603 435209   Fax 01603 435184
E-mail: tie.break@virgin.net
Artistic Director *David Farmer*

FOUNDED 1981. Specialises in high-quality theatre for children and young people, touring schools, youth centres, museums and festivals. Productions: *Breaking the Rules; George Speaks; Frog and Toad; Love Bites; Singing in the Rainforest; Boadicea – The Movie; Dinosaurs on Ice; The Invisible Boy; My Friend Willy; The Ugly Duckling; Almost Human.* New writing encouraged. Interested in low-budget, small-cast material only. School, educational and socially relevant material of special interest. Scripts welcome.

Torch Theatre

St Peter's Road, Milford Haven,
Pembrokeshire SA73 2BU
☎01646 694192   Fax 01646 698919
Artistic Director *Mike James*

FOUNDED 1976. Plays to a mixed audience hard to attract to new work on the whole. Committed to new work but financing has become somewhat prohibitive. Small-cast pieces with broad appeal welcome. Previous productions: *Frankie and Tommy; School for Wives; Tess of the d'Urbervilles.* The repertoire runs from Ayckbourn to Friel. Scripts sometimes welcome.

Traverse Theatre

Cambridge Street, Edinburgh EH1 2ED
☎0131 228 3223   Fax 0131 229 8443
Artistic Director *Philip Howard*
Literary Director *John Tiffany*
Literary Associate *Ella Wildridge*

The Traverse is the best-known theatre in Scotland for new writing; indeed it's policy is to put on nothing but new work by new writers. Also has a strong international programme of work in translation and visiting companies. Productions: *Knives in Hens* David Harrower; *Anna Weiss* Mike Cullen; *Greta* James Duthie; *Passing Places* Stephen Greenhorn; *Lazybed* Iain Crichton Smith. No unsolicited scripts. Writers welcome to make contact by phone or in writing.

Trestle Theatre Company

47–49 Wood Street, Barnet, Hertfordshire
EN5 4BS
☎0181 441 0349   Fax 0181 449 7036
Artistic Directors *Joff Chafer, Toby Wilsher*

FOUNDED 1981. Physical, mask theatre for

mostly student-based audiences (18–36 years). All work is devised by the company. Scripts which have the company's special brand of theatre in mind will be considered. No non-physical-based material. New writing welcome.

Tricycle Theatre
269 Kilburn High Road, London NW6 7JR
☎0171 372 6611   Fax 0171 328 0795
Artistic Director *Nicolas Kent*

FOUNDED 1980. Plays to a very mixed audience, in terms of both culture and class. Previous productions: *Two Trains Running* August Wilson; *The Day the Bronx Died* Michael Henry Brown; *Half the Picture* Richard Norton-Taylor and John McGrath; *Nativity* Nigel Williams; *Playboy of the West Indies* Mustapha Matura; *Joe Turner's Come and Gone* and *The Piano Lesson* August Wilson; *Pecong* Steve Carter; *A Love Song for Ulster* Bill Morrison; *Three Hotels* Jon Robin Baitz; *Nuremberg* adapt. from transcripts of the trials by Richard Norton-Taylor; *Srebrenica* adapt. Nicolas Kent. New writing welcome from women and ethnic minorities (particularly Black and Irish). Looks for a strong narrative drive with popular appeal, not 'studio' plays. Can only return scripts if postage coupons or s.a.e. are enclosed with original submission.

Tron Theatre Company
63 Trongate, Glasgow G1 5HB
☎0141 552 3748   Fax 0141 552 6657
Artistic Director *Irina Brown*

FOUNDED 1981. Plays to a broad cross-section of Glasgow and beyond, including international tours (Toronto 1990 & 1996; New York 1991; Montreal 1992). Recent productions: *Mate in Three* Vittorio Franceschi; *The Trick is to Keep Breathing* Janice Galloway/Michael Boyd; *Endgame* Beckett; *Good* C. P. Taylor; *Macbeth*; *Lavochkin-5 (La Funf in der Luft)* Alexei Shipenko, trans. Iain Heggie/Irina Brown. Interested in ambitious plays by UK and international writers. No unsolicited mss.

The Unearthly Theatre Company
150 Havelock Street, Preston, Lancashire PR1 7NJ
☎01772 886003   Fax 01772 886003
E-mail: moship@msn.com
Contact *James Miley, Gary Nixon, Michael Moss*

FOUNDED 1997. A new company operating from the University of Central Lancashire. Produces three plays a year, both contemporary and period. OUTPUT includes a new adaption of *Dracula*, an original sequel to *Dracula*

entitled *The Legacy*, a contemporary play, *Delirium* for World Aids Day '97, and *A Chorus of Disapproval*. Unsolicited material is not welcome; initial approach should be made in writing, enclosing an s.a.e. to ensure a response.

Unicorn Arts Theatre for Children
Arts Theatre, 6–7 Great Newport Street, London WC2H 7JB
☎0171 379 3280   Fax 0171 836 5366
Artistic Director *Tony Graham*

FOUNDED 1947 as a touring company, and took up residence in the Arts Theatre in 1967. Plays mainly to children between the ages of 4–12. Previous productions: *Alfie*; *Cinderella* by Stuart Paterson; *The Lost Child* by Mike Kenny. Runs the **Unicorn Arts Theatre National Young Playwrights' Competition** annually (for children between the ages of 6 and 16).

Upstairs at the Gatehouse
See **Ovation Productions** under **Film, TV and Video Production Companies**

Charles Vance Productions
Hampden House, 2 Weymouth Street, London W1N 3FD
☎0171 636 4343   Fax 0171 636 2323
Contact *Charles Vance, Jill Streatfeild*

In the market for medium-scale touring productions and summer-season plays. Hardly any new work and no commissions but writing of promise stands a good chance of being passed on to someone who might be interested in it. Occasional try-outs for new work in the Sidmouth repertory theatre. Send s.a.e. for return of mss.

Warehouse Theatre, Croydon
Dingwall Road, Croydon CR0 2NF
☎0181 681 1257   Fax 0181 688 6699
Artistic Director *Ted Craig*

South London's new writing theatre, seating 100–120. Produces up to six new plays a year and co-produces with companies who share the commitment to new work. Continually building upon a tradition of discovering and nurturing new writers, with activities including a monthly writers' workshop and the annual **International Playwriting Festival**. Previous productions: *Sugar Hill Blues* Kevin Hood; *Playing Sinatra* Bernard Kops; *Eva and the Cabin Boys* Sheila Dewey; *The Astronomers Garden* Kevin Hood; *Coming Up, Fat Souls* James Martin Charlton; *Trouble Sleeping* Nick Ward; *Iona Rain, The Blue*

Garden Peter Moffat. Unsolicited scripts welcome but it is more advisable to submit plays through the theatre's International Playwriting Festival. The theatre is committed to productions at least nine months in advance.

Watermill Theatre
Bagnor, Newbury, Berkshire RG20 8AE
☎01635 45834   Fax 01635 523726
Contact *Jill Fraser*

The Watermill tries to put on one new piece of work each year. Previous productions: *Deadwood* Alex Jones; *Hindsight* Richard Everett; *The Great Big Radio Show* Philip Glassboron and David Rhind-Tutt; *The Ugly Duckling* (now renamed *Honk*) George Stiles & Anthony Drewe.

Watford Palace Theatre
See **Palace Theatre**

West Yorkshire Playhouse
Playhouse Square, Leeds, West Yorkshire LS2 7UP
☎0113 2137800   Fax 0113 2137250

Committed to programming new writing as part of its overall policy. Before sending an unsolicited script please phone or write. The Playhouse does readings and workshops on new plays with writers from all over Britain and also has strong links with local writers and Yorkshire Playwrights. The theatre has writers-in-residence. Premières include: *A Passionate Woman* Kay Mellor; *Fathers Day* Maureen Lawrence; *The Beatification of Area Bay* Wole Soyinka; *The Winter Guest* Sharman Macdonald; *You'll Have Had Your Hole* Irvine Welsh.

Whirligig Theatre
14 Belvedere Drive, Wimbledon, London SW19 7BY
☎0181 947 1732   Fax 0181 879 7648
Contact *David Wood*

One play a year in major theatre venues, usually a musical for primary school audiences and weekend family groups. Interested in scripts which exploit the theatrical nature of children's tastes. Previous productions: *The See-Saw Tree; The Selfish Shellfish; The Gingerbread Man; The Old Man of Lochnagar; The Ideal Gnome Expedition; Save the Human; Dreams of Anne Frank; Babe, the Sheep-Pig.*

Michael White Productions Ltd
See **MW Entertainments Ltd** under **Film, TV and Video Production Companies**

White Bear Theatre Club
138 Kennington Park Road, London SE11 4DJ
Administration: 3 Dante Road, Kennington, London SE11 4RB
☎0171 793 9193   Fax 0171 277 0526
Contact *Michael Kingsbury*
Administrator *Julia Parr*

FOUNDED 1988. OUTPUT primarily new work for audiences aged 20–35. Unsolicited scripts welcome, particularly new work with a keen eye on contemporary issues, though not agitprop. Holds readings throughout the year. A recent production, *Absolution* by Robert Sherwood was nominated by the Writers' Guild for 'Best Fringe Play'.

Windsor Theatre Royal
See **Theatre Royal Windsor**

Wolsey Theatre Company
Civic Drive, Ipswich, Suffolk IP1 2AS
☎01473 218911   Fax 01473 212946
Artistic Director *Andrew Manley*
Contact *Eileen Kidd*

FOUNDED 1979. Tries to do one new play a year in the main house and studio. New writing encouraged. Unsolicited mss welcome. Previous productions: *Jane Eyre; Servant of Two Masters; Kafka's Dick; Talking Heads; The Country Wife; Sleeping Beauty; The Diary of Anne Frank.*

York Theatre Royal
St Leonard's Place, York YO1 2HD
☎01904 658162   Fax 01904 611534
Artistic Director *Damian Cruden*

Not a new writing theatre in the main. Previous productions: *Into the Woods; Macbeth; Tom Jones* (musical version adapted by John Doyle). Send synopses only.

The Young Vic
66 The Cut, London SE1 8LZ
☎0171 633 0133   Fax 0171 928 1585
Artistic Director *Tim Supple*

FOUNDED 1970. The Young Vic produces adventurous and demanding work for an audience with a youthful spirit. The main house is one of London's most exciting spaces and seats up to 500. In addition, a smaller, entirely flexible space, The Young Vic Studio, seats 100 and is used for experiment, performance, rehearsals and installations. 'We are not able to produce many new scripts at the moment; nor are we able to develop or read unsolicited scripts with the care they deserve. However, we are always happy to receive work.'

Festivals

Aldeburgh Poetry Festival

Goldings, Goldings Lane, Leiston, Suffolk
IP16 4EB
☎01728 830631   Fax 01728 832029
Contact *Michael Laskey*

Now in its tenth year, an annual international festival of contemporary poetry held over one weekend each November in Aldeburgh and attracting large audiences. Regular features include a two-week residency leading up to the festival, poetry readings, children's event, workshops, public masterclass, lecture, performance spot and the festival prize for the year's best first collection (see entry under **Prizes**).

Arundel Festival

The Arundel Festival Society Ltd, The Mary Gate, Arundel, West Sussex BN18 9AT
☎01903 883690   Fax 01903 884243
Administrator *Ms Julie Young*

Annual ten-day summer festival (21–31 August in 1998). Events include poetry, prose readings and lectures, open-air Shakespeare in Arundel Castle, concerts with internationally known artists, jazz, visual arts and active fringe.

Bath Fringe Festival

The Bell, 103 Walcot Street, Bath
BA1 5BW
☎01225 480079   Fax 01225 427441
Chair *David Stevenson*

FOUNDED 1981. Complementing the international music festival, the Fringe presents theatre, poetry, jazz, blues, comedy, cabaret, storytelling, carnival and more in venues, parks and streets of Bath during late May and early June.

Belfast Festival at Queen's

Festival House, 25 College Gardens, Belfast
BT9 6BS
☎01232 667687   Fax 01232 663733
Executive Director *Robert Agnew*

FOUNDED 1964. Annual three-week festival held in November. Organised by Queen's University in association with the **Arts Council of Northern Ireland**, the festival covers a wide variety of events, including literature. Programme available in September.

Birmingham Readers and Writers Festival

Festival Office, Central Library, Chamberlain Square, Birmingham B3 3HQ
☎0121 303 4244   Fax 0121 233 9702
Festival Director *Helen Cross*
Deputy Director *Matthew Gidley*

FOUNDED 1983. Annual ten-day festival held in November in arts venues and libraries in Birmingham. Concerned with all aspects of contemporary reading and writing, with visiting authors, workshops, performances, cabaret, conferences and special programmes for young people.

Book Now!

Langholm Lodge, 146 Petersham Road, Richmond, Surrey TW10 6UX
☎0181 831 6138   Fax 0181 940 7568
Director *Nigel Cutting*

FOUNDED 1992. Annual festival which runs throughout the month of November, administered by the Arts Section of Richmond Council. Principal focus is on poetry and serious fiction, but events also cover biography, writing for theatre, children's writing. Programme includes readings, discussions, workshops, debates, exhibitions, schools events. Writers to appear at past festivals include A. S. Byatt, Penelope Lively, Benjamin Zephaniah, Sir Dirk Bogarde, Roger McGough, Rose Tremain, John Mortimer and Sean Hughes.

Bradford Festival

Provincial House, Centenary Square, Bradford, West Yorkshire BD1 1NH
☎01274 309199   Fax 01274 724213
Director *Mark Fielding*

FOUNDED 1987. June/July; two weeks. The 'largest, award-winning annual community arts festival in the country'. Includes the Mela ('bazaar' or 'fair' in Urdu) reflecting the city's cultural mix, and Cafe Bradford in Centenary Square with music, street theatre, food, drink and spectacle.

Brighton Festival

Festival Office, 21–22 Old Steine, Brighton, East Sussex BN1 1EL
☎01273 292950   Fax 01273 622453

Contact *General Manager*

FOUNDED 1967. For 24 days every May, Brighton hosts England's largest mixed arts festival. Music, dance, theatre, film, opera, literature, comedy and exhibitions. Literary enquiries will be passed to the literature officer. Deadline October for following May.

Bury St Edmunds Festival
Borough Offices, Angel Hill, Bury St Edmunds, Suffolk IP33 1XB
☎01284 763233   Fax 01284 757070
Contact *Kevin Appleby, Festival Manager*

FOUNDED 1986. ANNUAL 17-day spring festival in various venues throughout this historic East Anglian town and outlying areas. Programme features classical music concerts and recitals, lunchtime jazz, theatre, comedy, walks, talks and exhibitions. 1998 highlights included The Hallé Orchestra, The European Chamber Orchestra, Jacques Loussier Trio and Larry Adler.

Buxton Festival
1 Crescent View, Hall Bank, Buxton, Derbyshire SK17 6EN
☎01298 70395   Fax 01298 72289
Contact *General Manager*

FOUNDED 1979. Annual two-and-a-half-week festival held in July. Rarely performed operas are staged in Buxton Opera House and the programme is complemented by a wide variety of other musical events, including recitals, Young Artists series, festival masses, chamber music and cabarets. Also, the Buxton Jazz Festival.

Canterbury Festival
Christ Church Gate, The Precincts, Canterbury, Kent CT1 2EE
☎01227 452853   Fax 01227 781830
Festival Director *Mark Deller*

FOUNDED 1984. Annual two-week festival held in October. A mixed programme of events including talks by visiting authors, readings and storytelling, walks, concerts in the cathedral, jazz, master classes, drama, visual arts, opera, film, cabaret and dance.

The Cheltenham Festival of Literature
Town Hall, Imperial Square, Cheltenham, Gloucestershire GL50 1QA
☎01242 521621   Fax 01242 256457
Festival Organiser *Sarah Smyth*

FOUNDED 1949. Annual festival held in October. The first purely literary festival of its

kind, this festival has over the past decade developed from an essentially local event into the largest and most popular in Europe. A wide range of events including talks and lectures, poetry readings, novelists in conversation, exhibitions, discussions and a large bookshop.

Chester Literature Festival
8 Abbey Square, Chester CH1 2HU
☎01244 319985   Fax 01244 341200
Chairman *John Elsley*

FOUNDED 1989. Annual festival during October, organised by local bookshops, writers' groups and Chester Arts Association. Major events sponsored by publishers. Authors taking part in the 1997 festival included Michael Holroyd, Dame Cleo Laine, Sarah Harrison, Prof. Norman Davies, Jonathan Gash, Dickie Bird, Robert Robinson, Robert Carrier, Jancis Robinson, Roger McGough.

Contact Young Playwrights' Festival
Oxford Road, Manchester M15 6JA
☎0161 274 3434
Contact *Sally Abbott (Head of Community and Education), Benedict Ayrton (Associate Director, Community and Education)*

FOUNDED 1986 and open to young people aged between 11 and 25 living in the North-west of England. The next festival will be held in June 1999 at the Contact Theatre with a deadline for scripts in February. All of the finalists work closely with professional writers and directors who help them to develop their work. All scripts submitted to the festival receive a critical analysis.

Dartington Literary Festival
See **Ways With Words**

The Festival of Dover
Dover District Council, White Cliffs Business Park, Dover, Kent CT16 3PD
☎01304 872058   Fax 01304 872062
Festival Organiser *Lisa Webb*

This annual community arts festival, now in its seventh year, presented a programme in 1998 of arts activities within the theme 'Coastal Landscapes'. In association with the White Cliffs Countryside Project, the festival featured a programme aimed at increasing awareness of our environment, including street theatre, concerts, open air spectaculars, walks, talks, workshops and exhibitions.

Dublin International Writers' Festival

An Chomhairle Ealaíon (The Arts Council), 70 Merrion Square, Dublin 2

☎00 353 1 6180200   Fax 00 353 1 6761302

Festival Director *Sinead MacAodha*

Biennial festival held in September. Features conference sessions, public interviews, debates, readings and exhibitions, with some of the world's leading authors in attendance.

Durham Literary Festival

Durham City Arts, Byland Lodge, Hawthorn Terrace, Durham City DH1 4TD

☎0191 386 6111 ext. 338 Fax 0191 386 0625

Contact *The Director*

FOUNDED 1989. Annual 2–3-week event, end of May–beginning of June, held at various locations in the city. Workshops, plus performances, cabaret, and other events. Although no festival was held in 1998, it is anticipated that it will take place again in 1999.

Edinburgh Book Festival

Scottish Book Centre, 137 Dundee Street, Edinburgh EH11 1BG

☎0131 228 5444   Fax 0131 228 4333

Director *Faith Liddell*

FOUNDED 1983. Europe's largest and liveliest public book event, now taking place on an annual basis. Held during the first fortnight of the Edinburgh International Festival, it presents an extensive programme for both adults and children including discussions, reading, lectures, demonstrations and workshops.

Exeter Festival

Festival Office, Civic Centre, Exeter, Devon EX1 1JN

☎01392 265200   Fax 01392 265366

Festival Organiser *Lesley Maynard*

FOUNDED 1980. Annual two-week festival with a variety of events including concerts, theatre, dance and exhibitions.

Greenwich and Docklands International Festival

6 College Approach, London SE10 9HY

☎0181 305 1818   Fax 0181 305 1188

Director *Bradley Hemmings*

FOUNDED 1970. Annual summer festival. Features a wide variety of events, including world music, theatre, dance, classical music, jazz, comedy, art, literature and free open-air events.

Guildford Book Festival

Old Coach House, Cuilfail, Lewes, East Sussex BN7 2BE

☎01273 478943   Fax 01273 478943

Book Festival Organiser *Joan König*

FOUNDED 1989. A ten-day celebration of books and writing held annually, during the autumn half-term, throughout the town. The programme includes literary lunches, poetry readings, a writer-in-residence, children's events, the Annual University Poetry Lecture; writing workshops and competitions, and bookshop events.

Haringey Literature Festival

Haringey Arts Council, Selby Centre, Selby Road, Tottenham, London N17 8JL

☎0181 801 9520   Fax 0181 885 2767

Festival Organiser *Dana Captainino*

FOUNDED 1995. Annual festival which runs from March to October. The programme is a mixture of poetry and literature, in the form of readings, discussions, workshops and masterclasses. Writers who have appeared at past festivals include: Fay Weldon, Louis de Bernières, Nick Hornby, Blake Morrison, Bernice Rubens, James Kelman, Jean Binta Breeze and Matthew Sweeney.

Harrogate International Festival

The Festival Office, 1 Victoria Avenue, Harrogate, North Yorkshire HG1 1EQ

☎01423 562303   Fax 01423 521264

Festival Director *William Culver Dodds*
Administrator *Fiona Goh*

FOUNDED 1966. Annual two-week festival at the end of July and beginning of August. Events include international symphony orchestras, chamber concerts, ballet, celebrity recitals, contemporary dance, opera, drama, jazz, comedy plus an international street theatre festival.

The Hay Festival

See **The Sunday Times Hay Festival**

Huddersfield Poetry Festival

c/o The Word Hoard, 46/47 Byram Arcade, Westgate, Huddersfield, West Yorkshire HD1 1ND

☎01484 452070   Fax 01484 455049

Contact *Dianne Darby*

Twice-yearly event consisting of a spring season in March/April of around four–six events combined with a participatory multi-arts collaborative project; and four days of writing workshops and performances in October exploring particular themes. Also occasional one-off events. Though very interested in local writers, the festival has a cosmopolitan outlook and features related performing arts including music, theatre and the visual arts.

Hull Literature Festival
City Arts, Central Library, Albion Street, Kingston upon Hull HU1 3TF
☎01759 883106   Fax 01759 883080
Director *David Porter*
FOUNDED 1992. Annual festival running in November.

Ilkley Literature Festival
Festival Office, Manor House Museum, Ilkley, West Yorkshire LS29 9DT
☎01943 601210
Director *David Porter*
FOUNDED 1973. Three festivals a year of 4–5 days' duration. Previous guests have included Tony Harrison, Sarah Dunant, Irina Ratushinskaya, Colin Thubron. Also presents children's events, storytellers, theatre and music, and creative writing workshops. Runs an open poetry competition. Telephone to join free mailing list.

International Playwriting Festival
Warehouse Theatre, Dingwall Road, Croydon CR0 2NF
☎0181 681 1257   Fax 0181 688 6699
FOUNDED 1985. Annual competition for full-length unperformed plays, judged by a panel of theatre professionals. Finalists given rehearsed readings during the festival week in November. Entries welcome from all parts of the world. For entry forms and details send an s.a.e. to the Festival Administrator. Deadline for entries usually by the first week of July. Previous winners produced at the theatre include: Kevin Hood *Beached*; Ellen Fox *Conversations with George Sandburgh After a Solo Flight Across the Atlantic*; Guy Jenkin *Fighting for the Dunghill*; James Martin Charlton *Fat Souls*; Peter Moffat *Iona Rain*; Dino Mahoney *YoYo*; Simon Smith *Fat Janet is Dead*.

Kent Literature Festival
The Metropole Arts Centre, The Leas, Folkestone, Kent CT20 2LS
☎01303 255070
Acting Festival Director *Ann Fearey*
FOUNDED 1980. Annual week-long festival held at the end of September which aims to bring the best in modern writing to a large audience. Visiting authors and dramatic presentations are a regular feature along with creative writing workshops, seminars, discussions and children's/family events. Also runs the **Kent Short Story Competition**.

King's Lynn, The Fiction Festival
19 Tuesday Market Place, King's Lynn, Norfolk PE30 1JW
☎01553 691661 (office hours) or 761919
Fax 01553 691779
Contact *Anthony Ellis*
FOUNDED 1989. Annual weekend festival held in March. Over the weekend there are readings and discussions, attended by guest writers of which there are usually eight. Previous guests have included Beryl Bainbridge, Malcolm Bradbury, Marina Warner, William Golding, Hilary Mantel, Elizabeth Jane Howard.

King's Lynn, The Poetry Festival
19 Tuesday Market Place, King's Lynn, Norfolk PE30 1JW
☎01553 691661 (office hours) or 761919
Fax 01553 691779
Contact *Anthony Ellis*
FOUNDED 1985. Annual weekend festival held at the end of September, with guest poets (usually eight). Previous guests have included Carol Ann Duffy, Paul Durcan, Gavin Ewart, Peter Porter, Stephen Spender. Events include readings and discussion panels.

Lancaster LitFest
Sun Street Studios, 23–29 Sun Street, Lancaster LA1 1ET
☎01524 62166   Fax 01524 841216
FOUNDED 1978. Regional Literature Development Agency, organising workshops, readings, residencies, publications. Year-round programme of literature-based events and annual festival in October featuring a wide range of writers from the UK and overseas. Organises annual poetry competition with winners receiving cash prizes and anthology publication.

City of London Festival
230 Bishopsgate, London EC2M 4QD
☎0171 377 0540   Fax 0171 377 1972
Director *Michael MacLeod*
FOUNDED 1962. Annual three-week festival held in June and July (1999: 22 June–15 July). Features over forty classical and popular music events alongside poetry and prose readings,

street theatre and open-air extravaganzas, in some of the most outstanding performance spaces in the world.

London New Play Festival

Diorama Arts Centre, 34 Osnabrook Street, London NW1 3ND
☎0171 209 2326

Artistic Director *Phil Setren*
Workshop Director *Christopher Preston*
Literary Manager *David Prescott*

FOUNDED 1989. Open to full-length and one-act plays which are assessed for originality, form, etc by a reading committee. Deadline for scripts is mid-January; details can be obtained from **The Writers' Guild**. In 1997, three plays and a number of readings were performed at the Riverside Studios, and a West End Platform Season was held at the Apollo Theatre, Shaftesbury Avenue. Offers writers workshops and discussions, and runs The Writers Group.

Ludlow Festival

Castle Square, Ludlow, Shropshire SY8 1AY
☎01584 875070   Fax 01584 877673

Contact *Festival Administrator*

FOUNDED 1959. Annual two-week festival held in the last week of June and first week of July with an open-air Shakespeare production held at Ludlow Castle and a varied programme of events including recitals, opera, dance, popular and classical concerts, literary and historical lectures.

Manchester Festival of Writing

Manchester Central Library, St Peter's Square, Manchester M2 5PD
☎0161 234 1973

Contact *Tang Lin*

FOUNDED 1990. An annual event organised by Manchester Libraries and Commonword community publishers. It consists of a programme of practical writing workshops on specific themes/genres run by well-known writers. Attendance at all workshops is free to Manchester residents.

National Student Drama Festival

See **University College, Scarborough** under **Writers' Courses**

Norfolk and Norwich Festival

16 Princes Street, Norwich, Norfolk NR3 1AE
☎01603 614921   Fax 01603 632303
E-mail: info@nnfest.easter-arts.co.uk

Festival Director *Marcus Davey*

FOUNDED 1772, this performing arts festival is the second oldest in the UK. Held annually in October (7th–18th in 1998), the festival includes talks by writers along with poetry and story-telling events.

North East Lincolnshire Literature Festival

Arts Development, North East Lincolnshire Council, Knoll Street, Cleethorpes, Lincolnshire DN35 8LN
☎01472 323000   Fax 01472 323005

Festival Programmer *Lynne Conlan*

FOUNDED 1997. Annual themed festival held in February/March. Reflecting the heritage of the area, the festival aims to make literature accessible to all ages and abilities through a varied and unusual programme. In 1998, the festival celebrated the 150th anniversary of the first passenger trains to Grimsby and Cleethorpes. Guests included Eric Chappell, Kathleen Rowntree, Linda McDougall and Max Ritchie.

Royal Court Young Writers' Festival

Royal Court Young People's Theatre, 309 Portobello Road, London W10 5TD
☎0181 960 4641   Fax 0181 960 1434

Contact *Carl Miller (Artistic Director)*

Open to young people up to the age of 25. The festival focuses on the process of playwriting and is open to young writers all over the country. Intensive work on the final draft of plays precedes production at the Royal Court Theatre Upstairs, before going on tour in the participating areas.

Salisbury Festival

Festival Office, 75 New Street, Salisbury, Wiltshire SP1 2PH
☎01722 323883   Fax 01722 410552

Director *Helen Marriage*

FOUNDED 1972. Annual festival held at the end of May/beginning of June. The 1998 festival included literary events with participants E. J. Howard, Claire Tomalin, John Mortimer, Jonathan Dimbleby and Lynne Reid Banks.

Scottish Young Playwrights Festival

Scottish Youth Theatre, Old Athenaeum Theatre, 179 Buchanan Street, Glasgow G1 2JZ
☎0141 332 5127   Fax 0141 333 1021

Artistic Director *Mary McCluskey*

The Scottish Young Playwrights project operates throughout Scotland. In every region an experienced theatre practitioner runs regular young writers' workshops aimed at developing the best possible scripts from initial ideas. A representative selection of scripts is then selected to form a showcase. The festival is mounted at the Old Athenaeum Theatre in December, in conjunction with the Royal Scottish Academy of Music and Drama. Scripts will be workshopped, revised and developed culminating in an evening presentation. Scripts are welcome throughout the year from young people aged 15–25 who are native Scots and/or resident in Scotland; synopses of unfinished scripts also considered. No restriction on style, content or intended media, but work must be original and unperformed. Further details from address above.

Stratford-upon-Avon Poetry Festival

The Shakespeare Centre, Henley Street, Stratford-upon-Avon, Warwickshire CV37 6QW
☎01789 204016   Fax 01789 296083
Festival Director *Roger Pringle*

FOUNDED 1953. Annual festival held on Sunday evenings during July and August. Readings by poets and professional actors.

The Sunday Times Hay Festival

Festival Office, Hay-on-Wye HR3 5BX
☎01497 821217   Fax 01497 821066
Festival Director *Peter Florence*

FOUNDED 1988. Annual May festival sponsored by *The Sunday Times*. Guests have included Salman Rushdie, Toni Morrison, Stephen Fry, Joseph Heller, Carlos Fuentes, Maya Angelou, Amos Oz, Arthur Miller.

Warwick & Leamington Festival

Warwick Arts Society, Northgate, Warwick CV34 4JL
☎01926 410747   Fax 01926 407606
Festival Director *Richard Phillips*

FOUNDED 1980. Annual festival lasting 12 days

in the first half of July. Basically a chamber and early music festival, with some open-air, large-scale concerts in Warwick Castle, the Festival also promotes plays by Shakespeare in historical settings. Large-scale education programme. Interested in increasing its literary content, both in performances and workshops.

Ways with Words

Droridge Farm, Dartington, Totnes, Devon TQ9 6JQ
☎01803 867311   Fax 01803 863688
Festival Director *Kay Dunbar*

Ways with Words runs a major literature festival at Dartington Hall in south Devon in July each year. Features over 100 writers giving lectures, readings, interviews, discussions, performances, master classes and workshops.

Ways with Words also runs literary weekends in Southwold (Suffolk), Bath, York and Bury St Edmunds, plus writing, reading and painting courses in the UK and abroad.

Wellington Literary Festival

Civic Offices, Tan Bank, Wellington, Telford, Shropshire TF1 1LX
☎01952 222935   Fax 01952 222936
Contact *Derrick Drew*

FOUNDED 1997. Annual festival held throughout October. Events include story telling, writers' forum, 'Pints and Poetry', children's poetry competition.

Writearound

Cleveland Arts, Gurney House, Gurney Street, Middlesbrough, Cleveland TS1 1JL
☎01642 262424
Contact *Mark Robinson*
E-mail: Cleveland.Arts@onyxnet.co.uk

FOUNDED 1989. Annual festival with a commitment to local writers. Held during October, featuring workshops and readings, plus guest writers and opportunities for new writers. Publishes anthologies of poetry by local children. Contact address above for further information. Programmes available in August.

Word for Word –
the Art of Translation

*The Reader** is a remarkable book on two counts. To come across a contemporary novel that stretches the imagination beyond literary London is unusual enough. But even more improbable, *The Reader* is a translation from German, a work of great power that owes almost as much to the creative skills of the translator as to the inspiration of the author Bernhard Schlink. Foreign authors are rarely served so well.

The exceptions prove the rule. Peter Høeg's *Miss Smilla's Feeling for Snow* has sold more than 700,000 copies and Jean-Dominique Bauby's *The Diving-Bell and the Butterfly* has exceeded 80,000 copies. But there are many other fine books that have either not made it in English at all or have been so sloppily translated as to rob them of any chance of cracking the English language market.

Little England culture is much to blame. Publishers cannot bring themselves to believe that foreign books, i.e. those written in another language, have anything worthwhile to say. Works in translation account for about three per cent of titles published in the United Kingdom; in France or Germany the figure rises to 30 and 40 per cent.

Then again, in at least one respect, Britain is wide open to foreign culture; it just happens that the US which provides many, if not most, of our trade books shares with us, give or take a few spellings, a common language. American dominance robs us of the incentive to extend our cultural reach.

Let it be said that translators themselves do not always help. There is a long established assumption in publishing that if you are at all familiar with a foreign language you should be able to turn in an acceptable English language version of a foreign text. But this simply is not true. It cannot be said too often; the ideal translator is also a gifted writer. He needs to have a feeling and fascination for language and the talent to convey the essence of the original work, echoing its style and tone. A word for word literal interpretation is bound to fail. As well as an intimate knowledge of a particular language, a good translation demands familiarity with other work by the same author not to mention an understanding and experience of his culture.

Some translators start with the advantage of being raised in a bilingual family, others acquire linguistic skills by working overseas. A university education in modern languages can be helpful but is not in itself a badge of competence, let alone proof of style and inspiration.

Because the translator is a creative artist in his own right, copyright law recognises the 'original' nature of his work with copyright protection that is distinct

---

The Reader, Bernhard Schlink – Phoenix Paperbacks

from the copyright of the author. This opens up the possibility of a recurring income over many years, even when the duration of the author's copyright is exhausted. For example, a writer knowledgeable in Russian might produce a marvellous new Chekhov translation thus bringing a play back into copyright for the benefit of the translator.

The downside to any such enterprise is that there can be no exclusive right to the translation of a particular work. Where one translator has trod profitably, another may soon follow in his footsteps. Working from the same source text, the result is likely to be two different but equally valid renditions. Nonetheless, for a popular book or play, the possibilities for argument between translators as to who owns what are legion. In the theatre, such disputes are further complicated by the tendency of some translators to rely rather too heavily on existing English language versions of a play to achieve their own interpretation. It has been known for a 'translator' to possess only the haziest notion of the language he was supposed to be working from. His defence was that he had a good dictionary.

Ideas for translating books or plays invariably start with a publisher or producer. It follows that the best chance of a commission comes from sending out sample material. But it is open to anyone to offer proposals. A writer who is bilingual in, say, French or German should watch the reviews and publishing lists for likely projects. The trick here is to secure an understanding with a prospective partner before trying to negotiate a commission. This is at least some protection against a publisher who might thank you profusely for the idea before sending it off to one of his regular panel of translators.

Knowledge of a rare language can help though it is no longer enough to be conversant with one of the minority European languages like Dutch or Danish. The use of English in these countries is now so extensive that writers are inclined to do their own translations or compose in English as the first language. Also, much depends on fashion. A few years ago, French dramatists seemed to lose their appeal. Now, the trend is moving back in their favour with a demand for translation of new work and new translations of the classics.

Payment for translation can be by royalty or by fee. If it is in the form of a lump sum, it should not be for the translation but for a specified use of the translator's work, for example, for the right to print 5000 copies for sale in the UK. Such an arrangement makes fair allowance for additional fees to be paid if further copies are sold or if the licence is extended to include America. For the translation of a book, the Model Contract drawn up by the Translators Association recommends that there should be an advance payment on account of royalties and a share of the proceeds from the sale of subsidiary rights such as serialisation. In the case of a play, the translator should receive a percentage of the gross box office receipts. The translator should be able to obtain additional payment if asked to edit a literary work as well as translate it; and there should be an additional fee for the preparation of an index for the translated edition. When translations are borrowed from public libraries, the translator receives a 30 per cent share of the full Public Lending Right payment.

Usually the rights owner, either author or publisher, accepts lower royalties on the translated edition, say, a 7½ per cent royalty on sales of a translated book compared with 10 per cent on sales in its original language. On a theatre production the original author might receive 6 per cent instead of 10 per cent. The author may also forego a share of secondary rights, e.g. of the proceeds from the sale of American rights. This means that some or all of the payment received by the translator is money that would otherwise have been paid to the original author. To that extent, the author is the person who is paying the translator.

Sometimes the foreign author of a work is so keen to see it translated that he will offer to pay the translation costs directly. In this case, a written contract between author and translator should specify the respective rights and set out how any proceeds from publication or production are to be divided.

Bursaries and prizes

A number of residential bursaries are offered by The British Centre for Literary Translation at the Department of Modern Languages and European History, The University of East Anglia, Norwich NR4 1TJ. For up-to-date information about bursaries abroad, contact the Cultural Attaché of the relevant embassy or bodies such as the French Institute, the Goethe Institut and the Italian Institute. The Arts Council offers bursaries to theatre translators under its Theatre Translation Schemes. The Translators Association administers several prizes for already published translations and the Arts Council sometimes contributes towards the cost of producing translations.

The Translators Association

The Translators Association is a subsidiary group within the Society of Authors. Published translators can apply for full membership. Translators in the making may apply for Associate Membership either when they have received an offer for a full-length translation or if they have had occasional translations of shorter material, e.g. articles, short stories and poems, published or performed commercially.

The Association's Model Contract, with explanatory notes, is available free to members; and the Association also issues Guidelines for translators of dramatic works. The Association's journal, *In Other Words*, contains a wide variety of articles, reviews and information.

The Translators Association, 84 Drayton Gardens, London SW10 9SB
(☎0171 373 6642)

European Publishers

Austria

Springer-Verlag KG
Sachsenplatz 4–6, PO Box 89, 1200 Vienna
☎00 43 1 3302415   Fax 00 43 1 3302426
FOUNDED 1924. *Publishes* anthropology, architecture, art, business, chemistry, computer science, economics, education, interior design, environmental studies, engineering, law, maths, dentistry, medicine, nursing, philosophy, physics, psychology, technology and general science.

Verlag Carl Ueberreuter
Alserstrasse 24, Postfach 306, A-1091 Vienna
☎00 43 1 404440   Fax 00 43 1 404445
FOUNDED 1548. *Publishes* fiction and general non-fiction: art, government, history, economics, political science, general science, science fiction, fantasy, music and dance.

Paul Zsolnay Verlag GmbH
Prinz-Eugenstrasse 30, Postfach 142, A-1041 Vienna
☎00 43 1 50576610   Fax 00 43 1 50576610
FOUNDED 1923. *Publishes* biography, fiction, general non-fiction, history, poetry.

Belgium

Brepols NV
Steenweg op Tielen 68, 2300 Turnhout
☎00 32 14 402500   Fax 00 32 14 428919
FOUNDED 1796. *Publishes* art, architecture, interior design, history, religion.

Facet NV
Willem Linnigstr 13, 2060 Antwerp
☎00 32 3 2274028   Fax 00 32 3 2273792
FOUNDED 1976. *Publishes* children's books.

Uitgeverij Lannoo NV
Kasteelstr 97, B-8700 Tielt
☎00 32 51 424211   Fax 00 32 51 401152
FOUNDED 1909. *Publishes* general non-fiction, art, biography, economics, gardening, health, history, management, nutrition, photography, poetry, government, political science, religion, travel.

Standaard Uitgeverij
Belgiëlei 147a, 2018 Antwerp
☎00 32 3 2395900   Fax 00 32 3 2308550
FOUNDED 1919. *Publishes* education, fiction, humour.

Denmark

Forlaget Apostrof ApS
Berggreensgade 24, Postboks 2580, DK-2100 Copenhagen
☎00 45 31 208420   Fax 00 45 31 208453
FOUNDED 1980. *Publishes* essays, fiction, humour, literature, literary criticism, general non-fiction, psychology, psychiatry.

Aschehoug Fakta
7 Vognmagergade, PO Box 2179, DK-1017 Copenhagen 0
☎00 45 33 919222   Fax 00 45 33 918218
FOUNDED 1977. *Publishes* cookery, health, how-to, maritime and nutrition.

Borgens Forlag A/S
Valbygardsvej 33, DK-2500 Valby
☎00 45 36 462100   Fax 00 45 36 441488
FOUNDED 1948. *Publishes* fiction, literature, literary criticism, science fiction, general non-fiction, art, crafts, education, environmental studies, essays, games, gay and lesbian, hobbies, health, nutrition, music, dance, philosophy, poetry, psychology, psychiatry, religion, social sciences, sociology.

Forum Publishers
Snaregade 4, DK-1205 Copenhagen K
☎00 45 33 147714   Fax 00 45 33 147791
FOUNDED 1940. *Publishes* fiction and mysteries.

GEC Gads Forlagsaktieselskab
Vimmelskaftet 32, DK-1161 Copenhagen K
☎00 45 33 150558   Fax 00 45 33 110800
FOUNDED 1855. *Publishes* general non-fiction, biological sciences, cookery, crafts, games, economics, education, English as a second language, environmental studies, gardening, history, law, mathematics, natural history, physics, plants, travel.

Gyldendalske Boghandel-Nordisk Forlag A/S
Klareboderne 3, DK-1001 Copenhagen K
☎00 45 33 110775   Fax 00 45 33 110323
FOUNDED 1770. *Publishes* fiction, art, biography, dance, dentistry, education, history, how-to, medicine, music, poetry, nursing, philosophy, psychology, psychiatry, general and social sciences, sociology.

Hekla Forlag
Valbygaardsvej 33, DK-2500 Valby
☎00 45 36 462100   Fax 00 45 36 441488
FOUNDED 1979. *Publishes* general fiction and non-fiction.

Høst & Søns Publishers Ltd
Købmagergade 62, Box 2212, DK-1018 Copenhagen
☎00 45 33 153031   Fax 00 45 33 155155
FOUNDED 1836. *Publishes* arts, crafts, environmental studies, games, hobbies, language, linguistics, regional interests, travel.

Egmont Lademann A/S
Gerdasgade 37, 2500 Valby
☎00 45 36 56600   Fax 00 45 36 44162
FOUNDED 1954. *Publishes* general non-fiction.

Lindhardt og Ringhof
Frederiksborggade 1, 2nd,, DK-1360 Copenhagen K
☎00 45 33 695000   Fax 00 45 33 695001
FOUNDED 1971. *Publishes* fiction and general non-fiction.

Munksgaard
Nørre Søgade 35, DK-1016 Copenhagen
☎00 45 33 127030   Fax 00 45 33 129387
FOUNDED 1917. *Publishes* fiction, general non-fiction, education, dentistry, medicine, nursing, psychology, psychiatry, general science, social sciences, sociology.

Nyt Nordisk Forlag Arnold Busck A/S
Købmagergade 49, DK-1150 Copenhagen K
☎00 45 33 111103   Fax 00 45 33 934490
FOUNDED 1896. *Publishes* fiction, art, biography, dance, dentistry, history, how-to, music, philosophy, religion, medicine, nursing, psychology, psychiatry, general and social sciences, sociology.

Politikens Forlag A/S
Vestergade 26, DK-1456 Copenhagen K
☎00 45 33 470707   Fax 00 45 33 470708
FOUNDED 1946. *Publishes* general non-fiction, art, crafts, dance, history, games, hobbies, music, natural history, sport, travel.

Samlerens Forlag A/S
Snaregade 4, DK-1205 Copenhagen K
☎00 45 33 131023   Fax 00 45 33 144314
FOUNDED 1942. *Publishes* essays, fiction, government, history, literature, literary criticism, political science.

Det Schønbergske Forlag A/S
Landemaerket 5, DK-1119 Copenhagen K
☎00 45 33 113066   Fax 00 45 33 330045
FOUNDED 1857. *Publishes* art, biography, fiction, history, humour, philosophy, poetry, psychology, psychiatry, travel

Spektrum Forlagsaktieselskab
4 Snaregade, DK-1205 Copenhagen K
☎00 45 33 147714   Fax 00 45 33 147791
FOUNDED 1990. *Publishes* general non-fiction.

Tiderne Skifter Forlag A/S
51 Pilestrede, 1001 DK-Copenhagen K
☎00 45 33 325772   Fax 00 45 33 144205
FOUNDED 1979. *Publishes* fiction, literature and literary criticism, essays, ethnology, photography, behavioural sciences.

Wangels Forlag AS
Gerdasgade 37, 2500 Valby
☎00 45 36 441120   Fax 00 45 36 441162
FOUNDED 1946. *Publishes* fiction.

Finland

Gummerus Publishers
Erottajankatu 5C, PO Box 2,
SF-00130 Helsinki
☎00 358 9 584301   Fax 00 358 9 58430200
FOUNDED 1872. *Publishes* fiction and general non-fiction.

Karisto Oy
Paroistentie 2, PO Box 102,
SF-13101 Hämeenlinna
☎00 358 3 6161551   Fax 00 358 3 6161565
FOUNDED 1900. *Publishes* fiction and general non-fiction.

Kirjayhtymä Oy
Urho Kekkosen Katu 4–6E,
SF-00100 Helsinki
☎00 358 9 6937641
Fax 00 358 9 69376366
FOUNDED 1958. *Publishes* fiction and general
non-fiction.

Otava Kustannusosakeyhtiö
Uudenmaankatu 8–12, PO Box 134,
00121 Helsinki
☎00 358 9 19961   Fax 00 358 9 643136
FOUNDED 1890. *Publishes* fiction, general non-
fiction, art, biography, education, history, how-
to.

Werner Söderström Osakeyhtiö (WSOY)
Bulevardi 12, PO Box 222, 00121 Helsinki
☎00 358 9 61681   Fax 00 358 9 6168405
FOUNDED 1878. *Publishes* fiction, general non-
fiction, education.

Tammi Publishers
Urho Kekkosen katu 4–6 E, PO Box 410,
00101 Helsinki
☎00 358 9 6937621   Fax 00 358 9 69376266
FOUNDED 1943. *Publishes* fiction, general non-
fiction.

France

Editions Arthaud SA
26 rue Racine, F–75278 Paris Codex 06
☎00 33 1 4051 3100   Fax 00 33 1 4329 2148
FOUNDED 1890. Imprint of **Flammarion SA**.
Publishes art, history, literature, literary criticism, esays, sport, travel.

Editions Belfond
12 avenue d'Italie, 75013 Paris
☎00 33 1 4416 0500   Fax 00 33 1 4416 0506
FOUNDED 1963. *Publishes* fiction, literature, literary criticism, essays, mysteries, romance,
poetry, general non-fiction, art, biography,
dance, health, history, how-to, music, nutrition.

Editions Bordas
17 rue Rémy-Dumoncel BP50, 75661 Paris
Cedex 14
☎00 33 1 4279 6200   Fax 00 33 1 4322 8518
FOUNDED 1946. *Publishes* education and general non-fiction.

Editions Calmann-Lévy SA
3 rue Auber, 75009 Paris
☎00 33 1 4742 3833   Fax 00 33 1 4742 7781
FOUNDED 1836. *Publishes* fiction, science fiction, fantasy, biography, history, humour, philosophy, psychology, psychiatry, social sciences, sociology, sport, economics.

Editions Denoël Sàrl
9 rue du Cherche-Midi, 75006 Paris
☎00 33 1 4439 7373   Fax 00 33 1 4439 7390
FOUNDED 1932. *Publishes* art, economics, fiction, science fiction, fantasy, government,
history, philosophy, general science, political
science, psychology, psychiatry, sport.

Librairie Arthème Fayard
75 rue des Saints-Pères, F-75006 Paris
☎00 33 1 4544 3845   Fax 00 33 1 4222 4017
FOUNDED 1854. *Publishes* biography, fiction,
history, dance, music, philosophy, religion,
social sciences, sociology, general science,
technology.

Flammarion SA
26 rue Racine, F–75278 Paris Cedex 06
☎00 33 1 4051 3100   Fax 00 33 1 4329 2148
FOUNDED 1875. *Publishes* general fiction and
non-fiction, art, architecture, gardening,
plants, interior design, literature, literary criticism, essays, medicine, nursing, dentistry, wine
and spirits.

Editions Gallimard
5 rue Sébastien-Bottin, 75007 Paris Cedex 07
☎00 33 1 4954 4200   Fax 00 33 1 4544 9919
FOUNDED 1911. *Publishes* fiction, poetry, art,
biography, dance, history, music, philosophy.

Société des Editions Grasset et Fasquelle
61 rue des Saints-Pères, 75006 Paris
☎00 33 1 4439 2200   Fax 00 33 1 4222 6418
FOUNDED 1907. *Publishes* fiction and general
non-fiction, essays, literature, literary criticism,
philosophy.

Hachette Groupe Livre
83 ave Marceau, 75116 Paris
☎00 33 1 4069 1600   Fax 00 33 1 4220 3993
FOUNDED 1826. *Publishes* fiction and general
non-fiction, architecture and interior design, art,
economics, education, general engineering,
government, history, language and linguistics,
political science, philosophy, general science,
self-help, social sciences, sociology, sport, travel.

Editions Robert Laffont
24 ave Marceau, 75381 Paris Cedex 08
☎00 33 1 5367 1400   Fax 00 33 1 5367 1490
FOUNDED 1941. *Publishes* fiction and non-fiction.

Librairie Larousse
17 rue de Montparnasse, 75298 Paris Cedex 06
☎00 33 1 4439 4400   Fax 00 33 1 4439 4343
FOUNDED 1852. *Publishes* general and social sciences, sociology, language, linguistics, technology.

Editions Jean-Claude Lattès
17 rue Jacob, F–75006 Paris
☎00 33 1 4441 7400   Fax 00 33 1 4325 3047
FOUNDED 1968. *Publishes* fiction and general non-fiction, biography, religion.

Les Editions Magnard Sàrl
20 rue Berbier-du-Mets, 75013 Paris
☎00 33 1 4408 8585   Fax 00 33 1 4408 4979
FOUNDED 1933. *Publishes* education.

Michelin et Cie (Services de Tourisme)
46 ave de Breteuil, F–75324 Paris Cedex 07
☎00 33 1 4566 1234   Fax 00 33 1 4566 1163
FOUNDED 1900. *Publishes* travel.

Les Editions de Minuit SA
7 rue Bernard-Palissy, 75006 Paris
☎00 33 1 4439 3920   Fax 00 33 1 4544 8236
FOUNDED 1942. *Publishes* fiction, essays, literature, literary criticism, philosophy, social science, sociology.

Fernand Nathan
9 rue Méchain, 75014 Paris
☎00 33 1 4587 5000   Fax 00 33 1 4331 2169
FOUNDED 1881. *Publishes* education, history, philosophy, psychology, psychiatry, general and social sciences, sociology.

Presses de la Cité
12 ave d'Italie, 75627 Paris
☎00 33 1 4416 0500   Fax 00 33 1 4416 0505
FOUNDED 1947. *Publishes* literature, literary criticism, essays, science fiction, fantasy, anthropology, biography, history, how-to, military science, travel.

Presses Universitaires de France (PUF)
108 blvd St-Germain, 75006 Paris 06
☎00 33 1 4634 1201   Fax 00 33 1 4634 6541
FOUNDED 1921. *Publishes* art, biography, dance, dentistry, government, general engineering, geography, geology, history, law, medicine, music, nursing, philosophy, psychology, psychiatry, religion, political and social sciences, sociology.

Editions du Seuil
27 rue Jacob, 75006 Paris Cedex 06
☎00 33 1 4046 5050   Fax 00 33 1 4329 0829
FOUNDED 1935. *Publishes* fiction, literature, literary criticism, essays, poetry, art, biography, dance, government, history, how-to, music, photography, philosophy, political science, psychology, psychiatry, religion, general and social sciences, sociology.

Les Editions de la Table Ronde
7 rue Corneille, 75006 Paris
☎00 33 1 4326 0395   Fax 00 33 1 4407 0930
FOUNDED 1944. *Publishes* fiction and general non-fiction, biography, history, psychology, psychiatry, religion.

Librairie Vuibert SA
20 rue Berbier-du-Mets, 75013 Paris
☎00 33 1 4441 7350   Fax 00 33 1 4325 7586
FOUNDED 1877. *Publishes* biological and earth sciences, chemistry, chemical engineering, economics, law, mathematics, physics.

Germany

Verlag C. H. Beck (OHG)
Wilhelmstr 9, 80801 Munich
☎00 49 89 381890   Fax 00 49 89 38189398
FOUNDED 1763. *Publishes* general non-fiction, anthropology, archaeology, art, dance, economics, essays, history, language, law, linguistics, literary criticism, music, philosophy, social sciences, sociology, theology.

Bertelsmann-Lexikon Verlag GmbH
Carl-Bertelsmann-Str, Postfach 33310, 33335 Gütersloh
☎00 49 5241 800   Fax 00 49 5241 75166
Publishes fiction and non-fiction, anthropology, art, biography, business, career development, economics, film, history, how-to, law, management, marketing, medicine, dentistry, nursing, radio, television, video, technology, travel.

Carlsen Verlag GmbH
Völckersstr 14–20, Postfach 500380, 22703 Hamburg

☎00 49 40 3910090   Fax 00 49 40 39100962
FOUNDED 1953. *Publishes* humour and general non-fiction.

Deutscher Taschenbuch Verlag GmbH & Co. KG (dtv)
Friedrichstr 1a, Postfach 400422, 80704 Munich
☎00 49 89 3817060   Fax 00 49 89 346428
FOUNDED 1961. *Publishes* fiction and general non-fiction; art, biography, computer science, dance, history, how-to, music, poetry, psychiatry, psychology, philosophy, religion, medicine, dentistry, nursing, social sciences, literature, literary criticism, essays, humour, travel.

Droemersche Verlagsanstalt Th. Knaur Nachfolger
Rauchstr 9–11, 81679 Munich
☎00 49 89 92710   Fax 00 49 89 9271168
FOUNDED 1901. *Publishes* fiction, general non-fiction, cookery, how-to, self-help, travel and general science.

Econ-Verlag GmbH
Kaiserswerthestr 282, Postfach 300321, 40403 Düsseldorf
☎00 49 211 43596   Fax 00 49 211 4359768
FOUNDED 1950. *Publishes* general non-fiction and fiction, economics, general science.

Falken-Verlag GmbH
Schöne Aussicht 21, Postfach 1120, 65521 Niederhausen
☎00 49 6127 7020   Fax 00 49 6127 702133
FOUNDED 1923. *Publishes* crafts, cookery, education, games, gardening, health, history, hobbies, how-to, humour, nutrition, photography, sport.

S Fischer Verlag GmbH
Hedderichstr 114, Postfach 700355, 60553 Frankfurt am Main
☎00 49 69 60620   Fax 00 49 69 6062214
FOUNDED 1886. *Publishes* fiction, general non-fiction, essays, literature, literary criticism.

Carl Hanser Verlag
Kolbergerstr 22, Postfach 860420, 81631 Munich
☎00 49 89 998300   Fax 00 49 89 984809
FOUNDED 1928. *Publishes* general non-fiction, poetry, computer science, economics, electronics, electrical, mechanical and general engineering, environmental studies, management, mathematics, medicine, nursing, dentistry, philosophy, physics.

Wilhelm Heyne Verlag
Türkenstr 5–7, 80333 Munich
☎00 49 89 286350   Fax 00 49 89 2800943
FOUNDED 1934. *Publishes* fiction, mystery, romance, humour, science fiction, fantasy, astrology, biography, cookery, film, history, how-to, occult, psychology, psychiatry, video.

Hoffmann und Campe Verlag
Harvestehuder Weg 42, Postfach 130444, 20139 Hamburg
☎00 49 40 441880   Fax 00 49 40 44188-290
FOUNDED 1781. *Publishes* fiction and general non-fiction; art, biography, dance, history, music, poetry, philosophy, psychology, psychiatry, general science, social sciences, sociology.

Ernst Klett Verlag GmbH
Rotebühlstr 77, Postfach 106016, 70049 Stuttgart
☎00 49 711 66720   Fax 00 49 711 628053
FOUNDED 1897. *Publishes* education, careers, geography, geology.

Gustav Lübbe Verlag GmbH
Scheidtbachstr 29–31, Postfach 200127, 51431 Bergisch Gladbach
☎00 49 2202 1210
FOUNDED 1963. *Publishes* fiction and general non-fiction, archaeology, biography, history, how-to.

Mosaik Verlag GmbH
Neumarkter Str 18, Postfach 800360, 81673 Munich 80
☎00 49 89 431890   Fax 00 49 89 43189674
Publishes animals, antiques, architecture and interior design, child care and development, cookery, crafts, economics, finance, career development, film, gardening, games, hobbies, health, house and home, human relations, nutrition, pets, self-help, sport, video, wine and spirits, women's studies.

Pestalozzi-Verlag Graphische Gesellschaft mbH
Am Pestalozziring 14, 91058 Erlangen
☎00 49 9131 60600   Fax 00 49 9131 773090
FOUNDED 1844. *Publishes* crafts, games, hobbies.

Rowohlt Taschenbuch Verlag GmbH
Hamburger Str 17, Postfach 1349, 21465 Reinbeck
☎00 49 40 72720   Fax 00 49 40 7272319
FOUNDED 1953. *Publishes* fiction and general non-fiction; archaeology, art, computer science,

crafts, education, essays, games and hobbies, gay and lesbian, government, history, literature, literary criticism, philosophy, political science, psychology, psychiatry, religion, general science, social sciences, sociology.

Springer-Verlag GmbH & Co KG
Heidelberger Platz 3, Postfach 311340, 10643 Berlin
☎00 49 30 82787   Fax 00 49 30 8214091
FOUNDED 1842. *Publishes* agriculture, architecture and interior design, astronomy, behavioural sciences, business, biological sciences, chemical engineering, chemistry, civil engineering, computer science, dentistry, economics, finance, geography, geology, health, nutrition, library and information sciences, management, marketing, mechanical engineering, electronics, electrical engineering, general engineering, physical sciences, earth sciences, environmental studies, law, mathematics, medicine, nursing, philosophy, psychology, psychiatry, physics, general science, technology.

Suhrkamp Verlag
Lindenstr 29–35, Postfach 101945, 60019 Frankfurt am Main
☎00 49 69 756010   Fax 00 49 69 75601522
FOUNDED 1950. *Publishes* biography, fiction, philosophy, poetry, psychology, psychiatry, general science.

K. Thienemanns Verlag
Blumenstr 36, 70182 Stuttgart
☎00 49 711 210550   Fax 00 49 711 2105539
FOUNDED 1849. *Publishes* fiction and general non-fiction.

Ullstein Buchverlage GmbH
13 Charlottenstr, 10969 Berlin
☎00 49 30 25913500 Fax 00 49 30 25913590
FOUNDED 1903. *Publishes* fiction, architecture and interior design, art, biography, dance, education, ethnology, geography, geology, government, health, history, how-to, military science, music, nutrition, poetry, political science, general science, social sciences, sociology, travel.

Italy

Adelphi Edizioni SpA
Via S. Giovanni sul Muro 14, 20121 Milan
☎00 39 2 72000975   Fax 00 39 2 89010337
FOUNDED 1962. *Publishes* fiction, art, biography, dance, music, philosophy, psychology, psychiatry, religion, general science.

Bompiana
Via Mecenate 91, 20138 Milan
☎00 39 2 50951   Fax 00 39 2 5065361
FOUNDED 1929. *Publishes* fiction and general non-fiction, art, drama, theatre and general science.

Bulzoni Editore SRL (Le Edizioni Universitarie d'Italia)
Via Dei Liburni 14, 00185 Rome
☎00 39 6 4455207   Fax 00 39 6 4450355
FOUNDED 1969. *Publishes* fiction, literature, literary criticism, essays, art, drama, general engineering, film, law, language, linguistics, philosophy, general science, social sciences, sociology, theatre, video.

Nuova Casa Editrice Licinio Cappelli GEM srl
Via Farini 14, I–40124 Bologna
☎00 39 51 239060   Fax 00 39 51 239286
FOUNDED 1851. *Publishes* fiction, art, biography, drama, film, government, history, music and dance, medicine, nursing, dentistry, philosophy, poetry, political science, psychology, psychiatry, religion, general science, social sciences, sociology, theatre, video.

Garzanti Editore
Via Senato 25, 20121 Milan
☎00 39 2 77871   Fax 00 39 2 76009233
FOUNDED 1861. *Publishes* fiction, literature, literary criticism, essays, art, biography, history, poetry, government, political science.

Giunti Publishing Group
Via Bolognese 165, 50139 Florence
☎00 39 55 66791   Fax 00 39 55 6679298
FOUNDED 1840. *Publishes* fiction, literature, literary criticism, essays, art, chemistry, chemical engineering, education, history, how-to, language arts, linguistics, mathematics, psychology, psychiatry, general science. Italian publishers of National Geographical Society books.

Gremese Editore SRL
Via Agnelli 88, 00151 Rome
☎00 39 6 65740507   Fax 00 39 6 65740509
FOUNDED 1978. *Publishes* fiction and non-fiction; art, astrology, cookery, crafts, dance, drama, environmental studies, fashion, games, hobbies, essays, literature, literary criticism, music, occult, parapsychology, photography, sport, travel, theatre, film, video, radio.

Istituto Geografico de Agostini SpA
Via Giovanni da Verrazzano 15, 28100 Novara
☎00 39 321 471830   Fax 00 39 321 471286
FOUNDED 1901. *Publishes* art, essays, gardening, plants, geology and geography, history, literature, literary criticism, regional interests, religion.

Longanesi & C
Corso Italia 13, 20122 Milan
☎00 39 2 8692640   Fax 00 39 2 72000306
FOUNDED 1946. *Publishes* fiction, art, biography, dance, history, how-to, medicine, nursing, dentistry, music, philosophy, psychology, psychiatry, religion, general and social sciences, sociology.

Arnoldo Mondadori Editore SpA
Via Mondadori, 20090 Segrate (Milan)
☎00 39 2 75421   Fax 00 39 2 75422302
FOUNDED 1907. *Publishes* fiction, mystery, romance, art, biography, dance, dentistry, history, how-to, medicine, music, poetry, philosophy, psychology, psychiatry, religion, nursing, general science, education.

Società Editrice Il Mulino
Str Maggiore 37, 40125 Bologna
☎00 39 51 256011   Fax 00 39 51 256034
FOUNDED 1954. *Publishes* dance, drama, economics, government, history, law, language, linguistics, music, philosophy, political science, psychology, psychiatry, social sciences, sociology, theatre.

Gruppo Ugo Mursia Editore SpA
Via Tadino 29, 20124 Milan
☎00 39 2 29403030   Fax 00 39 2 29525557
FOUNDED 1922. *Publishes* fiction, poetry, art, biography, education, history, maritime, philosophy, religion, sport, general and social sciences, sociology.

RCS Libri SpA
Via Mecenate 91, 20138 Milan
☎00 39 2 50952918   Fax 00 39 2 50952638
FOUNDED 1945. *Publishes* art, crafts, dance, environmental studies, games, hobbies, history, music, medicine, nursing, dentistry, outdoor recreation, general science.

Societa Editrice Internazionale – SEI
Corso Regina Margherita 176, 10152 Turin
☎00 39 11 52271   Fax 00 39 11 5211320
FOUNDED 1908. *Publishes* literature, literary criticism, essays, education, geography, geology, history, mathematics, philosophy, physics, religion, psychology, psychiatry.

Sonzogno
Via Mecenate 91, 20138 Milan
☎00 39 2 50951   Fax 00 39 2 5065361
FOUNDED 1818. *Publishes* fiction, mysteries, and general non-fiction.

Sperling e Kupfer Editori SpA
Via Borgonuovo 24, 20121 Milan
☎00 39 2 290341   Fax 00 39 2 6590290
FOUNDED 1899. *Publishes* fiction and general non-fiction, biography, economics, health, how-to, management, nutrition, general science, sport, travel.

Sugarco Edizioni SRL
Via Fermi 9, 21040 Carnago (Varese)
☎00 39 331 985511   Fax 00 39 331 985385
FOUNDED 1956. *Publishes* fiction, biography, history, how-to, philosophy.

Todariana Editrice
Via Gardone 29, 20139 Milan
☎00 39 2 55213405   Fax 00 39 2 55213405
FOUNDED 1967. *Publishes* fiction, poetry, science fiction, fantasy, literature, literary criticism, essays, language arts, linguistics, psychology, psychiatry, social sciences, sociology, travel.

The Netherlands

A.W. Bruna Uitgevers BV
Postbus 8411, 3503 RK Utrecht
☎00 31 30 2470411   Fax 00 31 30 2410018
FOUNDED 1868. *Publishes* fiction and general non-fiction; computer science, history, philosophy, psychology, psychiatry, general and social science, sociology.

Uitgeverij BZZTÔH
Laan van Meerdervoort 10, 2517 AJ Gravenhage
☎00 31 70 3632934   Fax 00 31 70 3631932
FOUNDED 1970. *Publishes* fiction, mysteries, general non-fiction, animals, astrology, biography, cookery, dance, humour, music, occult, pets, religion (Buddhist), romance, travel.

Elsevier Science BV
Sara Burgerhartstraat 25, PO Box 2400, 1000 CK Amsterdam
☎00 31 20 4853911   Fax 00 31 20 4852457
FOUNDED 1946. Parent company – Reed

Elsevier. *Publishes* sciences (all fields), management and professional, medicine, nursing, dentistry, economics, engineering (computer and general), mathematics, physics, psychology, psychiatry, social sciences, sociology, technology.

Uitgeverij Hollandia BV
Beukenlaan 20, Postbus 70, 3740 AB Baarn
☎00 31 35 5418941   Fax 00 31 35 5421917
FOUNDED 1899. *Publishes* fiction, maritime, travel.

Uitgeversmaatschappij J. H. Kok BV
Gildestraat 5, PO Box 130, 8260 AC Kampen
☎00 31 38 3392555   Fax 00 31 38 3327331
FOUNDED 1894. *Publishes* fiction, poetry, art, biography, crafts, education, environmental studies, games, history, hobbies, how-to, psychology, psychiatry, religion, general and social sciences, sociology, medicine, nursing, dentistry.

M & P Publishing House
Onderdoor 9, Postbus 170, 3990 DD Houten
☎00 31 30 6377736   Fax 00 31 30 6377736
FOUNDED 1974. *Publishes* general non-fiction.

Meulenhoff International
Herengracht 507, PO Box 100,
1000 AC Amsterdam
☎00 31 20 5533500   Fax 00 31 20 6258511
FOUNDED 1895. *Publishes* international co-productions, art and general non-fiction. Specialises in Dutch and translated literature, science fiction, non-fiction and children's.

Uitgeverij Het Spectrum BV
Montalbaendreef 2, Postbus 2073,
3500 GB Utrecht
☎00 31 30 2650650   Fax 00 31 30 2620850
FOUNDED 1935. *Publishes* science fiction, fantasy, literature, literary criticism, essays, mystery, crime, general non-fiction, computer science, history, astrology, occult, management, environmental studies, travel.

Time-Life Books BV
Ottho Heldringstr 5, 1066 AZ Amsterdam
☎00 31 20 5104371   Fax 00 31 20 6176594
Publishes art, cookery, gardening, plants, history, how-to, general science, parapsychology, behavioural sciences, biological sciences.

Unieboek BV
Onderdoor 7, Postbus 97, 3990 DB Houten
☎00 31 30 6377660   Fax 00 31 30 6377600

FOUNDED 1891. *Publishes* fiction, general non-fiction, architecture and interior design, government, political science, literature, literary criticism, essays, archaeology, cookery, history.

Uniepers BV
Heinkuitenstr. 26, Postbus 69,
1390 AB Abcoude
☎00 31 294 285111   Fax 00 31 294 283013
FOUNDED 1961. *Publishes* (mostly in co-editions) antiques, anthropology, archaeology, architecture and interior design, art, culture, dance, history, music, nature, natural history.

Veen Uitgevers Group
St Jacobsstr. 125, Postbus 14095,
3508 SC Utrecht
☎00 31 30 349211   Fax 00 31 20 349208
FOUNDED 1887. Part of Wolters Kluwer Trade Publishing. *Publishes* general non-fiction, fiction, essays, Dutch and foreign literature, literary criticism, travel, business,

Wolters Kluwer NV
Stadhouderskade 1, PO Box 818,
1000 AV Amsterdam
☎00 31 20 6070400   Fax 00 31 20 6070490
FOUNDED 1889. *Publishes* education, medical, technical encyclopedias, trade books and journals, law and taxation, periodicals.

Norway

H. Aschehoug & Co (W. Nygaard) A/S
Sehestedsgate 3, Postboks 363, 0102 Sentrum, Oslo
☎00 47 22 400400   Fax 00 47 22 206395
FOUNDED 1872. *Publishes* fiction and general non-fiction, general and social science, sociology.

J. W. Cappelens Forlag A/S
Maribosgaten 13, Postboks 350, 0101
Sentrum, Oslo
☎00 47 22 365000   Fax 00 47 22 365040
FOUNDED 1829. *Publishes* fiction, general non-fiction, religion.

N. W. Damm og Søn A/S
Tordenskioldsgt 6b, 0055 Oslo
☎00 47 22 471100   Fax 00 47 22 471149
FOUNDED 1845. *Publishes* fiction and general non-fiction.

Ex Libris Forlag A/S
Nordregt 22, Postboks 2130 Grünerlokka, 0505 Oslo
☎00 47 22 384450   Fax 00 47 22 385160
FOUNDED 1982. *Publishes* fiction, general non-fiction, cookery, health, nutrition, humour, human relations, publishing and book trade reference.

Gyldendal Norsk Forlag A/S
Sehestedsgt 4, Postboks 6860, 0130 St Olaf, Oslo
☎00 47 22 034100   Fax 00 47 22 034105
FOUNDED 1925. *Publishes* fiction, science fiction, fantasy, art, dance, biography, government, political science, history, how-to, music, social sciences, sociology, poetry, philosophy, psychology, psychiatry, religion.

Hjemmets Bokforlag AS
Tordenskioldsgate 6B, N-0055 Oslo
☎00 47 22 471000   Fax 00 47 22 471098
FOUNDED 1969. *Publishes* fiction and general non-fiction.

NKS-Forlaget
Majorstua, Pilestredet 46, Postboks 5853, 0308 Oslo
☎00 47 22 596000   Fax 00 47 22 596300
FOUNDED 1971. *Publishes* accountancy, childcare, English as a second language, health, nutrition, mathematics, natural history, general and social sciences, sociology.

Tiden Norsk Forlag
Storgt 23d, PO Box 8813, Youngstorget, 0028 Oslo
☎00 47 22 007100   Fax 00 47 22 007137
FOUNDED 1933. *Publishes* fiction, general non-fiction.

Portugal

Bertrand Editora Lda
Rua Anchieta 29 – 1d90, 1200 Lisbon
☎00 351 1 3479728   Fax 00 351 1 3468286
FOUNDED 1727. *Publishes* art, essays, literature, literary criticism, social sciences, sociology.

Editorial Caminho SARL
Al Santo Antonio dos Capuchos 6B, 1150 Lisbon
☎00 351 1 3152683   Fax 00 351 1 534346
FOUNDED 1977. *Publishes* fiction, government, political science.

Livraria Civilizacão (Américo Fraga Lamares & Ca Lda)
Rua Alberto Aires de Gouveia 27, 4000 Porto
☎00 351 2 2002286   Fax 00 351 2 312382
FOUNDED 1921. *Publishes* fiction, art, economics, history, social and political science, government, sociology.

Publicações Dom Quixote Lda
Rua Luciano Cordeiro 116-2, 1050 Lisbon
☎00 351 1 3158079   Fax 00 351 1 574595
FOUNDED 1965. *Publishes* fiction, poetry, education, history, philosophy, general and social sciences, sociology.

Publicações Europa-America Lda
Apdo 8, Estrada Lisbon-Sintra Km 14, 2726 Mem Martins Cedex
☎00 351 1 9211461   Fax 00 351 1 9217846
FOUNDED 1945. *Publishes* fiction, poetry, art, biography, dance, education, general engineering, history, how-to, music, philosophy, medicine, nursing, dentistry, psychology, psychiatry, general and social sciences, sociology, technology.

Gradiva – Publicações Lda
Rua Almeida e Sousa 21–r/c Esq, 1350 Lisbon
☎00 351 1 3974067   Fax 00 351 1 3953471
FOUNDED 1981. *Publishes* fiction, science fiction, fantasy, education, history, human relations, philosophy, general science.

Livros Horizonte Lda
Rua Chagas 17 - 1 Dto, 1120 Lisbon
☎00 351 1 3466917   Fax 00 351 1 3426921
FOUNDED 1953. *Publishes* art, education, history, psychology, psychiatry, social sciences, sociology.

Editorial Verbo SA
Rua Carlos Testa 1–2, 1000 Lisbon
☎00 351 1 3562131   Fax 00 351 1 3562139
FOUNDED 1959. *Publishes* education, history, general science.

Spain

Editorial Alhambra SA
Fernandez de la Hoz 9, 28010 Madrid
☎00 349 1 5940020   Fax 00 349 1 5921220
FOUNDED 1942. *Publishes* art, education, history, language arts, linguistics, medicine and nursing, dentistry, general science, psychology, psychiatry, philosophy.

Alianza Editorial SA
Juan Ignacio Luca de Tena 15, 28027 Madrid
☎00 349 1 7416600   Fax 00 349 1 3207480
FOUNDED 1965. *Publishes* fiction, poetry, art, history, mathematics, dance, music, philosophy, government, political and social sciences, sociology, general science.

Ediciones Anaya SA
Juan Ignacio Luca de Tena 15, 28027 Madrid
☎00 349 1 3938800   Fax 00 349 1 7426631
FOUNDED 1959. *Publishes* education.

Editorial Don Quijote
Compãs del Porvenir 6, 41013 Seville
☎00 349 5 4235080
FOUNDED 1981. *Publishes* fiction, literature, literary criticism, poetry, essays, drama, theatre, history.

EDHASA (Editora y Distribuidora Hispano – Americana SA)
Av Diagonal 519, 08029 Barcelona
☎00 349 3 4395104   Fax 00 349 3 4194584
FOUNDED 1946. *Publishes* fiction, literature, literary criticism, essays, history.

Editorial Espasa-Calpe SA
Apdo 547, Carretera de Irún Km 12, 200, 28080 Madrid
☎00 349 1 358 9689   Fax 00 349 1 358 9364
FOUNDED 1925. *Publishes* fiction, science fiction, fantasy, English as a second language, general non-fiction, biography, history, self-help, social sciences, sociology.

Ediciones Grijalbo SA
Aragó 385, 08013 Barcelona
☎00 349 3 4587000   Fax 00 349 3 4580495
FOUNDED 1942. *Publishes* fiction, general non-fiction, art, biography, history, government, political science, philosophy, psychology, psychiatry, religion, social sciences, sociology, technology.

Grupo Editorial CEAC SA
C/Peru 164, 08020 Barcelona
☎00 349 3 3075004   Fax 00 349 3 2660067
Formerly Editorial Timun Mas SA. *Publishes* education, technology, science fiction, fantasy.

Ediciones Hiperión SL
Calle Salustiano Ólózaga 14, 28001 Madrid
☎00 349 1 5576015   Fax 00 349 1 4358690
FOUNDED 1976. *Publishes* fiction, literature, literary criticism, essays, poetry, religions (Islamic and Jewish).

Editorial Luis Vives (Edelvives)
Dr Federico Rubio y Gali 1, 28039 Madrid
☎00 349 1 5347000   Fax 00 349 1 5531919
FOUNDED 1890. *Publishes* education.

Editorial Molino
Calabria 166 baixos, 08015 Barcelona
☎00 349 3 2260625   Fax 00 349 3 2266998
FOUNDED 1933. *Publishes* cookery, education, sport, fiction.

Mondadori España SA
Aragó 385, 08013 Barcelona
☎00 349 3 4587000   Fax 00 349 3 4159033
FOUNDED 1987. *Publishes* fiction, general non-fiction, biography, history, general science.

Editorial Planeta SA
Córsega 273, 08008 Barcelona
☎00 349 3 4154100   Fax 00 349 3 2177140
FOUNDED 1952. *Publishes* fiction and general non-fiction.

Plaza y Janés SA
Enrique Granados 86–88, 08008 Barcelona
☎00 349 3 4151100   Fax 00 349 3 4156976
FOUNDED 1959. *Publishes* fiction and general non-fiction.

Santillana SA
Juan Bravo 38, 28006 Madrid
☎00 349 1 3224500   Fax 00 349 1 3224475
FOUNDED 1964. *Publishes* fiction, essays, literature, literary criticism, travel.

Editorial Seix Barral SA
Córsega 270, 4, 08008 Barcelona
☎00 349 3 2186400   Fax 00 349 3 2184773
FOUNDED 1945. *Publishes* fiction, poetry, drama, theatre.

Tusquets Editores
Iradier 24 baixos, 08017 Barcelona
☎00 349 3 4174170   Fax 00 349 3 4176703
FOUNDED 1969. *Publishes* fiction, art, biography, eroticism, essays, history, literature, literary criticism, social sciences, sociology.

Ediciones Versal SA
Calabria 108, 08015 Barcelona
☎00 349 3 3257404   Fax 00 349 3 4236898
FOUNDED 1984. *Publishes* general non-fiction, biography, literature, literary criticism, essays.

Sweden

Albert Bonniers Förlag AB
Box 3159, Sveavägen 56, S-103 63 Stockholm
☎00 46 8 6968000   Fax 00 46 8 6968630
FOUNDED 1837. *Publishes* fiction and general non-fiction.

Bokförlaget Bra Böcker AB
Södra Vägen, S-26380 Höganäs
☎00 46 42 339000   Fax 00 46 42 330504
FOUNDED 1965. *Publishes* fiction, geography, geology, history.

Brombergs Bokförlag AB
Box 12886, Industrigaton 4A,
S-112 98 Stockholm
☎00 46 8 6503390   Fax 00 46 8 6500160
FOUNDED 1973. *Publishes* fiction, general non-fiction, government, political science, general science.

Bokförlaget Forum AB
PO Box 14115, Gamla Brogatan, Riddargatan
23A, S-107 23 Stockholm
☎00 46 8 6968440   Fax 00 46 8 6968368
FOUNDED 1944. *Publishes* fiction and general non-fiction.

Bokförlaget Natur och Kultur
Box 27323, Karlavägen 31,
S-102 54 Stockholm
☎00 46 8 4538600   Fax 00 46 8 4538790
FOUNDED 1922. *Publishes* fiction and general non-fiction, biography, history, psychology, psychiatry, general science.

Norstedts Förlag AB
Box 2052, Tryckerigatan 4,
S-103 12 Stockholm
☎00 46 8 7893000   Fax 00 46 8 7893038
FOUNDED 1823. *Publishes* fiction and general non-fiction.

AB Rabén och Sjögren Bokförlag
PO Box 45022, Kungstengatan 49, S-104 30
Stockholm
☎00 46 8 4570300   Fax 00 46 8 4570331
FOUNDED 1942. *Publishes* fiction and general non-fiction.

Richters Förlag AB
Ostra Förstadsgatan 46, 205 75 Malmö
☎00 46 40 380600   Fax 00 46 40 933708
FOUNDED 1942. *Publishes* fiction.

Tiden Barn-och Ungdomsforlaget AB
Box 45022, S-104 30 Stockholm
☎00 46 8 4570300   Fax 00 46 8 4570334
FOUNDED 1912. *Publishes* fiction, general non-fiction, poetry, history, government, political science, social sciences, sociology, psychology, psychiatry.

B Wählströms Bokförlag AB
Box 30022, S-104 25 Stockholm
☎00 46 8 6198600   Fax 00 46 8 6189761
FOUNDED 1911. *Publishes* fiction and general non-fiction.

Switzerland

Arche Verlag AG, Raabe und Vitali
Postfach 112, CH-8030 Zurich
☎00 41 1 2522410   Fax 00 41 1 2611115
FOUNDED 1944. *Publishes* literature and literary criticism, essays, biography, fiction, poetry, music, dance, travel.

Artemis Verlags AG
Munstergasse 9, CH-8024 Zurich
☎00 41 1 2521100   Fax 00 41 1 2624792
FOUNDED 1943. *Publishes* art, architecture and interior design, biography, history, philosophy, political science, government, travel.

Diogenes Verlag AG
Sprecherstr 8, CH-8032 Zurich
☎00 41 1 2548511   Fax 00 41 1 2528407
FOUNDED 1952. *Publishes* fiction, essays, literature, literary criticism, mysteries, art, drama, theatre, philosophy.

Langenscheidt AG Zürich-Zug
Postfach 326, CH-8021 Zurich
☎00 41 1 2115000   Fax 00 41 1 2122149
Publishes language arts and linguistics.

Larousse (Suisse) SA
3 Route du Grand-Mont, CH-1052 Le
Mont-sur-Lausanne
☎00 41 22 369140
Publishes dictionaries, reference and textbooks.

Neptun-Verlag
Fidlerstr, Postfach 171, CH-8272 Ermatingen
☎00 41 72 642020   Fax 00 41 72 642023
FOUNDED 1946. *Publishes* history and travel.

Orell Füssli Verlag
Nuschderstr 22, CH-8022 Zurich
☎00 41 1 2113630   Fax 00 41 1 4667412
FOUNDED 1519. *Publishes* art, biography, economics, education, geography, geology, history, how-to.

Editions Payot Lausanne
18 ave de la Gare, CP 529, CH-1001 Lausanne
☎00 41 21 3290264   Fax 00 41 21 3290266
FOUNDED 1875. *Publishes* general non-fiction, anthropology, dance, education, history, law, medicine, nursing, dentistry, music, literature, literary criticism, essays, general science.

Sauerländer AG
Laurenzenvorstadt 89, CH-5001 Aarau
☎00 41 62 8368626   Fax 00 41 62 8368620
FOUNDED 1807. *Publishes* biography, education, history, poetry, medicine, nursing, dentistry, general science, social sciences, sociology.

Scherz Verlag AG
Theaterplatz 4–6, CH-3000 Berne 7
☎00 41 31 3277117   Fax 00 41 31 3277171
FOUNDED 1939. *Publishes* fiction and general non-fiction; biography, history, psychology, psychiatry, philosophy, parapsychology.

European Television Companies

Austria

ORF (Österreichisher Rundfunk)
Würzburggasse 30, A–1136 Vienna
☎00 43 1 87 8780   Fax 00 43 1 87 8783766

Belgium

Radio-Télévision Belge de la Communauté Française (RTBF)
Boulevard Auguste Reyers 52,
B–1044 Brussels
☎00 32 2 737 2560   Fax 00 32 2 737 2556

Vlaamse Radio en Televisie-omroep (VRT)
Auguste Reyerslaan 52, B–1043 Brussels
☎00 32 2 741 3111   Fax 00 32 2 736 5786

Vlaamse Televisie Maatschappij (VTM) (cable)
Medialaan 1, B–1800 Vilvoorde
☎00 32 2 255 3211   Fax 00 32 2 252 5141

Denmark

Danmarks Radio–TV
TV Byen, DK–2860 Søborg
☎00 45 35 20 3040   Fax 00 45 35 20 3023

TV Danmark
Indiakaj 12, DK–2100 Copenhagen 0
☎00 45 35 43 0522   Fax 00 45 35 43 0655

TV–2 Danmark
Rugaardsvej 25, DK–5100 Odense C
☎00 45 65 91 1244   Fax 00 45 65 91 3322

Finland

MTV3 Finland
Ilmalantori 2, SF–00240 Helsinki
☎00 358 9 15001   Fax 00 358 9 1500707

Yleisradio Oy (YLE)/TV1/TV2
PO Box 00024 Yleisradio,
SF–00240 Helsinki
☎00 358 9 14801   Fax 00 358 9 14803215

France

France 2
22 ave Montaigne, 75387 Paris Cedex 08
☎00 33 1 44 21 42 42Fax 00 33 1 44 21 51 45

France 3
116 ave du Président Kennedy,
75790 Paris Cedex 16
☎00 33 1 42 30 13 13Fax 00 33 1 46 47 92 94

La Sept/Arte (cable & satellite)
50 ave Théophile Gautier, 75016 Paris
☎00 33 1 44 14 77 77Fax 00 33 1 44 14 77 00

M6 (Métropole Television)
89 ave Charles de Gaulle,
92575 Neuilly sur Seine
☎00 33 1 41 92 66 66Fax 00 33 1 41 92 66 10

Arte Geie (cable & satellite)
2a rue de le Fonderie, 67080 Strasbourg
☎00 33 3 88 14 22 22Fax 00 33 3 88 22 22 00

Canal + (pay TV)
85–89 Quai André Citroën,
75711 Paris Cedex 15
☎00 33 1 44 25 10 00Fax 00 33 1 44 25 12 34

La Cinquième
18 rue Horace-Vernet, 92136 Issey Les
Moulineaux
☎00 33 1 41 46 55 55Fax 00 33 1 41 08 02 22

RFO (Radio Télévision Française d'Outre-mer)
5 ave du Recteur Poincaré, 75782 Paris
☎00 33 1 42 15 71 00Fax 00 33 1 42 15 74 37

TF1
1 Quai du Pont du Jour, 92656 Boulogne
☎00 33 1 41 41 12 34Fax 00 33 1 41 41 28 40

Germany

ARD – Das Erste
ARD Büro, Bertramstr 8, 60320 Frankfurt am
Main
☎00 49 69 59 0607   Fax 00 49 69 15 52075

ZDF (Zweites Deutsches Fernsehen)
ZDF-Strasse 1, 55127 Mainz
☎00 49 61 31 701   Fax 00 49 61 31 72157

Ireland

Radio Telefis Éireann (RTE – RTE 1)
Donnybrook, Dublin 4
☎00 353 1 208 3111   Fax 00 353 1 208 3080

Teilefis na Gaelige
Baile na hAbhann, Co Na Gaillimhe
☎00 353 91 505050   Fax 00 353 91 505021

Italy

RAI (RadioTelevisione Italiana)
Viale Mazzini 14, 00195 Rome
☎00 39 6 3878   Fax 00 39 6 3725680

Tele piu'
Via Piranesi 46, 20137 Milan
☎00 39 2 700 271   Fax 00 39 2 700 27201

The Netherlands

AVRO (Algemene Omroep Vereniging)
Postbus 2, 1200 JA Hilversum
☎00 31 35 671 79 11 Fax 00 31 35 671 74 39

IKON
Postbus 10009, 1201 EA Hilversum
☎00 31 35 672 72 72 Fax 00 31 35 621 51 00

NCRV (Nederlandse Christelijke Radio Vereniging)
Postbus 25000, 1202 HBC Hilversum
☎00 31 35 671 99 11 Fax 00 31 35 671 92 85

NOS (Nederlandse Omroep Stichting)
Postbus 26600, 1202 JT Hilversum
☎00 31 35 677 92 22 Fax 00 31 35 624 20 23

NPS (Nederlandse Programma Stichting)
Postbus 29000, 1202 MA Hilversum
☎00 31 35 677 93 33 Fax 00 31 35 677 4959

TROS (Televisie en Radio Omroep Stichting)
Postbus 28450, 1202 LL Hilversum
☎00 31 35 671 57 15
Fax 00 31 35 671 52 36

VARA
Postbus 1200, AD Hilversum
☎00 31 35 671 19 11
Fax 00 31 35 671 13 33

Veronica (VOO)
Laapersveld 75, 1213 VB Hilversum
☎00 31 35 671 67 16 Fax 00 31 35 624 97 71

VPRO
Postbus 11, 1200 JC Hilversum
☎00 31 35 671 29 11
Fax 00 31 35 671 22 54

Norway

NRK (Norsk Rikskringkasting)
Bjørnstjerne Bjørnsons Plass 1, N–0340 Oslo
☎00 47 23 04 7000

TVNorge
Sagveien 17, 0459–Oslo 4
☎00 47 22 38 7800   Fax 00 47 22 35 1000

TV2
Postboks 2, N–5002 Bergen
☎00 47 55 90 8070   Fax 00 47 55 90 8090

Portugal

Radiotelevisão Portuguesa (RTP)
Av 5 de Outubro 197, 1000 Lisbon
☎00 35 11 793 1774   Fax 00 35 11 796 6227

SIC (Sociedade Independente de Comunicação
Estrada da Outurela 119, 2796 Carnaxide
☎00 35 11 417 9400   Fax 00 35 11 417 3119

TVI (Televisão Independente)
Edificio Altejo 6, rua Matigna, 1900–Lisbon
☎00 35 11 861 1600   Fax 00 35 11 868 7968

TVI (Televisão Independente)
Rua Márió Castelhano 40, Queluz de Baixo,
2745 Barcarena
☎00 35 11 434 7500   Fax 00 35 11 435 5076

Spain

RTVE (Radiotelevision Española)
Edificio Prado del Rey, E–28223 Madrid
☎00 349 1 581 7000   Fax 00 349 1 581 7757

RTVM (Radiotelevision Madrid)
Zurbano 71, E–28010 Madrid
☎00 349 1 581 5404   Fax 00 349 1 581 5412

TVE (Televisión Española, SA)
O'Donnell 77, 28007 Madrid
☎00 349 1 346 8723   Fax 00 349 1 346 9777

Antena 3
Avda. Isla Graciosa, E–28700 Madrid
☎00 349 1 623 0500   Fax 00 349 1 651 3664

Sweden

SVT (Sveriges Television)
Oxenstiernsgatan 26–34, S–10510 Stockholm
☎00 46 8 784 0000   Fax 00 46 8 784 1500

TV4
Storangskroken 10, S–11579 Stockholm
☎00 46 8 459 4000   Fax 00 46 8 459 4444

Switzerland

SBC (Swiss Broadcasting Corp.)
Giacomettistr 3, CH–3000 Bern 15
☎00 41 31 350 91 11 Fax 00 41 31 350 92 86

Schweizer Fernsehen DRS
Fernsehenstrasse 1–4, CH–8052 Zurich
☎00 41 1 305 66 11   Fax 00 41 1 305 56 60

TSR (Télévision Suisse Romande)
Quai Ernest Ansermet 20,
CH–1211 Geneva 8
☎00 41 22 708 99 11 Fax 00 41 22 708 98 00

RTSI (Radiotelevisione svizzera di lingua Italiana)
Postfach 235, CH–6903 Lugarno
☎00 41 91 803 51 11 Fax 00 41 91 803 91 50

US Publishers

International Reply Coupons (IRCs)

For return postage, send IRCs, available from post offices. Letters, 60 pence; mss according to weight.

ABC–Clio, Inc.

Suite 350, 501 South Cherry Street, Denver CO 80222
☎001 303 333 3003   Fax 001 303 333 4037
Website: www.abc-clio.com
Publisher *Rolf A Janke*

FOUNDED 1955. *Publishes* non-fiction: reference, including mythology, native American studies, government and politics, history, military and war, women's studies/issues, current world issues. About 35–40 titles a year. No unsolicited mss; synopses and ideas welcome.
Royalties paid annually. *UK subsidiary* **ABC-Clio Ltd**, Oxford.

Abingdon Press

201 Eighth Avenue South, Box 801, Nashville TN 37202–0801
☎001 615 749 6404   Fax 001 615 749 6512
Editorial Director *Harriett Jane Olson*

Publishes non-fiction: religious (lay and professional), children's religious and academic texts. About 100 titles a year. Approach in writing only with synopsis and samples. IRCs essential.

Harry N. Abrams, Inc.

100 Fifth Avenue, New York NY 10011
☎001 212 206 7715   Fax 001 212 645 8437
CEO/President/Editor-in-chief
Paul Gottlieb

Publishes illustrated books: art, architecture, nature, entertainment and children's. No fiction. Submit completed mss (no dot matrix), together with sample illustrations.

Academy Chicago Publishers

363 W. Erie Street, Chicago IL 60610
☎001 312 751 7300   Fax 001 312 751 7306
Website: http://www.academychicago.com
Senior Editor *Anita Miller*

FOUNDED 1975. *Publishes* fiction: mystery and mainstream; non-fiction: history, women's studies. No romance, children's, young adult, religious, sexist or avant-garde. 12 titles in 1997.
IMPRINT **Cassandra Editions** ('Lost' Women

Writers). Send first three chapters only, accompanied by IRCs; no synopses or ideas.
Royalties paid twice-yearly. *Distributed* in the UK and Europe by Gazelle, Lancaster.

Ace Science Fiction & Fantasy

See **Berkley Publishing Group**

Adams Media Corporation

260 Center Street, Holbrook MA 02343
☎001 781 767 8100   Fax 001 781 767 0994
President *Robert L. Adams*

FOUNDED 1980. *Publishes* general non-fiction: careers, business, personal finance, relationships, parenting and maternity, self-improvement, reference, cooking, sports, games and humour.
TITLES *Adams Streetwise Small Business Start-up; The New Living Heart; Small Miracles; The Everything Baby Names Book; The Lost Lennon Interviews; Knock 'em Dead with Great Answers to Tough Interview Questions.* Ideas welcome.

Addison-Wesley Longman Inc.

The Addison-Wesley Longman General Publishing Group is in the process of being sold. 'During the transition process the editorial staff is unable to give adequate time to freelance contributions, so we are not able to accept freelance or unsolicited mss at this point.'

University of Alabama Press

Box 870380, Tuscaloosa AL 35487
☎001 205 348 5180   Fax 001 205 348 9201
Director *Nicole Mitchell*

Publishes academic books in the fields of American history, American literature, history of science and technology, linguistics, archaeology, rhetoric and speech communication, Judaic studies, political science and public administration, with special emphasis on Southern regional studies. About 40 titles a year.

Aladdin Books

See **Simon & Schuster Children's Publishing Division**

University of Alaska Press
1st Floor, Gruening Building, PO Box 756240, University of Alaska, Fairbanks AK 99775–6240
☎001 907 474 5831   Fax 001 907 474 5502
Manager *Debbie Van Stone*
Managing Editor *Carla Helfferich*
Acquisitions *Pam Odom*

Traces its origins back to 1927 but was relatively dormant until the early 1980s. *Publishes* scholarly works about Alaska and the North Pacific rim, with a special emphasis on circumpolar regions. 5–10 titles a year. No fiction or poetry.

DIVISIONS
Ramuson Library Historical Translation Series *Marvin Falk* TITLES *The Great Russian Navigator, A. I. Chirikov; Journals of the Priest Ioann Veniaminov in Alaska, 1923 to 1836.* **Oral Biography Series** *William Schneider* TITLES *The Life I've Been Living; Kusiq: An Eskimo Life History from the Arctic Coast of Alaska.* **Monograph Series** *Carla Helfferich* TITLES *Intertidal Bivalves: A Guide to the Common Marine Bivalves of Alaska.* **Classic Reprint Series** *Terrence Cole* TITLES *Fifty Years Below Zero, A Lifetime of Adventure in the Far North; The Thousand-Mile War, World War II in Alaska and the Aleutians.* **Lanternlight Library** Informal non-fiction covering Northern interest. TITLES *Aleutian Echoes; Bear Man of Admiralty Island: A Biography of Allen E. Hasselborg.* Unsolicited mss, synopses and ideas welcome.

Allen Lane
See **Penguin Putnam Inc**

AMACOM
1601 Broadway, New York NY 10019–7406
☎001 212 903 8417   Fax 001 212 903 8083
Publisher *Hank Kennedy*

Owned by American Management Association. *Publishes* business books only, including general management, business communications, sales and marketing, finance, computers and information systems, human resource management and training, career/personal growth skills, research development, project management and manufacturing, quality/customer service titles. 65–70 titles a year. TITLES *Corporate Executions; The Great Transition; Knock Your Socks Off Answers; Straight Talk About Gays in the Workplace; Diary of a Small Business Owner.* Proposals welcome.
Royalties paid twice-yearly.

Anchor
See **Bantam Doubleday Dell Publishing Group, Inc.**

Anvil
See **Krieger Publishing Co., Inc.**

Appaloosa Publications
See **Sovereign**

Ann Arbor Paperbacks
See **University of Michigan Press**

Archway
See **Pocket Books**

University of Arizona Press
1230 North Park Avenue, Suite 102, Tucson AZ 85719–4140
☎001 520 621 1441   Fax 001 520 621 8899
Director *Stephen Cox*
Editor-in-Chief *Christine Szuter*

FOUNDED 1959. *Publishes* academic non-fiction, particularly with a regional/cultural link, plus Native-American and Hispanic literature. About 50 titles a year.

Arkana
See **Penguin Putnam Inc**

University of Arkansas Press
McIlroy House, 201 Ozark Avenue, Fayetteville AR 72701
☎001 501 575 3246   Fax 001 501 575 6044
Acting Director *John Coghlan*

FOUNDED 1980. *Publishes* scholarly monographs, poetry and general trade including essays, biography, etc. Particularly interested at present in scholarly works in history, politics, sociology and literary criticism. About 30 titles a year. TITLES *Movement and Modernism: Yeats, Eliot, Lawrence, Williams, and Early Twentieth Century Dance* Terri Mester; *Breaking the Silence: The Little Rock Women's Emergency Committee to Open Our Schools, 1958–1963* Sara Murphy; *Postmodernism and a Sociology of the Absurd* Stanford Lyman.
Royalties paid annually.

Aspect
See **Warner Books Inc.**

Atheneum Books for Young Readers
See **Simon & Schuster Children's Publishing Division**

Atlantic Monthly Press
See **Grove/Atlantic Inc**

AUP (Associated University Presses)
AUP New Jersey titles are handled in the UK by **Golden Cockerel Press** (see **UK Publishers**).

Avery Publishing Group, Inc.
120 Old Broadway, Garden City Park, New York NY 11040
☎001 516 741 2155   Fax 001 516 742 1892
Managing Editor *Rudy Shur*
FOUNDED 1976. *Publishes* adult trade non-fiction, specialising in childbirth, childcare, alternative health, self-help, New Age and natural cooking. About 50 titles a year. TITLES *Prescription for Nutritional Healing, 2nd ed.* James Balch, MD and Phyllis Balch, CNC; *Secrets of Fat-Free Cooking* Sandra Woodruff; *How to Teach Your Baby to Read* Glenn Doman. No unsolicited mss; synopses and ideas welcome if accompanied by s.a.e..
Royalties paid twice-yearly.

Avon Books
1350 Avenue of the Americas, New York NY 10019
☎001 212 261 6800   Fax 001 212 261 6895
Senior Vice President/Publisher *Lou Aronica*
FOUNDED 1941. A division of the Hearst Corporation. *Publishes* hardcover, trade and mass-market paperbacks. Fiction: contemporary and historical romance, literary fiction, science fiction and fantasy, mystery and suspense thrillers, commercial fiction, and young adult. Non-fiction: history, health, sports, humour, film, parenting and childcare, gay and lesbian studies, music, self-help, psychology, true crime, science, current events, business, nature, inspirational and literary non-fiction. 461 titles in 1997. IMPRINTS **Camelot**; **Bard**; **Eos**; **Twilight**; **Flare**. Submit query letter and sample chapter.

Back Bay Books
See **Little, Brown & Company, Inc.**

Badboy
See **Masquerade Books**

Baker Book House
PO Box 6287, Grand Rapids MI 49516–6287
☎001 616 676 9185   Fax 001 616 676 9573
Website: http://www.bakerbooks.com
President *Dwight Baker*
Director of Publications *Allan Fisher*
FOUNDED 1939. Began life as a used-book store and began publishing in earnest in the 1950s, primarily serving the evangelical Christian market. About 165 titles a year. Additional information for authors on website.

DIVISIONS/IMPRINTS
Baker Books *Paul Engle* Publishes religious non-fiction and fiction, Bible reference, professional (pastors and church leaders) books, children's books. About 80 titles a year. TITLES *Turning Points* Mark Noll; *Praise Jerusalem!* Augusta Trobaugh; *Overcoming the Dark Side of Leadership* Gary McIntosh and Samuel Rima Sr.; *Willow* Norm Bomer, illus. Stan Myers. Proposals welcome (request guidelines, specifying non-fiction, fiction, professional or children's). No unsolicited mss.
Baker Academic *Jim Weaver* Publishes college/seminary textbooks, religious reference books, biblical studies monographs. About 30 titles a year. TITLES *John Calvin and the Will* Dewey Hoitenga Jr; *The Evangelical Left* Millard Erickson. Proposals welcome (guidelines available on request). No unsolicited mss. **Fleming H. Revell** *Linda Holland* FOUNDED 1870. A family-owned business until 1978, Revell was one of the first Christian publishers to take the step into secular publishing. Joined Baker Book House in 1992. *Publishes* adult fiction and non-fiction for evangelical Christians. About 45 titles a year. TITLES *Your Love and Marriage* Willard Harley; *In Search of Morality* Robert A. Schuller. Synopses and ideas welcome.
Chosen Books *Jane Campbell* FOUNDED 1971; joined Baker Book House in 1992. *Publishes* charismatic adult non-fiction for evangelical Christians. About 10 titles a year. TITLES *The Twilight Labyrinth* George Otis Jr. Synopses or ideas welcome.
Royalties paid twice-yearly.

Balch Institute Press
See **Golden Cockerel Press** under **UK Publishers**

The Ballantine Publishing Group (Ballantine/Del Rey/Fawcett/Ivy/One World)
201 East 50th Street, New York NY 10022
☎001 212 572 2713   Fax 001 212 572 4912
Website: http://www.randomhouse.com
Group President *Linda Grey*
Snr. Div. VP/Publisher, Ballantine *Clare Ferraro*
Div. VP/Executive Editor, One World *Cheryl Woodruff*
FOUNDED 1952. Division of **Random House,**

Inc. *Publishes* fiction and non-fiction, science fiction. 475 titles in 1997.

IMPRINTS **Ballantine Books; Del Rey; Fawcett Columbine; Fawcett Crest; Fawcett Gold Medal; Fawcett Juniper; Ivy; House of Collectibles; One World.**

Banner Books
See **University Press of Mississippi**

Bantam Doubleday Dell Publishing Group, Inc.
1540 Broadway, New York NY 10036
☎001 212 354 6500   Fax 001 212 302 7985
Website: http://www.bdd.com

Chairman/CEO *Jack Hoeft*
President/COO *Erik Engstrom*
Group Snr. VP/Publisher, Bantam Books *Irwyn Applebaum*
Group Snr. VP/Publisher, Doubleday *Arlene Friedman*
Group Snr. VP/Publisher, Dell Publishing *Carole Baron*
President/Publisher BDD Audio Publishing *Jenny Frost*
President/Publisher, Books for Young Readers *Craig Virden*

Owned by Bertelsmann, the international media company which bought **Random House, Inc.** in March 1998. *Publishes* general commercial fiction: mysteries, westerns, romance, war, science fiction and fantasy, crime and thrillers, adventure; non-fiction, including New Age, African-American/Latino, feminist, gay/lesbian studies; young readers and children's.

DIVISIONS/IMPRINTS
Bantam Books; Doubleday; Dell Publishing; Broadway Books; Books for Young Readers; BBD Audio Publishing; Anchor; Island; Laurel Leaf; Loveswept; New Age Books; New Sciences; Peacock Press; Skylark; Spectra; Starfire; Sweet Dreams; Yearling Books. Most work comes through agents. No unsolicited mss.

Bard
See **Avon Books**

Barron's Educational Series
250 Wireless Boulevard, Hauppauge NY 11788
☎001 516 434 3311   Fax 001 516 434 3723
Chairman/President *Manuel H. Barron*
Managing Editor *Grace Freedson*
FOUNDED 1942. *Publishes* adult non-fiction, children's fiction and non-fiction, test preparation materials and language materials/tapes, cook-

books, gardening, pets, business, art and painting. No adult fiction. 200 titles a year. Unsolicited mss, synopses and ideas for books welcome.
Royalties paid twice-yearly.

Basic Books
See **HarperCollins Publishers, Inc.**

Beacon Press
25 Beacon Street, Boston MA 02108
☎001 617 742 2110   Fax 001 617 723 3097
Director *Helene Atwan*
Publishes general non-fiction. About 50 titles a year. Does not accept unsolicited mss. For further information, refer to www.beacon.org

Bedford Books
See **St Martin's Press, Inc.**

Beech Tree Books
See **William Morrow & Co., Inc.**

Berkley Publishing Group
200 Madison Avenue, New York NY 10016
☎001 212 951 8800   Fax 001 212 213 6706
Website: http:/www.putnam.com
Publisher/Snr VP/Editor-in-Chief *Leslie Gelbman*
FOUNDED 1954. Subsidiary of **The Putnam Berkley Publishing Group.** *Publishes* paperbacks: general interest fiction and non-fiction. About 700 titles a year. IMPRINTS **Ace Science Fiction & Fantasy** Submit synopsis and first three chapters; **Berkley Books; Berkley Prime Crime; Boulevard; Charter/Diamond; Jove.**
Royalties paid twice-yearly.

H. & R. Block
See **Simon & Schuster Trade Division**

Boulevard
See **Berkley Publishing Group**

Boyds Mills Press
815 Church Street, Honesdale PA 18431
☎001 717 253 1164   Fax 001 717 253 0179
Publisher *Kent Brown Jr*
Editorial Director *Larry Rosler*
A subsidiary of Highlights for Children, Inc. FOUNDED 1990 as a publisher of children's trade books. *Publishes* children's fiction, non-fiction and poetry. About 50 titles a year. TITLES *Sharp Horns on the Moon* Carole Crowe; *Lemonade Sun* Rebecca Kai Dotlich; *One Room School* Laurence Pringle; *Poison Dart Frogs* Jennifer Owings

Dewey. Unsolicited mss, synopses and ideas for books welcome. No romance or fantasy novels.

Royalties paid twice-yearly.

Bradford Books
See **The MIT Press**

Brassey's, Inc.
22883 Quicksilver Drive, Dulles VA 20166
☎001 703 260 0602   Fax 001 703 260 0701
E-mail: brasseys@aol.com
Managing Director *Jim Sutton*
Editorial Director *Don McKeon*
FOUNDED 1983. Associated with **Brassey's** of London. *Publishes* non-fiction titles on defence and military affairs, national and international, current affairs, foreign policy, history, biography, intelligence and sports. About 30 titles a year. TITLES *Raiders and Blockaders: The American Civil War Afloat* William N. Still Jr., et al; *Baseball Prospectus: 1998 Edition* Gary Huckabay, et al; *Hitler: The Pathology of Evil* George Victor; *Blue Helmets: The Strategy of UN Military Operations* John Hillen; *The Bicycle in Wartime* Jim Fitzpatrick. No unsolicited mss; synopses and ideas welcome.

Royalties paid annually.

Broadway Books
See **Bantam Doubleday Dell Publishing Group, Inc.**

Browndeer Press
See **Harcourt Brace Children's Books Division**

Bulfinch Press
See **Little, Brown & Company, Inc.**

Bullseye Books
See **Random House, Inc.**

Buzz Books
See **St Martin's Press, Inc.**

University of California Press
2120 Berkeley Way, Berkeley CA 94720
☎001 510 642 4247   Fax 001 510 643 7127
Director *James H. Clark*
Publishes scholarly and scientific non-fiction; some fiction and poetry in translation. 300 titles in 1997. Preliminary letter with outline preferred.

Camelot
See **Avon Books**

Carol Publishing Group
120 Enterprise Avenue, Secaucus NJ 07094
☎001 201 866 0490   Fax 001 201 866 8159
Publisher *Steven Schragis*
FOUNDED 1989. *Publishes* some fiction but mostly non-fiction: biography and autobiography, history, science, humour, how-to, illustrated and self-help. 175 titles in 1997.

Carolrhoda Books, Inc.
241 First Avenue North, Minneapolis MN 55401
☎001 612 332 3344   Fax 001 612 332 7615
Editorial Director *Amy Gelman*
Submissions Editor *Rebecca Poole*
Publishes children's: nature, biography, history, beginners' readers, world cultures, photo essays and historical fiction. Please send s.a.e. for author guidelines.

Cassandra Editions
See **Academy Chicago Publishers**

Chapters
See **Houghton Mifflin Co.**

Charlesbridge Publishing
85 Main Street, Watertown MA 02172
☎001 617 926 0329   Fax 001 617 926 5720
Website: http://www.charlesbridge.com
Chairman *Brent Farmer*
Managing Editor *Elena Dworkin Wright*
FOUNDED 1980 as an educational publisher focusing on teaching thinking processes. *Publishes* children's educational programmes, non-fiction picture books and multicultural fiction for 3- to 12-year-olds. 24 titles in 1997. Complete mss or proposals welcome with self-addressed envelope and IRCs. Mss should be paged, with suggested illustrations described for each page.

Charter/Diamond
See **Berkley Publishing Group**

University of Chicago Press
5801 South Ellis Avenue, Chicago IL 60637–1496
☎001 773 702 7700   Fax 001 773 702 9756
FOUNDED 1891. *Publishes* academic non-fiction only. 266 titles in 1997.

Children's Press
See **Grolier, Inc.**

Chosen Books
See **Baker Book House**

Chronicle Books
85 Second Street, Sixth Floor, San Francisco CA 94105
☎001 415 777 7240   Fax 001 800 858 7787
Website: http://chronbooks.com
Publisher *Jack Jensen*
Publishing Director *Caroline Herter*
FOUNDED 1966. Division of Chronicle Publishing Co. *Publishes* fiction and non-fiction and children's books. Also stationery and gift items. About 200 titles a year.
  DIVISIONS **Children's** *Victoria Rock*; **Fiction** *Jay Schaefer* **Giftworks** *Caroline Herter*. Query or submit outline/synopsis and sample chapters and artwork.
  Royalties paid twice-yearly.

Clarion Books
See **Houghton Mifflin Co.**

Clarkson Potter
See **The Crown Publishing Group**

Classic Reprint
See **University of Alaska Press**

Cobblehill Books
See **Penguin Putnam Inc**

Crescent Books
See **Random House, Inc.**

The Crown Publishing Group
201 East 50th Street, New York NY 10022
☎001 212 572 2409   Fax 001 212 940 7408
Website: http://www.randomhouse.com
President/Publisher *Chip Gibson*
FOUNDED 1933. Division of **Random House, Inc.** *Publishes* popular trade fiction and non-fiction. 267 titles in 1997.
  IMPRINTS **Clarkson Potter** *Lauren Shakely*; **Harmony** *Leslie Meredith*; **Living Language**; *Kathy Mintz* **Three Rivers Press** *Steve Magnuson*; **Crown** *Steve Ross*.

DAW Books, Inc.
375 Hudson Street, 3rd Floor, New York NY 10014–3658
☎001 212 366 2096/Submissions: 366 2095
Fax 001 212 366 2090
Publishers *Elizabeth R. Wollheim, Sheila E. Gilbert*
Submissions Editor *Peter Stampfel*
FOUNDED 1971 by Donald and Elsie Wollheim as the first mass-market publisher devoted to science fiction and fantasy. *Publishes* science fiction/fantasy, and some horror. No short stories, anthology ideas or non-fiction. Unsolicited mss, synopses and ideas for books welcome. About 36 titles a year. TITLES *River of Blue Fire* Tad Williams; *Sword-Born* Jennifer Roberson; *The Compass of the Soul* Sean Russell.
  Royalties paid twice-yearly.

Dearborn Financial Publishing, Inc.
155 N. Wacker Drive, Chicago IL 60606–1719
☎001 312 836 4400   Fax 001 312 836 1021
President *Dennis Blitz*
Chairman *Robert C. Kyle*
Vice President *Carol Luitjens* (Textbook, Course, Training-Securities)
A niche publisher serving the financial services industries. Formerly part of Longman. *Publishes* real estate, insurance, financial planning, securities, commodities, investments, banking, professional education, motivation and reference titles, investment reference and how-to books for the consumer (personal finance, real estate) and small business owner. About 150 titles a year.
DIVISIONS/IMPRINTS
Trade/Professional *Cynthia Zigmund* TITLES *100 Ways to Beat the Market; Buyer Beware; Home Office Know-How.* **Textbook: Real Estate Education Company** *Carol Luitjens* TITLES *Modern Real Estate Practice* (14th ed.); *Real Estate Confronts Reality; Realty Bluebook* (32nd ed.). **Insurance and Security Training** *Carol Luitjens* TITLES Insurance: *Retirement Planning; Variable Contracts; Distributions from Qualified Plans*; Securities: *PassTrak Series 7 License Exam Manual; PassTrak Series 7 Q&A.* **Upstart Publishing Company** *Robin Nominelli* TITLES *The Business Planning Guide; The Market Planning Guide.* **Commodity Trend Service** *Dennis Blitz* TITLES *Futures Charts.* Unsolicited mss, synopses and ideas welcome.
  Royalties paid twice-yearly.

Del Rey
See **The Ballantine Publishing Group**

Dell Publishing
See **Bantam Doubleday Dell Publishing Group, Inc.**

Derrydale
See **Random House, Inc.**

Michael di Capua Books
See **HarperCollins Publishers**

Dial Books for Young Readers

375 Hudson Street, New York NY
10014–3657
☎001 212 366 2800   Fax 001 212 366 2020
Queries *Submissions Coordinator*
FOUNDED 1961. A division of Penguin Putnam
Books for Young Readers. *Publishes* children's
books, including picture books, beginning
readers, fiction and non-fiction for middle
grade and young adults. 70 titles a year.
IMPRINTS Hardcover only: **Dial Books for
Young Readers**; **Dial Books**; hardcover and
paperback editions: **Dial Easy-to-Read**. No
unsolicited mss accepted; query letters with
return postage only.
Royalties paid twice-yearly.

Dimensions for Living

Box 801, Nashville TN 37203–0801
☎001 615 749 6000   Fax 001 615 749 6512
Acquisitions Editor *Joseph A. Crowe*
FOUNDED 1992. *Publishes* non-fiction books
for laity (inspirational, Christian living and self-
help). 20 titles in 1997.

Doubleday

See **Bantam Doubleday Dell Publishing
Group, Inc.**

Dragonfly Books

See **Random House, Inc.**

Lisa Drew Books

See **Simon & Schuster Trade Division**

Thomas Dunne Books

See **St Martin's Press, Inc.**

Sanford J. Durst Publications

11 Clinton Avenue, Rockville Centre,
New York NY 11570
☎001 516 766 4444   Fax 001 516 766 4520
Owner *Sanford J. Durst*
FOUNDED 1975. *Publishes* non-fiction: numis-
matic and related, philatelic, legal and art. Also
children's books. About 12 titles a year.
Royalties paid twice-yearly.

Dushkin/McGraw-Hill

See **The McGraw-Hill Companies**

Dutton/Dutton Children's Books

See **Penguin Putnam Inc**

Eaglebrook

See **William Morrow and Co., Inc.**

Edge Books

See **Henry Holt & Co Inc.**

William B. Eerdmans Publishing Co.

255 Jefferson Avenue SE, Grand Rapids MI
49503
☎001 616 459 4591   Fax 001 616 459 6540
President *William B. Eerdmans Jr*
Vice President/Editor-in-Chief *Jon Pott*
FOUNDED 1911 as a theological and reference
publisher. Gradually began publishing in other
genres with authors like C. S. Lewis, Dorothy
Sayers and Malcolm Muggeridge on its lists.
Publishes religious: theology, biblical studies,
ethical and social concern, social criticism and
children's. 130 titles in 1997.
DIVISIONS
Children's *Judy Zylstra* **Other** *Jon Pott* TITLES
The Promise of Winter Marty & Marty; *Systematic
Theology* Wolfhart Pannenberg; *Dear Zoë* Max de
Pree; *God's Little Seeds* Bijou Le Tord; *Bioethics:
A Primer for Christians* Gilbert Meilaender. Unso-
licited mss, synopses and ideas welcome.
Royalties paid twice-yearly.

Eos

See **Avon Books**

M. Evans & Co., Inc.

216 East 49th Street, New York NY 10017
☎001 212 688 2810   Fax 001 212 486 4544
Chairman *George C. de Kay*
FOUNDED 1954 as a packager. Began publishing
in 1962. Best known for its popular psychology
and medicine books, with titles like *Body
Language, Open Marriage, Pain Erasure* and
Aerobics. Publishes general non-fiction and west-
ern fiction. TITLES *The Arthritis Breakthrough*
Henry Scammell; *Total Concentration* Harold
Levinson; *Born in Blood* and *Dungeon, Fire and
Sword* John J. Robinson; *Dr Atkins' Diet
Revolution* Robert Atkins. About 40 titles a year.
No unsolicited mss; query first. Synopses and
ideas welcome.
Royalties paid twice-yearly.

Everyman's Library

See **The Knopf Publishing Group**

Faber & Faber, Inc.

53 Shore Road, Winchester MA 08190
☎001 617 721 1427   Fax 001 617 729 2783
Chairman *Thomas Kelleher*
Part of the UK-based company. *Publishes* fiction

and non-fiction for adults. About 100 titles a year. No unsolicited mss.

Royalties paid twice-yearly.

Facts On File, Inc.
11 Penn Plaza, New York NY 10001
☎001 212 967 8800   Fax 001 212 967 9196
President *Mark McDonnell*
Publisher *Laurie E. Likoff*

Started life in the early 1940s with News Digest subscription series to libraries. Began publishing on specific subjects with the Checkmark Books series and developed its current reference and trade book programme in the 1970s. *Publishes* general trade, young adult trade and academic reference for the school and library markets. *Specialises* in single subject encyclopedias. About 135 titles a year. No fiction, cookery or popular non-fiction.

DIVISIONS

General Reference *Laurie Likoff* TITLES *Literary A–Z Series; Eyewitness History Series; Stonehenge.* **Academic Reference** *Eleanora Von Dehsen* TITLES *Maps on File; Encyclopedia of Black Women in America.* **Adult Trade** *James Chambers* TITLES *Mafia Encyclopedia; It's Only Rock 'n' Roll.* **Young Adult** *Nicole Bowen* TITLES *Global Profiles Series; American Historic Places; Career Ideas for Kids.* **Electronic Publishing** *Antonio Gomez* TITLES *Understanding Drugs and Alcohol CD-ROM; The American Indian Multimedia CD-ROM.* Unsolicited synopses and ideas welcome; no mss. Send query letter in the first instance.

Royalties paid twice-yearly.

Farrar, Straus & Giroux, Inc.
19 Union Square West, New York NY 10003
☎001 212 741 6900   Fax 001 212 633 9385
President/Chief Executive *Roger W. Straus III*
Snr Vice-President/Editor-in-Chief
Jonathan Galassi

FOUNDED 1946. *Publishes* general fiction, non-fiction, juveniles. About 190 titles a year.

DIVISIONS

Children's Books *Margaret Ferguson*. Publishes fiction and non-fiction, books and novels for children and young adults. Approximately 100 titles a year. Submit synopsis and sample chapters (copies of artwork/photographs as part of package). **Hill & Wang** *Elisabeth Sifton*
IMPRINTS **MIRASOL Libros Juveniles**; **Noonday Press** *Elisabeth Dyssegaard*; **North Point Press; Sunburst Books**.

Fawcett
See **The Ballantine Publishing Group**

Donald I. Fine Books
See **Penguin Putnam Inc**

Fireside
See **Simon & Schuster Trade Division**

Flare
See **Avon Books**

Fodor's Travel Publications
See **Random House, Inc.**

Forge
See **St Martin's Press, Inc.**

The Free Press
See **Simon & Schuster Trade Division**

Samuel French, Inc.
45 West 25th Street, New York NY 10010
☎001 212 206 8990   Fax 001 212 206 1429
Senior Editor *William Talbot*
Acquisitions Editor *Lawrence Harbison*

FOUNDED 1830. *Publishes* plays in paperback: Broadway and off-Broadway hits, light comedies, mysteries, one-act plays and plays for young audiences. Unsolicited mss welcome. No synopses. 50 titles in 1997.

Royalties paid annually (books); twice-yearly (amateur productions); monthly (professional productions). *Overseas associates* in London, Toronto and Sydney.

The Globe Pequot Press
PO Box 833, 6 Business Park Road, Old Saybrook CT 06475
☎001 860 395 0440   Fax 001 860 395 1418
President *Linda Kennedy*
Associate Publisher *Michael K. Urban*

Publishes regional and international travel, how-to, personal finance, and outdoor recreation. About 100 titles a year. TITLES include the *Off The Beaten Path* series, of which there are currently 50 titles, e.g. *Ohio: Off the Beaten Path.* Also publishes the *Recommended Country Inns* guides. Unsolicited mss, synopses and ideas welcome, particularly for travel and outdoor recreation books.

Royalties paid.

Grammercy Books
See **Random House, Inc.**

Greenwillow Books
See **William Morrow and Co., Inc.**

Griffin Trade Paperbacks
See **St Martin's Press**

Grolier, Inc.
Sherman Turnpike, Danbury CT 06816
☎001 203 797 3500   Fax 001 203 797 3197
Chairman/Chief Executive Officer
   Arnaud Lagardere
FOUNDED 1895. *Publishes* juvenile non-fiction,
encyclopedias, speciality reference sets, children's
fiction and picture books. Aout 600 titles a year.
   DIVISIONS **Children's Press**; **Grolier
Educational**; **Grolier Reference**; **Orchard
Books**; **Franklin Watts** (see entry).

Grosset & Dunlap
See **The Putnam & Grosset Group**

Grove/Atlantic Inc.
841 Broadway, New York NY 10003–4793
☎001 212 614 7850   Fax 001 212 614 7886
President/Publisher *Morgan Entrekin*
Senior Editor *Anton Mueller*
FOUNDED 1952. *Publishes* general fiction and
non-fiction. 93 titles in 1997.
   IMPRINTS **Atlantic Monthly Press**; **Grove
Press**.

Gulliver Books
See **Harcourt Brace Children's Books
Division**

**Harcourt Brace Children's Books
Division**
525 B Street, Suite 1900, San Diego
CA 92101–4495
☎001 619 231 6616   Fax 001 619 699 6777
Vice President/Publisher *Louise Pelan*
A division of Harcourt Brace & Company.
Publishes fiction, poetry and non-fiction cover-
ing a wide range of subjects: biography, envi-
ronment and ecology, history, travel, science
and current affairs for children and young
adults. About 175 titles a year.
   IMPRINTS **Browndeer Press**; **Gulliver
Books**; **Gulliver Green® Books** Ecology and
environment; **Harcourt Brace Children's
Books**; **Harcourt Brace Paperbacks**;
Odyssey Paperbacks Novels; **Red Wagon
Books** For ages 6 months to 3 years; **Voyager
Paperbacks** Picture books; **Silver Whistle**.
No unsolicited mss.

Hard Candy
See **Masquerade Books**

Harlequin Historicals
See **Silhouette Books**

Harmony
See **The Crown Publishing Group**

HarperCollins Publishers, Inc.
10 East 53rd Street, New York NY 10022
☎001 212 207 7000   Fax 001 212 207 7797
Website: http://www.harpercollins.com
President/Chief Executive Officer
   Anthea Disney
FOUNDED 1817. Owned by News Corp-
oration. *Publishes* general fiction, non-fiction
and college textbooks in hardcover, trade
paperback and mass-market formats.

DIVISIONS/IMPRINTS
Adult Trade *Judith Regan* President/Publisher;
Harper Reference *Linda Cunningham* Vice
President/Publishing Director; **HarperCollins
Children's Books** *Susan Katz* President/Pub-
lisher; **Harper Paperbacks** *Marjorie Braman* Snr
VP/Publishing Director; **Harper Audio** *Linda
Cunningham* Vice President/Publishing Director;
Harper Prism *John Douglas* Executive Editor;
Michael di Capua Books *Michael di Capua*
Vice President/Publisher; **Regan Books** *Judith
Regan* President/Publisher; **Basic Books**.
   SUBSIDIARY **Zondervan Publishing House**
(see entry).

Harvard University Press
79 Garden Street, Cambridge MA 02138
☎001 617 495 2611   Fax 001 617 496 4677
Editor-in-Chief *Aida D. Donald*
Publishes scholarly non-fiction only: general
interest, science and behaviour, social science,
history, humanities, psychology, political science, sociology, economics, law, business,
classics, religion, cultural studies. 120 new titles
a year and 80–90 paperbacks. Free book catalogue available.

Hearst Books/Hearst Marine Books
See **William Morrow & Co., Inc.**

Hill & Wang
See **Farrar, Straus & Giroux, Inc**

Hippocrene Books, Inc.
171 Madison Avenue, New York NY 10016
☎001 212 685 4371   Fax 001 212 779 9338
President/Editorial Director *George
   Blagowidow*

FOUNDED 1971. *Publishes* general non-fiction and reference books. Particularly strong on foreign language dictionaries, language studies, military history and international cookbooks. No fiction. Send brief summary, table of contents and one chapter for appraisal. S.a.e. essential for response. For manuscript return include sufficient postage cover (IRCs).

Holiday House, Inc.
425 Madison Avenue, New York
NY 10017
☎001 212 688 0085   Fax 001 212 421 6134
Vice President/Editor-in-Chief *Regina Griffin*
Publishes children's general fiction and non-fiction (pre-school to secondary). About 50 titles a year. TITLES *Which Way to the Revolution? A Book About Maps* Bob Barner; *Young, Black and Determined: A Biography of Lorraine Hansberry* Patricia and Frederick McKissack. Submit synopsis and three sample chapters for novels and chapter books; complete mss (without artwork) for picture books. Mss will not be returned without return postage.

Henry Holt & Co Inc.
115 West 18th Street, New York
NY 10011
☎001 212 886 9200   Fax 001 212 633 0748
President/CEO *Michael Naumann*
FOUNDED 1866. Henry Holt is one of the oldest publishers in the United States. *Publishes* fiction, by both American and international authors, biographies, and books on history and politics, ecology and psychology. IMPRINTS **Edge Books**; **John Macrae Books**; **Bill Martin Jr Books**; **Metropolitan Books**; **Owl Books**; **Red Feather Books**.

Houghton Mifflin Co.
222 Berkeley Street, Boston MA 02116
☎001 617 351 5000
Contact *Submissions Editor*
FOUNDED 1832. *Publishes* literary fiction and general non-fiction, including autobiography, biography and history. Also school and college textbooks; children's fiction and non-fiction. Average 100 titles a year. Queries only for adult material; synopses, outline and sample chapters for children's non-fiction; complete mss for children's fiction. IRCs required with all submissions/queries.
DIVISIONS **Clarion Books** (children's and young adult); **Mariner Books** (trade paperback imprint); **Chapters** (cookbooks) .

House of Collectibles
See **The Ballantine Publishing Group**

Hudson River Editions
See **Simon & Schuster Trade Division**

University of Illinois Press
1325 South Oak Street, Champaign
IL 61820–6903
☎001 217 333 0950   Fax 001 217 244 8082
Editorial Director *Richard L. Wentworth*
Publishes non-fiction, scholarly and general, with special interest in Americana, women's studies, African–American studies, American music and regional books. About 110–120 titles a year.

Indiana University Press
601 North Morton Street, Bloomington
IN 42404–3797
☎001 812 855 4203   Fax 001 812 855 7931
Director *John Gallman*
Publishes scholarly non-fiction in the following subject areas: African studies, anthropology, Asian studies, Afro-American studies, environment and ecology, film, folklore, history, Jewish studies, literary criticism, medical ethics, Middle East studies, military, music, paleontology, philanthropy, philosophy, politics, religion, semiotics, Russian and East European studies, Victorian studies, women's studies, a few fiction reprints. Query in writing in first instance.

University of Iowa Press
Kuhl House, 119 West Park Road, Iowa City
IA 52242
☎001 319 335 2000   Fax 001 319 335 2055
Interim Director *Holly Carver*
FOUNDED 1969 as a small scholarly press publishing about five books a year. Now publishing about 35 a year in a variety of scholarly fields, plus local interest, short stories, autobiography and poetry. No unsolicited mss; query first. Unsolicited ideas and synopses welcome.
Royalties paid annually.

Iowa State University Press
2121 South State Avenue, Ames IA 50010
☎001 515 292 0140   Fax 001 515 292 3348
Director *Linda Speth*
Editor-in-Chief *Gretchen Van Houten*
FOUNDED 1934 as an offshoot of the university's journalism department. *Publishes* scholarly books and textbooks, agriculture, aeronautics,

environmental studies, regional history, journalism, and veterinary medicine.
Royalties paid annually; sometimes twice yearly.

Irwin/McGraw-Hill
See **The McGraw-Hill Companies**

Island
See **Bantam Doubleday Dell Publishing Group, Inc.**

Ivy
See **The Ballantine Publishing Group**

JellyBean Press
See **Random House, Inc.**

Jove
See **Berkley Publishing Group**

University Press of Kansas
2501 West 15th Street, Lawrence
KS 66049–3905
☎001 785 864 4154   Fax 001 785 864 4586
Director *Fred M. Woodward*
FOUNDED 1946. Became the publishing arm for all six state universities in Kansas in 1976. *Publishes* scholarly books in American history, women's studies, presidential studies, social and political philosophy, political science, military history and environmental. About 50 titles a year. Proposals welcome.
Royalties paid annually.

Jean Karl Books
See **Simon & Schuster Children's Publishing Division**

Kent State University Press
Kent OH 44242–0001
☎001 330 672 7913   Fax 001 330 672 3104
Director *John T. Hubbell*
Editor-in-Chief *Julia Morton*
FOUNDED 1965. *Publishes* scholarly works in history and biography, literary studies and general non-fiction. 25–30 titles a year. Queries welcome; no mss.
Royalties paid annually.

The Knopf Publishing Group
201 East 50th Street, New York NY 10022
☎001 212 751 2600   Fax 001 212 572 2593
President/Editor-in-Chief *Sonny Mehta*
FOUNDED 1915. Division of **Random House, Inc.** *Publishes* fiction and non-fiction, poetry, juvenile. 134 titles in 1997. IMPRINTS **Alfred A.**

Knopf Inc.; **Everyman's Library**; **Pantheon Books**; **Schocken Books**; **Vintage Books**; **Random House AudioBooks**; **Random House Large Print Publishing**.

Krieger Publishing Co., Inc.
PO Box 9542, Melbourne FL 32902–9542
☎001 407 724 9542   Fax 001 407 951 3671
Website: http://www.web4u.com/
  krieger-publishing/
Chairman *Robert E. Krieger*
President *Donald E. Krieger*
Editorial Head *Mary Roberts*
FOUNDED 1970. *Publishes* education and communications, history, medical science, psychology, chemistry, physical and natural sciences, reference, space sciences, technology and engineering.
IMPRINTS **Anvil**; **Exploring Community History Series**; **Open Forum**; **Orbit**; **Professional Practices in Adult Education and Human Resource Development**; **Public History**. Unsolicited mss welcome. Not interested in synopses/ideas.
Royalties paid yearly.

Lanternlight Library
See **University of Alaska Press**

Laurel Leaf
See **Bantam Doubleday Dell Publishing Group, Inc.**

Lehigh University Press
See **Golden Cockerel Press** under **UK Publishers**

Lerner Publications Co.
241 First Avenue North, Minneapolis
MN 55401
☎001 612 332 3344   Fax 001 612 332 7615
Editorial Director *Gar Willets*
Publishes children's and young adults: art, nature, biography, history, world cultures, world and US geography, aviation, sports, fiction, mysteries, physical science. 90 titles in 1997. Please send IRCs for author guidelines.

Little Simon
See **Simon & Schuster Children's Publishing Division**

Little, Brown and Company, Inc.
3 Center Plaza, Boston MA 021008
☎001 617 227 0730
Website: http://www.littlebrown.com

President/CEO *Charles E. Hayward*
Vice-President/Publisher, Trade
Sarah Crichton

Division of Time Warner Trade Publishing. FOUNDED 1837. *Publishes* contemporary popular fiction and literary fiction. Also non-fiction: cookbooks, biographies, drama, history, mysteries, poetry, art, photography, reference, science, sport, travel and children's. 305 titles in 1997.

IMPRINTS **Back Bay Books; Bulfinch Press**. No unsolicited mss. Query letter in the first instance.

Living Language
See **The Crown Publishing Group**

Llewellyn Publications
PO Box 64383, St Paul
MN 55164-0383
☎001 612 291 1970   Fax 001 612 291 1908
President/Publisher *Carl L. Weschcke*
Acquisitions Manager *Nancy J. Mostad*

Division of Llewellyn Worldwide Ltd. FOUNDED 1901. *Publishes* self-help and how-to: astrology, alternative health, tantra, Fortean studies, tarot, yoga, Santeria, dream studies, metaphysics, magic, witchcraft, herbalism, shamanism, organic gardening, women's spirituality, graphology, palmistry, parapsychology. Also fiction with an authentic magical or metaphysical theme. About 100 titles a year. TITLES *Slavic Sorcery* Kenneth Johnson; *Celtic Women's Spirituality* Edain McCoy; *Inner Passages, Outer Journeys* David Cumes, MD; *Twelve Faces of Saturn* Bill Tierney. Unsolicited mss welcome; proposals preferred. IRCs essential in all cases. Books are distributed in the UK by Airlift Book Co.

Lodestar Books
See **Penguin Putnam Inc**

Lothrop, Lee & Shepard
See **William Morrow and Co., Inc.**

Louisiana State University Press
Baton Rouge LA 70893
☎001 504 388 6294   Fax 001 504 388 6461
Director *L. E. Phillabaum*

Publishes non-fiction: Southern history, American history, Southern literary criticism, American literary criticism, biography, political science, music (jazz) and Latin American studies. About 70 titles a year. Send IRCs for mss guidelines.

Loveswept
See **Bantam Doubleday Dell Publishing Group, Inc.**

The Lyons Press
31 West 21st Street, New York NY 10010
☎001 212 620 9580   Fax 001 212 929 1836
Managing Director *Nick Lyons*
Senior Editor *Bryan Oettel*

Publishes outdoor, nature, sports, gardening and angling titles, plus cookery, woodwork and art. About 80 titles a year. No unsolicited mss; synopses and ideas welcome.

Royalties paid twice-yearly.

Margaret K. McElderry Books
See **Simon & Schuster Children's Publishing Division**

McFarland & Company, Inc., Publishers
PO Box 611, Jefferson NC 28640
☎001 336 246 4460   Fax 001 336 246 5018
President/Editor-in-Chief *Robert Franklin*
Vice President *Rhonda Herman*
Editors *Steve Wilson, Virginia Tobiassen*

FOUNDED 1979. A library reference and upper-end speciality market press publishing scholarly books in many fields: international studies, performing arts, popular culture, sports, women's studies, music and fine arts, business, history, war memoirs and librarianship. *Specialises* in general reference. Especially strong in cinema studies. No fiction, poetry, children's, New Age or inspirational/devotional works. About 150 titles a year. TITLES *Heads of States and Governments; International Holidays; African Placenames; Opera Companies and Houses; Christopher Lee and Peter Cushing; The Sexual Harassment of Women; The Recreation Handbook.* No unsolicited mss; send query letter first. Synopses and ideas welcome.

Royalties paid annually.

The McGraw-Hill Companies
1221 Avenue of the Americas, New York
NY 10020
☎001 212 512 2000
Contact *Submissions Editor*

FOUNDED 1873. US parent of the UK-based **McGraw-Hill Book Co. Europe**. *Publishes* a wide range of educational, professional, business, science, engineering and computing books.

DIVISIONS **Educational & Professional Publishing Group; Professional Publishing**

Group; Business Books; Electronic Publishing; Irwin/McGraw-Hill; Health Professions Division; McGraw-Hill Higher Education; WCB/McGraw Hill; Dushkin/McGraw-Hill; Osborne/McGraw-Hill.

John Macrae Books
See **Henry Holt & Co Inc.**

Mariner Books
See **Houghton Mifflin Co.**

Bill Martin Jr Books
See **Henry Holt & Co Inc.**

Masquerade Books
801 Second Avenue, New York NY 10017
☎001 212 661 7878   Fax 001 212 986 7355
Publisher *Richard Kasak*
FOUNDED 1989. *Publishes* erotic fiction. 120 titles in 1997. IMPRINTS **Badboy; Hard Candy; Rhinoceros; Masquerade; Rosebud.**

University of Massachusetts Press
PO Box 429, Amherst MA 01004–0429
☎001 413 545 2217   Fax 001 413 545 1226
Director *Bruce Wilcox*
Senior Editor *Clark Dougan*
FOUNDED 1964. *Publishes* scholarly, general interest, African-American, ethnic, women's and gender studies, cultural criticism, architecture and environmental design, literary criticism, poetry, philosophy, biography, history, sociology. Unsolicited mss considered but query letter preferred in the first instance. Synopses and ideas welcome. 40 titles in 1997.
Royalties paid annually.

Margaret K. McElderry Books
See **Simon & Schuster Children's Publishing Division**

Mentor
See **Penguin Putnam Inc**

Meridian
See **Penguin Putnam Inc**

Metropolitan Books
See **Henry Holt & Co Inc.**

The University of Michigan Press
PO Box 1104, 839 Greene Street, Ann Arbor MI 48106
☎001 313 764 4388   Fax 001 313 936 0456
Director *Colin Day*

FOUNDED 1930. *Publishes* non-fiction, textbooks, literary criticism, theatre, economics, political science, history, classics, anthropology, law studies, women's studies, English as a second language. 166 titles in 1997.

IMPRINTS
University of Michigan Press *LeAnn Fields* Specialises in monographs in anthropology, economics, classics, women's studies, theatre, political science. **Ann Arbor Paperbacks** TITLES *The Legacy of Tiananmen – China in Disarray* James A. R. Miles; *James Joyce and the Art of Mediation* David Weir; *Discovering American Culture* Cheryl L. Delk. No unsolicited mss.
Royalties paid twice-yearly.

The Millbrook Press, Inc.
2 Old New Milford Road, PO Box 335, Brookfield CT 06804
☎001 203 740 2220   Fax 001 203 775 5643
School/Library Publisher *Jean Reynolds*
Trade Publisher *Judy Korman*
Managing Editor *Colleen Seibert*
FOUNDED 1989. *Publishes* mainly non-fiction, children's and young adult, for trade, school and public library. About 120 titles a year. TITLES *Crafts From Your Favourite Fairy Tales; Round and Square: A Book of Shapes; Mother Teresa: Helping the Poor, Snakes and Slithery Creatures.*
Royalties paid twice-yearly.

Minstrel Books
See **Pocket Books**

MIRASOL Libros Juveniles
See **Farrar, Straus & Giroux, Inc**

University Press of Mississippi
3825 Ridgewood Road, Jackson MS 39211–6492
☎001 601 982 6205   Fax 001 601 982 6217
Director/Publisher *Dr Richard Abel*
Associate Director/Editor-in-Chief *Seetha A-Srinivasan*
FOUNDED 1970. The non-profit book publisher partially supported by the eight State universities. *Publishes* scholarly and trade titles in literature, history, American culture, Southern culture, African-American, women's studies, popular culture, folklife, ethnic, performance, art and photography, and other liberal arts. About 50 titles a year.

IMPRINTS
Muscadine Books *JoAnne Prichard* Regional trade titles. TITLES *The New Orleans Garden; The*

Crawfish Book; The Catfish Book. **Banner Books** Paperback reprints of significant fiction and non-fiction. TITLES *Savage Holiday* Richard Wright; *Dark Princess* W. E. B. DuBois. Send letter of enquiry, prospectus, table of contents and sample chapter prior to submission of full mss.

Royalties paid annually. *Represented* world-wide. UK representatives: **Roundhouse Publishing Ltd.**

University of Missouri Press
2910 LeMone Boulevard, Columbia
MO 65201–8227
☎001 573 882 7641   Fax 001 573 884 4498
Director/Editor-in-Chief *Beverly Jarrett*

Publishes academic: history, literary criticism, intellectual history and related humanities disciplines and short stories – usually four volumes a year. TITLES *Shades of Blue and Gray, An Introductory Military History of the Civil War* Herman Hattaway; *Orphan Trains to Missouri* Michael D. Patrick and Evelyn Goodrich Trickel; *The Catholic Imagination in American Literature* Ross Labrie. Best approach is by letter. Send one short story for consideration, and synopses for academic work. About 50 titles a year.

The MIT Press
5 Cambridge Ctr., Cambridge MA 02142
☎001 617 253 5646   Fax 001 617 258 6779
Managing Editor *Michael Sims*

Publishes scholarly and professional, technologically sophisticated books, including computer science and artificial intelligence, economics, architecture, cognitive science, neuroscience, environmental studies, linguistics and philosophy. 25 titles in 1997. IMPRINT **Bradford Books**.

The Modern Library
See **Random House, Inc.**

Monograph Series
See **University of Alaska Press**

William Morrow & Co., Inc.
1350 Avenue of the Americas, New York
NY 10019
☎001 212 261 6500   Fax 001 212 261 6595
Editor-in-Chief *Betty Kelly*

FOUNDED 1926. *Publishes* fiction, poetry and general non-fiction. Approach in writing only. No unsolicited mss or proposals for adult books. Proposals read only if submitted through a literary agent. About 600 titles a year.

IMPRINTS **Hearst Books/Hearst Marine**

Books *Betty Rice*; **Quill Trade Paperbacks** *Toni Sciarra*; **Morrow Junior Books** *David Reuther*; **Lothrop, Lee & Shepard** *Susan Pearson*; **Greenwillow Books** *Susan Hirschman*; **Eaglebrook** *Joann Davis*; **Mulberry Books/Beech Tree Books** (trade paperbacks) *David Reuther*, **Rob Weisbach Books** *Rob Weisbach*.

Mulberry Books
See **William Morrow and Co., Inc.**

Muscadine Books
See **University Press of Mississippi**

Mysterious Press
See **Warner Books Inc.**

University of Nevada Press
MS 166, Reno NV 89557–0076
☎001 702 784 6573   Fax 001 702 784 6200
Director *Ronald Latimer*
Editor-in-Chief *Margaret Dalrymple*

FOUNDED 1960. *Publishes* serious fiction, Native American studies, natural history, Western Americana, Basque studies and regional studies. About 40 titles a year including reprints. Unsolicited material welcome if it fits in with areas published, or offers a 'new and exciting' direction.

Royalties paid twice-yearly.

New Age Books
See **Bantam Doubleday Dell Publishing Group, Inc.**

University Press of New England
23 South Main Street, Hanover
NH 03755–2048
☎001 603 643 7100   Fax 001 603 643 1540
Acting Director *Peter Gilbert*
Editorial Director *Philip Pochoda*

FOUNDED 1970. A scholarly book publisher sponsored by six institutions of higher education in the region: Brandeis, Dartmouth, Middlebury, Tufts, Wesleyan and the University of New Hampshire. *Publishes* general and scholarly non-fiction; plus poetry through the Wesleyan Poetry Series and Hardscrabble Books fiction of New England. About 75 titles a year.

IMPRINTS **Wesleyan University Press** Interdisciplinary studies, history, literature, women's studies, government and public issues, biography, poetry, natural history and environment. Unsolicited material welcome.

Royalties paid annually. *Overseas associates:* UK – University Presses Marketing; Europe – Trevor Brown Associates.

University of New Mexico Press
1720 Lomas Boulevard NE, Albuquerque
NM 87131–1591
☎001 505 277 2346   Fax 001 505 277 9270
Director *Elizabeth C. Hadas*
Editor *Larry Durwood Ball*

Publishes scholarly and regional books. No fiction, how-to, children's, humour, self-help, technical or textbooks. 53 titles in 1997.

New Sciences
See **Bantam Doubleday Dell Publishing Group, Inc.**

Noonday Press
See **Farrar, Straus & Giroux, Inc**

North Point Press
See **Farrar, Straus & Giroux, Inc**

University of North Texas Press
PO Box 311336, Denton TX 76203–1336
☎001 940 565 2142   Fax 001 940 565 4590
Director *Frances B. Vick*
Associate Director/Editorial Director
   Charlotte M. Wright
Associate Director/Marketing *Gretchen Finn*

FOUNDED 1987. *Publishes* folklore, ecology, regional interest, contemporary, social issues, history, military, women's issues, writing and publishing reference. Publishes the Vassar Miller Poetry Prize winner each year. About 14 titles a year. TITLES *A Sniper in the Tower* Gary Lavergne; *Whatever Happened to Jacy Farrow?* Ceil Cleveland. No unsolicited mss. Approach by letter in the first instance. Synopses and ideas welcome.
Royalties paid annually.

W. W. Norton & Company
500 Fifth Avenue, New York NY 10110
☎001 212 354 5500   Fax 001 212 869 0856

FOUNDED 1923. *Publishes* quality fiction, poetry and non-fiction, college textbooks, professional and medical books. About 300 titles a year. No unsolicited mss.

NTC/Contemporary Publishing Group
4255 West Touhy Avenue, Lincolnwood
IL 60646–1975
☎001 847 679 5500   Fax 001 847 679 2494
Publisher *Christine Albritton*
Editorial Director *John Nolan*
FOUNDED 1947. *Publishes* general adult non-

fiction and adult education books. 600 titles in 1997. Submissions require s.a.e. for response.

Odyssey Paperbacks
See **Harcourt Brace Children's Books Division**

University of Oklahoma Press
1005 Asp Avenue, Norman OK 73019–0445
☎001 405 325 5111   Fax 001 405 325 4000
Director *John N. Drayton*

FOUNDED 1928. *Publishes* general scholarly non-fiction only: American Indian studies, history of American West, classical studies, literary theory and criticism, anthropology, archaeology, natural history, political science and women's studies. About 100 titles a year.

One World
See **The Ballantine Publishing Group**

Onyx
See **Penguin Putnam Inc**

Open Forum
See **Krieger Publishing Co., Inc.**

Orbit
See **Krieger Publishing Co., Inc.**

Orchard Books
See **Grolier, Inc.**

Osborne/McGraw Hill
See **The McGraw-Hill Companies**

Owl Books
See **Henry Holt & Co Inc.**

Pantheon Books
See **The Knopf Publishing Group**

Paragon House
2700 University Avenue, Suite 200, St Paul
MN 55114–1016
☎001 612 644 3087   Fax 001 612 644 0997
Executive Director *Gordon L. Anderson*

FOUNDED 1982. *Publishes* non-fiction: reference and academic. Subjects include history, religion, philosophy, New Age, Jewish interest, self-help, political science, international relations, psychology.
Royalties paid twice-yearly.

Peacock Press
See **Bantam Doubleday Dell Publishing Group, Inc.**

Pelican Publishing Company

Box 3110, Gretna LA 70054–3110
☎001 504 368 1175

Editor-in-Chief *Nina Kooij*

Publishes general non-fiction: popular history, cookbooks, travel, art, business, children's, editorial cartoon, architecture, golf, Scottish interest, and motivational. About 85 titles a year. Initial enquiries required for all submissions.

Pelion Press

See **Rosen Publishing Group, Inc.**

Penguin Putnam Inc

375 Hudson Street, New York NY 10014
☎001 212 366 2000   Fax 001 212 366 2666
Website: http://www.penguin.com

Chairman *Michael Lynton*
President *Phyllis Grann*
Snr. Vice-President, Penguin Putnam Inc/President, Dutton/Plume/Signet
Elaine Koster

Penguin Putnam is a division of the Penguin Group, which is owned by Pearson plc. The group is the second-largest trade book publisher in the world. *Publishes* fiction and non-fiction in hardback and paperback; adult and children's. IMPRINTS include **Allen Lane; Arkana; DAW Books** (see entry); **Dutton; Donald I. Fine; Mentor; Meridian; Onyx; Penguin Classics; Plume; Roc Books; Signet; Signet Classics; Topaz; Truman M. Talley Books; Viking.**
   Children's Division IMPRINTS **Dial Books for Young Readers; Cobblehill Books; Dutton Children's Books; Lodestar Books; Viking Children's Books; Puffin; Frederick Warne.**
Royalties paid twice-yearly.

University of Pennsylvania Press

4200 Pine Street, Philadelphia PA 19104–4011
☎001 215 898 1671   Fax 001 215 898 0404

Director *Eric Halpern*

FOUNDED 1896. *Publishes* serious non-fiction: scholarly, reference, professional, textbooks and semi-popular trade. No original fiction or poetry. TITLES *ABC of Architecture; Penn Greek Drama Series; Captain Watson's Travels in America; A Different Kind of War Story.* About 70 titles a year. No unsolicited mss but synopses and ideas for books welcome.
Royalties paid annually.

Perigee Books

See **The Putnam Berkley Publishing Group**

Philomel Books

See **The Putnam & Grosset Group**

Picador USA

See **St Martin's Press, Inc.**

Players Press

PO Box 1132, Studio City CA 91614-0132
☎001 818 789 4980

Chairman *William-Alan Landes*
Managing Director *David Cole*

FOUNDED 1965 as a publisher of plays; now publishes across the entire range of performing arts: plays, musicals, theatre, film, cinema, television, costume, puppetry, plus technical theatre and cinema material. 53 titles in 1997. TITLES *Principles of Stage Combat Handbook; Stage Crafts Handbook; Scenes for Acting & Directing, vol 2; Performance One – Monologues for Women; Period Costume for Stage and Screen – Medieval to 1500; Three Sisters.* No unsolicited mss; synopses/ideas welcome. Send query letter.
   Royalties paid twice-yearly. *Overseas* subsidiaries in Canada, Australia and the UK.

Plenum Publishing

233 Spring Street, New York NY 10013
☎001 212 620 8000   Fax 001 212 463 0742

Executive Editor, Plenum Trade Books
Linda Greenspan Regan

FOUNDED 1946. *Publishes* quality non-fiction for the intelligent layman and the professional: trade science, social sciences, health, psychology, anthropology and criminology. Over 300 titles a year. Queries only. DIVISION **Plenum Trade** About 20–35 titles a year.

Plume

See **Penguin Putnam Inc**

Pocket Books

1230 Avenue of the Americas, New York NY 10020
☎001 212 698 7000   Fax 001 212 698 7439

President/Publisher *Gina Centrello*

FOUNDED 1939. A division of Simon & Schuster Consumer Group. *Publishes* trade paperbacks and hardcovers; mass-market, reprints and originals. IMPRINTS **Archway; Minstrel Books; Pocket Star Books; Washington Square Press.**

Power Kids Press

See **Rosen Publishing Group, Inc.**

Price, Stern, Sloan
See **The Putnam & Grosset Group**

Princeton Review
See **Random House, Inc.**

Public History
See **Krieger Publishing Co., Inc.**

Puffin
See **Penguin Putnam Inc**

The Putnam & Grosset Group
200 Madison Avenue, New York NY 10016
☎001 212 951 8700   Fax 001 212 532 3693
Chairman *Margaret Frith*
President *Douglas Whiteman*
**President & Publisher, G. P. Putnam's
Sons** *Nancy Paulsen*
President & Publisher, Grosset & Dunlap
Jane O'Connor

The children's book division of **The Putnam
Berkley Publishing Group** (see entry).
IMPRINTS **G. P. Putnam's Sons** *Kathy
Dawson* Senior Editor; **Philomel Books** *Patricia
Lee Gauch* Editorial Director; **Grosset &
Dunlap** *Catherine Daly-Weir* Senior Editor;
Price, Stern, Sloan *Lara Bergen* Editor-in-
Chief. All imprints *publish* picture books, activity
books, fiction and non-fiction for children.

**The Putnam Berkley Publishing
Group** (a member of **Penguin
Putnam Inc.**)
200 Madison Avenue, New York NY 10016
☎001 212 951 8400   Fax 001 212 213 6706
Website: http://www.putnam.com
Chief Executive Officer *Phyllis Grann*
President *David Shanks*

FOUNDED 1838. *Publishes* general fiction and
non-fiction, including children's. Also business, how-to, nutrition and general fiction
under the **Berkley** imprints. **Putnam &
Grosset Group** is the children's book division
(see entry).

DIVISIONS
Berkley Mass-market paperback division (see
entry). **Perigee Books** *John Duff* Trade paperback division. Non-fiction: cookbooks, crafts,
humour, music & dance, health, nutrition, psychology, self-help, social sciences and sociology,
biography, child care and development, behavioural sciences, business, human relations,
education. **Putnam** Hardcover division,
includes **G. P. Putnam Sons**, **Grosset/**

Putnam and **Jeremy P. Tarcher** imprints.
Riverhead Books *Susan J. Petersen* Hardcovers
and trade paperbacks – fiction and non fiction,
including spirituality, religion, biography,
African-American works and travel.
Royalties paid twice-yearly.

Questar
See **Warner Books Inc.**

Quill Trade Paperbacks
See **William Morrow and Co., Inc.**

Rand McNally & Co.
8255 North Central Park Avenue, Skokie
IL 60076
☎001 847 329 8100   Fax 001 847 673 0539
Executive Editor *Jon Leverenz*

FOUNDED 1856. *Publishes* world atlases and
maps, road atlases of North America and
Europe, city and state maps of the United
States and Canada, educational wall maps,
atlases and globes, plus children's products.
Includes electronic publications. 30 titles in
1997.

Random House, Inc.
201 East 50th Street, New York NY 10022
☎001 212 751 2600   Fax 001 212 572 8700
Website: http://www.randomhouse.com
Chairman/Chief Executive Officer
Alberto Vitale

FOUNDED 1925. The world's largest English-
language general trade book publisher. Owned
by Advance Publications Inc. until it was
bought by the German media company,
Bertelsmann, in March 1998. 2036 titles in
1997. Submissions via agents preferred.

DIVISIONS
**Random House Trade Publishing
Group** IMPRINTS **Random House Adult Trade
Books** AUTHORS Truman Capote, Gore Vidal,
Maya Angelou, Norman Mailer, General Colin
Powell; **Villard Books** AUTHORS Robert
Fulghum, Roxanne Pulitzer, Whitney Otto;
The Modern Library; **Times Books** (see
entry); **Princeton Review**; **Random House
Reference & Information Publishing**
Publishes reference works in both book and elec-
tronic formats. TITLES *Random House Webster's
College Dictionary; Random House Webster's College
Thesaurus*.
    The Knopf Publishing Group (see entry).
    The Crown Publishing Group (see entry).
    The Ballantine Publishing Group (see
entry).

Random House Children's Publishing
AUTHORS include Roald Dahl, Theodore Geisel (Dr Seuss), Leo Lionni. IMPRINTS **Dragonfly Books**; **Knopf Paperbacks**; **Bullseye Books**; **Children's Media** CD-ROMs and videos; **Random House Entertainment**.

Random House Value Publishing General interest books across a wide range of categories. IMPRINTS **Wing Books**; **Crescent Books**; **Grammercy Books**; **Children's Classics**; **JellyBean Press**; **Derrydale**.

Fodor's Travel Publications Travel guides in both book and electronic format.

Royalties paid twice-yearly.

Rawson Associates
See **Simon & Schuster Trade Division**

Red Feather Books
See **Henry Holt & Co Inc.**

Red Wagon Books
See **Harcourt Brace Children's Books Division**

Regan Books
See **HarperCollins Publishers, Inc.**

Fleming H. Revell
See **Baker Book House**

Rhinoceros
See **Masquerade Books**

Riverhead Books
See **The Putnam Berkley Publishing Group**

Riverside Publishing Co.
See **Houghton Mifflin Co.**

Roc Books
See **Penguin Putnam Inc**

Rosebud
See **Masquerade Books**

The Rosen Publishing Group, Inc.
29 East 21st Street, New York NY 10010
☎001 212 777 3017   Fax 001 212 253 6915
President *Roger Rosen*
Editorial Director *Patra McSharry Sevastiades*
Executive Editor *Jane Kelly Kosek*
Editors *Gina Ng, Jennifer Croft, Michele Drohan, Erica Smith, Erin Hovanec*
Reference Editors *Margaret Haerens, Christine Slovey*

Publishes non-fiction books (supplementary to the curriculum, reference and self-help) for a young adult audience. Reading levels are years 7–12 and 4–6 (books for teens with literacy problems). Areas of interest include health, religion, careers, self-esteem, sexuality, drug abuse prevention, personal safety, African studies and a wide variety of other multicultural titles. About 150 titles a year.

IMPRINTS
Pelion Press Music titles; **Power Kids Press** *Caroline Levchuck, Helen Packard* Non-fiction books for Reception up to Year 4 that are supplementary to the curriculum. Subjects include conflict resolution, character building, health, safety, drug abuse prevention, history, self-help, religion and multicultural titles. 144 titles a year. For all imprints, write with outline and sample chapters.

Rutgers University Press
100 Joyce Kilmer Avenue, Piscataway NJ 08854–8099
☎001 732 445 7762   Fax 001 732 445 7039
Editor-in-Chief *Leslie Mitchner*
FOUNDED 1936. *Publishes* scholarly books, regional and social sciences. Unsolicited mss, synopses and ideas for books welcome. No original fiction or poetry. About 70 titles a year.
Royalties paid annually.

St Martin's Press, Inc.
175 Fifth Avenue, New York NY 10010
☎001 212 674 5151   Fax 001 212 420 9314
Chairman/Chief Executive *John Sargent*
President/Publisher (Trade Division) *Sally Richardson*
FOUNDED 1952. A subsidiary of **Macmillan Publishers** (UK), St Martin's Press made its name and fortune by importing raw talent from the UK to the States and has continued to buy heavily in the UK. *Publishes* general fiction, especially mysteries and crime; and adult non-fiction: history, self-help, political science, travel, biography, scholarly, popular reference, college textbooks. 1600 titles in 1997.
IMPRINTS **Picador USA**; **Griffin Trade Paperbacks**; **St Martin's Paperbacks (Mass)**; **Thomas Dunne Books**; **Tor**; **Forge**; **Bedford Books**; **Buzz Books**.

Scarecrow Press, Inc.
4720 Boston Way, Lanham Maryland 20706
☎001 301 459 3366   Fax 001 301 459 2118
Associate Publisher *Shirley Lambert*

FOUNDED 1950 as a short-run publisher of library reference books. Acquired by **University Press of America, Inc.** in 1995. *Publishes* reference, scholarly and monographs (all levels) for libraries. Reference books in all areas except sciences, specialising in the performing arts, music, cinema and library science. About 165 titles a year. Publisher for the Medical Library Association, Society of American Archivists, Children's Literature Association, Institute of Jazz Studies of Rutgers – the State University of New Jersey, the American Theological Library Association. Also publisher of *VOYA* (Voice of Youth Advocates); six issues a year. Unsolicited mss welcome but material will not be returned unless requested and accompanied by return postage. Unsolicited synopses and ideas for books welcome.

Royalties paid annually.

Schocken Books
See **The Knopf Publishing Group**

Scholastic, Inc.
555 Broadway, New York NY 10012
☎001 212 343 6100   Fax 001 212 343 6390
Website: http://www.scholastic.com/
Executive Vice President/Publisher
Barbara Marcus
Senior Vice-President/Publisher *Jean Feiwel*
FOUNDED 1920. The world's largest publisher and distributor of children's books in the English language. *Publishes* picture books and fiction for middle grade (8–12-year-olds) and young adults: family stories, friendship, humour, fantasy, mysteries and school. Also non-fiction: biography and multicultural subjects. About 500 titles a year. Mss with outlines and three sample chapters welcome.

Anne Schwartz Books
See **Simon & Schuster Children's Publishing Division**

Scott Foresman-Addison Wesley
1900 E Lake Avenue, Glenview IL 60025–2086
☎001 847 729 3000   Fax 001 847 486 3999
President, School Publishing Group
Kathryn Costello
FOUNDED 1896. Merged with **Addison-Wesley Longman Publishing Co.** in 1996. *Publishes* elementary and secondary education materials. 1300 titles in 1997.

Scribner
See **Simon & Schuster Trade Division**

Signet/Signet Classics
See **Penguin Putnam Inc**

Silhouette Books
300 East 42nd Street, New York NY 10017
☎001 212 682 6080   Fax 001 212 682 4539
Editorial Manager *Tara Gavin*
FOUNDED 1979 as an imprint of **Simon & Schuster** and was acquired by a wholly owned subsidiary of Toronto-based Harlequin Enterprises Ltd in 1984. *Publishes* category, contemporary romance fiction and historical romance fiction only. Over 360 titles a year across a number of imprints.

IMPRINTS
Silhouette Romance *Joan Marlow Golan*; **Silhouette Desire** *Melissa Senate*; **Silhouette Special Edition** *Tara Gavin*; **Silhouette Intimate Moments** *Leslie Wainger*, **Silhouette Yours Truly** *Leslie Wainger*; **Harlequin Historicals** *Tracy Farrell*. **Steeple Hill** *Tara Gavin* New imprint launched in 1997 to publish *Love Inspired* a line of inspirational contemporary romances with stories designed to 'lift readers' spirits and gladden their hearts'. No unsolicited mss. Submit query letter in the first instance or write for detailed submission guidelines/tip sheets.

Royalties paid twice-yearly. *Overseas associates* worldwide.

Silver Whistle
See **Harcourt Brace Children's Books Division**

Simon & Schuster Children's Publishing Division
1230 Avenue of the Americas, New York NY 10020
☎001 212 698 7200
President and Publisher *Rick Richter*
A division of the Simon & Schuster Consumer Group. *Publishes* pre-school to young adult, picture books, hardcover and paperback fiction, non-fiction, trade, library and mass-market titles.

IMPRINTS
Aladdin Books *Ellen Krieger* Picture books, paperback fiction and non-fiction reprints and originals, and limited series for ages pre-school to young adult; **Atheneum Books for Young Readers** *Jonathan Lanman* Picture books, hardcover fiction and non-fiction books across all genres for ages 3 to young adult. Two lines within this imprint are **Jean Karl Books** quality

fantasy-fiction and **Anne Schwartz Books** distinct picture books and high-quality fiction; **Little Simon** *Robin Corey* Mass-market novelty books (pop-ups, board books, colouring & activity) and merchandise (book and audiocassette) for ages birth through 8; **Margaret K. McElderry Books** *Margaret K. McElderry* Picture books, hardcover fiction and non-fiction trade books for children ages 3 to young adult; **Simon & Schuster Books for Young Readers** *Stephanie Owens Lurie* Picture books, hardcover fiction and non-fiction for children ages 3 to young adult. **Simon Spotlight** *Robin Corey* New imprint devoted exclusively to children's media tie-ins and licensed properties.

For submissions to all imprints: send envelope (US size 10) for guidelines, attention: *Manuscript Submissions Guidelines.*

Simon & Schuster Trade Division (Division of Simon & Schuster Consumer Group)

1230 Avenue of the Americas, New York NY 10020
☎001 212 698 7000   Fax 001 212 698 7007
President/Publisher *Carolyn K. Reidy*
Publishes fiction and non-fiction.

DIVISIONS
The Free Press *Paula Barker Duffy* VP & Publisher, *Elizabeth Maguire* VP & Editorial Director; **Fireside/Touchstone** *Mark Gompertz* VP & Publisher, *Trish Todd*; **Scribner** *Susan Moldow* VP & Publisher, *Nan Graham* VP & Editor-in-Chief; **Simon and Schuster** *David Rosenthal* VP & Publisher, *Michael V. Korda* Senior VP & Editor-in-Chief; **Trade Paperbacks** *Mark Gompertz* VP & Publisher, *Trish Todd* VP & Editor-in-Chief.

IMPRINTS
H. & R. Block; Lisa Drew Books; Fireside; The Free Press; Free Press Paperbacks; Hudson River Editions; Rawson Associates; Scribner; Scribner Classics; Scribner Paperback Fiction; S&S Libros eñ Espanol; Simon & Schuster; Touchstone. No unsolicited mss.
Royalties paid twice-yearly.

Simon Spotlight
See **Simon & Schuster Children's Publishing Division**

Skylark
See **Bantam Doubleday Dell Publishing Group, Inc.**

Southern Illinois University Press
PO Box 3697, Carbondale IL 62902
☎001 618 453 2281   Fax 001 618 453 1221
Director *Rick Stetter*
FOUNDED 1953. *Publishes* scholarly and general interest non-fiction books and educational materials, specialising in theatre, film, modern literary studies, rhetoric, criminal justice and aviation. 50 titles a year.
Royalties paid annually.

Sovereign/Appaloosa Publications
128 Reynolds Road £2, Lexington KY 40517
☎001 606 971 0080   Fax 001 606 971 9190
E-mail: sovpublish@aol.com
Chairman *Dorothy Deering*
Managing Director *B. Richardson*
FOUNDED 1996. *Publishes* fiction and non-fiction, cookbooks and children's books. 4 titles in 1997.
DIVISION **Appaloosa** *James Russo* TITLES *The Final Prophet; The Curse of Cain; Freddie the Firefly; Too Safe for Strangers.* Unsolicited mss, synopses and ideas for books welcome. No pornography.
Royalties paid twice-yearly.

Spectra
See **Bantam Doubleday Dell Publishing Group, Inc.**

Stackpole Books
5067 Ritter Road, Mechanicsburg PA 17055
☎001 717 796 0411   Fax 001 717 796 0412
President *M. David Detweiler*
Vice President/Editorial Director *Judith Schnell*
FOUNDED 1933. *Publishes* outdoor sports, nature, photography, military reference, history, fishing, woodworking and carving. 75 titles in 1997.
Royalties paid twice-yearly.

Stanford University Press
Stanford CA 94305-2235
☎001 415 723 9434   Fax 001 415 725 3457
Director *Norris Pope*
Publishes non-fiction: scholarly works in all areas of the humanities, social sciences, natural sciences, history and literature. About 120 titles a year. No unsolicited mss; query in writing first.

Starfire
See **Bantam Doubleday Dell Publishing Group, Inc.**

Steeple Hill
See **Silhouette Books**

Sterling Publishing Co. Inc.
387 Park Avenue South, 5th Floor, New York NY 10016–8810
☎001 212 532 7160   Fax 001 212 213 2495
President/Editor *Lincoln Boehm*
Executive Vice-President/Editorial Director *Charles Nurnberg*
Contact *Sheila Anne Barry*
FOUNDED 1949. *Publishes* non-fiction: reference and information books, science, nature, arts and crafts, architecture, home improvement, history, photography, children's humour, complementary health, wine and food, social sciences, sports, music, psychology, New Age, occult, woodworking, pets, hobbies, gardening, puzzles and games. 600 titles in 1997.

Stonehenge Press
See **Time-Life Inc.**

Sunburst Books
See **Farrar, Straus & Giroux, Inc**

Susquehanna University Press
See **Golden Cockerel Press** under **UK Publishers**

Sweet Dreams
See **Bantam Doubleday Dell Publishing Group, Inc.**

Syracuse University Press
1600 Jamesville Avenue, Syracuse NY 13244–5160
☎001 315 443 5541   Fax 001 315 443 5545
Director *Robert Mandel*
FOUNDED 1943. *Publishes* scholarly books in the following areas: contemporary Middle East studies, international affairs, Irish studies, Iroquois studies, women and religion, Jewish studies, peace studies. About 50 titles a year. TITLES *Intellectual Life in Arab East* M. Buheiry; *Middle Eastern Lives* M. Kramer. SERIES TITLES include *Irish Studies; Modern Jewish History; Syracuse Studies on Peace and Conflict Resolution; Space, Pace & Society* (geography series); *Television; New York Classics; New York State History & Culture; Writing About Women.* Also

co-publishes with a number of organisations such as the American University of Beirut. No unsolicited mss. Send query letter with IRCs.
Royalties paid annually.

Truman M. Talley
See **Penguin Putnam Inc**

Jeremy P. Tarcher
See **The Putnam Berkley Publishing Group**

Temple University Press
Broad and Oxford Streets, Philadelphia PA 19122
☎001 215 204 8787   Fax 001 215 204 4719
E-mail: tempress@astro.ocis.temple.edu
Editor-in-Chief *Janet M. Francendese*
Publishes scholarly non-fiction: American history, Latin American studies, gay and lesbian studies, ethnic studies, psychology, Asian American studies, anthropology, law, cultural studies, sociology, women's studies, health care and disability, philosophy, public policy, labour studies, urban and environmental studies, photography and Black studies. About 60 titles a year. Authors generally academics. Write in first instance.

University of Tennessee Press
293 Communications Building, Knoxville TN 37996
☎001 615 974 3321   Fax 001 615 974 3724

FOUNDED in 1940. *Publishes* scholarly and regional non-fiction. 35 titles in 1997.
Royalties paid twice-yearly.

University of Texas Press
PO Box 7819, Austin TX 78713-7819
☎001 512 471 7233/Editorial: 471 4278
Fax 001 512 320 0668
Director *Joanna Hitchcock*
Assistant Director/Executive Editor *Theresa J. May*

Publishes scholarly non-fiction: anthropology, archaeology, cultural geography, Latin/Mexican/ Native American studies, politics, biology and earth sciences, environmental, American/ Texan urban studies, Texana, women's, film, cultural, media studies, Middle Eastern studies, regional cookbooks, natural history, Latin American/Middle Eastern literature in translation, art and architecture, classics. Unsolicited material welcome in above subject areas only. About 90 titles a year and 12 journals. TITLES *A*

John Graves Reader John Graves; *Journey Through Kurdistan* Mary Ann Bruni; *Twentieth Century Latin American Poetry: A Bilingual Anthology* ed. Stephen Tapscott.

Royalties paid annually.

Three Rivers Press
See **The Crown Publishing Group**

Time-Life Inc.
2000 Duke Street, Alexandria VA 22314
☎001 703 838 7000   Fax 001 703 838 7474
President/Chief Executive *George Artandi*

FOUNDED 1961. *Publishes* non-fiction: art, cooking, crafts, food, gardening, health, history, home maintenance, nature, photography, science. No unsolicited mss. About 300 titles a year.

DIVISIONS/IMPRINTS **Time-Life Books**; **Time-Life Education**; **Time-Life International**; **Time-Life Music**; **Time-Life Video & Television**; **Stonehenge Press**.

Times Books
201 East 50th Street, New York
NY 10022
☎001 212 572 2170   Fax 001 212 940 7464
Publisher *Peter Bernstein*

FOUNDED 1959. A division of **Random House**. *Publishes* general non-fiction and consumer reference. 53 titles in 1997. Unsolicited mss not considered. Letter essential.

Topaz
See **Penguin Putnam Inc**

Tor
See **St Martin's Press, Inc.**

Touchstone
See **Simon & Schuster Trade Division**

Twilight
See **Avon Books**

Tyndale House Publishers, Inc.
351 Executive Drive, Carol Stream
IL 60188
☎001 630 668 8300   Fax 001 630 668 8311
Chairman *Kenneth N. Taylor*
President *Mark D. Taylor*

FOUNDED 1962 by Kenneth Taylor. Non-denominational religious publisher of around 100–150 titles a year for the evangelical Christian market. Books cover a wide range of categories from home and family to inspirational, theology, doctrine, Bibles, general reference and fiction. Also produces video material, calendars and audio books for the same market. No poetry. TITLES *New Living Translation; Left Behind; Tribulation Force; Walking With the Savior; Home with a Heart.* No unsolicited mss; they will be returned unread. Synopses and ideas considered. Send query letter summarising contents of books and length. Include a brief biography, detailed outline and sample chapters. IRCs essential for response or return of material. No audio cassettes, disks or video tapes in lieu of mss. Response time around 6–12 weeks. No phone calls. Send s.a.e. for free catalogue and full submission guidelines.

Royalties paid annually.

University Press of America, Inc.
4720 Boston Way, Lanham MD 20706
☎001 301 459 3366   Fax 001 301 459 2118
Publisher *James E. Lyons*

FOUNDED 1975. *Publishes* scholarly monographs, college and graduate level textbooks. No children's, elementary or high school. About 450 titles a year. Submit outline or request proposal questionnaire.

Royalties paid annually. Distributed by Oxford Publicity Partners, Oxford.

Upstart Publishing Company
See **Dearborn Financial Publishing, Inc.**

Van Nostrand Reinhold
115 Fifth Avenue, New York NY 10003
☎001 212 254 3232   Fax 001 212 475 2548
Chief Executive Officer *Marianne J. Russell*

FOUNDED 1848. A division of International Thomson Publishing, Inc. *Publishes* professional and reference information products in the following fields: culinary arts/hospitality, architecture/design, environmental sciences and business technology. 110 titles in 1997.

Viking/Viking Children's Books
See **Penguin Putnam Inc**

Villard Books
See **Random House, Inc.**

Vintage Books
See **The Knopf Publishing Group**

Voyager Paperbacks
See **Harcourt Brace Children's Books Division**

J. Weston Walch, Publisher

321 Valley Street, PO Box 658, Portland
ME 04104-0658
☎001 207 772 2846   Fax 001 207 772 3105
President *Suzanne Sanborn Austin*
Editor-in-Chief *Lisa French*
Acquisitions Editor *Kate O'Halloran*

FOUNDED 1927. *Publishes* supplementary educational materials for secondary schools across a wide range of subjects, including art, business, technology, careers, literacy, mathematics, science, music, social studies, special needs, etc. Always interested in ideas from secondary school teachers who develop materials in the classroom. 100 titles in 1997. Unsolicited mss, synopses and ideas welcome.

Royalties paid twice-yearly.

Walker & Co.

435 Hudson Street, New York NY 10014
☎001 212 727 8300   Fax 001 212 727 0984
Contact *Submissions Editor*

FOUNDED 1959. *Publishes* mystery, childrens and non-fiction. Please contact the following editors in advance before sending any material to be sure of their interest, then follow up as instructed: **Mystery** *Michael Seidman* 60–70,000 words. Send first three chapters and 3-5 page synopsis. **Trade non-fiction** *George Gibson* Permission and documentation must be available with mss. Submit prospectus first, with sample chapters and marketing analysis. **Books for Young Readers** *Emily Easton* Fiction and non-fiction. Query before sending non-fiction proposals. Especially interested in young science, historical picture books and contemporary fiction for middle grades and young adults.

Frederick Warne

See **Penguin Putnam Inc**

Warner Books Inc.

1271 Avenue of the Americas, New York
NY 10020
☎001 212 522 7200   Fax 001 212 522 7991
Chief Executive Officer *Laurence J. Kirshbaum*
VP/Executive Editor *Rick Horgan*

FOUNDED 1961. *Publishes* fiction and non-fiction, audio books, gift books, electronic and multimedia products. 349 titles in 1997.

IMPRINTS **Aspect** *Betsy Mitchell*; **Mysterious Press** *William Malloy*; **Questar**; **Warner**

Treasures; **Warner Vision**. Query or submit outline with sample chapters and letter.

Washington Square Press

See **Pocket Books**

Washington State University Press

Cooper Publications Building, Pullman
WA 99164-5910
☎001 509 335 3518   Fax 001 509 335 8568
Director *Thomas H. Sanders*

FOUNDED 1928. Revitalised in 1984 to publish hardcover originals, trade paperbacks and reprints. *Publishes* mainly on the history, prehistory and culture of the Northwest United States (Washington, Idaho, Oregon, Montana, Alaska) and British Columbia, but works that focus on national topics or other regions may also be considered. 8–10 titles a year. TITLES *Terra Pacifica: People and Places in the Northwest States and Western Canada; Snowbound; Trail to the Klondike; Grand Coulee: Harnessing a Dream; Raise Hell and Sell Newspapers: Alden J. Blethen and 'The Seattle Times'*. Unsolicited mss and queries welcome.

Royalties paid annually.

Franklin Watts

(A Division of Grolier Publishing), Sherman Turnpike, Danbury CT 06816
☎001 203 797 3500   Fax 001 203 797 6986
Vice President/Publisher *John W. Selfridge*
Executive Editor *Mark Friedman*
Science Editor *Melissa Stewart*

FOUNDED 1942 and acquired by **Grolier** in 1975. *Publishes* non-fiction: curriculum-based material for ages 5–18 across a wide range of subjects, including history, social sciences, natural and physical sciences, health and medicine, biography. Over 100 titles a year. No unsolicited mss. Synopses and ideas considered. Address samples to 'Submissions' and include IRCs if response required. Be prepared for a three-month turnaround.

Royalties paid twice-yearly.

WCB/McGraw-Hill

See **The McGraw-Hill Companies**

Rob Weisbach Books

See **William Morrow & Co., Inc.**

Wesleyan University Press

See **University Press of New England**

Wing Books

See **Random House, Inc.**

Yearling Books
See **Bantam Doubleday Dell Publishing Group, Inc.**

Zondervan Publishing House
5300 Patterson Avenue SE, Grand Rapids
MI 49530
☎001 616 698 6900   Fax 001 616 698 3421

President/Chief Executive *Bruce E. Ryskamp*
FOUNDED 1931. Subsidiary of **HarperCollins Publishers, Inc.** *Publishes* Protestant religion, Bibles, books, audio & video, computer software, calendars and speciality items. TITLES *Old Testament Theology; The C. S. Lewis Readers' Encyclopedia; How to Thrive as a Small-Church Pastor; NIV Young Discoverer's Bible.*

US Agents

Adler & Robin Books, Inc.
3000 Connecticut Avenue, Suite 317,
Washington DC 20008
☎001 202 986 9275   Fax 001 202 986 9485
President/Agent *Bill Adler Jr*
Senior Agent *Lisa M. Swayne*
E-mail: adlerbooks@earthlink.net
FOUNDED 1988. *Handles* popular adult fiction
and non-fiction. Unsolicited synopses and
queries welcome. Send letter with outline or
proposal and sample chapters if possible. Electronic submissions accepted. No reading fee.
CLIENTS H. Michael Fruse, Richard Laermer,
Arthur J. Magida, W. S. Penn. *Commission* Home
15%; UK 20%.

The Ahearn Agency, Inc.
2021 Pine Street, New Orleans LA 70118
☎001 504 861 8395   Fax 001 504 866 6434
President *Pamela G. Ahearn*
E-mail: pahearn@aol.com
FOUNDED 1992. *Handles* general and genre fiction, and non-fiction. Particularly interested in
women's fiction, suspense fiction and historical
romance. No children's books, poetry, autobiography, plays, screenplays or short fiction.
Reading fee charged to unpublished authors.
Send brief query letter with s.a.e. for reply in
the first instance. CLIENTS include John Ames,
Meagan McKinney, Laura Joh Rowland, Marc
Vargo. *Commission* Home 15%; Translation
and UK 20%. *Overseas associates* in Europe and
Latin America.

Marcia Amsterdam Agency
Suite 9A, 41 West 82nd Street, New York
NY 10024
☎001 212 873 4945
Contact *Marcia Amsterdam*
FOUNDED 1969. *Specialises* in mainstream fiction,
horror, suspense, humour, young adult, TV and
film scripts. No poetry, books for the 8–10 age
group or how-to. No unsolicited mss. First
approach by letter only and enclose IRCs. No
reading fee for outlines and synopses. CLIENTS
include George Burt, James Hatfield, L. E.
Hawes, Ruby Jean Jensen, Robert Leininger,
William H. Lovejoy, Isaac Millman, Patricia
Rowe. *Commission* Home 15%; Dramatic 10%;
Foreign 20%.

Bart Andrews & Associates Inc
7510 Sunset Boulevard, Suite 100,
Los Angeles CA 90046–3418
☎001 310 271 9916
Contact *Bart Andrews*
FOUNDED 1982. General non-fiction: show
business, biography and autobiography, film
books, trivia, TV and nostalgia. No scripts. No
fiction, poetry, children's or science. No books
of less than major commercial potential.
Specialises in working with celebrities on autobiographies. No unsolicited mss. 'Send a brilliant
letter (with IRCs for response) extolling your
manuscript's virtues. Sell me!' CLIENTS include
J. Randy Taraborrelli, Wayne Newton, Bart
Andrews. No reading fee. *Commission* Home &
Translation 15%. *Overseas associates* **Abner Stein**,
London.

Joseph Anthony Agency
15 Locust Court Road, 20 Mays Landing,
New Jersey NJ 08330
☎001 609 625 7608
Contact *Joseph Anthony*
FOUNDED 1964. *Handles* all types of novel and
scripts for TV: 2-hour mini-series, screenplays
and ½-hour sitcoms. No poetry, short stories or
pornography. *Specialises* in action, romance and
detective novels. Last sale to **Silhouette Books**
by writer Karen Alaire. Unsolicited mss welcome. Return postage essential. Reading fee
charged to new writers: novels $85; screenplays
$100. CLIENTS include Ed Adair, Robert Long,
Joseph McCullough, Sandi Wether. Signatory
of the Writer's Guild of America. *Commission*
Home 15%; Dramatic & Translation 20%.

The Artists Group
10100 Santa Monica Boulevard, Suite 2490,
Los Angeles CA 90067
☎001 310 552 1100   Fax 001 213 277 9513
Contact *Robert Malcolm, Hal Stalmaster*
FOUNDED 1978. Screenplays and plays for film
and TV. No unsolicited mss. Write with list of
credits, if any. No reading fee. *Commission* 10%.

Malaga Baldi Literary Agency
2112 Broadway, Suite 403, New York
NY 10023
☎001 212 579 5075

Contact *Malaga Baldi*

FOUNDED 1986. *Handles* quality fiction and non-fiction. No scripts. No westerns, men's adventure, science fiction/fantasy, romance, how-to, young adult or children's. Writers of fiction should send mss with covering letter, including IRCs for return of mss and stamped addressed postcard for notification of receipt. Allow ten weeks minimum for response. For non-fiction, approach in writing with a proposal, table of contents and two sample chapters. No reading fee. CLIENTS include Margaret Erhart, Daniel Harris, Felice Picano, Daniel Pool, David J. Skal. *Commission* 15%. *Overseas associates* **Abner Stein**, **Marsh & Sheil Ltd**, UK; Japan Uni.

The Balkin Agency, Inc.

PO Box 222, Amherst MA 01004
☎001 413 548 9835   Fax 001 413 548 9836
Contact *Richard Balkin*

FOUNDED 1973. *Handles* adult non-fiction only. No reading fee for outlines and synopses. *Commission* Home 15%; Foreign 20%.

Maximilian Becker Agency
See **Aleta M. Daley**

Meredith Bernstein Literary Agency, Inc.

2112 Broadway, Suite 503A, New York NY 10023
☎001 212 799 1007   Fax 001 212 799 1145
Contact *Meredith Bernstein, Elizabeth Cavanaugh*

FOUNDED 1981. Fiction and non-fiction of all types. Send query letter first; unpublished authors welcome. IRCs essential for response. CLIENTS include Marilyn Campbell, Georgina Gentry, Patricia Ireland, David Jacobs, Nancy Pickard. *Commission* Home & Dramatic 15%; Translation 20%. *Overseas associates* **Abner Stein**, UK; Lennart Sane, Holland, Scandinavia and Spanish language; Thomas Schluck, Germany; Bardon Chinese Media Agency; William Miller, Japan; Frederique Porretta, France; Agenzia Letteraria, Italy.

Reid Boates Literary Agency

PO Box 328, 69 Cooks Crossroad, Pittstown NJ 08867-0328
☎001 908 730 8523   Fax 001 908 730 8931
Contact *Reid Boates*
E-mail: rboatesla@aol.com

FOUNDED 1985. *Handles* general fiction and non-fiction. *Specialises* in journalism and media, serious self-help, biography and autobiography, true crime and adventure, popular science, current affairs, trade reference and quality fiction. No scripts. No science fiction, fantasy, romance, western, gothic, children's or young adult. Enquire by letter with IRCs in first instance. No reading fee. CLIENTS include Dr James Rippe, Stephen Singular, Jon Winokur and the estate of Ava Gardner. *Commission* Home & Dramatic 15%; Translation 20%. *Overseas associates* Michael Meller, UK & Germany; Kyoshi Asano, Japan; Raquel de la Concha, Spanish languages; Eliane Baristi, France.

Georges Borchardt, Inc.

136 East 57th Street, New York NY 10022
☎001 212 753 5785   Fax 001 212 838 6518

FOUNDED 1967. Works mostly with established/published authors. *Specialises* in fiction, biography, and general non-fiction of unusual interest. Unsolicited mss not read. *Commission* Home, UK, Dramatic 15%; Translation 20%. *UK associates* **Sheil Land Associates Ltd** (Richard Scott Simon), London.

Brandt & Brandt Literary Agents, Inc.

1501 Broadway, New York NY 10036
☎001 212 840 5760   Fax 001 212 840 5776
Contact *Carl D. Brandt, Gail Hochman, Marianne Merola, Charles Schlessiger*

FOUNDED 1914. *Handles* non-fiction and fiction. No poetry or children's books. No unsolicited mss. Approach by letter describing background and ambitions. No reading fee. *Commission* Home & Dramatic 15%; Foreign 20%. *UK associates* **A. M. Heath & Co. Ltd**.

Pema Browne Ltd

Pine Road, HCR Box 104B, Neversink NY 12765
☎001 914 985 2936   Fax 001 914 985 7635
Contact *Pema Browne, Perry Browne*

FOUNDED 1966. ('Pema rhymes with Emma.') *Handles* mass-market mainstream and hardcover fiction: romance, men's adventure, horror, humour, children's picture books and young adult; non-fiction: how-to, religion and reference. No unsolicited mss; send query letter with IRCs. No fax queries. Also handles illustrators' work. CLIENTS include Linda Cargill, Gary J. Grappo, Miriam Moore. *Commission* Home 15%; Translation 20%; Dramatic 10%; Overseas authors 20%.

Sheree Bykofsky Associates, Inc.
11 East 47th Street, New York NY 10017
☎001 212 308 1253
Contact *Sheree Bykofsky*
FOUNDED 1985. *Handles* adult fiction and non-fiction. No scripts. No children's, young adult, horror, science fiction, romance, westerns, occult or supernatural. *Specialises* in popular reference, self-help, psychology, biography and highly commercial or highly literary fiction. No unsolicited mss. Send query letter first with brief synopsis or outline and writing sample (1–3 pp) for fiction. IRCs essential for reply or return of material. No phone calls. No reading fee. CLIENTS include Richard Carlson & Benjamin Shield, Martin Edelston, Glenn Ellenbogen, Merrill Furman, Don Gabor, Alan Lakein, Nancy Mair, Ed Morrow, Adele Wilcox. *Commission* Home 15%; UK (including sub-agent's fee) 25%. Member of the Association of Authors' Representatives.

Maria Carvainis Agency, Inc.
235 West End Avenue, New York NY 10023
☎001 212 580 1559   Fax 001 212 877 3486
Contact *Maria Carvainis*
FOUNDED 1977. *Handles* fiction: literary and mainstream, contemporary women's, mystery, suspense, fantasy, historical, children's and young adult novels; non-fiction: business, finance, women's issues, political and film biography, medicine, psychology and popular science. No film scripts unless from writers with established credits. No science fiction. No unsolicited mss; they will be returned unread. Queries only, with IRCs for response. No reading fee. *Commission* Domestic & Dramatic 15%; Translation 20%.

Martha Casselman, Literary Agent
PO Box 342, Calistoga CA 94515-0342
☎001 707 942 4341
Contact *Martha Casselman*
FOUNDED 1979. *Handles* all types of non-fiction. No fiction at present. Main interests: food/cookery, biography, current affairs, popular sociology. No scripts, textbooks, poetry, coming-of-age fiction or science fiction. Especially interested in cookery with an appeal to the American market for possible co-publication in UK. Send queries and brief summary, with return postage. No mss. If you do not wish return of material, please state so. Also include, where applicable, any material on previous publications, reviews, brief biography. No proposals via fax. No reading fee. *Commission* Home 15%.

The Catalog Literary Agency
PO Box 2964, Vancouver WA 98668
☎001 360 694 8531
Contact *Douglas Storey*
FOUNDED 1986. *Handles* popular, professional and textbook material in all subjects, especially business, health, money, science, technology, computers, electronics and women's interests; also how-to, self-help, mainstream fiction and children's non-fiction. No genre fiction. No scripts, articles, screenplays, plays, poetry or short stories. No reading fee. No unsolicited mss. Query with an outline and sample chapters and include IRCs. CLIENTS include Don Brown, Malcolm S. Foster, Deborah Wallace. *Commission* 15%.

The Linda Chester Literary Agency
Rockefeller Center, 630 Fifth Avenue, New York NY 10111
☎001 219 439 0881   Fax 001 212 439 9858
Contact *Joanna Pulcini*
FOUNDED 1978. *Handles* literary and commercial fiction and non-fiction in all subjects. No scripts, children's or textbooks. No unsolicited mss. No reading fee for solicited material. *Commission* Home & Dramatic 15%; Translation 25%.

Connie Clausen & Associates
250 East 87th Street, Apt. 16H, New York NY 10128
☎001 212 427 6135   Fax 001 212 996 7111
Agents *Stedman Mays, Mary M. Tahan*
Handles non-fiction work such as memoirs, biography, true crime, true stories, how-to, psychology, spirituality, relationships, style, health/nutrition, fashion/beauty, women's issues, humour and cookbooks. No fiction. Books include Quentin Crisp's *Resident Alien*; *What the IRS Doesn't Want You to Know* Marty Kaplin and Naomi Weiss; *A Flat Stomach ASAP: The Fastest Way to Perfect Abs* Ellington Darden; *The Rules* Ellen Fein & Sherrie Schneider; *It's About Time ... Age-Defying Beauty & Well-Being* Dayle Hadden. Send query letter only. Include IRCs. UK *associates* **David Grossman Literary Agency Ltd**.

Hy Cohen Literary Agency Ltd
PO Box 43770, Up. Montclair NJ 07043
☎001 973 783 9494   Fax 001 973 783 9867
President *Hy Cohen*
FOUNDED 1975. Fiction and non-fiction. No scripts. Unsolicited mss welcome, but synopsis

with sample 100 pp preferred. IRCs essential. No reading fee. *Commission* Home & Dramatic 10%; Foreign 20%. *Overseas associates* **Abner Stein**, UK.

Ruth Cohen, Inc.
Box 7626, Menlo Park CA 94025
☎001 650 854 2054
President *Ruth Cohen*

FOUNDED 1982. Works mostly with established/published authors but will consider new writers. *Specialises* in high-quality mystery and women's fiction, plus historical romance. No poetry, short stories or film scripts. No unsolicited mss. Send opening 10 pp with synopsis. Include enough IRCs for return postage or materials *will not be returned*. No reading fee. *Commission* Home & Dramatic 15%; Foreign 20%.

Frances Collin Literary Agent
PO Box 33, Wayne PA 19087–0033
☎001 610 254 0555   Fax 001 610 254 5029
Contact *Frances Collin*

FOUNDED 1948. Successor to Marie Rodell. *Handles* general fiction and non-fiction. No scripts. No unsolicited mss. Send query letter only, with IRCs for reply, for the attention of Marsha Kear. No reading fee. Rarely accepts non-professional writers or writers not represented in the UK. *Overseas associates* worldwide.

Don Congdon Associates, Inc.
156 Fifth Avenue, Suite 625, New York NY 10010–7002
☎001 212 645 1229   Fax 001 212 727 2688
Contact *Don Congdon, Michael Congdon, Susan Ramer*

FOUNDED 1983. *Handles* fiction and non-fiction. No academic, technical, romantic fiction, or scripts. No unsolicited mss. Approach by letter in the first instance. No reading fee. *Commission* Home 10%; UK & Translation 19%. *Overseas associates* **The Marsh Agency** (Europe), **Abner Stein** (UK), Michelle Lapautre (France), Tuttle Mori Agency (Japan).

The Connor Literary Agency
2911 West 71st Street, Richfield MN 55423
☎001 612 866 1486   Fax 001 612 869 4074
Contact *Marlene Connor, John Lynch*

FOUNDED 1985. *Handles* general non-fiction, contemporary women's fiction, popular fiction, Black fiction and non-fiction, how-to, mysteries and crafts. Particularly interested in illustrated books. No unsolicited mss; send query letter in the first instance. Previously published authors preferred. CLIENTS include Simplicity Pattern Company, *Essence Magazine*, Bonnie Allen, Ron Elmore, Nadezda Obradovic. *Commission* Home 15%; UK & Translation 25%. *Overseas associates* in England, Spain, Japan, France and Germany.

Richard Curtis Associates, Inc
171 East 74th Street, Second Floor, New York NY 10021
☎001 212 772 7363   Fax 001 212 772 7393
Contact *Richard Curtis*
E-mail: rcurtis@curtisagency.com

FOUNDED 1969. *Handles* genre and mainstream fiction, plus commercial non-fiction. Scripts rarely. *Specialises* in electronic rights and multimedia.

Curtis Brown Ltd
10 Astor Place, New York NY 10003
☎001 212 473 5400
Book Rights *Laura Blake Peterson, Ellen Geiger, Peter L. Ginsberg, Emilie Jacobson, Ginger Knowlton, Perry Knowlton, Jennifer McDonald, Marilyn E. Marlow, Andrew Pope, Clyde Taylor, Maureen Walters, Mitchell Walters*
Film, TV, Audio Rights *Timothy Knowlton, Edwin Wintle*
Translation *Dave Barbor*

FOUNDED 1914. *Handles* general fiction and non-fiction. Also some scripts for film, TV and theatre. No unsolicited mss; queries only, with IRCs for reply. No reading fee. *Overseas associates* Representatives in all major foreign countries.

Aleta M. Daley/ Maximilian Becker Agency
444 East 82nd Street, New York NY 10028
☎001 212 744 1453   Fax 001 212 249 2088
1021 Budapest, Széher lit 72, Hungary
☎/fax 00 36 1 200 3148
Contact *Aleta M. Daley*

FOUNDED 1950. *Handles* non-fiction and fiction; also scripts for film and TV. No unsolicited mss. Send query letter in the first instance with sample chapters or a proposal. No reading fee, but handling fee is charged to cover postage, telephone, etc. *Commission* Home 15%; UK 20%.

Joan Daves Agency

21 West 26th Street, New York
NY 10010-1003
☎001 212 685 2663   Fax 001 212 685 1781
Director *Jennifer Lyons*
FOUNDED 1952. Literary fiction and non-fiction. No romance or textbooks. No scripts. Send query letter in the first instance. 'A detailed synopsis seems valuable only for non-fiction work. Material submitted should specify the author's background, publishing credits and similar pertinent information.' No reading fee. CLIENTS include Frederick Franck, Frank Browning, Suzy McKee Charnas, John Maclean, Elizabeth Holtzman, Melvin Jules Bukret, Christina Shea, Roger Shattack, Leora Tannenbaum and the estates of Isaac Babel, Heinrich Böll and Martin Luther King Jr. *Commission* Home 15%; Dramatic 10–25%; Foreign 20%.

Elaine Davie Literary Agency

620-L Park Avenue, Rochester NY 14607
☎001 716 442 0830
President *Elaine Davie*
FOUNDED 1986. *Handles* all types of adult fiction and non-fiction, specialising in books by and for women. Particularly interested in commercial genre fiction. No scripts. No short stories, anthologies, poetry or children's. Submit synopsis and sample chapters or complete mss together with IRCs. No reading fee. *Commission* Home 15%; Dramatic & Translation 20%.

Anita Diamant Literary Agency

310 Madison Avenue, Suite 1105, New York
NY 10017
☎001 212 687 1122
Contact *John Talbot, Robin Rue*
FOUNDED 1917. *Handles* fiction and non-fiction. No academic, children's, science fiction and fantasy, poetry, articles, short stories, screenplays or teleplays. Works in association with Hollywood film agent. No unsolicited mss. Write with description of work, short synopsis and details of publishing background. No reading fee. CLIENTS include V. C. Andrews, Frederic Bean, Linda Howard, William W. Johnstone, Janice Kaiser, Richard Lederer, Mark McGarrity, Andrew Neiderman, Duane Schultz, Richard S. Wheeler. *Commission* Home & Dramatic 15%; Translation 20%. *Overseas associates* **A. M. Heath & Co. Ltd**, UK.

Sandra Dijkstra Literary Agency

1155 Camino del Mar, Suite 515–C, Del Mar
CA 92014
☎001 619 755 3115
Contact *Debra Ginsberg*
FOUNDED 1981. *Handles* quality and commercial non-fiction and fiction, including some genre fiction. No scripts. No westerns, contemporary romance or poetry. Willing to look at children's projects. *Specialises* in quality fiction, mystery/thrillers, psychology, self-help, science, health, business, memoirs, biography. Dedicated to promoting new and original voices and ideas. For fiction: send brief synopsis (1 page) and first 50 pages; for non-fiction: send proposal with overview, chapter outline, author biog. and two sample chapters. All submissions should be accompanied by IRCs. No reading fee. *Commission* Home 15%; Translation 20%. *Overseas associates* **Abner Stein**, UK; Ursula Bender, Agence Hoffman, Germany; Monica Heyum, Scandinavia; Luigi Bernabo, Italy; M. Casanovas, Spain; Caroline Van Gelderen, Netherlands; M. Kling (La Nouvelle Agence), France; William Miller, The English Agency, Japan.

Dykeman Associates, Inc.

4115 Rawlins, Dallas TX 75219-3661
☎001 214 528 2991   Fax 001 214 528 0241
Contact *Alice Dykeman, Barry Franke PhD.*
FOUNDED 1974. *Handles* non-fiction, fiction, screen and teleplays. No unsolicited mss; send outline or synopsis. Editing available. *Commission* 15%.

Jane Dystel Literary Management

One Union Square West, Suite 904, New York NY 10003
☎001 212 627 9100   Fax 001 212 627 9313
Website: www.dystel.com
Contact *Jane Dystel, Miriam Goderich, Todd Keithley*
FOUNDED 1991. *Handles* non-fiction and fiction. *Specialises* in politics, history, biography, cookbooks, current affairs, celebrities, commercial and literary fiction. No reading fee. CLIENTS include Lorene Cary, Thomas French, Dan Gearino, Lynne Rossetto Kasper, Gus Lee, Alice Medrich, Thomas Moran, Barack Obama, Mary Russell, Elaine St James, Michael Tucker.

Educational Design Services, Inc.

PO Box 253, Wantagh NY 11793
☎001 718 539 4107/516 221 0995
President *Bertram Linder*

Vice President *Edwin Selzer*

FOUNDED 1979. *Specialises* in educational material and textbooks for sale to school markets. IRCs must accompany submissions. *Commission* Home 15%; Foreign 25%.

Elek International Rights Agents

457 Broome Street, New York NY 10013
☎001 212 431 9368   Fax 001 212 966 5768

Contact *Kelly Duignan*
Website: theliteraryagency.com

FOUNDED 1979. *Handles* adult non-fiction and children's picture books. No scripts, novels, psychology, New Age, poetry, short stories or autobiography. No unsolicited mss; send letter of enquiry with IRCs for reply; include résumé, credentials, brief synopsis. No reading fee. CLIENTS Tedd Arnold, Dr Robert Ballard, Patrick Brogan, Robert Bateman, Laura Cornell, Chris Dodd, Dan Drexler, Tracy Harrast, Sally Placksin, Betsy Treitler. *Commission* Home 15%; Dramatic & Foreign 20%. Through wholly-owned subsidiary The Content Company Inc., licenses and manages clients' intellectual property for development into electronic formats - CD-ROM/CD-I/DVD/On-Line/CD-Plus,   etc. 'We manage our own website where clients' projects are promoted. Additionally, we feature their published works and provide links to Amazon.com for consumer purchases.'

Ann Elmo Agency, Inc.

60 East 42nd Street, New York NY 10165
☎001 212 661 2880/1 Fax 001 212 661 2883

Contact *Lettie Lee, Mari Cronin, Andree Abecassis*

FOUNDED in the 1940s. *Handles* literary and romantic fiction, mysteries and mainstream; also non-fiction in all subjects, including biography and self-help. Some children's (8–12-year-olds). Query letter with outline of project in the first instance. No reading fee. *Commission* Home 15–20%. *Overseas associates* **John Johnson Ltd**, UK.

Frieda Fishbein Associates

PO Box 723, Bedford NY 10506
☎001 914 234 7232   Fax 001 914 234 4196

President *Janice Fishbein*
Associates *Heidi Carlson, Douglas Michael*

FOUNDED 1925. Eager to work with new/unpublished writers. *Specialises* in historical romance, historical adventure, male adventure, mysteries, thrillers, family sagas, 'non-reporting' and how-to. Also plays and screenplays. No poetry, magazine articles, short stories or young children's. First approach with query letter. No

reading fee for outlines at our request or for published authors working in the same genre. CLIENTS include Gary Bohlke, Lisa Dillman, Herbert Fisher, Jeanne Mackin, William Seebring, Robert Simpson, Alicen White. *Commission* Home & Dramatic 10%; Foreign 20%.

ForthWrite Literary Agency & Speakers Bureau

28990 Pacific Coast Highway, Suite 106, Malibu CA 90265
☎001 310 457 5785   Fax 001 310 457 9785

Contact *Wendy Keller*

FOUNDED 1988. *Specialises* in non-fiction: business (marketing, finance, management and sales), alternative health, popular psychology, history (English and Scottish), self-help, home and health, crafts, computer, how-to, animal care. Handles electronic, foreign (translation and distribution) and resale rights for previously published books. Send query letter with IRCs. *Commission* Foreign 20%.

Robert A. Freedman Dramatic Agency, Inc.

Suite 2310, 1501 Broadway, New York NY 10036
☎001 212 840 5760

President *Robert A. Freedman*
Vice President *Selma Luttinger*

FOUNDED 1928 as Brandt & Brandt Dramatic Department, Inc.. Took its present name in 1984. Works mostly with established authors. *Specialises* in plays, film and TV scripts. Unsolicited mss not read. *Commission* Dramatic 10%.

Max Gartenberg, Literary Agent

521 Fifth Avenue, Suite 1700, New York NY 10175
☎001 212 860 8451   Fax 001 973 535 5033

Contact *Max Gartenberg*

FOUNDED 1954. Works mostly with established/published authors. *Specialises* in non-fiction and trade fiction. Query first. CLIENTS include Linda Davis, Ralph Hickok, Charles Little, Howard Owen, David Roberts, Ralph Sawyer. *Commission* Home & Dramatic 10%; 15% on initial sale, 10% thereafter; Foreign 15/20%.

Gelfman Schneider Literary Agents, Inc.

250 West 57th Street, Suite 2515, New York NY 10107
☎001 212 245 1993   Fax 001 212 245 8678

Contact *Deborah Schneider, Jane Gelfman*

FOUNDED 1919 (London), 1980 (New York). Formerly John Farquharson Ltd. Works mostly with established/published authors. *Specialises* in general trade fiction and non-fiction. No poetry, short stories or screenplays. No reading fee for outlines. Submissions must be accompanied by IRCs. *Commission* Home 15%; Dramatic 15%; Foreign 20%. *Overseas associates* **Curtis Brown Group Ltd**, UK.

Goldberg Literary Agents, Inc.
255 West 84th Street, New York NY 10024
☎001 212 799 1260
Editorial Director *Kathrine Butler*
FOUNDED 1974. *Handles* fiction and non-fiction. No unsolicited mss. Send query letter describing work in the first instance. *Commission* Home 10%; UK 20%. *Overseas associate* Peter Knight, UK.

Sanford J. Greenburger Associates, Inc.
15th Floor, 55 Fifth Avenue, New York NY 10003
☎001 212 206 5600   Fax 001 212 463 8718
Contact *Heide Lange, Faith Hamlin, Beth Vesel, Theresa Park*
Handles fiction and non-fiction. No unsolicited mss. First approach with query letter, sample chapter and synopsis. No reading fee.

The Charlotte Gusay Literary Agency
10532 Blythe Avenue, Los Angeles CA 90064
☎001 310 559 0831   Fax 001 310 559 2639
Contact *Charlotte Gusay*
FOUNDED 1988. *Handles* fiction, both literary and commercial, plus non-fiction: children's and adult humour, parenting, gardening, women's and men's issues, feminism, psychology, memoirs, biography, travel. No science fiction, horror, short pieces or collections of stories. No unsolicited mss; send query letter first, then if your material is requested, send succinct outline and first three sample chapters for fiction, or proposal for non-fiction. No response without IRCs. No reading fee. *Commission* Home 15%; Dramatic 10%; Translation & Foreign 25%.

Joy Harris Literary Agency, Inc.
156 Fifth Avenue, Suite 617, New York NY 10010
☎001 212 924 6269   Fax 001 212 924 6609
Contact *Joy Harris, Kassandra Duane, Leslie Daniels*

Handles adult non-fiction and fiction. No unsolicited mss. Query letter in the first instance. No reading fee. *Commission* Home & Dramatic 15%; Foreign 20%. *Overseas associates* Michael Meller, Germany; **Abner Stein**, UK; Tuttle Mori, Japan/China; Eliane Benisti, France.

John Hawkins & Associates, Inc.
71 West 23rd Street, Suite 1600, New York NY 10010
☎001 212 807 7040   Fax 001 212 807 9555
Contact *John Hawkins, William Reiss*
FOUNDED 1893. *Handles* film and TV rights and software. No unsolicited mss; send queries with 1–3 page outline and 1 page c.v. IRCs necessary for response. No reading fee. *Commission* Apply for rates.

The Jeff Herman Agency, Inc.
332 Bleecker Street, Suite 6–31, New York NY 10014
☎001 212 941 0540   Fax 001 212 941 0614
Contact *Jeffrey H. Herman*
Handles all areas of non-fiction, textbooks and reference and commercial fiction. No scripts. No unsolicited mss. Query letter with IRCs in the first instance. No reading fee. Jeff Herman publishes a useful reference guide to the book trade called *The Writer's Guide to Book Editors, Publishers & Literary Agents* (Prima). *Commission* Home 15%; Translation 10%.

Susan Herner Rights Agency, Inc.
PO Box 303, Scarsdale NY 10583
☎001 914 725 8967   Fax 001 914 725 8969
Contact *Susan N. Herner, Sue P. Yuen*
FOUNDED 1987. Adult fiction and non-fiction in all areas. No children's books. *Handles* film and TV rights and software. Send query letter with outline and sample chapters. No reading fee. *Commission* Home 15%; Dramatic & Translation 20%. *Overseas associates* **David Grossman Literary Agency Ltd**, UK.

Frederick Hill Associates
1842 Union Street, San Francisco CA 94123
☎001 415 921 2910   Fax 001 415 921 2802
Contact *Fred Hill, Bonnie Nadell, Irene Moore*
FOUNDED 1979. General fiction and non-fiction. No scripts. Send query letter detailing past publishing history if any. IRCs required. CLIENTS include David Foster Wallace, Katherine Neville, Richard North Patterson. *Commission* Home & Dramatic 15%; Foreign 20%. *Overseas associates* **Mary Clemmey Literary Agency**, UK.

Hull House Literary Agency
240 East 82nd Street, New York NY 10028
☎001 212 988 0725   Fax 001 212 794 8758
President *David Stewart Hull*
Associate *Lydia Mortimer*

FOUNDED 1987. *Handles* commercial fiction, mystery, biography, military history. No scripts, poetry, short stories, romance, science fiction and fantasy, children's or young adult. No unsolicited mss; send single-page letter describing project briefly, together with short biographical note and list of previous publications if any. IRCs essential. No reading fee. *Commission* Home 15%; Translation 20%.

IMG Literary
22 East 71st Street, New York NY 10021–4911
☎001 212 772 8900   Fax 001 212 772 2617
Contact *David Chalfant (Vice President), Meghan Sercombe*

FOUNDED 1986. A wholly-owned subsidiary of IMG, The Mark McCormack Group of Companies. *Handles* non-fiction and fiction. No science fiction, fantasy, poetry or photography. No scripts. Query first. Submissions should include brief synopsis (typed), sample chapters (50 pp maximum), publishing history, etc. CLIENTS include Pat Conroy, Jan Morris, Arnold Palmer, Dianne Pugh, Tiger Woods. *Commission* Home & Dramatic 15%; Foreign 20%. *Overseas associates* worldwide.

Kidde, Hoyt & Picard Literary Agency
333 East 51st Street, New York NY 10022
☎001 212 755 9461/9465
Fax 001 212 223 2501
Chief Associate *Katharine Kidde*
Associate *Laura Langlie*

FOUNDED 1981. *Specialises* in mainstream and literary fiction, romantic fiction (historical and contemporary), and quality non-fiction in humanities and social sciences (biography, history, current affairs, the arts). No reading fee. Query first, include s.a.e. CLIENTS include Michael Cadnum, Bethany Campbell, Jim Oliver, Patricia Robinson. *Commission* 15%.

Kirchoff/Wohlberg, Inc.
866 United Nations Plaza, Suite 525,
New York NY 10017
☎001 212 644 2020   Fax 001 212 223 4387
Authors' Representative *Elizabeth Pulitzer-Voges*

FOUNDED 1930. *Handles* books for children and young adults, specialising in children's picture books. No adult material. No scripts for TV, radio, film or theatre. Send letter of enquiry with synopsis or outline and IRCs for reply or return. No reading fee.

Paul Kohner, Inc.
9300 Wilshire Boulevard, Suite 555, Beverly Hills CA 90212
☎001 310 550 1060   Fax 001 310 276 1083
Contact *Gary Salt, Beth Bohn*

FOUNDED 1938. *Handles* a broad range of books for subsidiary rights sales to film and TV. Few direct placements with publishers as film and TV scripts are the major part of the business. *Specialises* in true crime, biography and history. Non-fiction preferred to fiction for the TV market but anything 'we feel has strong potential' will be considered. No short stories, poetry, science fiction or gothic. Unsolicited material will be returned unread, if accompanied by s.a.e. Approach via a third-party reference or send query letter with professional résumé. No reading fee. CLIENTS Ed McBain, Tony Huston, John Katzenbach, Charles Marowitz, Alan Sharp, Donald Westlake. *Commission* Home & Dramatic 10%; Publishing 15%.

Barbara S. Kouts, Literary Agent
PO Box 560, Bellport NY 11713
☎001 516 286 1278   Fax 001 516 286 1538
Contact *Barbara S. Kouts*

FOUNDED 1980. *Handles* fiction, non-fiction and children's. No romance, science fiction or scripts. No unsolicited mss. Query letter in the first instance. No reading fee. CLIENTS include Hal Gieseking, Nancy Mairs, Robert San Souci. *Commission* Home 10%; Foreign 20%.

Peter Lampack Agency, Inc.
551 Fifth Avenue, Suite 1613, New York NY 10176
☎001 212 687 9106   Fax 001 212 687 9109
Contact *Peter Lampack, Sandra Blanton, Loren Soeiro*

FOUNDED in 1977. *Handles* commercial fiction: male action and adventure, contemporary relationships, historical, mysteries and suspense, literary fiction; also non-fiction from recognised experts in a given field, plus biographies, autobiographies. Also handles theatrical, motion picture, and TV rights from book properties. No original scripts or screenplays, series or episodic material. Best approach by letter in first instance. No reply without s.a.e. 'We will respond within three weeks and invite the submission of manuscripts which we would like to examine.' No reading fee. No unsolicited mss. CLIENTS include J. M. Coetzee, Clive Cussler, Martha Grimes, Judith Kelman, Johanna Kingsley, Jessica March, Doris Mortman, David Osborn, Gerry Spence, Fred Mustard Stewart. *Commission* Home & Dramatic 15%; Translation & UK 20%.

The Lazear Agency, Inc.
430 First Avenue North, Suite 416, Minneapolis MN 55401
☎001 612 332 8640   Fax 001 612 332 4648
Contact *Christi Cardenas, Cheryl Kissel, Jonathon Lazear, Wendy Lazear, Jeff McGuiness, Susie Moncur*

FOUNDED 1984. *Handles* fiction: mysteries, suspense, young adult and literary; also true crime, addiction recovery, biography, travel, business, and scripts for film and TV, CD-ROM and CD-I, broad band interactive television. Children's books from previously published writers. No poetry or stage plays. Approach by letter, with description of mss, short autobiography and IRCs. No reading fee. CLIENTS include Noah Adams, Andrei Codrescu, Al Franken, Jane Goodall, Merrill Lynch, Harvey Mackay, Gary Paulsen, The Pillsbury Co., Will Weaver, Bailey White. *Commission* Home & Dramatic 15%; Translation 20%.

Levant & Wales, Literary Agency, Inc.
108 Hayes Street, Seattle WA 98109
☎001 206 284 7114   Fax 001 206 284 0190
E-mail: waleslit@aol.com
Contact *Elizabeth Wales, Adrienne Reed*

FOUNDED 1988. *Handles* quality fiction and non-fiction. No scripts except via sub-agents. No genre fiction, westerns, romance, science fiction or horror. Special interest in 'Pacific Rim', West, West Coast, and Pacific Northwest clients. No unsolicited mss; send query letter with publication list and writing sample. No reading fee. No e-mail queries longer than one page. *Commission* Home 15%; Dramatic & Translation 20%.

Ellen Levine, Literary Agency, Inc.
Suite 1801, 15 East 26th Street, New York NY 10010-1505
☎001 212 899 0620   Fax 001 212 725 4501
Contact *Diana Finch, Elizabeth Kaplan, Louise Quayle, Ellen Levine*

FOUNDED 1980. *Handles* all types of books. No scripts. No unsolicited mss, nor any other material unless requested. No telephone calls. First

approach by letter; send US postage or IRCs for reply, otherwise material not returned. No reading fee. *Commission* Home 15%; Foreign 20%. *UK Associate* **A. M. Heath & Co. Ltd** .

Ray Lincoln Literary Agency
Elkins Park House, Suite 107-B, 7900 Old York Road, Elkins Park PA 19027
☎001 215 635 0827   Fax 001 215 782 8882
Contact *Mrs Ray Lincoln*

FOUNDED 1974. *Handles* adult and children's fiction and non-fiction: biography, science, nature and history. Scripts as spin-offs from book mss only. No poetry or plays unless adaptations from published book. Keenly interested in adult biography, in all types of children's books (age five and upwards, not illustrated), in fine adult fiction, science and nature. No unsolicited mss; send query letter first, including IRCs for response. If interested, material will then be requested. No reading fee. Postage fee for projects handled by the agency. *Commission* Home & Dramatic 15%; Translation 20%.

Literary & Creative Artists Agency
3543 Albemarle Street NW, Washington DC 20008
☎001 202 362 4688   Fax 001 202 362 8875
Contact *Muriel G. Nellis, Jane F. Roberts, Elizabeth Pokempner, Jennifer Steinbach, Leslie Toussaint*

FOUNDED 1981. *Specialises* in a broad range of non-fiction. No poetry, pornography, academic or educational textbooks. No unsolicited mss; query letter in the first instance. Include IRCs for response. No reading fee. *Commission* Home 15%; Dramatic 20%; Translation 20–25%.

Sterling Lord Literistic, Inc.
65 Bleecker Street, New York NY 10012
☎001 212 780 6050
Contact *Peter Matson, Sterling Lord*

FOUNDED 1979. *Handles* all genres, fiction and non-fiction, plus scripts for TV, radio, film and theatre. Unsolicited mss will be considered. Prefers letter outlining all non-fiction. No reading fee. *Commission* Home 15%; UK & Translation 20%. *Overseas associates* **Peters Fraser & Dunlop Group Ltd**, UK.

Richard P. McDonough, Literary Agent
34 Pinewood, Irvine, CA 92604
☎001 949 654 5480   Fax 001 949 654 5470
Contact *Richard P. McDonough*

FOUNDED 1986. General non-fiction and literary fiction. Film scripts should be addressed to *Steve Grossman*. No genre fiction. No unsolicited mss; query first and include IRCs. No reading fee. CLIENTS John Dufresne, Robert Gordon, Jane Holtz Kay, Mary Leonhardt, Thomas Lynch, M. R. Montgomery, William Sullivan. *Commission* 15%.

McIntosh & Otis, Inc.

310 Madison Avenue, New York
NY 10017
☎001 212 687 7400   Fax 001 212 687 6894
President *Eugene H. Winick*
Adult Books *Sam Pinkus, Jakki Spicer,*
   Barbara Kennedy
Children's *Dorothy Markinko, Renée Cho*
Motion Picture/Television *Evva Pryor*
FOUNDED 1928. Adult and juvenile literary fiction and non-fiction. No textbooks or scripts. No unsolicited mss. Query letter indicating nature of the work plus details of background. IRCs for response. No reading fee. *Commission* Home & Dramatic 15%; Foreign 20%. *UK Associates* **A. M. Heath & Co. Ltd**, London.

Denise Marcil Literary Agency, Inc.

685 West End Avenue, Suite 9C, New York
NY 10025
☎001 212 932 3110
President *Denise Marcil*
FOUNDED 1977. *Specialises* in non-fiction: health, alternative health and medicine, careers and personal finance books for a Generation-X audience, pop culture, popular reference. Fiction: big commercial thrillers. Query letters only, with IRCs. CLIENTS include Rosanne Bittner, Arnette Lamb, Carla Neggers, Dr William Sears. *Commission* Home & Dramatic 15%; Foreign 20%.

Betty Marks

176 East 77th Street, Apt. 9F, New York
NY 10021
☎001 212 535 8388
Contact *Betty Marks*
FOUNDED 1969. Works mostly with established/published authors. *Specialises* in journalists' non-fiction and novels. No unsolicited mss. Query letter and outline in the first instance. *Commission* Home 15%; Foreign 20%. *Overseas associates* **Abner Stein**, UK; Mohrbooks, Germany; International Editors, Spain & Portugal; Rosemary Buchman, Europe; Tuttle Mori, Japan.

The Evan Marshall Agency

6 Tristam Place, Pine Brook NJ 07058–9445
☎001 973 882 1122   Fax 001 973 882 3099
Contact *Evan Marshall*
FOUNDED 1987. *Handles* general adult fiction and non-fiction. No unsolicited mss; send query letter first. *Commission* Home 15%; UK & Translation 20%.

Mews Books Ltd

c/o Sidney B. Kramer, 20 Bluewater Hill,
Westport CT 06880
☎001 203 227 1836   Fax 001 203 227 1144
Contact *Sidney B. Kramer, Fran Pollak*
FOUNDED 1970. *Handles* adult fiction and non-fiction, children's, pre-school and young adult. No scripts, short stories or novellas (unless by established authors). *Specialises* in cookery, medical, health and nutrition, scientific non-fiction, children's and young adult. Unsolicited material welcome. Presentation must be professional. Partial submissions should include summary of plot/characters, one or two sample chapters, personal credentials and brief on target market. No reading fee. If material is accepted, agency asks $350 circulation fee (4–5 publishers), which will be applied against commissions (waived for published authors). Charges for photocopying, postage expenses, telephone calls and other direct costs. Principal agent is an attorney and former publisher (a founder of Bantam Books). Offers consultation service through which writers can get advice on a contract or on publishing problems. *Commission* Home 15%; Film & Translation 20%. *Overseas associates* **Abner Stein**, UK.

Maureen Moran Agency

PO Box 20191, Parkwest Station, New York
NY 10025
☎001 212 222 3838   Fax 001 212 531 3464
Contact *Maureen Moran*
Formerly Donald MacCampbell, Inc. *Handles* novels only. No scripts, non-fiction, science fiction, westerns or suspense. *Specialises* in romance. No unsolicited mss; approach by letter. No reading fee. *Commission* US Book Sales 10%; First Novels US 15%.

Howard Morhaim Literary Agency

841 Broadway, Suite 604, New York
NY 10003
☎001 212 529 4433   Fax 001 212 995 1112
Contact *Howard Morhaim*
FOUNDED 1979. *Handles* general adult fiction and non-fiction. No scripts. No children's or

young adult material, poetry or religious. No unsolicited mss. Send query letter with synopsis and sample chapters for fiction; query letter with outline or proposal for non-fiction. No reading fee. *Commission* Home 15%; UK & Translation 20%. *Overseas associates* worldwide.

Henry Morrison, Inc.
PO Box 235, Bedford Hills NY 10507
☎001 914 666 3500   Fax 001 914 241 7846
Contact *Henry Morrison*

FOUNDED 1965. *Handles* general fiction, crime and science fiction, and non-fiction. No scripts unless by established writers. Unsolicited material welcome; but send query letter with outline of proposal (1–5 pp) in the first instance. No reading fee. CLIENTS Beverly Byrne, Joe Gores, Robert Ludlum. *Commission* Home 15%; UK & Translation 20%.

Ruth Nathan Agency
53 East 34th Street, Suite 207, New York NY 10016
☎001 212 481 1185   Fax 001 212 481 1185
FOUNDED 1984. *Specialises* in illustrated books, fine art & decorative arts, historical fiction with emphasis on Middle Ages, true crime, showbiz. Query first. No unsolicited mss. No reading fee. *Commission* 15%.

B. K. Nelson Literary Agency
84 Woodland Road, Pleasantville NY 10570–1322
☎001 914 741 1322   Fax 001 914 741 1324
President *Bonita K. Nelson*

FOUNDED 1979. *Specialises* in business, self-help, how-to, political, autobiography, celebrity biography. Major motion picture and TV documentary success. No unsolicited mss. Letter of inquiry. Reading fee charged. *Commission* 20%. Lecture Bureau for Authors founded 1994; Foreign Rights Catalogue established 1995; BK Nelson Infomercial Marketing Co. 1996, primarily for authors and endorsements, and Red Pepper Productions for motion picture production in 1998.

New Age World Services & Books
62091 Valley View Circle #2, Joshua Tree CA 92252
☎001 760 366 2833   Fax 001 760 366 2890
Contact *Victoria E. Vandertuin*

FOUNDED 1957. New Age fiction and non-fiction, young adult fiction and non-fiction, and poetry. No scripts, drama, missionary, biogra-

phy, sports, erotica, humour, travel or cookbooks. *Specialises* in New Age, self-help, health and beauty, meditation, yoga, channelling, how-to, metaphysical, occult, psychology, theology, religion, lost continents, time travel. Unsolicited mss and queries welcome. Reading fee charged. *Commission* Home 15%; Foreign 20%.

New England Publishing Associates, Inc.
Box 5, Chester CT 06412
☎001 203 345 7323   Fax 001 203 345 3660
Contact *Elizabeth Frost-Knappman, Edward W. Knappman*

FOUNDED 1983. *Handles* non-fiction and (clients only) fiction. *Specialises* in current affairs, history, science, women's studies, reference, psychology, biography, true crime. No textbooks or anthologies. No scripts. Unsolicited mss considered but query letter or phone call preferred first. No reading fee. CLIENTS include Lary Bloom, Kathryn Cullen-DuPont, Hartford Curant, Sharon Edwards, Elizabeth Lewin, Philip Ginsburg, Michael Golby, William Gross, Dandi Mackall, Mike Nevins, William Packard, John Philpin, Art Plotnik, Carl Rollyson, Robert Sherrill, Orion Magazine, Claude Summers, Ian Tattersall, Ann Waldron. *Commission* Home 15%. *Overseas associates* throughout Europe and Japan; Scott-Ferris, UK. Dramatic rights: **Renaissance**, Los Angeles.

The Betsy Nolan Literary Agency
224 West 29th Street, 15th Floor, New York NY 10001
☎001 212 967 8200   Fax 001 212 967 7292
Contact *Betsy Nolan, Carla Glasser, Donald Lehr*

FOUNDED 1980. *Specialises* in non-fiction: popular culture, music, gardening, biography, childcare, cooking, how-to. Some literary fiction, film & TV rights. No unsolicited mss. Send query letter with synopsis first. No reading fee. *Commission* Home 15%; Foreign 20%.

The Otte Co
9 Goden Street, Belmont MA 02178–3002
☎001 617 484 8505
Contact *Jane H. Otte, L. David Otte*

FOUNDED 1973. *Handles* adult fiction and non-fiction. No scripts. No unsolicited mss. Approach by letter. No reading fee. *Commission* Home 15%; Dramatic 7½%; Foreign 20%.

Richard Parks Agency
138 East 16th Street, Suite 5B, New York
NY 10003
☎001 212 254 9067
Contact *Richard Parks*
FOUNDED 1989. *Handles* general trade fiction
and non-fiction: literary novels, mysteries and
thrillers, commercial fiction, science fiction,
biography, pop culture, psychology, self-help,
parenting, medical, cooking, gardening, etc.
No scripts. No technical or academic. No
unsolicited mss. Fiction read by referral only.
No reading fee. CLIENTS include Scott
Campbell, Jonathan Lethem, Joseph McBeide,
Audrey Schulman, Joel Simon. *Commission*
Home 15%; UK & Translation 20%. *Overseas
associates* **The Marsh Agency**, **Barbara Levy
Literary Agency**. Member of the Association
of Authors' Representatives.

James Peter Associates, Inc.
PO Box 772, Tenafly NJ 07670
☎001 201 568 0760   Fax 001 201 568 2959
Contact *Bert Holtje*
FOUNDED 1971. Non-fiction only. 'Many of
our authors are historians, psychologists, physi-
cians – all are writing trade books for general
readers.' No scripts. No fiction or children's
books. *Specialises* in history, popular culture,
business, health, biography and politics. No
unsolicited mss. Send query letter first, with
brief project outline, samples and biographical
information. No reading fee. CLIENTS include
Jim Wright, Alan Axelrod, Charles Phillips,
David Stutz, Carol Turkington. A member of
the Association of Authors' Representatives.
Commission 15%.

Stephen Pevner, Inc.
248 West 73rd Street, 2nd Floor, New York
NY 10023
☎001 212 496 0474   Fax 001 212 496 0796
Contact *Stephen Pevner*
FOUNDED 1991. *Handles* pop culture, novels
and film-related books. Also handles TV, film,
theatre and radio scripts. Approach in writing
with synopsis (include first chapters for a novel).
No reading fee. *Commission* Home 15%.

Alison J. Picard Literary Agent
PO Box 2000, Cotuit MA 02635
☎001 508 477 7192   Fax 001 508 420 0762
Contact *Alison Picard*
FOUNDED 1985. *Handles* mainstream and literary
fiction, contemporary and historical romance,

children's and young adult, mysteries and
thrillers; plus non-fiction. No short stories unless
suitable for major national publications, and no
poetry. Rarely any science fiction and fantasy.
Particularly interested in expanding non-fiction
titles. Approach with written query. No reading
fee. *Commission* 15%. *Overseas associates* **A. M.
Heath & Co. Ltd**, UK.

Pinder Lane & Garon-Brooke Associates Ltd
159 West 53rd Street, New York NY 10019
☎001 212 489 0880   Fax 001 212 489 7104
Owner Agents *Dick Duane, Robert Thixton*
Vice President *Jean Free*
Agent *Nancy Coffey*
FOUNDED 1951. Fiction and non-fiction: his-
tory and historical romance, suspense/thrillers,
political intrigue, horror/occult, self-help. No
category romance, westerns or mysteries. No
unsolicited mss. First approach by query letter.
No reading fee. CLIENTS include Virginia
Coffman, Lolita Files, Eric Harry, Chris
Heimerdinger, Michael Pinson, Rosemary
Rogers, Richard Steinberg, Major Chris
Stewart. *Commission* Home 15%; Dramatic
10–15%; Foreign 30%. *Overseas associates* **Abner
Stein**, UK; Translation: Bernard Kurman.

Arthur Pine Associates, Inc.
250 West 57th Street, New York NY 10107
☎001 212 265 7330   Fax 001 212 265 4650
Contact *Richard S. Pine, Lori Andiman,
Sarah Piel*
FOUNDED 1970. *Handles* fiction and non-fiction (adult books only). No scripts, children's,
autobiographical (unless celebrity), textbooks
or scientific. No unsolicited mss. Send query
letter with synopsis, including IRCs in first
instance. All material must be submitted to the
agency on an exclusive basis with s.a.e.
Commission 15%.

PMA Literary & Film Management, Inc.
Box 1817, Old Chelsea Sta., New York
NY 10011
☎001 212 929 1222   Fax 001 212 206 0238
President *Peter Miller*
Vice President *Jennifer Robinson*
Associates *Eric Wilinski, Yuri Skujins*
FOUNDED 1976. Commercial fiction, non-
fiction and screenplays. *Specialises* in books with
motion picture and television potential, and in
true crime. No poetry, pornography, non-

commercial or academic. No unsolicited mss. Approach by letter with one-page synopsis. Editing service available for unpublished authors (non-obligatory). Fee recoupable out of first monies earned. CLIENTS include Ann Benson, Vincent T. Bugliosi, Jay R. Bonansinga, Wensley Clarkson, Michael Eberhardt, Christopher Cook Gilmore, John Glatt, Chris Rogers, Ted Sennett, Rob Thomas, Gene Walden, Steven Yount. *Commission* Home 15%; Dramatic 10–15%; Foreign 20–25%.

Susan Ann Protter Literary Agent

110 West 40th Street, Suite 1408, New York NY 10018–3616
☎001 212 840 0480

Contact *Susan Protter*

FOUNDED 1971. *Handles* general fiction, mysteries, thrillers, science fiction and fantasy; non-fiction: history, general reference, biography, true crime, science, health and parenting. No romance, poetry, westerns, religious, children's or sport manuals. No scripts. First approach with letter, including IRCs. No reading fee. CLIENTS include Lydia Adamson, Terry Bisson, David G. Hartwell, John G. Cramer, Kathleen McCoy PhD, Lynn Armistead McKee, Rudy Rucker, Barbara C. Unell. *Commission* Home & Dramatic 15%; Foreign 25%. *Overseas associates* **Abner Stein**, UK; agents in all major markets.

Puddingstone Literary/ SBC Enterprises, Inc.

11 Mabro Drive, Denville NJ 07834–9607
☎001 973 366 3622

Contact *Alec Bernard, Eugenia Cohen*

FOUNDED 1972. *Handles* trade fiction, non-fiction, film and telemovies. No unsolicited mss. Send query letter with IRCs. No reading fee. *Commission* varies.

Quicksilver Books, Literary Agents

50 Wilson Street, Hartsdale NY 10530
☎001 914 946 8748

President *Bob Silverstein*

FOUNDED 1973. *Handles* literary fiction and mainstream commercial fiction: blockbuster, suspense, thriller, contemporary, mystery and historical; and general non-fiction, including self-help, psychology, holistic healing, ecology, environmental, biography, fact crime, New Age, health, nutrition, enlightened wisdom and spirituality. No scripts, science fiction and fantasy, pornographic, children's or romance.

UK material being submitted must have universal appeal for the US market. Unsolicited material welcome but must be accompanied by IRCs for response, together with biographical details, covering letter, etc. No reading fee. CLIENTS include John Harricharan, Vasant Lad, Ted Libbey, Dorothy Nolte, Arthur Reber, Barrymore Scherer, Grace Speare, Melvin van Peebles. *Commission* Home & Dramatic 15%; Translation 20%.

Helen Rees Literary Agency

123 N. Washington Street, 5th Floor, Boston MA 02114
☎001 617 723 5232 ext 233
Fax 001 617 723 5211

Contact *Joan Mazmanian*

FOUNDED 1982. *Specialises* in books on health and business; also handles biography, autobiography and history; quality fiction. No scholarly, academic or technical books. No scripts, science fiction, children's, poetry, photography, short stories, cooking. No unsolicited mss. Send query letter with IRCs. No reading fee. CLIENTS include Donna Carpenter, Alan Dershowitz, Alexander Dubcek, Harry Figgie Jr, Senator Barry Goldwater, Sandra Mackey, Price Waterhouse. *Commission* Home 15%; Foreign 20%.

Renaissance, A Literary/ Talent Agency

8523 Sunset Boulevard, Los Angeles CA 90069
☎001 310 289 3636   Fax 001 310 289 3637

President *Joel Gotler*
Literary Associates *Steven Fisher, Alan Nevins, Irv Schwartz, Brian Lipson*

FOUNDED 1934. Fiction and non-fiction; film and TV rights. No unsolicited mss. Send query letter with IRCs in the first instance. No reading fee. *Commission* Home 10–15%.

Rights Unlimited, Inc.

101 West 55th Street, Suite 2D, New York NY 10019
☎001 212 246 0900   Fax 001 212 246 2114

Contact *Bernard Kurman*

FOUNDED 1985. *Handles* adult fiction, non-fiction. No scripts, poetry, short stories, educational or literary works. Unsolicited mss welcome; query letter with synopsis preferred in the first instance. No reading fee. CLIENTS Charles Berlitz, Gyo Fujikawa, Norman Lang. *Commission* Home 15%; Translation 20%.

Rosenstone/Wender

3 East 48th Street, 4th Floor, New York
NY 10017
☎001 212 832 8330   Fax 001 212 759 4524

Contact *Phyllis Wender, Susan Perlman Cohen, Sonia E. Pabley*

FOUNDED 1981. *Handles* fiction, non-fiction, children's and scripts for film, TV and theatre. No material for radio. No unsolicited mss. Send letter outlining the project, credits, etc. No reading fee. *Commission* Home 15%; Dramatic 10%; Foreign 20%. *Overseas associates* La Nouvelle Agence, France; Andrew Nurnberg, Netherlands; The English Agency, Japan; Mohrbooks, Germany; Ole Licht, Scandinavia.

Shyama Ross 'The Write Therapist'

2000 North Ivar Avenue, Suite 3, Hollywood CA 90068
☎001 213 465 2630   Fax 001 213 465 8597

Contact *Shyama Ross*

FOUNDED 1979. *Handles* non-fiction trade books: New Age, health and fitness, philosophy, psychology, trends, humour, business, mysticism; also fiction: thrillers, romance, suspense, mystery, contemporary. No scripts. Story analyst for screenplays. No Christian evangelical, travel, sleazy sex or children's. *Specialises* in humour, how-to, mainstream fiction, healing and women's issues. New writers welcome. Query by letter with brief outline of contents and background (plus IRCs). Fee charged ($125 for up to 50,000 words) for detailed analysis of mss. Professional editing also available (rates per page or hour). *Commission* Home & Film rights 15%; Translation 20%.

Jane Rotrosen Agency

318 East 51st Street, New York NY 10022
☎001 212 593 4330   Fax 001 212 935 6985

Contact *Meg Ruley, Andrea Cirillo, Ruth Kagle, Stephanie Tade*

Handles commercial fiction: romance, horror, mysteries, thrillers and fantasy and popular non-fiction. No scripts, educational, professional or belles lettres. No unsolicited mss; send query letter in the first instance. No reading fee. *Commission* Home 15%; UK & Translation 20%. *Overseas associates* worldwide and film agents on the West Coast.

Victoria Sanders Literary Agency

241 Avenue of the Americas, Suite 11H, New York NY 10014
☎001 212 633 8811   Fax 001 212 633 0525

Contact *Victoria Sanders, Diane Dickensheid*

FOUNDED 1993. *Handles* general trade fiction and non-fiction, plus ancillary film and television rights. CLIENTS Connie Briscoe, Yolanda Joe, Alexander Smalls, Colin Kersey, J. M. Redmann. *Commission* Home & Dramatic 15%; Translation 20%.

Sandum & Associates

144 East 84th Street, New York NY 10028
☎001 212 737 2011

Contact *Howard E. Sandum*

FOUNDED 1987. *Handles* all categories of general adult non-fiction, plus occasional fiction. No scripts. No children's, poetry or short stories. No unsolicited mss. Third-party referral preferred but direct approach by letter, with synopsis, brief biography and IRCs, is accepted. No reading fee. CLIENTS include James Cowan, Bro. Victor d'Arvila-Latourrette, Adele Getty, Barbara Lachman. *Commission* Home & Dramatic 15%; Translation & Foreign 20%. *Overseas associates* Scott Ferris Associates.

SBC Enterprises, Inc.

See **Puddingstone Literary**

Jack Scagnetti Talent & Literary Agency

5118 Vineland Avenue, Suite 102, North Hollywood CA 91601
☎001 818 762 3871

Contact *Jack Scagnetti*

FOUNDED 1974. Works mostly with established/published authors. *Handles* non-fiction, fiction, film and TV scripts. No reading fee for outlines. *Commission* Home & Dramatic 10%; Foreign 15%.

Schiavone Literary Agency, Inc.

236 Trails End, West Palm Beach FL 33413–2135
☎001 561 966 9294   Fax 001 561 966 9294

President *James Schiavone*
E-mail: profschia@aol.com

FOUNDED 1997. *Handles* fiction and non-fiction (all genres). *Specialises* in biography, autobiography, celebrity memoirs. No poetry or scripts. No unsolicited mss; send query with brief biosketch, synopsis, outline and sample chapters (enclose IRCs). No reading fee. CLIENTS Sandra E. Bowen, Lajla Kraichnan, Bernard Leopold, Michael Ugarte PhD. *Commission* Home 15%; Foreign & Translation 20%. *Overseas associates* in Europe.

Susan Schulman, A Literary Agency

454 West 44th Street, New York NY 10036
☎001 212 713 1633/4/5
Fax 001 212 581 8830

FOUNDED 1979. *Specialises* in non-fiction of all types but particularly in psychology-based self-help for men, women and families. Other interests include business, the social sciences, biography, language and linguistics. Fiction interests include contemporary fiction, including women's, mysteries, historical and thrillers 'with a cutting edge'. Always looking for 'something original and fresh'. No unsolicited mss. Query first, including outline and three sample chapters with IRCs. No reading fee. Represents properties for film and television, and works with agents in appropriate territories for translation rights. *Commission* Home & Dramatic 15%; Translation 20%. *Overseas associates* Plays: **Rosica Colin Ltd** and **The Agency Ltd**, UK; Children's books: Marilyn Malin, UK, Commercial fiction: **MBA Literary Agents** UK.

Shapiro-Lichtman-Stein Talent Agency

8827 Beverly Boulevard, Los Angeles CA 90048
☎001 310 859 8877   Fax 001 310 859 7153

FOUNDED 1969. Works mostly with established/published authors. *Handles* film and TV scripts. Unsolicited mss will not be read. *Commission* Home & Dramatic 10%; Foreign 20%.

The Shepard Agency

Pawling Savings Bank Building, Suite 3, Southeast Plaza, Brewster NY 10509
☎001 914 279 2900/3236
Fax 001 914 279 3239

Contact *Jean Shepard, Lance Shepard*

FOUNDED 1987. *Handles* non-fiction: business, food, self-help and travel; some fiction: adult, children's and young adult and the occasional script. No pornography. *Specialises* in business. Send query letter, table of contents, sample chapters and IRCs for response. No reading fee. *Commission* Home & Dramatic 15%; Translation 20%.

Lee Shore Agency Ltd

440 Friday Road, Pittsburgh PA 15209
☎001 412 821 0440   Fax 001 412 821 6099
E-mail: LeeShore1@aol.com
Website: http://www.olworld.com/olworld/m_lshore/

Contact *Cynthia Sterling, Jennifer Blose, Kristine L. Habun*

FOUNDED 1988. *Handles* non-fiction, including textbooks, and mass-market fiction: horror, romance, mystery, westerns, science fiction. Also some young adult and, more recently, screenplays. *Specialises* in New Age, self-help, how-to and quality fiction. No children's. No unsolicited mss. Send IRCs for guidelines before submitting work. Reading fee charged. CLIENTS include Mel Blount, Francisco Cruz, Dr Laura Essen, Dr Lynn Hawker, Susan Sheppard. *Commission* Home 15%; Dramatic 20%.

Bobbe Siegel Literary Agency

41 West 83rd Street, New York NY 10024
☎001 212 877 4985   Fax 001 212 877 4985

Contact *Bobbe Siegel*

FOUNDED 1975. Works mostly with established/published authors. *Specialises* in literary fiction, detective, suspense, historical, fantasy, biography, how-to, women's interest, fitness, health, beauty, sports, pop psychology. No scripts. No cookbooks, crafts, children's, short stories or humour. First approach with letter including IRCs for response. No reading fee. Critiques given if the writer is taken on for representation. CLIENTS include Michael Buller, Eileen Curtis, Margaret Mitchell Dukore, Primo Levi, John Nordahl, Curt Smith. *Commission* Home 15%; Dramatic & Foreign 20%. (Foreign/Dramatic split 50/50 with subagent.) *Overseas associates* in various countries, including **John Pawsey** in the UK.

The Evelyn Singer Agency, Inc.

PO Box 594, White Plains NY 10602
☎001 914 949 1147/914 631 5160

Contact *Evelyn Singer*

FOUNDED 1951. Works mostly with established/published authors. *Handles* fiction and non-fiction, both adult and children's. Adult: health, medicine, how-to, diet, biography, celebrity, conservation, political, serious novels, suspense and mystery. Children's: educational non-fiction for all ages and fiction for the middle/teen levels. No picture books unless the author is or has an experienced book illustrator. No formula romance, poetry, sex, occult, textbooks or specialised material unsuitable for trade market. No scripts. No unsolicited mss. First approach with letter giving writing background, credits, publications, including date of publication and publisher. IRCs essential. No phone calls. No reading fee. 'Accepts writers who have earned at least $25,000 from freelance writing.'

CLIENTS include John Armistead, Mary Elting, Franklin Folsom, William F. Hallstead, Rose Wyler. *Commission* Home 15%; Dramatic 20%; Foreign 25%. *Overseas associates* **Laurence Pollinger Limited**, UK.

Michael Snell Literary Agency
PO Box 1206, Truro MA 02666–1206
☎001 508 349 3718
President *Michael Snell*
Vice President *Patricia Smith*

FOUNDED 1980. Adult non-fiction, especially science, business and women's issues. *Specialises* in business and computer books (professional and reference to popular trade how-to); general how-to and self-help on all topics, from diet and exercise to parenting, relationships, health, sex, psychology and personal finance, plus literary and suspense fiction. No unsolicited mss. Send outline and sample chapter with return postage for reply. No reading fee for outlines. Brochure available on how to write a book proposal. Rewriting, developmental editing, collaborating and ghostwriting services available on a fee basis. Send IRCs. *Commission* Home 15%.

Southern Writers
Whitney Bank Building, Suite 1138,
635 Gravier Street, New Orleans
LA 70130–2801
☎001 504 525 5150
President *William Griffin*

FOUNDED 1979. *Handles* fiction and non-fiction of general interest. No scripts, short stories, poetry, autobiography or articles. No unsolicited mss. Approach in writing with query. Reading fee charged to authors unpublished in the field. *Commission* Home 15%; Dramatic & Translation 20%.

The Spieler Agency
154 West 57th Street, Room 135, New York
NY 10019
☎001 212 757 4439   Fax 001 212 333 2019
The Spieler Agency/West, 1328 Sixth Street, #3, Berkeley, CA 94710
☎001 510 528 2616 Fax 001 510 528 8117
Contact *Joseph Spieler, Lisa M. Ross, John Thornton, Ada Muellner (New York); Victoria Shoemaker (Berkeley)*

FOUNDED 1980. *Handles* literary fiction and non-fiction. No how-to or genre romance. *Specialises* in history, science, ecology, social issues and business. No scripts. Approach in writing with IRCs. No reading fee. CLIENTS include James

Chace, Evan Eisenberg, Paul Hawken, Joe Kane, Walter Laqueur, Akio Morita, Marc Reisner, Peter Senge, Jan Swafford. *Commission* Home 15%; Translation 20%. *Overseas associates* **Abner Stein, The Marsh Agency**, UK.

Philip G. Spitzer Literary Agency
50 Talmage Farm Lane, East Hampton
NY 11937
☎001 516 329 3650   Fax 001 516 329 3651
Contact *Philip Spitzer*

FOUNDED 1969. Works mostly with established/published authors. *Specialises* in general non-fiction and fiction – thrillers. No reading fee for outlines. *Commission* Home & Dramatic 15%; Foreign 20%.

Lyle Steele & Co. Ltd
Literary Agents
511 East 73rd Street, Suite 6, New York
NY 10021
☎001 212 288 2981
President *Lyle Steele*

FOUNDED 1985. *Handles* general non-fiction and category fiction, including mysteries (anxious to see good British mysteries), thrillers, horror and occult. Also North American rights to titles published by major English publishers. No scripts unless derived from books already being handled. No romance. No unsolicited mss: query with IRCs in first instance. No reading fee. *Commission* 10%. *Overseas associates* worldwide.

Gloria Stern Agency
2929 Buffalo Speedway, Suite 2111, Houston
TX 77098
☎001 713 963 8360   Fax 001 713 963 8460
Contact *Gloria Stern*

FOUNDED 1976. *Specialises* in non-fiction, including biography, history, politics, women's issues, self-help, health, science and education; also adult fiction. No scripts, how-to, poetry, short stories or unsolicited mss. First approach by letter stating content of book, including one chapter, qualifications as author and IRCs. No reading fee. *Commission* Home 10–15%; Dramatic 10%; Foreign 20% shared; Translation 20% shared. *Overseas associates* **A. M. Heath & Co. Ltd**, UK, and worldwide.

Gloria Stern Agency (Hollywood)
12535 Chandler Boulevard, Suite 3, North Hollywood CA 91607
☎001 818 508 6296   Fax 001 818 508 6296
Contact *Gloria Stern*

FOUNDED 1984. *Handles* film scripts, genre (romance, detective, thriller and sci-fi) and mainstream fiction; electronic media. 'No books containing gratuitous violence.' Approach with letter, biography and synopsis. Reading fee charged by the hour. *Commission* Home 15%; Offshore 20%.

Jo Stewart Agency

201 East 66th Street, Suite 18G, New York NY 10021
☎001 212 879 1301

Contact *Jo Stewart*

FOUNDED 1978. *Handles* fiction and non-fiction. No scripts. No unsolicited mss; send query letter first. No reading fee. *Commission* Home 10%; Foreign 20%; Unpublished 15%. *Overseas associates* **John Johnson (Authors' Agent) Ltd**, UK.

Gunther Stuhlmann Author's Representative

PO Box 276, Becket MA 01223
☎001 413 623 5170

Contact *Gunther Stuhlmann, Barbara Ward*

FOUNDED 1954. *Handles* literary fiction, biography and serious non-fiction. No film/TV scripts unless from established clients. No short stories, detective, romance, adventure, poetry, technical or computers. Query first with IRCs, including sample chapters and synopsis of project. '*We take on few new clients.*' No reading fee. CLIENTS include Isabel Bolton, Julieta Campos, B. H. Friedman, Anaïs Nin, Richard Powers, Otto Rank. *Commission* Home 10%; Foreign 15%; Translation 20%.

The Tantleff Office

375 Greenwich Street, Suite 700, New York NY 10013
☎001 212 941 3939   Fax 001 212 941 3948

Contact (scripts) *Jack Tantleff, Jill Bock, Charmaine Ferenczi*

FOUNDED 1986. *Handles* primarily scripts for theatre, film and TV, and represents actors. Does not handle books. No unsolicited mss; queries only. No reading fee. CLIENTS include Brian Friel, Marsha Norman, Mark O'Donnell. *Commission* 10%.

2M Communications Ltd

121 West 27th Street, Suite 601, New York NY 10001
☎001 212 741 1509   Fax 001 212 691 4460

Contact *Madeleine Morel*

FOUNDED 1982. *Handles* non-fiction only: everything from pop psychology and health to cookery books, biographies and pop culture. No scripts. No fiction, children's, computers or science. No unsolicited mss; send letter with sample pages and IRCs. No reading fee. CLIENTS include David Steinman, Janet Wolfe, Donald Woods. *Commission* Home & Dramatic 15%; Translation 20%. *Overseas associates* EAIS, France; Thomas Schluck Agency, Germany; Asano Agency, Japan; Living Literary Agency, Italy; Nueva Agencia Literaria Internacional, Spain.

Susan P. Urstadt, Inc.

PO Box 1676, New Canaan CT 06840
☎001 203 972 8226   Fax 001 203 966 2249

President *Susan P. Urstadt*

FOUNDED 1975. *Specialises* in decorative arts, antiques, gardening, cookery, biography, history, sports, natural history, environment and popular reference. No unsolicited fiction or children's. Query with outline, sample chapter, author biography and IRCs to cover return postage. *Commission* Home 15%; Dramatic & Foreign 20%.

Van der Leun & Associates

22 Division Street, Easton CT 06612
☎001 203 259 4897

Contact *Patricia Van der Leun*

FOUNDED 1984. *Handles* fiction and non-fiction. No scripts. No science fiction, fantasy or romance. *Specialises* in art and architecture, science, biography and fiction. No unsolicited mss; query first, with proposal and short biography. No reading fee. CLIENTS include Robert Fulghum, Marion Winik, Arthur Zajonc. *Commission* 15%. *Overseas associates* **Abner Stein**, UK; Michelle Lapautre, France; English Agency, Japan; Carmen Balcells, Spain; Lijnkamp Associates, The Netherlands; Karin Schindler, South America; Susanna Zevi, Italy.

Wallace Literary Agency, Inc.

177 East 70th Street, New York NY 10021
☎001 212 570 9090   Fax 001 212 772 8979

Contact *Lois Wallace, Thomas C. Wallace*

FOUNDED 1988. No unsolicited mss. No faxed queries. *Commission* Rates upon application. *UK representative* **A. M. Heath & Co. Ltd**; *French representative* Michelle Lapautre; *all other European representation* **Andrew Nurnberg Associates**; *Japanese representative* Tuttle-Mori.

John A. Ware Literary Agency

392 Central Park West, New York NY 10025
☎001 212 866 4733   Fax 001 212 866 4734

Contact *John Ware*

FOUNDED 1978. *Specialises* in non-fiction: biography, history, current affairs, investigative journalism, science, inside looks at phenomena, medicine and psychology (academic credentials required). Also handles literary fiction, mysteries/thrillers, sport, oral history, Americana and folklore. Unsolicited mss not read. Send query letter first with IRCs to cover return postage. No reading fee. CLIENTS include Caroline Fraser, Jon Krakauer, Jack Womack. *Commission* Home & Dramatic 15%; Foreign 20%.

Waterside Productions, Inc.
2191 San Elijo Avenue, Cardiff by the Sea CA 92007-1839
☎001 619 632 9190   Fax 001 619 632 9295
Contact *William Gladstone*
FOUNDED 1982. *Handles* general non-fiction: computers and technology, psychology, science, business, sports. All types of multimedia. No unsolicited mss; send query letter. No reading fee. *Commission* Home 15%; Dramatic 20%; Translation 25%. *Overseas associates* **Serafina Clarke**, UK; Asano Agency, Japan; Ulla Lohren, Sweden; Ruth Liepman, Germany; Vera Le Marie, EAIS, France; Bardon Chinese Media Agency, China; Grandi & Vitali, Italy; DRT, Korea; Mercedes Casanovas, Spain.

Watkins Loomis Agency, Inc.
133 East 35th Street, Suite 1, New York NY 10016
☎001 212 532 0080   Fax 001 212 889 0506
Contact *Nicole Aragi*
FOUNDED 1904. *Handles* fiction and non-fiction. No scripts for film, radio, TV or theatre. No science fiction, fantasy or horror. No reading fee. No unsolicited mss. Approach in writing with enquiry or proposal and s.a.e. *Commission* Home 15%; UK & Translation 20%. *Overseas associates* **Abner Stein**; **The Marsh Agency**, UK.

Wecksler-Incomco
170 West End Avenue, New York NY 10023
☎001 212 787 2239   Fax 001 212 496 7035
Contact *Sally Wecksler, Joann Amparan*
FOUNDED 1971. *Handles* non-fiction: business, reference, biographies, performing arts and heavily illustrated books. Send queries only. No unsolicited mss. No reading fee. Foreign rights. *Commission* Home 15%; Translation 20%; British rights 20%.

Cherry Weiner Literary Agency
28 Kipling Way, Manalapan NJ 07726
☎001 732 446 2096   Fax 001 732 792 0506
Contact *Cherry Weiner*
FOUNDED 1977. *Handles* more or less all types of genre fiction: science fiction and fantasy, romance, mystery, westerns. No scripts. No non-fiction. No unsolicited mss. No submissions except through referral. No reading fee. *Commission* 15%. *Overseas associates* **Abner Stein**, UK; Thomas Schluck, Germany; International Editors Inc., Spain.

Wieser & Wieser, Inc.
118 East 25th Street, New York NY 10010
☎001 212 260 0860   Fax 001 212 505 7186
Contact *Olga B. Wieser, George J. Wieser, Jake Elwell*
FOUNDED 1976. Works mostly with established/published authors. *Specialises* in literary and mainstream fiction, serious and popular historical fiction, and general non-fiction: business, finance, aviation, sports, photography, cookbooks, travel and popular medicine. No poetry, children's, science fiction or religious. No unsolicited mss. First approach by letter with IRCs. No reading fee for outlines. *Commission* Home & Dramatic 15%; Foreign 20%.

Ruth Wreschner, Authors' Representative
10 West 74th Street, New York NY 10023
☎001 212 877 2605   Fax 001 212 595 5843
Contact *Ruth Wreschner*
FOUNDED 1981. Works mostly with established/published authors but 'will consider very good first novels, both mainstream and genre, particularly British mystery writers'. *Specialises* in popular medicine, psychology, health, self-help, business. No screenplays or dramatic plays. First approach with query letter and IRCs. For fiction, send a synopsis and first 25 pp; for non-fiction, an outline and two sample chapters. No reading fee. *Commission* Home 15%; Foreign 20%.

Ann Wright Representatives
165 West 46th Street, Suite 1105, New York NY 10036–2501
☎001 212 764 6770   Fax 001 212 764 5125
Contact *Dan Wright*
FOUNDED 1961. *Specialises* in screenplays for film and TV. Also handles novels, drama and fiction. No academic, scientific or scholarly.

Approach by letter; no reply without IRCs. Include outline and credits only. New film and TV writers encouraged. No reading fee. CLIENTS include Alexander Barnett, Theodore Bonnet, Tom Dempsey, Max C. Garrick Jr., Jerry D. Hoffman, George Lupu, John Peer Nugent, Kevin O'Morrison, David Reynolds, Ying Zhu. Signatory to the Writers Guild of America Agreement. *Commission* Home varies according to current trend (10–20%); Dramatic 10% of gross.

Writers House, Inc.

21 West 26th Street, New York NY 10010
☎001 212 685 2400   Fax 001 212 685 1781

Contact *Albert Zuckerman, Amy Berkower, Merrilee Heifetz, Susan Cohen, Susan Ginsburg, Fran Lebowitz, Karen Solem, Robin Rue*

FOUNDED 1974. *Handles* all types of fiction, including children's and young adult, plus narrative non-fiction: history, biography, popular science, pop and rock culture. *Specialises* in popular fiction, women's novels, thrillers and children's. Represents novelisation rights for film producers such as New Line Cinema. No scripts. No professional or scholarly. For consideration of unsolicited mss, send letter of enquiry, 'explaining why your book is wonderful, briefly what it's about and outlining your writing background'. No reading fee. CLIENTS include Virginia Andrews, Barbara Delinsky, Ken Follett, Eileen Goudge, Stephen Hawking, Linda Howard, Michael Lewis, Robin McKinley, Ann Martin, Andrew Neiderman, Francine Pascal, Ridley Pearson, Nora Roberts, Cynthia Voigt, F. Paul Wilson. *Commission* Home & Dramatic 15%; Foreign 20%. Albert Zuckerman is author of *Writing the Blockbuster Novel*, published by **Little, Brown & Co.** and **Warner Paperbacks**.

Susan Zeckendorf Associates, Inc.

171 West 57th Street, Suite 11B, New York NY 10019
☎001 212 245 2928   Fax 001 212 977 2643

President *Susan Zeckendorf*

FOUNDED 1979. Works with new/unpublished writers. *Specialises* in literary fiction, commercial women's fiction, international espionage, thrillers and mysteries. Non-fiction interests: science, parenting, music and self-help. No category romance, science fiction or scripts. No unsolicited mss. Send query letter describing mss. No reading fee. CLIENTS include Linda Dahl, James N. Frey, Marjorie Jaffe, Laurie Morrow, Una-Mary Parker, Jerry E. Patterson. *Commission* Home & Dramatic 15%; Foreign 20%. *Overseas associates* **Abner Stein**, UK; V. K. Rosemarie Buckman, Europe, South America; Tom Mori, Japan, Taiwan. Film & TV representative: Joel Gotler at **Renaissance**.

US Media Contacts in the UK

ABC News Intercontinental Inc.
8 Carburton Street, London W1P 7DT
☎0171 637 9222   Fax 0171 631 5084
Bureau Chief & Director of News Coverage, Europe, Middle East & Africa *Rex Granum*

Alaska Journal of Commerce
16 Cavaye Place, London SW10 9PT
☎0171 370 1737   Fax 0171 370 7751
Bureau Chief *Robert Gould*

The Associated Press
12 Norwich Street, London EC4A 1BP
☎0171 353 1515   Fax 0171 353 8118
Chief of Bureau/Managing Director
  Myron L. Belkind

The Baltimore Sun
11 Kensington Court Place, London W8 5BJ
☎0171 460 2200   Fax 0171 460 2211
Bureau Chief *Bill Glauber*

Billboard
23 Ridgmount Street, 3rd Floor, London
WC1E 7AH
☎0171 631 0407   Fax 0171 323 2314
International Deputy Editor *Thom Duffy*

Bloomberg Business News
City Gate House, 39–45 Finsbury Square,
London EC2A 1PX
☎0171 330 7500   Fax 0171 374 6138
London Bureau Chief *Paul Sillitoe*

Bridge News
78 Fleet Street, London EC4Y 1HY
☎0171 842 4000   Fax 0171 583 5032
Chief Correspondent (UK) *Timothy Penn*

Business Week
34 Dover Street, London W1X 4BR
☎0171 491 8985   Fax 0171 409 7152
Bureau Chief *Stanley Reed*

Cable News Network Inc. (CNN)
CNN House, 19–22 Rathbone Place, London
W1P 1DF
☎0171 637 6800   Fax 0171 637 6868
Bureau Chief *Charles Hoff*

CBC Television and Radio
43/51 Great Titchfield Street, London
W1P 8DD
☎0171 412 9200   Fax 0171 631 3095
London Bureau Manager *Sue Phillips*

CBS News
68 Knightsbridge, London SW1X 7LL
☎0171 581 4801   Fax 0171 581 4431
Assistant Bureau Chief *John Paxson*

Chicago Tribune Press Service
169 Piccadilly, London W1V 9DD
☎0171 499 8769   Fax 0171 499 8781
Chief European Correspondent *Ray Moseley*

CNBC
8 Bedford Avenue, London WC1B 3NQ
☎0171 927 6758   Fax 0171 636 2628
Bureau Chief *Karen Nye*

Cox Newspapers
The Atlanta Journal Constitution, 29 Ferry
Street, Isle of Dogs, London E14 3DT
☎0171 537 0765   Fax 0171 537 0766
European Correspondent *Lou Salome*

Dow Jones Telerate-Commodities & Finance
10 Fleet Place, Limeburner Lane, London
EC4M 7RB
☎0171 832 9293   Fax 0171 832 9894
Senior Editor, Europe, Middle East & Africa *Arjen Bongard*

Fairchild Publications of New York
121 Kingsway, London WC2B 6PA
☎0171 831 3607   Fax 0171 831 6485
Bureau Chief *James Fallon*

Forbes Magazine
51 Charles Street, London W1X 7PA
☎0171 495 0120   Fax 0171 495 0170
European Bureau Manager *Howard Banks*

Futures World News
2 Royal Mint Court, Dexter House, London
EC3N 4QN
☎0171 867 8867   Fax 0171 867 1368
London Bureau Chief *Barbara Kollmeyer*

The Globe and Mail
43–51 Great Titchfield Street, London
W1P 8DD
☎0171 323 0449   Fax 0171 323 0428
European Correspondent *Madelaine Drohan*

International Herald Tribune
63 Long Acre, London WC2E 9JH
☎0171 836 4802   Fax 0171 240 2254
London Correspondent *Tom Buerkle*

Journal of Commerce
Totara Park House, 3rd Floor, 34/36 Gray's Inn Road, London WC1X 8HR
☎0171 430 2495   Fax 0171 837 2168
Chief European Correspondent *Bruce Barnard*

Los Angeles Times
150 Brompton Road, London SW3 1HX
☎0171 823 7315   Fax 0171 823 7308
Bureau Chief *William D. Montalbano*

Market News Service, Inc.
Wheatsheaf House, 4 Carmelite Street, London EC4Y 0BN
☎0171 353 4462   Fax 0171 353 9122
Bureau Chief *Jon Hurdle*

McGraw-Hill International
34 Dover Street, London W1X 4BR
☎0171 493 0538   Fax 0171 493 9896
Bureau Chief *David Brezovec*

National Public Radio
Room G-10 East Wing, Bush House, Strand, London WC2B 4PH
☎0171 557 1089   Fax 0171 379 6486
London Bureau Chief *Michael Goldfarb*

NBC News Worldwide Inc.
8 Bedford Avenue, London WC1B 2NQ
☎0171 637 8655   Fax 0171 636 2628
Bureau Chief *Karen Curry*

The New York Times
66 Buckingham Gate, London SW1E 6AU
☎0171 799 5050   Fax 0171 799 2962
Chief Correspondent *William Hodge*

Newsweek
18 Park Street, London W1Y 4HH
☎0171 629 8361   Fax 0171 408 1403
Bureau Chief *Stryker McGuire*

People Magazine
Brettenham House, Lancaster Place, London
WC2E 7TL
☎0171 499 4080   Fax 0171 322 1125
Special Correspondent *Jerene Jones*

Philadelphia Inquirer
36 Agate Road, London W6 0AH
☎0181 932 8854   Fax 0181 932 8856
Correspondent *Fawn Vrazo*

Reader's Digest Association Ltd
11 Westferry Circus, Canary Wharf, London
E14 4HE
☎0171 715 8000   Fax 0171 715 8716
Editor-in-Chief, British Edition *Russell Twisk*
(See under **UK Publishers** and **Magazines**)

Time Magazine
Brettenham House, Lancaster Place, London
WC2E 7TL
☎0171 499 4080   Fax 0171 322 1230
Bureau Chief *Barry Hillenbrand*
(See entry under **Magazines**)

USA Today
10 Wardour Street, London W1V 3HG
☎0171 559 5859   Fax 0171 559 5895
Chief European Correspondent *David Lynch*

Voice of America
IPC, 76 Shoe Lane, London EC4A 3JB
☎0171 410 0960   Fax 0171 410 0966
Bureau Chief/Senior Editor *Paul Francuch*

Wall Street Journal
10 Fleet Place, London EC4M 7RB
☎0171 832 9200   Fax 0171 832 9201
London Bureau Chief *Lawrence Ingrassia*

Washington Post
18 Park Street, London W1Y 4HH
☎0171 629 8958   Fax 0171 629 8950
Bureau Chief *T. R. Reid*

Who Weekly
Brettenham House, Lancaster Place, London
WC2E 7TL
☎0171 322 1118   Fax 0171 322 1199
Special Correspondent *Moira Bailey*

Worldwide Television News (WTN)
The Interchange, Oval Road, Camden Lock, London NW1 7DZ
☎0171 410 5200   Fax 0171 410 8302
President *Robert E.Burke*

Professional Associations and Societies

ABSA

See **Association for Business Sponsorship of the Arts**

ABSW

See **Association of British Science Writers**

ALCS

See **Authors' Licensing & Collecting Society**

Alliance of Literary Societies

Birmingham and Midland Institute, Margaret Street, Birmingham B3 3BS
☎0121 236 3591
President *Gabriel Woolf*
Chairman *H. W. Woodward*
Honorary Secretary *To be appointed*
FOUNDED 1974. Acts as a liaison body between member societies and, when necessary, as a pressure group. Deals with enquiries and assists in preserving buildings and places with literary connections. Over 80 societies hold membership. A directory of literary societies is maintained and the ALS produces an annual fanzine, *Chapter One*, which is distributed to affiliated societies, carrying news of personalities, activities and events. Details of this and advertising rates from Kenneth Oultram, Editor, Chapter One, Clatterwick Hall, Little Leigh, Northwich, Cheshire CW8 4RJ (☎01606 891303).

Arvon Foundation

Totleigh Barton, Sheepwash, Beaworthy, Devon EX21 5NS
☎01409 231338   Fax 01409 231338
E-mail: t-barton@ arvonfoundation.org
Website: http://www.arvonfoundation.org
Lumb Bank, Heptonstall, Hebden Bridge, West Yorkshire HX7 6DF
☎01422 843714   Fax 01422 843714
E-mail: l-bank@arvonfoundation.org
Moniack Mhor, Teavarran, Kiltarlity, Beauly, Inverness-shire IV4 7HT
☎01463 741675
E-mail: m-mhor@arvonfoundation.org
President *Terry Hands*
Chairman *Sir Robin Chichester-Clark*

National Director *David Pease*
FOUNDED 1968. Offers people of any age (over 16) and any background the opportunity to live and work with professional writers. Five-day residential courses are held throughout the year at Arvon's three centres, covering poetry, narrative, drama, writing for children, songwriting and the performing arts. A number of bursaries towards the cost of course fees are available for those on low incomes, the unemployed, students and pensioners. Runs a biennial poetry competition (see under **Prizes**).

Association for Business Sponsorship of the Arts (ABSA)

Nutmeg House, 60 Gainsford Street, Butlers Wharf, London SE1 2NY
☎0171 378 8143   Fax 0171 407 7527
ABSA exists to promote and encourage partnerships between the private sector and the arts, to their mutual benefit and to that of the community at large. It provides a wide range of services to over 300 business members as well as to 600 arts organisations and museums through the ABSA Development Forum. To enable individual business people to share their skills with the arts, ABSA manages the Placement Scheme and the NatWest Board Bank through its Business in the Arts programme. On behalf of the Department for Culture, Media and Sport and the Department of Education for Northern Ireland, Absa manages the Pairing Scheme, an incentive programme for new and established sponsors of the arts. Increasingly, ABSA is working with forward-looking businesses to determine the future of business/arts partnerships through its Creative Forum for Culture and the Economy. With the support of its Patron, HRH The Prince of Wales, it is exploring and developing new ways for business, the arts and society to interact. ABSA runs its programmes from London and through a network of offices nationwide.

Association of American Correspondents in London

12 Norwich Street, London EC4A 1BP
☎0171 353 1515   Fax 0171 936 2229
Contact *Sandra Marshall*

Subscription £90 (Organisations)

FOUNDED 1919 to serve the professional interests of its member organisations, promote social cooperation among them, and maintain the ethical standards of the profession. (An extra £30 is charged for each department of an organisation which requires separate listing in the Association's handbook.)

Association of American Publishers, Inc

71 Fifth Avenue, 2nd Floor, New York, NY 10003 USA

☎001 212 255 0200   Fax 001 212 255 7007
E-mail: tmckee@aap.publishers.org
Website: http://www.publishers.org

Also at: 1718 Connecticut Avenue, NW, Washington, DC 2000

☎001 202 232 3335 Fax 001 202 745 0694

Contact *Tom McKee*

FOUNDED 1970. For information about subscription rates and membership, contact the Association's website.

Association of Authors' Agents

c/o Sheil Land Associates Ltd, 43 Doughty Street, London WC1N 2LF

☎0171 405 9351   Fax 0171 831 2127

President *Vivien Green*
Membership £50 p.a.

FOUNDED 1974. Membership voluntary. The AAA maintains a code of practice, provides a forum for discussion, and represents its members in issues affecting the profession.

Association of British Editors

Broadvision, 49 Frederick Road, Edgbaston, Birmingham B15 1HN

☎0121 455 7949   Fax 0121 454 6187

Executive Director/Honorary Secretary
Jock Gallagher
Subscription £50 p.a.

FOUNDED 1985. Independent organisation for the study and enhancement of journalism worldwide. Established to protect and promote the freedom of the Press. Members are expected to 'maintain the dignity and rights of the profession; consider and sustain standards of professional conduct; exchange ideas for the advancement of professional ideals; work for the solution of common problems'. Membership is limited, but open to persons who have immediate charge of editorial or news policies in all media.

Association of British Science Writers (ABSW)

23 Savile Row, London W1X 2NB

☎0171 439 1205   Fax 0171 973 3051

Administrator *Barbara Drillsma*
Membership £25 p.a.; £20 (Associate)

ABSW has played a central role in improving the standards of science journalism in the UK over the last 40 years. The Association seeks to improve standards by means of networking, lectures and organised visits to institutional laboratories and industrial research centres. Puts members in touch with major projects in the field and with experts worldwide. A member of the European Union of Science Journalists' Associations, ABSW is able to offer heavily subsidised places on visits to research centres in most other European countries, and hosts reciprocal visits to Britain by European journalists. Membership open to those who are considered to be *bona fide* science writers/editors, or their film/TV/radio equivalents, who earn a substantial part of their income by promoting public interest in and understanding of science. Runs the administration and judging of the **Glaxo Science Writers' Awards**, for outstanding science journalism in newspapers, journals and broadcasting.

Association of Christian Writers (formerly Fellowship of Christian Writers)

73 Lodge Hill Road, Farnham, Surrey GU10 3RB

☎01252 715746   Fax 01252 715746
E-mail: adminacw@dial.pipex.com

Administrator *Mr W. G. Crawford*
Subscription £10 (Single); £12.50 (Family & Overseas)

FOUNDED in 1971 'to inspire and equip men and women to use their talents and skills with integrity to devise, write and market excellent material which comes from a Christian worldview. In this way we seek to be an influence for good and for God in this generation.' *Publishes* a quarterly magazine. Runs three training events each year, biennial conference, competitions, postal workshops, area groups, prayer support and manuscript criticism.

Association of Freelance Journalists

5 Beacon Flats, Kings Haye Road, Wellington, Telford, Shropshire TF1 1RG
Website: http://members.tripod.com/
~media_2/afj.html

Founding President *Martin Scholes*

Subscription £30 p.a.

Offers membership to local correspondents, those making a modest sum writing for the specialist press and those writing for a hobby, with or without an income. Members receive a laminated press card, newsletters, information networking, discounts on services, etc.

Association of Freelance Writers
Sevendale House, 7 Dale Street, Manchester
M1 1JB
☎0161 228 2362   Fax 0161 228 3533
Contact *Angela Cox*
Subscription £29 p.a.

FOUNDED in 1995 to help and advise new and established freelance writers. Members receive a copy of *Freelance Market News* each month which gives news, views and the latest advice and guidelines about publications at home and abroad. Other benefits include one free appraisal of prose or poetry each year, reduced entry to **The Writers Bureau** writing competition, reduced fees for writing seminars and discounts on books for writers.

Association of Golf Writers
106 Byng Drive, Potters Bar, Hertfordshire
EN6 1UJ
☎01707 654112   Fax 01707 654112
Honorary Secretary *Mark Garrod*

FOUNDED 1938. Aims to cooperate with golfing bodies to ensure best possible working conditions.

Association of Illustrators
First Floor, 32–38 Saffron Hill, London
EC1N 8FH
☎0171 831 7377   Fax 0171 831 6277
Contact *Stephanie Smith*

FOUNDED 1973 to promote illustration and illustrators' rights, and encourage professional standards. The AOI is a non-profit-making trade association dedicated to its members, to protecting their interests and promoting their work. Talks, seminars, a newsletter, regional groups, legal and portfolio advice as well as a number of related publications such as *Rights, The Illustrator's Guide to Professional Practice*, and *Survive, The Illustrator's Guide to a Professional Career*.

Association of Independent Libraries
Leeds Library, 18 Commercial Street, Leeds,
West Yorkshire LS1 6AL
☎01132 453071
Chairman *Geoffrey Forster*

Established to 'further the advancement, conservation and restoration of a little-known but important living portion of our cultural heritage'. Members include the **London Library, Devon & Exeter Institution, Linen Hall Library** and **Plymouth Proprietary Library**.

Association of Learned and Professional Society Publishers
48 Kelsey Lane, Beckenham,
Kent BR3 3NE
☎0181 658 0459   Fax 0181 663 3583
Secretary-General *Bernard Donovan*

FOUNDED 1972 to foster the publishing activities of learned societies and academic and professional bodies. Membership is limited to such organisations, those publishing on behalf of member organisations and those closely associated with the work of academic publishers.

Association of Little Presses
25 St Benedict's Close, Church Lane, London
SW17 9NX
E-mail: upton@globalnet.co.uk
Co-ordinator *Laurence Upton*
Subscription £12.50 p.a.

FOUNDED 1966 as a loosely knit association of individuals running little presses, who grouped together for mutual self-help and encouragement. First acted as a pressure group to extend the availability of grant aid to small presses and later became more of an information exchange, advice centre and general promoter of small press publishing. Currently represents over 300 publishers and associates throughout Britain. Membership is open to presses and magazines as well as to individuals and institutions.

ALP publishes a twice-yearly magazine, *Poetry and Little Press Information* (PALPI); a *Catalogue of Little Press Books in Print*; information booklets such as *Getting Your Poetry Published* (over 35,000 copies sold since 1973) and *Publishing Yourself: Not Too Difficult After All* which advises those who are thinking of self-publishing, and a regular newsletter.

ALP organises frequent bookfairs. Its main focus, that of supporting members' presses, brings it into contact with organisations worldwide. Over 80% of all new poetry in Britain is published by small presses and magazines but the Association is by no means solely devoted to publishers of poetry; its members produce everything from comics to cookery, novels and naval history.

Association of Scottish Motoring Writers

c/o Scottish and Universal Newspapers,
5/15 Bank Street, Airdrie ML6 6AF
☎01236 748048   Fax 01236 748098
Contact *John Murdoch*
Subscription £45 (Full); £25 (Associate)

FOUNDED 1961. Aims to co-ordinate the activities of, and provide shared facilities for, motoring writers resident in Scotland. Membership is by invitation only.

Author-Publisher Network

12 Mercers, Hawkhurst, Kent TN18 4LH
☎01580 753346
Admin: SKS, St Aldhelm, 20 Paul Street,
Frome, Somerset BA11 1DX
☎01373 451777
Chairman *Clive Brown*
Secretary *Denis Long*
Subscription £25 (p.a.)

FOUNDED 1993. The association aims to provide an active forum for writers publishing their own work. An information network of ideas and opportunities for self-publishers. Explores the business and technology of writing and publishing. Regular newsletter, supplements, seminars and workshops, etc.

Authors North

c/o The Society of Authors, 84 Drayton
Gardens, London SW10 9SB
☎0171 373 6642
Secretary *Ray Dunbobbin*

A group within **The Society of Authors** which organises meetings for members living in the North of England.

Authors' Club

40 Dover Street, London W1X 3RB
☎0171 499 8581   Fax 0171 409 0913
Secretary *Mrs Ann Carter*

FOUNDED in 1891 by Sir Walter Besant, the Authors' Club welcomes as members writers, publishers, critics, journalists, academics and anyone involved with literature. Administers the **Authors' Club Best First Novel Award; Sir Banister Fletcher Award; Marsh Biography Award** and the **Marsh Award for Children's Literature in Translation**. Membership fee: apply to secretary.

Authors' Licensing & Collecting Society (ALCS)

Marlborough Court, 14–18 Holborn, London
EC1N 2LE
☎0171 395 0600   Fax 0171 395 0660
E-mail: alcs@alcs.co.uk
Website: http:/www.alcs.co.uk
Secretary General *Christopher Zielinski*
Subscription £5.88 incl. VAT (UK; free to members of **The Society of Authors**, **The Writers' Guild, NUJ, BAJ** and **CIOJ**); £5 (Residents of EU countries); £7 (Overseas)

FOUNDED 1977. The British collecting society for all writers and their heirs, ALCS is a non-profit organisation whose principle purpose is to ensure that hard-to-collect revenues due to authors are efficiently collected and speedily distributed. Established to give assistance to writers in their battle to make a better living through the protection and exploitation of collective rights, ALCS has distributed some £32m. to British writers since its creation. On joining, members license ALSC to administer on their behalf those rights which an author is unable to exercise as an individual or which are best handled on a collective basis. Chief among these are: photocopying, cable retransmission (including the fees for BBC Prime and BBC World Service programming), rental and lending rights (but not British Public Lending Right), off-air recording, electronic rights, the performing right and public reception of broadcasts. The society is a prime resource and a leading authority on copyright matters and writers' collective interests. It maintains a watching brief on all matters affecting copyright both in Britain and abroad, making representations to UK government authorities and the EU. Consult the ALCS website or contact the office for application forms and further information.

BAAA

See **British American Arts Association**

BACB

See **British Association of Communicators in Business**

BAFTA (British Academy of Film and Television Arts)

195 Piccadilly, London W1V 0LN
☎0171 734 0022   Fax 0171 734 1792
Chief Executive *Jane Clarke*
Subscription £155 p.a. (Over 30); £75 p.a. (Under 30); £80 p.a. (Country); £70 p.a. (Overseas); £54 (Initial entry fee)

FOUNDED 1947. Membership limited to 'those who have contributed to the industry' over a minimum period of three years. Best known for its annual awards ceremonies, now held separately for film, television, children's programmes and interactive entertainment, the Academy runs a full programme of screenings, seminars, masterclasses, debates, lectures etc. It also actively supports training and educational projects.

Also BAFTA Scotland, BAFTA Wales, BAFTA North, BAFTA LA, BAFTA East Coast (USA) run separate programmes and, in the case of Scotland and Wales, hold their own awards.

BAPA
See **British Amateur Press Association**

BAPLA (British Association of Picture Libraries and Agencies)
18 Vine Hill, London EC1R 5DX
☎0171 713 1780   Fax 0171 713 1211
Represents 95 per cent of the British picture library and agency industry offering more than 300 million pictures. The Association offers advice on pricing, an annual membership directory, a picture-sourcing database, and *publishes* a quarterly industry magazine, *Light Box*.

BASCA (British Academy of Songwriters, Composers and Authors)
The Penthouse, 4 Brook Street, London W1Y 1AA
☎0171 629 0992   Fax 0171 629 0993
Chairman *Guy Fletcher*
Subscription from £35 + VAT p.a.

FOUNDED 1947. The Academy offers advice and support for songwriters and composers and represents members' interests to the music industry. It also issues a standard contract between publishers and writers and a collaborators' agreement. Members receive the Academy's quarterly magazine and can attend fortnightly legal and financial seminars and creative workshops. The Academy administers Britain's annual awards for composers, the Ivor Novello Awards, now in their 43rd year.

The Bibliographical Society
c/o The Wellcome Institute Library, 183 Euston Road, London NW1 2BE
☎0171 611 7244   Fax 0171 611 8703
President *R. Myers*
Honorary Secretary *D. Pearson*

Subscription £28 p.a.

Aims to promote and encourage the study and research of historical, analytical, descriptive and textual bibliography, and the history of printing, publishing, bookselling, bookbinding and collecting; to hold meetings at which papers are read and discussed; to print and publish works concerned with bibliography; to form a bibliographical library. Awards grants and bursaries for bibliographical research. *Publishes* a quarterly magazine called *The Library*.

Book Packagers Association
93A Blenheim Crescent, London W11 2EQ
☎0171 221 9089
Secretary *Rosemary Pettit*
Subscription £150 p.a.; Associate membership £75 p.a.; Overseas membership £100 p.a.
Aims to provide members with a forum for the exchange of information, to improve the image of packaging and to represent the interests of members. Activities include meetings, seminars, the provision of standard contracts and a joint stand at the London Book Fair.

Book Trust
Book House, 45 East Hill, London SW18 2QZ
☎0181 516 2977   Fax 0181 516 2978
Chief Executive *Brian Perman*
Subscription £25 p.a.; £28 (Overseas)

FOUNDED 1925. Book Trust, the independent educational charity promoting books and reading, includes Young Book Trust (formerly Children's Book Foundation). The Trust offers a book information service (free to the public and on subscription to the trade); administers many literary prizes (including the **Booker**); carries out surveys, *publishes* useful reference books and resource materials; houses a children's book reference library, and promotes children's books through activities like Children's Book Week.

Book Trust Scotland
The Scottish Book Centre, 137 Dundee Street, Edinburgh EH11 1BG
☎0131 229 3663   Fax 0131 228 4293
Contact *Kathryn Ross*

FOUNDED 1956. Book Trust Scotland works with schools, libraries, writers, artists, publishers, bookshops and individuals to promote the pleasures of reading to people of all ages. It provides a book information service which draws on the children's reference library (a copy of every children's book published in the previous twelve months), the Scottish children's book collection, a range of press cuttings on Scottish literary themes and a number of smaller collections of Scottish books. Book Trust Scotland administers **The Fidler Award** and the **The Stakis Prize for the Scottish Writer of the Year**; and *publishes* guides to Scottish books and writers, both adult and children's. Book Trust Scotland also produces a range of children's reading posters, literary guides and Scottish poetry posters.

Booksellers Association of Great Britain & Ireland

Minster House, 272 Vauxhall Bridge Road, London SW1V 1BA
☎0171 834 5477   Fax 0171 834 8812
E-mail: 100437.2261@compuserve.com

Chief Executive *Tim Godfray*

FOUNDED 1895. The BA helps 3,300 independent, chain and multiple members to sell more books and reduce costs. It represents members' interests to publishers, Government, authors and others in the trade as well as offering marketing assistance, running training courses, conferences, seminars and exhibitions. Together with **The Publishers Association**, coordinates the World Book Day initiative. *Publishes* directories, catalogues, surveys and various other publications connected with the book trade and administers the **Whitbread Book of the Year and Literary Awards**.

British Academy of Film and Television Arts

See **BAFTA**

British Academy of Songwriters, Composers and Authors

See **BASCA**

British Amateur Press Association (BAPA)

2 New Houses, Pant, Merthyr Tydfil CF48 2AB
E-mail: ep@ribbon.demon.co.uk

Honorary Secretary *Ms E. Pearson*

A non-profit-making, non-sectarian hobby organisation (founded in 1890) to 'promote the fellowship of amateur writers, artists, editors, printers, publishers and other craftsmen/women. To encourage them to edit, print and publish, *as a hobby*, magazines and newsletters, etc' by letterpress and other processes, including photocopiers and computer DTP/word-processors. Not an outlet for placing work commercially, only with other members in their private publications circulated within the association and amongst friends. A fraternity providing contacts between amateur writers, poets, editors, artists, etc. Postal enquiries only, please enclose first-class stamp to the Secretary at the above address.

British American Arts Association

118 Commercial Street, London E1 6NF
☎0171 247 5385   Fax 0171 247 5256

Director *Jennifer Williams*

A non-profit organisation working in the field of arts and education. BAAA conducts research, organises conferences, produces a quarterly newsletter and is part of an international network of arts and education organisations. As well as a specialised arts and education library, BAAA has a more general library holding information on opportunities for artists and performers both in the UK and abroad. BAAA is not a grant-giving organisation.

British Association of Communicators in Business (BACB)

42 Borough High Street, London SE1 1XW
☎0171 378 7139   Fax 0171 387 7140

Membership Secretary *Sheila Ayinla*

FOUNDED 1949. The Association aims to be the 'market leader for those involved in corporate media management and practice by providing professional, authoritative, dynamic, supportive and innovative services'.

British Association of Journalists

88 Fleet Street, London EC4Y 1PJ
☎0171 353 3003   Fax 0171 353 2310

General Secretary *Steve Turner*
Subscription National newspaper staff, national broadcasting staff, national news agency staff: £12.50 a month. Other seniors, including magazine journalists, PRs and freelances who earn the majority of their income from journalism: £7.50 a month. Journalists under 24: £5 a month. Student journalists: Free.

FOUNDED 1992. Aims to protect and promote the industrial and professional interests of journalists.

British Association of Picture Libraries and Agencies

See **BAPLA**

British Copyright Council

Copyright House, 29–33 Berners Street,
London W1P 4AA
☎0171 306 4066   Fax 0171 306 4050

Contact *The Secretary*

Works for the national and international acceptance of copyright and acts as a lobby/watchdog organisation on behalf of creators, publishers and performers on copyright and associated matters. Publications include *Guide to the Law of Copyright and Rights in Performances in the UK*; *Photocopying from Books and Journals*. An umbrella organisation which does not deal with individual enquiries.

The British Council

10 Spring Gardens, London SW1A 2BN
☎0171 930 8466/Press Office: 0171 389 487
Fax 0171 839 6347

Head of Literature *Dr Alastair Niven*

The British Council promotes Britain abroad. It provides access to British ideas, talents, expertise and experience in education and training, books and periodicals, the English language, literature and the arts, sciences and technology. An independent, non-political organisation, the British Council works in 109 countries running a mix of offices, libraries, resource centres and English teaching operations.

British Equestrian Writers' Association

Priory House, Station Road, Swavesey,
Cambridge CB4 5QJ
☎01954 232084   Fax 01954 231362

Contact *Gillian Newsum*
Subscription £15

FOUNDED 1973. Aims to further the interests of equestrian sport and improve, wherever possible, the working conditions of the equestrian press. Membership is by invitation of the committee. Candidates for membership must be nominated and seconded by full members and receive a majority vote of the committee.

British Film Commission

70 Baker Street, London W1M 1DJ
☎0171 224 5000   Fax 0171 224 1013

Press & Public Relations Manager
Tina McFarling

FOUNDED 1991 the BFC is funded through the Department for Culture, Media and Sport. Its remit is to promote the United Kingdom as an international production centre, to encourage the use of British artists and technicians, technical services, facilities and locations, and to provide wide-ranging support to those filming and contemplating filming in the UK.

British Film Institute

21 Stephen Street, London W1P 2LN
☎0171 255 1444   Fax 0171 436 7950

Membership from £11.95 p.a.

FOUNDED 1933. Exists to encourage the development of film, television and video in the UK. Its divisions include: National Film and Television Archive; BFI on the South Bank (National Film Theatre, London Film Festival and Museum of the Moving Image); **BFI Production**; **BFI National Film Library**; and BFI Information & Education (including Publishing, *Sight and Sound*). It also provides programming support to a regional network of 36 film theatres.

British Guild of Beer Writers

The Maltings, Old School Lane, Stanford,
Bedfordshire SG18 9JL
☎01462 851420

Secretary *Barry Bremner*
Subscription £40 p.a.

FOUNDED 1988. Aims to improve standards in beer writing and at the same time extend public knowledge of beers and brewing. Publishes a directory of members with details of their publications and their particular areas of interest; this is then circulated to newspapers, magazines, trade press and broadcasting organisations. As part of the plan to improve writing standards and to achieve a higher profile for beer, the Guild offers annual awards, The Gold and Silver Tankard Awards, to writers and broadcasters judged to have made the most valuable contribution towards this end in their work. Meetings are held regularly.

British Guild of Travel Writers

90 Corringway, London W5 3HA
☎0181 998 2223

Chairman *Gary Buchanan*
Honorary Secretary *Brenda Birmingham*
Subscription £75 p.a.

The professional association of travel writers, broadcasters, photographers and editors which aims to serve its members' professional interests by acting as a forum for debate, discussion and 'networking'. The Guild *publishes* an annual Year Book giving full details of all its members, holds monthly meetings and has a monthly newsletter. Members are required to earn the majority of their income from travel reporting.

British Science Fiction Association

1 Long Row Close, Everdon, Daventry, Northants NN11 3BE
☎01327 361661
E-mail: bsfa@enterprise.net

Membership Secretary *Paul Billinger*
Subscription £19 p.a. (Reduction for unwaged)

FOUNDED originally in 1958 by a group of authors, readers, publishers and booksellers interested in science fiction. With a worldwide membership, the Association aims to promote the reading, writing and publishing of science fiction and to encourage SF fans to maintain contact with each other. Also offers postal writers workshop, a magazine chain and an information service. *Publishes Matrix* bi-monthly newsletter with comment and opinions, news of conventions, etc. Contributions from members welcomed; *Vector* bi-monthly critical journal – reviews of books and magazines; *Focus* bi-annual magazine with articles, original fiction and letters column. For further information, contact the Membership Secretary at the above address or on e-mail.

British Screen Finance

14–17 Wells Mews, London W1P 3FL
☎0171 323 9080   Fax 0171 323 0092

Contact *Simon Perry, Emma Berkofsky*

A private company aided by government grant; shareholders are Rank, Channel 4, Granada and Pathé. Exists to invest in British films specifically intended for cinema release in the UK and worldwide. Divided into two functions: project development (contact *Emma Berkofsky*), and production investment (contact *Simon Perry*). British Screen also manages the European Co-production Fund which exists to support feature films co-produced by the UK with other European countries. British Screen develops around 40 projects per year, and has invested in 115 British feature film productions in the last ten years.

British Society of Magazine Editors (BSME)

137 Hale Lane, Edgware, Middlesex HA8 9QP
☎0181 906 4664   Fax 0181 959 2137

Contact *Gill Branston*

Holds regular lunches and industry forums as well as an annual awards dinner.

Broadcasting Press Guild

Tiverton, The Ridge, Woking, Surrey GU22 7EQ
☎01483 764895   Fax 01483 764895

Membership Secretary *Richard Last*
Subscription £15 p.a.

FOUNDED 1973 to promote the professional interests of journalists specialising in writing or broadcasting about the media. Organises monthly lunches addressed by top broadcasting executives, and annual TV and radio awards. Membership by invitation.

BSME

See **British Society of Magazine Editors**

Bureau of Freelance Photographers

Focus House, 497 Green Lanes, London N13 4BP
☎0181 882 3315   Fax 0181 886 5174

Membership Secretary *James Clancy*
Subscription £40 p.a. (UK); £50 p.a. (Overseas)

FOUNDED 1965. Assists members in selling their pictures through monthly *Market Newsletter* and offers advisory, legal assistance and other services.

Campaign for Press and Broadcasting Freedom

8 Cynthia Street, London N1 9JF
☎0171 278 4430   Fax 0171 837 8868

Subscription £12 p.a. (concessions available); £25 p.a. (Institutions); £20 p.a. (Organisations)

Broadly based pressure group working for more accountable and accessible media in Britain. Advises on right of reply and takes up the issue of the portrayal of minorities. Members receive *Free Press* (bi-monthly), discounts on publications and news of campaign progress.

The Caravan Writers' Guild

Hillside House, Beach Road, Benllech, Anglesey LL74 8SW
☎01248 852248   Fax 01248 852107

Contact *The Secretary*
Subscription £5 Joining fee plus £10 p.a.

Guild for writers active in the specialist fields of caravan and camping journalism.

Careers Writers' Association

71 Wimborne Road, Colehill, Wimborne, Dorset BH21 2RP
☎01202 880320

Membership Secretary *Barbara Buffton*

FOUNDED 1979. The association aims to promote high standards of careers writing, improve access to sources of information, provide a network for members to exchange information and experience, hold meetings on topics of relevance and interest to members. Also produces an occasional newsletter and maintains a membership list. Forges links with organisations sharing related interests, and maintains regular contact with national education and training bodies, government agencies and publishers.

Chartered Institute of Journalists

2 Dock Offices, Surrey Quays Road, London SE16 2XU
☎0171 252 1187   Fax 0171 232 2302
General Secretary *Christopher Underwood*
Subscription £155
FOUNDED 1884. The Chartered Institute is concerned with professional journalistic standards and with safeguarding the freedom of the media. It is open to writers, broadcasters and journalists (including self-employed) in all media. Affiliate membership (£105) is available to part-time or occasional practitioners and to overseas journalists who can join the Institute's International Division. Members also belong to the IOJ (TU) – Institute of Journalists, an independent trade union which protects, advises and represents them in their employment or freelance work; negotiates on their behalf and provides legal assistance and support. The IOJ (TU) is a certificated trade union which represents members' interests in the workplace, and is also a constituent member of the National Council in the Training of Journalists and the Independent Unions Training Council.

Children's Book Circle

c/o Macmillan Publishers Ltd, 25 Eccleston Place, London SW1W 9NF
☎0171 881 8000   Fax 0171 881 8001
Membership Secretary *Gaby Morgan*
The Children's Book Circle provides a discussion forum for anybody involved with children's books. Monthly meetings are addressed by a panel of invited speakers and topics focus on current and controversial issues. Administers the **Eleanor Farjeon Award**.

Children's Book Foundation

See **Book Trust**

Circle of Wine Writers

44 Oaklands Avenue, Droitwich, Worcestershire WR9 7BT
☎01905 773707   Fax 01905 773707
Vice Chairman *Philippe Boucheron*
Membership £25 p.a.
FOUNDED 1962. Open to all *bona fide* authors,

broadcasters, journalists and photographers currently being published, as well as lecturers and tutors, all of whom are professionally engaged in communicating about wines and spirits. Aims to improve the standard of writing, broadcasting and lecturing about wines, spirits and beers; to contribute to the growing knowledge and interest in wine; to promote wines and spirits of quality and to comment adversely on faulty products or dubious practices; to establish and maintain good relations with the news media and the wine trade; to provide members with a strong voice with which to promote their views; to provide a programme of workshops, meetings, talks and tastings.

Clé, The Irish Book Publishers Association

Cultural Offices, Temple Bar, 2, Republic of Ireland
☎00 353 1 8729090
President *Michael Gill*
Administrator *Orla Martin*
FOUNDED 1970 to promote Irish publishing, protect members' interests and train the industry.

Comedy Writers' Association of Great Britain

61 Parry Road, Ashmore Park, Wolverhampton, West Midlands WV11 2PS
☎01902 722729   Fax 01902 722729
Contact *Ken Rock*
FOUNDED 1981 to assist and promote the work of comedy writers. The Association is a self-help group designed to encourage and advise its members to sell their work. It is an international organisation with representatives in Britain, Germany, Cyprus, Sweden, Belgium, Luxembourg, Czechoslovakia, Denmark, Finland and Canada. International seminar with videos of foreign TV comedy programmes, bookshop and business club where members can discuss opportunities. Members often come together to work jointly on a variety of comedy projects for British and overseas productions. *Publishes* regular magazines and monthly market information.

Comhairle nan Leabhraichean/The Gaelic Books Council

22 Mansfield Street, Glasgow G11 5QP
☎0141 337 6211   Fax 0141 353 0515
Chairman *Boyd Robertson*
Director *Ian MacDonald*
FOUNDED 1968 and now a charitable company

with its own bookshop. Encourages and promotes Gaelic publishing by giving grants to publishers and writers; providing editorial and word-processing services; retailing Gaelic books; producing a catalogue of all Gaelic books in print, and answering enquiries about them.

Commercial Radio Companies Association

77 Shaftesbury Avenue, London W1V 7AD
☎0171 306 2603   Fax 0171 470 0062
Chief Executive *Paul Brown*
Research and Communications Manager
Rachell Fox

The CRCA is the trade body for the independent radio stations. It represents members' interests to Government, the **Radio Authority**, trade unions, copyright organisations and other bodies.

The Copyright Licensing Agency Ltd

90 Tottenham Court Road, London
W1P 0LP
☎0171 436 5931   Fax 0171 436 3986
E-mail: cla@cla.co.uk
Website: http://www.cla.co.uk
Chief Executive/Secretary *Peter Shephard*

FOUNDED 1982 by the **Authors' Licensing and Collecting Society (ALCS)** and the **Publishers Licensing Society Ltd (PLS)**, the CLA administers collectively photocopying and other copying rights that it is uneconomic for writers and publishers to administer for themselves. The Agency issues collective and transactional licences, and the fees it collects, after the deduction of its operating costs, are distributed at regular intervals to authors and publishers via their respective societies (i.e. ALCS or PLS). Since 1987 CLA has distributed over £50 million.

Council for British Archaeology

Bowes Morrell House, 111 Walmgate, York
YO1 2UA
☎01904 671417   Fax 01904 671384
Information Officer *Mike Heyworth*

FOUNDED 1944 to represent and promote archaeology at all levels. Its aims are to improve the public's awareness in and understanding of Britain's past; to carry out research; to survey, guide and promote the teaching of archaeology at all levels of education; to publish a wide range of academic, educational, general and bibliographical works (see **CBA Publishing**).

Council of Academic and Professional Publishers
See **The Publishers Association**

Crime Writers' Association (CWA)

60 Drayton Road, Kings Heath, Birmingham
B14 7LR
Secretary *Judith Cutler*
Membership £40 (Town); £35 (Country)

Full membership is limited to professional crime writers, but publishers, literary agents, booksellers, etc., who specialise in crime are eligible for Associate membership. The Association has regional chapters throughout the country, including Scotland. Meetings are held monthly in central London, with informative talks frequently given by police, scenes of crime officers, lawyers, etc., and a weekend conference is held annually in different parts of the country. Produces a monthly newsletter for members called *Red Herrings* and presents various annual awards.

The Critics' Circle

c/o The Stage (incorporating Television Today), 47 Bermondsey Street, London
SE1 3XT
☎0171 403 1818 ext 106 (Catherine Cooper)
Fax 0171 357 9287
President *Allen Robertson*
Honorary General Secretary *Charles Hedges*
Subscription £18 p.a.

Membership by invitation only. Aims to uphold and promote the art of criticism (and the commercial rates of pay thereof) and preserve the interests of its members: professionals involved in criticism of film, drama, music and dance.

Department for Culture, Media and Sport

2–4 Cockspur Street, London SW1Y 5DH
☎0171 211 6000   Fax 0171 211 6270
Senior Press Officer, Arts *Toby Sargent*

The Department for Culture, Media and Sport has responsibilities for Government policies relating to the arts, museums and galleries, public libraries, sport, broadcasting, Press standards, the built heritage, the film and music industries, tourism and the National Lottery. It funds **The Arts Council**, national museums and galleries, **The British Library** (including the new library building at St Pancras), the Public Lending Right and the Royal Commission on Historical Manuscripts. It is responsible within Government for the public library service in England,

and for library and information matters generally, where they are not the responsibility of other departments.

Directory & Database Publishers Association

93A Blenheim Crescent, London
W11 2EQ
☎0171 221 9089
Website: directory-publisher.co.uk
Contact *Rosemary Pettit*
Subscription £115–1140 p.a.

FOUNDED 1970 to promote the interests of *bona fide* directory publishers and protect the public from disreputable and fraudulent practices. The objectives of the Association are to maintain a code of professional practice to safeguard public interest; to raise the standard and status of directory publishing throughout the UK; to promote business directories as a medium for advertising; to protect the legal and statutory interests of directory publishers; to foster bonds of common interest among responsible directory publishers and to provide for the exchange of technical, commercial and management information between members. Meetings, seminars, conference, newsletter awards, fairs.

Drama Association of Wales

The Library, Singleton Road, Splott, Cardiff
CF2 2ET
☎01222 452200   Fax 01222 452277
Contact *Gary Thomas*

Runs a large playscript lending library; holds an annual playwriting competition (see under **Prizes**); offers a script-reading service (£10 per script) which usually takes three months from receipt of play to issue of reports. From plays submitted to the reading service, selected scripts are considered for publication of a short run (250–750 copies). Writers receive a percentage of the cover price on sales and a percentage of the performance fee.

East Anglian Writers

47 Christchurch Road, Norwich, Norfolk
NR2 3NE
☎01603 455503   Fax 01603 455503
Chairman *Michael Pollard*

A group of over 80 professional writers living in Norfolk and Suffolk. Informal pub meetings, occasional speakers' evenings and contact point for professional writers new to the area.

Edinburgh Bibliographical Society

Dept of Special Collections, Edinburgh University Library, George Square, Edinburgh
EH8 9LJ
☎0131 650 3412   Fax 0131 650 6863
Honorary Secretary *Dr M. Simpson*
Subscription £10; £15 (Institution);
  £5 (Students)

FOUNDED 1890. Organises lectures on bibliographical topics and visits to libraries. *Publishes* a biennial journal called *Transactions*, which is free to members, and other occasional publications.

Educational Publishers Council

See **The Publishers Association**

Electronic Publishers' Forum

See **The Publishers Association**

The English Association

University of Leicester, University Road, Leicester LE1 7RH
☎0116 252 3982   Fax 0116 252 2301
Chief Executive *Helen Lucas*

FOUNDED 1906 to promote understanding and appreciation of the English language and its literatures. Activities include sponsoring a number of publications and organising lectures and conferences for teachers, plus annual sixth-form conferences. Publications include *Year's Work in Critical and Cultural Theory, English, Use of English, Primary English, Essays and Studies* and *Year's Work in English Studies*.

ETmA (Educational Television & Media Association)

37 Monkgate, York YO3 7PB
☎01904 639212   Fax 01904 639212
E-mail: josie.key@etma.u-net.com
Administrator *Josie Key*

The ETmA is a 'dynamic association' comprising a wide variety of users of television and other electronic media in education. Annual awards scheme (video competition), and annual conferences. New members always welcome.

Federation of Entertainment Unions

1 Highfield, Twyford, Nr Winchester, Hampshire SO21 1QR
☎01962 713134   Fax 01962 713288
Secretary *Steve Harris*

Plenary meetings six times annually and meetings of The Film and Electronic Media Committee six times annually on alternate months. Additionally, there are Training & European Committees. Represents the following unions: British Actors' Equity Association; Broadcasting Entertainment Cinematograph and Theatre Union; Musicians' Union; AEEU; **National Union of Journalists**; **The Writers' Guild of Great Britain**.

The Federation of Worker Writers and Community Publishers (FWWCP)

PO Box 540, Burslem, Stoke on Trent
ST6 6DR
☎01782 822327   Fax 01782 822327
E-mail: fwwcp@mcmail.com
Website: http://www.fwwcp.mcmail.com

Administrator/Coordinator *Tim Diggles*

The FWWCP is a federation of writing groups who are committed to writing and publishing based on working-class experience and creativity. The FWWCP is the membership's collective national voice and has for some time been given funding by **The Arts Council**. Founded in 1976, it comprises around 50 member groups, each one with its own identity, reflecting its community and membership. They represent over 5000 people who regularly (often weekly) meet to offer constructive criticism, produce books and tapes, perform and share skills, offering creative and critical support. There are writers' workshops of long standing; adult literacy organisations; groups working mainly in oral and local history; groups and local networks of writers who come together to publish, train or perform; groups with a specific remit to further the aims of a section of the community such as the homeless or disabled. Although diverse in nature, member organisations share the aim to make writing and publishing accessible to people and encourage them to take an active, cooperative and democratic role in writing, performing and publishing. The main activities include training days and weekends to learn and share skills, a quarterly magazine, a major annual festival of writing and networking between member organisations. The FWWCP has published a number of anthologies and is willing to work with other organisations on publishing projects. Membership is only open to groups but individuals will be put in touch with groups which can help them, and become friends of the Federation. Contact the above address for an information leaflet.

Fellowship of Christian Writers

See **Association of Christian Writers**

Foreign Press Association in London

11 Carlton House Terrace, London
SW1Y 5AJ
☎0171 930 0445   Fax 0171 925 0469

Contact *Davina Crole, Catherine Flury*
Membership (not incl. VAT) £100 p.a.
    (Full); £92.40 (Associate Journalists);
    £142 (Associate Non-Journalists)

FOUNDED 1888. Non-profit-making service association for foreign correspondents based in London, providing a variety of press-related services.

The Gaelic Books Council

See **Comhairle nan Leabhraichean**

The Garden Writers' Guild

c/o Institute of Horticulture, 14/15 Belgrave Square, London SW1X 8PS
☎0171 245 6943

Contact *Angela Clarke*
Subscription £15; (£10 to Institute of Horticulture members)

FOUNDED 1990. Aims to revise the status and standing of gardening communicators. Administers an annual awards scheme. Operates a mailing service and organises press briefing days.

General Practitioner Writers' Association

West Carnliath, Strathtay, Perth PH9 0PG
☎01887 840380   Fax 01887 840380

Contact *Professor F. M. Hull*
Subscription £30 p.a.; £40 (Joint)

FOUNDED 1986 to promote and improve writing activities within and for general practices. Open to general practitioners, practice managers, nurses, etc. and professional journalists writing on anything pertaining to general practice. Very keen to develop input from interested parties who work mainly outside the profession. Regular workshops, discussions and a twice-yearly journal, *The GP Writer*.

Guild of Agricultural Journalists

Charmwood, 47 Court Meadow, Rotherfield, East Sussex TN6 3LQ
☎01892 853187

Honorary General Secretary *Don Gomery*
Subscription £30 p.a.

FOUNDED 1944 to promote a high professional standard among journalists who specialise in agriculture, horticulture and allied subjects. Represents members' interests with representative bodies in the industry; provides a forum through meetings and social activities for members to meet eminent people in the industry; maintains contact with associations of agricultural journalists overseas; promotes schemes for the education of members and for the provision of suitable entrants into agricultural journalism.

Guild of Editors
See **The Newspaper Society**

The Guild of Erotic Writers
CTCK PO Box 8431, Deptford, London SE8 4BP
☎0973 767086
Contact *Elizabeth Coldwell, Zak Jane Keir*
Subscription £10 p.a.

FOUNDED 1995. Aims to provide a network for all authors of erotic fiction, both published and unpublished and to promote erotica as a valid form of writing. Members receive quarterly newsletters and a tip sheet on getting work accepted, together with discounts on conferences and events, and a manuscript-reading service (also available to non-members at 'very competitive rates' – short stories £4.50 for members, £7 non-members).

The Guild of Food Writers
48 Crabtree Lane, London SW6 6LW
☎0171 610 1180   Fax 0171 610 1180
Administrator *Christina Thomas*
Subscription £45

FOUNDED 1945. The objects of the Guild include 'to bring together professional food writers including journalists, broadcasters and authors, to print and issue an annual list of members, to extend the range of members' knowledge and experience by arranging discussions, tastings and visits, and to encourage the development of new writers by every means including competitions and awards. The Guild aims to contribute to the growth of public interest in, and knowledge of, the subject of food and to campaign for improvements in the quality of food.'

Guild of Motoring Writers
30 The Cravens, Smallfield, Surrey RH6 9QS
☎01342 843294   Fax 01342 844093
General Secretary *Sharon Scott-Fairweather*
FOUNDED 1944. Represents members' interests and provides a forum for members to exchange information.

The Guild of Regional Film Writers
45 Tides Way, Marchwood, Southampton, Hampshire SO40 4LE
☎01703 872956   Fax 01703 872956
E-mail: drv.movieman@virgin.net
Chairman *Darren Vaughan*
Subscription £40 p.a.

FOUNDED 1986. Aims to encourage, support and promote the work of regional film writers and broadcasters within the industry. Works closely with distributors, exhibitors and other industry bodies. Members are invited to 'Cinema Days' weekends thrice yearly where new movies are screened and press conferences held. Prospective members should supply three relevant cuttings/tapes for approval.

Humberside Writers' Association (HWA)
'Fairoaks', West Promenade, Driffield, East Yorkshire YO25 7TZ
☎01377 255542
Chairman *Glynn S. Russell*
Annual membership fee £2

FOUNDED 1987 by local writers, would-be writers and people interested in new writing who gathered together with the backing of their regional arts association to create a platform for local scribblers, published or otherwise. Organises and promotes writing-related events and workshops within the Humberside area. *Publishes* information about events, competitions, workshops, publications and any other news, local or national, about opportunities of interest to members. Holds regular meetings (last Wednesday of the month) to which writers, publishers and agents are invited; plus day schools, readings, newsletter and library/resource unit.

Independent Publishers Guild
25 Cambridge Road, Hampton, Middlesex TW12 2JL
☎0181 979 0250   Fax 0181 979 6393
Secretary *Yvonne Messenger*
Subscription approx. £75 p.a.

FOUNDED 1962. Membership open to independent publishers, packagers and suppliers, i.e. professionals in allied fields. Regular meetings, conferences, seminars, mailings and a quarterly bulletin.

Independent Television Association
See **ITV Network Centre**

Independent Theatre Council

12 The Leathermarket, Weston Street,
London SE1 3ER
☎0171 403 1727/6698 (general/training) Fax
0171 403 1745

Contact *Charlotte Jones*

The management association and representative
body for small/middle-scale theatres (up to
around 350 seats) and touring theatre companies.
Negotiates contracts and has established standard
agreements with Equity on behalf of all professionals working in the theatre. Negotiations
with the **Theatre Writers' Union** and **The
Writers' Guild** for a contractual agreement
covering rights and fee structure for playwrights
were concluded in 1991. Terms and conditions
were renegotiated and updated in April 1997.
Copies of the minimum terms agreement can be
obtained from The Writers' Guild. *Publishes* a
booklet, *A Practical Guide for Writers and
Companies* (£3.50 plus p&p), giving guidance to
writers on how to submit scripts to theatres and
guidance to theatres on how to deal with them.

Institute of Copywriting

PO Box 1561, Wedmore BS28 4TD
☎01934 713563   Fax 01934 713492

Secretary *Alex Middleton*

FOUNDED 1991 to promote copywriters and
copywriting (writing publicity material). Maintains a code of practice. Membership is open to
students as well as experienced practitioners.
Runs training courses (see entry under **Writers'
Courses**). Has a list of approved copywriters.
Answers queries relating to copywriting. Contact
the Institute for a free booklet.

Institute of Translation and Interpreting (ITI)

377 City Road, London EC1V 1NA
☎0171 713 7600   Fax 0171 713 7650
E-mail: iti@compuserve.com
Website: www.iti.org.uk

The ITI is a professional association of translators
and interpreters aiming to promote the highest
standards in translating and interpreting. It has
strong corporate membership and runs professional development courses and conferences,
sometimes in conjunction with its language,
regional and subject network. Membership is
open to those with a genuine and proven involvement in translation and interpreting (including students). ITI's Directory of Members, its
bi-monthly Bulletin and other publications are
available from the Secretariat. The Secretariat
offers a free referral service whereby enquirers
can be given the names of suitable members for
any interpreting/translating assignment. ITI is a
full and active member of FIT (International
Federation of Translators).

International Association of Puzzle Writers

42 Brigstocke Terrace, Ryde, Isle of Wight
PO33 2PD
☎01983 811688

Contact *Dr Jeremy Sims*

FOUNDED 1966 for writers of brainteasing puzzles, crosswords and word games, and for designers of games in general. Enquiries from publishers seeking material welcome. Aims to provide
support and information and to promote the art
of puzzle writing and games design to publishers,
games manufacturers and the general public.
Publishes bi-monthly newsletter – contributions
welcome. Membership is free but stamps or
IRCs are necessary to cover the costs of postage
of the newsletter. For further information, send
s.a.e. to the above address.

International Cultural Desk

6 Belmont Crescent, Glasgow G12 8ES
☎0141 339 0090   Fax 0141 337 2271
E-mail: icd@dial.pipex.com

Development Manager *Hilde Bollen*
Information Officer *Anne Robb*

FOUNDED 1994. Aims to assist the Scottish cultural community to operate more effectively in
an international context by providing timely
and targeted information and advice. The Desk
provides and disseminates information on
funding sources, international opportunities
and cultural policy development in Europe,
and also assists with establishing contacts internationally. The Desk is not a funding agency.
Publishes Communication, a bi-monthly information update about forthcoming international
opportunities across the whole range of cultural
and artistic activity, and *InFocus*, a series of specialised guides with an international focus.

Irish Book Publishers Association

See **Clé**

Irish Copyright Licensing Agency Ltd

19 Parnell Square, Dublin 1, Republic of
Ireland
☎00 353 1 872 9202   Fax 00 353 1 872 2035

Administrator *Orla O'Sullivan*

FOUNDED 1992 by writers and publishers in

Ireland to provide a scheme through which rights holders can give permission, and users of copyright material can obtain permission, to copy.

Irish Writers' Union
19 Parnell Square, Dublin 1 Republic of Ireland
☎00 353 1 872 1302   Fax 00 353 1 872 6282
Secretary *Mara Rainwater*
Subscription £20 p.a.
FOUNDED1986 to promote the interests and protect the rights of writers in Ireland.

Isle of Man Authors
24 Laurys Avenue, Ramsey, Isle of Man IM8 2HE
☎01624 815634
Secretary *Mrs Beryl Sandwell*
Subscription £5 p.a.
An association of writers living on the Isle of Man, which has links with **The Society of Authors**.

ITI
See **Institute of Translation and Interpreting**

ITV Network Centre
200 Gray's Inn Road, London WC1X 8HF
☎0171 843 8000   Fax 0171 843 8158
The ITV Network Centre, wholly owned by the ITV companies, independently commissions and schedules the television programmes which are shown across the ITV network. As a successor to the Independent Television Association, it also provides a range of services to the ITV companies where a common approach is required.

IVCA (International Visual Communication Association)
Bolsover House, 5–6 Clipstone Street, London W1P 8LD
☎0171 580 0962   Fax 0171 436 2606
Chief Executive *Wayne Drew*
The IVCA is a professional association representing the interests of the users and suppliers of visual communications. In particular it pursues the interests of producers, commissioners and manufacturers involved in the non-broadcast and independent facilities industries and also business event companies. It represents all sizes of company and freelance individuals, offering information and advice services, publications, a professional network, special interest groups, a magazine and a variety of events including the UK's Film and Video Communications Festival.

The Library Association
7 Ridgmount Street, London WC1E 7AE
☎0171 636 7543   Fax 0171 436 7218
E-mail: info@la-hq.org.uk
http://www.la-hq.org.uk
Chief Executive *Ross Shimmon*
The professional body for librarians and information managers, with 25,000 individual and institutional members. **Library Association Publishing** produces 30–35 new titles each year and has over 250 in print. The *LA Record* is the monthly magazine for members. Further information from Information Services, The Library Association.

The Media Society
56 Roseneath Road, London SW11 6AQ
Contact *Peter Dannheisser*
Subscription £25 p.a.; £10 Entry fee
FOUNDED 1973. A registered charity which aims to provide a forum for the exchange of knowledge and opinion between those in public and political life, the professions, industry and education. Meetings (about 10 a year) usually take the form of luncheons and dinners in London with invited speakers. The society also acts as a 'think tank' and submits evidence and observations to royal commissions, select committees and review bodies.

Medical Journalists' Association
2 St George's Road, Kingston-upon-Thames, Surrey KT2 6DN
☎0181 549 1019   Fax 0181 255 4964
Chairman *John Illman*
Honorary Secretary *Jenny Sims*
Subscription £30 p.a.
FOUNDED 1967. Aims to improve the quality and practice of medical and health journalism and to improve relationships and understanding between medical and health journalists and the health and medical professions. Regular meetings with senior figures in medicine and medico politics; teach-ins on particular subjects to help journalists with background information; weekend symposium for members with people who have newsworthy stories in the field; awards for medical journalists offered by various commercial sponsors, plus MJA's own award financed by members. *Publishes* a detailed directory of members and freelances and two-monthly newsletter.

Medical Writers' Group

The Society of Authors, 84 Drayton Gardens, London SW10 9SB
☎0171 373 6642   Fax 0171 373 5768
Contact *Jacqueline Granger-Taylor*

FOUNDED 1980. A specialist group within **The Society of Authors** offering advice and help to authors of medical books. Administers Medical Prizes.

National Association of Writers Groups

The Arts Centre, Biddick Lane, Washington, Tyne & Wear NE38 2AB
☎0191 416 9751   Fax 0191 4311263
Contact *Brian Lister*

FOUNDED 1995 with the object of furthering the interests of writers' groups throughout the UK. A registered charity, No: 1059047, NAWG is strictly non-sectarian and non-political. *Publishes* a bi-monthly newsletter, distributed to member groups; gives free entry to competitions for group anthologies, poetry, short stories, articles, novels and sketches; holds an annual open festival of writing with 40 workshops, seminars, individual surgeries led by professional, high-profile writers. Membership open to all writers' groups – there are no restrictions or qualifications required for joining; 120 groups are affiliated so far.

National Association of Writers in Education

PO Box 1, Sheriff Hutton, York YO60 7YU
☎01653 618429   Fax 01653 618429
Contact *Paul Munden*
Subscription £12 p.a.

FOUNDED 1991. Aims to promote the contribution of living writers to education and to encourage both the practice and the critical appreciation of creative writing. Has over 400 members. Organises national conferences and training courses. *Publishes* a directory of writers who work in schools, colleges and the community (available on the Internet on www.nawe.co.uk) and a magazine, *Writing in Education*, issued free to members three times per year.

National Campaign for the Arts

Francis House, Francis Street, London SW1P 1DE
☎0171 828 4448   Fax 0171 931 9959
E-mail: newmail@artscampaign.org
Director *Jennifer Edwards*

FOUNDED 1984 to represent the cultural sector in Britain and to make sure that the problems facing the arts are properly put to Government, at local and national level. The NCA is an independent body relying on finance from its members. Involved in all issues which affect the arts: public finance, education, broadcasting and media affairs, the fight against censorship, the rights of artists, the place of the arts on the public agenda and structures for supporting culture. Membership open to all arts organisations (except government agencies) and to individuals. Literature subscriptions available.

National Literacy Trust

Swire House, 59 Buckingham Gate, London SW1E 6AS
☎0171 828 2435   Fax 0171 931 9986
Website: www.literacytrust.org.uk
Director *Neil McClelland*
Subscription £14 p.a.

FOUNDED 1993. A charitable organisation (Registered Charity No: 1015539) which aims to work with others to enhance literacy standards in the UK, to encourage more reading and writing for pleasure and to seek to raise the profile of literacy in the context of social and technological change. Maintains a database of literacy initiatives in the UK, now available on its website; provides training and consultancy on literacy, organises seminars and conferences, undertakes media campaigns and *publishes* a quarterly magazine, *Literacy Today*. Runs Reading is Fundamental, UK which provides books free to children and, in 1999, is organising the National Year of Reading for the government.

National Poetry Foundation

See **Organisations of Interest to Poets**

The National Small Press Centre

See **Organisations of Interest to Poets**

National Union of Journalists

Acorn House, 314 Gray's Inn Road, London WC1X 8DP
☎0171 278 7916   Fax 0171 837 8143
E-mail: NUJ@mc1.poptel.org.uk
General Secretary *John Foster*
Subscription £148.50 p.a. (Freelance) or 1% of annual income if lower; minimum contribution £57.75

Represents journalists in all sectors of publishing, print and broadcast. Responsible for wages and conditions agreements which apply across the industry. Provides advice and representation for its members, as well as administering unemployment and other benefits. *Publishes* various guides and magazines: *Freelance Directory, Fees Guide, The Journalist* and *The Freelance* (see **Magazines**).

NETWORKING for Women in Film, Video and Television

c/o Vera Media, 30–38 Dock Street, Leeds, West Yorkshire LS10 1JF
☎0113 242 8646   Fax 0113 245 1238
E-mail: networking@vera-media.demon.co.uk
Contact *Jane Howarth, Al Garthwaite*
Subscription £15 p.a.
FOUNDED 1989. A membership organisation for women working, seeking work, studying or in any way involved in film, video or television. Media studies departments, libraries, careers services are also welcome to join. *Publishes* a quarterly 20–page newsletter with news of activities, upcoming events, reviews, information about production funds, courses, etc. Entries of up to 40 words may be sent for inclusion in the Members' Index circulated throughout the membership to assist geographical/interest-based networking and employment. Contributions to the newsletter are welcome from all members. Advice, help and a campaigning voice for women in media are also on offer.

New Playwrights Trust

Interchange Studios, 15 Dalby Street, London NW5 3NQ
☎0171 284 2818   Fax 0171 482 5292
E-mail: npt@easynet.co.uk
Executive Director *Jonathan Meth*
Subscription (information on rates available by post)
New Playwrights Trust is the national research and development organisation for writing for all forms of live and recorded performance. *Publishes* a range of information pertinent to writers on all aspects of development and production in the form of pamphlets, and a six-weekly journal which also includes articles and interviews on aesthetic and practical issues. NPT also runs a script-reading service and a link service between writers and producers, organises seminars and conducts research projects. The latter includes research into the use of bilingual techniques in playwriting (*Two Tongues*), documentation of training programmes for writers (*Going Black Under the Skin*) and an investigation of the relationship between live art and writing (*Writing Live*).

New Producers Alliance (NPA)

9 Bourlet Close, London W1P 7PJ
☎0171 580 2480   Fax 0171 580 2484
FOUNDED 1992; current membership of over 1300. Aims to encourage the production of commercial feature films for an international audience and to educate and inform feature film producers, writers and directors. The NPA is an independent networking organisation providing members with access to contacts, information, free legal advice and general help regarding film production. *Publishes* a monthly newsletter and organises meetings, workshops and seminars. The NPA does not produce films so please do not send scripts or treatments.

The New SF Alliance (NSFA)

c/o BBR Magazine, PO Box 625, Sheffield, South Yorkshire S1 3GY
Contact *Chris Reed*
FOUNDED 1989. Committed to supporting the work of new writers and artists by promoting independent and small press publications worldwide. 'Help with finding the right market for your material by providing a mail-order service which allows you to sample magazines, and various publications including *BBR* magazine and *Scavenger's Newsletter*, which features the latest market news and tips.'

Newspaper Conference

See **The Newspaper Society**

The Newspaper Society

Bloomsbury House, 74–77 Great Russell Street, London WC1B 3DA
☎0171 636 7014   Fax 0171 631 5119
Director *David Newell*
Young Newspaper Executives'
  Association *David Brown*
The association of publishers of the regional and local press, representing 1,400 regional daily and weekly, paid for and free, newspaper titles in the UK. The Newspaper Conference is an organisation within the Society for London editors and representatives of regional newspapers. Bloomsbury House is also home to the Guild of Editors and to the Young Newspaper Executives' Association.

NPA

See **New Producers Alliance**

NSFA

See **The New SF Alliance**

Outdoor Writers' Guild

PO Box 520, Bamber Bridge, Preston,
Lancashire PR5 8LF
☎01772 696732   Fax 01772 696732
Secretary *Terry Marsh*
Subscription £35 p.a.; Joining fee £10

FOUNDED 1980 to promote, encourage and
assist the development and maintenance of
professional standards among those involved in
all aspects of outdoor journalism. Membership
is not limited to writers but includes other outstanding professional media practitioners in the
outdoor world such as broadcasters, photographers, filmmakers, editors, publishers and illustrators. *Publishes* a quarterly journal, *Bootprint*,
and an annual *Handbook and Directory* (£25;
free to members) as well as guidelines, codes of
practice and advice notes. Presents five Awards
for Excellence jointly with the Camping and
Outdoor Leisure Association (COLA), and its
own Award for Photographic Excellence.

PACT (Producers Alliance for Cinema and Television)

45 Mortimer Street, London W1N 7TD
☎0171 331 6000   Fax 0171 331 6700
Chief Executive *Shaun Williams*
Membership Officer *David Alan Mills*

FOUNDED 1991. PACT is the trade association
of the UK independent television and feature
film production sector and is a key contact
point for foreign producers seeking British co-
production, co-finance partners and distributors. Works for producers in the industry at
every level and operates a members' regional
network throughout the UK with a divisional
office in Scotland. Membership services
include: a dedicated industrial relations unit;
discounted legal advice; a varied calendar of
events; business advice; representation at international film and television markets; a comprehensive research programme; various publications: a monthly magazine, an annual
members' directory; affiliation with European
and international producers' organisations;
extensive information and production advice.
Lobbies actively with broadcasters, financiers
and governments to ensure that the producer's
voice is heard and understood in Britain and
Europe on all matters affecting the film and
television industry.

PAPA

See **The Professional Authors' and
Publishers' Association**

PEN

7 Dilke Street, London SW3 4JE
☎0171 352 6303   Fax 0171 351 0220
General Secretary *Gillian Vincent*
Membership £40 (London/Overseas);
    £35 (members living over 50 miles from
    London)

English PEN is part of International PEN, a
worldwide association of published writers
which fights for freedom of expression and
speaks out for writers who are imprisoned or
harassed for having criticised their governments,
or for publishing other unpopular views.
FOUNDED in London in 1921, International
PEN now consists of 130 centres in almost 100
countries. PEN originally stood for poets, essayists and novelists, but membership is now also
open to published playwrights, editors, translators and journalists. A programme of talks and
discussions is supplemented by a twice-yearly
mailing and annual congress at one of the centre
countries.

Performing Right Society

29–33 Berners Street, London W1P 4AA
☎0171 580 5544   Fax 0171 306 4050

Collects and distributes royalties arising from
the performance and broadcast of copyright
music on behalf of its composer, lyricist and
music publisher members and members of affiliated societies worldwide.

Periodical Publishers Association (PPA)

Queens House, 28 Kingsway, London
WC2B 6JR
☎0171 404 4166   Fax 0171 404 4167
Contact *Daska Davis*

FOUNDED 1913 to promote and protect the
interests of magazine publishers in the UK.

The Personal Managers' Association Ltd

1 Summer Road, East Molesey, Surrey
KT8 9LX
☎0181 398 9796   Fax 0181 398 9796
Co-chairs *Jane Annakin, Marc Berlin, Tim Corrie*
Secretary *Angela Adler*
Subscription £250 p.a.

An association of artists' and dramatists' agents
(membership not open to individuals). Monthly
meetings for exchange of information and discussion. Maintains a code of conduct and acts as
a lobby when necessary. Applicants screened. A

high proportion of play agents are members of the PMA.

The Picture Research Association
Head Office: 455 Finchley Road, London NW3 6HN
☎0171 431 9886   Fax 0171 431 9887
Chairman *Emma Krikler*
Subscription Members: Introductory £35; Full £45; Associate £40. Magazine only: £25 per year quarterly
FOUNDED 1977 as the Society of Picture Researchers & Editors. The Picture Research Association is a professional body for picture researchers, managers, picture editors and all those involved in the research, management and supply of visual material to all forms of the media. The Association's main aims are to promote the interests and specific skills of its members internationally; to promote and maintain professional standards; to bring together those involved in the research and publication of visual material; to provide a forum for the exchange of information and to provide guidance to its members. Free advisory service for members, regular meetings, quarterly magazine, monthly newsletter and Freelance Register.

Player–Playwrights
9 Hillfield Park, London N10 3QT
☎0181 883 0371
President *Jack Rosenthal*
Contact *Peter Thompson* (at the above address)
Subscription £10 (Joining fee); £6 p.a. thereafter, plus £1 per attendance
FOUNDED 1948. A society giving opportunity for writers new to stage, radio and television, as well as others finding difficulty in achieving results, to work with writers established in those media. At weekly meetings (7.45–10.00 p.m., Mondays, St Augustine's Hall, Queen's Gate, London SW7), members' scripts are read or performed by actor members and afterwards assessed and dissected in general discussion. Newcomers and new acting members are always welcome.

Poetry Book Society
See **Organisations of Interest to Poets**

Poetry Ireland
See **Organisations of Interest to Poets**

The Poetry Society
See **Organisations of Interest to Poets**

Private Libraries Association
16 Brampton Grove, Kenton, Harrow, Middlesex HA3 8LG
☎0181 907 6802   Fax 0181 907 6802
Honorary Secretary *Frank Broomhead*
Membership £25 p.a.
FOUNDED 1956. An international society of book collectors. The Association's objectives are to promote and encourage the awareness of the benefits of book ownership, and the study of books, their production, and ownership; to publish works concerned with this, particularly those which are not commercially profitable, to hold meetings at which papers on cognate subjects can be read and discussed. Lectures and exhibitions are open to non-members.

Producers Alliance for Cinema and Television
See **PACT**

The Professional Authors' and Publishers' Association (PAPA)
292 Kennington Road, London SE11 4LD
☎0171 582 1477   Fax 0171 582 4084
Contact *Tom Deegan, Andy Dempsey*
FOUNDED 1993 to provide self-publishing authors with an imprint, a book production, promotion and marketing service, thereby enabling them to avoid exploitation by so-called 'subsidy' or 'partnership' publishers. Authors using the Association's New Millenium imprint own the stock of books and receive the greater proportion of the profits on book sales.

The Publishers Association
1 Kingsway, London WC1B 6XF
☎0171 565 7474   Fax 0171 836 4543
Chief Executive *Ronnie Williams, OBE*
The national UK trade association for books, learned journals, and electronic publications, with around 300 member companies in the industry. Very much a trade body representing the industry to Government and the European Commission, and providing services to publishers. *Publishes* the *Directory of Publishing* in association with **Cassell**. Also home of the General Books Council (trade books), the Educational Publishers Council (school books), PA's International Division (BDC), the Council of Academic and Professional Publishers, and the Electronic Publishers' Forum.

Publishers Licensing Society Ltd

5 Dryden Street, Covent Garden, London
WC2E 9NW
☎0171 829 8486   Fax 0171 829 8488
Manager *Caroline Elmslie*

FOUNDED in 1981, the PLS obtains mandates
from publishers which grant PLS the authority to
license photocopying of pages from published
works. PLS aims to maximise revenue from
licences for mandating publishers and to expand
the range and repertoire of mandated publishers
available to licence holders. It supports the
Copyright Licensing Agency (CLA) in its
efforts to increase the number of legitimate users
through the issuing of licences and vigorously
pursues any infringement of copyright works
belonging to rights' holders.

Publishers Publicity Circle

48 Crabtree Lane, London SW6 6LW
☎0171 385 3708   Fax 0171 385 3708
Contact *Christina Thomas*

Enables book publicists from both publishing
houses and freelance PR agencies to meet and
share information regularly. Meetings, held
monthly in central London, provide a forum for
press journalists, television and radio researchers
and producers to meet publicists collectively. A
directory of the PPC membership is published
each year and distributed to over 2500 media
contacts.

Radio Authority

Holbrook House, 14 Great Queen Street,
London WC2B 5DG
☎0171 430 2724

The Radio Authority plans frequencies, awards
licences, regulates programming and advertising, and plays an active role in the discussion
and formulation of policies which affect the
Independent Radio Industry and its listeners.
The number of Independent Radio stations,
now over 200, continues to increase with new
licences being advertised on a regular basis.

The Romantic Novelists' Association

1 Beechwood Court, The Street, Syderstone,
King's Lynn, Norfolk PE31 8TR
☎01485 578594   Fax 01485 578138
Contact *John Johnson*
Subscription Full & Associate: £25 p.a.;
£30 (Overseas, non-EU); New Writers:
£55; £60 (Overseas, non-EU)

Membership is open to published writers of
romantic fiction (modern or historical), or those
who have had two or more full-length serials
published. Associate membership is open to publishers, editors, literary agents, booksellers, librarians and others having a close connection with
novel writing and publishing. Membership, in
the New Writers' Scheme, is available to writers
who have not yet had a full-length novel published. New Writers must submit a manuscript
each September. The mss receive a report from
experienced published members and the reading
fee is included in the subscription of £55.
Meetings are held in London and the regions
with interesting guest speakers. The *RNA News*
is published quarterly and issued free to members. The Association makes two annual awards:
The Major Award for the Romantic Novel of
the Year, and **The New Writers Award** for the
best published novel by a new writer.

Royal Festival Hall Literature Office

Performing Arts Department, Royal Festival
Hall,, London SE1 8XX
☎0171 921 0907   Fax 0171 928 2049
Head of Literature *Antonia Byatt*

The Royal Festival Hall presents a year-round
literature programme covering all aspects of
writing. Regular series range from New Voices
to Fiction International and there is a biennial
Poetry International Festival. Literature events
are now programmed in the Voice Box, Purcell
Room and Queen Elizabeth Hall. To join the
free mailing list, phone 0171 921 0734.

Royal Society of Literature

1 Hyde Park Gardens, London W2 2LT
☎0171 723 5104   Fax 0171 402 0199
President *Lord Jenkins of Hillhead*
Subscription £30 p.a.

FOUNDED 1823. Membership by application to
the Secretary. Fellowships are conferred by the
Society on the proposal of two Fellows.
Membership benefits include lectures, discussion
meetings and poetry readings in the Society's
rooms. Lecturers have included Patrick Leigh
Fermor, Germaine Greer, Seamus Heaney, John
Mortimer and Tom Stoppard. Presents the **W.
H. Heinemann Prize** and the **Winifred
Holtby Prize**.

Royal Television Society

Holborn Hall, 100 Gray's Inn Road, London
WC1X 8AL
☎0171 430 1000   Fax 0171 430 0924
E-mail: royaltvsociety@btinternet.com

Website: www.rts.org.uk
Subscription £57 p.a.
FOUNDED 1927. Covers all disciplines involved in the television industry. Provides a forum for debate and conferences on technical, social and cultural aspects of the medium. Presents various awards including journalism, programmes, technology, design and commercials. *Publishes Television Magazine* eight times a year for members and subscribers.

Science Fiction Foundation

c/o Liverpool University Library, PO Box 123, Liverpool L69 3DA
☎0151 794 2696/2733   Fax 0151 794 2681
Contact *Andy Sawyer*

The SFF is a national academic body for the furtherance of science fiction studies. *Publishes* a thrice-yearly magazine, *Foundation* (see entry under **Magazines**), which features academic articles and reviews of new fiction. It also has a reference library (see entry under **Library Services**), housed at Liverpool University.

Scottish Daily Newspaper Society

48 Palmerston Place, Edinburgh EH12 5DE
☎0131 220 4353   Fax 0131 220 4344
Director *Mr J. B. Raeburn*
FOUNDED 1915. Trade association representing publishers of Scottish daily and Sunday newspapers.

Scottish Library Association

Scottish Centre for Information & Library Services, 1 John Street, Hamilton, Strathclyde ML3 7EU
☎01698 458888   Fax 01698 458899
Director *Robert Craig*
FOUNDED 1908 to bring together everyone engaged in or interested in library work in Scotland. The Association has over 2300 members, covering all aspects of library and information work. Its main aims are the promotion of library services and the qualifications and status of librarians.

Scottish Newspaper Publishers Association

48 Palmerston Place, Edinburgh EH12 5DE
☎0131 220 4353   Fax 0131 220 4344
Director *Mr J. B. Raeburn*
FOUNDED around 1905. The representative body for the publishers of paid-for weekly and associated free newspapers in Scotland. Represents the interests of the industry to Government, public

and other bodies and provides a range of services including marketing of *The Scottish Weekly Press*, industrial relations, and education and training. It is an active supporter of the Press Complaints Commission.

Scottish Print Employers Federation

48 Palmerston Place, Edinburgh EH12 5DE
☎0131 220 4353   Fax 0131 220 4344
Director *Mr J. B. Raeburn*
FOUNDED 1910. Employers' organisation and trade association for the Scottish printing industry. Represents the interests of the industry to Government, public and other bodies and provides a range of services including industrial relations. Negotiates a national wages and conditions agreement with the Graphical, Paper and Media Union, as well as education, training and commercial activities. The Federation is a member of Intergraf, the international confederation for employers' associations in the printing industry. In this capacity its views are channelled on the increasing number of matters affecting print businesses emanating from the European Union.

Scottish Publishers Association

Scottish Book Centre, 137 Dundee Street, Edinburgh EH11 1BG
☎0131 228 6866   Fax 0131 228 3220
E-mail: enquiries@scottishbooks.org
Director *Lorraine Fannin*
Administrator *Davinder Bedi*
Marketing Manager *Alison Rae*
SBMG/Training *Allan Shanks*

The Association represents over 70 Scottish publishers, from multinationals to very small presses, in a number of capacities, but primarily in the cooperative promotion and marketing of their books. The SPA also acts as an information and advice centre for both the trade and general public. *Publishes* seasonal catalogues, membership lists, the annual *Directory of Publishing in Scotland* and regular newsletters. Represents members at international book fairs; runs an extensive training programme in publishing skills; carries out market research; and encourages export initiatives. Also provides administrative back-up for the Scottish Book Marketing Group, a cooperative venture with Scottish booksellers.

The Society of Authors in Scotland

24 March Hall Crescent, Edinburgh EH16 5HL
☎0131 667 5230
Secretary *Alanna Knight*
The Scottish branch of **The Society of**

Authors, which organises business meetings, social and bookshop events in Scotland.

The Society of Authors

84 Drayton Gardens, London SW10 9SB
☎0171 373 6642   Fax 0171 373 5768
E-mail: authorsoc@writers.org.uk
General Secretary *Mark Le Fanu*
Subscription £65/70 p.a.

FOUNDED 1884. The Society of Authors is an independent trade union with some 6000 members. It advises on negotiations with publishers, broadcasting organisations, theatre managers and film companies; assists with complaints and takes action for breach of contract, copyright infringement, etc. Together with **The Writers' Guild**, the Society has played a major role in advancing the Minimum Terms Agreement for authors. Among the Society's publications are *The Author* (a quarterly journal) and the *Quick Guides* series to various aspects of writing (all free of charge to members). Other services include vetting of contracts, emergency funds for writers, and various special discounts. There are groups within the Society for scriptwriters, children's writers and illustrators, educational writers, medical writers and translators. Authors under 35 or over 65, not earning a significant income from their writing, may apply for lower subscription rates. Contact the Society for a free booklet giving further information.

Society of Civil Service Authors

4 Top Street, Wing, Nr Oakham, Rutland
LE15 8SE
Membership Secretary *Mrs Joan Hykin*
Subscription £15 p.a.

FOUNDED 1935. Aims to encourage authorship by present and past members of the Civil Service and to provide opportunities for social and cultural relationships between civil servants who are authors or who aspire to be authors. Annual competitions, open to members only, are held for short stories, poetry, sonnets, travel articles, humour, etc. Members receive *The Civil Service Author*, a bi-monthly magazine. Occasional meetings in London, one or two weekends outside London.

Society of Freelance Editors and Proofreaders (SFEP)

Mermaid House, 1 Mermaid Court, London
SE1 1HR
☎0171 403 5141

Chair *Kathleen Lyle*
Vice-chair *Sue Deeley*

Secretary *Shelagh Brown*
Subscription £40 p.a. (Individuals) plus £10.00 joining fee; Corporate membership available

FOUNDED 1988 in response to the growing number of freelance editors and their increasing importance to the publishing industry. Aims to promote high editorial standards by disseminating information through advice and training, and to achieve recognition of the professional status of its members. The Society also supports moves towards recognised standards of training and qualifications, and is currently putting in place accredited and registered membership of SFEP.

Society of Indexers

Mermaid House, 1 Mermaid Court, London
SE1 1HR
☎0171 403 4947   Fax 0171 357 0903
Secretary *Christine Shuttleworth*
Subscription £40 p.a.; £60 (Institutions)

FOUNDED 1957. *Publishes The Indexer* (bi-annual, April and October) and a quarterly newsletter. Issues an annual list of members and *Indexers Available (IA)*, which lists members and their subject expertise. In addition, the Society runs an open-learning course entitled *Training in Indexing* and recommends rates of pay (currently £13 per hour).

Society of Sussex Authors

Bookends, Lewes Road, Horsted Keynes, Haywards Heath, West Sussex RH17 7DP
☎01825 790755   Fax 01825 790755
Contact *Michael Legat*
Subscription £10 p.a.

FOUNDED 1968 to promote the interests of its members and of literature, particularly within the Sussex area. Regular meetings and exchange of information; plus social events. Membership restricted to writers who live in Sussex and who have had at least one book commercially published, or other writings used professionally. Meetings are held six times a year in Lewes.

Society of Women Writers and Journalists

110 Whitehall Road, London E4 6DW
☎0181 529 0886
Honorary Secretary *Jean Hawkes*
Subscription £25 (Town); £21 (Country); £15 (Overseas). £10 Joining fee

FOUNDED 1894. The first of its kind to be run as an association of women engaged in journalism.

Aims to encourage literary achievement, uphold professional standards, and establish social contacts with other writers. Lectures given at monthly lunchtime meetings. Offers advice to members and has regular seminars, etc. *Publishes* a quarterly society journal, *The Woman Journalist*.

Society of Young Publishers
12 Dyott Street, London WC1A 1DF
Website: http://www.thesyp.demon.co.uk
Subscription £20 p.a.; £15 (Student/unwaged)

Provides facilities whereby members can increase their knowledge and widen their experience of all aspects of publishing. Open to those in related occupations, with associate membership available for over-35s. *Publishes* a monthly newsletter called *Inprint* and holds meetings on the last Wednesday of each month at **The Publishers Association**. Please enclose an s.a.e. when writing to the Society.

The South and Mid-Wales Association of Writers (S.A.M.W.A.W)
c/o I.M.C. Consulting Group, Denham House, Lambourne Crescent, Cardiff CF4 5ZW
☎01222 761170   Fax 01222 761304
Contact *Julian Rosser*
Subscription £7 (Single); £12 (Joint)

FOUNDED 1971 to foster the art and craft of writing in all its forms. Provides a common meeting ground for writers, critics, editors, adjudicators from all over the UK and abroad. Organises an annual residential weekend conference and a day seminar in May and October respectively. Holds competitions, two for members only and two which are open to the public, in addition to **The Mathew Pritchard Award for Short Story Writing**.

South Eastern Writers' Association
47 Sunningdale Avenue, Leigh-on-Sea, Essex SS9 1JY
☎01702 77083   Fax 01702 77083
President *Marion Hough*

FOUNDED 1989 to bring together experienced and novice writers, in an informal atmosphere. Non-profit-making, the Association holds a annual residential weekend each spring at Bulphan, Essex. Free workshops and discussion groups included in the overall cost. Previous guest speakers: Simon Brett, Jonathan Gash, George Layton, Maureen Lipman, Terry Pratchett, Jack Rosenthal.

Sports Writers' Association of Great Britain
c/o English Sports Council Press Office, 16 Upper Woburn Place, London WC1H 0QP
☎0171 273 1555   Fax 0171 383 0273
Secretary *Mary Fitzhenry*
Subscription £23 p.a. incl. VAT (London); £11.75 incl. VAT (Regional)

FOUNDED 1948 to promote and maintain a high professional standard among journalists who specialise in sport in all its branches and to serve members' interests. *Publishes* quarterly bulletin for members.

Theatre Writers' Union
See **The Writers' Guild of Great Britain**

The Translators Association
84 Drayton Gardens, London SW10 9SB
☎0171 373 6642   Fax 0171 373 5768
E-mail: authorsoc@writers.org.uk
Secretary *Gordon Fielden*

FOUNDED 1958 as a subsidiary group within **The Society of Authors** to deal exclusively with the special problems of literary translators into the English language. Members are entitled to all the benefits and services of the Association, in addition to those of the Society, without extra charge. These include free legal and general advice and assistance on all matters relating to translators' work, including the vetting of contracts and information about improvements in rates of remuneration. Membership is normally confined to translators who have had their work published in volume or serial form or produced in this country for stage, television or radio. Translators of work for industrial firms or government departments are in certain cases admitted to membership if their work, though not on general sale, is published by the organisation commissioning the work. The Association administers several prizes for translators of published work and maintains a database to enable members' details to be supplied to publishers who are seeking a translator for a particular work.

Ver Poets
Haycroft, 61–63 Chiswell Green Lane, St Albans, Hertfordshire AL2 3AL
☎01727 867005
Chairman *Ray Badman*
Editor/Organiser *May Badman*
Membership £10 p.a.; £12.50 or US$25 (Overseas)

FOUNDED 1966 to promote poetry and to help

poets. With postal and local members, holds meetings in St Albans; runs a poetry bookstall for members' books and publications from other groups; publishes members' work in anthologies and organises poetry competitions, including the annual **Ver Poets Open** competition. Gives help and advice whenever they are sought and makes information available to members about other poetry groups, events and opportunities for publication.

Voice of the Listener and Viewer
101 Kings Drive, Gravesend, Kent DA12 5BQ
☎01474 352835   Fax 01474 35112
E-mail: vlv@btinternet.com

The citizen's voice in broadcasting is an independent, non-profit-making society working to ensure independence and high standards in broadcasting. It is also the only consumer body speaking for listeners and viewers on the whole range of broadcasting issues. VLV is funded by its members and is free from sectarian, commercial and political affiliations. Holds public lectures, seminars and conferences, and has frequent contact with MPs, civil servants, the BBC and independent broadcasters, regulators, academics and other consumer groups. VLV has responded to all parliamentary and public enquiries on broadcasting since 1984 and to all consultation documents issued by the ITC and Radio Authority since 1990. The VLV does not handle complaints.

W.A.T.C.H.
See **Writers and their Copyright Holders**

Welsh Academy
3rd Floor, Mount Stuart House, Mount Stuart Square, Cardiff CF1 6DQ
☎01222 492025   Fax 01222 492930
Administrator *Margaret Harlin*

FOUNDED 1968. The Welsh Academy is the English Language section of **Yr Academi Gymreig**, the national society of Welsh writers. The Academy exists to promote English literature in Wales. Organises readings and an annual conference (usually held in May). There are three tiers of membership: Fellow (max. 12, an honorary position offered to those who have made an outstanding contribution to the literature of Wales over a number of years); Member (open to all who are deemed to have made a contribution to the literature of Wales whether writers, editors or critics); Associate Member (open to all who are interested in the Academy's work). Publications include: *BWA*, the Welsh

Academy's newsletter; *The Oxford Companion to the Literature of Wales*; *Writing in Wales*; *The Literature of Wales in Secondary Schools*; *How the Earth Was Formed Quiz And Other Poems and Stories by Children*; *The New Welsh Review*; *A Bibliography of Anglo-Welsh Literature*; *Interweave*.

Welsh Books Council (Cyngor Llyfrau Cymru)
Castell Brychan, Aberystwyth, Ceredigion SY23 2JB
☎01970 624151   Fax 01970 625385
Director *Gwerfyl Pierce Jones*
Head of Editorial Department *Dewi Morris Jones*

FOUNDED 1961 to stimulate interest in Welsh literature and to support authors. The Council distributes the government grant for Welsh language publications and promotes and fosters all aspects of both Welsh and Welsh-interest book production. Its Editorial, Design, Marketing and Children's Books departments and wholesale distribution centre offer central services to publishers in Wales. Writers in Welsh and English are welcome to approach the Editorial Department for advice on how to get their manuscripts published. *Books in Wales/Llais Llyfrau* is a quarterly publication which includes book lists, reviews and articles on various aspects of Welsh writing and publishing (see entry under **Magazines**).

Welsh Union of Writers
4 Teilo Street, Pontcanna, Cardiff CF1 9JN
☎01222 640041
E-mail: John.A.Harrison@btinternet.com
Secretary *John Harrison*
Subscription £10 p.a.; £5 Joining fee

FOUNDED 1982. Independent union. Full membership by application to persons born or working in Wales with at least one publication in a quality journal or other outlet. Associate membership now available for other interested supporters. Lobbies for writing in Wales, represents members in disputes; annual conference and occasional events and publications.

West Country Writers' Association
Malvern View, Garway Hill, Hereford, Herefordshire HR2 8EZ
☎01981 580495
President *Christopher Fry*
Honorary Secretary *Mrs Anne Double*
Subscription £10 p.a.

FOUNDED 1951 in the interest of published

authors with an interest in the West Country. Meets to discuss news and views and to listen to talks. Conference and newsletters.

Women in Publishing
c/o The Bookseller, 12 Dyott Street, London WC1A 1DF
Contact *Information Officer*
Membership £20 p.a. (Individuals); £15 (Unwaged); £25 (if paid for by company)

Aims to promote the status of women working within the publishing industry and related trades, to encourage networking, and to provide training for career and personal development. Meetings held on the second Wednesday of the month at **The Publishers Association** (see entry for address) at 6.30 pm. Monthly newsletter.

Women Writers Network (WWN)
23 Prospect Road, London NW2 2JU
☎0171 794 5861
Membership Secretary *Cathy Smith*
Subscription £30 p.a. (Full); £20 p.a. (Overseas); £20 p.a. ('Newsletter only' membership)

FOUNDED 1985. Provides a forum for the exchange of information, support, career and networking opportunities for working women writers. Meetings, seminars, excursions, newsletter and directory. Full membership includes free admission to monthly meetings, a directory of members and a monthly newsletter. Details from the Membership Secretary at the above address.

Writers and their Copyright Holders (W.A.T.C.H.)
The Library, The University of Reading, PO Box 223, Whiteknights, Reading, Berkshire RG6 6AE
☎0118 9318783   Fax 0118 9316636
Website: http:www.lib.utexas.edu/Libs/ HRC/WATCH
Contact *Dr David Sutton*

FOUNDED 1994. Provides an on-line database of information about the copyright holders of literary authors. The database is available free of charge on the Internet and the Web. W.A.T.C.H. is the successor project to the Location Register of English Literary Manuscripts and Letters, and continues to deal with location register enquiries.

The Writers' Guild of Great Britain (incorporating The Theatre Writers' Union)
430 Edgware Road, London W2 1EH
☎0171 723 8074   Fax 0171 706 2413
E-mail: postie@wggb.demon.uk
Website: http.www.writers.org.uk/guide
General Secretary *Alison V. Gray*
Annual subscription 1% of that part of the author's income earned in the areas in which the Guild operates, with a basic subscription of £70 and a maximum of £920

FOUNDED 1959. The Writers' Guild is the writers' trade union, affiliated to the TUC. It represents writers in film, radio, television, theatre and publishing. The Guild has negotiated agreements on which writers' contracts are based with the BBC, Independent Television companies, and **PACT** (the Producers' Alliance for Cinema and Television). Those agreements are regularly renegotiated, both in terms of finance and conditions. In 1997, the Guild membership joined with that of the Theatre Writers' Union to create a new, more powerful union.

In 1979, together with the Theatre Writers' Union, the Guild negotiated the first ever industrial agreement for theatre writers, the TNC Agreement, which covers the **Royal National Theatre**, the **Royal Shakespeare Company**, and the **English Stage Company**. Further agreements have been negotiated with the Theatre Management Association which covers regional theatre and the **Independent Theatre Council**, the organisation which covers small theatres and the Fringe.

The Guild initiated a campaign over ten years ago which achieved the first ever publishing agreement for writers with the publisher W. H. Allen. Jointly with **The Society of Authors**, that campaign has continued and each year sees new agreements with more publishers. Perhaps the most important breakthrough came with **Penguin** on 20 July 1990. The Guild now also has agreements covering **HarperCollins**, **Random House Group**, **Transworld** and others.

The Guild regularly provides individual help and advice to members on contracts, conditions of work, and matters which affect a member's life as a professional writer. Members are given the opportunity of meeting at craft meetings, which are held on a regular basis throughout the year. Membership is by a points system. One major piece of work (a full-length book, an hour-long television or radio play, a feature film, etc.) entitles the author to full membership;

writers who do not qualify for Full Membership may qualify for Associate Membership; they currently pay the basic subscription only of £70. A new type of membership was launched in July 1997 called Candidate Membership. This is open to all those who wish to be involved in writing but have not yet had work published. The subscription fee for this is £35.

Yachting Journalists' Association

3 Friars Lane, Maldon, Essex CM9 6AG
☎01621 855943/0468 962936(mobile)
Fax 01621 852212

Honorary Secretary *Peter Cook*
Subscription £30 p.a.

To further the interest of yachting, sail and power, and to provide support and assistance to journalists in the field; current membership is just over 230 with 16 from overseas. A handbook, listing details of members and subscribing PR organisations, press facility recommendations, forthcoming events and other useful information, is published annually in April at a cost to non-members and non-advertisers of £5. Information for inclusion should be submitted by the end of February. The YJA organises the Yachtsman of the Year Awards which are in their 43rd year. Presented annually at the beginning of January, they consist of the Yachtsman of the Year, Young Sailor of the Year and Global Achievement Awards.

Young Newspaper Executives' Association

See **The Newspaper Society**

Yr Academi Gymreig

3rd Floor, Mount Stuart House, Mount Stuart Square, Cardiff CF1 6DQ
☎01222 492064   Fax 01222 492930

Administrator *Sharon Krieger*

FOUNDED 1959. National society of Welsh writers. Aims to encourage writing in Welsh. *Publishes Taliesin*, plus books on Welsh literature and an English/Welsh dictionary. Organises readings, conferences and general literary events. Various tiers of membership available.

Liable to Libel

You might think that writers have enough on their plates without being dragged through the courts whenever one or several of their readers feel unjustly pilloried or gratuitously insulted. Most of us can barely get through a week without someone giving us the elbow – the boss, a colleague, the children. That's life. But there are those extra sensitive souls who can only bear to see their names in print when the reference is accompanied by extravagant praise. Anything that passes as an insult has the aggrieved party rushing off to the nearest lawyer.

The care that writers must take in treading the minefield of libel was illustrated recently by a prominent notice in *The Stage*.

> 'In Fay Weldon's book *Worst Fears*, one of the main characters is called Jenny Linden. Unfortunately, this character's name is almost identical to that of the actress Jennie Linden. We wish to clarify that the character is in no way connected to Jennie Linden and that any similarities are entirely coincidental. We apologise unreservedly to Jennie Linden for any distress and embarrassment caused by any connection between the character and Jennie Linden.'

Having to apologise for choosing a name at random may seem tough on Miss Weldon but as the law stands, if you are sued for libel your opponent need not prove that you intended to discredit him or even that he has been harmed by whatever you have said. All that is necessary is to indicate that a hurt to reputation has been suffered.

The ease of proving libel in British courts, relative to other countries, has made London the libel capital of the world. Over in America, for example, a 'public figure' has to show malice by the author to succeed in winning damages. Not here. It may be that the incorporation of the European Convention on Human Rights will eventually extend freedom of expression. Meanwhile, we have to be satisfied with recent piecemeal reforms that have gone some way to reducing the financial risk of putting words on paper.

Where libel has been committed unintentionally or 'innocently' one way out of the trap is an 'offer to make amends'. This escape clause has been available since the 1950s but until two years ago it was rarely taken up because it was hedged by so many technicalities. Now, under the 1996 Defamation Act, the rules have been tightened to allow for a speedy and relatively inexpensive resolution of disputes. If you did not intend to defame and can show that you were not reckless, you can avoid further litigation by offering a published apology, a sum in compensation and a settlement of costs. If the amount to be paid cannot be agreed mutually a judge can make an order.

There is a downside as Daniel Eilon, a solicitor with Campbell Hooper, points out: 'The offer of amends is not so much a defence as an orderly surrender. If you use it, you cannot plead any of the other recognised defences such as justification, fair comment, privilege and innocent dissemination.'

So what if you are in fighting mood? It is a complete defence to prove that a statement, however defamatory, is true in substance and in fact. The trouble with pleading justification, however, is that every significant detail of a statement must be proved to be true, a hard trick to pull.

Another line of defence is to prove that the words complained of are fair comment on a matter of public interest. The defence will fail if the defendant is shown to have been actuated by malice (merely disliking the plaintiff is insufficient) or the facts on which he based the comment were untrue. But fair comment allows for critics to do their worst. 'Every latitude must be given to opinion and to prejudice ... Mere exaggeration, or even gross exaggeration, would not make the comment unfair. However wrong the opinion expressed may be in point of truth, or however prejudiced the writer, it may still be within the prescribed limit.' (*Merivale v. Carson, 1887*) Again, 'comments may be fair, although wrong; they may be fair although expressed with violence and heat. A critic is entitled to use ridicule, sarcasm and irony, as weapons so long as he does not use them unfairly.' (*Digby v. Financial News, 1907*)

Privilege covers 'fair and accurate' reports of public judicial proceedings while innocent dissemination applies only to distributors (not authors, editors or publishers).

To rely on this defence, a defendant must show that he has taken reasonable care in relation to the publication of the statement; had no reason to believe that he was contributing to the publication of a defamatory statement; and no effective control over the maker of the statement. This defence came into force in 1996.

To choose one of these defences is to cut off any line of retreat. There can be no resort to an offer to make amends.

Lawyers have criticised the 1996 Act for failing to allow for a greater degree of flexibility in settling disputes while welcoming long overdue changes in Britain's archaic and, in many ways, anarchic libel laws. The time limit for starting an action for defamation has been cut from three years to one. (This will curb the use of 'gagging writs' such as those used by the late Robert Maxwell.) There is a new summary procedure under which every defamation claim can come before a judge at an early stage. The judge assesses whether the claim is suitable for summary disposal, or whether it should go for trial, with or without a jury. He has power to award damages up to £10,000. This makes it easier for an ordinary citizen to seek redress against a rich opponent who, otherwise, is liable to keep a trial going as long as possible in the hope that a plaintiff will run out of patience and money.

There have been fewer massive libel awards of late but a successful action can still bring in a tidy fortune.

For reasons lost in the deliberations of the jury rooms, awards are invariably out of all proportion to damage suffered. It used to be the rule that compensation for a serious libel should roughly correspond to the price of a good house. Somewhere along the line, the house became a mansion. Speaking up for press colleagues who have found themselves in the High Court, William Rees-Mogg points out that 'if newspaper vans ran amok in London and crashed freely into innocent pedestrians, that would cost their proprietors less than a few defamatory paragraphs'.

For those with the gambling instinct, the chance of jackpot winnings is a powerful draw. It may be a safe general rule, as the Book of Proverbs tells us that 'A good name is rather to be chosen than great riches'. But, in the wonderful world of libel, lawyers are ready to admit that some plaintiffs go for the money. Some time ago, a famous critic was offered a settlement plus an apology or double the money and no apology. He decided he could live without the apology.

There is some hope that the lid has been put on outrageous libel awards now that the Court of Appeal can provide guidelines. Many reformers would go further. They want the responsibility of a jury to be limited to saying if damages should be substantial, moderate, nominal or contemptuous. The judge would then decide on the appropriate figure. A useful compromise would compel juries to explain their calculations. As Lord Donaldson has observed, 'having to give reasons puts a substantial premium on ensuring that the head rules the heart'.

Every writer is responsible for his own work. But this should not mean that when he makes mistakes he alone carries the can. Journalists are usually covered by their employers who take on the whole cost of a libel action. If it were otherwise many of our best known columnists would be out of business. When, early in the year, Alan Clark won his case against the London *Evening Standard* for 'passing off' a spoof diary as his own, the costs amounted to £250,000. How many journalists could afford that?

Sadly, book publishers are less protective of those who serve their commercial interests. A typical publishing contract includes a warranty clause which entitles the publisher to be indemnified by the author against damages and costs if any part of the work turns out to be libellous.

Publishers excuse their weakness of backbone by arguing that only the author is in a position to know whether or not a work is libellous and that the onus should be on the author to check facts before they are published. But why, asks Mark Le Fanu of the Society of Authors, should the risk be borne by the author alone when a publisher deliberately gambles on making money out of a book?

> 'While it is true that a writer of fiction is much more likely than the publisher to know whether or not a person has been defamed (whether intentionally or unintentionally), the issue is much less clear-cut with non-fiction. Authors are not experts in the arcane mysteries of the "fair comment" defence to a libel claim. Publishers are well aware that certain sorts of books (e.g. biographies of the living, business exposés, etc) inevitably carry a libel risk.'

In fairness, it must be said that the indemnity is rarely invoked unless a publisher feels he has been deceived or misled. But, at the very least, the author should insist that his publisher has the manuscript read for libel and that his contract does not specify unlimited liability.

Libel insurance offers some sort of safeguard and a publisher who is insured is clearly preferable to one who is not. But most insurance policies carry severe limitations, not least a ceiling on the payout of damages. Also, reading for libel can be expensive for a book that is in any way controversial. As Richard West discovered when he wrote an investigative volume, 'The lawyer who read it for libel got £1000. The lawyer who wrote in to the publisher to complain on behalf of his client was probably paid about £5000'. Since West himself earned about £500 for his efforts he concluded, not unreasonably, that authorship was a mug's game.

To make matters worse, the risks of encountering a libel action have increased substantially with the extension of 'no win, no fee' litigation to all claims for damages. It is already commonplace to hear solicitors advertising on commercial radio for prospective clients to come forward. Allowing actions to be funded by solicitors working for a success fee is bound to appeal to the easily offended. Even if a loony case fails to get to court, a cost-conscious publisher may choose to play safe by amending a text to a point where it loses its cutting edge and thus its sales appeal. It is not unknown for an entire book to be jettisoned to save on lawyers' bills.

Peter Marsh, a barrister specialising in defamation, offers these tips for writers about to embark on a controversial project.

> 'If the subject or subjects of critical comment are still alive, beware; if you are writing a book about real life incidents but have changed names to avoid identification, take extreme care in the choice of names for your characters; remember that damage to a person's reputation can be caused by innuendo. For example, to write of someone that most people thought he was taking advantage of the Inland Revenue may suggest some improper and unethical practice. If a living person is going to be the subject of comment which is expressly or implicitly derogatory, make absolutely sure your facts are correct and can be substantiated. Otherwise, your publisher is going to be propelled into the courtroom naked of a defence.'

Is there anything to be said for those who bring libel actions? No better summary of the risks and tribulations for all but the excessively rich appears in Adam Raphael's absorbing indictment, *Grotesque Libels*.

> 'The problems of a libel action can be stated quite simply. The law is highly technical and the pleadings so complex that even its skilled practitioners often differ on the most basic questions. The costs of the lawyers involved are so high that they make the fees charged by any

other profession appear to be a mere bagatelle. The opportunities for obstruction and delay are such that it can take as long as five years to bring a libel action to court. When it eventually does reach the court, the damages left to the whim of a jury are so uncertain that the result is often no sounder than a dodgy fruit machine. A libel action has in fact more in common with a roulette wheel than justice. The net result for both plaintiffs and defendants is that such actions are a nightmare with only the lawyers able to sleep soundly.'

No wonder Bernard Levin asserts 'If I were libelled (I have frequently been) and were given the choice of suing or having all my toenails pulled out with red-hot pincers while listening to *Pelléas et Mélisande*, I think it would be a close run thing.'

As for those who are unable to keep out of the courts, the best advice comes from Tom Crone in his book on *Law and the Media*. The libel litigant, he says, must possess two prime qualities – 'a strong nerve and a deep pocket'.

Literary Societies

Most literary societies exist on a shoestring budget; it is a good idea to enclose an A5 s.a.e. with all correspondence needing a reply.

Margery Allingham Society

2B High Green, Winchelsea, East Sussex
TN36 4HB
☎01797 222363   Fax 01797 222363
Contact *Mrs Pat Wat*
Subscription £8 p.a.

FOUNDED 1988 to promote interest in and study of the works of Margery Allingham. The London Society *publishes* two issues of the newsletter, *The Bottle Street Gazette* per year. Contributions welcome. Two social events a year. Open membership.

Jane Austen Society

Carton House, Redwood Lane, Medstead, Alton, Hampshire GU34 5PE
☎01705 475855   Fax 01705 788842
E-mail: rosemary@sndc.demon.co.uk
Website: http://www.sndc.demon.co.uk/jas.htm
Honorary Secretary *Susan McCartan*
Subscription UK: £10 (Annual);
    £15 (Joint); £30 (Corporate); £150 (Life);
    Overseas: £12 (Annual); £18 (Joint);
    £33 (Corporate); £180 (Life)

FOUNDED 1940 to promote interest in and enjoyment of Jane Austen's novels and letters. The society has branches in Bath & Bristol, Midlands, London, Oxford, Kent and Hampshire. There are independent Societies in North America and Australia.

William Barnes Society

75 Prince of Wales Road, Dorchester, Dorset
DT1 1PS
☎01305 264405
Contact *Mrs Pamela Holden*
Subscription £6 p.a.

FOUNDED 1983 to provide a forum in which admirers of the Dorset poet could share fellowship and pleasure in his work. William Barnes (1801–86) is best known as the writer of Dorset dialect poetry. His interest in dialect prompted him to become a learned philologist and he published many papers in defence of native English against the incursions of French and Latin. Quarterly meetings and newsletter.

The Baskerville Hounds

6 Bramham Moor, Hill Head, Fareham, Hampshire PO14 3RU
☎01329 667325
Chairman *Philip Weller*
Subscription £6 p.a.

FOUNDED 1989. An international Sherlock Holmes society specialising solely in studies of *The Hound of the Baskervilles* and its Dartmoor associations. *Publishes* a quarterly newsletter, an annual journal and specialist monographs. It also organises many social functions, usually on Dartmoor. Open membership.

The Beckford Society

15 Healey Street, London NW1 8SR
☎0171 267 7750   Fax 01985 213195
Secretary *Sidney Blackmore*
Subscription £10 (min.) p.a.

FOUNDED 1995 to promote an interest in the life and works of William Beckford (1760–1844) and his circle. Encourages Beckford studies and scholarship through exhibitions, lectures and publications, including an annual journal, *The Beckford Journal*, and occasional newsletters.

Arnold Bennett Society

106 Scotia Road, Burslem, Stoke on Trent, Staffordshire ST6 4ET
☎01782 816311
Secretary *Mrs Jean Potter*
Subscription £6 (Single); £7 (Family);
    £5 (Unwaged)

Aims to promote interest in the life and works of 'Five Towns' author Arnold Bennett and other North Staffordshire writers. Annual dinner. Regular functions in and around Buslem. Quarterly newsletter. Open membership.

E. F. Benson Society

The Old Coach House, High Street, Rye, East Sussex TN31 7JF
☎01797 223114   Fax 0171 580 0763
Secretary *Allan Downend*
Subscription £7.50 (UK/Europe);
    £12.50 (Overseas)

FOUNDED 1985 to promote the life and work of

E. F. Benson and the Benson family. Organises social and literary events, exhibitions and talks. *Publishes* a quarterly newsletter and annual journal, *The Dodo,* postcards and reprints of E. F. Benson articles and short stories. Holds an archive which includes the Seckersen Collection (transcriptions of the Benson collection at the Bodleian Library in Oxford).

E. F. Benson/The Tilling Society
5 Friars Bank, Pett Road, Guestling, East Sussex TN35 4ET
Contact *Cynthia Reavell*
Subscription Full starting membership (members receive all back newsletters) £22 (UK); £26 (Overseas); or Annual Membership (members receive only current year's newsletters) £8 (UK); £10 (Overseas).

FOUNDED 1982 for the exchange of news, information and speculation about E. F. Benson and his *Mapp & Lucia* novels. Readings, discussions and twice-yearly newsletter. Acts as a clearing house for every sort of news and activity concerning E. F. Benson.

The Betjeman Society
35 Eaton Court, Boxgrove Avenue, Guildford, Surrey GU1 1XH
☎01483 560882
Honorary Secretary *John Heald*
Subscription £7 (Individual); £9 (Family); £3 (Student); £2 extra each category for overseas members

Aims to promote the study and appreciation of the work and life of Sir John Betjeman. Annual programme includes poetry reading, lectures, discussions, visits to places associated with Betjeman, and various social events. Meetings are held in London and other centres. Regular newsletter and annual journal, *The Betjemanian.*

The Bewick Society
c/o The Dean's Office, Faculty of Arts and Design, University of Northumbria, Squires Building, Sandyford Road, Newcastle upon Tyne NE1 8ST
☎0191 227 3138   Fax 0191 227 4077
Chairman *Kenneth McConkey*
Subscription £7 p.a.

FOUNDED 1988 to promote an interest in the life and work of Thomas Bewick, wood-engraver and naturalist (1753–1828). Organises related events and meetings, and is associated with the Bewick birthplace museum.

Biggles & Co
See **The W. E. Johns Society**

Birmingham Central Literary Association
c/o Birmingham & Midland Institute, Margaret Street, Birmingham B3 3DS
☎0121 236 3591
Contact *The Honorary Secretary*
Holds fortnightly meetings at the Birmingham Midland Institute to discuss the lives and work of authors and poets. Holds an annual dinner to celebrate Shakespeare's birthday.

The George Borrow Society
The Gables, 112 Irchester Road, Rushden, Northants NN10 9XQ
☎01933 312965   Fax 01933 312965
President *Sir Angus Fraser, KCB TD*
Honorary Secretary *Dr James H. Reading*
Honorary Treasurer *Mrs Ena R. J. Reading*
Subscription £8 p.a.

FOUNDED 1991 to promote knowledge of the life and works of George Borrow (1803–81), traveller, linguist and writer. The Society holds biennial conferences (with published proceedings) and informal intermediate gatherings, all at places associated with Borrow. *Publishes* the *George Borrow Bulletin* twice yearly, a newsletter containing scholarly articles, publications relating to Borrow, reports of past events and news of forthcoming events. Member of the **Alliance of Literary Societies** and corporate associate member of the Centre of East Anglian Studies (CEAS) at the University of East Anglia, Norwich (Borrow's home city for many years).

Elinor Brent-Dyer
See **Friends of the Chalet School**

British Fantasy Society
2 Harwood Street, Heaton Norris, Stockport, Cheshire SK4 1JJ
☎0161 476 5368
President *Ramsey Campbell*
Vice-President *Jan Edwards*
Secretary *Robert Parkinson*
Subscription from £17 p.a.(Apply to secretary.)

FOUNDED 1971 for devotees of fantasy, horror and related fields in literature, art and the cinema. *Publishes* a regular newsletter with information and reviews of new books and films, plus related fiction and non-fiction magazines. Annual conference at which the **British Fantasy Awards** are presented. These awards are voted on by the membership and are not an open competition.

The Brontë Society
Brontë Parsonage Museum, Haworth,
Keighley, West Yorkshire BD22 8DR
☎01535 642323   Fax 01535 647131
Contact *Membership Secretary*
Subscription £15 p.a.(UK/Europe);
£7.50 (Student); £5 (Junior – up to age
14); £22 (Overseas); Joint subscriptions and
life membership also available

FOUNDED 1893. Aims and activities include the
preservation of manuscripts and other objects
related to or connected with the Brontë family,
and the maintenance and development of the
museum and library at Haworth. The society
holds regular meetings, lectures and exhibitions; and *publishes* information relating to the
family, a bi-annual society journal *Transactions*
and a bi-annual *Gazette*. Freelance contributions for either publication should be sent to
the Publications Secretary at the address above.

The Browning Society
163 Wembley Hill Road, Wembley Park,
Middlesex HA9 8EL
☎0181 904 8401
Honorary Secretary *Ralph Ensz*
Subscription £15 p.a.

FOUNDED 1969 to promote an interest in the
lives and poetry of Robert and Elizabeth
Barrett Browning. Meetings are arranged in
the London area, one of which occurs in
December at Westminster Abbey to commemorate Robert Browning's death.

The John Buchan Society
Limpsfield, 16 Ranfurly Road, Bridge of Weir
PA11 3EL
☎01505 613116
Secretary *Russell Paterson*
Subscription £10 (Full/Overseas);
£4 (Associate); £6 (Junior);
£20 (Corporate); £90 (Life)

To perpetuate the memory of John Buchan and
to promote a wider understanding of his life and
works. Holds regular meetings and social gatherings, *publishes* a journal, and liaises with the John
Buchan Centre at Broughton in the Scottish
borders.

The Burns Federation
The Dick Institute, Elmbank Avenue,
Kilmarnock, Strathclyde KA1 3BU
☎01563 5726469 Fax 01563 529661/572469
Chief Executive *Shirley Bell*

Subscription £12 p.a.(Individual);
£25 (Club subscription)

FOUNDED 1885 to encourage interest in the life
and work of Robert Burns and keep alive the
old Scottish Tongue. The Society's interests go
beyond Burns himself in its commitment to the
development of Scottish literature, music and
arts in general. *Publishes* the quarterly *Burns
Chronicle/Burnsian*.

The Byron Society
Byron House, 6 Gertrude Street, London
SW10 0JN
☎0171 352 5112
Honorary Director, Byron Society *Mrs
Elma Dangerfield OBE*
Subscription £18 p.a.

Also: Newstead Abbey Byron Society,
Newstead Abbey, Newstead Abbey Park,
Nottingham NG15 8GE
☎01623 797392 (Contact: *Mrs Maureen Crisp*)

FOUNDED 1876; revived in 1971. Aims to promote knowledge and discussion of Lord Byron's
life and works, and those of his contemporaries,
through lectures, readings, concerts, performances and international conferences. *Publishes*
annually in April *The Byron Journal*, a scholarly
journal – £5 plus 60p postage.

Randolph Caldecott Society
Clatterwick Hall, Little Leigh, Northwich,
Cheshire CW8 4RJ
☎01606 891303
Honorary Secretary *Kenneth N. Oultram*
Subscription £7–£10 p.a.

FOUNDED 1983 to promote the life and work
of artist/book illustrator Randolph Caldecott.
Meetings held in the spring and autumn in
Caldecott's birthplace, Chester. Guest speakers,
outings, newsletter, exchanges with the society's American counterpart. (Caldecott died
and was buried in St Augustine, Florida.) A
medal in his memory is awarded annually in
the US for children's book illustration.

The Carlyle Society, Edinburgh
Dept of English Literature, The University of
Edinburgh, David Hume Tower, George
Square, Edinburgh EH8 9JX
Fax 0131 650 6898
E-mail: ian.campbell@ed.ac.uk
Contact *The President*
Subscription £2 p.a.; £10 (Life); $20 (US)

FOUNDED 1929 to examine the lives of
Thomas Carlyle and his wife Jane, his writings,

contemporaries, and influences. Meetings are held about six times a year and occasional papers are published annually. Enquiries should be addressed to the President of the Society at the above address or to the Secretary at 15 Lennox Street, Edinburgh EH4 1QB.

Lewis Carroll Society

Acorns, Dargate, Near Faversham, Kent ME13 9HG
Fax 01227 751339
Secretary *Sarah Stanfield*
Subscription Individual: £13 (UK); £15 (Europe); £17 (Outside Europe); £10 (Retired rate); £2 (Additional family members); Institutions: £26 (UK); £28 (Europe); £30 (Outside Europe)

FOUNDED 1969 to bring together people with an interest in Charles Dodgson and promote research into his life and works. *Publishes* bi-annual journal *The Carrollian*, featuring scholarly articles and reviews; a newsletter (*Bandersnatch*) which reports on Carrollian events and the Society's activities; and *The Lewis Carroll Review*, a book reviewing journal. Regular meetings held in London with lectures, talks, outings, etc.

Lewis Carroll Society (Daresbury)

Clatterwick Hall, Little Leigh, Northwich, Cheshire CW8 4RJ
☎01606 891303
Honorary Secretary *Kenneth N. Oultram*
Subscription £5 p.a.

FOUNDED 1970. To promote the life and work of Charles Dodgson, author of the world-famous *Alice's Adventures*. Holds regular meetings in the spring and autumn in Carroll's birthplace, Daresbury, Cheshire. Guest speakers, theatre visits and a newsletter. Appoints annually a 10-year-old 'Alice', who is available for public engagements.

Friends of the Chalet School

4 Rock Terrace, Coleford, Bath, Somerset BA3 5NF
☎01373 812705   Fax 01373 813517
Contact *Ann Mackie-Hunter, Clarissa Cridland*
Subscription £7.50 p.a.; £6 (Under-18); Outside UK: details on application

FOUNDED 1989 to promote the works of Elinor Brent-Dyer. The society has members worldwide; *publishes* four newsletters a year and runs a lending library.

The Raymond Chandler Society

6 Barkers Road, Nether Edge, Sheffield S7 1SE
☎0114 255 6302   Fax 0114 255 6302
UK Contact *Simon Beckett*
Subscription £15 p.a.(£7 concessions)

Although based in Germany, the Society has an international membership. Its foremost concerns are with Raymond Chandler's works and his influence and reception within a historical and contemporary context, but it is also concerned with the genre of the 'crime novel' in general. Presents the 'Marlowe' awards (see entry under **Prizes**). *Publishes* the *Chandler Yearbook*, a scholarly publication containing reviews and articles on crime writing in both English and German. The Society attends international conferences such as 'Shots on Page' and 'Bouchercon', and organises the Chandler Symposium, usually held in Ulm, Germany in July.

The Chesterton Society UK

11 Lawrence Leys, Bloxham, Near Banbury, Oxfordshire OX15 4NU
☎01295 720869
Honorary Secretary *Robert Hughes, KHS*
Subscription £10 p.a.

FOUNDED 1964 to promote the ideas and writings of G. K. Chesterton.

The Children's Books History Society

25 Field Way, Hoddesdon, Hertfordshire EN11 0QN
☎01992 464885   Fax 01992 464885
E-mail: cbhs@abcgarrett.demon.co.uk
Membership Secretary *Mrs Pat Garrett*
Subscription £10 p.a.

ESTABLISHED 1969. Aims to promote an appreciation of children's books and to study their history, bibliography and literary content. The Society holds approximately six meetings per year in London and a summer meeting to a collection, or to a location with a children's book connection. Three newsletters issued annually, also an occasional paper. The Society constitutes the British branch of the Friends of the Osborne and Lillian H. Smith Collections in Toronto, Canada, and also liaises with the **Library Association**. In 1990, the Society established its biennial Harvey Darton Award for a book, published in English, which extends our knowledge of some aspect of British children's literature of the past. 1998 joint-winners: John Goldthwaite *The Natural History of Make-Believe* and Peter Newbolt *G. A. Henty 1832–1902: a bibliographi-*

cal study of his British editors with short accounts of his publishers, illustrators and designers etc.

The John Clare Society

The Stables, 1A West Street, Helpston, Peterborough PE6 7DU
☎01733 252678
Honorary Secretary *Mrs J. Mary Moyse*
Subscription £9.50 (Individual);
£12.50 (Joint); £7.50 (Fully Retired);
£9.50 (Joint Retired); £10 (Group/Library);
£3 (Student, Full-time); £12.50 sterling draft/$25 (Overseas)

FOUNDED 1981 to promote a wider appreciation of the life and works of the poet John Clare (1793–1864). Organises an annual festival in Helpston in July; arranges exhibitions, poetry readings and conferences; and *publishes* an annual society journal and quarterly newsletter.

Wilkie Collins Society

47 Hereford Road, Acton, London W3 9JW
Chairman *Andrew Gasson*
Membership Secretary *Paul Lewis* (at above address)
Subscription £8.50 (UK); $12.50 (US) (Outside Europe, remittance must be in sterling)

FOUNDED 1980 to provide information on and promote interest in the life and works of Wilkie Collins, one of the first English novelists to deal with the detection of crime. *The Woman in White* appeared in 1860 and *The Moonstone* in 1868. *Publishes* newsletters, reprints of Collins' work and an occasional journal.

The Arthur Conan Doyle Society

PO Box 1360, Ashcroft, British Columbia Canada V0K 1A0
☎001 250 453 2045   Fax 001 250 453 2075
Joint Organisers *Christopher Roden, Barbara Roden*
Membership Contact *R. Dixon-Smith*, 59 Stonefield, Bar Hill, Cambridge CB3 8TE
Subscription £16 (UK); £16 (Overseas); Family rates available

FOUNDED 1989 to promote the study and discussion of the life and works of Sir Arthur Conan Doyle. Occasional meetings, functions and visits. *Publishes* an annual journal and twice-yearly news magazine, together with reprints of Conan Doyle's writings.

The Rhys Davies Trust

10 Heol Don, Whitchurch, Cardiff CF4 2AU
☎01222 623359   Fax 01222 529202
Contact *Meic Stephens*

FOUNDED 1990 to perpetuate the literary reputation of the Welsh prose writer, Rhys Davies (1901–78), and to foster Welsh writing in English. Organises competitions in association with other bodies such as **The Welsh Academy**, puts up plaques on buildings associated with Welsh writers, offers grant-aid for book production, etc.

The Dickens Fellowship

48 Doughty Street, London WC1N 2LF
☎0171 405 2127   Fax 0171 831 5175
Honorary General Secretary *Edward G. Preston*
Subscription £5 (First year); £8.50 (Renewal)

FOUNDED 1902. The Society's particular aims and objectives are: to bring together lovers of Charles Dickens; to spread the message of Dickens, his love of humanity ('the keynote of all his work'); to remedy social injustice for the poor and oppressed; to assist in the preservation of material and buildings associated with Dickens. Annual conference. *Publishes* journal called *The Dickensian* (available at special rate to members) and organises a full programme of lectures, discussions, visits and conducted walks throughout the year. Branches worldwide.

Early English Text Society

Christ Church, Oxford OX1 1DP
Fax 01865 794199
Executive Secretary *R. F. S. Hamer* (at above address)
Editorial Secretary *Dr H. L. Spencer* (at Exeter College, Oxford OX1 3DP)
Membership Secretary *Dr W. E. J. Collier* (at Buffers Cottage, Station Road, Hope, Derbyshire S33 2RR)
Subscription £15 p.a.(UK); $30 (US); $35 (Canada)

FOUNDED 1864. Concerned with the publication of early English texts. Members receive annual publications (one or two a year) or may select titles from the backlist in lieu.

The Eighteen Nineties Society

(incorporating **The Francis Thompson Society**, Founded 1963)
97D Brixton Road, London SW9 6EE
☎0171 582 4690
Patron *HRH Princess Michael of Kent*

President *Countess of Longford CBE*
Chairman *Martyn Goff OBE*
Honorary Secretary G. *Krishnamurti*
Subscription £20 p.a.(UK); $35 (US)

FOUNDED 1963 to bring together admirers of the work of Francis Thompson, the Society widened its scope in 1972 to embrace the artistic and literary scene of the entire decade (Impressionism, Realism, Naturalism, Symbolism). Assists members' research into the literature and art of the period; mounts exhibitions; *publishes* an annual journal and quarterly newsletter, plus biographies of neglected writers and artists of the period under the general title of *Makers of the Nineties.*

The George Eliot Fellowship

71 Stepping Stones Road, Coventry,
Warwickshire CV5 8JT
☎01203 592231
Contact *Mrs Kathleen Adams*
Subscription £10 p.a.; £100 (Life);
Concessions for pensioners

FOUNDED 1930. Exists to honour George Eliot and promote interest in her life and works. Readings, memorial lecture, birthday luncheon and functions. Issues a quarterly newsletter and an annual journal. Awards an annual prize for a George Eliot essay.

Folly (Fans of Light Literature for the Young)

21 Warwick Road, Pokesdown,
Bournemouth, Dorset BH7 6JW
☎01202 432562
E-mail: folly@sims.abel.co.uk
Contact *Mrs Sue Sims*
Subscription £6 p.a.(UK); £7 (Europe);
£8.50 (Worldwide)

FOUNDED 1990 to promote interest in a wide variety of children's authors – with a bias towards writers of girls' books and school stories. *Publishes* three magazines a year.

The Franco-Midland Hardware Company

6 Bramham Moor, Hill Head, Fareham,
Hampshire PO14 3RU
☎01329 667325
Chairman *Philip Weller*
Subscription £15 p.a.

FOUNDED 1989. 'The world's leading Sherlock Holmes correspondence study group and the most active Holmesian society in Britain.' *Publishes* bi-annual journal, a bi-annual news

magazine and at least six specialist monographs a year. It provides certificated self-study courses and organises monthly functions at Holmes-associated locations. Open membership.

The Gaskell Society

Far Yew Tree House, Over Tabley,
Knutsford, Cheshire WA16 0HN
☎01565 634668
E-mail: JoanLeach@aol.com
Website: http://www.lang.nagoya-ac.jp/
~matsuoka/Gaskell.html
Honorary Secretary *Joan Leach*
Subscription £8 p.a.; £12 (Overseas)

FOUNDED 1985 to promote and encourage the study and appreciation of the life and works of Elizabeth Cleghorn Gaskell. Meetings held in Knutsford, Manchester and London; residential study weekends and visits; annual journal and bi-annual newsletter.

The Ghost Story Society

PO Box 1360, Ashcroft, British Columbia
Canada V0K 1A0
☎001 250 453 2045   Fax 001 250 453 2075
E-mail: ashtree@mail.netshop.net
Joint Organisers *Barbara Roden,*
Christopher Roden
Subscription UK: £13 (Surface mail)/
£14.50 (Airmail); $23 (US); $29.50 (Canadian)

FOUNDED 1988. Devoted mainly to supernatural fiction in the literary tradition of M. R. James, Walter de la Mare, Algernon Blackwood, E. F. Benson, A. N. L. Murphy, R. H. Malden, etc. *Publishes* a thrice-yearly journal, *All Hallows*, which includes new fiction in the genre and non-fiction of relevance to the genre.

The Gothic Society

Chatham House, Gosshill Road, Chislehurst,
Kent BR7 5NS
☎0181 467 8475   Fax 0181 295 1967
Contact *Jennie Gray*
Subscription £22.50 p.a.; £26 (Overseas)

FOUNDED 1990 for the amusement of 'those who delight in morbid, macabre and black-hued themes, both ancient and modern Gothick!' *Publishes* high-quality paperbacks on related subjects, and four large-format illustrated magazines yearly together with a quarterly newsletter. Some scope for original and imaginative fiction, but main preference is for history, biography and intelligent but amusing essays on the arts. Members have a definite advantage over writers outside the Society. (Also see **The Gargoyle's Head** under **Small Presses**.)

Rider Haggard Appreciation Society

27 Deneholm, Whitley Bay, Tyne & Wear
NE25 9AU
☎0191 252 4516   Fax 0191 252 4516
E-mail: 106251.3413@compuserve.com
Contact *Roger Allen*
Subscription £8 p.a.(UK); £10 (Overseas)
FOUNDED 1985 to promote appreciation of the life and works of Sir Henry Rider Haggard, English novelist, 1856–1925. News/books exchange, and meetings every two years.

The Thomas Hardy Society

PO Box 1438, Dorchester, Dorset
DT1 1YH
☎01305 251501
Honorary Secretary *Miss Eileen Johnson*
Subscription £12 (Individual);
£16 (Corporate); £15 (Individual
Overseas); £20 (Corporate Overseas)
FOUNDED 1967 to promote the reading and study of the works and life of Thomas Hardy. Thrice-yearly journal, events and a biennial conference.

The Henty Society

Fox Hall, Kelshall, Royston, Hertfordshire
SG8 9SE
☎01763 287208
Honorary Secretary *Mrs Ann J. King*
Subscription £12 p.a.(UK); £15 (Overseas)
FOUNDED 1977 to study the life and work of George Alfred Henty, and to publish research, bibliographical data and lesser-known works, namely short stories. Organises conferences and social gatherings in the UK and Canada, and *publishes* quarterly bulletins to members. Published in 1996: *G. A. Henty (1832–1902) a Bibliographical Study* by Peter Newbolt.

Sherlock Holmes Society (Northern Musgraves)

Overdale, 69 Greenhead Road, Huddersfield, West Yorkshire HD1 4ER
☎01484 426957   Fax 01484 426957
Contact *David Stuart Davies, Kathryn White*
Subscription £17 p.a.(UK)
FOUNDED 1987 to promote enjoyment and study of Sir Arthur Conan Doyle's Sherlock Holmes through publications and meetings. One of the largest Sherlock Holmes societies in Great Britain. Honorary members include Bert Coules, Richard Lancelyn Green, Edward Hardwicke and Douglas Wilmer. Past honorary members: Dame Jean Conan Doyle, Peter Cushing and Jeremy Brett. Open membership. Lectures, presentations and consultation on matters relating to Holmes and Conan Doyle available.

The Sherlock Holmes Society of London

13 Crofton Avenue, Orpington, Kent
BR6 8DU
☎01689 811314
Membership Secretary *R. J. Ellis*
Subscription £9.50 p.a.(Associate); £14 (Full)
FOUNDED 1951 to promote the study of the life and work of Sherlock Holmes and Dr Watson, and their creator, Sir Arthur Conan Doyle. Offers correspondence and liaison with international societies, and a bi-annual society journal.

Sherlock Holmes

See **The Franco–Midland Hardware Company**

Hopkins Society

Library, Museum & Gallery, Earl Road, Mold, Flintshire CH7 1AP
☎01352 758403   Fax 01352 700236
Contact *Sandra Wynne*
Subscription £5 p.a.
FOUNDED 1990 to celebrate the life and work of Gerard Manley Hopkins; to inform members of any publications, courses or events about the poet. Holds an annual lecture on Hopkins in the spring; produces two newsletters a year; sponsors and organises educational projects based on Hopkins' life and works.

W. W. Jacobs Appreciation Society

3 Roman Road, Southwick, West Sussex
BN42 4TP
☎01273 871017   Fax 01273 871017
Contact *A. R. James*
FOUNDED 1988 to encourage and promote the enjoyment of the works of W. W. Jacobs, and stimulate research into his life and work. *Publishes* a quarterly newsletter free to those who send s.a.e. (9 x 4ins). Contributions welcome but no payment made. Preferred lengths 600–1200 words. No subscription charge. Biography, bibliography, directories of plays and films are available for purchase.

Richard Jefferies Society
Eidsvoll, Bedwells Heath, Boars Hill, Oxford
OX1 5JE
☎01865 735678

Honorary Secretary *Lady Phyllis Treitel*
Membership Secretary *Mrs Sheila Povey*
Subscription £7 p.a.(Individual); £8 (Joint);
Life membership for those over 50

FOUNDED 1950 to promote understanding of
the work of Richard Jefferies, nature/country
writer, novelist and mystic (1848–87). Produces
newsletters, reports and an annual journal;
organises talks, discussions and readings. Library
and archives. Assists in maintaining museum in
Jefferies' birthplace at Coate near Swindon.
Membership applications should be sent to
Margaret Evans, 23 Hardwell Close, Grove, Nr
Wantage, Oxon OX12 0BN.

Jerome K. Jerome Society
The Birthplace Museum, Belsize House,
Bradford Street, Walsall, West Midlands
WS1 1PN
☎01922 629000   Fax 01922 721065

Honorary Secretary *Tony Gray*
Subscription £5 p.a.(Ordinary);
£25 (Corporate); £6 (Joint); £2.50 (Under
21/Over 65)

FOUNDED 1984 to stimulate interest in Jerome
K. Jerome's life and works (1859–1927). One
of the Society's principal activities is the support of a small museum in the author's birthplace, Walsall. Meetings, lectures, events and a
twice-yearly newsletter *Idle Thoughts*. Annual
dinner in Walsall near Jerome's birth date (2nd
May).

The W. E. Johns Society
Canna, West Drive, Bracklesham Bay,
Chichester, West Sussex PO20 8PF
☎01243 671209

Contact *Jenny Schofield*
Subscription £8 p.a.

Publishes bi-annual magazine, *Biggles Flies Again*
and usually holds two meetings (in Hertford
and Nottingham) each year.

Johnson Society
Johnson Birthplace Museum, Breadmarket
Street, Lichfield, Staffordshire WS13 6LG
☎01543 264972

Hon. General Secretary *Mrs Norma Hooper*
Subscription £7.50 p.a.; £10 (Joint)

FOUNDED 1910 to encourage the study of the
life, works and times of Samuel Johnson (1709–
1784) and his contemporaries. The Society is
committed to the preservation of the Johnson
Birthplace Museum and Johnson memorials.

Johnson Society of London
255 Baring Road, Grove Park, London
SE12 0BQ
☎0181 851 0173
E-mail: jsl@nbbl.demon.co.uk
Website: http://www.nbbl.demon.co.uk/
index.html

Honorary Secretary *Mrs Z. E. O'Donnell*
Subscription £10 p.a.; £12.50 (Joint)

FOUNDED 1928 to promote the knowledge and
appreciation of Dr Samuel Johnson and his
works. Regular meetings from October to
April in the Vestry Hall of St Edmund the King,
Lombard Street in London on the second Saturday of each month, and a commemoration
ceremony around the anniversary of Johnson's
death (December) held in Westminster Abbey.

The Just William Society
15 St James' Avenue, Bexhill-on-Sea,
East Sussex TN40 2DN
☎01424 216065

Secretary *Michael Vigar*
Treasurer *Phil Woolley*
Subscription £7 p.a.(UK); £10 (Overseas);
£5 (Juvenile/Student); £15 (Family)

FOUNDED 1994 to further knowledge of
Richmal Crompton's *William* and *Jimmy* books.
An annual 'William' meeting is held in April,
although this is not currently organised by the
Society. The Honorary President of the Society
is Richmal Crompton's niece, Richmal Ashbee.

The Keats–Shelley Memorial Association (Inc)
1 Lewis Road, Radford Semele, Warwickshire
CV31 1UB

Contact *Honorary Treasurer* (at 10 Lansdowne
Road, Tunbridge Wells, Kent TN1 2NJ.
☎01892 533452 Fax 01892 519142)
Subscription £10 p.a.; £100 (Life)

FOUNDED 1909 to promote appreciation of the
works of Keats and Shelley, and their contemporaries. One of the Society's main tasks is the
preservation of 26 Piazza di Spagna in Rome as
a memorial to the British Romantic poets in
Italy, particularly Keats and Shelley. *Publishes*
an annual review of Romantic Studies called
the *Keats-Shelley Review* and arranges events
and lectures for Friends. The review is edited

by *Angus Graham-Campbell*, c/o Eton College, Windsor, Berkshire SL4 6EA.

Kent & Sussex Poetry Society
Costens, Carpenters Lane, Hadlow, Kent
TN11 0EY
☎01732 851404

Contact *Honorary Secretary* (at above address)
Subscription £6 p.a.; £3 (non-attending); £2 (per meeting)

FOUNDED 1946 to promote the enjoyment of poetry. Monthly meetings, including readings by major poets, and a monthly workshop. *Publishes* an annual folio of members' work based on Members' Competition, adjudicated and commented upon by a major poet, and runs an Open Poetry Competition (see entry under **Prizes**) bi-annually.

Kent Fantasy Society
68 Bellevue Road, Ramsgate, Kent CT11 8DN
☎01843 590502

Secretary *Barbara A. Stone*
Newsletter Editor *David L. Stone*
Subscription £7.50 (6 months); £14 (1 year)

FOUNDED in 1997 to promote interest in the genre and to provide a meeting place for enthusiasts. Also encourages new talent by publishing the work of six new writers per year in the regular newsletter, *Wonderland*, which includes book reviews, genre news, competitions, letters and regular small press listing. Please send s.a.e with enquiries.

The Kilvert Society
The Old Forge, Kinnersley, Hereford
HR3 6QB
☎01544 327426

Secretary *Mr M. Sharp*
Subscription £5 p.a.; £50 (Life)

FOUNDED 1948 to foster an interest in the Diary, the diarist and the countryside he loved. *Publishes* three newsletters each year; during the summer holds three weekends of walks, commemoration services and talks.

The Kipling Society
Tree Cottage, 2 Brownleaf Road, Brighton, East Sussex BN2 6LB
☎01273 303719   Fax 01273 303719
Website: http://www.kipling.org.uk

Honorary Secretary *Mr J. W. Michael Smith*
Subscription £20 p.a.

FOUNDED 1927. The Society's main activities are: maintaining a specialised library in London; answering enquiries from the public (schools, publishers, writers and the media); arranging a regular programme of lectures, especially in London and in Sussex, and an annual luncheon with guest speaker; maintaining a small museum and reference at The Grange, in Rottingdean near Brighton; issuing a quarterly journal. This is a literary society for all who enjoy the prose and verse of Rudyard Kipling (1865–1936) and are interested in his life and times. Please contact the Secretary by letter, telephone or fax for further information.

The Kitley Trust
Toadstone Cottage, Edge View, Litton, Derbyshire SK17 8QU
☎01298 871564

Contact *Rosie Ford*

FOUNDED 1990 by a teacher in Sheffield to promote the art of creative writing, in memory of her mother, Jessie Kitley. Activities include: bi-annual poetry competitions; a 'Get Poetry' Day (distribution of children's poems in shopping malls); annual sponsorship of a writer for a school; campaigns; organising conferences for writers and teachers of writing. Funds are provided by donations and profits (if any) from competitions.

Charles Lamb Society
1A Royston Road, Richmond, Surrey
TW10 6LT
☎0181 940 3837

General Secretary *Mrs M. R. Huxstep*
Subscription £12 p.a.(Single); £18 (Joint & Corporate); US$28 (Overseas Personal); US$42 (Overseas Corporate)

FOUNDED 1935 to promote the study of the life, works and times of English essayist Charles Lamb (1775–1834). Holds regular monthly meetings and lectures in London and organises society events over the summer. Annual luncheon in February. *Publishes* a quarterly bulletin, *The Charles Lamb Bulletin*. Contributions of Elian interest are welcomed by the editor *Dr Duncan Wu* at Dept of English Literature, University of Glasgow, Glasgow G12 8QQ (E-mail: dwu@englit.arts.gla.ac.uk/☎0141 332 3836). Membership applications should be sent to the General Secretary at the Richmond address above. The Society's library is housed in the **Guildhall Library**, Aldermanbury, London EC2P 2EJ (☎0171 606 3030). Member of the **Alliance of Literary Societies**. Registered Charity No: 803222.

Lancashire Authors' Association
Heatherslade, 5 Quakerfields, Westhoughton,
Bolton, Lancashire BL5 2BJ
☎01942 791390

General Secretary *Eric Holt*
Subscription £9 p.a.; £12 (Joint);
£1 (Junior)

FOUNDED 1909 for writers and lovers of
Lancashire literature and history. Aims to foster
and stimulate interest in Lancashire history and
literature as well as in the preservation of the
Lancashire dialect. Meets four times a year on
Saturday at various locations. *Publishes* a quarterly journal called *The Record* which is issued
free to members and holds eight annual competitions (open to members only) for both
verse and prose. Comprehensive library with
access for research to members.

The Philip Larkin Society
c/o Centre for Educational Studies, The
University of Hull, Hull HU6 7RX
☎01482 847930   Fax 01482 466133
E-mail: jhw@palsoc.karoo.co.uk

Contact *Mrs Janet Whitehead*
Subscription £18 (Full rate);
£12 (Unwaged/Senior Citizen);
£8 (Student)

FOUNDED in 1995 to promote awareness of the
life and work of Philip Larkin (1922–1985) and
his literary contemporaries; to bring together
all those who admire Larkin's work as a poet,
writer and librarian; to bring about publications
on all things Larkinesque. Organises a programme of events ranging from lectures to
rambles exploring the countryside of Larkin's
schooldays.

The D. H. Lawrence Society
Dept of French, University of Hull,
Cottingham Road, Hull HU6 7RX
Contact *Dr Catherine Greensmith*
Subscription £10; £9 (Concession);
£11 (Joint); £12 (European); £15 (RoW)

FOUNDED 1974 to increase knowledge and the
appreciation of the life and works of D. H.
Lawrence. Monthly meetings, addressed by
guest speakers, are held in the library at
Eastwood (birthplace of DHL). Organises visits
to places of interest in the surrounding countryside, supports the activities of the D. H.
Lawrence Centre at Nottingham University,
and has close links with DHL Societies worldwide. *Publishes* two newsletters and one journal
each year, free to members.

The T. E. Lawrence Society
PO Box 728, Oxford OX2 6YP
Contact *Gigi Horsfield*
Subscription £16 (UK); £20 (Overseas)

FOUNDED 1985 as a non-profit making, educational, registered charity to advance awareness
of the life and work of Thomas Edward
Lawrence and to promote research into his life
and work. *Publishes* four newsletters and two
journals per year. A biennial symposium is
held, usually in Oxford, to bring members
together to share both academic and social
interests. The Society encourages the formation of regional groups of which, currently,
there are five: three in England (Northwest,
London, Dorset), one in Europe (Netherlands)
and one in the USA (Eastern States).

The Leamington Literary Society
15 Church Hill, Leamington Spa,
Warwickshire CV32 5AZ
☎01926 425733

Honorary Secretary *Mrs Margaret Watkins*
Subscription £6 p.a.

FOUNDED 1912 to promote the study and
appreciation of literature and the arts. Holds
regular meetings every second Tuesday of the
month (except August) at the Regent Hotel,
Leamington Spa. The Society has published
various books of local interest.

Wyndham Lewis Society
18 Coltsfoot Road, Ware, Hertfordshire
SG12 7NW
E-mail: swol@cableol.co.uk

Contact *Mrs Sam Brown*
Subscription £10 p.a.(UK/Europe);
£12 p.a.(Institutions); US$25 (Rest of
World) US$30 (Institutions, RoW) (US
dollar subs to be sent to Wyndham Lewis
Society, Hugh Anson-Cartwright, 229
College Street, Toronto, Ontario M5T
1R4, Canada – all cheques payable to The
Wyndham Lewis Society)

FOUNDED 1974 to promote recognition of the
value of Lewis's works and encourage scholarly
research on the man, his painting and his writing.
Publishes inaccessible Lewis writings; the annual
society journal *The Wyndham Lewis Annual* plus
two newsletters; and reproduces Lewis's paintings. The journal is edited by *Paul Edwards*,
School of English, Bath Spa University College,
Newton St. Loe, Bath BA2 9BN.

William Morris Society
Kelmscott House, 26 Upper Mall,
Hammersmith, London W6 9TA
☎0181 741 3735

Contact *David Rodgers*
Subscription £13.50 p.a.

FOUNDED 1953 to promote interest in the life,
work and ideas of William Morris (1834–1923),
English poet and craftsman.

Violet Needham Society
c/o 19 Ashburnham Place, London
SE10 8TZ
☎0181 692 4562

Honorary Secretary *R. H. A. Cheffins*
Subscription £6 p.a.(UK & Europe);
£9 (outside Europe)

FOUNDED 1985 to celebrate the work of children's author Violet Needham and stimulate critical awareness of her work. *Publishes* thrice-yearly *Souvenir*, the Society journal with an accompanying newsletter; organises meetings and excursions to places associated with the author and her books. The journal includes articles about other children's writers of the 1940s and '50s and on ruritanian fiction. Contributions welcome.

The Edith Nesbit Society
73 Brookehowse Road, London SE6 3TH
Chairman *Nicholas Reed*
Treasurer *Nicholas Wright*
Subscription £5 p.a.; £7.50 (Joint);
£50 (Life)

FOUNDED in 1996 to celebrate the life and work of Edith Nesbit (1858–1924), best known as the author of *The Railway Children*. The Society's activities include a regular newsletter, booklets, talks and visits to relevant places.

The Wilfred Owen Association
17 Belmont, Shrewsbury, Shropshire
SY1 1TE
☎01743 235904

Chairman *Helen McPhail*
Subscription Adults £4 (£6 Overseas);
£2 (Senior Citizens/Students/
Unemployed); £10 (Groups/Institutions)

FOUNDED 1989 to commemorate the life and works of Wilfred Owen by promoting readings, visits, talks and performances relating to Owen and his work, and supporting appropriate academic and creative projects. Membership is international with 600 members. *Publishes* a newsletter twice a year. Speakers are available for schools or clubs etc. Special events in 1998 to commemorate the 80th anniversary of Owen's death.

The Elsie Jeanette Oxenham Appreciation Society
32 Tadfield Road, Romsey, Hampshire
SO51 5AJ
☎01794 517149   Fax 01794 517149

Contact *Ms Ruth Allen*
Subscription £6 p.a.

FOUNDED 1989 to promote the works of Elsie J. Oxenham. Publishes a newsletter, *The Abbey Chronicle*, three times a year.

Thomas Paine Society U.K.
43 Wellington Gardens, Selsey, West Sussex
PO20 0RF
☎01243 605730
E-mail: tompainesociety@mrm.co.uk
Website: www.mrm.co.uk

President *The Rt. Hon. Michael Foot*
Honorary Secretary/Treasurer *Eric Paine*
Subscription (Minimum) £10 p.a.(UK);
£20 (Overseas); £5 (Unwaged/Pensioners)

FOUNDED 1963 to promote the life and work of Thomas Paine, and continues to expound his ideals. Meetings, newsletters, lectures and research assistance. Membership badge. The Society has members worldwide and keeps in touch with American and French Thomas Paine associations. *Publishes* magazine, *Bulletin*, twice yearly and holds occasional exhibitions and talks on Paine's life.

Mervyn Peake Society
2 Mount Park Road, Ealing, London
W5 2RP
☎0181 566 9307   Fax 0181 991 0559
E-mail: 101367.1376@compuserve.com

Contact *Frank Surry*
Subscription £12 p.a. (UK & Europe);
£5 (Students/OAPs/Unwaged);
£12 (Institutions); £14 (All other
countries); £16 (Institutions overseas)

FOUNDED 1975 to promote a wider understanding of Mervyn Peake's achievements as novelist, poet, painter and illustrator. Membership is opn to all, irrespective of native language or country of residence. *Publishes The Mervyn Peake Review* annually and the *MPS Newsletter* quarterly. Holds an AGM.

The John Polidori Literary Society

Ebenezer House, 31 Ebenezer Street, Langley Mill, Nottinghamshire NG16 4DA
☎0181 560 9916

Founder & President *Franklin Charles Bishop*
Subscription £15 p.a.

FOUNDED 1990 to promote and encourage appreciation of the life and works of John William Polidori MD (1795–1821) – novelist, poet, tragedian, philosopher, diarist, essayist, reviewer, traveller and one of the youngest students to obtain a medical degree (at the age of 19). He was one-time intimate of the leading figures in the Romantic movement and travelling companion and private physician to Lord Byron. He was a pivotal figure in the infamous Villa Diodati ghost story sessions in which he assisted Mary Shelley in the creation of her *Frankenstein* tale. As a result of this, Polidori introduced into literature the enduring icon of the vampire portrayed as an aristocratic, handsome seducer with his seminal work *The Vampyre – A Tale*, published in 1819. The birthplace of Polidori, in Great Pulteney Street, London, was honoured in 1998 by the erection of a City of Westminster Green Plaque award. Members receive exclusive newsletters, invitations to unique social events and publication offers. International membership in USA, Canada and France.

The Beatrix Potter Society

32 Etchingham Park Road, Finchley, London N3 2DT
☎0181 346 8031

Secretary *Mrs Marian Werner*
Subscription UK: £10 p.a.(Individual);
£15 (Institutional); Overseas: £15 (or US$25/Can./Aust.$30, Individual);
£22 (US$35/Can./Aust.$47, Institutional)

FOUNDED 1980 to promote the study and appreciation of the life and works of Beatrix Potter (1866–1943). Potter was not only the author of *The Tale of Peter Rabbit* and other classics of children's literature; she was also a landscape and natural history artist, diarist, farmer and conservationist, and was responsible for the preservation of large areas of the Lake District through her gifts to the National Trust. The Society upholds and protects the integrity of the inimitable and unique work of the lady, her aims and bequests. Holds regular talks and meetings in London with visits to places connected with Beatrix Potter. Biennial International Study Conferences are held in the UK and occasionally in the USA. The Society has an active publishing programme.

The Powys Society

The Old School House, George Green Road, George Green, Wexham, Buckinghamshire SL3 6BJ
☎01753 578632
E-mail: gostik@premier.co.uk

Honorary Secretary *Chris Gostick*
Subscription £13.50 (UK); £16 (Overseas);
£6 (Students)

The Society (with a membership of 350) aims to promote public education and recognition of the writings, thought and contribution to the arts of the Powys family; particularly of John Cowper, Theodore and Llewelyn, but also of the other members of the family and their close associates. The Society holds two major collections of Powys published works, letters, manuscripts and memorabilia. *Publishes* the *Powys Society Newsletter* in April, June and November and *The Powys Journal* in August. Organises an annual conference as well as lectures and meetings in Powys places.

The Arthur Ransome Society Ltd

Abbot Hall Art Gallery, Kirkland, Kendal, Cumbria LA9 5AL
☎01539 722464   Fax 01539 722494

Chairman *M. Temple*
Secretary *Bill Janes*
Contact *Gillian Riding*
Subscription £5 (Junior); £10 (Student);
£15 (Adult); £20 (Family/Overseas);
£40 (Corporate); Concessions for retired persons

FOUNDED 1990 to celebrate the life and promote the works and ideas of Arthur Ransome, author of the world-famous *Swallows and Amazons* titles for children and biographer of Oscar Wilde. TARS seeks to encourage children and adults to engage in adventurous pursuits, to educate the public about Ransome and his works, and to sponsor research into his literary works and life.

The Followers of Rupert

31 Whiteley, Windsor, Berkshire SL4 5PJ
☎01753 865562

Membership Secretary *Mrs Shirley Reeves*
Subscription UK: £9.50; £11.50 (Joint);
Europe, airmail: £10.50 (Individual);
£12.50 (Joint); Worldwide, airmail:
£12.50 (Individual); £14.50 (Joint)

FOUNDED in 1983. The Society caters for the growing interest in the Rupert Bear stories, past, present and future. *Publishes* the *Nutwood*

Newsletter quarterly which gives up-to-date news of Rupert and information on Society activities. A national get-together of members – the Followers Annual – is held during the autumn in venues around the country.

The Ruskin Society of London
351 Woodstock Road, Oxford OX2 7NX
☎01865 310987/515962
Honorary Secretary *Miss O. E. Forbes-Madden*
Subscription £10 p.a.

FOUNDED 1986 to promote interest in John Ruskin (1819–1900) and his contemporaries. All aspects of Ruskinia are introduced. Functions are held in London. *Publishes* the annual *Ruskin Gazette*, a journal concerned with Ruskin's influence.

The Dorothy L. Sayers Society
Rose Cottage, Malthouse Lane,
Hurstpierpoint, West Sussex BN6 9JY
☎01273 833444   Fax 01273 835988
Contact *Christopher Dean*
Subscription £12 p.a.; US$24 p.a.

FOUNDED 1976 to promote the study of the life, works and thoughts of Dorothy Sayers; to encourage the performance of her plays and publication of her books and books about her; to preserve original material and provide assistance to researchers. Acts as a forum and information centre, providing material for study purposes which would otherwise be unavailable. Annual seminars and other meetings. Co-founder of the Dorothy L. Sayers Centre in Witham. *Publishes* bi-monthly bulletin and other papers.

The Shaw Society
51 Farmfield Road, Downham, Bromley,
Kent BR1 4NF
☎0181 697 3619   Fax 0181 697 3619
Honorary Secretary *Ms Barbara Smoker*
Subscription £10 p.a.(Individual); £15 (Joint)

FOUNDED 1941 to promote interest in the life and works of G. Bernard Shaw. Meetings are held on the last Friday of every month (except July, August and December) at Conway Hall, Red Lion Square, London WC1 (6.30pm for 7pm) at which speakers are invited to talk on some aspect of Shaw's life or works. Monthly playreadings are held on the first Friday of each month (except August). A 'Birthday Tribute' is held at Shaw's Corner, Ayot St Lawrence in Hertfordshire on the weekend nearest to Shaw's birthday (26th July). *Publishes* a quarterly newsletter and a magazine, *The Shavian*, which appears approximately every nine months.

The Robert Southey Society
1 Lewis Terrace, Abergarwed, Resoluen,
Neath SA11 4DL
☎01639 711480
Contact *Robert King*
Subscription £10 p.a.

FOUNDED 1990 to promote the work of Robert Southey. *Publishes* an annual newsletter and arranges talks on his life and work. Open membership.

The Friends of Shandy Hall (The Laurence Sterne Trust)
Shandy Hall, Coxwold, York YO6 4AD
☎01347 868465
Honorary Secretary *Mrs J. Monkman*
Subscription £6 (Annual); £60 (Life)

Promotes interest in the works of Laurence Sterne and aims to preserve the house in which they were created (open to the public). *Publishes* annual journal *The Shandean*. An Annual Memorial Lecture is delivered at Shandy Hall each summer.

Robert Louis Stevenson Club
5 Albyn Place, Edinburgh EH2 4NJ
☎0131 225 6665   Fax 0131 220 1015
Contact *Alistair J. R. Ferguson*
Subscription £10 p.a.(Individual); £80 (Life)

FOUNDED 1920 to promote the memory of Robert Louis Stevenson and interest in his works. *Publishes* yearbook and quarterly newsletter for members.

The R. S. Surtees Society
Manor Farm House, Nunney, Near Frome,
Somerset BA11 4NJ
☎01373 836937   Fax 01373 836574
Contact *Mrs Joan Wright*
Subscription £10

FOUNDED 1979 to republish the works of R. S. Surtees and others.

The Tennyson Society
Central Library, Free School Lane, Lincoln
LN2 1EZ
☎01522 552862   Fax 01522 552858
E-mail: kathleenjefferson@lincolnshire.gov.uk
Honorary Secretary *Miss K. Jefferson*
Subscription £8 p.a.(Individual);
     £10 (Family); £15 (Corporate); £125 (Life)

FOUNDED 1960. An international society with membership worldwide. Exists to promote the study and understanding of the life and work of

Alfred, Lord Tennyson. The Society is concerned with the work of the Tennyson Research Centre, 'probably the most significant collection of mss, family papers and books in the world'. *Publishes* annually the *Tennyson Research Bulletin*, which contains articles and critical reviews; and organises lectures, visits and seminars. Annual memorial service at Somersby in Lincolnshire.

The Edward Thomas Fellowship
Butlers Cottage, Halswell House, Goathurst, Bridgwater, Somerset TA5 2DH
☎01278 662856
Secretary *Richard Emeny*
Subscription £5 p.a.(Single); £7 p.a.(Joint)
FOUNDED 1980 to perpetuate and promote the memory of Edward Thomas and to encourage an appreciation of his life and work. The Fellowship holds a commemorative birthday walk on the Sunday nearest the poet's birthday, 3 March; issues newsletters and holds various events.

The Francis Thompson Society
See **The Eighteen Nineties Society**

The Trollope Society
9A North Street, Clapham, London SW4 0HN
☎0171 720 6789   Fax 0171 978 1815
Contacts *John Letts, Phyllis Eden*
FOUNDED 1987 to study and promote Anthony Trollope's works. Linked with the publication of the first complete edition of his novels.

The Walmsley Society
April Cottage, No 1 Brand Road, Hampden Park, Eastbourne, East Sussex BN22 9PX
☎01323 506447
Honorary Secretary *Fred Lane*
Subscription £8 p.a.; £10 (Family); £7 (Students/Senior Citizens)
FOUNDED 1985 to promote interest in the art and writings of Ulric and Leo Walmsley. Two annual meetings, one held in Robin Hood's Bay on the East Yorkshire coast, spiritual home of the author Leo Walmsley. The Society also seeks to foster appreciation of the work of his father Ulric Walmsley. *Publishes* a journal twice-yearly and newsletters, and is involved in other publications which benefit the aims of the Society.

Mary Webb Society
15 Melbourne Rise, Gains Park, Shrewsbury, Shropshire SY3 5DA
Secretary *Mary Palmer*

Subscription £7.50 p.a.
FOUNDED 1972. Attracts members from the UK and overseas who are devotees of the literature of Mary Webb and of the beautiful Shropshire countryside of her novels. *Publishes* annual journal in September, organises summer schools in various locations related to the authoress's life and works. Archives; lectures; tours arranged for individuals and groups.

H. G. Wells Society
49 Beckingthorpe Drive, Bottesford, Nottingham NG13 0DN
Honorary Secretary *J. R. Hammond*
Subscription £14 (UK/EU); £17 (Overseas); £20 (Corporate); £8 (Concessions)
FOUNDED 1960 to promote an interest in and appreciation of the life, work and thought of Herbert George Wells.

The Charles Williams Society
26 Village Road, London N3 1TL
Contact *Honorary Secretary*
FOUNDED 1975 to promote interest in, and provide a means for, the exchange of views and information on the life and work of Charles Walter Stansby Williams (1886–1945).

The Henry Williamson Society
16 Doran Drive, Redhill, Surrey RH1 6AX
☎01737 763228
Membership Secretary *Mrs Margaret Murphy*
Subscription £8 p.a.; £10 (Family); £4 (Students)
FOUNDED 1980 to encourage, by all appropriate means, a wider readership and deeper understanding of the literary heritage left by the 20th-century English writer Henry Williamson (1895–1977). *Publishes* annual journal.

The P. G. Wodehouse Society
108 Balmoral Road, Northampton NN2 6JZ
☎01604 239216
President *Richard Briars*
Contact *Richard Morris*
Subscription £15 p.a.
Relaunched in May 1997 to advance the genius of P. G. Wodehouse. Publications include *Wooster Source* and the *By The Way* newsletter. Regular national and international group meetings. Members in most countries throughout the world. Society patrons include Rt. Hon. Tony

Blair MP, Sir Edward Cazelet (Wodehouse's grandson) and Stephen Fry.

WW2 HMSO PPBKS Society
3 Roman Road, Southwick, West Sussex
BN42 4TP
☎01273 871017   Fax 01273 871017
Contact *A. R. James*
Subscription £2 p.a.

FOUNDED 1994 to encourage collectors of, and promote research into HM Stationery Office's World War II series of paperbacks, most of which were written by well-known authors, although, in many cases, anonymously. *Publishes* bi-monthly newsletter for those who send s.a.e. (9 x 4 ins). Contributors welcome; preferred length 600–1200 words but no payment made. Bibliography available for purchase (£3); Collectors' Guide (£5).

Yorkshire Dialect Society
51 Stepney Avenue, Scarborough, North Yorkshire YO12 5BW
☎01723 371296
Secretary *Michael Park*

Subscription £6 p.a.

FOUNDED 1897 to promote interest in and preserve a record of the Yorkshire dialect. *Publishes* dialect verse and prose writing. Two journals to members annually. Details of publications are available from the Librarian, YDS, School of English, University of Leeds, Leeds, West Yorkshire LS2 9JT.

Francis Brett Young Society
48 Meadow Croft, Hagley, Stourbridge, West Midlands DY9 0LJ
☎01562 887255
Honorary Secretary *Mrs Joan Willcox*
Subscription £7 p.a.(Individuals);
    £10 (Couples sharing a journal);
    £5 (Students); £7 (Organisations/Overseas);
    £70 (Life); £100 (Joint, Life)

FOUNDED 1979. Aims to provide a forum for those interested in the life and works of English novelist Francis Brett Young and to collate research on him. Promotes lectures, exhibitions and readings; *publishes* a regular newsletter.

Arts Councils and Regional Arts Boards

The Arts Council of England

14 Great Peter Street, London SW1P 3NQ
☎0171 333 0100   Fax 0171 973 6590
Chairman *Gerry Robinson*
Secretary General *Peter Hewitt*

The 1998/99 government grant dispensed by the Arts Council stands at approximately £184.6 million. From this fund the Arts Council supports arts organisations, artists, performers and others: grants can also be made for particular productions, exhibitions and projects. Grants available to individuals are detailed in the free Arts Council folder: *Development Funds 1998/99*. The total amount set aside for literature in 1998/99 is £1,563,888.

Drama Director *Anna Stapleton* New writing is supported through *Theatre Writing Allocations* (contact the Drama Department for more details).

Literature Director *Gary McKeone* The Literature Department has defined support for writers, education, access to literature including the touring of authors and literary exhibitions, cultural diversity, and an international view of writing including more translation into English among its top priorities. Professor Andrew Motion is chairman of the Literature Advisory Panel. This year the Arts Council will be giving at least 15 grants of £7,000 each to individual writers. Applicants must have at least one published book. Details available from the Literature Department.

The Arts Council/ An Chomhairle Ealaíon

70 Merrion Square, Dublin 2
☎00 353 1 6180200   Fax 00 353 1 6761302
Literature Officer *Sinead MacAodha*

The Irish Arts Council has programmes under six headings to assist in the area of literature and the book world: a) Writers; b) Literary Organisations; c) Publishers; d) Literary Magazines; e) Participation Programmes; f) Literary Events and Festivals. It also gives a number of annual bursaries (see **Arts Council Literature Bursaries, Ireland**) and organises the **Dublin International Writers' Festival**.

The Arts Council of Northern Ireland

MacNeice House, 77 Malone Road, Belfast BT9 6AQ
☎01232 385200   Fax 01232 661715
Literature Officer *Ciaran Carson*

Funds book production by established publishers, programmes of readings, literary festivals, writers-in-residence schemes and literary magazines and periodicals. Occasional schools programmes and anthologies of children's writing are produced. Annual awards and bursaries for writers are available. Holds information also on various groups associated with local arts, workshops and courses.

Scottish Arts Council

12 Manor Place, Edinburgh EH3 7DD
☎0131 226 6051   Fax 0131 225 9833
Literature Director *Jenny Brown*
Literature Officer *Shonagh Irvine*
Literature Secretary *Catherine Allan*

The Council's work for Scottish-based writers who have a track record of publication includes: bursaries (considered twice yearly); travel and research grants (considered three times yearly); writing fellowships (posts usually advertised) and an international writing fellowship (organised reciprocally with the Canada Council). Also publishes lists of Scottish writers' groups, workshops, circles, awards and literary agents.

The Arts Council of Wales

Museum Place, Cardiff CF1 3NX
☎01222 394711   Fax 01222 221447
Senior Literature Officer *Tony Bianchi*
Senior Officer: Dance and Drama *Anna Holmes*

Funds literary magazines and book production; *Writers on Tour* and bursary schemes; **Welsh Academy, Welsh Books Council, Hay-on-Wye Literature Festival** and **Ty Newydd Writers' Centre** at Cricieth; also children's literature, annual awards and translation projects. The Council aims to develop theatrical experience among Wales-based writers through a variety of schemes – in particular, by funding writers on year-long attachments.

English Regional Arts Boards

5 City Road, Winchester, Hampshire
SO23 8SD
☎01962 851063   Fax 01962 842033
E-mail: info.erab@artsfb.org.uk
Website: http://www.arts.org.uk
Chief Executive *Christopher Gordon*
Assistant *Carolyn Nixson*

English Regional Arts Boards is the representative body for the 10 Regional Arts Boards (RABs) in England. Its Winchester secretariat provides project management, services and information for the members, and acts on their behalf in appropriate circumstances. Scotland, Northern Ireland and Wales have their own Arts Councils. The three Welsh Regional Arts Associations are now absorbed into the Welsh Arts Council. RABs are support and development agencies for the arts in the regions. Policies are developed in response to regional demand, and to assist new initiatives in areas of perceived need; they may vary from region to region.

DIRECT GRANTS FOR WRITERS

Most RABs designate part of their budgets for allocation direct to writers, but often it is a minor proportion which new or aspiring playwrights stand little chance of receiving. Money is more readily available for professional writers, although allocations are now often made for appearances in schools, community settings, theatre workshops, etc rather than to support the writer at his work, because of the emphasis placed on community access to the arts. New writing is also encouraged through the funding of small presses and grants to theatre companies for play commissions. Write for details of the schemes available from individual Boards or access the Regional Arts Pages on the Website.

Cleveland Arts

Ground Floor, Gurney House, Gurney Street, Middlesbrough, Cleveland TS1 1JL
☎01642 262424   Fax 01642 262429
Contact *Literature Development Officer*

Not one of the Regional Arts Boards, Cleveland Arts is an independent arts development agency working in the county of Cleveland. The company works in partnership with local authorities, public agencies, the business sector, schools, colleges, individuals and organisations to coordinate, promote and develop the arts – crafts, film, video, photography, music, drama, dance, literature, public arts, disability, Black arts, community arts. The Literature Development Officer promotes writing classes, poetry readings and cabarets, issues a free newsletter and assists publishers and writers.

East Midlands Arts

Mountfields House, Epinal Way, Loughborough, Leicestershire LE11 0QE
☎01509 218292   Fax 01509 262214
Literature Officer *Sue Stewart*
Drama Officer *Helen Flach*

Covers Leicestershire, Rutland, Nottinghamshire, Derbyshire (excluding the High Peak district) and Northamptonshire. A comprehensive information service for regional writers includes an extensive *Writers' Information Pack*, with details of local groups, workshops, residential writing retreats, publishers and publishing information, regional magazines which offer a market for work, advice on approaching the media, on unions, courses and grants. A directory of writers is available to aid people using the *Artists At Your Service* scheme and to establish *Writers' Attachments*. Writers' bursaries are granted for work on a specific project – all forms of writing are eligible except local history and biography. Writing for the theatre can come under the aegis of both Literature and Drama. A list of writers' groups is available, plus *Foreword*, the literature newsletter.

Eastern Arts Board

Cherry Hinton Hall, Cambridge CB1 4DW
☎01223 215355   Fax 01223 248075
Literature Officer *Emma Drew*
Drama Officer *Alan Orme*
Cinema & Broadcast Media Officer *Martin Ayres, Caroline Norbury*

Covers Bedfordshire, Cambridgeshire, Essex, Hertfordshire, Norfolk, Suffolk and Lincolnshire. Policy emphasises quality and access. Support is given to publishers and literature promoters based in the EAB region, also to projects which develop audiences for literature performances and publishing, including electronic media. Bursaries offered annually to individual published writers. Lists of literary groups, workshops, local writing courses and writers working in the educational sector supplied. Also provides advice on applying for National Lottery funds.

London Arts Board

Elme House, 3rd Floor, 133 Long Acre, London WC2E 9AF
☎0171 240 1313/Help Line: 0171 240 4578
Fax 0171 240 4580
Principal Literature Officer *John Hampson*
Principal Drama Officer *Sue Timothy*

The London Arts Board is the Regional Arts

Board for the Capital, covering the 32 boroughs and the City of London. Potential applicants for support for literature and other arts projects should contact the Board for information.

North West Arts Board

Manchester House, 22 Bridge Street,
Manchester M3 3AB
☎0161 834 6644   Fax 0161 834 6969
E-mail: nwarts-info@mcrl.poptel.org.uk

Media Officer – Literature Bronwen Williams
Performing Arts Officer – Drama Ian
  Tabbron

NWAB covers Cheshire, Greater Manchester, Merseyside, Lancashire and the High Peak district of Derbyshire. Offers financial assistance to a great variety of organisations and individuals through a number of schemes, including Writers' Bursaries, Residencies and Placements and the Live Writing scheme. NWAB publishes a directory of local writers groups, a directory of writers and a range of information covering topics such as performance and publishing. For further details contact the Literature Department.

Northern Arts Board

9–10 Osborne Terrace, Jesmond, Newcastle upon Tyne NE2 1NZ
☎0191 281 6334   Fax 0191 281 3276
E-mail: nab@norab.demon.co.uk
Website: http://www.poptel/org.uk/arts/

Head of Published and Broadcast Arts
  Janice Campbell

Covers Cumbria, Durham, Northumberland, Teesside and Tyne and Wear, and was the first regional arts association in the country to be set up by local authorities. It supports both organisations and writers and aims to stimulate public interest in artistic events. Offers Writers Awards for published writers to release them from work or other commitments for short periods of time to enable them to concentrate on specific literary projects. It also has a film/TV script development fund operated through the Northern Production Fund. A separate scheme for playwrights is operated by the Northern Playwrights Society. Northern Arts makes drama awards to producers only. Also funds writers' residencies, and has a fund for publications. Contact list of regional groups and workshops available.

South East Arts

10 Mount Ephraim, Tunbridge Wells, Kent
TN4 8AS
☎01892 515210   Fax 01892 549383

Literature Officer Anne Downes

Drama Officer Linda Lewis

Covers Kent, Surrey, East and West Sussex (excluding the London boroughs). The literature programme aims to raise the profile of contemporary literature across the region, to support new and established writers and encourages creative reading schemes. Priorities include live literature schemes, writers' residencies, and bursaries for writers living in the region. A regular newsletter is available.

South West Arts

Bradninch Place, Gandy Street, Exeter, Devon
EX4 3LS
☎01392 218188   Fax 01392 413554
E-mail: swarts@mail.zynet.co.uk

Director of Media & Published Arts
  David Drake
Director of Performing Arts Nick Capaldi
Media & Published Arts Administrator
  Sara Williams

Covers the county formerly known as Avon, Cornwall, Devon, Dorset (excluding Bournemouth, Christchurch and Poole), Gloucestershire and Somerset. 'The central theme running through the Board's aims are promoting quality and developing audiences for new work.' The literature policy aims to promote a healthy environment for writers of all kinds and to encourage a high standard of new writing. There is direct investment in small presses, publishers and community groups. Literary festivals, societies and arts centres are encouraged. The theatre department aims to support the development of theatre writing by funding the development of literary management programmes of dramaturgy and seasons of new plays. List of regional groups and workshops available from the Information Service.

Southern Arts

13 St Clement Street, Winchester, Hampshire
SO23 9DQ
☎01962 855099   Fax 01962 861186

Literature Officer Keiren Phelan
Film, Video & Broadcasting Officer Jane
  Gerson
Theatre Officer Nick Young

Covers Berkshire, Buckinghamshire, Hampshire, the Isle of Wight, Oxfordshire, Wiltshire and South East Dorset. The Literature Department funds fiction and poetry readings, festivals, magazines, bursaries, a literature prize, publications, residencies and a scheme which subsidises writers working in education and the community.

West Midlands Arts

82 Granville Street, Birmingham B1 2LH
☎0121 631 3121   Fax 0121 643 7239
Literature Officer *Adrian Johnson*

There are special criteria across the art forms, so contact the Information Office for details of *New Work & Commissioning* and other schemes as well as for the *Reading (Correspondence Mss Advice) Service*. There are contact lists of writers, storytellers, writing groups etc. WMA supports the regional publication, *Raw Edge Magazine*: contact PO Box 4867, Birmingham B3 3HD.

Yorkshire & Humberside Arts

21 Bond Street, Dewsbury, West Yorkshire WF13 1AY
☎01924 455555   Fax 01924 466522
E-mail: yharts-info@geo2.poptel.org.uk
Literature Officer *Steve Dearden*
Drama Officer *Shea Connolly*
Administrator *Jill Leahy*

'Libraries, publishing houses, local authorities and the education service all make major contributions to the support of literature. Recognising the resources these agencies command, Yorkshire & Humberside Arts actively seeks ways of acting in partnership with them, whilst at the same time retaining its particular responsibility for the living writer and the promotion of activities currently outside the scope of these agencies.' Funding goes to **Yorkshire Art Circus** (community publishing); poetry publishers **Arc Publications** and **Smith/ Doorstop**; *Live Writing*, a scheme which subsidises projects involving professional writers at all levels as well as writing and community groups; and awards for local independent publishers. Also offers support for literature in performance and for the **Ilkley Literature Festival**, The Word Hoard and *the text* magazine. It has a bursary scheme for writers; holds a list of workshops and writers' groups throughout the region. *Publishes* an on-line directory and a newsletter, *Write Angles*, bi-monthly. Contact the Literature Officer.

Writers' Courses, Circles and Workshops

Courses

Courses are listed under country and county

ENGLAND

Berkshire

University of Reading
Centre for Continuing Education, London Road, Reading, Berkshire RG1 5AQ
☎0118 9318347

Creative writing courses usually include *Life into Fiction; Poetry Workshop; Getting Started; Writers Helping Writers* (with **Southern Arts'** help, the course includes visits from well-known writers); *Writing Fiction*. There is also a support group for teachers of creative writing, a public lecture by a writer, a reading by students of their work and various Saturday workshops. Fees vary depending on the length of course. Concessions available.

Buckinghamshire

Missenden Abbey
Great Missenden, Buckinghamshire
HP16 0BD
☎01494 890296   Fax 01494 863697

Residential courses, weekend workshops and a regular writers circle available. The 1997 programme included *Writing Magazine Articles and Getting Them Published; Writing Comedy for Television and Radio; The Art of Travel Writing; A Creative Approach to Non-Fiction Writing; Writing Poetry; Writing for Children.*

National Film & Television School
Beaconsfield Studios, Station Road, Beaconsfield, Buckinghamshire HP9 1LG
☎01494 671234   Fax 01494 674042
http://www.nftsfilm-tv.ac.uk

Full-time screenwriting course, designed for students who already have experience of writing in other fields, offers an intensive programme of writing combined with an understanding of the practical stages involved in the making of film and television drama. Range of work covers comedy, TV series and serials, short film, adaptation for the screen and narrative. The ability to collaborate successfully is developed through exercises and projects shared with students in other specialisations. 'We encourage the formation of working partnerships which will continue after graduation.

Cambridgeshire

National Extension College
18 Brooklands Avenue, Cambridge CB2 2HN
☎01223 316644   Fax 01223 313586

Runs a number of home-study courses on writing. Courses include: *Essential Editing; Creative Writing; Writing for Money; Copywriting; Essential Desktop Publishing; Essential Design.* Contact the NEC for copy of the *Guide to Courses* which includes details of fees.

PMA Training
PMA House, Free Church Passage, St Ives, Cambridgeshire PE17 4AY
☎01480 300653   Fax 01480 496022
E-mail: admin@pma-group.com
Website: www.pma-group.co.uk

One-/two-/three-day editorial, PR, design and publishing courses held in central London. High-powered, intensive courses run by Fleet Street journalists and magazine editors. Courses include: *News Writing; Journalistic Style; Feature Writing; Investigative Reporting; Basic Writing Skills.* Fees range from £150 to £600 plus VAT. Special rates for freelancers.

Cheshire

The College of Technical Authorship – Distance Learning Course
The College of Technical Authorship, PO Box 7, Cheadle, Cheshire SK8 3BY
☎0161 437 4235   Fax 0161 437 4235

Distance learning courses for City & Guilds Tech 536, Part 1, Technical Communication Techniques, and Part 2, Technical Authorship.

Individual tuition by correspondence and fax; includes some practical work done at home. Contact: John Crossley, DipDistEd, DipM, MCIM, FISTC, LCGI.

Cleveland

University of Leeds

Adult Education Centre, 37 Harrow Road, Middlesbrough, Cleveland TS5 5NT
☎01642 814987
E-mail: r.k.o'rourke.@leeds.ac.uk

Creative writing courses held throughout Cleveland, North and West Yorkshire in the autumn, spring and summer terms. These are held weekly and as non-residential summer schools. Courses carrying undergraduate credit are part-time and offered in a range of subjects at beginners, intermediate and advanced levels. A range of professional development courses for writers and Writing Development Workers which carry postgraduate credit are also offered. These include: *Black Writing Development*; *Creating Community Theatre*; *Writing and Cross Art Forms*. Contact *Rebecca O'Rourke* for details.

Cumbria

Higham Hall College

Bassenthwaite Lake, Cockermouth, Cumbria CA13 9SH
☎017687 76276   Fax 017687 76013

Residential courses. Summer 1998 programme included *Memoir Writing* and *The Art of Lying (Creative Writing)*. Detailed brochure available.

Derbyshire

Real Writers

PO Box 170, Chesterfield, Derbyshire S40 1FE
Correspondence course with personal tuition from working writers. In addition to the support and appraisal service, runs an annual short story competition.

Writers' Summer School, Swanwick

The Hayes, Swanwick, Derbyshire
A week-long summer school of informal talks and discussion groups, forums, panels, quizzes and competitions, and 'a lot of fun'. Open to everyone, from absolute beginners to published authors. Held in August from late Saturday to Friday morning. Cost (1998) £192+, all inclusive. Contact the Secretary, *Brenda Courtie* at The New Vicarage, Parson's Street, Woodford Halse, Daventry, Northants NN11 3RE (☎07050 630949).

Devon

Dartington College of Arts

Totnes, Devon TQ9 6EJ
☎01803 862224   Fax 01803 863569
Website: http://www.dartington.ac.uk

BA(Hons) course in *Performance Writing*: exploratory approach to writing as it relates to performance. The course is part of a performance arts programme which encourages interdisciplinary work with Arts Management, Music, Theatre, Visual Performance. The programme includes a range of elective modules in emerging art forms which are available to all. Contact Subject Director, Performance Writing: *Caroline Bergvall*.

Exeter & Devon Arts Centre

Bradninch Place, Gandy Street, Exeter, Devon EX4 3LS
☎01392 219741   Fax 01392 499929

The centre is closed for rebuilding until early 1999. Literature events and classes/workshops will continue in other venues. For full details, brochures are available from the Centre.

University of Exeter

Exeter, Devon EX4 4QW
☎01392 264580

BA(Hons) in Drama with a third-year and postgraduate option in *Playwriting*. Contact *Professor Peter Thomson*.

Dorset

Bournemouth University

School of Media Arts and Communication, Poole House, Talbot Campus, Fern Barrow, Poole, Dorset BH12 5BB
☎01202 595553   Fax 01202 595530

Three-year, full-time BA(Hons) course in *Scriptwriting for Film and Television*. Contact *Sue Sykes*, Programme Adiminstrator.

Essex

National Council for the Training of Journalists

Latton Bush Centre, Southern Way, Harlow, Essex CM18 7BL
☎01279 430009   Fax 01279 438008
E-mail: NCTJ@itecharlow.co.uk
Website: http://www.itecharlow.co.uk/nctj

For details of journalism courses, both full-time and via distance learning, please write to the NCTJ enclosing a large s.a.e.

Hampshire

Highbury College, Portsmouth

Dovercourt Road, Cosham, Portsmouth,
Hampshire PO6 2SA
☎01705 383131   Fax 01705 378382

Courses include: one-year *Pre-entry Magazine Journalism* (mainly post-graduate intake). Run under the auspices of the Periodicals Training Council. 20-week *Pre-entry Newspaper Journalism* course, run under the auspices of the National Council for Training of Journalists. One-year Post-Graduate Diploma in *Broadcasting Journalism*, run under the auspices of the Broadcast Journalism Training Council. Contact the Secretary, ☎01705 283287.

King Alfred's College of Higher Education

Winchester, Hampshire SO22 4NR
☎01962 841515   Fax 01962 842280

Three-year course on *Drama, Theatre and Television Studies*, including *Writing for Devised Community Theatre* and *Writing for Television Documentary*. Contact *Tim Prentki*.

MA course in *Theatre for Development* – one year, full-time course with major project overseas or in the UK. MA course in *Writing for Children* (subject to validation) available on either a one- or two-year basis. Enquiries: Admissions Officer, ☎01962 827235; Programme enquiries: *Jo Roffey*, ☎01962 827375.

University of Southampton New College

Part-time Adult Continuing Education,
Southampton SO17 1BJ
☎01703 592833   Fax 01703 594060

Creative writing courses, writers' register (full year of support for writers) and writers' workshops. Courses are held in local/regional centres. New for 1998/99: Certificate of Higher Education in *Writing*.

Hertfordshire

West Herts College

Faculty of Visual Communication, Hempstead Road, Watford, Hertfordshire WD1 3EZ
☎01923 812654 (Admissions)

The 24-week postgraduate course in *Writing and Production for the Media* covers two options: *Creative, Business and Technical Writing* and *Radio Writing and Production*. The college also offers a postgraduate diploma in *Publishing* with an option in *Multimedia Publishing*. Contact the Admissions Secretary on the number above.

Humberside

Hull College of Further Education

Queen's Gardens, Hull,
North Humberside HU1 3DG
☎01482 329943   Fax 01482 219079

Offers part-time day/evening writing courses, including *Novel Writing* and *Short Story Writing*, at various centres within the city. Most courses begin each academic term and last for a period of ten weeks. Publishes an anthology of students' work each year entitled, *Embryo*. Contact *Ed Strauss*.

Kent

Kent Enterprises

The Oast House, Plaxtol, Sevenoaks,
Kent TN15 0QG
☎01732 810561   Fax 01732 810632

Wide range of courses (one-/two-/three-day) including screenwriting and other key creative roles in film and television and *How to Write Bestselling Novels*. Courses run throughout the year and concessions are available for members of certain trade organisations. Contact *Joan Harrison*.

University of Kent at Canterbury

Unit for Part-time Study, Keynes College,
Canterbury, Kent CT2 7NP
☎01227 823662

Creative writing courses. Contact *Vicki Inge*.

Lancaster

Chrysalis – The Poet In You

Mashiters, Tatham, Lancaster LA2 8PH
☎015242 62996

Offers courses, workshops and one-to-one sessions. The course consists of Part 1, 'for those who feel drawn to reading more poetry as well as wanting to start to write their own', and Part 2, 'a more advanced course designed for those who are already writing and who want to go more deeply into its process and technique'. Brochure available from the address above.

Edge Hill University College

St Helen's Road, Ormskirk,
Lancashire L39 4QP
☎01695 575171

Offers a two-year, part-time MA in *Writing Studies*. Combines advanced-level writers' workshops with closely related courses in poetics of writing and contemporary writing in English. There is also provision for MPhil- and

PhD-level research in writing and poetics. A full range of creative writing courses is available at undergraduate level, in poetry and fiction writing which may be taken as part of a modular BA.

Lancaster University

Department of Creative Writing, Lonsdale College, Bailrigg, Lancaster LA1 4YN
☎01524 594169

Offers practical graduate and undergraduate courses in writing fiction, poetry and scripts. All based on group workshops – students' work-in-progress is circulated and discussed. Visiting writers have included: Carol Ann Duffy, Kazuo Ishiguro, Bernard MacLaverty, David Pownall. Contact *Linda Anderson* for details.

Leicestershire

Leicester Adult Education College, Writing School

Leicester Adult Education College, Wellington Street, Leicester LE1 6HL
☎0116 2334343   Fax 0116 2334344

Offers a wide range of creative writing and journalism courses throughout the year with occasional masterclasses and talks. Manuscript appraisal by post for short stories and articles. For details contact *Valerie Moore*.

London

Black Coral Training

130 Lea Valley Techno Park, Ashley Road, London N17 9LN
☎0181 880 4860

Courses on offer: *Writing for Short Film Production*, Foundation and Intermediate; *Screenwriting*, Foundation, Intermediate & Advanced; *Working with Writers, Actors and Directors*, Foundation & Intermediate; *Script Reading*, Foundation; *Script Editing*, Foundation & Intermediate; *Writing for TV/Radio Drama*, Foundation & Intermediate. TV Intermediate courses carry 50% concessionary places. Also runs Script City, a three-year screenwriting and development training programme.

The Central School of Speech and Drama

Embassy Theatre, Eton Avenue, London NW3 3HY
☎0171 722 8183   Fax 0171 722 4132

Post-Graduate Diploma in *Advanced Theatre Practice*. One-year, full-time course aimed at providing a grounding in principal areas of professional theatre practice – *Writing, Dramaturgy, Directing, Performance, Puppetry* and *Design*, with an emphasis on collaboration between the various strands. Entrants to the *Writing* strand are required to submit two pieces of writing together with completed application form. Prospectus available. Writing and Dramaturgy Tutor: *Nick Wood*.

The City Literary Institute

Humanities Dept, Stukeley Street, London WC2B 5LJ
☎0171 430 0542

The Writing School offers a wide range of courses from *Radio Drama Writing* and *Writing for Children* to *Autobiographical Writing* and *Writing Short Stories*. The Department offers information and advice during term time.

City University

Northampton Square, London EC1V 0HB
☎0171 477 8268

Creative writing classes include: *Writer's Workshop; Wordshop* (poetry); *Writing Comedy; Playwright's Workshop; Writing Freelance Articles for Newspapers; Women Writer's Workshop; Creative Writing; Fiction Short and Long; Feature Journalism; Writing for Children*. Contact: Courses for Adults.

The Drill Hall

16 Chenies Street, London WC1B 7EX
☎0171 631 1353   Fax 0171 631 4468

Holds a number of writing classes and workshops. In 1998, Kate Pullinger held a one-day workshop on writing short stories and playwright Kay Adshead ran a 10-week course designed for 'anybody who wants to write a play within a supportive group atmosphere'.

The London Academy of Playwriting

75 Hillfield Park, London N10 3QU
☎0181 444 5228   Fax 0181 444 5228

Two-year, part-time, post-graduate course in playwriting. Directors: *Tony Dinner* and *Sonja Lyndon*.

London College of Printing

Elephant & Castle, London SE1 6SB
☎0171 514 6562/7667
E-mail: b.daly@lcpdt.linst.ac.uk
Website: http://www.linst.ac.uk/lcp/dali/summer

Courses in journalism. Short courses run by DALI (Developments at the London Institute) at the address above: *Guide to Magazine Writing/*

News Writing/Feature Writing;/Freelance Journalism/Proof Reading/Subbing on the Screen; also *Sub-editing and Law for Journalists.* In the summer of 1998, it launched full-time courses for short periods of 2–10 weeks. For individuals and companies there are 'tailor-made training' services. For further details or advice call 0171 514 6560. Prospectus and information leaflets available.

London School of Journalism
22 Upbrook Mews, London W2 3HG
☎0171 706 3790   Fax 0171 706 3780
Correspondence courses with an individual and personal approach. Students remain with the same tutor throughout their course. Options include: *Short Story Writing; Writing for Children; Poetry; Freelance Journalism; Improve Your English; English for Business; Journalism and Newswriting.* Fees vary but range from £195 for *Enjoying English Literature* to £375 for *Journalism and Newswriting.* Contact the Student Administration Office at the above address.

Middlesex University
School of Communication, Cultural & Media Studies, White Hart Lane, London N17 8HR
☎0181 362 5000   Fax 0181 362 6878
Undergraduate courses (full-time, part-time, associate) for those interested in writing, publishing and the media. Writing & Publishing Studies Set includes: *Editing* and *Marketing* (contact *Juliet Gardiner*); BA(Hons) Writing Programme includes: *Journalism, Scriptwriting* and *Narrative* and *Poetry Workshops* (contact *Susanna Gladwin*).

Roehampton Institute London
Department of Drama: Theatre, Film and Television, Roehampton Lane, London SW15 5PU
☎0181 392 3230   Fax 0181 392 3289
Three-year BA(Hons) programmes in *Drama and Theatre Studies* and *Film and Television Studies* include courses on writing for stage and screen. Contact *Jeremy Ridgman.*

Thames Valley University
St Mary's Road, London W5 5RF
☎0181 579 5000
Offers a course in *Scriptwriting for Television, Stage and Radio.* Aims to provide the fundamental principles of the craft of script writing.

University of Westminster
Harrow Campus, Watford Road, Harrow, Middlesex HA1 3TP
☎0171 911 5903
The 1997 Summer School courses included

Scriptwriting for Film and Television and *Broadcast Journalism.*

Greater Manchester
University of Manchester
Department of English and American Studies, Arts Building, Oxford Road, Manchester M13 9PL
☎0161 275 3054   Fax 0161 275 3054
E-mail: alex.sherwood@man.ac.uk
Offers a one-year MA in *Novel Writing.* Contact *Alex Sherwood.*

University of Salford
Admissions Office, Departmenmt of Media and Performance, Adelphi, Peru Street, Salford, Greater Manchester M3 6EQ
☎0161 295 6027
MA in *Television and Radio Scriptwriting.* Two-year, part-time course taught by professional writers and producers. Also offers a number of Masterclasses with leading figures in the radio and television industry.

Password Training Ltd
23 New Mount Street, Manchester M4 4DE
☎0161 953 4071   Fax 0161 953 4001
Password Training provides training for publishers, writers' groups and individual writers in Internet publishing, planning, production, design, marketing, costing and distribution. Clients have included the Federation of Worker Writers and Community Publishers, The Arts Council, Regional Arts Boards, Yorkshire Art Circus and Corridor Community Press. For further details, contact *Claire Turner.*

The Writers Bureau
Sevendale House, 7 Dale Street, Manchester M1 1JB
☎0161 228 2362   Fax 0161 228 3533
Comprehensive home-study writing course with personal tuition service from professional writers (fee £249). Fiction, non-fiction, articles, short stories, novels, TV, radio and drama all covered in detail. Trial period, guarantee and no time limits. ODLQC accredited. Quote Ref. EH99. Free enquiry line: 0800 856 2008

The Writers Bureau College of Journalism
Address/☎ as The Writers Bureau above
Home-study course covering all aspects of journalism. Real-life assignments assessed by qualified tutors with the emphasis on getting into print and enjoying the financial rewards.

Comprises 28 modules and three handbooks with special introductory offers. Ref: EHJ99. Free enquiry line: 0800 298 7008.

The Writers College
Address/☎ as The Writers Bureau above
The Art of Writing Poetry Course from The Writers Bureau sister college. A home-study course with a more 'recreational' emphasis. The 60,000-word course has 17 modules and lets you complete six written assignments for tutorial evaluation. Fees: £99. Quote Ref. EHP99. Free enquiry line: 0800 856 2008.

Merseyside
University of Liverpool
Centre for Continuing Education,
19 Abercromby Square, Liverpool L69 7ZG
☎0151 794 6900 (24 hrs) Fax 0151 794 2544

Courses ahve included: *Introduction to Creative Writing; The Short Story and the Novel; Poetry Workshops; Biography and Autobiography; Science Fiction and Fantasy; Women's Writing; Writing for Children; Travel Writing; Introduction to Journalism; The Art and Craft of Songwriting; Scripting for Radio; Scripting for Theatre; Scripting for Comedy; Scripting for Film and Television; Scriptwriting for Women.* Most courses are run in the evening over 10 or 20 weeks and you may, if wished, work towards a university qualification in Creative Writing. Weekend and summer residential courses are possible. No pre-entry qualifications required. Fees vary with concessions for the unwaged and those in receipt of benefit. For further information and copy of current prospectus, phone or write to Keith Birch, Head of Creative Arts (address as above).

Norfolk
University of East Anglia
School of English & American Studies,
Norwich, Norfolk NR4 7TJ
☎01603 593262

UEA has a history of concern with contemporary literary culture. Among its MA programmes is one in *Creative Writing*, Stream 1: Prose Fiction; Stream 2: Poetry; Stream 3: Script and Screenwriting.

Nottinghamshire
The Nottingham Trent University
Humanities Faculty Office (Post Graduate Studies), Clifton Lane, Nottingham NG11 8NS
☎01115 941 8418 Fax 0115 948 6632
MA in *Writing*. Workshop-based, it focuses on

the development of your own feature-writing, fiction, lifewriting and poetry. Current visiting professors: Michele Roberts and Miranda Seymour. Application forms available from the above address. For more information contact *Helen Muskett* on 0115 941 8418 ext 6335.

Somerset
Bath Spa University College
Newton Park, Bath BA2 9BN
☎01225 875875 Fax 01225 875444
Postgraduate Diploma/MA in *Creative Writing*. Includes poetry, fiction, playwriting and scriptwriting. Visiting writers have included Roy Fisher, Marion Lomax, William Stafford and Fay Weldon. Contact Clare Brandram Jones for details.

Institute of Copywriting
PO Box 1561, Wedmore, Somerset
BS28 4TD
☎01934 713563 Fax 01934 713492
E-mail: institute@dial.pipex.com
Website: http://dspace.dial.pipex.com/
   institute/copy.htm
Comprehensive home-study course covering all aspects of copywriting, including advice on becoming a self-employed copywriter. Each student has a personal tutor who is an experienced copywriter and who provides detailed feedback on the student's assignments. Also a two-day residential course.

University of Bristol
Department for Continuing Education,
8–10 Berkeley Square, Bristol BS8 1HH
☎0117 9287172 Fax 0117 9254975
Courses in Bristol and throughout the surrounding counties (Dorset, Gloucestershire, Somerset, Wiltshire). *Women and Writing*, for women who write or would like to begin to write (poetry, fiction, non-fiction, journals); *Certificate in Creative Writing*. Detailed brochure available.

Staffordshire
Keele University
The Centre for Continuing and Professional Education, Keele University, (Freepost ST1666), Newcastle under Lyme, Staffordshire ST5 5BG
☎01782 583436
Weekend courses on literature and creative writing. The 1998 programme included fiction writing and writing for children. Also runs

study days where major novelists or poets read and discuss their work.

Surrey

Royal Holloway College

University of London, Egham Hill, Egham, Surrey TW20 0EX
☎01784 443922   Fax 01784 431018
Three-year BA course in *Theatre Studies* during which playwriting can be studied as an option in the second or third year. Contact *Dan Rebellato* or *David Wiles*.

University of Surrey

School of Educational Studies, University of Surrey, Guildford, Surrey GU2 5XH
☎01483 259750   Fax 01483 300803
The programme 'Courses For All' includes several *Creative Writing* courses, held at the University, the Guildford Institute and throughout the county. For details contact the Enrolment Secretary or *Dr Brian Crossley FRSA*, Creative Writing Consultant.

Sussex

Chichester Institute of Higher Education

Bishop Otter College, College Lane, Chichester, West Sussex PO19 4PE
☎01243 816000   Fax 01243 816080
Postgraduate Certificate/Diploma MA in *Creative Writing*. Contact *Ms Jan Ainsley*, Head of English Studies for details.

The Earnley Concourse

Earnley, Chichester, West Sussex PO20 7JL
☎01243 670392   Fax 01243 670832
Offers a range of residential and non-residential courses throughout the year. The 1997 programme included *Writing for Publication; You Can Sell What You Write*. Brochure available.

Scriptwriters Tutorials

Wish Hill, Sandy Lane, Mayfield, East Sussex TN20 6UE
☎01435 873914   Fax 0171 720 7047
Offers professional *one-to-one* scriptwriting tuition by working writers in film, television, radio or stage. Beginners, intermediate and advanced courses. Script evaluation service and correspondence courses. Tutors based in London, Oxford and the southern counties.

University of Sussex

Centre for Continuing Education, Education Development Building, Falmer, Brighton, East Sussex BN1 9RG
☎01273 678537   Fax 01273 678848
Postgraduate Diploma in *Dramatic Writing*: the student is treated as a commissioned writer working in theatre, TV, radio or film – one-year, part-time from April to March, Convenor *Richard Crane*. Certificate in *Creative Writing*: short fiction, novel and poetry for imaginative writers – one-year, part-time, Convenor *Richard Crane*. Postgraduate Diploma in *Creative Writing and Personal Development*: for writers working in care services and self exploration, Convenor *Celia Hunt*. Contact for all courses: *Yvonne Barnes*.
  Other accredited courses on campus and at locations in East and West Sussex. Contact: *Lisa Templeton*.

Tyne & Wear

University of Newcastle upon Tyne

Centre for Continuing Education, Newcastle upon Tyne NE1 7RU
☎0191 222 5680
Writing-related courses include: *Writing From the Inside Out; Dramatic Writing for Film, TV and Radio; Writing Workshops*. Contact the Secretary, Adult Education Programme.

Warwickshire

University of Warwick

Open Studies, Continuing Education Department, Coventry, Warwickshire CV4 7AL
☎01203 523831
Creative writing courses held at the university or in regional centres. Subjects include: *Starting to Write; Prose and Poetry Writing; Creative Writing; Writing for Radio; Screenwriting for Beginners*. A one-year certificate in *Creative Writing* is available.

West Midlands

Sandwell College

Smethwick Campus, Crocketts Lane, Smethwick B66 3BU
☎0121 556 6000
Creative writing courses held afternoons/ evenings, from September to July. General courses covering short stories, poetry, autobiography, etc. Also women's writing courses. Contact *Roz Goddard*.

University of Birmingham

School of Continuing Studies, Edgbaston, Birmingham B15 2TT
☎0121 414 5607/7259   Fax 0121 414 5619

Day and weekend classes, including creative writing, writing playscripts for beginners. Courses are held at locations throughout Birmingham, the West Midlands, Hereford & Worcester and Shropshire. Detailed course brochures are available from the above address. Please specify which course you are interested in.

The University also offers an MA course in *Playwriting Studies,* established by David Edgar in 1970. Contact *Brian Crow* at the Department of Drama and Theatre Arts (☎0121 414 5993).

Wiltshire

Marlborough College

Marlborough, Wiltshire SN8 1PA
☎01672 892388/9   Fax 01672 892476

Summer school with literature and creative writing included in its programme. Caters for residential and day students. Brochure available giving full details and prices.

Yorkshire

Hull College

Queen's Gardens, Hull, East Yorkshire HU1 3DG
☎01482 329943   Fax 01482 219079

Offers part-time day/evening writing courses in *Novel Writing* and *Short Story Writing,* at Hull College, Part Street Centre. Courses begin each academic term. An anthology of students' work is published each year. Contact: *Gwynneth Yates.*

The Northern School of Film and Television

Leeds Metropolitan University, 2 Queen Square, Leeds, West Yorkshire LS2 8AF
☎0113 2831900   Fax 0113 2831901

The NSFTV offers a Postgraduate Diploma/MA course in *Fiction Screenwriting.* One to two years, full-time. Currently, six graduates working on *The Bill.* Contact: *Ian Macdonald.*

Open College of the Arts

Houndhill, Worsbrough, Barnsley, South Yorkshire S70 6TU
☎01226 730495   Fax 01226 730838
E-mail: open.arts@ukonline.co.uk
Website: http//www.ukonline.co.uk/openarts/index.htm

The OCA correspondence course, *Starting to Write,* offers help and stimulus, without an emphasis on commercial success, from experienced writers/tutors. Subsequent levels available include specialist poetry, fiction and biographical writing courses. Audio-cassette versions of these courses are available.

Sheffield Hallam University

School of Cultural Studies, Sheffield Hallam University, Collegiate Crescent, Sheffield S10 2BP
☎0114 2254408   Fax 0114 2254403

Offers MA in *Creative Writing* (one-year, full-time/two-year, part-time course).

University College Bretton Hall

School of English and Communication Media, Faculty of Art, University College Bretton Hall, West Bretton, Wakefield, West Yorkshire WF4 4LG
☎01924 830261   Fax 01924 830521

Offers one-year full-time/two-years part-time MA course in *Creative Writing* designed for competent though not necessarily published writers. Contact *Rob Watson* for details.

University College, Scarborough

North Riding College, Filey Road, Scarborough, North Yorkshire YO11 3AZ
☎01723 362392   Fax 01723 362392
Website: http://www.ucscarb.ac.uk

BA Single Honours and Combined Honours Degree in which *Theatre Studies* contains *Writing for Theatre.* Contact *Dr Eric Prince.* University College Scarborough also works closely with the Stephen Joseph Theatre and its artistic director Alan Ayckbourn. The theatre sustains a policy for staging new writers. (See entry under **Theatre Producers.**) The College hosts the annual National Student Drama Festival which includes the International Student Playscript Competition (details from The National Information Centre for Student Drama at UCS; e-mail: nsdf@ucscarb.ac.uk or from *Clive Wolfe* on 0181 883 4586).

University of Leeds

See under *Cleveland*

University of Sheffield

Division of Adult Continuing Education, 196–198 West Street, Sheffield S1 4ET
☎0114 2227000   Fax 0114 2227001

Creative writing courses and workshops.

IRELAND

Dingle Writing Courses Ltd

Ballintlea, Ventry, Co. Kerry Republic of Ireland

☎00 353 66 59052   Fax 00 353 66 59052

An autumn programme of weekend and five-day residential courses for beginners and experienced writers alike. Tutored by professional writers the courses take place in 'an inspirational setting overlooking Inch strand'. The 1998 course offers poetry, fiction, starting to write, writing for television and writing for theatre and film. Tutors include Paul Durcan, Michael Donaghy, Evelyn Conlon, Anne Enright, Pat Boran and Michael Harding. All-inclusive price (1998): £135 (weekend) or £300 (5 days). Brochures and further information available from directors, *Abigail Joffe* or *Nicholas McLachlan* at the address above.

University of Dublin (Trinity College)

Graduates Studies Office, Arts Building, Trinity College, Dublin 2 Republic of Ireland
☎00 353 1 608 1561   Fax 00 353 1 671 2821
E-mail: elang@tcd.ie

Offers a M.Phil. *Creative Writing* course. A one-year, full-time course intended for students who are seriously committed to writing, are practising, or prospective authors. Contact Admissions at the address above.

Queen's University of Belfast

Institute of Continuing Education, Belfast BT7 1NN
☎01232 273323

Courses have included *Creative Writing* and *Journal Writing*.

University of Ulster

Short Course Unit, Room 17C21, Belfast BT37 0QB
☎01232 365131

Creative writing course/workshop, usually held in the autumn and spring terms. Concessions available. Contact the Administrative Officer.

SCOTLAND

University of Aberdeen

Centre for Continuing Education, Regent Building, Regent Walk, Aberdeen AB24 3FX
☎01224 272449   Fax 01224 272478

Creative writing evening class held weekly, taught by published author. Participants may join at any time.

University of Dundee

Institute for Education and Lifelong Learning, Nethergate, Dundee DD1 4HN
☎01382 344128

Various creative writing courses held at the University and elsewhere in Dundee, Perthshire and Angus. Detailed course brochure available.

Edinburgh University

Centre for Continuing Education, 11 Buccleuch Place, Edinburgh EH8 9LW
☎0131 650 4400   Fax 0131 667 6097
E-mail: cce@ed.ac.uk

Several writing-orientated courses and summer schools. Beginners welcome. Intensive two-week course in *Playwriting* is held in July, culminating in a rehearsed reading by professional actors and recorded on video for participants to take away. Free tuition in word-processing and use of computer room. Course brochure available.

University of Glasgow

Department of Adult and Continuing Education, 59 Oakfield Avenue, Glasgow G12 8LW
☎0141 330 4032/4394 (Brochure/Enquiries)

In 1997–98 ran several writers' workshops and courses at all levels; all friendly and informal. Daytime and evening meetings. Tutors are all experienced, published writers in various fields.

University of St Andrews

School of English, The University, St Andrews, Fife KY16 9AL
☎01334 462666   Fax 01334 462655

Offers postgraduate study in *Creative Writing*. Candidates choose two topics from: *Fiction: The Novel; Craft and Technique in Poetry; The Short Story*, and also write their own poetry and/or prose for assessment.

7:84 Summer School

See **7:84 Theatre Company Scotland** under **Theatre Producers**

WALES

Tŷ Newydd Writers' Centre

Llanystumdwy, Cricieth, Gwynedd LL52 0LW
☎01766 522811   Fax 01766 523095

Residential writers' centre set up by the Taliesin Trust with the support of the **Arts Council of Wales** to encourage and promote writing in both English and Welsh. Most courses run from Monday evening to Saturday morning. Each course has two tutors and takes a maximum of 16 participants. The centre offers a wide range of specific courses for writers at all levels of experience. Early booking essential. Fee £275 inclusive. People on low incomes may be eligible for a grant or bursary. Course leaflet available. (Also see **Organisations of Interest to Poets**.)

University of Glamorgan
Treforest, Pontypridd CF37 1DL
☎01443 482551

MA in *Writing* – a two-year part-time Master of Arts degree for writers of fiction and poets. ESTABLISHED 1993. Contact *Professor Tony Curtis* at the School of Humanities and Social Sciences.
    Also, BA in Theatre and Media Drama. Modules include *Scriptwriting: Theatre, Radio, TV and Video*. Contact *Steven Blandford*.

University of Wales, Bangor
Department of English, College Road, Bangor LL57 2DG
☎01248 382102   Fax 01248 382102

Offers undergraduate and postgraduate degrees in creative writing, including writing fiction, writing poetry, writing for the theatre, writing for film and the media. Modules also available in contemporary literature, adaptation, film studies, modern American and British fiction, poetry and drama, children's literature and women's writing, and the opportunity to combine study with other creative and performing arts, languages or film studies. PhD course in *Creative and Critical Writing*. Visiting writers have included Margaret Atwood, Ted Hughes, and Nobel prize winners Derek Walcott and William Golding.

Circles and Workshops

Directory of Writers' Circles
Oldacre, Horderns Park Road, Chapel-en-le-Frith, High Peak SK23 9SY
☎01298 812305
E-mail: jillie@cix.compulink.co.uk
Website: http://www.cix.co.uk/~oldacre

Comprehensive directory of writers' circles, containing contacts and addresses of more than 600 groups and circles meeting throughout the country. Some overseas entries too. Available from *Jill Dick* at the above address. £5 post free.

Alston Hall
Alston Lane, Longridge, Preston, Lancashire PR3 3BP
☎01772 784661   Fax 01772 785835

Holds regular day-long creative writing workshops, also weekend residential courses. Brochure available.

Annual Writers' Conference
'Chinook', Southdown Road, Winchester, Hampshire SO21 2BY
☎01703 712307
Conference Director *Barbara Large*

Having grown over the past 18 years from a creative writing workshop, this event is now the largest writers' conference in the country attracting international authors, playwrights, poets, agents and editors who give workshops, lectures and seminars to help writers harness

their creativity and develop technical skills. The 1999 conference will be held over the weekend of 25–27 June at King Alfred's University College, Winchester.

Carmarthen Writers' Circle
Lower Carfan, Tavern Spite, Whitland, Pembrokeshire SA34 0NP
☎01994 240441

FOUNDED 1989. The Circle meets on the second Monday of every month upstairs at the Queen's Hotel in Carmarthen. Both beginners and experienced writers welcome. Activities include competitions, workshops and 'poet and pints' evenings. For more information, contact *Jenny White* at the address above.

Children's Novel Writers' Folio
See **Short Story Writers' Folio**

Chiltern Writers' Group
Marsh Green House, Bassetsbury Lane, High Wycombe HP11 1QY
☎01494 451654

Invites writers, publishers, editors and agents to speak at its monthly meetings at Wendover Public Library. Regular newsletter and competitions. Annual subscription: £15; concessions: £10. Non-members meeting: £3. Contact *Diana Atkinson* at the above address.

Concordant Poets Folios

87 Brookhouse Road, Farnborough,
Hampshire GU14 0BU

Founded through popular demand ten years ago to encourage and assist poets, while studying techniques and possible marketing outlets. Each poem included is discussed and advised upon from several different viewpoints, with poets gaining valuable knowledge while building (via postal method) a circle of friends with mutual interests. Whether beginner, intermediate or advanced, there is a suitable place in one of the eight folios. For details and enrolment form please send s.a.e. to *Barbara Horsfall*.

The Cotswold Writers' Circle

Dar-es-Salaam, Beeches Park, Hampton Fields, Minchinhampton, Gloucestershire GL6 9BA

The Circle meets fortnightly in Cirencester. Activities include organising and running two competitions, publishing an anthology of Circle work, etc. Contact *Charles Hooker*, Honorary Treasurer, for details of the Circle's activities.

Croftspun

Drakemyre Croft, Cairnorrie, Methlick, Ellon, Aberdeenshire AB41 7JN
☎01651 806252

Publishes a small booklet entitled *The Cottage Guide to Writers' Postal Workshops*, a directory giving the contact names and addresses of postal folios for writers (£2 post free – cheques payable to *Mrs C. M. Gill*).

Destructive Writers

56 Crampton Street, London SE17
☎0181 986 2263

DW is a group of people who write; some already have (relatively) long experience in writing, some have been or are being published, others are just beginning. DW meets twice a month to discuss stories, exchange tips and ideas, useful information, etc.

'Sean Dorman' Manuscript Society

Cherry Tree, Crosemere Road, Cockshutt, Ellesmere, Shropshire SY12 0JP
☎01939 270293

FOUNDED 1957. The Society provides mutual help among writers and aspiring writers in England, Wales and Scotland. By means of circulating manuscript parcels, members receive constructive criticism of their own work and read and comment on the work of others. Each 'Circulator' has up to nine participants and members' contributions may be in any medium: short stories, chapters of a novel, poetry, magazine articles, etc. Members may join two such circulators if they wish. Each circulator has a technical section and a letters section in which friendly communication between members is encouraged, and all are of a general nature apart from one, specialising in mss for the Christian market. Full details and application forms available on receipt of s.a.e. Director: *Mary Driver*. Subscription £6.50 p.a.

Equinoxe Screenwriting Workshops

Association Equinoxe, 4 Square du Roule, 75008 Paris, France
☎00 33 1 5353 4488   Fax 00 33 1 5353 4489

FOUNDED 1993, with Jeanne Moreau as president, to promote screenwriting and to establish a link between European and American film production. In association with Canal+, Sony Pictures Entertainment and Media Programme of the European Union, Equinoxe supports young writers of all nationalities by creating a screenwriting community capable of appealing to an international audience. Open to selected professional screenwriters able to speak either English or French fluently. To date, Equinoxe has helped 95 European and American authors to perfect and promote scripts. 24 of these have been brought to the screen and a further 6 are in production. Contact *Claire Dubert* for further information.

Euroscript

PO Box 81, Shepperton, Middlesex TW19 9ND
☎01932 267522   Fax 01932 267522
Website: www.euroscript.co.uk

Euroscript, a MEDIA project of the EU to advance European scriptwriting, is a distance training project working in EU languages. It develops screenplays, reads, selects and promotes scripts and writers. Also runs workshops and supports writers' groups. Write or access the website for further information.

Gay Authors Workshop

BM Box 5700, London WC1N 3XX
☎0181 520 5223

Established 1978 to encourage and support lesbian/gay writers. Regular meetings and a newsletter. Contact *Kathryn Byrd*. Membership £5; £2 unwaged.

Historical Novel Folio

17 Purbeck Heights, Mount Road, Parkstone, Poole, Dorset BH14 0QP
☎01202 741897

An independent postal workshop – single folio dealing with any period before World War II. Send s.a.e. for details. Contact: *Doris Myall-Harris*.

The International Inkwell

See under **Editorial, Research and Other Services**

London Screenwriters' Workshop

114 Whitfield Street, London W1P 5RW
☎0171 242 2134

Established by writers in 1983 as a forum for contact, information and tuition. LSW helps new and developing writers in the film, TV and video industries. Organises a continuous programme of workshops, events with industry figures, seminars and courses. Free monthly events and magazine newsletter every two months. Contact *Ben Davies*. Membership £30 p.a..

London Writer Circle

15 Lower Park Road, Loughton, Essex IG10 4NB
☎0181 508 6916

FOUNDED 1924. Aims to help and encourage writers of all grades. Monthly evening meetings with well-known speakers on aspects of literature and journalism, and workshops for short story writing, poetry and feature writing. Occasional social events and quarterly magazine. Subscription: £16 (Town); £9 (Country); £6 (Overseas). Contact *Margaret Owen*, Membership Secretary at the above address.

The Mill Writer's Group

Blaenllain, Dihewyd, Lampeter, Ceredigion SA48 7QR
☎01570 471284

FOUNDED in 1997. The weekly meetings are intended for the published and un-published in all genres, as a forum in which ideas are discussed, views shared, encouragement given etc. Work published bi-monthly in *A Word's Worth*, sold in local shops. Contact *Amanda J. Jones*.

Nottingham Writers Contact

U.A.E.C. Centre, 16 Shakespeare Street, Nottingham NG1 4GF
☎01159 288913

A group of professional and amateur writers which meets every third Saturday in the month at the U.A.E.C. Centre, 10.00am–12.30pm. 'If you are visiting the city contact Keith Taylor at the above telephone number.'

NWP (North West Playwrights)

Contact Theatre, Oxford Road, Manchester M15 6JA
☎0161 274 4418   Fax 0161 274 4418

FOUNDED 1982. Award-winning organisation whose aim is to develop and promote new theatre writing. Operates a script-reading service, Commission and Residency Award Scheme, The Lowdown newsletter and the Summer Workshops – an annual showing of six workshopped plays by local writers. Previous participants include Charlotte Keatley, Kevin Fegan, Lavinia Murray and James Stock. Services available only to North West writers.

QueenSpark Books

See entry under **Small Presses**

Scribo

Flat 1, 31 Hamilton Road, Boscombe, Bournemouth, Dorset BH1 4EQ
☎01202 302533

FOUNDED in the early '70s, Scribo circulates folios (published and unpublished work) to its members, who currently number about 40. The only criteria for joining is that you must be actively engaged in writing novels. Forum folios discuss anything of interest to novelists; problems are shared and information exchanged. Manuscript folios offer friendly criticism and advice. Besides 'general' mss folios there are four specialist folios: crime; aga-saga/ saga/romance; Gothic suspense; fantasy/science-fiction. A new folio has been launched for the more literary novelist. 'No pornography.' Contact: *K. Sylvester, P. A. Sylvester*. No s.a.e., no reply.

Short Story Writers' Folio/ Children's Novel Writers' Folio

5 Park Road, Brading, Sandown, Isle of Wight PO36 0HU
☎01983 407697

Postal workshops – members receive constructive criticism of their work and read and offer advice on fellow members' contributions. Send an s.a.e. for further details. Contact: *Mrs Dawn Wortley-Nott*.

Southport Writers' Circle

32 Dover Road, Southport, Merseyside PR8 4TB

Runs a poetry competition (see **Prizes**). Contact *Alison Chisholm*.

Southwest Scriptwriters

149 St Andrew's Road, Montpelier, Bristol
BS6 5EL
☎0117 9445424   Fax 0117 9445413
FOUNDED 1994 to offer encouragement and
advice to those writing for stage, screen, radio
and TV in the region. The group, which
attracts professional writers, enthusiasts and students, meets regularly at the Theatre Royal,
Bristol to read aloud and provide critical feedback on members' work, discuss writing technique and exchange market information.
Catherine Johnson, writer-in-residence at the
Bristol Old Vic, acts as Honorary President and
is able to offer information and advice on
members' writing. Subscription: £5 p.a.
Contact the Secretary, *John Colborn* for details.

Speakeasy – Milton Keynes Writers' Group

46 Wealdstone Place, Springfield, Milton
Keynes MK6 3JG
☎01908 663860
Invites lovers of the written and spoken word
to their monthly meetings on the first Friday of
each month, 7.45pm. Full and varied programme including Local Writers Nights where
work can be read and performed. Contact:
Martin Brocklebank. Also runs an Annual Open
Creative Writing Competition. Send s.a.e. for
entry form to address above.

University of Stirling

Education Policy & Development, Airthrey
Castle, Stirling FK9 4LA
☎01786 467940   Fax 01786 463398
Offers 10-week courses from the beginning of
February, held in Airthrey Castle. *Writers
Workshop*: aspiring writers are invited to join a
lively and friendly group which offers help and
stimulus with many different kinds of writing.
The workshop format means students produce a
fair body of writing and receive feedback and
encouragement. A 10-week course, held on
Thursday evenings. *115 Creative Writing: Absolute
Beginners*: a course designed for those who would
like to write but lack the confidence or experience for a writers' workshop. Held on Monday
evenings. For further information or an application form, contact *Paula Douglas*, Open Studies
Secretary at the address above.

Sussex Playwrights' Club

2 Princes Avenue, Hove, East Sussex BN3 4GD
☎01273 734985
FOUNDED 1935. Aims to encourage the writing
of plays for stage, radio and TV by giving
monthly dramatic readings of members' work
by experienced actors, mainly from local drama
groups. Gives constructive critical suggestions as
to how work might be improved, and suggests
possible marketing. Membership is not confined to writers but to all who are interested in
theatre in all its forms, and all members are
invited to take part in such discussions. Guests
are always welcome at a nominal 50p. Meetings
held at New Venture Theatre, Bedford Place,
Brighton, East Sussex. Subscription: £5 p.a.
Contact the Secretary, *Mrs Constance Cox* for
details.

Ways With Words

See under **Festivals**

Women & Words

73 Stillingfleet Road, Barnes, London
SW13 9AF
☎0181 255 9578   Fax 0181 255 9578
Aims to provide a space where women interested in writing can meet, share ideas, experiences and work in progress in an informal
atmosphere. Holds weekly meetings, Saturday
10am–12pm (£1.50 per session). Membership
(optional) entitles you to a monthly newsletter
and members' directory. Contact *Anne Cotgreave*
for further information.

Workers' Educational Association

National Office: Temple House, 17 Victoria
Park Square, London E2 9PB
☎0181 983 1515   Fax 0181 983 4840
FOUNDED in 1903, the WEA is a voluntary body
with members drawn from all walks of life. It
runs writing courses and workshops throughout
the country and all courses are open to everyone.
Branches in most towns and many villages, with
13 district offices in England and 1 in Scotland.
Contact your district WEA office for courses in
your region. All correspondence should be
addressed to the District Secretary.

Cheshire, Merseyside & West Lancashire:
7/8 Bluecoat Chambers, School Lane,
Liverpool L1 3BX (☎0151 709 8023)

Eastern: Botolph House, 17 Botolph Lane,
Cambridge CB2 3RE (☎01223 350978)

East Midlands: 16 Shakespeare Street,
Nottingham NG1 4GF (☎01159 475162)

London: 4 Luke Street, London EC2A 4NT
(☎0171 388 7261/387 8966)

Northern: 51 Grainger Street, Newcastle upon
Tyne NE1 5JE (☎0191 232 3957)

North Western: 4th Floor, Crawford House, University Precinct Centre, Oxford Road, Manchester M13 9GH (☎0161 273 7652)

South Eastern: 4 Castle Hill, Rochester, Kent ME1 1QQ (☎01634 842140)

South Western: Martin's Gate Annexe, Bretonside, Plymouth, Devon PL4 0AT (☎01752 664989)

Thames & Solent: 6 Brewer Street, Oxford OX1 1QN (☎01865 246270)

Western: 40 Morse Road, Redfield, Bristol BS5 9LB (☎01179 351764)

West Mercia: 78–80 Sherlock Street, Birmingham B5 6LT (☎0121 666 6101)

Yorkshire North: 6 Woodhouse Square, Leeds, W. Yorkshire LS3 1AD (☎01132 453304)

Yorkshire South: Chantry Buildings, 6–20 Corporation Street, Rotherham S60 1NG (☎01709 837001)

Scottish Association: Riddle's Court, 322 Lawnmarket, Edinburgh EH1 2PG (☎0131 226 3456)

Writers in Oxford

Indexed as: Writers in Oxford
41 Kingston Road, Oxford OX2 6RH
☎01865 513844

FOUNDED 1992. Open to published authors, playwrights, poets and journalists. Linked to **The Society of Authors** but organised locally. Arranges a programme of meetings, seminars and social functions. Publishes newsletter, *The Oxford Writer*. Subscription: £15 p.a. Contact the Secretary, *Maggie Black* for details.

The Writers' Workshop

Barlows, Frieth, Buckinghamshire RG9 6PR
☎01442 871004

The Writers' Workshop at Frieth offers classes and workshops in creative writing, plus professional assessments, for three 10-week terms per year, in pleasant countryside near High Wycombe.

Yorkshire Playwrights

3 Trinity Road, Scarborough, North Yorkshire YO11 2TD
☎01723 367449   Fax 01723 367449

FOUNDED 1989 out of an initiative by Jude Kelly and William Weston of the **West Yorkshire Playhouse**. A group of professional writers of plays for stage, TV and radio whose aims are to encourage the writing and performance of new plays in Yorkshire. Open to any writers living in Yorkshire who are members, preferably, of the **The Writers' Guild/Theatre Writers Union**, or **The Society of Authors**. Contact the Administrator, *Ian Watson* for an information sheet.

Editorial, Research and Other Services

Lesley & Roy Adkins
Longstone Lodge, Aller, Langport, Somerset
TA10 0QT
☎01458 250075   Fax 01458 250858

Contact *Lesley Adkins, Roy Adkins*

Offers indexing, research, copy-editing, manuscript criticism/advice, contract writing for publishers, rewriting, book reviews and feature writing. *Special interests* archaeology (worldwide), history and heritage. See also **Lesley & Roy Adkins Picture Library**.

Anagram Editorial Service
26 Wherwell Road, Guildford, Surrey GU2 5JR
☎01483 533497   Fax 01483 306848
E-mail: mjb@'anagram.u-net.com

Contact *Martyn Bramwell*

Full range of editorial services available from project development through commissioning, editing and proof-reading to production of finished books. Specialises in earth sciences, natural history, environment, general science and technology. Also author of over 30 non-fiction titles for young readers. Clients include UK, German, American and Middle East publishers, United Nations agencies (UNEP, FAO) and international conservation organisations.

Arioma
1 St Albans, Clarach Road, Borth, Ceredigion
SY24 5LN
☎01970 871296   Fax 01970 871733

Contact *Moira Smith*

FOUNDED 1987. Staffed by ex-London journalists, who work mainly with authors wanting to self-publish. Editing, indexing, ghost writing, cover design, plus initial help with marketing and publicity. Sample chapter and synopsis required. All types of book welcome, but work must be of a 'sufficiently high standard'. Rates on application. Please send s.a.e. with all submissions.

Astron Ltd
77 New Bond Street, London W1Y 9DB
☎0171 495 2230   Fax 0171 495 4472

Managing Director *Colin Ancliffe*

In addition to a long-standing database of permanent job-seekers within publishing, Astron has a freelance register with details of a large number of experienced people available to undertake all types of freelance assignments within the publishing field.

Authors' Research Services
32 Oak Village, London NW5 4QN
☎0171 284 4316

Contact *Richard Wright*

Research and document supply service, particularly to authors, academics and others without easy access to London libraries and sources of information. Also indexing of books and journals. Rates negotiable.

Black Ace Production
PO Box 6557, Forfar DD8 2YS
☎01307 465096   Fax 01307 465494

Directors *Hunter Steele, Boo Wood*

FOUNDED 1990. Book production and text processing, including text capture (or scanning), editing, proofing to camera-ready/film, printing and binding, jacket artwork and design. Delivery of finished books; can sometimes help with distribution.

Brooks Krikler Research
455 Finchley Road, London NW3 6HN
☎0171 431 9886   Fax 0171 431 9887

Contact *Emma Krikler*

Provides a full picture-research service to all those involved in publishing and the media. Educational and non-educational books, magazines, advertising, CD-ROM & multimedia, brochures, video and computer games manufacturers and designers. The service includes finding, editing and providing images, negotiating all reproduction charges inclusive of full copyright clearance. Has special arrangements with photographic libraries worldwide and a variety of photographers can undertake commissioned work. An on-line service is available with all requests.

D. Buckmaster
Wayfarer House, 51 Chatsworth Road,
Torquay, Devon TQ1 3BJ
☎01803 294663

Contact *Mrs D. Buckmaster*

General editing of mss, specialising in traditional themes in religious, metaphysical and esoteric subjects. Also success and inspirational books or articles.

Graham Burn Productions

9–13 Soulbury Road, Linslade, Leighton Buzzard, Bedfordshire LU7 7RL
☎01525 377963/376390   Fax 01525 382498

Offers complete production services to writers wishing to publish their own material, and pre-press and print services to other publishers.

CIRCA Research and Reference Information Ltd

13–17 Sturton Street, Cambridge CB1 2SN
☎01223 568017   Fax 01223 354643
Approx. turnover £500,000

ESTABLISHED 1989. An editorial co-operative specialising in researching, writing and editing of reference works on international politics and economics, including *Cassell Dictionary of Modern Britain; Cassell Dictionary of Modern Politics; Dorling Kindersley World Reference Atlas; Keesing's UK Record; People in Power.* All work is fee-based.

Combrógos Literary Agency

See entry under **UK Agents**.

Creative Communications

11 Belhaven Terrace, Glasgow G12 0TG
☎0141 334 9577   Fax 0141 334 9577
Contact *Ronnie Scott*

Creative Comunications delivers professional corporate communication services to leading Scottish organisations. It also provides effective writing (including copywriting and script writing), editing and newspaper design, and consults on all aspects of communications. Recent activities include developing copy for World Wide Web and interactive CD-ROM projects.

The Critical Eye

c/o Breese Books Ltd, 164 Kensington Park Road, London W11 2ER

ESTABLISHED 1994. The Critical Eye provides an honest and direct assessment, from a publisher's point of view, of the first 50 pages of manuscripts submitted by writers. This is probably the only critical evaluation service run by an established publisher. The cost of a Critical Eye report and evaluation is currently £125. A detailed information pack is available on request.

E. Glyn Davies

Cartref, 21 Claremont Avenue, Bishopston, Bristol BS7 8JD
☎0117 9756793   Fax 0117 9246248
Contact *E. Glyn Davies*

Editorial services for writers whose first language is not English: rewriting, revision, proof-reading, translation into English. Quotations on request.

Deeson Editorial Services

Ewell House, Faversham, Kent ME13 8UP
☎01795 535468   Fax 01795 535469
Contact *Dr Tony Deeson, Dominic Deeson*

ESTABLISHED 1959. A comprehensive research/writing/editing service for books, magazines, newspapers, articles, annual reports, submissions, presentations. Design and production facilities. Specialists in scientific, technical, industrial and business-to-business subjects including company histories.

Flair for Words

5 Delavall Walk, Eastbourne, East Sussex BN23 6ER
☎01323 640646
Directors *Cass and Janie Jackson*

ESTABLISHED 1988. Offers wide range of services to writers, whether beginners or professional, through the Flair Network. Offers assessment, editing and advisory service. Publishes bi-monthly newsletter, handbooks on all aspects of writing, and audio tapes.

Kathleen M. Gill

11 Cranmore Close, Aldershot, Hampshire GU11 3BH
☎01252 325881
Contacts *Kathie Gill*

ESTABLISHED over 19 years (previously F. G. & K. M. Gill). Proof-reading, copy-editing and indexing services. Fiction and non-fiction (all subjects). Clients include UK, North American and continental publishers. Rates on application.

Indexing Specialists

202 Church Road, Hove, East Sussex BN3 2DJ
☎01273 738299   Fax 01273 323309
Contact *Richard Raper*
Website: http://www.pavilion.co.uk/indspec

ESTABLISHED over 30 years. Indexes in a wide

range of subjects for all manner of books, journals and other publications. Also offers copy-editing and proof-reading services. Quotations available on request.

Ink Inc. Ltd
1 Angelsea Road, Kingston on Thames, Surrey KT1 2EW
☎0181 549 3174
E-mail: richpark1@hotmail.com
Managing Director *Richard Parkes*
Editorial Head *Barbara Leedham*

Publishing consultants. Clients range from very small dtp operations to large plcs. Advises on every aspect of publishing, including production, design, editorial, marketing, distribution and finance. Also takes on editorial, design, production and project management work.

The International Inkwell, a writers' retreat
Cafe du Livre, Rue de la Mairie, 11170 Montolieu, Aude, France
☎00 33 468248117   Fax 00 33 468248321
E-mail: 11320.616@compuserve.com
London address: 96 Edith Grove, Chelsea, London SW10
☎01304 369799)
Contact *Lucia Stuart*

Set in the French medieval village of Montolieu, which boasts 14 bookshops to a population of 800, The International Inkwell rents rooms for writers. Open from June to September, groups are welcome for writing courses, reading weeks or forums. For further details contact Lucia Stuart at the address in France from May to September or the London address from November to April.

J G Editorial
54 Mount Street, Lincoln LN1 3JG
☎01522 821246   Fax 01522 821247
E-mail: jennigoss@compuserve.com
Contact *Jenni Goss*

ESTABLISHED 1988. Freelance editors with 21 years' experience offering full editorial service to authors and typesetters. Independent critique service for fiction, general non-fiction and academic/business (no poetry) – includes structure and presentation; rewriting/ghosting; word processing/presentation/keying; project management; editorial reports; copy and disk editing (IBM); proofreading. Quotations on request.

J. P. Lethbridge
245 St Margaret's Road, Ward End, Birmingham B8 2DY
☎0121 783 0548
Contact *J. P. Lethbridge*

Experienced historical researcher. Searching through old newspapers and checking birth, marriage and death certificates a speciality. Special interest in crime. Rates negotiable.

The Literary Consultancy
PO Box 12939, London N8 9WA
☎0181 372 3922/374 2812
Fax 0181 372 3922/374 2812
Contact *Rebecca Swift, Hannah Griffiths*

Founded in 1996 by former publishers to offer an editorial service and advice for aspiring writers. 'Excellent connections with publishers and agents.' Will provide an appraisal of fiction, poetry and most categories of non-fiction. Charges range from £40 for a short story, £65 for three chapters and synopsis, to £300 for a full mss of 300 pages.

LJC Permission Services
8 Burstow House, Skipton Way, Horley, Surrey RG6 8LP
☎07000 782332   Fax 07000 782331
Contacts *Robert Young, Louisa Clements*

A copyright clearing agency used widely by publishers and authors who wish to reproduce copyright material. The agency undertakes to obtain permission for articles, photographs, artwork and music to be reproduced in another publication or on cassettes. Part of the service includes preparing acknowledgement copy if requested and negotiating the reproduction fee with the copyright holder. Full breakdown of costs on larger projects. Large database of copyright sources. Multimedia permissions also undertaken. Fixed fee per permission.

Duncan McAra
28 Beresford Gardens, Edinburgh EH5 3ES
☎0131 552 1558   Fax 0131 552 1558
Contact *Duncan McAra*

Consultancy on all aspects of general trade publishing: editing, rewriting, copy-editing, proof-reading. *Specialises* in art, architecture, archaeology, biography, military, travel and books of Scottish interest. Also runs a literary agency (see **UK Agents**).

Deborah Manley

57 Plantation Road, Oxford OX2 6JE
☎01865 310284

Contact *Deborah Manley*

Offers (to publishers) editorial reports, copy-editing, writing, rewriting, research, anthologising, indexing, proof-reading and caption copy. Specialises mainly in children's, reference and travel. NUJ rates.

Minett Media

6 Middle Watch, Swavesey, Cambridge
CB4 5RN
☎01954 230250   Fax 01954 232019
E-mail: info@minettmedia.co.uk &
100673.655@compuserve.com
Website: http://www.minettmedia.co.uk

Contact *Dr Steve Minett, Gunnel Minett*

Minett Media specialises in the pro-active and strategic management of trade press activities. Produces press releases and feature articles for multi-national business-to-business companies, offering a comprehensive editorial service (including site visits anywhere in Europe, writing draft text, securing approval and best effort at publication in the international trade press). Also offers media databases for internet users and complete-package production of business-to-business, multi-language customer magazines (including translation, design, artwork, repro, printing and distribution) and enquiry database management.

Murder Files

Marienau, Brimley Road, Bovey Tracey,
Devon TQ13 9DH
☎01626 833487   Fax 01626 835797

Contact *Paul Williams*

Crime writer and researcher specialising in UK murders. Can provide information on thousands of well-known and less well-known cases dating from 1400. Copies of press cuttings relating to murder available for cases from 1920 onwards. Research also undertaken for general enquirers, writers, TV, radio, video, etc. Rates on application.

New Authors Showcase

Rivendell, Kingsgate Close, Torquay, Devon
TW2 8QA
☎01803 326617   Fax 01803 326617
E-mail: newauthors@compuserve.com
Website: http://ourworld.compuserve.com/
  homepages/newauthors

Contact *Barrie E. James*

Formed in August 1997. A modern internet site for new unpublished authors to display their work to publishers. Web pages available for published authors to advertise their work. All literary work considered, including poetry. No reading fee. First approach should be by regular mail including an s.a.e.

Northern Writers Advisory Services (NWAS)

77 Marford Crescent, Sale, Cheshire
M33 4DN
☎0161 969 1573

Contact *Jill Groves*

Offers publishing services such as copy-editing, proof-reading, and typesetting. Does much of its work with societies (mainly local history), self publishers and small presses. NWAS's specialist subject is history, especially local and family history. Also handles biographies. Rates on application, but 'very reasonable'.

Ormrod Research Services

Weeping Birch, Burwash, East Sussex
TN19 7HG
☎01435 882541   Fax 01435 882541

Contact *Richard Ormrod*

ESTABLISHED 1982. Comprehensive research service: literary, historical, academic, biographical, commercial. Critical reading with report, editing, indexing, proof-reading, ghosting. Verbal quotations available.

Pages Editorial & Publishing Services

Ballencrieff Cottage, Ballencrieff Toll,
Bathgate, West Lothian EH48 4LD
☎01506 632728   Fax 01506 635444
E-mail: pages@clara.net

Contact *Susan Coon*

Contract-publishing service for magazines and newsletters, including journalism, editing, advertising, production and mailing. Also editorial advice, word processing and short-run publishing service for authors and publishers.

Roger Palmer Limited, Media Contracts and Copyright

23c Tavistock Place, London WC1H 9SE
☎0171 383 5454   Fax 0171 383 3234
E-mail: contracts@rogerpalmerltd.co.uk

Contact *Roger Palmer, Stephen Aucutt,
  Angela Elkins*

ESTABLISHED 1993. Drafts, advises on and negotiates all media contracts (on a regular or *ad hoc* basis) for publishers, literary and merchandising agents, authors, packagers, charities and others. Manages and operates clients' complete contracts functions, undertakes contractual audits, devises contracts and permissions systems, advises on copyright and related issues and provides training and seminars on an individual or group basis. Growing private client list, with special rates for members of **The Society of Authors**. Roger Palmer (Managing Director) was for many years Contracts and Intellectual Property Director of the Hodder & Stoughton Group; Stephen Aucutt (Director) was previously Contracts Manager for Reed Children's Books, and Angela Elkins has considerable experience in publishing, music and broadcasting.

Patent Research
Dachsteinstr. 12a, D–81825 Munich
Germany
☎00 49 89 4307833
Contact *Gerhard Everwyn*

All world, historical patents for researchers, authors, archives, museums and publishers. Rates on application.

Penman Literary Service
185 Daws Heath Road, Benfleet, Essex
SS7 2TF
☎01702 557431
Contact *Mark Sorrell*

ESTABLISHED 1950. Advisory, editorial and typing service for authors. Rewriting, ghosting, proof-reading; critical assessment of mss.

Perfect English
11 Hill Square, Upper Cam, Dursley,
Gloucestershire GL11 5NJ
☎01453 547320   Fax 01453 547266
E-mail: alexanderassoc@compuserve.com
Contact *James Alexander*

'Meticulous reading and editing to remove errors of spelling, grammar, punctuation, word choice and meaning. Mss returned fully checked and as perfect as possible within the structure and style of the original material.' Rates on application.

Readers Reports International
See **The Authors' Representative Co.** under **UK Agents**.

Reading & Righting (Robert Lambolle Services)
618B Finchley Road, London NW11 7RR
☎0181 455 4564   Fax 0181 455 4564
Contact *Robert Lambolle*

Reader/literary editor, with agency, publishing and theatre experience. Offers detailed manuscript evaluation, analysis of prospects and next-step guidelines. Fiction, non-fiction, drama and screenplays. Special interests include cinema, the performing arts, popular culture, psychotherapy and current affairs. Also editorial services, creative writing workshops and lectures. Services do not include representing writers in an agent's capacity. Send s.a.e. for detailed leaflet on procedure and terms.

Scriptmate
See **Book-in-Hand Ltd** under **Small Presses**

Strand Editorial Services
16 Mitchley View, South Croydon, Surrey
CR2 9HQ
☎0181 657 1247   Fax 0181 657 1247
Contact *Derek Bradley*

All stages of editorial production of house journals, magazines, newsletters, publicity material, etc. Short-term, long-term and emergency projects. Sub-editing, proof-reading, and book reviews (education, training and business). Reasonable rates (negotiable).

Teral Research Services
45 Forest View Road, Moordown,
Bournemouth, Dorset BH9 3BH
☎01202 516834   Fax 01202 516834
Contact *Terry C. Treadwell*

All aspects of research undertaken but specialises in all military, aviation, naval and defence subjects, both past and present. Extensive book and photographic library, including one of the best collections of World War One aviation photographs. Terms by arrangement.

WORDSmith
2 The Island, Thames Ditton, Surrey KT7 0SH
☎0181 339 0945   Fax 0181 339 0945
Contact *Michael Russell*

Copy-editing, both on paper and on-screen. Specialises in rewriting and abridging, particularly new writer fiction. Also magazine articles and stories, company literature, user guides, copywriting, film-script editing. Everything from 2000 to 200,000 words. Please phone for details.

The Writers Advice Centre for Children's Books

Palace Wharf, Rainville Road, London
W6 9HN
☎0181 874 7347   Fax 0181 874 7347

Contact *Louise Jordan*

Offers editorial and marketing advice to children's writers – both published and unpublished – by Readers who are all currently connected with children's publishing. Plus personal introductions to publishers/agents where appropriate. Also runs courses and small agenting service.

The Writers' Exchange

14 Yewdale, Clifton Green, Swinton
M27 8GN
☎01706 877480

Contact *Mike Wright, The Secretary*

FOUNDED 1978. Full range of copywriting, ghostwriting and editorial services, including appraisal service for amateur writers preparing to submit material to or having had material rejected by, literary agents and/or publishers. Novels, short stories, film, TV, radio, and stage plays. Send s.a.e. for details.

Press Cuttings Agencies

The Broadcast Monitoring Company

89½ Worship Street, London EC2A 2BE
☎0171 377 1742   Fax 0171 377 6103

Television, radio, national and European press monitoring agency. Cuttings from national and all major European press available seven days a week, with early morning delivery. Also monitoring of all news and current affairs programmes – national, international and satellite. Retrospective research service and free telephone notification. Sponsorship evaluation from all media sources.

Durrants Press Cuttings Ltd

103 Whitecross Street, London EC1Y 8QT
☎0171 588 3671   Fax 0171 374 8171

Wide coverage of all print media sectors; foreign press in association with agencies abroad; current affairs and news programmes from UK broadcast media. High speed, early morning press cuttings from the national press. Overnight delivery via courier to most areas or first-class mail. Well presented, laser printed, A4 cuttings. Monthly reading fee of £70 plus 85p per cutting.

International Press-Cutting Bureau

224–236 Walworth Road, London SE17 1JE
☎0171 708 2113   Fax 0171 701 4489
Contact *Robert Podro*

Covers national, provincial, trade, technical and magazine press. Cuttings are normally sent twice weekly by first-class post and there are no additional service charges or reading fees. Subscriptions for 100 and 250 cuttings are valid for six months. Larger subscriptions expire after one year even if the total number of cuttings subscribed for has not been reached. 100 cuttings (£146, plus VAT); 250 (£330, plus VAT).

Press Express

3rd Floor, 53–56 Great Sutton Street, London EC1V 0DE
☎0171 689 0123   Fax 0171 251 1412
Contact *Charles Stuart-Hunt*

High-speed overnight press cuttings.

The Prominent Information Company

Bear Wharf, 27 Bankside, London SE1 9DP
☎0171 203 3500   Fax 0171 203 0101
Contact *Gary Forrest*

Offers an overnight national press monitoring service with same day, early morning delivery. Also coverage of regional papers and weekly/monthly business/trade magazines. Rates on application.

Romeike & Curtice

Hale House, 290–296 Green Lanes, London N13 5TP
☎0800 289543   Fax 0181 882 6716
Contact *Mary Michael*

Covers national and international dailies and Sundays, provincial papers, consumer magazines, trade and technical journals, national radio/TV logs and teletext services. Back research and advertising checking services are also available.

We Find It (Press Clippings)

103 South Parade, Belfast BT7 2GN
☎01232 646008   Fax 01232 646008
Contact *Avril Forsythe*

Specialises in Northern Ireland press and magazines, both national and provincial. Rates on application.

Bursaries, Fellowships and Grants

Aosdána

An Chomhairle Ealaíon (The Arts Council), 70 Merrion Square, Dublin 2, Republic of Ireland
☎00 353 1 6180200   Fax 00 353 1 6761302
Registrar of Aosdána *Patricia Quinn*

Aosdána is an affiliation of creative artists engaged in literature, music and the visual arts, and consists of not more than 200 artists who have gained a reputation for achievement and distinction. Membership is by competitive sponsored selection and is open to Irish citizens or residents only. Members are eligible to receive an annuity for a five-year term to assist them in pursuing their art full-time.
Award IR£8000 (annuity).

Arts Council Literature Bursaries, Ireland

An Chomhairle Ealaíon (The Arts Council), 70 Merrion Square, Dublin 2, Republic of Ireland
☎00 353 1 6180200   Fax 00 353 1 6761302
Literature Officer *Sinéad MacAodha*

Bursaries in literature awarded to creative writers of fiction, poetry and drama in Irish and English to enable concentration on, or completion of, specific projects. A limited number of bursaries may be given to non-fiction projects. Open to Irish citizens or residents only. Final entry date 3rd April.
Award IR£3,000–8,000 (£6,000–16,000 over two years).

Arts Council Theatre Writing Bursaries

Arts Council of England, 14 Great Peter Street, London SW1P 3NQ
☎0171 333 0100 ext 431   Fax 0171 973 6590
Contact *John Johnston*

Intended to provide experienced playwrights with an opportunity to research and develop a play for the theatre independently of financial pressures and free from the need to write for a particular market. Bursaries are also available for theatre translation projects. Writers must be resident in England. Writers resident in Wales, Scotland or Northern Ireland should approach their own Arts Council. Final entry date 6 January 1999.
Award £3500.

Arts Council Writers' Awards

14 Great Peter Street, London SW1P 3NQ
☎0171 333 0100   Fax 0171 973 6590
Literature Assistant *Sarah Sanders*

ESTABLISHED 1965. The Arts Council offers 15 awards a year. Applications should be accompanied by a c.v., description and sample of work in progress, statement of annual income and three copies of a previously published creative work. Judges will make their choices principally on the grounds of artistic quality, basing that judgment on their reading of work in progress and evidence before them of the writer's past achievement. Past winners include: Richard Beard, Elleke Boehmer, Catherine Byron, Julia Darling, Maura Dooley, Tony Flynn, Michael Hofmann, Matthew Kneale, Rory Maclean, Pratima Mitchell, Margaret Mulvihill, Charles Osborne, Brian Patten, Zeeba Sadiq, Jo Shapcott, Jane Solomon. Final entry date 30 September.
Award 15 awards of £7000.

The Authors' Contingency Fund

The Society of Authors, 84 Drayton Gardens, London SW10 9SB
☎0171 373 6642   Fax 0171 373 5768

This fund makes modest grants to published authors who find themselves in sudden financial difficulties.

The Authors' Foundation

The Society of Authors, 84 Drayton Gardens, London SW10 9SB
☎0171 373 6642   Fax 0171 373 5768

Annual grants to writers whose publisher's advance is insufficient to cover the costs of research involved. Application by letter to The Authors' Foundation giving details, in confidence, of the advance and royalties, together with the reasons for needing additional funding. Grants are sometimes given even if there is no commitment by a publisher, so long as the applicant has had a book published and the new work will almost certainly be published. £50,000 was distributed in 1997. Contact the

Society of Authors for an information sheet. Final entry date 30 April.

The K. Blundell Trust
The Society of Authors, 84 Drayton Gardens, London SW10 9SB
☎0171 373 6642   Fax 0171 373 5768

Annual grants to writers whose publisher's advance is insufficient to cover the costs of research. Author must be under 40, has to submit a copy of his/her previous book and the work must 'contribute to the greater understanding of existing social and economic organisation'. Application by letter. Contact the Society of Authors for an information sheet. Final entry date 30 April. Total of £15,000 available.

Alfred Bradley Bursary Award
c/o Network Radio Drama, BBC North, New Broadcasting House, Oxford Road, Manchester M60 1SJ
☎0161 244 4254
Contact *Melanie Harris*

ESTABLISHED 1992. Biennial award in commemoration of the life and work of the distinguished radio producer Alfred Bradley. Aims to encourage and develop new writing talent in the BBC North region. There is a change of focus for each award; the theme for the 1997 award was Verse Drama. Entrants must live or work in the North region. The award is given to help authors to pursue a career in writing for radio. Support and guidance is given from regional BBC radio producers. Previous winners: Lee Hall, Mandy Precious.
Award up to £6000 over 2 years.

British Academy Small Personal Research Grants
10 Carlton House Terrace, London SW1Y 5AH
☎0171 969 5200   Fax 0171 969 5300
Contact *Assistant Secretary, Research Grants*

Quarterly award to further original creative research at postdoctoral level in the humanities and social sciences. Entrants must no longer be registered for postgraduate study, and must be resident in the UK. Final entry dates end of September, November, February and April.
Award maximum £5000.

Cholmondeley Awards
The Society of Authors, 84 Drayton Gardens, London SW10 9SB
☎0171 373 6642   Fax 0171 373 5768
FOUNDED 1965 by the late Dowager Marchioness of Cholmondeley. Annual non-competitive awards for the benefit and encouragement of poets of any age, sex or nationality, for which submissions are not required. Presentation date: June. 1997 winners: Alison Brackenbury, Gillian Clarke, Tony Curtis, Anne Stevenson.
Award (total) £8000, usually shared.

The Economist/Richard Casement Internship
The Economist, 25 St James's Street, London SW1A 1HG
☎0171 839 7000
Contact *Business Affairs Editor (re. Casement Internship)*

For a journalist under 24 to spend three months in the summer writing for *The Economist* about science and technology. Applicants should write a letter of introduction along with an article of approximately 600 words suitable for inclusion in the Science and Technology Section. Competition details normally announced in the magazine late January and 4–5 weeks allowed for application.

European Jewish Publication Society
37–43 Sackville Street, London W1X 2DL
☎0171 333 8111   Fax 0171 333 0660
Contact *Dr Colin Shindler, Dr Sidney Brichto*

ESTABLISHED in 1995 to help fund the publication of books of European Jewish interest which would otherwise remain unpublished. Helps with the marketing, distribution and promotion of such books. Publishers who may be interested in publishing works of Jewish interest should approach the Society with a proposal and manuscript in the first instance. Books which have been supported include: *Double or Nothing* Thelma Ruby and Peter Frye; *The Slow Mirror and Other Stories* Sonja Lyndon and Sylvia Paskin; *Jewish Carpets* Anton Felton; *Selected Poems of Lotte Kramer* Lotte Kramer.
Grant £3000 (maximum)

Fulbright T. E. B. Clarke Fellowship in Screenwriting
The Fulbright Commission, Fulbright House, 62 Doughty Street, London WC1N 2LS
☎0171 404 6880   Fax 0171 404 6834
Contact *Programme Director*

Award offered to a young (normally, under 35) British film screenwriter to spend nine months in the US developing his/her expertise and experience. The successful candidate will follow postgraduate courses in screenwriting at a US institution, attend real-life story conferences and write a screenplay and some treatments during the award period. At the time of going to press, funding for this award was unconfirmed for 1999/2000. Please contact the Fulbright Commission for further information. Full details and application forms for all Fulbright awards (Fulbright Postgraduate Awards, Fulbright Scholarship Grants) are available on the Internet at: http://www.fulbright.co.uk

Award Air travel and grant of £18,000 plus approved tuition fees.

Fulton Fellowship

David Fulton (Publishers) Ltd, Ormond House, 26/27 Boswell Street, London WC1N 3JD
☎0171 405 5606   Fax 0171 831 4840
E-mail: david.fulton@fultonbooks.co.uk
Contact *David Fulton*

The Fulton Fellowship in Special Education was ESTABLISHED in 1995 with The Centre for the Study of Special Education, Westminster College, Oxford. The Fellowship, worth £2000, has been extended to offer schools as well as individual teachers the chance to share work their staff have done or are doing collaboratively through written publication to a wider audience. 1997 Fellow: Tim O'Brien.

The Tony Godwin Award

The Tony Godwin Memorial Trust, c/o Laurence Pollinger Limited, 18 Maddox Street, London W1R 0EU
☎0171 629 9761   Fax 0171 629 9765
Contact *Lesley Hadcroft* (at above address)
Chairman *Iain Brown* (0171 627 4244)

Biennial award established to commemorate the life of Tony Godwin, a prominent publisher in the 1960s/70s. Open to all young people (under 35 years old) who are UK nationals and working, or intending to work, in publishing. The award provides the recipient with the means to spend at least one month as the guest of an overseas publishing house in order to learn about international publishing. The recipient is expected to submit a report upon return to the UK. Final entry date for next award: 31 December, 1999. Previous winners: George Lucas (Hodder), Richard Scrivener (Penguin).

Prize Bursary of approx. US$5000.

Eric Gregory Trust Fund

The Society of Authors, 84 Drayton Gardens, London SW10 9SB
☎0171 373 6642   Fax 0171 373 5768

Annual competitive awards of varying amounts are made each year for the encouragement of young poets under the age of 30 who can show that they are likely to benefit from an opportunity to give more time to writing. Open only to British-born subjects resident in the UK. Final entry date, 31 October. Presentation date, June. Contact the Society of Authors for further information. 1997 winners: Matthew Clegg, Sarah Corbett, Polly Clark, Tim Kendal, Graham Nelson, Matthew Welton.

Award (total) £22,000.

The Guardian Research Fellowship

Nuffield College, Oxford OX1 1NF
☎01865 278520   Fax 01865 278676
Contact *Warden's Secretary*

One-year fellowship endowed by the Scott Trust, owner of *The Guardian*, to give someone working in the media the chance to put their experience into a new perspective, publish the outcome and give a *Guardian* lecture. Applications welcomed from journalists and management members, in newspapers, periodicals or broadcasting. Research or study proposals should be directly related to experience of working in the media. Accommodation and meals in college will be provided, and a 'modest' supplementary stipend might be arranged to ensure the Fellow does not lose out from the stay. Advertised annually in November.

Hawthornden Castle Fellowship

Hawthornden Castle, The International Retreat for Writers, Lasswade, Midlothian EH18 1EG
☎0131 440 2180
Administrator *Adam Czerniawski*

ESTABLISHED 1982 to provide a peaceful setting where published writers can work without disturbance. The Retreat houses five writers at a time, who are known as Hawthornden Fellows. Writers from any part of the world may apply for the fellowships. No monetary assistance is given, nor any contribution to travelling expenses, but once arrived at Hawthornden, the writer is the guest of the Retreat. Applications on forms provided must be made by the end of September for the following calendar year. Previous winners include: Les Murray, Alasdair Gray, Helen Vendler, Olive Senior, Hilary Spurling.

Francis Head Bequest

The Society of Authors, 84 Drayton Gardens, London SW10 9SB
☎0171 373 6642   Fax 0171 373 5768

Provides grants to published British authors over the age of 35 who need financial help during a period of illness, disablement or temporary financial crisis.

Ralph Lewis Award

University of Sussex Library, Brighton, East Sussex BN1 9QL
☎01273 678158   Fax 01273 678441

ESTABLISHED 1985. Triennial award set up by Ralph Lewis, a Brighton author and art collector who left money to fund awards for promising manuscripts which would not otherwise be published. The award is given in the form of a grant to a UK-based publisher in respect of an agreed three-year programme of publication of literary works by new authors or by established authors using new styles or forms. No direct applications from writers. Previous winners: **Peterloo Poets** (1989–91); **Serpent's Tail** (1992–94); **Stride Publications** (1997–99).

London Arts Board: Publishing New Writing Fund

London Arts Board, Elme House, 133 Long Acre, London WC2E 9AF
☎0171 240 1313   Fax 0171 240 4580

Aims to support and develop small presses and literary magazines in the publishing of new or under-represented fiction and poetry. This fund is only open to groups for whom publishing is a central activity. Contact the Principal Literature Officer for further details and deadline.

Macaulay Fellowship

An Chomhairle Ealaíon (The Arts Council), 70 Merrion Square, Dublin 2, Republic of Ireland
☎00 353 1 6180200   Fax 00 353 1 6761302

Literature Officer Sinead MacAodha

To further the liberal education of a young creative artist. Candidates for this triennial award must be under 30 on 30 June, or 35 in exceptional circumstances, and must be Irish citizens or residents. The Fellowship is offered on rotation between Music, Visual Arts and Literature (Literature in 1999).
Award IR£3500.

The John Masefield Memorial Trust

The Society of Authors, 84 Drayton Gardens, London SW10 9SB
☎0171 373 6642   Fax 0171 373 5768

This trust makes occasional grants to professional poets (or their immediate dependants) who are faced with sudden financial problems.

Somerset Maugham Trust Fund

The Society of Authors, 84 Drayton Gardens, London SW10 9SB
☎0171 373 6642   Fax 0171 373 5768

The annual awards arising from this Fund are designed to encourage young writers to travel and to acquaint themselves with other countries. Candidates must be under 35 and their publishers must submit a published literary work in volume form in English. They must be British subjects by birth. Final entry date 31 December. Presentation in June. 1997 winners: Rhidian Brook *The Testimony of Taliesin Jones*; Kate Clanchy *Slattern*; Philip Hensher *Kitchen Venom*; Francis Spufford *I May Be Some Time*.
Awards £5000 each.

MIDAS

See **The PAWS (Public Awareness of Science) Drama Script Fund**

National Poetry Foundation Grants

27 Mill Road, Fareham, Hampshire PO16 0TH
☎01329 822218

Contact *Johnathon Clifford*

The **National Poetry Foundation** considers applications for grant aid of up to £1000 where other funding is not available and the product will benefit poetry in general. Send details together with s.a.e. to NPF (Grants) at the above address.

The Airey Neave Trust

40 Charles Street, London W1X 7PB
☎0171 495 0554   Fax 0171 491 1118

Contact *Hannah Scott*

INITIATED 1989. Annual research fellowships for up to three years – towards a book or paper – for serious research connected with national and international law, and human freedom. Must be attached to a particular university in Britain. Interested applicants should come forward with ideas, preferably before March in any year.

New London Writers' Awards

London Arts Board, Elme House, 133 Long Acre, London WC2E 9AF
☎0171 240 1313   Fax 0171 240 4580
Contact *John Hampson*

ESTABLISHED 1993/94. Four bursaries, of £3,500 each, are awarded annually to London writers. Application form available from the above address. Final entry date: 16 October 1998. The four winners in 1996/97 were Mark de Brito, Jean McNeil, Cliff Ashcroft and Tony Hanania.

Newspaper Press Fund

Dickens House, 35 Wathen Road, Dorking, Surrey RH4 1JY
☎01306 887511   Fax 01306 876104
Director/Secretary *Peter Evans*

Aims to relieve distress among journalists and their dependants. Limited help available to non-member journalists. Continuous and/or occasional financial grants; also retirement homes for eligible beneficiaries. Further information and subscription details available from The Secretary or via the Reuter Foundation website on: www.foundation.reuters.com.npf

Northern Arts Literary Fellowship

Northern Arts, 10 Osborne Terrace, Jesmond, Newcastle upon Tyne NE2 1NZ
☎0191 281 6334   Fax 0191 281 3276
Contact *Published & Broadcast Arts Department*

A competitive fellowship. Contact the Northern Arts for details.

Northern Arts Writers Awards

Northern Arts, 10 Osborne Terrace, Jesmond, Newcastle upon Tyne NE2 1NZ
☎0191 281 6334   Fax 0191 281 3276
Contact *Published & Broadcast Arts Department*

Bi-annual awards, offered to established authors resident in the Northern Arts area on the basis of literary merit. Application spring/summer. Also available, one-month residencies at the Tyrone Guthrie Centre, Ireland.
Award Variable.

The PAWS (Public Awareness of Science) Drama Script Fund

The PAWS Office, OMNI Communications, Osborne House, 111 Bartholomew Road, London NW5 2BJ
☎0171 267 2555/voice mail: 0171 428 0961
Fax 0171 482 2394
Contacts *Barrie Whatley, Andrew Millington*

ESTABLISHED 1994. Annual award aimed at encouraging television scriptwriters to include science and engineering scenarios in their work. Grants (currently £2000) are given to selected writers to develop their script ideas into full treatments; prizes are awarded for the best of these treatments (Grand Prix currently £5000). The PAWS Fund holds meetings enabling writers to meet scientists and engineers and also offers a contacts service to put writers in 'one-to-one' contact with specialists who can help them develop their ideas.

The PAWS Drama Script Fund is in the process of starting an associated project, MIDAS, which will offer an annual prize (to be shared by writer and producer, and expected to be £5000) for the best television drama broadcast in the UK that makes a contribution to the public's awareness of science or engineering. For further details contact the PAWS office above.

Pearson Playwrights' Scheme

3 Burlington Gardens, London W10X 1LE
☎0171 411 2000
Contact *Jack Andrews*

Awards bursaries to playwrights. Applicants must be sponsored by a theatre which then submits the play for consideration by a panel. Each award allows the playwright a twelve-month attachment. Applications invited via theatres in October 1998. For up-to-date information, contact Jack Andrews. 1997 winner: Peter Moffat *Nabokov's Gloves*.

The Margaret Rhondda Award

The Society of Authors, 84 Drayton Gardens, London SW10 9SB
☎0171 373 6642   Fax 0171 373 5768

Competitive award given to a woman writer as a grant-in-aid towards the expenses of a research project in journalism. Triennial (next awarded: 1999). Final entry date 31 December 1998. Presentation date May. 1996 winner: Laura Spinney.
Award (total) approx. £1000.

The Royal Literary Fund

144 Temple Chambers, Temple Avenue, London EC4Y 0DA
☎0171 353 7150
Secretary *Mrs Fiona Clark*

Grants and pensions are awarded to published authors in financial need, or to their dependants. Examples of author's works are needed for assessment by Committee. Write for further details and application form.

Southern Arts Writer's Award

13 St Clement Street, Winchester, Hampshire
SO23 9DQ
☎01962 855099   Fax 01962 861186
Contact *Literature Officer*

Offers an annual award of £3500 to a published
writer living in the region to assist a specific
project. Awards can be used to cover a period
of unpaid leave while writing from home, to
finance necessary research and travel, or to purchase equipment. Final entry date: 16 October.

Laurence Stern Fellowship

Department of Journalism, City University,
Northampton Square, London EC1V 0HB
☎0171 477 8224   Fax 0171 477 8594
Contact *Bob Jones*
Website: http://www.city.ac.uk/journalism

FOUNDED 1980. Awarded to a young journalist
experienced enough to work on national stories. It gives them the chance to work on the
national desk of the *Washington Post*. Benjamin
Bradlee, the *Post*'s Vice-President-at-Large,
selects from a shortlist drawn up in March/
April. 1998 winner: Caroline Daniel. Full
details available on the Web.

Thames Television Theatre Writers' Scheme

See **Pearson Playwrights' Scheme**

David Thomas Prize

The Financial Times (W), 1 Southwark
Bridge, London SE1 9HL
☎0171 873 3000   Fax 0171 873 3924
Managing Editor *Robin Pauley*

FOUNDED 1991. Annual award in memory of
David Thomas, *FT* journalist killed on assignment in Kuwait in April 1991, whose 'life was
characterised by original and radical thinking
coupled with a search for new subjects and
orthodoxies to challenge'. The award will provide an annual study/travel grant to enable the
recipient to take a career break to explore a
theme in the fields of industrial policy, Third
World development or the environment.
Entrants may be of any nationality; age limits
vary. A given theme which changes from year to
year is announced in the early autumn. The 1997
theme was: 'What is the future of work?'.
Entrants should submit up to 800 words on the
theme, together with a brief c.v. and proposal
outlining how the award could be used to

explore the theme further. Award winners will
be required to write an essay of 1500–2000
words at the end of the study period which will
be considered for publication in the newspaper.
Final entry date end December/early January.
Prize £3000 travel grant.

Tom-Gallon Trust

The Society of Authors, 84 Drayton Gardens,
London SW10 9SB
☎0171 373 6642   Fax 0171 373 5768

A biennial award is made from the Trust Fund
to fiction writers of limited means who have
had at least one short story accepted. Authors
wishing to enter should send a list of their
already published fiction, giving the name of
the publisher or periodical in each case and the
approximate date of publication; one published
short story; a brief statement of their financial
position; an undertaking that they intend to
devote a substantial amount of time to the
writing of fiction as soon as they are financially
able to do so; and an s.a.e. for the return of
work submitted. Final entry date 20 September
1998. Presentation date June.
Award £1000.

The Betty Trask Awards

The Society of Authors, 84 Drayton Gardens,
London SW10 9SB
☎0171 373 6642   Fax 0171 373 5768

These annual awards are for authors who are
under 35 and Commonwealth citizens, awarded
on the strength of a first novel (published or
unpublished) of a traditional or romantic nature.
The awards must be used for a period or periods
of foreign travel. Final entry date 31 January.
Presentation June. Contact The Society of
Authors for an information sheet. Previous win-
ners: Alex Garland *The Beach*; Josie Barnard *Poker
Face*; Ardashir Vakil *Beach Boy*; Diran Adebayo
Some Kind of Black; Sanjida O'Connell *Theory of
Mind*.
Award (total) £25,000.

The Travelling Scholarships

The Society of Authors, 84 Drayton Gardens,
London SW10 9SB
☎0171 373 6642   Fax 0171 373 5768

Annual, non-competitive awards for the benefit of British authors, to enable them to travel
abroad. 1997 winners: William Palmer, Jo
Shapcott and James Simmons.
Award (total) £6000.

UEA Writing Fellowship

University of East Anglia, University Plain, Norwich, Norfolk NR4 7TJ

☎01603 592734   Fax 01603 593522

Director of Personnel & Registry Services
  J. R. L. Beck

ESTABLISHED 1971. Awarded to a writer of established reputation in any field for a period of six months, January to end June. The duties of the Fellowship are discussed at an interview. It is assumed that one activity will be the pursuit of the Fellow's own writing. In addition the Fellow will be expected to (a) offer an undergraduate creative writing course in the School of English and American Studies during the Spring semester, and to read and grade work received or offer workshops, tutorials, and/or visits to seminars; (b) make contact with groups around the county. An office and some limited secretarial assistance will be provided, and some additional funds will be available to help the Fellow with the activities described above. Applications for the fellowship should be lodged with the Director of Personnel & Registry Services in the autumn; candidates should submit at least two examples of recent work. Previous winner: Alison Fell.
  Award £5000 plus free flat on campus.

The David T. K. Wong Fellowship

School of English and American Studies, University of East Anglia, Norwich, Norfolk NR4 7TJ

☎01603 592810   Fax 01603 507728

An annual fellowship founded by retired Hong Kong senior civil servant, journalist and businessman, David Wong, to give writers the chance to produce a work of fiction in English set in the Far East. The aim of the Fellowship is 'to promote better understanding of the Far East and excellence in the writing of literature'. Applications will be considered from published and unpublished writers of any age and nationality. An original piece of fiction must be submitted with an application form, available from the above address, by 31 October. 1998 winner: Po Wah Lam.
  Award £25,000.

Prizes

ABSW/Glaxo Science Writers' Awards

Association of British Science Writers, 23 Savile Row, London W1X 2NB

☎0171 439 1205   Fax 0171 973 3051

ABSW Administrator *Barbara Drillsma*

A series of annual awards for outstanding science journalism in newspapers, journals and broadcasting.

J. R. Ackerley Prize

English Centre of International PEN, 7 Dilke Street, London SW3 4JE

☎0171 352 6303   Fax 0171 351 0220

Commemorating the novelist/autobiographer J. R. Ackerley, this prize is awarded for a literary autobiography, written in English and published in the year preceding the award. Entry restricted to nominations from the Ackerley Trustees only ('please do not submit books'). Previous winners include: John Osborne *Almost a Gentleman*; Barry Humphries *More Please*; Blake Morrison *And When Did You Last See Your Father?*; Paul Vaughan *Something in Linoleum*; Tim Lott *The Scent of Dried Roses*.

Acorn-Rukeyser Chapbook Contest

Mekler & Deahl, Publishers, 237 Prospect Street South, Hamilton, Ontario, Canada L8M 2Z6

☎001 905 312 1779   Fax 001 905 312 8285
E-mail: meklerdeahl@globalserve.net

Contact *James Deahl, Gilda Mekler*

ESTABLISHED in 1996, this annual award is named after the poets Milton Acorn and Muriel Rukeyser to honour their achievements as populist poets. Poets may enter as many as 30 poems for a fee of £5. Final entry date: 31 October. Contact the above address for a copy of the rules. 1997 winner: Linda Rogers *Picking the Stones*.

Prize (Canadian) $100 and publication of the manuscript.

Age Concern Book of the Year

See **The Seebohm Trophy**

Aldeburgh Poetry Festival Prize

Goldings, Goldings Lane, Leiston, Suffolk IP16 4EB

☎01728 830631   Fax 01728 832029

Festival Coordinator *Michael Laskey*

ESTABLISHED 1989 by the Aldeburgh Poetry Trust. Sponsored by the Aldeburgh Bookshop for the best first collection published in Britain or the Republic of Ireland in the preceding twelve months. Open to any first collection of poetry of at least 40 pp. Final entry date: 1 October. Previous winners include: Donald Atkinson, Susan Wicks, Gwyneth Lewis, Glyn Wright, Robin Robertson.

Prize £500, plus an invitation to read at the following year's festival.

Alexander Prize

Royal Historical Society, University College London, Gower Street, London WC1E 6BT

☎0171 387 7532   Fax 0171 387 7532

Contact *Literary Director*

Awarded for a historical essay of not more than 8000 words. Competitors may choose their own subject for the essay, but must submit their choice for approval in the first instance to the Literary Director of the Royal Historical Society.

Prize £250.

Allied Domecq Playwright Award

c/o Scope Ketchum Sponsorship, Tower House, 8–14 Southampton Street, London WC2E 7HA

☎0171 379 3234   Fax 0171 465 8241

Contact *Lucy McCrickard, Nathalie Curry*

ESTABLISHED 1995. Biennial award, founded by Allied Domecq and the **Bush Theatre** in London, to encourage new writing talent. Open to writers (over the age of 18) who have not yet had a play produced professionally. Entrants must submit a 1000-word outline plus examples of previously completed work. First winner: Jacinta Stringer.

Prize £5000 to help with development of the outline; if appropriate, the play will be staged at the Bush Theatre.

An Duais don bhFilíocht i nGaeilge

An Chomhairle Ealaíon (The Arts Council), 70 Merrion Square, Dublin 2, Republic of Ireland

☎00 353 1 6180200   Fax 00 353 1 6761302

Literature Officer *Sinead MacAodha*

Triennial award for the best book of Irish poetry.

Works must have been published in the Irish language in the preceding three years. Next award in 2001.

Prize £1500.

Hans Christian Andersen Awards

IBBY, Nonnenweg 12, Postfach CH-4003, Basle, Switzerland

☎00 41 61 272 2917   Fax 00 41 61 272 2757

E-mail: ibby@eye.ch

Executive Director Leena Maissen

The highest international prizes for children's literature: The Hans Christian Andersen Award for Writing ESTABLISHED 1956; The Hans Christian Andersen Award for Illustration ESTABLISHED 1966. Candidates are nominated by National Sections of IBBY (The International Board on Books for Young People). Biennial prizes are awarded, in even-numbered years, to an author and an illustrator whose body of work has made a lasting contribution to children's literature. Next award 1998. 1996 winners: Award for Writing: Uri Orlev (Israel); Award for Illustration: Klaus Ensikat (Germany).

Award Gold medals.

Eileen Anderson Central Television Drama Award

Central Broadcasting, Central Court, Gas Street, Birmingham B1 2JT

☎0121 634 4245   Fax 0121 634 4414

Head of Regional Affairs Kevin Johnson

ESTABLISHED 1987 with money left by the late Dr Eileen Anderson and contributed to by **Central Television**, this is an annual award to encourage new theatre writing in the Midlands. Open to all new plays or an adaptation commissioned or premièred by a building-based theatre company in the Central region. Previous winners include: David Edgar *Pentecost* (premièred at the **Royal Shakespeare Company**'s The Other Place in Stratford); Sean Street *Honest John* (premièred on Community Tour by the **Royal Theatre Northampton**); Vilma Hollingbery & Michael Napier Brown *Is This the Day?* (premièred at the Royal Theatre Northampton); Lucy Gannon *Wicked Old Nellie* (**Derby Playhouse**); Timberlake Wertenbaker *The Love of the Nightingale* (commissioned by the Royal Shakespeare Company's The Other Place); Pam Gem's *The Blue Angel* (premièred at the Royal Shakespeare Company's The Other Place) and Rod Dungate for *Playing By The Rules* (premièred at the **Birmingham Repertory Theatre**).

Prize £1500, plus trophy worth an additional £500 designed each year by a local college of education. A plaque is awarded to the theatre which commissioned the work.

Angus Book Award

Cultural Services, County Buildings, Forfar DD8 3WF

☎01307 461460   Fax 01307 462590

Contact Gavin Drummond (Director of Cultural Services)

ESTABLISHED 1995. Designed to try to help teenagers develop an interest in and enthusiasm for reading. Eligible books are read and voted on by third-year schoolchildren in all eight Angus secondary schools. 1998 winner: Robert Swindells *Unbeliever*.

Prize £250 cheque, plus trophy in the form of a replica Pictish stone.

Arc Short Stories Competition

ARC Publications, Nanholme Mill, Shaw Wood Road, Todmorden, Lancashire OL14 6DA

☎01706 812338   Fax 01706 818948

Contact Rosemary Jones

ESTABLISHED 1988. Annual award set up to stimulate the writing and reading of quality short fiction. Open to all living in the area covered by the three Northern regional arts boards (**North West Arts**, **Northern Arts**, **Yorkshire & Humberside Arts**) as well as Derbyshire and Lincolnshire. Final entry date: 30 June. Please send s.a.e. for entry forms which are available from March onwards.

Prize Guaranteed same-year publication in anthology, plus small cash prize.

The Aristeion Prize

Commission of the European Communities, Culture Unit, Rue de la Loi 200, B–1049 Brussels, Belgium

☎00 32 22 99 92 40   Fax 00 32 22 99 92 83

Contact The Culture Unit

ESTABLISHED 1990 to bring knowledge and appreciation of European literature to a wider public and to celebrate the strength and diversity of the European literary tradition. Nominations are submitted from the EFTA/EEA countries and EU Member States of their best works of literature and translation from the last three years. Sponsored by the Commission. 1997 winners: Antonio Tabucchi *Sostiene Pereira* (Literary Prize); Hans-Christian Oeser *Butcher Boy* by Patrick McCabe (Translation Prize).

Prize 20,000 ecus (about £14,000) for each category.

The Rosemary Arthur Award

National Poetry Foundation, 27 Mill Road, Fareham, Hampshire PO16 0TH
Contact *Johnathon Clifford*

ESTABLISHED 1989. Annual award to get poets of merit published in book form. Anyone resident in the UK who has not previously had a book published may submit 40 poems together with s.a.e. and £5 reading fee at any time during the year. The winner is announced in February. The 1999 award will be the last.

Award Complete funding for a book of the poet's work, plus £100 and an engraved carriage clock.

Arvon Foundation International Poetry Competition

Kilnhurst, Kilnhurst Road, Todmorden, Lancashire OL14 6AX
☎01706 816582   Fax 01706 816359
Contact *David Pease*

ESTABLISHED 1980. Biennial competition (next in 2000) for poems written in English and not previously broadcast or published. There are no restrictions on the number of lines, themes, age of entrants or nationality. No limit to the number of entries. Entry fee: £5 per poem. Previous winners: Paul Farley *Laws of Gravity*; Don Paterson *A Private Bottling*.

Prize (1st) £5000 and £5000 worth of other prizes sponsored by Duncan Lawrie Limited.

The Asher Prize
See **Medical Prizes**

Authors' Club First Novel Award

Authors' Club, 40 Dover Street, London W1X 3RB
☎0171 499 8581   Fax 0171 409 0913
Contact *Mrs Ann Carter*

ESTABLISHED 1954. This award is made for the most promising work published in Britain by a British author, and is presented at a dinner held at the Authors' Club. Entries for the award are accepted from publishers by the end of the year in question and must be full-length – short stories are not eligible. Joint 1997 winners: Diran Adebayo *Some Kind of Black*; Rhidian Brook *The Testimony of Taliesin Jones*.

Award £750.

BAAL Book Prize

BAAL Publications Secretary, Centre for Language & Communication, University of Wales, Cardiff, PO Box 94, Cardiff CF1 3XB
☎01222 874243   Fax 01222 874242

E-mail: sarangi@cardiff.ac.uk
Contact *Dr Srikant Sarangi*

Annual award made by the British Association for Applied Linguistics to an outstanding book in the field of applied linguistics. Final entry at the end of Oct/Nov. Nominations from publishers only. Previous winners: Ruth Lesser and Lesley Milroy *Linguistics and Aphasia*; *Dictionary of British Sign Language*; Susan Berk-Seligson *The Bilingual Courtroom*; Joshua A. Fishman *Reversing Language Shift*; Deborah Cameron *Verbal Hygiene*; Marco Jacquemet *Credibility in Court*.

The Barclays Bank Prize
See **Lakeland Book of the Year Awards**

Verity Bargate Award

The Soho Theatre Company, 21 Dean Street, London W1V 6NE
☎0171 287 5060   Fax 0171 287 5061
Contact *Paul Syrett, Literary Manager*

To commemorate the late Verity Bargate, founder and director of the **Soho Theatre Company**. This award is presented bi-annually for a new and unperformed full-length play. Send s.a.e. for details; if submitting scripts, enclose one s.a.e. script-size and one standard-size. The Soho Theatre Company also runs many courses for new writers. Previous winners: Adrian Pagan, Frazer Grace, Lyndon Morgans, Diane Samuels, Judy Upton, Angela Meredith.

Award £1500, plus production by the Soho Theatre Company.

The Herb Barrett Award

Mekler & Deahl, Publishers, 237 Prospect Street South, Hamilton, Ontario, Canada L8M 2Z6
☎001 905 312 1779   Fax 001 905 312 8285
E-mail: meklerdeahl@globalserve.net
Contact *James Deahl*

ESTABLISHED in 1996, this annual award is named in honour of Herb Barrett, founder of the Hamilton Chapter of the Canadian Poetry Association. Poets may enter one or two haiku for a fee of £5, or three or more haiku for a fee of £7.50. Final entry date: 30 November. Contact the above address for a copy of the rules. 1997 winners: Giovanni Malito, Elizabeth St Jacques, Sandra Fuhringer.

Prize (Canadian) $75, $50 and $25; anthology publication for the winners and all other worthy entries.

The Shaunt Basmajian Chapbook Award

Canadian Poetry Association, PO Box 22571, St George Postal Outlet, Toronto, Ontario, Canada M5S 1V0
E-mail: cpa@zap.wwdc.com
Contact *Allan Briesmaster*

ESTABLISHED 1996. Annual award named in honour of poet Shaunt Basmajian, a founder of the Canadian Poetry Association. Up to 24 pages of poetry may be submitted for an entry fee of Canadian $15. Open to any type of poetry. A copy of the rules is available from the above address.
Prize (Canadian) $100 and publication of the winning manuscript.

H. E. Bates Short Story Competition

Events Team, Directorate of Environment Services, Northampton Borough Council, Cliftonville House, Bedford Road, Northampton NN4 7NR
☎01604 238791   Fax 01604 238796
Contact *Liz Carroll-Wheat*

Named after the late H. E. Bates, one of the masters of the short story form. Entries should preferably be typed, 2000 words maximum on any subject. Any writer resident in Great Britain is eligible and there are categories for children under 11 and under 16.
Prize (1st) £200.

BBC Wildfire Magazine Awards for Nature Writing

BBC Wildlife Magazine, Broadcasting House, Whiteladies Road, Bristol BS8 2LR
☎0117 9738402   Fax 0117 9467075

Annual competition for professional and amateur writers. The competition was suspended in 1997 and at the time of going to press plans for its future resumption were unknown.

BBC Wildlife Magazine Poetry Awards

PO Box 229, Bristol BS99 7JN
☎0117 9738402   Fax 0117 9467075
Contact *Rosamund Kidman Cox*

Annual award for a poem, the subject of which must be the natural world and/or our relationship with it. Entrants may submit one poem only of no more than 50 lines with the entry form which appears in the magazine. Closing date for entries varies from year to year. 1997 winner: Matthew Barton.
Prizes Poet of the Year: £500, publication in the magazine, plus reading of the poem on Radio 4's *Poetry Please*; eight runners-up prizes: £75 plus publication in the magazine; four young poets awards.

Samuel Beckett Award

c/o Faber & Faber, 3 Queen Square, London WC1N 3AU
☎0171 465 0045   Fax 0171 465 0034
Contact *Editorial Department*

The rules for this award are currently under review.

David Berry Prize

Royal Historical Society, University College London, Gower Street, London WC1E 6BT
☎0171 387 7532   Fax 0171 387 7532

Annual award for an essay of not more than 10,000 words on Scottish history. Candidates may select any subject from the relevant period, providing it has been submitted to, and approved by, the Council of the Royal Historical Society.
Prize £250.

Besterman Medal

See **The Library Association Besterman Medal**

The BFC Mother Goose Award

Books for Children, 4 Furzeground Way, Stockley Park, Uxbridge, Middlesex UB11 1DP
☎0181 606 3061   Fax 0181 606 3099
Contact *Marisa Ryder, Editorial Coordinator*

ESTABLISHED 1979. Annual award for the most exciting newcomer to British children's book illustration. 1997 winner: Clare Jarrett *Catherine and the Lion*.
Prize £1000, plus Golden Egg trophy.

Birdwatch Bird Book of the Year

c/o Birdwatch Magazine, 3D/F Leroy House, 436 Essex Road, Islington, London N1 3QP
☎0171 704 9495
Contact *Dominic Mitchell*

ESTABLISHED in 1992 to acknowledge excellence in ornithological publishing – an increasingly large market with a high turnover. Annual award. Entries, from publishers, must offer an original and comprehensive treatment of their particular ornithological subject matter and must have a broad appeal to British-based readers. Previous winners: *Terns of Europe and North America* Klaus Malling Olsen and Hans Larsson; *Birds in Europe – Their Conservation Status* Graham Tucker and Melanie Heath; *The Birds of Israel* Hadoram Shirihai.

James Tait Black Memorial Prizes
University of Edinburgh, David Hume Tower, George Square, Edinburgh EH8 9JX
☎0131 650 3619   Fax 0131 650 6898
Contact *Department of English Literature*

ESTABLISHED 1918 in memory of a partner of the publishing firm of **A. & C. Black Ltd**. Two prizes, one for biography and one for fiction. Closing date for submissions: 30 September. Each prize is awarded for a book published in Britain in the previous twelve months. Prize winners are announced in December each year. 1997 winners: Roy Foster *W. B. Yeats: A Life, Vol. 1*; Andrew Miller *Ingenious Pain*. Previous winners include: Diarmaid MacCulloch *Thomas Cranmer: A Life*; Graham Swift *Last Orders*; Alice Thompson *Justine*; Christopher Priest *The Prestige*; Gitta Sereny *Albert Speer: His Battle with Truth*; Alan Hollinghurst *The Folding Star*; Doris Lessing *Under My Skin*; Caryl Phillips *Crossing the River*; Richard Holmes *Dr Johnson and Mr Savage*.
Prizes £3000 each.

Boardman Tasker Award
14 Pine Lodge, Dairyground Road, Bramhall, Stockport, Cheshire SK7 2HS
☎0161 439 4624
Contact *Dorothy Boardman*

ESTABLISHED 1983, this award is given for a work of fiction, non-fiction or poetry, whose central theme is concerned with the mountain environment and which can be said to have made an outstanding contribution to mountain literature. Authors of any nationality are eligible, but the book must have been published or distributed in the UK for the first time between 1 November 1998 and 31 October 1999. Entries from publishers only. 1997 winner: Paul Pritchard *Deep Play (Bâton Wicks)*.
Prize £2000 (at Trustees' discretion).

Booker Prize for Fiction
Book Trust, Book House, 45 East Hill, London SW18 2QZ
☎0181 516 2977   Fax 0181 516 2978
Contact *Sandra Vince*

The leading British literary prize, set up in 1968 by Booker McConnell Ltd, with the intention of rewarding merit, raising the stature of the author

in the eyes of the public and increasing the sale of the books. The announcement of the winner has been televised live since 1981, and all books on the shortlist experience a substantial increase in sales. Eligible novels must be written in English by a citizen of Britain, the Commonwealth, the Republic of Ireland or South Africa, and must be published in the UK for the first time between 1 October and 30 September of the year of the prize. Self-published books are no longer accepted. Entries are accepted from UK publishers who may each submit not more than two novels within the appropriate scheduled publication dates. The judges may also ask for certain other eligible novels to be submitted to them. Annual award. Previous winners include: James Kelman *How Late It Was, How Late*; Ben Okri *The Famished Road*; Michael Ondaatje *The English Patient*; Barry Unsworth *Sacred Hunger*; Roddy Doyle *Paddy Clarke Ha, Ha, Ha*; Pat Barker *The Ghost Road*; Graham Swift *Last Orders*. 1997 winner: Arundhati Roy *God of Small Things*.
Prize £20,000 winner; £1000, shortlist.

Author of the Year Award
Booksellers Association of Great Britain and Ireland
272 Vauxhall Bridge Road, London SW1V 1BA
☎0171 834 5477   Fax 0171 834 8812
Contact *Administrator*

Founded as part of the BA Annual Conference to involve authors more closely in the event. Authors must be British or Irish. Not an award open to entry but voted on by the BA's membership. 1998 winner: Louis de Bernières.
Award £1000 plus trophy.

Border Television Prize
See **Lakeland Book of the Year Awards**

The BP Natural World Book Prize
Book Trust, Book House, 45 East Hill, London SW18 2QZ
☎0181 516 2977   Fax 0181 516 2978
Contact *Sandra Vince*

ESTABLISHED in 1996 as an amalgamation of the Natural World Book Prize (the magazine of the Wildlife Trusts) and the BP Conservation Book Prize. Award for a book on creative conservation of the environment. Entries from UK publishers only. 1997 winner: Graham Harvey *The Killing of the Countryside*.
Prizes (1st) £5000; Runner-up: £1000.

The Michaél Breathnach Literary Memorial Award

Cló Iar-Chonnachta Teo, Indreabhán, Conamara, Co. Galway Republic of Ireland
☎00 353 91 593307   Fax 00 353 91 593362
Editor *Nóirín Ní Ghrádaigh*

As part of its 10-year celebration, **Cló Iar-Chonnachta** has established an annual award for the best Irish-language work in any literary form: novel, drama, poetry collection or short story collection. Open to writers aged under 30 years. Closing date for entries: 1 December annually.
Prize IR£1000.

Bridport Arts Centre
The Bridport Prize

Arts Centre, South Street, Bridport, Dorset DT6 3NR
☎01308 427183   Fax 01308 427183
Contact *Bridport Prize Administrator*

Annual competition for poetry and short story writing. Unpublished work only, written in English. Winning stories are read by leading London literary agent and an anthology of prize-winning entries is published. Also runs a Young Writers' Competition with variable prizes. Final entry date: 30 June (1 May for Young Writers' award). Send s.a.e. for entry forms.
Prizes £2,500, £1000 & £500 in each category, plus supplementary runners-up prizes.

Katharine Briggs Folklore Award

The Folklore Society, University College London, Gower Street, London WC1E 6BT
☎0171 387 5894
Contact *The Convenor*

ESTABLISHED 1982. An annual award in November for the book, published in Britain and Ireland between 1 June and 30 May in the previous calendar year, which has made the most distinguished non-fiction contribution to folklore studies. Intended to encourage serious research in the field which Katharine Briggs did so much to establish. The term folklore studies is interpreted broadly to include all aspects of traditional and popular culture, narrative, belief, custom and folk arts.
Prize £50, plus engraved goblet.

British Book Awards

Publishing News, 43 Museum Street, London WC1A 1LY
☎0171 404 0304   Fax 0171 242 0762
ESTABLISHED 1988. Viewed by the book trade as the one to win, 'The Nibbies' are presented annually in February. The 1998 Awards were in the following categories: Children's Book; Distributor; Editor; Publisher Marketing; Bookshop Marketing; Illustrated Book; Sales Representative; Newcomer; Design and Production; Lifetime Achievement; Author; Book; Independent Bookseller; Chain Bookseller; Services to Bookselling; Publisher. Each winner receives the prestigious Nibbie and the awards are presented to those who have made the most impact in the book trade during the previous year. Previous winners: Alan Bennett, Salman Rushdie, Dava Sobel, Sebastian Faulks, Jung Chang, Anne Fine, Books etc., Waterstone's, Ottakar's, and publishers **Transworld**, **Fourth Estate** and **Little, Brown**. For further information contact: Merric Davidson, 12 Priors Heath, Goudhurst, Cranbrook, Kent TN17 2RE (☎/Fax 01580 212041).

British Comparative Literature Association/British Centre for Literary Translation Competition

Dept of Literature, University of Essex, Wivenhoe Park, Colchester, Essex CO4 3SQ
Competition Secretary *Dr Leon Burnett*

ESTABLISHED 1983. Annual competition open to unpublished literary translations from all languages. Maximum submission 25 pages. Special prizes for translations from Swedish (biennial). Final entry date: 31 January.
Prizes (1st) £350; (2nd) £200; (3rd) £100; plus publication for all winning entries in the Association's annual journal *Comparative Criticism* (**Cambridge University Press**). Other entries may receive commendations.

British Fantasy Awards

2 Harwood Street, Heaton Norris, Stockport, Cheshire SK4 1JJ
☎0161 476 5368 (after 6 p.m.)
Secretary *Robert Parkinson*

Awarded by the **British Fantasy Society** by members at its annual conference for Best Novel and Best Short Story categories, among others. Not an open competition. Previous winners include: Ramsey Campbell, Dan Simmons, Michael Marshall Smith, Thomas Ligotti.

British Literature Prize

See **David Cohen British Literature Prize**

British Press Awards

Press Gazette, Quantum House, 19 Scarbrook Road, Croydon, Surrey CR9 1LX
☎0181 565 4200   Fax 0181 565 4395

'The Oscars of British journalism'. Open to all British morning and Sunday newspapers sold nationally and news agencies. March event. Run by the *Press Gazette*.

British Science Fiction (Association) Award

60 Bournemouth Road, Folkestone, Kent CT19 5AZ
☎01303 252939

Award Administrator *Chris Hill*

ESTABLISHED 1966. The BSFA awards a trophy each year in three categories – novel, short fiction and artwork – published in the preceding year. Previous winners: Iain Banks *Feersum Endjinn*; Paul di Filippo *The Double Felix*.

James Cameron Award

City University, Department of Journalism, Northampton Square, London EC1V 0HB
☎0171 477 8221   Fax 0171 477 8594

Contact *The Administrator*

Annual award for journalism to a reporter of any nationality, working for the British media, whose work is judged to have contributed most during the year to the continuance of the Cameron tradition. Administered by City University Department of Journalism. 1997 winner: Fergal Keane, BBC.

Cardiff International Poetry Competition

PO Box 438, Cardiff CF1 6YA
☎01222 492025   Fax 01222 492930

Contact *Margaret Harlin*

ESTABLISHED 1986. An annual competition for unpublished poems in English of up to 50 lines. Launched in the spring with an autumn closing date.

Prize (total) £5000.

Carey Award

Society of Indexers, Mermaid House, 1 Mermaid Court, London SE1 1HR
☎0171 403 4947   Fax 0171 357 0903

Secretary *Christine Shuttleworth*

A private award made by the Society to a member who has given outstanding services to indexing. The recipient is selected by Council with no recommendations considered from elsewhere.

Carnegie Medal

See **The Library Association Carnegie Medal**

The Raymond Chandler Society's 'Marlowe' Award for Best International Crime Novel

Heidenheimerstr. 106, 89075 Ulm Germany
☎0114 255 6302 (UK contact)
Fax 0114 255 6302

Contact *Simon Beckett (UK), Dr William R. Adamson (Germany)*

ESTABLISHED 1991. Annual award to the best English language crime novel. Awards also for best German language crime novel and best German language crime short story. Entry details from UK contact number. Submissions direct to the Society. Previous international 'Marlowe' winners include: Sara Paretsky, Minette Walters, Michael Connelly.

Sid Chaplin Short Story Competition

Shildon Town Council, Civic Centre Square, Shildon, Co Durham DL4 1AH
☎01388 772563   Fax 01388 777648

Contact *Mrs J. M. Stafford*

FOUNDED 1986. Annual themed short story competition (1997 subject was 'Hopes and Dreams'). Maximum 3000 words; £1 entrance fee (Juniors free). All stories must be unpublished and not broadcast and/or performed. *Prizes* (1st) £300; (2nd) £150; (3rd) £75; (Junior) £50.

Children's Book Award

The Federation of Children's Book Groups, The Old Malt House, Aldbourne, Wiltshire SN8 2DW
☎01672 540629   Fax 01672 541280

Coordinator *Marianne Adey*

ESTABLISHED 1980. Awarded annually for best book of fiction suitable for children. Unique in that it is judged by the children themselves. Previous winners include: Dick King-Smith *Harriet's Hare*; Ian Strachan *The Boy in the Bubble*; Mick Inkpen *Threadbear*, Robert Swindells *Room 13*; Elizabeth Laird *Kiss the Dust*; Jaqueline Wilson *The Suitcase Kid* and *Double Act*.

Award A splendid silver and oak sculpture made by Graham Stewart and Tim Stead, plus portfolio of letters, drawings and comments from the children who took part in the judging; category winners receive silver bowls designed by the same artists and portfolios.

Children's Book Circle Eleanor Farjeon Award

See **Eleanor Farjeon Award**

Arthur C. Clarke Award for Science Fiction

60 Bournemouth Road, Folkestone, Kent
CT19 5AZ
☎01303 252939   Fax 01303 252939
Administrator *Paul Kincaid*

ESTABLISHED 1986. The Arthur C. Clarke Award is given yearly to the best science fiction novel with first UK publication in the previous calendar year. Both hardcover and paperback books qualify. Made possible by a generous donation from Arthur C. Clarke, this award is selected by a rotating panel of six judges nominated by the **British Science Fiction Association** and the **Science Fiction Foundation**. Previous winners include: Amitar Ghosh *The Calcutta Chromosome*; Paul J. McAuley *Fairyland*; Pat Cadigan *Fools*; Jeff Noon *Vurt*; Marge Piercy *Body of Glass*; Pat Cadigan *Synners*; Colin Greenland *Take Back Plenty*.
Award £1000 plus trophy.

The Cló Iar-Chonnachta Literary Award

Cló Iar-Chonnachta Teo, Indreabhán,
Conamara, Co. Galway, Republic of Ireland
☎00 353 91 593307   Fax 00 353 91 593362
Editor *Nóirín Ní Ghrádaigh*

As part of its 10-year celebration, **Cló Iar-Chonnachta** has established an annual prize for a newly written and unpublished work in the Irish language. Awarded 1996 for the best novel, 1997 for the best poetry collection, and 1998 for the best short story collection or drama. Last date of entry for 1999 Award: 1 December 1998.
Prize IR£5000.

David Cohen British Literature Prize in the English Language

Arts Council of Great Britain, 14 Great Peter Street, London SW1P 3NQ
☎0171 333 0100   Fax 0171 973 6590
Literature Director *Gary McKeone*
Literature Assistant *Valerie Olteanu*

ESTABLISHED 1993. By far the most valuable literature prize in Britain, the British Literature Prize, launched by the **Arts Council**, is awarded biennially. Anyone is eligible to suggest candidates and the award recognises writers who use the English language and who are British citizens, encompassing dramatists as well as novelists, poets and essayists. The prize is for a lifetime's achievement rather than a single play or book

and is donated by the David Cohen Family Charitable Trust in association with Coutts Bank. The David Cohen Trust was set up in 1980 by David Cohen, general practitioner and son of a property developer. The Trust has helped composers, choreographers, dancers, poets, playwrights and actors. The Council is providing a further £10,000 to enable the winner to commission new work, with the dual aim of encouraging young writers and readers. 1997 winner: Dame Muriel Spark. Previous winners: Harold Pinter, V. S. Naipaul.
Award £30,000, plus £10,000 towards new work.

Collins Biennial Religious Book Award

HarperCollins Publishers, 77–85 Fulham Palace Road, London W6 8JB
☎0181 741 7070   Fax 0181 307 4064
Contact *Jeremy Yates-Round*

Biennial award given for the book which has made the most distinguished contribution to the relevance of Christianity in the modern world, written by a living citizen of the Commonwealth, the Republic of Ireland or South Africa. Previous winners include: John MacQuarrie *Jesus Christ in Modern Thought*. The award scheme is currently on hold – all enquiries to Jeremy Yates-Round.
Award £5000.

The Commonwealth Writers Prize

Book Trust, Book House, 45 East Hill, London SW18 2QZ
☎0181 516 2977   Fax 0181 516 2978
Contact *Sandra Vince*

ESTABLISHED 1987. An annual award to reward and encourage the upsurge of new Commonwealth fiction. Any work of prose or fiction is eligible, i.e. a novel or collection of short stories. No drama or poetry. The work must be written in English by a citizen of the Commonwealth and be first published in the year before its entry for the prize. Entries must be submitted by the publisher to the region of the writer's Commonwealth citizenship. The four regions are: Africa, Eurasia, S. E. Asia and South Pacific, Caribbean and Canada. 1998 winners: Peter Carey *Jack Maggs* (Best Book); Tim Wynveen *Angel Falls* (Best First Book).
Prizes £10,000 for Best Book; £3000 for Best First Book; 8 prizes of £1000 for each best and first best book in four regions.

The Thomas Cook/Daily Telegraph Travel Book Award

Buckden Wood, Perry Road, Buckden, Huntingdon PE18 9XQ
☎01480 812218   Fax 01480 812981
E-mail: jennifer@egan-and-talbot.demon.co.uk
Contact *Jennifer Rigby, Publishing*

FOUNDED in 1980 by The Thomas Cook Group. Annual award given to the author of the book, published (in the English language) in the previous year, which most inspires the reader to want to travel. Submissions by publishers only. Previous winners: Gavin Bell *In Search of Tusitala: Travels in the South Pacific after Robert Louis Stevenson*; William Dalrymple *City of Djinns*; Nik Cohn *The Heart of the World*; Stanley Stewart *Frontiers of Heaven*. 1997 winner: Nicholas Crane *Clear Waters Rising*.
Award £7500.

The Duff Cooper Prize

54 St Maur Road, London SW6 4DP
☎0171 736 3729   Fax 0171 731 7638
Contact *Artemis Cooper*

An annual award for a literary work of biography, history, politics or poetry, published by a recognised publisher (member of **The Publishers Association**) during the previous 12 months. The book must be submitted by the publisher, not the author. Financed by the interest from a trust fund commemorating Duff Cooper, first Viscount Norwich (1890–1954). 1997 winner: Diarmaid MacCulloch *Cranmer*.
Prize £2500.

Rose Mary Crawshay Prize

The British Academy, 10 Carlton House Terrace, London SW1Y 5AX
☎0171 969 5200   Fax 0171 969 5300
Contact *British Academy Secretary*

ESTABLISHED 1888 by Rose Mary Crawshay, this prize is given for a historical or critical work by a woman of any nationality on English literature, with particular preference for a work on Keats, Byron or Shelley. The work must have been published in the preceding three years.
Prizes normally two of approximately £500 each.

Crime Writers' Association (Cartier Diamond Dagger)

60 Drayton Road, Kings Heath, Birmingham B14 7LR
Contact *The Secretary*

An annual award for a lifetime's oustanding contribution to the genre. 1997 winner: Colin Dexter, creator of Inspector Morse.

Crime Writers' Association (John Creasey Memorial Dagger for Best First Crime Novel)

60 Drayton Road, Kings Heath, Birmingham B14 7LR
Contact *The Secretary*

ESTABLISHED 1973 following the death of crime writer John Creasey, founder of the **Crime Writers' Association**. This award, sponsored by **Chivers Press**, is given annually for the best crime novel by an author who has not previously published a full-length work of fiction. Nominations from publishers only. Previous winners include: Laurie King *A Grave Talent*; Doug J. Swanson *Big Town*. 1997 winner: Paul Johnston *The Body Politic*.
Award Dagger, plus cheque.

Crime Writers' Association (The CWA/The Macallan Gold Dagger for Non-Fiction)

60 Drayton Road, Kings Heath, Birmingham B14 7LR
Contact *The Secretary*

Annual award for the best non-fiction crime book published during the year. Nominations from publishers only. Previous winners include: Antonia Fraser *The Gunpowder Plot*; Martin Beales *Dead Not Buried*; David Canter *Criminal Shadows*; Alexandra Artley *Murder in the Heart*; Charles Nicholl *The Reckoning*; John Bossy *Giordano Bruno and the Embassy Affair*. 1997 winner: Paul Britton *The Jigsaw Man*.
Award Dagger, plus cheque (sum varies).

Crime Writers' Association (The CWA/The Macallan Gold and Silver Daggers for Fiction)

60 Drayton Road, Kings Heath, Birmingham B14 7LR
Contact *The Secretary*

Two annual awards for the best crime fiction published during the year. Nominations for Gold Dagger from publishers only. Previous winners include: Val McDermid *The Mermaids Singing*; Minette Walters *The Scold's Bridle*; Patricia Cornwell *Cruel and Unusual*; Ben Elton *Popcorn* (Gold); Peter Lovesey *The Summons*; Peter Høeg *Miss Smilla's Feeling for Snow*; Sarah Dunant *Fatlands*; Peter Lovesey *Bloodhounds* (Silver). 1997 winners: Ian Rankin *Black and*

Blue (Gold); Janet Evanovich *Three to Get Deadly* (Silver).
Award Dagger, plus cheque (sum varies).

Crime Writers' Association (The CWA/The Macallan Short Story Dagger)

60 Drayton Road, Kings Heath, Birmingham B14 7LR

Contact *The Secretary*

ESTABLISHED 1993. An award for a published crime story. Publishers should submit three copies of the story by 30 September. 1997 winner: Reginald Hill *On the Psychiatrist's Couch*.
Prize Dagger, plus cheque.

Harvey Darton Award

See **The Children's Books History Society** under **Literary Societies**

The Hunter Davies Prize

See **Lakeland Book of the Year Awards**

Isaac & Tamara Deutscher Memorial Prize

Department of International Relations, London School of Economics, Houghton Street, London WC2A 2AE
☎0171 955 7181

Secretary *Dr Justin Rosenberg*

An annual award in recognition of, and as an encouragement to, outstanding research in or about the Marxist tradition. Made to the author of an essay or full-scale work published or in manuscript. Final entry date 1 May.
Award £250.

George Devine Award

17A South Villas, London NW1 9BS
☎0171 267 9793 (evenings)

Contact *Christine Smith*

Annual award for a promising new playwright writing for the stage in memory of George Devine, artistic director of the **Royal Court Theatre**, who died in 1965. The play, which can be of any length, does not need to have been produced. Send two copies of the script, plus outline of work, to Christine Smith by March. Information leaflet available.
Prize £5000.

Denis Devlin Memorial Award for Poetry

An Chomhairle Ealaíon (The Arts Council), 70 Merrion Square, Dublin 2, Republic of Ireland

☎00 353 1 6180200   Fax 00 353 1 6761302

Literature Officer *Sinead MacAodha*

Triennial award for the best book of poetry in English by an Irish poet, published in the preceding three years. Next award 2001.
Award £1500.

Dog Watch Open Poetry Competition

267 Hillbury Road, Warlingham, Surrey CR6 9TL
☎01883 622121

Contact *Michaela Edridge*

ESTABLISHED 1993. Dog Watch is a charity that rescues and finds new homes for badly abused dogs. The annual prize is awarded only to authors of unpublished works. Final entry date is 1st September each year and entrants should send s.a.e. for details.
Prize (1st) £50; (2nd) £30; (3rd) £20.

Drama Association of Wales Playwriting Competition

The Library, Singleton Road, Splott, Cardiff CF2 2ET
☎01222 452200   Fax 01222 452277

Contact *Gary Thomas*

Annual competition held to promote the writing of one-act plays in English and Welsh of between 20 and 45 minutes' playing time. The theme of the competition is changed each year – the 1998 title was *Shadows*. Application forms from the above address.
Prizes awarded for Best Play for an All Female Cast, Best Play in the Welsh Language, Best Play for a Children's/Youth Cast, Best Author Under 25, Best Adult Play and Best Overall Play.

Eccles Prize

Columbia Business School, 834 Uris Hall, 3022 Broadway, New York NY 10027, USA
☎001 212 854 2747   Fax 001 212 854 3050

Contact *Office of Public Affairs*

ESTABLISHED 1986 by Spencer F. Eccles in commemoration of his uncle, George S. Eccles, a 1922 graduate of the Business School. Annual award for excellence in economic writing. One of the US's most prestigious book prizes. Books must have a business theme and be written for a general audience. Previous winners: *The Warburgs* Ron Chernow; *The New Palgrave Dictionary of Money and Finance* ed. Peter Newman, Murray Milgate and John Eatwell; *The Prize* Daniel Yergin.

The T.S. Eliot Prize

The Poetry Book Society, Book House, 45 East Hill, London SW18 2QZ
☎0181 870 8403/877 1615(24-hr answer-phone

Contact *Clare Brown, Director*

ESTABLISHED 1993. Annual award named after T. S. Eliot, one of the founders of the Poetry Book Society. Open to books of new poetry published in the UK and Republic of Ireland during the year and over 32 pages in length. At least 75 per cent of the collection must be previously unpublished in book form. Final entry date is in July. Previous winners: Ciaran Carson *First Language*; Paul Muldoon *The Annals of Chile* ; Mark Doty *My Alexandria*; Les Murray *Subhuman Redneck Poems*; Don Paterson *God's Gift to Women*.

The Encore Award

The Society of Authors, 84 Drayton Gardens, London SW10 9SB
☎0171 373 6642   Fax 0171 373 5768

ESTABLISHED 1990. Awarded to an author who has had one (and only one) novel previously published. Details from **The Society of Authors**. 1998 joint winners: Alan Warner *These Demented Lands* and Timothy O'Grady *I Could Read the Sky*.
Prize (total) £7500.

Envoi Poetry Competition

Envoi, 44 Rudyard Road, Biddulph Moor, Stoke on Trent, Staffordshire ST8 7JN
☎01782 517892

Contact *Roger Elkin*

Run by *Envoi* poetry magazine. Competitions are featured regularly, with prizes of £200, plus three annual subscriptions to *Envoi*. Winning poems along with full adjudication report are published. Send s.a.e. to Competition Secretary, 17 Millcroft, Bishops Stortford, Hertfordshire CM23 2BP.

Esquire/Apple/Waterstone's Non-Fiction Award

National Magazine Co Ltd, 72 Broadwick Street, London W1V 2BP
☎0171 439 5000   Fax 0171 312 3920

Editor *Peter Howarth*

ESTABLISHED 1993 by *Esquire* as a major annual literary award. 1996 winner: Peter Godwin *Mukina*. The award was suspended for 1997 and at the time of going to press its future is uncertain.

European Literary Prize/European Translation Prize

See **The Aristeion Prize**

Geoffrey Faber Memorial Prize

Faber & Faber Ltd, 3 Queen Square, London WC1N 3AU
☎0171 465 0045   Fax 0171 465 0034

ESTABLISHED 1963 as a memorial to the founder and first chairman of **Faber & Faber**, this prize is awarded in alternate years for the volume of verse and the volume of prose fiction published in the UK in the preceding two years, which is judged to be of greatest literary merit. Authors must be under 40 at the time of publication and citizens of the UK, Commonwealth, Republic of Ireland or South Africa. 1997 winner: Emily Perkins *Not Her Real Name*.
Prize £1000.

Eleanor Farjeon Award

c/o Children's Book Circle, Transworld Children's Books, 61–63 Uxbridge Road, London W5 5SA
☎0181 231 6648   Fax 0181 231 6727

Contact *Naomi Cooper*

This award, named in memory of the much-loved children's writer, is for distinguished services to children's books either in this country or overseas, and may be given to a librarian, teacher, publisher, bookseller, author, artist, reviewer, television producer, etc. Nominations from members of the **Children's Book Circle**. 1997 winner: *Michael Rosen*.
Award £750.

The Fidler Award

c/o Book Trust Scotland, The Scottish Book Centre, 137 Dundee Street, Edinburgh EH11 1BG
☎0131 229 3663   Fax 0131 228 4293

Sponsored by Hodder Children's Books for an unpublished novel for children aged 8–12, to encourage authors new to writing for this age group. Authors should not previously have had a novel published for this age group. The award is administered by **Book Trust Scotland**. Final entry date: end October. Previous winners: Theresa Breslin *Simon's Challenge*; Catherine McPhail *Run Zan Run*; John Smithwhaite *The Falcon's Crest*. 1997 winner: Mark Leyland *Slate Mountain*.
Award £1000, plus publication.

Fish (Publishing) Short Story Prize

Fish Publishing, Durrus, Bantry, Co Cork, Republic of Ireland
☎00 353 27 61246   Fax 00 353 27 61246
E-mail: fishpublishing@tinet.ie
Website: www.midnet.it/beara/fish.htm
Contact *Clem Cairns, Jula Walton*

ESTABLISHED 1994. Annual award which aims to discover, encourage and publish exciting new literary talent. Stories of 5000 words maximum which have not been published previously may be entered; an entry fee of £8 is charged for the first entry and £5 thereafter. Closing date: mid-November. Honorary Patrons: Roddy Doyle and Dermot Healy. Previous winners: Karl Iagnemma *Dog Days*; Molly McCloskey *The Stranger*.
Prize £1000; the best 15 stories are published.

Sir Banister Fletcher Award

Authors' Club, 40 Dover Street, London W1X 3RB
☎0171 499 8581   Fax 0171 409 0913
Contact *Mrs Ann Carter*

This award was created by Sir Bannister Fletcher, who was president of the **Authors' Club** for many years. The prize is donated by Nelson Hurst & Marsh, insurance brokers, and is presented annually for the best book on architecture or the fine arts published in the preceding year. Submissions: Fletcher Award Committee, RIBA, 66 Portland Place, London W1N 4AD. Previous winners: Richard Weston *Alvar Aalto*; Dr Megan Aldrich *Gothic Revival*; Professor Thomas Markus *Building and Power*; John Onians *Bearers of Meaning: Classical Orders in Antiquity*; Sir Michael Levey *Giambattista Tiepolo: His Life and Art*; John Allan *Berthold Lubetkin – Architecture and The Tradition of Progress*; Professor David Watkin *Sir John Soane, Enlightenment Thought and the Royal Academy*.
Award £1000.

The John Florio Prize

See **The Translators Association Awards**

The Forward Prizes for Poetry

Colman Getty PR, Carrington House, 126–130 Regent Street, London W1R 5FE
☎0171 439 1783   Fax 0171 439 1784
Contact *Liz Sich, Margot Weale*

ESTABLISHED 1992. Three awards, sponsored by Forward Publishing, Waterstone's and Tolman Cunard, for the best collection of poetry, the best first collection of poetry, and the best single poem which is not already part of an anthology or collection. All entries must be published in the UK or Eire and submitted by poetry publishers (collections) or newspaper and magazine editors (single poems). Individual entries of poets' own work are not accepted. 1997 winners: Jamie McKendrick, Robin Robertson, Lavinia Greenlaw.
Prizes £10,000 for best collection; £5000 for best first collection; £1000 for best single poem.

Anne Frankel Prize

Sight and Sound, British Film Institute, 21 Stephen Street, London W1P 1PL
☎0171 255 1444   Fax 0171 436 2327
Contact *The Administrator*

ESTABLISHED 1991. Annual prize for young film critics in memory of the late Anne Frankel, who wrote on film. Age limit for entrants is 25. Entrants must submit three examples of their film writing which must have been published in local or national newspapers and periodicals (these can include student newspapers). Final entry date usually end October.
Prize £500.

The Frogmore Poetry Prize

The Frogmore Press, 42 Morehall Avenue, Folkestone, Kent CT19 4EF
Contact *Jeremy Page*

ESTABLISHED 1987. Awarded annually and sponsored by the Frogmore Foundation. The winning poem, runners-up and short-listed entries are all published in the magazine. Previous winners have been: David Satherley, Caroline Price, Bill Headdon, John Latham, Diane Brown, Tobias Hill, Mario Petrucci, Gina Wilson.
Prize The winner receives 100 guineas and a life subscription to the biannual literary magazine *The Frogmore Papers*.

David Gemmell Cup

Hastings' Writers Group, 39 Emmanuel Road, Hastings, East Sussex TN34 3LB
☎01424 442471
Contact *Mrs R. Bartholomew*

ESTABLISHED 1988. Annual award to encourage writers of short fiction (1500 words) resident in East and West Sussex, Kent, Surrey, London and London boroughs. Final entry date: end of August; entry forms, which are essential, are available from May (enclose s.a.e). The competition is organised by Hastings

Writers' Group and is presented by its sponsor David Gemmell. Previous winners: Jenny Jackson, Wendy Brewer, Barbara Couvela, Stella Radford, Carol Bostock, Sarah Mills.

Prizes (1st) £250 plus David Gemmell Cup; (2nd) £150; (3rd) £100; (4th) £50; (5th) £30; (6th) £20. Additionally, certificates of commendation issued at the discretion of the judge, David Gemmell.

The Gladstone History Book Prize

Royal Historical Society, University College London, Gower Street, London WC1E 6BT
☎0171 387 7532   Fax 0171 387 7532
Contact *Executive Secretary*

A new annual award for the best new work on any historical subject which is not primarily related to British history, published in the UK in the preceding calendar year. The book must be the author's first (solely written) history book and be an original and scholarly work of historical research.
Prize £1000.

Glaxo Science Writers' Awards
See **ABSW/Glaxo Science Writers' Awards**

Glenfiddich Awards
4 Bedford Square, London WC1B 3RA
☎0171 255 1100   Fax 0171 631 0602

A series of awards to writers and broadcasters who have contributed most to the civilised appreciation of food and drink through articles, books, illustration and photography published in the UK. Also covers TV and radio programmes, as well as a Special Award for outstanding work or event. 1998 winners: Food Book of the Year: *The Book of Jewish Food* Claudia Roden; Drink Book of the Year: *The Wild Bunch* Patrick Matthews; Food Writer of the Year: Philippa Davenport for work in the *Financial Times*; Drink Writer of the Year: Richard Ehrlich for work in the *Independent on Sunday*; Magazine Cookery Writer of the Year: Philippa Davenport for work in *Country Living*; Newspaper Cookery Writer of the Year: Simon Hopkinson for work in *The Independent*; Restaurant Writer of the Year: Fay Maschler for work in the *Evening Standard*; Wine Writer of the Year: Richard Neill for work in *Decanter* and *The Daily Telegraph*; Regional Writer of the Year: Gillian Glover for work in *The Scotsman*; Television Programme of the Year: *A Cook on the Wild Side*, presented and produced by Hugh Fearnley-Whittingstall, directed by Andrew Palmer, executive producer

Eleanor Stephens (Keo Films for Ch4 in association with Stephens Kerr); Radio Programme of the Year: no award made; Visual Award: Jason Lowe for photography in *Malt Whisky* by Charles MacLean; 1998 Special Awards: Ann Bagnall, Southover Press and *The Food Programme*, BBC Radio 4; 1998 Glenfiddich Trophy Winner: Fay Maschler.

Award Overall winner (chosen from the category winners) £3000, plus the Glenfiddich Trophy (which is held for one year); category winners £800 each, plus a case of Glenfiddich Single Malt Scotch Whisky and an engraved commemorative quaich.

Edgar Graham Book Prize
c/o Department of Development Studies, School of Oriental and African Studies, Thornhaugh Street, Russell Square, London WC1H 0XG
☎0171 436 7295   Fax 0171 323 6605
Contact *The Secretary*

ESTABLISHED 1984. Biennial award in memory of Edgar Graham. Aims to encourage research work in Third World agricultural and industrial development. Open to published works of original scholarship on agricultural and/or industrial development in Asia and/or Africa. No edited volumes. Next award 2000; final entry date 31 March 2000.
Prize £1500.

Kate Greenaway Medal
See **The Library Association Kate Greenaway Medal**

The Guardian Children's Fiction Award
The Guardian, 119 Farringdon Road, London EC1R 3ER
☎0171 239 9694   Fax 0171 713 4366
Children's Book Editor *Joanna Carey*

ESTABLISHED 1967. Annual award for an outstanding work of fiction for children by a British or Commonwealth author, first published in the UK in the preceding year, excluding picture books and previous winners. Final entry date: late January. No application form necessary. Previous winners: Henrietta Branford *Fire, Bed and Bone*; Melvin Burgess *Junk*; Lesley Howarth *MapHead*; Rachel Anderson *Paper Faces*; Hilary McKay *The Exiles*; William Mayne *Low Tide*; Sylvia Waugh *The Mennyms*; Philip Pullman *Dark Materials I: Northern Lights*; Alison Prince *The Sherwood Hero*.
Award £1500.

The Guardian Fiction Prize

The Guardian, 119 Farringdon Road, London EC1R 3ER
☎0171 278 2332   Fax 0171 837 2114
Contact *Literary Editor*

ESTABLISHED 1965. An annual award for a novel published by a British, Irish or Commonwealth writer, which is chosen by the literary editor in conjunction with the paper's regular reviewers of fiction. Previous winners include: James Buchan *Heart's Journey into Winter*; Seamus Deane *Reading in the Dark*; Candia McWilliam *Debatable Land*; Alasdair Gray *Poor Things*; Alan Judd *The Devil's Own Work*; Pat Barker *The Eye in the Door*; Anne Michaels *Fugitive Pieces*.
Prize £5000.

W. H. Heinemann Prize

Royal Society of Literature, 1 Hyde Park Gardens, London W2 2LT
☎0171 723 5104   Fax 0171 402 0199

ESTABLISHED 1945. Works of any kind of literature may be submitted by publishers under this award, which aims to encourage genuine contributions to literature. Books must be written in the English language and have been published in the previous year; translations are not eligible for consideration. Preference tends to be given to publications which are unlikely to command large sales: poetry, biography, criticism, philosophy, history. Final entry date: 31 October. Up to three awards may be given. Previous winners: Tony Harrison *The Shadow of Hiroshima* and *Permanently Bard*; Frank McCourt *Angela's Ashes*.
Prize £5000.

Felicia Hemans Prize for Lyrical Poetry

University of Liverpool, PO Box 147, Liverpool, Merseyside L69 3BX
☎0151 794 2458   Fax 0151 794 2454
Contact *The Registrar*

ESTABLISHED 1899. Annual award for published or unpublished verse. Open to past or present members and students of the University of Liverpool. One poem per entrant only. Closing date 1 May.
Prize £30.

Heywood Hill Literary Prize

10 Curzon Street, London W1Y 7FJ
☎0171 629 0647
Contact *John Saumarez Smith*

ESTABLISHED 1995 by the Duke of Devonshire to reward a lifetime's contribution to the enjoy-

ment of books. Three judges chosen annually. No applications are necessary for this award. 1997 winner: John Nicoll of **Yale University Press**.
Prize £10,000.

David Higham Prize for Fiction

c/o Book Trust, Book House, 45 East Hill, London SW18 2QZ
☎0181 516 2977   Fax 0181 516 2978
Contact *Sandra Vince*

ESTABLISHED 1975. An annual award for a first novel or book of short stories published in the UK in the year of the award by an author who is a citizen of Britain, the Commonwealth, the Republic of Ireland or South Africa. Previous winners: Vikram Chandra *Red Earth and Pouring Rain*; Fred D'Aguiar *The Longest Memory*; Nicola Barker *Love Your Enemies*; John Loveday *Halo*; Elspeth Barker *O Caledonia*; Linda Grant *The Cast Iron Shore*. 1997 winner: Ronald Wright *A Scientific Romance*.
Award £1000.

William Hill Sports Book of the Year

Greenside House, Station Road, Wood Green, London N22 4TP
☎0181 918 3731   Fax 0181 918 3728
Contact *Graham Sharpe*

ESTABLISHED 1989. Annual award introduced by Graham Sharpe of bookmakers William Hill. Sponsored by William Hill and thus dubbed the 'bookie' prize, it is the first, and only, Sports Book of the Year award. Final entry date: September. Previous winners include: Simon Kuper *Football Against the Enemy*; Stephen Jones *Endless Winter*; Nick Hornby *Fever Pitch: A Fan's Life*; Colin McRae *Dark Trade*; Simon Hughes *A Lot of Hard Yakka*.
Prize (reviewed annually) £10,000 package including £6000 cash, hand-bound copy, £750 free bet and a day at the races. Runners-up prizes.

Hilton House Poet of the Year/Open Competitions

Hilton House (Publishers), Hilton House, 39 Long John Hill, Norwich, Norfolk NR1 2JP
☎01603 449845
Contact *Michael K. Moore*

ESTABLISHED 1995. Annual awards to promote interest in poetry and to encourage high standards. Unpublished poems only, of up to 30 lines; no limit to number of entries. Best poems selected will be published in Hilton House anthology series for that year. Entrants for all competitions must apply for rules and entry forms. Final entry dates: 31st March (Poet of the Year); 31st August (Open Competition). 1997 winners: Fred Alson, Maureen Cronin Settle. *Prizes* (for both competitions) 1st £200; 2nd £100; 3rd £150.

Also Hilton House Poet of the Year Best Collection/Open Competition Best Collection – for collections of 6–10 poems. Entry dates as above. *Prizes* (for both competitions) 1st 30 books containing prizewinner's collection; 2nd 20 books; 3rd 10 books.

Calvin & Rose G. Hoffman Prize

King's School, Canterbury, Kent CT1 2ES
☎01227 595501

Contact *The Headmaster*

Annual award for distinguished publication on Christopher Marlowe, established by the late Calvin Hoffman, author of *The Man Who was Shakespeare* (1955) as a memorial to himself and his wife. For unpublished works of at least 5000 words written in English for their scholarly contribution to the study of Christopher Marlowe and his relationship to William Shakespeare. Final entry date: 1 September. Previous winners: Prof. Dr Kurt Tetzeli von Rosador, Dr R. Dutton, Prof. R. Danson, Prof. T. Cartelli, Dr David Pascoe, Dr Lisa Hopkins, Prof. J. Shapiro, Prof. J. Bate, Dr Ruth Lunney.

Winifred Holtby Prize

Royal Society of Literature, 1 Hyde Park Gardens, London W2 2LT
☎0171 723 5104   Fax 0171 402 0199

ESTABLISHED 1966 by Vera Brittain who gave a sum of money to the RSL to provide an annual prize in honour of Winifred Holtby who died at the age of 37. Administered by the **Royal Society of Literature**. The prize is for the best regional novel of the year written in the English language. The writer must be of British or Irish nationality, or a citizen of the Commonwealth. Translations, unless made by the author himself of his own work, are not eligible for consideration. If in any year it is considered that no regional novel is of sufficient merit the prize money may be awarded to an author, qualified as aforesaid, of a literary work of non-fiction or poetry, concerning a regional subject. Publishers are invited to submit works (three copies of each) published during the current year to the Secretary, labelled 'Winifred Holtby Prize'. Final entry date: 31 October. Previous winners:

Rohinton Mistry *A Fine Balance*; Paul Watkins *Archangel*; Jim Crace *Signals of Distress*.
Prize £800.

L. Ron Hubbard's Writers of the Future Contest

PO Box 218, East Grinstead, West Sussex RH19 4GH

Contest Administrator *Andrea Grant-Webb*

ESTABLISHED 1984 by L. Ron Hubbard to encourage new and amateur writers of science fiction, fantasy and horror. Quarterly awards with an annual grand prize. Entrants must submit a short story of up to 10,000 words, or a novelette less than 17,000 words, which must not have not been previously published. The contest is open only to those who have been published professionally. Previous winners: Roge Gregory, Malcolm Twigg, Janet Martin, Alan Smale, Ken Rand. Send s.a.e. for entry form.

Prizes (1st) £640, (2nd) £480 and (3rd) £320 each quarter; Annual Grand Prize: £2,500. All winners are awarded a trip to the annual L. Ron Hubbard Achievement Awards which include a series of professional writers' workshops, and are published in the *L. Ron Hubbard Presents Writers of the Future* anthology.

Ilkley Literature Festival Poetry Competition

Manor House Museum, Ilkley, West Yorkshire LS29 9DT
☎01943 601210

Contact *David Porter*

Annual open poetry competition run by the **Ilkley Literature Festival**. Final entry date: August each year. Entry fee: £2.50 per poem. Previous winners: Anthony Dunn, John Sewell.
Prize (total) £600.

The Richard Imison Memorial Award

The Society of Authors, 84 Drayton Gardens, London SW10 9SB
☎0171 373 6642   Fax 0171 373 5768

Contact *The Secretary, The Broadcasting Committee*

Annual award established 'to perpetuate the memory of Richard Imison, to acknowledge the encouragement he gave to writers working in the medium of radio, and in memory of the support and friendship he invariably offered writers in general, and radio writers in particular'.

Administered by the Society of Authors and generally sponsored by the Peggy Ramsay Foundation, the purpose is 'to encourage new talent and high standards in writing for radio by selecting the radio drama by a writer new to radio which, in the opinion of the judges, is the best of those submitted.' An adaptation for radio of a piece originally written for the stage, television or film will not be eligible. Any radio drama first transmitted in the UK between 1 January and 31 December by a writer or writers new to radio, is eligible, provided the work is an original piece for radio and it is the first dramatic work by the writer(s) that has been broadcast. Submission may be made by any party to the production in the form of two copies of an audio cassette (not-returnable) accompanied by a nomination form. 1997 winners: Rosemary Kay *Wilde Belles*; John Waters *Holy Secrets*.

Prize £1000.

The Independent/Scholastic Story of the Year

Postal box address changes each year (see below)

ESTABLISHED 1993. Open competition for the best short story for children aged 6–9. One story per entrant (between 1500–2500 words). Details of the competition, including the postal box address, are published in *The Independent* in March/April of each year.

Prize £2000; two runners-up of £500 each. The winning story will be published in the newspaper and in an anthology published by **Scholastic Children's Books**, along with a selection of the best entries.

The International IMPAC Dublin Literary Award

Dublin City Public Libraries, Administrative Headquarters, Cumberland House, Fenian Street, Dublin 2 Republic of Ireland
☎00 353 1 6619000   Fax 00 353 1 6761628

ESTABLISHED 1995. Sponsored by a US-based productivity improvement firm, IMPAC, this prize is awarded for a work of fiction written and published in the English language or written in a language other than English and published in English translation. Initial nominations are made by municipal public libraries in major and capital cities worldwide, each library putting forward up to three books to the international panel of judges in Dublin. 1998 winner: Herta Müller *The Land of Green Plums*.

Prize IR£100,000 (if the winning book is in English translation, the prize is shared IR£75,000 to the author and IR£25,000 to the translator).

International Reading Association Literacy Award

International Reading Association,
800 Barksdale Road, PO Box 8139, Newark, Delaware 19714-8139, USA
☎001 302 731 1600   Fax 001 302 731 1057

Director of Research *Alan E. Frostrup, Executive Director*

The International Reading Association is a non-profit education organisation devoted to improving reading instruction and promoting literacy worldwide. In addition to the US $10,000 award presented each year on International Literacy Day (September 8), the organisation gives more than 25 awards in recognition of achievement in reading research, writing for children, media coverage of literacy, and literacy instruction.

International Student Playscript Competition

See **University College, Scarborough** under **Writers' Courses, Circles and Workshops**

Irish Times International Fiction Prize

The Irish Times Ltd, 10–16 D'Olier Street, Dublin 2, Republic of Ireland
☎00 353 1 679 2022   Fax 00 353 1 670 9383

Administrator, Book Prizes *Gerard Cavanagh*

FOUNDED 1989. Biennial award to the author of a work of fiction written in the English language and published in Ireland, the UK or the US in the two years of the award. Next award to be announced in October 1999, the short list having been announced in September. Books are nominated by literary critics and editors only. Previous winners: J. M. Coetzee *The Master of Petersburg*; E. Annie Proulx *The Shipping News*; Norman Rush *Mating*; Louis Begley *Wartime Lies*; Seamus Deane *Reading in the Dark*.

Prize IR£7500.

Irish Times Irish Literature Prizes

The Irish Times Ltd, 10–16 D'Olier Street, Dublin 2, Republic of Ireland
☎00 353 1 679 2022   Fax 00 353 1 670 9383

Administrator, Book Prizes *Gerard Cavanagh*

FOUNDED 1989. Biennial prizes awarded in

three different categories: fiction (a novel, novella or collection of short stories), non-fiction prose (history, biography, autobiography, criticism, politics, sociological interest, travel, current affairs and belles-lettres), and poetry (collection or a long poem or a sequence of poems, or a revised/updated edition of a previously published selection/collection). The author must have been born in Ireland or be an Irish citizen, but may live in any part of the world. Books are nominated by literary editors and critics, and are then called in from publishers. Previous winners: Paddy Devlin *Straight Left* (non-fiction); Kathleen Ferguson *A Maid's Tale* (fiction); Robert Greacen *Collected Poems*; Brian Keenan *An Evil Cradling*; John MacKenna *The Fallen and Other Stories*.

Prizes IR£5,000 each category.

The Jennings Brothers Prize
See **Lakeland Book of the Year Awards**

Jewish Quarterly Literary Prizes
PO Box 2078, London W1A 1JR
☎0171 629 5004   Fax 0171 629 5110
Contact *Gerald Don*

Formerly the H. H. Wingate Prize. Annual awards (one for fiction and one for non-fiction) for works which best stimulate an interest in and awareness of themes of Jewish interest. Books must have been published in the UK in the year of the award and be written in English by an author resident in Britain, the Commonwealth, Israel, Republic of Ireland or South Africa. Previous winners: Anne Michaels *Fugitive Pieces*; Claudia Roden *The Book of Jewish Food*; Amos Oz *Black Box*; Anton Gill *The Journey Back from Hell*; Bernice Rubens *Kingdom Come*; Leo Abse *Wotan My Enemy*; Ronald Harwood *Home*; Alan Isler *The Prince of West End Avenue*; Theo Richmond *Konin: A Quest*; Clive Sinclair *The Lady With the Laptop*; W. G. Sebald *The Emigrants*.

Prizes Fiction: £4000; Non-fiction: £3000.

Mary Vaughan Jones Award
Cyngor Llyfrau Cymru (Welsh Books Council), Castell Brychan, Aberystwyth, Dyfed SY23 2JB
☎01970 624151   Fax 01970 625385
Contact *The Administrator*

Triennial award for distinguished services in the field of children's literature in Wales over a considerable period of time.

Award Silver trophy.

Kent & Sussex Poetry Society Open Competition
8 Edward Street, Southborough, Tunbridge Wells, Kent TN4 0HP
☎01892 543862
Chairman *Clive R. Eastwood*

Annual competition. Entry fee £3 per poem, maximum 40 lines. Closing date: 31 January 1999. Judge for 1999 will be Gillian Clarke.

Prizes (total) £1000.

Kent Short Story Competition
Kent Literature Festival, The Metropole Arts Centre, The Leas, Folkestone, Kent CT20 2LS
☎01303 255070
Contact *Ann Fearey*

ESTABLISHED 1992. For a short story of up to 3000 words by anyone over the age of 16. Sponsored by Midland Bank and supported by Saga and Shepway District Council. Send s.a.e. for entry forms, available from March.

Prizes (1st) £275; (2nd) £150; (3rd) £100.

Kraszna-Krausz Book Awards
122 Fawnbrake Avenue, London SE24 0BZ
☎0171 738 6701   Fax 0171 738 6701
Administrator *Andrea Livingstone*

ESTABLISHED 1985. Annual award to encourage and recognise oustanding achievements in the publishing and writing of books on the art, practice, history and technology of photography and the moving image (film, television, video and related screen media). Books in any language, published worldwide, are eligible. Entries must be submitted by publishers only. Prizes for books on still photography alternate annually with those for books on the moving image (1998: photography). Previous winners: Ruth Vasey *The World According to Hollywood, 1918–1939*; Richard Taylor *The Encyclopedia of Animation Techniques*; Eve Arnold *In Retrospect*; Larry J. Schaaf *Records of the Dawn of Photography*.

Prizes £10,000 in each of the main categories; £1000 special commendations.

Lakeland Book of the Year Awards
Cumbria Tourist Board, Ashleigh, Holly Road, Windermere, Cumbria LA23 2AQ
☎015394 44444   Fax 015394 44041
Contact *Sheila Lindsay*

Five annual awards set up by Cumbrian author Hunter Davies and the Cumbria Tourist Board. The **Hunter Davies Prize** was established in 1984 and is awarded for the book which best helps visitors or residents enjoy a greater love or understanding of any aspect of life in Cumbria and the Lake District. Three further awards were set up in 1993 with funding from the private sector: **The Tullie House Prize** is for the book which best helps develop a greater appreciation of the built and/or natural environment of Cumbria; **The Barclays Bank Prize** is for the best small book on any aspect of Cumbrian life, its people or culture, and **The Border Television Prize** is for the book which best illustrates the beauty and character of Cumbria. A new award was established in 1997, **The Jennings Brothers Prize for the Best Guide Book**. Final entry date mid-March. 1997 winners: Hunter Davies Prize: Andrew Wilson *A President's Love Affair with the Lake District*; Border Television Prize: John Satchell *Family Album*; Barclays Bank Prize: John and Anne Nuttall *The Tarns of Lakeland, Vol 2*; Tullie House Prize: Val Corbett *A Rhythm, a Rite and a Ceremony*; Jennings Brothers Prize: Gordon Thorburn and John Baxter *The Appleby Rai*.

Prize £100 and certificate.

Lancashire County Library/NWB Children's Book of the Year Award

Lancashire County Library Headquarters, 143 Corporation Street, Preston, Lancashire PR1 2UQ
☎01772 264010   Fax 01772 555919
Manager, Young People's Service *Jean Wolstenholme*

ESTABLISHED 1986. Annual award sponsored by the National Westminster Bank for a work of original fiction suitable for 11–14–year–olds. The winner is chosen by 13–14–year–old secondary school pupils in Lancashire. Books must have been published between 1 September and 31 August in the year of the award and authors must be UK residents. Final entry date: 1 September each year. Recent winners: Robert Westall *Gulf*; Brian Jacques *Salamandastron*; Ian Strachan *The Boy in the Bubble*; Garry Kilworth *The Electric Kid*; Frances Hendry *Chandra*. 1997 winner: Elizabeth Hawkins *The Sea of Peril*. To celebrate the tenth anniversary of the award, all previous winners were judged for the 'Books Across Europe Award'. Ian Strachan's *The Boy in the Bubble* was voted the overall winner.

Prize £500 plus engraved glass decanter.

The Library Association Besterman Medal

7 Ridgmount Street, London WC1E 7AE
☎0171 636 7543   Fax 0171 436 7218
ESTABLISHED 1970. Sponsored by Whitaker.

Awarded annually for an outstanding bibliography or guide to literature first published in the UK during the preceding year. Recommendations for the award are invited from members of **The Library Association**. Among criteria taken into consideration in making the award are: authority of the work and quality of articles or entries; accessibility and arrangement of the information; scope and coverage; quality of indexing; adequacy of references; accuracy of information; physical presentation; and the originality of the work. Previous winners include: Heather Creaton *Bibliography of Printed Works on London History to 1939*; John McIlwaine *Africa: A Guide to Reference Material*; Katherine Pantzer *A Short-title Catalogue of Books Printed in England, Scotland, Ireland and English Books Printed Abroad 1475–1640 Vol 3*.

Award Medal.

The Library Association Carnegie Medal

7 Ridgmount Street, London WC1E 7AE
☎0171 636 7543   Fax 0171 436 7218

ESTABLISHED 1936. Presented for an outstanding book for children written in English and first published in the UK during the preceding year. This award is not necessarily restricted to books of an imaginative nature. Previous winners include: Melvyn Burgess *Junk*; Anne Fine *Flour Babies*; Theresa Breslin *Whispers in the Graveyard*.

Award Medal.

The Library Association Kate Greenaway Medal

7 Ridgmount Street, London WC1E 7AE
☎0171 636 7543   Fax 0171 436 7218

ESTABLISHED 1955. Presented annually for the most distinguished work in the illustration of children's books first published in the UK during the preceding year. Previous winners include: Helen Cooper *The Baby Who Wouldn't Go To Bed*; Alan Lee *Black Ships Before Troy*; Gregory Rogers *Way Home*.

Award Medal.

The Library Association McColvin Medal

7 Ridgmount Street, London WC1E 7AE
☎0171 636 7543   Fax 0171 436 7218
ESTABLISHED 1970. Sponsored by Whitaker. Annual award for an outstanding reference book first published in the UK during the preceding year. Books eligible for consideration include: encyclopedias, general and special;

dictionaries, general and special; biographical dictionaries; annuals, yearbooks and directories; handbooks and compendia of data; atlases. Recommendations invited from members of **The Library Association**. Previous winners include: Colin Matthew *The Gladstone Diaries*; Ray Desmond *Dictionary of British and Irish Botanists*; Edward Peget-Tomlinson *The Illustrated History of Canal and River Navigation*.
Award Medal.

The Library Association Walford Award
7 Ridgmount Street, London WC1E 7AE
☎0171 636 7543   Fax 0171 436 7218

Awarded to an individual who has made a sustained and continual contribution to British bibliography over a period of years. The nominee need not be resident in the UK. The award is named after Dr A. J. Walford, a bibliograper of international repute. Previous winners include: Prof. Stanley Wells, Prof. J. D. Pearson and Prof. R. C. Alston.
Award Cash prize and certificate.

The Library Association Wheatley Medal
7 Ridgmount Street, London WC1E 7AE
☎0171 636 7543   Fax 0171 436 7218

ESTABLISHED 1962. Sponsored by Whitaker. Annual award for an outstanding index first published in the UK during the preceding three years. Whole work must have originated in the UK and recommendations for the award are invited from members of **The Library Association**, the **Society of Indexers**, publishers and others. Previous winners include: Elizabeth Moys *British Tax Encyclopedia*; Paul Nash *The World of Environment 1972–1992*; Richard Raper *The Works of Charles Darwin*.
Award Medal.

Lichfield Prize
c/o Tourist Information Centre, Donegal House, Bore Street, Lichfield, Staffordshire WS13 6NE
☎01543 252109   Fax 01543 417308
Contact *Mrs Alison Bessey* (at Lichfield District Council on 01543 414000 ext. 2047)

ESTABLISHED 1988. Biennial award initiated by Lichfield District Council to coincide with the Lichfield Festival. Run in conjunction with James Redshaw Booksellers of Lichfield and 1997 Prize co-sponsors, **Hodder & Stoughton** publishers. Awarded for a previously unpublished novel based upon the geographical area of

Lichfield district, contemporary or historical, but not futuristic. Previous winners include: Valerie Kershaw *Rockabye*; Gary Coyne *The Short Caution*. Next award 1999. Final entry date in April of that year.
Prize £5000, plus possible publication.

Literary Review Grand Poetry Competition
See *Literary Review* under **Magazines**

London Writers Competition
See **Wandsworth London Writers Competition**

Longman-*History Today* Book of the Year Award
c/o History Today, 20 Old Compton Street, London W1V 5PE
☎0171 439 8315
Contact *Peter Furtado, Marion Soldan*

ESTABLISHED 1993. Annual award set up as joint initiative between the magazine *History Today* and the publisher **Addison Wesley Longman** to mark the past links between the two organisations, to encourage new writers, and to promote a wider public understanding of, and enthusiasm for, the study and publication of history. Submissions are made by publishers only. Previous winners: Andrew Gordon *The Rules of the Game: Jutland and British Naval Command*; Orlando Figes *A People's Tragedy: The Russian Revolution 1891–1924*; Paul Binski *Westminster Abbey and the Plantagenets*; Nicholas Timmins *Five Giants: A Biography of the Welfare State*.
Prize £1000 (see *History Today* from July 1998).

Lost Poet
PO Box 136, Norwich, Norfolk NR3 3LJ
☎01603 440944   Fax 01603 440940
Contact *Tricia Frances*

Lost Poet runs four literary competitons per year. All profits go to the work of The Sayana Wolf Trust who fund personal development courses and community projects for British and North American children and adults. For more details, send s.a.e. to the above address.
Prizes reflect the amount of entries received.

Sir William Lyons Award
The Guild of Motoring Writers, 30 The Cravens, Smallfield, Surrey RH6 9QS
☎01342 843294   Fax 01342 844093
Contact *Sharon Scott-Fairweather*

An annual competitive award to encourage young people in automotive journalism and to foster interests in motoring and the motor industry. Entrance by two essays and interview with Awards Committee. Applicants must be British, aged 17–23 and resident in UK. Final entry date 31 August. Presentation date in December.

Award £1000 plus trophy.

The Macallan/*Scotland on Sunday* Short Story Competition

Scotland on Sunday, 20 North Bridge, Edinburgh EH1 1YT
☎0131 243 3602   Fax 0131 220 2443
Contact *Rosemary Goring*

ESTABLISHED 1990. Annual competition to recognise the best in new Scottish writing. Stories are accepted from those who were born or are living in Scotland, or from Scots living abroad. Up to three stories per applicant permitted. Maximum 3000 words per story. Final entry date in March. The top 20 entries are published in a book in conjunction with the **Scottish Arts Council**. Previous winners: Alan Spence, Ali Smith, Chris Dolan, Michael Faber, Anne Donovan.

Prizes 1st £6000; 2nd £600; four runners-up receive £100 each. Winning story is published in *Scotland on Sunday* and four of six shortlisted will be broadcast on BBC Radio Scotland.

McColvin Medal

See **The Library Association McColvin Medal**

Agnes Mure Mackenzie Award

The Saltire Society, 9 Fountain Close, 22 High Street, Edinburgh EH1 1TF
☎0131 556 1836   Fax 0131 557 1675
Administrator *Kathleen Munro*

ESTABLISHED 1965. Biennial award in memory of the late Dr Agnes Mure Mackenzie for a published work of distinguished Scottish historical research of scholarly importance (including intellectual history and the history of science). Editions of texts are not eligible. The 1998 award is open to books published between 1st January 1997 and 31st December 1998. Nominations are invited and should be sent to the Administrator. Previous winner: Stephen Boardman *The Early Stewart Kings, Robert II and Robert III*.

Prize Bound and inscribed copy of the winning publication.

W. J. M. Mackenzie Book Prize

Political Studies Association, Dept of Politics, University of Nottingham, Nottingham NG7 2RD
☎0115 9514797   Fax 0115 9514797
PSA Executive Director *Victoria Leach*

ESTABLISHED 1987. Annual award to best work of political science published in the UK during the previous year. Submissions from publishers only. Final entry date in June. Previous winners: James Mayall *Nationalism and International Society*; Brian Barry *Theories of Justice;* Avi Shlaim *Collusion Across the Jordan*; Colin Crouch *Industrial Relations and European State Tradition*; Iain Hampsher-Monk *A History of Modern Political Thought;* Patrick Dunleavy *Democracy, Bureaucracy and Public Choice*; Ivor Crewe and Anthony King *The S.D.P.*

Prize £100, plus travel/attendance at three-day annual conference.

McKitterick Prize

Society of Authors, 84 Drayton Gardens, London SW10 9SB
☎0171 373 6642   Fax 0171 373 5768
Contact *Awards Secretary*

Annual award for a full-length work in the English language, first published in the UK or unpublished. Open to writers over 40 who have not had any adult novel published other than the one submitted. Closing date 16 December. 1997 winner: Patricia Duncker *Hallucinating Foucault*.

Prize £4–5000.

Enid McLeod Prize

Franco-British Society, Room 623, Linen Hall, 162–168 Regent Street, London W1R 5TB
☎0171 734 0815   Fax 0171 734 0815
Executive Secretary *Miss Louise Laing*

ESTABLISHED 1982. Annual award to the author of the work of literature published in the UK which, in the opinion of the judges, has contributed most to Franco-British understanding. Any full-length work written in English by a citizen of the UK, Commonwealth, Republic of Ireland, Pakistan, Bangladesh and South Africa. No English translation of a book written originally in any other language will be considered. Nominations from publishers for books published between 1 January and 31 December of the year of the prize. Previous winners: Gillian Tindall *Célestine, Voices from a French Village*; Jonathan Keates *Stendhal;* Sebastian Faulks *Birdsong*; Margaret Crosland *Simone de*

Beauvoir – The Woman and Her Work; Frank Giles *The Locust Years*.
Prize Cheque.

Macmillan Prize for a Children's Picture Book

Macmillan Children's Books, 25 Eccleston Place, London SW1W 9NF
☎0171 881 8000   Fax 0171 881 8001
Contact *The Marketing Dept.*

Set up in order to stimulate new work from young illustrators in art schools, and to help them start their professional lives. Fiction or non-fiction. **Macmillan** have the option to publish any of the prize winners.
Prizes (1st) £1000; (2nd) £500; (3rd) £250.

Macmillan Silver PEN Award

The English Centre of International PEN, 7 Dilke Street, London SW3 4JE
☎0171 352 6303   Fax 0171 351 0220

Sponsored by **Macmillan Publishers**. An annual award for a volume of short stories written in English by a British author and published in the UK in the year preceding the prize. Nominations by the PEN Executive Committee only. Previous winners: Jane Gardham *Going into a Dark House*; Nicola Barker *Love Your Enemies*; Pauline Melville *Shape-Shifter*; Fay Weldon *Wicked Women*. 1997 winner: Clive Sinclair *The Lady With the Laptop*.
Prize £500, plus silver pen.

The Mail on Sunday Novel Competition

Postal box address changes each year (see below)

Annual award ESTABLISHED 1983. Judges look for a story/character that springs to life in the 'tantalising opening 50–150 words of a novel'. Details of the competition, including the postal box address, are published in The Mail on Sunday in July/August. 1997 winners: Jude Rodger, Nicola Richardson, Michael Ryan, Kate Spencer, Karen Martin, Pat Simpson.
Awards (1st) £400 book tokens and a weekend writing course at the **Arvon Foundation**; (2nd) £300 tokens; (3rd) £200 tokens; three further prizes of £150 tokens each.

The Mail on Sunday/John Llewellyn Rhys Prize

Book Trust, Book House, 45 East Hill, London SW18 2QZ
☎0181 516 2977   Fax 0181 516 2978
Contact *Sandra Vince*

ESTABLISHED 1942. An annual young writer's award for a memorable work of any kind. Entrants must be under the age of 35 at the time of publication; books must have been published in the UK in the year of the award. The author must be a citizen of Britain or the Commonwealth, writing in English. Previous winners: Matthew Kneale *Sweet Thames*; Jason Goodwin *On Foot to the Golden Horn*, Melanie McGrath *Motel Nirvana*. 1997 winner: Nicola Barker *Heading Inland*.
Prize £5000 (1st); £500 for shortlisted entries.

Marsh Award for Children's Literature in Translation

Authors' Club, 40 Dover Street, London W1X 3RB
☎0171 499 8581   Fax 0171 409 0913
Contact *Mrs Ann Carter*

ESTABLISHED 1995 and sponsored by the Marsh Christian Trust, the award aims to encourage translation of foreign children's books into English. It is a biennial award (next award: 1998), open to British translators of books for 4 – 16-year-olds, published in the UK by a British publisher. Any category will be considered with the exception of encyclopedias and reference. No electronic books. First winner: Anthea Bell *A Dog's Life* by Christine Nostlinger.
Prize £750.

Marsh Biography Award

Authors' Club, 40 Dover Street, London W1X 3RB
☎0171 499 8581   Fax 0171 409 0913
Contact *Mrs Ann Carter*

A biennial award for the most significant biography published over a two-year period by a British publisher. Next award October 1999. Previous winners: Hugh & Mirabel Cecil *Clever Hearts*; Patrick Marnham *The Man Who Wasn't Maigret*; Selina Hastings *Evelyn Waugh*. 1997 winner: Jim Ring *Erskine Childers*.
Award £3500, plus silver trophy presented at a dinner.

Kurt Maschler Award

Book Trust, Book House, 45 East Hill, London SW18 2QZ
☎0181 516 2977   Fax 0181 516 2978
Contact *Sandra Vince*

ESTABLISHED 1982. Annual award for 'a work of imagination in the children's field in which text and illustration are of excellence and so presented that each enhances, yet balances the other'. Books published in the current year in the UK by a British author and/or artist, or by someone resident for ten years, are eligible. Previous winners: Kathy Henderson and Patrick Benson *The Little Boat*; Trish Cooke, illus. Helen Oxenbury *So Much*; Karen Wallace, illus. Mike Bostock *Think of an Eel*; Raymond Briggs *The Man*; Colin McNaughton *Have You Seen Who's Just Moved in Next Door to Us?*; Babette Cole *Drop Dead*. 1997 winner: William Mayne and Jonathan Heale (illus.) *Lady Muck*.

Award £1000 plus bronze Emil trophy.

MCA Book Prize

122 Fawnbrake Avenue, London SE24 0BZ
☎0171 738 6701   Fax 0171 738 6701
Administrator *Andrea Livingstone*
k-k@dial.pipex.com

ESTABLISHED 1993. Annual award sponsored by the Management Consultancies Association to recognise and reward books that contribute stimulating, original and progressive ideas on management. Entries should have been published first in the UK during the calendar year of the Award and written by British subjects living in the UK. Submissions by publishers only. Previous winners: Mary Bragg *Reinventing Influence*; Colin Egan *Creating Organizational Advantage*; Clive Morton *Becoming World Class*; Richard Whittington *What is Strategy and Does it Matter?*.

Prizes £5000 for best management book published. In addition, a special commendation for younger writers, carrying an award of £2000 for best management book by a writer under 40 may be given.

Medical Prizes

The Society of Authors, 84 Drayton Gardens, London SW10 9SB
☎0171 373 6642   Fax 0171 373 5768
Contact *Jacqueline Granger-Taylor*

Annual award in five categories: basic book, advanced author book, advanced edited book, medical history, first textbook, published in the UK in the year preceding the awards. Previous winners: Rona M. Mackie *Clinical Dermatology* 4th edition; C. P. Warlow, M. S. Dennis, J. van Gijn, G. J. Hankey, P. A. G. Sandercock, J. M. Bamford, J. Wardlow *Stroke*; John C. Bennett and Richard P. McLaughlin *Orthodontic Management of the Dentition with the Preadjusted Appliance*; John Pickup and Gareth Williams *Textbook of Diabetes*; Arthur Hollman *Sir Thomas Lewis: Pioneer Cardiologist*. **The Asher Prize** for a first textbook: Andrew R. Houghton and David Gray *Making Sense of the ECG*.

Prizes £1000 (each category).

Mere Literary Festival Open Competition

The Mere & District Linkscheme, Limpers Hill, Mere, Wiltshire BA12 6BD
☎1747 860475

Contact *Mrs Adrienne Howell (Events Organiser)*

Annual open competition which alternates between short stories and poetry. The winners are announced at the Mere Literary Festival during the second week of October. The 1999 competition is for poetry with a closing date for entries in July. For further details, including entry fees and forms, contact the address above.

Cash prizes.

Meyer-Whitworth Award

Arts Council of England, 14 Great Peter Street, London SW1P 3NQ
☎0171 333 0100 ext 431   Fax 0171 973 6590
Contact *The Drama Director*

In 1908 the movement for a National Theatre joined forces with that to create a memorial to William Shakespeare. The result was the Shakespeare Memorial National Theatre Committee, the embodiment of the campaign for a National Theatre. This award, bearing the name of but two protagonists in the movement, has been established to commemorate all those who worked for the SMNT. Endowed by residual funds of the SMNT, the award is intended to help further the careers of UK playwrights who are not yet established, and to draw contemporary theatre writers to the public's attention. The award is given to the writer whose play most nearly satisfies the following criteria: a play which embodies Geoffrey Whitworth's dictum that 'drama is important in so far as it reveals the truth about the relationships of human beings with each other and the world at large'; a play which shows promise of a developing new talent; a play in which the writing is of individual quality. Nominations from professional theatre companies. Plays must have been written in the English language and produced professionally in the UK in the 12 months preceding the award. Candidates will have had no more than two of their plays professionally produced.

Award £8000.

MIND Book of the Year/ Allen Lane Award

Granta House, 15–19 Broadway, London E15 4BQ
☎0181 519 2122 ext. 225   Fax 0181 522 1725

ESTABLISHED 1981. Annual award, in memory

of Sir Allen Lane, for the author of a book published in the current year (fiction or non-fiction), which furthers public understanding of mental health problems. 1998 winner: Jenny Diski *Skating to Antarctica*.
Award £1000.

The Mitchell Prize for Art History/The Eric Mitchell Prize

c/o The Burlington Magazine, 14–16 Duke's Road, London WC1H 9AD
☎0171 388 8157   Fax 0171 388 1230
Executive Director *Caroline Elam*

ESTABLISHED 1977 by art collector, philan-thropist and businessman, Jan Mitchell, to draw attention to exceptional achievements in the his-tory of art. Consists of two prizes: The Mitchell Prize, given for an outstanding and original con-tribution to the study and understanding of visual arts, and The Eric Mitchell Prize, given for the most outstanding first book in this field. The prizes are awarded to authors of books in English that have been published in the previous 12 months (i.e. 1 January – 31 December 1997 for the 1998 award). Books are submitted by pub-lishers before the end of February. Previous win-ners: The Mitchell Prize: *Nicolas Poussin* Elizabeth Cropper and Charles Dempsey; The Eric Mitchell Prize: *The Triumph of Vulcan* Suzanne Brown Butters.
Prizes $15,000 (Mitchell Prize); $5000 (Eric Mitchell Prize)

Scott Moncrieff Prize
See **The Translators Association Awards**

The Montagu of Beaulieu Trophy
Guild of Motoring Writers, 30 The Cravens, Smallfield, Surrey RH6 9QS
☎01342 843294   Fax 01342 844093
Contact *Sharon Scott-Fairweather*

First presented by Lord Montagu on the occa-sion of the opening of the National Motor Museum at Beaulieu in 1972. Awarded annu-ally to a member of the **Guild of Motoring Writers** who, in the opinion of the nominated jury, has made the greatest contribution to recording in the English language the history of motoring or motor cycling in a published book or article, film, television or radio script, or research manuscript available to the public.
Prize Trophy.

The Mother Goose Award
See **The BFC Mother Goose Award**

Shiva Naipaul Memorial Prize
The Spectator, 56 Doughty Street, London WC1N 2LL
☎0171 405 1706   Fax 0171 242 0603
Contact *Emma Bagnall*

ESTABLISHED 1985. Annual prize given to an English language writer of any nationality under the age of 35 for an essay of not more than 4000 words describing a culture alien to the writer. Final entry date is in March. Previous winner: John Gimlette.
Prize £3000.

NASEN Special Educational Needs Book and Software Awards
The Educational Publishers Council, The Publishers Association, 1 Kingsway, London WC2B 6XF
☎0171 565 7474   Fax 0171 836 4543
ESTABLISHED 1992. Organised by the National Association for Special Education Needs (NASEN) and the **Educational Publishers Council**. Three awards: *The Children's Book Award*, for the book that most successfully pro-vides a positive image of children with special needs; *The Academic Book Award* celebrates the work of authors and editors who have made an outstanding contribution to the theory and prac-tice of special education; and *The Software Awards* for broad application to a range of areas across the curriculum. Books must have been published in the UK within the year preceding the award. 1997 winners: Dorothy Hogan *Charlie's Eye* (Children's); Patricia Howlin *Autism. Preparing for Adulthood* (Academic); Widgit – First Keys & SEMERC – Pages (Joint Winners, Software).
Prize £500.

New London Writers Award
London Arts Board, 133 Long Acre, London WC2E 9AF
☎0171 240 1313   Fax 0171 240 4580
E-mail: jhn@lonab.demon.co.uk
Contact *John Hampson, Principal Literature Officer*

ESTABLISHED 1993/4. Annual award to writers resident in London who have had published one (and no more) full-length work of fiction or poetry and currently are at work on their second book. Final entry date: October 1999. Prospective applicants should contact the LAB to check details and for application forms. Previous winners: Cliff Ashcroft, Jean McNeil, Tony Hanania, Mark Angelo de Brito.
Prize £4000.

Nobel Prize

The Nobel Foundation, PO Box 5232,
102 45 Stockholm, Sweden
☎00 46 8 663 0920   Fax 00 46 8 660 3847
Contact *Information Section*

Awarded yearly for outstanding achievement in physics, chemistry, physiology or medicine, literature and peace. FOUNDED by Alfred Nobel, a chemist who proved his creative ability by inventing dynamite. In general, individuals cannot nominate someone for a Nobel Prize. The rules vary from prize to prize but the following are eligible to do so for Literature: members of the Swedish Academy and of other academies, institutions and societies similar to it in membership and aims; professors of history of literature or of languages at universities or colleges; Nobel Laureates in Literature; presidents of authors' organisations which are representative of the literary activities of their respective countries. British winners of the literature prize, first granted in 1901, include Rudyard Kipling, John Galsworthy and Winston Churchill. Recent winners: Seamus Heaney; Camilio Jose Cela (Spain); Octavio Paz (Mexico); Nadine Gordimer (South Africa); Derek Walcott (St Lucia); Toni Morrison (USA); Kenzaburo Oe (Japan); Wislawa Szymborska (Poland). Nobel Laureate in Literature 1997: Dario Fo (Italy).

Prize 1996: SEK7,500,000 (about £700,000), increasing each year to cover inflation.

The Noma Award for Publishing Africa

PO Box 128, Witney, Oxfordshire OX8 5XU
☎01993 775235   Fax 01991 709265
Contact *Mary Jay, Secretary to the Managing Committee*

ESTABLISHED 1979. Annual award, founded by the late Shoichi Noma, President of Kodansha Ltd, Tokyo, to encourage the publication of works by African writers and scholars within Africa. The award is for an outstanding book, published in Africa by an African writer, in three categories: scholarly and academic; literature and creative writing; children's books. Entries, by publishers only, by 31 March for a title published in the previous year. Maximum number of three entries. Previous winners: Paul Tiyambe Zeleza *A Modern Economic History of Africa – Vol 1: The Nineteenth Century*; Marlene van Niekerk *Triomf*; Kitia Touré *Destins Parallèles*; A. Adu Boahen *Mfantsipim and the Making of Ghana: A Centenary History 1876–1976*.

Prize US$ 10,000 and presentation plaque.

C. B. Oldman Prize

Aberdeen University Library, Queen Mother Library, Meston Walk, Aberdeen AB24 3UE
☎01224 272592   Fax 01224 487048
Contact *Richard Turbet*

ESTABLISHED 1989 by the International Association of Music Libraries, UK Branch. Annual award for best book of music bibliography, librarianship or reference published the year before last (i.e. books published in 1996 considered for the 1998 prize). Previous winners: Michael Twyman, Andrew Ashbee, Michael Talbot, Donald Clarke, John Parkinson, John Wagstaff, Stanley Sadie, William Waterhouse, Richard Turbet.

Prize £150.

Orange Prize for Fiction

Book Trust, 45 East Hill, London SW18 2QZ
☎0181 516 2977   Fax 0181 516 2978
Contact *Sandra Vince*

ESTABLISHED 1996. Annual award founded by a group of senior women in publishing to 'create the opportunity for more women to be rewarded for their work and to be better known by the reading public'. Awarded for a full-length novel written in English by a woman of any nationality, and published in the UK between 1 April and 31 March of the following year. 1998 winner: Carol Shields *Larry's Party*.

Prize £30,000 and a work of art (a limited edition bronze figurine to be known as 'The Bessie' in acknowledgement of anonymous prize endowment).

The Orwell Prize

The Political Quarterly, (Literary Editor), 8a Bellevue Terrace, Edinbugh EH7 4DT
☎0131 557 2517   Fax 0131 557 2517
Contact *Bernard Crick*

Jointly ESTABLISHED in 1993 by the George Orwell Memorial Fund and the *Political Quarterly* to encourage and reward writing in the spirit of Orwell's 'What I have most wanted to do ... is to make political writing into an art'. Two categories: book or pamphlet; newspaper and/or articles, features, columns, or sustained reportage on a theme. Submissions by editors or publishers only. 1997 winners: Ian Bell (journalism); Peter Godwin (book).

Prizes £1000 for each category.

Outposts Poetry Competition

Outposts, 22 Whitewell Road, Frome, Somerset BA11 4EL
☎01373 466653

Contact *Roland John*

Annual competition for an unpublished poem of not more than 60 lines run by **Hippopotamus Press**.

Prizes 1st £500, 2nd £200, 3rd £100.

OWG/COLA Awards for Excellence

Outdoor Writers' Guild, PO Box 520, Bamber Bridge, Preston, Lancashire PR5 8LF

☎01772 696732   Fax 01772 696732

Contact *Terry Marsh*

ESTABLISHED 1980. Annual award by the **Outdoor Writers' Guild** and the Camping & Outdoor Leisure Association to raise the standard of outdoor writing, journalism and broadcasting. Winning categories include best guidebook, best outdoor book, best feature, best photojournalism, best technical report. Open to OWG members only. Final entry date March.

Prize (total) £1250.

Catherine Pakenham Award

The Sunday Telegraph, 1 Canada Square, Canary Wharf, London E14 5DT

☎0171 538 6259   Fax 0171 513 2512

Contact *Lucy Goodwin*

ESTABLISHED in 1970, the award is designed to ecourage women journalists as they embark on their careers. Open to women aged 18–25 who have had at least one piece of work published. Previous winners: Elizabeth Brooks, Esther Oxford, Polly Toynbee.

Award £1000 and a writing commission with one of the Telegraph publications; three runner-up prizes of £200 each.

The Parker Pen Sonnet Romantic Novel of the Year 1998

11 Cranborne Gardens, Manor Road, Oadby, Leicester LE2 4EZ

☎0116 2715695

Contact *Award Organiser*

ESTABLISHED 1960. Formerly known as the Romantic Novelists' Association Major Award. Sponsorship for the 1998 award is by Parker Pen. Annual award for the best romantic novel of the year, open to non-members as well as members of the **Romantic Novelists' Association**. Novels must be published between specified dates which vary year to year. Authors must be based in the UK. 1997 winner: Susan Gee *The Hours of the Night*. Previous winners include: Rosamunde Pilcher *Coming Home*; Susan Kay

Phantom; Reay Tannahill *Passing Glory*; Elizabeth Buchan *Consider the Lily*; Charlotte Bingham *A Change of Heart*. Contact the Organiser for entry form.

Award £5000.

Peer Poetry Competition

26(w) Arlington House, Bath Street, Bath, Somerset BA1 1QN

☎01225 445298

Contact *Paul Amphlett*

Winners of this competition are chosen by poets and subscribers to *Peer Poetry* magazine. £10 paid for all qualifying groups of poems; *Peer Poetry* prints all qualifying entries. 'No size limits, eclectic range, for 35+ poets.' Entry fee: £4.50 for approximately 200 lines, 1000 words, presented double-column, single sides, name and address on reverse. Entry fee to poets who order the magazine (from address above): £7 inc. p&p. Closing dates: end April/October. Two s.a.e.s, one A4 size, essential; no entry form required.

PEN Awards

See **Macmillan Silver PEN Award**; **The Stern Silver PEN Non-Fiction Award**

Peterloo Poets Open Poetry Competition

2 Kelly Gardens, Calstock, Cornwall PL18 9SA

☎01822 833473

Contact *Lynn Chambers*

ESTABLISHED 1986. Annual competition for unpublished English language poems of not more than 40 lines. Final entry date 2 March. Previous winners: John Watts, David Craig, Rodney Pybus, Debjani Chatterjee, Donald Atkinson, Romesh Gunesekera, Shafi Ahmed, Anna Crowe, Carol Ann Duffy, Mimi Khalvati, John Lyons, M. R. Peacocke, Carol Shergold, David Simon, Maureen Wilkinson, Chris Woods.

Prize £4000 (1st).

Poem of the Month Competition

Erix Publications, 27 Old Gloucester Street, London WC1N 3XX

A monthly competition for poems of any style and length. No limit to the number of entries but they must be original work and previously unpublished. Entry fee of £3 per poem. Closing date is the last day of every month.

Prize £100. Winning poem will be published in *Poem of the Month* on the Internet (www.writing.co.uk).

Poetry Business Competition

The Studio, Byram Arcade, Westgate,
Huddersfield, West Yorkshire HD1 1ND
☎01484 434840   Fax 01484 426566

Contact *The Competition Administrator*

ESTABLISHED 1986. Annual award which aims
to discover and publish new writers. Entrants
should submit a manuscript of poems. Entry
fee £15. Winners will have their work published by the **Poetry Business** under the
Smith/Doorstop imprint. Final entry date: end
of October. Previous winners include: Pauline
Stainer, Michael Laskey, Mimi Khalvati, David
Morley, Julia Casterton, Liz Cashdan, Moniza
Alvi, Selima Hill. Send s.a.e. for full details.

Prize Publication of full collection; runners-
up have pamphlets; 20 complimentary copies.
Also cash prize (£1000) to be shared equally
between all winners.

Poetry Life Poetry Competition

Poetry Life, 14 Pennington Oval, Lymington,
Hampshire SO41 8BQ

Contact *Adrian Bishop*

ESTABLISHED 1993. Open competition for original poems in any style which have not been published in a book. Maximum length of 80 lines.
Entry fee of £3 per poem. Send s.a.e. for details.

Prize £500 (1st); £100 (2nd); £50 each (3rd
& 4th).

The Poetry Society's National Poetry Competition

The Poetry Society, 22 Betterton Street,
London WC2H 9BU
☎0171 420 9880   Fax 0171 240 4818

Contact *Competition Organiser*

One of Britian's major open poetry competitions. Closing date: 31 October. Poems on any
theme, up to 40 lines. For rules and entry form
send s.a.e. to the Competition Organiser at the
above address.

Prizes (1st) £5000; (2nd) £1000; (3rd) £500;
10 commendations of £50 plus a Mont Blanc
pen.

Peter Pook Humorous Novel Competition

See **Emissary Publishing** under
UK Publishers

The Portico Prize

The Portico Library, 57 Mosley Street,
Manchester M2 3HY
☎0161 236 6785

Contact *Miss Emma Marigliano*

ESTABLISHED 1985. Administered by the
Portico Library in Manchester. Biennial award
(odd-numbered years) for a published work of
fiction or non-fiction set wholly or mainly in
the North-West/Cumbria. Previous winners
include: John Stalker *Stalker*; Alan Hankinson
Coleridge Walks the Fells; Jenny Uglow *Elizabeth
Gaskell: A Habit of Stories*.

Prize £2500.

The Dennis Potter Television Play of the Year Award

Room 6022, BBC TV Centre, Wood Lane,
London W12 7RJ
☎0181 225 9513

ESTABLISHED 1994 in memory of the late television playwright to 'bring out courageous and
imaginative voices'. Annual award for writers
who have not had single plays produced on
television. Nominees are put forward by independent and BBC producers. 1998 winner:
Nick Stafford *Pity*.

Prize A commission for a first draft of single
drama.

Premio Langhe Ceretto – Per La Cultura Del Cibo

Biblioteca Civica 'G. Ferrero', Via Paruzza 1,
12051 Alba, Italy
☎00 39 173 290092   Fax 00 39 173 362075

Contact *Gianfranco Maggi*

ESTABLISHED 1991. Annual award, founded by
the wine company F. Lli Ceretto, for published
works dealing with historical, scientific, dieto-
logical, gastronomical or sociological aspects of
food and wine. Previous winners: E. Gowers,
A. Kanafani-Zahar, J. Bottero, S. L. Kaplan.

The Premio Valle Inclán

See **The Translators Association Awards**

The Mathew Prichard Award for Short Story Writing

95 Celyn Avenue, Lakeside, Cardiff CF2 6EL
Competition Secretary *Mrs Betty Persen*
Organiser *Philip Beynon*

ESTABLISHED 1996 to provide sponsorship and
promote Wales and its writers. Competition
open to all writers in English; the final entry
date is 1 March each year.

Prizes (1st) £1000; (2 runners–up) £250 each.

Pulitzer Prizes

The Pulitzer Prize Board, 709 Journalism,
Columbia University, New York NY 10027,
USA
☎001 212 854 3841/2

Awards for journalism in US newspapers, and for published literature, drama and music by American nationals. Deadlines: 1 February (journalism); 1 March (music); 1 March (drama); 1 July for books published between 1 Jan–30 June, and 1 Nov for books published between 1 July–31 Dec (literature). 1997 winners included: Steven Millhauser *Martin Dressler: The Tale of an American Dreamer*, Frank McCourt *Angela's Ashes*; Lisel Mueller *Alive Together: New and Selected Poems*; Richard Kluger *Ashes to Ashes: America's Hundred-Year Cigarette War, the Public Health and the Unabashed Triumph of Philip Morris*.

Puppy Lifeline Short Story and Poetry Competition

Farplace, Sidehead, Westgate, Co Durham DL13 1LE
☎01388 517397   Fax 01388 517044
Contact *Jan Edwards, National Fundraising Officer*

ESTABLISHED 1997 to help raise funds for Puppy Lifeline's rescue and rehoming work. Annual competition for writers and poets. Closing date for entries is 31 July each year. Submissions can be any length up to 5000 words; entry fee of £3 per short story and £2 per poem, payable to Puppy Lifeline. Send s.a.e. for details.

Prizes £100 (story); £60 (poem) plus runners-up prizes.

Real Writers

PO Box 170, Chesterfield, Derbyshire S40 1FE

ESTABLISHED 1994. Annual short story competition. Entry fee: £4. Optional critiques. Entry forms, rules and further details available from the above address.

Prize (1st) £1000.

Trevor Reese Memorial Prize

Institute of Commonwealth Studies, University of London, 28 Russell Square, London WC1B 5DS
☎0171 580 5876   Fax 0171 255 2160
Contact *Seminar and Conference Secretary*

ESTABLISHED 1979 with the proceeds of contributions to a memorial fund to Dr Trevor Reese, Reader in Commonwealth Studies at the Institute and a distinguished scholar of imperial history (d.1976). Biennial award (next award 2000) for a scholarly work, usually by a single author, in the field of Imperial and Commonwealth History published in the preceding two academic years. Final entry date: March 2000. All correspondence relating to

the prize should be marked *Trevor Reese Memorial Prize*.
Prize £1000.

Regional Press Awards

Press Gazette, Quantum House, 19 Scarbrook Road, Croydon, Surrey CR9 1LX
☎0181 565 4200   Fax 0181 565 4395

Comprehensive range of journalist and newspaper awards for the regional press. Five newspapers of the year, by circulation and frequency, and a full list of journalism categories. Open to all regional journalists, whether freelance or staff. June event. Run by the *Press Gazette* .

Renault UK Journalist of the Year Award

Guild of Motoring Writers, 30 The Cravens, Smallfield, Surrey RH6 9QS
☎01342 843294   Fax 01342 844093
Contact *Sharon Scott-Fairweather*

Originally the Pierre Dreyfus Award and ESTABLISHED 1977. Awarded annually by Renault UK Ltd in honour of Pierre Dreyfus, president director general of Renault 1955–75, to the member of the **Guild of Motoring Writers** who is judged to have made the most outstanding journalistic effort during the year.
Prize (1st) £1500, plus trophy.

The Rhône–Poulenc Prizes for Science Books

COPUS, c/o The Royal Society, 6 Carlton House Terrace, London SW1Y 5AG
☎0171 451 2579/2580   Fax 0171 451 2693
Contact *Imelda Topping*

ESTABLISHED 1988 by COPUS (Committee on the Public Understanding of Science) with the Science Museum. Sponsored by Rhône-Poulenc. Annual awards for popular non-fiction science and technology books judged to contribute most to the public understanding of science. Books must be published during the previous calendar year in their first English edition in the UK. The prizes, totalling £20,000, are divided between two categories: the Rhône-Poulenc Prize awarded for a book for general readership, and the Junior Prize for books written primarily for young people. Final entry date: January. 1997 winners: Alan Walker and Pat Shipman *The Wisdom of Bones*; Nick Arnold *Horrible Science* (series) (Junior Prize).

Prizes Rhône-Poulenc Prize £10,000; Junior Prize £10,000.

Rhyme International Prize

c/o Orbis Magazine, 27 Valley View,
Primrose, Jarrow, Tyne & Wear NE32 5QT
☎0191 4897055   Fax 0191 4301297
E-mail: Mshields12@aol.com or
MikeShields@compuserve.com

Contact *Mike Shields*

ESTABLISHED 1982. Annual competition aimed
at promoting rhyming poetry. Minimum entry
fee £5 (£2.50 per poem). Entries may fall into
two categories: rhymed poems of less than 50
lines; or formal: sonnet, villanelle, etc. Final
entry date: end September.
Prize (total) £1500.

John Llewellyn Rhys Prize

See **The Mail on Sunday/John Llewellyn
Rhys Prize**

Rio Tinto David Watt
Memorial Prize

Rio Tinto Plc, 6 St James's Square, London
SW1Y 4LD
☎0171 930 2399   Fax 0171 930 3249

Contact *The Administrator*

INITIATED in 1987 to commemorate the life and
work of David Watt. Annual award, open to
writers currently engaged in writing for English
language newspapers and journals, on international and political affairs. The winners are
judged as having made 'outstanding contributions towards the greater understanding and
promotion of national and international political issues'. Entries must have been published
during the year preceding the award. Final
entry date 31 March. The 1997 winner was
John Lloyd for his article 'Right and left to right
and wrong?', published in the *New Statesman*.
Previous winners include: Máire Nic Suibhne
for 'A paler shade of orange', published in the
Guardian Weekend; Martin Wolf for 'If you go
down to the woods today', published in the
Financial Times and David Rose for 'Silent
Revolution', published in the *Observer*.
Prize £5000.

Rogers Prize

Academic Trust Funds, Room 234,
University of London, Senate House, London
WC1E 7HU
☎0171 636 8000 ext. 3147

Contact *The Secretary of the Academic Trust
Funds*

Annual award for an essay or dissertation on
alternately a medical or surgical subject, which
is named and appointed by the University of

London – in 1998 for 'An Essay for an
Advance in Medicine'. Essays and dissertations
must be in English and shall be typewritten or
printed and submitted by 30 June.
Prize £250.

Romantic Novelists' Association
Major Award

See **The Parker Pen Sonnet Romantic
Novel of the Year 1998**

Rooney Prize for Irish Literature

Rooney Prize, Strathin, Templecarrig,
Delgany, Co. Wicklow, Republic of Ireland
☎00 353 1 287 4769   Fax 00 353 1 287 2595

Contact *Jim Sherwin, Barbara Norman*

ESTABLISHED 1976. Annual award to encourage young Irish writing to develop and continue. Authors must be Irish, under 40 and
published. A non-competitive award with no
application procedure.
Prize IR£5000.

Royal Economic Society Prize

c/o University of York, York YO1 5DD
☎01904 433764   Fax 01904 433575/9

Contact *Prof. Mike Wickens*

Annual award for the best article published in
The Economic Journal. Open to members of the
Royal Economic Society only. Next award
1999. Final entry date: December 1998. Previous
winners: Drs O. P. Attanasio & Guglielmo
Weber; Prof. M. H. Pesaran; Prof. J. Pemberton.
Prize £3000.

Royal Society of Literature Awards

See **Winifred Holtby Memorial Prize** and
W. H. Heinemann Prize

Runciman Award

Anglo-Hellenic League, Flat 4, 68 Elm Park
Gardens, London SW10 9PB
☎0171 352 2676   Fax 0171 351 5657

Contact *The Administrator*

ESTABLISHED 1985. Annual award, founded by
the Anglo-Hellenic League and funded by the
Onassis Foundation, to promote Anglo-Greek
understanding and friendship. Named after Sir
Steven Runciman, former chairman of the
Anglo-Hellenic League. Prizes are offered for
works in three historical categories: Greece
from earliest times to the foundation of
Constantinople, capital of the Roman Empire
at Byzantium, in 324; Byzantium and post-
Byzantium from 324 until 1821; the modern
Hellenic world from 1821 to the present.

Awards may be given for a work of fiction, drama or non-fiction; concerned academically or non-academically with the history of any period; biography or autobiography, the arts, archaeology; a guide book or a translation from the Greek of any period. Final entry date in February; awards presented in May. Previous winners include: *The Empire of Manuel I Komnenos 1143–1180* Paul Magdalino; *Crete: the Battle and the Resistance* Antony Beevor; *A Concise History of Greece* Richard Clogg; *An Introduction to Modern Greek Literature* Roderick Beaton; *The Diffusion of Classical Art in Antiquity* Sir John Boardman.
Awards up to £9000.

The SAGA Prize
Book Trust, Book House, 45 East Hill, London SW18 2QZ
☎0181 870 9055   Fax 0181 874 4790
Contact *Sandra Vince*
ESTABLISHED 1995. Annual award for the best unpublished novel by a black writer born in Great Britain or the Republic of Ireland and having a black African ancestor. Established by Marsha Hunt and sponsored by The SAGA Group. Mss must be unpublished and of no more than 80,000 words. Entry fee of £15 per mss. Final entry date is in June. 1997 winner: Judith Bryan *Bernard and the Cloth Monkey*.
Prize £3000 plus publication.

Sagittarius Prize
Society of Authors, 84 Drayton Gardens, London SW10 9SB
☎0171 373 6642   Fax 0171 373 5768
ESTABLISHED 1990. For first published novel by an author over the age of 60. Final entry date: mid–December. 1997 winner: Barbara Hardy *London Lovers*.
Prize £2000.

The Saltire Literary Awards
Saltire Society, 9 Fountain Close, 22 High Street, Edinburgh EH1 1TF
☎0131 556 1836   Fax 0131 557 1675
Administrator *Kathleen Munro*
ESTABLISHED 1982. Annual awards, one for Book of the Year, the other for Best First Book by an author publishing for the first time. Open to any author of Scottish descent or living in Scotland, or to anyone who has written a book which deals with either the work and life of a Scot or with a Scottish problem, event or situation. Nominations are invited from editors of leading newspapers, magazines and periodicals.

Previous winners: Scottish Book of the Year: *Grace Notes* Bernard MacLaverty; Best First Book: *A Painted Field* Robin Robertson.
Prizes £5000 (Scottish Book); £1500 (First Book).

Sandburg–Livesay Anthology Contest
Mekler & Deahl, Publishers, 237 Prospect Street South, Hamilton, Ontario, Canada L8M 2Z6
☎001 905 312 1779   Fax 001 905 312 8285
E-mail: meklerdeahl@globalserve.net
Contact *James Deahl, Gilda Mekler*
FOUNDED 1996. Annual award named after the poets Carl Sandburg and Dorothy Livesay to honour their achievement as populist poets. Up to ten poems may be entered for a fee of £5. A copy of the rules is available from the above address. Final entry date: 31 October. 1997 winners: Ronnie R. Brown (Canada), Joan Woodcock (UK).
Prizes 1st £50, 2nd £25; anthology publication for the winners and all other worthy entries.

Aileen and Albert Sanders Memorial Trophy
13 Milton Crescent, Leicester LE4 0PA
☎0116 2341420
Contact *Ivan Sanders*
Annual poetry competition. Entry fees: £5 for up to two poems, £10 for up to five (maximum per competitor). Rules and entry forms available from the address above.
Prizes 1st £500 plus trophy and certificate; nine runners-up prizes and certificates.

Schlegel–Tieck Prize
See **The Translators Association Awards**

Scottish Arts Council Book Awards
Scottish Arts Council, 12 Manor Place, Edinburgh EH3 7DD
☎0131 226 6051   Fax 0131 225 9833
Literature Officer *Gavin Wallace*
A number of awards are given biannually to authors of published books in recognition of high standards in new writing from new and established writers. Authors should be Scottish, resident in Scotland or have published books of Scottish interest. Applications from publishers only.
Award £1000 each.

Scottish Book of the Year
See **The Saltire Literary Awards**

Scottish International Open Poetry Competition
42 Tollerton Drive, Irvine, Ayrshire KA12 0ER
Contact *The Administrator*

ESTABLISHED in 1972 in association with Ayrshire Writers and Artists Society by Henry Mair and patronised by Hugh MacDiarmid. Open to poets worldwide for poems written in English or Scots and which have not been published or broadcast. All entries to be accompanied by an s.a.e. or IRCs (for international entries). Contact the administrator for further details.

Prizes 1st £100 and The MacDiarmid Trophy; Scottish section, The Clement Wilson Trophy; International Trophy.

The Scottish Writer of the Year Prize
See **The Stakis Prize for the Scottish Writer of the Year Prize**

SCSE Book Prizes
Department of Education Studies, University of Reading, Bulmershe Court, Reading, Berkshire RG6 1HY
☎01189 318861   Fax 01189 318863
Contact *Professor P. Croll*

Annual awards given by the Standing Conference on Studies in Education for the best book on education published during the preceding year and for the best book by a new author. Nomination by members of the Standing Conference and publishers.

Prizes £1000 and £500.

The Seebohm Trophy – Age Concern Book of the Year
1268 London Road, London SW16 4ER
☎0181 679 8000/0181 765 7456
Contact *Vinnette Marshall, Jane Marsh*

ESTABLISHED 1995. Annual award in memory of the late Lord Seebohm, former President of Age Concern England. Awarded to the author and publisher of a non-fiction title published in the previous calendar year which, in the opinion of the judges, is most successful in promoting the well-being and understanding of older people. Final entry by the end of March for presentation in October. 1997 winner: *Epidemiology in Old Age* eds. S. Ebrahim and A. Kalache.

Prize £1000 (author); Trophy (publisher), for one year.

Seeds Poetry Contest
412–701 King Street West, Suite 412, Toronto, Ontario, Canada M5V 2W7
E-mail: writers@pathcom.com
Website: http://www.pathcom.com/~writers

International competition for poems which are optimistic expressions of life, society and nature (the theme of *Seeds* magazine). No electronic submissions. Entry fee: US$15. Deadline at the end of April.

Prizes 1st $100 and publication in *Seeds* magazine and website.

Bernard Shaw Translation Prize
See **The Translators Association Awards**

Signal Poetry for Children Award
Thimble Press, Lockwood, Station Road, South Woodchester, Stroud, Gloucestershire GL5 5EQ
☎01453 873716/872208   Fax 01453 878599
Contact *Nancy Chambers*

This award is given annually for particular excellence in one of the following areas: single-poet collections published for children; poetry anthologies published for children; the body of work of a contemporary poet; critical or educational activity promoting poetry for children. All books for children published in Britain are eligible regardless of the original country of publication. Unpublished work is not eligible. Previous winners include: Philip Gross *The All-Nite Café*; Helen Dunmore *Secrets*.

Award £100 plus certificate designed by Michael Harvey.

André Simon Memorial Fund Book Awards
5 Sion Hill Place, Bath BA1 5SJ
☎01225 336305   Fax 01225 421862
Contact *Tessa Hayward*

ESTABLISHED 1978. Three awards given annually for the best book on drink, best on food and special commendation in either. Previous winners: Claudia Roden *The Book of Jewish Food*; Clive Coats *Côte d'Or*; Maria Kaneva-Johnson *The Melting Pot – Balkan Food and Cookery*; Janet Mendel *Traditional Spanish Cooking*; Sophie D. Coe and Michael D. Coe *The True History of Chocolate* (special commendation).

Awards £2000 (best books); £1000 (special commendation); £200 to shortlisted books.

Smarties Book Prize

Book Trust, Book House, 45 East Hill,
London SW18 2QZ
☎0181 516 2977   Fax 0181 516 2978
Contact *Sandra Vince*

ESTABLISHED 1985 to encourage high standards
and stimulate interest in books for children, this
prize is given for a children's book (fiction),
written in English by a citizen of the UK or an
author resident in the UK, and published in the
UK in the year ending 31 October. There are
three age-group categories: 5 and under, 6–8
and 9–11. Previous winners include: *Ginger*
Charlotte Voake (5 and under, gold); *The Owl
Tree* Jenny Nimmo (6–8, gold); *Harry Potter and
the Philosopher's Stone* J. K. Rowling (9–11,
gold).
  Prizes in each category: £2,500 (gold);
£1000 (silver); £500 (bronze).

W. H. Smith Literary Award

W. H. Smith Ltd., Audrey House, Ely Place,
London EC1N 6SN
☎0171 269 2625   Fax 0171 269 2635
Contact *Anna Passey*

FOUNDED 1959. Annual prize awarded to a UK,
Republic of Ireland or Commonwealth citizen
for the most oustanding contribution to English
literature, published in English in the UK in the
preceding year. Writers cannot submit work
themselves. Previous winners include: Alice
Munro *Open Secrets*; Vikram Seth *A Suitable Boy*;
Michèle Robert *Daughters of the House*; Thomas
Pakenham *The Scramble for Africa*; Derek Walcott
Omeros; Simon Schama *Landscape and Memory*.
Four previous winners have gone on to win the
Nobel Prize for Literature – Derek Walcott,
Nadine Gordimer, Patrick White and Seamus
Heaney.
  Prize £10,000.

W. H. Smith's Thumping Good Read Award

W. H. Smith Ltd., Greenbridge Road,
Swindon, Wiltshire SN3 3LD
☎01793 616161   Fax 01793 562590
Contact *Catherine Hickson*

ESTABLISHED 1992 to promote new writers of
popular fiction. Books must have been published in the 12 months preceding the award.
Submissions, made by publishers, are judged by
a panel of customers to be the most un-put-
down-able from a shortlist of six. Final entry
date: February each year. Previous winners:
Robert Harris *Fatherland*; Thomas Eidson *St*

Agnes' Stand; Andrew Klavan *True Crime*. 1998
winner: Douglas Kennedy *The Big Picture*.
  Award £5000.

W. H. Smith's Young Writers' Competition

Dept. GWC, PO Box 985, Swindon
SN38 7XU
☎01793 451300

Annual awards for poems or prose by anyone
in the UK aged 16 or under. There are four
age groups. Over 60 individual winners have
their work included in a paperback every year.
  Prize (total) over £7000.

Sony Radio Awards

Alan Zafer & Associates, 47–48 Chagford
Street, London NW1 6EB
☎0171 723 0106   Fax 0171 724 6163
E-mail: zafer@compuserve.com
Contact *Alan Zafer*

ESTABLISHED 1981 by the **Society of
Authors**. Sponsored by Sony and presented in
association with the Radio Academy. Annual
awards to recognise excellence in radio broadcasting. Entries must have been broadcast in
the UK between 1 January and 31 December
in the year preceding the award. The categories
for the awards are reviewed each year.

Southern Arts Literature Prize

Southern Arts, 13 St Clement Street,
Winchester, Hampshire SO23 9DQ
☎01962 855099   Fax 01962 861186
Contact *Literature Officer*

ESTABLISHED 1991, this prize is awarded annually to an author living in the **Southern Arts**
region for the most promising work of prose or
poetry published during the year. The 1998
prize will be awarded for literary non-fiction.
Previous winner: Jon Stallworthy *Louis
MacNeice* (biography). Final entry date: 30 June.
  Prize £1000, plus a craft commission to the
value of £600.

Southport Writers' Circle Poetry Competition

32 Dover Road, Southport, Merseyside
PR8 4TB
Contact *Mrs Hilary Tinsley*

For previously unpublished work. Entry fee:
£1.50 first poem, plus £1 for each subsequent
entry. Open category (any subject any form) and
humorous category; maximum 40 lines. Closing
date: end April. Poems must be entered under a

pseudonym, accompanied by a sealed envelope marked with the pseudonym and title of poem, containing s.a.e. Entries must be typed on A4 paper and be accompanied by the appropriate fee payable to Southport Writers' Circle. No application form is required. Envelopes should be marked 'Poetry Competition'. Postal enquiries only. No calls.

Prizes (1st) £100; (2nd) £50; (3rd) £25 in each category.

Ian St James Awards

c/o The New Writers' Club, PO Box 60, Cranbrook, Kent TN17 2ZR
☎01580 212626   Fax 01580 212041

ESTABLISHED 1989. Administered by the New Writers' Club. Presented annually to approximately 10 writers of short stories. These awards are 'an opportunity for talented and as yet unpublished writers to achieve recognition'. Ian St James is a successful novelist who hopes to attract both literary and commercial fiction from aspiring writers. Winning entries are published in a paperback anthology. The Ian St James Awards are open to international writers who have not had a novel or novella previously published. Final entry date: 30 April each year. Previous top prize winners: Kate Atkinson *Karmic Mothers*; Joshua Davidson *The Saviour*; Anna McGrail *The Welfare of the Patient*. Entry forms available from around October from above address.

Award Top prize: £2000 plus runners-up cash prizes. Shortlisted stories are published throughout the year in *The New Writer* magazine.

The Stakis Prize for the Scottish Writer of the Year Prize

c/o Book Trust Scotland, The Scottish Book Centre, 137 Dundee Street, Edinburgh EH11 1BG
☎0131 229 3663   Fax 0131 228 4293

Contact *Kathryn Ross*

ESTABLISHED 1987. Sponsored by Stakis for the best substantial work of an imaginative nature, including TV and radio scripts and writing for children (for 8–16 years), first published, performed, filmed or transmitted between 1st August and 31st July. Writers born in Scotland, or who have Scottish parents, or who have been resident in Scotland for a considerable period, or who take Scotland as their inspiration are all eligible. Submissions accepted in English, Scots or Gaelic. Recent winners: Janice Galloway, Alan Spence and Aonghas MacNeacail.

Prize £10,000, plus £1,000 to each of the other four shortlisted writers.

Stand Magazine Poetry Competition

Stand Magazine, 179 Wingrove Road, Newcastle upon Tyne NE4 9DA
☎0191 273 3280

Contact *The Administrator*

Biennial award for poems written in English and not yet published, broadcast or under consideration elsewhere. Next award 2000. Final entry date: 30 June 2000. Send s.a.e. for entry form.

Prize (total) £2500.

Stand Magazine Short Story Competition

Stand Magazine, 179 Wingrove Road, Newcastle upon Tyne NE4 9DA
☎0191 273 3280

Contact *The Administrator*

Biennial award for short stories written in English and not yet published, broadcast or under consideration elsewhere. Next award 1999. Closing date: 30 June 1999. Send s.a.e. for entry form.

Prize (total) £2500.

Staple First Editions Project/ Staple Open Poetry Competition

Tor Cottage, 81 Cavendish Road, Matlock, Derbyshire DE4 3HD
☎01629 582764

Contact *Donald Measham*

Two biennial open competitions run by *Staple* magazine. The Open Poetry Competition is run on even years and the First Editions Project, which is for single-author collections (poetry, prose), is on odd years. Final entry date: 1 February. Publication of winning poetry monograph, July 2000; of fiction collection, March 2001.

Prizes Poetry: 1st £250 and £50 of Carcanet books of poet's choice; 2nd £100 and £25 of Carcanet books; 3rd £50 and 10 prizes of £20. First Editions Project: half shares of £500, complimentary copies, publication, promotion and distribution to subscribers and to the book trade.

The Stern Silver PEN Non-Fiction Award

English Centre of International PEN, 7 Dilke Street, London SW3 4JE
☎0171 352 6303   Fax 0171 351 0220

ESTABLISHED 1986 and sponsored, from 1997, by the family of James Stern in memory of their father. An annual award for an outstanding work of non-fiction written in English and published in England in the year preceding the prize. Nominations by the PEN Executive Committee only. Please do not submit books. Previous winners: John Hale *The Civilization of Europe in the Renaissance*; Eric Hobsbawm *Age of Extremes*; Neal Ascherson *Black Sea*; Hugo Vickers *The Kiss*.

Prize £1000, plus silver pen.

Sunday Times Award for Excellence in Writing

The Sunday Times, 1 Pennington Street, London E1 9XW
☎0171 782 5774   Fax 0171 782 5798
Contact *The Literary Editor*

ESTABLISHED 1987. Annual award to fiction and non-fiction writers. The panel consists of *Sunday Times* journalists, publishers and other figures from the book world. 1997 winner: Harold Pinter. Previous winners: Anthony Burgess, Seamus Heaney, Stephen Hawking, Ruth Rendell, Muriel Spark, William Trevor, Martin Amis, Ted Hughes. No applications; prize at the discretion of the Literary Editor.

Sunday Times Award for Small Publishers

Independent Publishers Guild, 25 Cambridge Road, Hampton, Middlesex TW12 2JL
☎0181 979 0250   Fax 0181 979 6393
Contact *Yvonne Messenger*

ESTABLISHED 1988, the first winner was **Fourth Estate**. Open to any publisher producing between five and forty titles a year, which must primarily be original titles, not reprints. Entrants are invited to submit their catalogues for the last twelve months, together with two representative titles. Previous winners: **Nick Hern Books**; **Tarquin Publications**; **Ellipsis**. 1997 winner: **Bradt Publications**.

Sunday Times Young Writer of the Year Award

The Society of Authors, 84 Drayton Gardens, London SW10 9SB
☎0171 373 6642   Fax 0171 373 5768
Contact *Awards Secretary*

ESTABLISHED 1991. Annual award given on the strength of the promise shown by a full-length published work of fiction, non-fiction, poetry or drama. Entrants must be British citizens, res-

ident in Britain and under the age of 35 at the closing date of 31 December. The work must be by one author, in the English language, and published in Britain during the 12 months prior to the closing date. Full details available from the above address. Previous winners: Katherine Pierpoint *Truffle Beds*; Andrew Cowan *Pig*; William Dalrymple *City of Djinns*; Simon Armitage *Xanadu and Kid*.

Prize £5000.

The Talkies

9–10 Barnard Mews, London SW11 1QU
☎0171 582 0536   Fax 0171 582 4917
Contact *Peter Dean, Sean King, Samantha Warren*

Annual award ESTABLISHED in 1995 by *Talking Business* magazine to recognise the best in spoken word publishing, production, design and retailing. There are 19 awards with the 'Talkie of the Year' being picked from the winners of all the categories. Contact *Talking Business* for entry form. Final entry date: late July. Previous Talkie of the Year winners: *Alan Bennett Diaries*; *This Sceptred Isle*.

Prizes Framed certificate for all winners, plus logo award for Best Reader and Talkie of the Year.

Reginald Taylor and Lord Fletcher Essay Prize

Journal of the British Archaeological Association, Institute of Archaelogy, 36 Beaumont Street, Oxford OX1 2PG
Contact *Dr Martin Henig*

A biennial prize, in memory of the late E. Reginald Taylor and of Lord Fletcher, for the best unpublished essay, not exceeding 7500 words, on a subject of archaeological, art history or antiquarian interest within the period from the Roman era to AD 1830. The essay should show *original* research on its chosen subject, and the author will be invited to read the essay before the Association. The prize is now included in the British Archaeological Awards scheme and the presentation will be made along with the other awards in November 2000. The essay may be published in the journal of the Association if approved by the Editorial Committee. Closing date for entries is 1 June 2000. All enquiries by post please. No phone calls. Send s.a.e. for details.

Prize £300 and a medal.

The Teixeira Gomes Prize

See **The Translators Association Awards**

Telegraph Young Food & Drink Writer of the Year Award

The Daily Telegraph, 1 Canada Square, Canary Wharf, London E14 5DT
☎0171 538 6259   Fax 0171 513 2512

Contact *Vicky Hurley*

ESTABLISHED 1997. An award designed to allow young people, between the ages of 18 and 25, to review a meal, wherever eaten, showing talent and a sense of humour.

Prizes Winner and runner-up will have an opportunity to write a feature on food and drink at a restaurant abroad. Second prize is likewise to write a 500-word piece that will be placed next to the winners. Five further runners-up will each receive a bottle of port and a book.

David Thomas Prize

See entry under **Bursaries, Fellowships and Grants**

Anne Tibble Poetry Competition

Events Team, Directorate of Environment Services, Northampton Borough Council, Cliftonville House, Bedford Road, Northampton NN4 7NR
☎01604 238791   Fax 01604 238796

Entries should preferably be typed, 20 lines maximum, any subject. Writers must be resident in the UK; categories for children under 11 and under 16.

Prize £200 (1st).

The Times Educational Supplement Books and Resources Awards

Times Educational Supplement, Admiral House, 66–68 East Smithfield, London E1 9XY
☎0171 782 3000   Fax 0171 782 3200

Contact *Literary Editor*

ESTABLISHED 1973. Annual awards made for the best books used in schools, and for innovative mixed media resources (first awarded in 1996). The books must have been published in Britain. Previous winners: Junior Information Book Award: *What's the Big Idea? Time and the Universe* Mary and John Gribbin; Senior Information Book Award: *Big Bang* Heather Cooper and Nigel Henbest. Primary Mathematics Schoolbook Award: *Learning Mathematics in the Nursery: Desirable Approaches* The Early Childhood Mathematics Group; Secondary Mathematics Schoolbook Award: *Nelson Secondary Maths Extension Book* Jim Noonan, Paula Barker, Terry Bevis, Gay Cain, Brian Martin, Christine Mitchell, Robert Powell, Gwen Wood.

The Tir Na N-Og Award

Cyngor Llyfrau Cymru (Welsh Books Council), Castell Brychan, Aberystwyth, Dyfed SY23 2JB
☎01970 624151   Fax 01970 625385

An annual award given to the best original book published for children in the year prior to the announcement. There are three categories: Best Welsh Fiction; Best Welsh Non-fiction; Best English Book with an authentic Welsh background.

Awards £1000 (each category).

TLS/Blackwells Poetry Competition

Times Literary Supplement, Admiral House, 66–68 East Smithfield, London E1 9XY
☎0171 782 3000

Contact *Mick Imlah (Poetry Editor, TLS)*

ESTABLISHED 1997. Annual open competition. Final entry date: 1 November 1998. 1997 winner: Douglas Weir.

Prizes £2000; three runners-up £500 each.

Marten Toonder Award

An Chomhairle Ealaíon (The Arts Council), 70 Merrion Square, Dublin 2, Republic of Ireland
☎00 353 1 6180200   Fax 00 353 1 6761302

Literature Officer *Sinead MacAodha*

A triennial award for creative writing. Next award will be offered in Literature in 2001. Given to an established writer in recognition of achievement. Open to Irish citizens or residents only.

Award IR£4500.

The Translators Association Awards

The Translators Association, 84 Drayton Gardens, London SW10 9SB
☎0171 373 6642   Fax 0171 373 5768

Contact *Kate Pool*

Various awards for translations into English from, for example, Dutch and Flemish (The Vondel Translation Prize), French (Scott Moncrieff Prize), German (Schlegel-Tieck Prize), Italian (The John Florio Prize), Portuguese (The Teixeira Gomes Prize), Spanish (The Premio Velle Inclán), and Swedish (Bernard Shaw Translation Prize).

The Betty Trask Prize

See entry under **Bursaries, Fellowships and Grants**

The Trewithen Poetry Prize

Treskewes Cottage, Trewithen Moor,
Stithians, Truro, Cornwall TR3 7DU
Contact *Competition Secretary*

ESTABLISHED 1995 in order to promote poetry
with a rural theme. Entry forms available from
the above (enclose s.a.e.). Closing date: 31
October. Entry fee of £2.50 for first poem,
£1.50 for subsequent entries. Previous winners
include: Elizabeth Rapp, David Smart, Sylvia
Oldroyd, Ann Drysdale.

Prizes (total) £600 plus publication in *The
Trewithen Chapbook.*

The Tullie House Prize

See **Lakeland Book of the Year Awards**

UNESCO/PEN Short Story Competition

English Centre of International PEN,
7 Dilke Street, London SW3 4JE
☎0171 352 6303

ESTABLISHED 1993. Biennial award, funded by
UNESCO and administered by the English
Centre of PEN. It is intended to reward the
efforts of those who write in English despite
the fact that it is not their mother tongue (the
Irish, Scots and Welsh are not eligible). Entries
in the form of short stories not exceeding 1500
words should be submitted to the writer's
home country PEN centre and not to the
London office. The top three entries are then
forwarded to the English PEN centre for final
judging. Final entry date: end December of
year preceding award. First awarded March
1993. Previous winners: Jerome Mandel,
Aleksander Hemon, Ding Shihezhi.

Prizes (1st) $3000; (2nd) $2000; (3rd) $500.

Unicorn Arts Theatre National Young Playwrights' Competition

Unicorn Theatre for Children, Arts Theatre,
Great Newport Street, London WC2H 7JB
☎0171 379 3280   Fax 0171 836 5366
Contact *Ruth Burgess*

Annual awards to young playwrights aged 6–16
for plays on a theme decided by the theatre.
Three age groups: 6–8; 9–12; 13–16. The plays
are judged by a committee of writers. The
winners take part in workshops on the plays
with members of the Unicorn Theatre professional company, with rehearsed readings on
stage the following spring. Final entry date: end
December.

T. E. Utley Memorial Award

111 Sugden Road, London SW11 5ED
☎0171 228 3900
Contact *The Secretary*

Annual award ESTABLISHED 1988 in memory of
the political journalist T. E. Utley. In 1996,
two awards were given for unpublished essays
by aspiring journalists who were still at school
or university.

Prizes £2500 (under 25); £1500 (under 18).

Ver Poets Open Competition

Haycroft, 61–63 Chiswell Green Lane, St
Albans, Hertfordshire AL2 3AL
☎01727 867005
Contact *May Badman*

Various competitions are organised by **Ver
Poets**, the main one being the annual Open for
unpublished poems of no more than 30 lines
written in English. Entry fee: £2.50 per poem.
Entries must be made under a pseudonym, with
name and address on form or separate sheet.
Vision On, the anthology of winning and selected
poems, and the adjudicators' report are normally
available from mid-June. Final entry date: 30
April. Back numbers of the anthology are available for £2, post-free.

Prizes (1st) £500; (2nd) £300; two runners-
up £100.

Vogue Talent Contest

Vogue, Vogue House, Hanover Square,
London W1R 0AD
☎0171 499 9080   Fax 0171 408 0559
Contact *Frances Bentley*

ESTABLISHED 1951. Annual award for young
writers and journalists (under 25 on 1 January
in the year of the contest). Final entry date:
mid–April. Entrants must write three pieces of
journalism on given subjects.

Prizes £1000, plus a month's paid work
experience with *Vogue*; (2nd) £500.

The Vondel Translation Prize

See **The Translators Association Awards**

Wadsworth Prize for Business History

Business Archives Council, The Clove
Building, 4 Maguire Street, London SE1 2NQ
☎0171 407 6110
Chairman *Mrs Lenore Symons*

ESTABLISHED 1978. Annual award for the best
book published on British business history.

Previous winners: Dr Richard Saville *Bank of Scotland, A History 1695–1995*; Dr T. R. Gourvish and Dr R. Wilson *The British Brewing Industry: A History*.
Prize £500.

Arts Council of Wales Book of the Year Awards

Arts Council of Wales, Museum Place, Cardiff CF1 3NX
☎01222 394711   Fax 01222 221447
Contact *Tony Bianchi*

Annual non-competitive prizes awarded for works of exceptional literary merit written by Welsh authors (by birth or residence), published in Welsh or English during the previous calendar year. There is one major prize in English, the Book of the Year Award, and one major prize in Welsh, Gwobr Llyfr y Flwyddyn. Shortlists of three titles in each language are announced in April; winners announced in May.
Prizes £3000 (each); £1000 to each of four runners-up.

Walford Award

See **The Library Association Walford Award**

(Wandsworth) London Writers Competition

Room 224A, The Town Hall, Wandsworth High Street, London SW18 2PU
☎0181 871 7037   Fax 0181 871 7630
Contact *Wandsworth Arts Office*

An annual competition, open to all writers of 16 or over who live, work or study in the Greater London area. Previously unpublished work may be submitted in the poetry or short story categories.
Prizes £1000 for each category, divided between the top three entries; plus two runners-up.

The Harri Webb Prize

10 Heol Don, Whitchurch, Cardiff CF4 2AU
☎01222 623359   Fax 01222 529202
Contact *Meic Stephens*

ESTABLISHED 1995. Annual competition to commemorate the Welsh poet, Harri Webb (1920–94), for a single poem in any of the categories in which he wrote: ballad, satire, song, polemic. The poems are chosen by three adjudicators; no submissions. 1997 winner: Steve Short.
Prize £100.

The Weidenfeld Translation Prize

European Humanities Research Centre, The Queen's College, Oxford OX1 4AW
☎01865 279183/244701
Contact *The Fellows' Secretary*

ESTABLISHED in 1996 by publisher Lord Weidenfeld to encourage good translation into English. Annual award to the translator(s) of a work of fiction, poetry or drama written in any living European language. Submissions from publishers only. For further information, contact Dr David Constantine at the Queen's College address above. 1997 winner: Colin Smith *The King Amaz'd* by Gonzalo Torrente Ballester.
Prize £1000.

Wellington Town Council Award

Civic Offices, Tan Bank, Wellington, Telford, Shropshire TF1 1LX
☎01952 222935   Fax 01952 222936
Contacts *Martin Scholes, Derrick Drew*

ESTABLISHED 1995. Annual short story competition to promote the ancient town of Wellington, now part of the Wellington annual literary festival. Open to all for a minimum fee of £2.50; prizes are sponsored so all entry fee monies go to charity. 1997 winners: Charles Warren (Overall winner); Michael Herschell (Best Shropshire Entry); Lucy Lind and Lilian Parker (Joint winners, Best Story for Children).
Prizes Trophies and money.

Wheatley Medal

See **The Library Association Wheatley Medal**

Whitbread Book of the Year and Literary Awards

Minster House, 272 Vauxhall Bridge Road, London SW1V 1BA
☎0171 834 5477   Fax 0171 834 8812
Contact *Gillian Cronin*

ESTABLISHED 1971. Publishers are invited to submit books for this annual competition designed for writers who have been resident in Great Britain or the Republic of Ireland for three years or more. The awards are made in two stages. First, nominations are selected in four categories: novel, first novel, biography and poetry. One of these is then voted by the panel of judges as Whitbread Book of the Year. 1997 winners: Jim Crace *Quarantine* (novel); Pauline Melville *The Ventriloquist* (first novel); Graham Robb *Victor Hugo* (biography); Ted Hughes *Tales From Ovid* (poetry and Book of the Year).

For the first time, in 1996, the Children's Award was separated out into the Whitbread Children's Book of the Year Award, the 1997 winner being Andrew Norriss for *Aquila*.

Awards £21,000 (Book of the Year); £10,000 (Children's); £2000 (all nominees).

Whitfield Prize

Royal Historical Society, University College London, Gower Street, London WC1E 6BT
☎0171 387 7532   Fax 0171 387 7532
Contact *Executive Secretary*

ESTABLISHED 1977. An annual award for the best new work within a field of British history, published in the UK in the preceding calendar year. The book must be the author's first (solely written) history book and be an original and scholarly work of historical research. Final entry date: end December.

Prize £1000.

John Whiting Award

Arts Council of England, 14 Great Peter Street, London SW1P 3NQ
☎0171 333 0100 ext 6431 Fax 0171 973 6590
Contact *The Drama Director*

FOUNDED 1965. Annual award to commemorate the life and work of the playwright John Whiting (*The Devils, A Penny for a Song*). Any writer who has received during the previous two calendar years an award through the **Arts Council's Theatre Writing Schemes** or who has had a première production by a theatre company in receipt of annual subsidy is eligible to apply. Awarded to the writer whose play most nearly satisfies the following criteria: a play in which the writing is of special quality; a play of relevance and importance to contemporary life; a play of potential value to the British theatre. Closing date for entries: 7 January 1999.

Prize £6000.

Alfred and Mary Wilkins International £2000 Prize Memorial Poetry Competition

Birmingham & Midland Institute, 9 Margaret Street, Birmingham B3 3BS
☎0121 236 3591   Fax 0121 212 4577
Administrator *Mr P. A. Fisher*

An annual competition for an unpublished poem not exceeding 40 lines, written in English by an author over the age of 15. The poem should not have been entered for any other poetry competition. Nineteen prizes awarded in all.

Prizes (total) £2000.

Griffith John Williams Memorial Prize

3rd Floor, Mount Stuart House, Mount Stuart Square, Cardiff CF1 6DQ
☎01222 492064   Fax 01222 492930
Contact *Dafydd Rogers*

FOUNDED 1965. Biennial award in honour of the first president of the **Welsh Academy** which aims to promote writing in Welsh. Entries must be the first published work of authors/poets writing in Welsh. Work must have been published in the two-year period preceding the award.

Award £400.

Raymond Williams Community Publishing Prize

Literature Dept, Arts Council of England, 14 Great Peter Street, London SW1P 3NQ
☎0171 333 0100   Fax 0171 973 6590
Contact *Karen Woods*

ESTABLISHED 1990. Award for published work of outstanding creative and imaginative quality which reflects the voices and experiences of the people of particular communities. Submissions may be in the form of poetry, fiction, biography, autobiography, drama, providing they are literary in quality and intent. They are likely to be produced by small community or cooperative presses, but other forms of publication will be considered. Final entry date: end April. Winner announced in July. 1997 winner: *Portobello, Its People, Its Past, Its Present* by Sharon Whetlor and Liz Bartlett, published by the Kensington & Chelsea Community History Group.

Prizes (1st) £3000; runner-up £2000. Prizes are divided between publisher and author.

H. H. Wingate Prize

See **Jewish Quarterly Literary Prize**

Wolfson History Prizes

Wolfson Foundation, 18–22 Haymarket, London SW1Y 4DQ
☎0171 930 1057   Fax 0171 930 1036
Contact *Executive Secretary*

ESTABLISHED 1972. An award made annually to authors of published historical works, with the object of encouraging historians to communicate with general readers as well as with their professional colleagues. Previous winners: Fiona MacCarthy *William Morris*; John G. C. Rohl *The Kaiser and His Court: Wilhelm II and the Government of Germany*; Lord Skidelsky *John Maynard Keynes: The Economist as Saviour 1920–1937*.

Prize (total) £25,000.

Woolwich Young Radio Playwrights' Competition

Independent Radio Drama Productions Ltd, PO Box 518, Manningtree, Essex CO11 1XD
Contact *Marja Giejgo*

ESTABLISHED 1990 and sponsored by the Woolwich Plc, with writer Carla Lane as patron. This is a national scheme which aims to discover and professionally produce radio drama writing talent among young people aged 25 and under. The competition involves national and regional script writing competitions with various workshop programmes at independent and BBC local radio stations. Send s.a.e. for further details. Writers selected for production receive a **Writers' Guild** approved contract.

The Writers Bureau Poetry and Short Story Competition

The Writers Bureau, Sevendale House, 7 Dale Street, Manchester M1 1JB
☎0161 228 2362
Competition Secretary *Angela Cox*

ESTABLISHED 1994. Annual award. Poems should be no longer than 40 lines and short stories no more than 2000 words. £3.50 entry fee.
Prizes in each category: (1st) £300; (2nd) £200; (3rd) £100.

The Writers' Guild Awards

430 Edgware Road, London W2 1EH
☎0171 723 8074   Fax 0171 706 2413

Originally ESTABLISHED 1961 and relaunched in 1991. Five categories of awards: radio (original drama, comedy/light entertainment, dramatisations); theatre (West End, fringe, regional, children's); books (non-fiction, fiction, children's); film (best screenplay); television (original play/film, original drama series, original drama serial, dramatisation/adaptation, situation comedy, light entertainment, children's). There are also awards for: Non-English Language, New Writer of the Year (won by Ayub Khan-Din in 1997), Lifetime Achievement (won by John McGrath in 1997) and The Writers' Guild Award which is given to an individual or institution in recognition of their outstanding contribution towards the developing and fostering of new writing in any field represented by the Guild (won by Gordon House of BBC World Service in 1997). The various short-lists are prepared by a different jury in each category and presented to the full Guild membership for its final vote.

Xenos Short Story Competition

Xenos magazine, 29 Poplar Street, Haslingden, Rossendale BB4 5LY
☎01706 211590
E-mail: xenos@xenos.demon.co.uk
Website: http://www.xenos.demon.co.uk

Two annual short story competitions open to all. Each competition has a specific theme; send s.a.e. or IRC for details. No entries accepted without an official entry form (photocopies accepted) and the appropriate fee. Closing dates: 30 June and 31 December.
Prizes Three cash prizes of £50 (plus publication) per competition; three runners-up receive an annual subscription plus publication.

Yorkshire Open Poetry Competition

See **Ilkley Literature Festival Poetry Competition**

Yorkshire Post Art and Music Awards

Yorkshire Post, PO Box 168, Wellington Street, Leeds, West Yorkshire LS1 1RF
☎0113 2432701   Fax 0113 2388909
Contact *Margaret Brown*

Two annual awards made to the authors whose work has contributed most to the understanding and appreciation of art and music. Books should have been published in the preceding year in the UK. Previous winners: Charles Hemming *British Landscape Painters: A History and Gazetteer;* David Cairns *Berlioz: The Making of An Artist.*
Award £1000 each.

Yorkshire Post Best First Work Award

Yorkshire Post, PO Box 168, Wellington Street, Leeds, West Yorkshire LS1 1RF
☎0113 2432701   Fax 0113 2388909
Contact *Margaret Brown*

An annual award for a work by a new author published during the preceding year. Previous winners include: Harriet O'Brien *Forgotten Land.*
Prize £1000.

Yorkshire Post Book of the Year Award

Yorkshire Post, PO Box 168, Wellington Street, Leeds, West Yorkshire LS1 1RF
☎0113 2432701   Fax 0113 2388909
Contact *Margaret Brown*

An annual award for the book (either fiction or

non-fiction) which, in the opinion of the judges, is the best work published in the preceding year. 1997 winner: John Ehrman *The Younger Pitt, Vol. III: The Consuming Struggle*. *Prize* £1200.

Young Science Writer Award
The Daily Telegraph, 1 Canada Square, Canary Wharf, London E14 5DT
☎0171 538 6259   Fax 0171 513 2512
Contact *Vicky Hurley*

ESTABLISHED 1987, this award is designed to bridge the gap between science and writing, challenging the writer to come up with a piece in no more than 700 words that is friendly, informative and, above all, understandable. Open to two age groups: 16–19 and 20–28.

Award Winners and runners-up receive cash prizes and have the opportunity to have their pieces published on the science pages of *The Daily Telegraph*. The winner also gets an all expenses paid trip.

Writers' Earnings From Lending and Copying

Here is a little known fact. While Public Lending Right, which every writer has heard about, has £5 million to spread between 27,000 authors, the largely unsung Authors' Licensing and Collecting Society hands out £10 million to 35,000 writers. And while PLR remains static (the latest figure is the same as for the two previous years) the ALCS goes from strength to strength.

Actually, it is a little unfair to suggest that the ALCS keeps its corporate head down. It now sends out a regular newsletter and has even created an eye-catching logo. But the fact remains that while books on library shelves, or their absence, remains an ever interesting topic for press pundits, the activities of the ALCS which include collecting and redistributing payments for photocopying, cable transmission, off-air recording and electronic rights do not have the same emotive power to excite. A pity, because that is where the money is and that is where more of it will come from. Even librarians recognise this as they give less of their attention to hard print and more to electronic information.

The ALCS reaches out to all those rights which an author is unable to exercise individually and are thus best handled on a collective basis. Some of these rights come as a surprise. Despite hefty pressure from interest groups, the British government has resisted a levy on the sale of blank audio and video cassettes to compensate writers and other artists for home recordings. But France, Germany and Switzerland are more accommodating and British writers are entitled to their share which, if it were not for the ALCS, would go uncollected.

Recent initiatives range from Byline, a service to journalists by which freelance material is licensed worldwide to a scheme allowing authors 'equitable remuneration' for the rental of videos and other recordings of their work. But the biggest source of ALCS income, around 58% of the total, is from licensing deals on photocopying.

Membership of the ALCS is via one of the writers' organisations. If, say, you are a member of the Society of Authors you automatically belong to the ALCS and will profit accordingly. On the other hand, it is as well to register items of work as they become available to the public. Not all media promoters hand over fees willingly. Every bit of additional information gathered by the ALCS helps it to become more effective as a policing as well as a collecting agency.

Meanwhile, what of PLR? It is, it seems, destined to be the poor relation of the ALCS. When, in 1951, a scheme for recompensing authors for books borrowed from public libraries was first mooted, it was suggested that each library loan should be valued at one old penny or around 20p in current money. Instead the rate per loan is 2.07p which means that the only authors who do well out of PLR are the 93 at the top of the popularity poll who each get the maximum payout of £6000. Of the rest, twelve thousand authors receive less than £100 and ten thousand fail to register for any payment at all. Compare this to Finland where the average payment is £2,470 or Denmark where it is £1,657. Here, it is just £216.

Still, on the principle that every little helps, PLR is not to be ignored. To qualify, an author must be resident in the United Kingdom or Germany (the latter as part of a reciprocal deal). For a book to be eligible it must be printed, bound and put on sale with an ISBN. It must not be mistaken for a newspaper or periodical, or be a musical score. Crown copyright is excluded, also books where authorship is attributed to a company or association. But - and this is where mistakes often occur - the author does not have to own copyright to be eligible for PLR. Anyone who has disclaimed copyright as part of a flat fee commission, for instance, will still have a claim if his name is on the title page.

Under PLR, the sole writer of a book may not be its sole author. Others named on the title page or elsewhere in the book, such as illustrators, translators, compilers, editors and revisers, may have a claim to authorship. Share sizes must reflect the relative level of contributions. But translators may apply, without reference to other authors, for a 30 per cent fixed share (to be divided equally between joint translators). Similarly, an editor or compiler may register a 20 per cent share provided he has written 10 per cent of the book or at least 10 pages of text. Joint editors or compilers must divide the 20 per cent share equally.

Authors and books can be registered for PLR only when application is made during the author's lifetime. However, once an author is registered, the PLR on his books continues for the period of copyright, i.e., 70 years after death. If he wishes, an author can assign PLR to other people and bequeath it by will. If a co-author is dead or untraceable, the remaining co-author can still register for a share of PLR so long as he provides supporting evidence as to why he alone is making application.

A note on German PLR. This is collected by the ALCS and is made on author name for all works of fiction. But authors of non-fiction works must register their titles with the Wissenschaft department of the VG Wort. Each registration calls for a fee of up to 650DM. If this is judged to be worthwhile, contact the ALCS for registration forms. Bear in mind that under the German system there is a 10 per cent deduction for administration, a further 10 per cent for a 'social fund', which is set aside for making *ex gratia* payments to authors who are in need, and yet another 45 per cent for 'social security'. After the 65 per cent deductions, the remaining amount is divided between the authors (who take 70 per cent) and the publishers (who take 30 per cent).

There are various ideas for extending PLR. Much thought, for example, has gone into the question of rewarding authors of reference books which are consulted on library premises but rarely taken out on loan. Complex sampling procedures have been rejected as too expensive and time consuming. Instead, payment is likely to be based on the average number of loans of a book in the lending stock. Also, there is a good argument for extending PLR to talking books, school and university libraries and to all authors living in the European Union. The latter might persuade other European countries to follow Germany's example with reciprocity payments to UK authors. But any extension of PLR must surely wait on extra funding. A government committed to raising educational standards might be expected to do a little more to strengthen what is, after all, the backbone of literacy.

PLR application forms and details can be obtained from: The Registrar, PLR Office, Bayheath House, Prince Regent Street, Stockton on Tees, Cleveland TS18 1DF (☎01642 604699).

The Authors' Licensing & Collecting Society (ALCS), Marlborough Court, 14–18 Holborn, London EC1N 2LE (☎0171 395 0600).

Library Services

Aberdeen Central Library

Rosemount Viaduct, Aberdeen AB25 1GW
☎01224 652500   Fax 01224 641985

Open 9.00 am to 8.00 pm Monday to Friday
(Reference & Local Studies: 9.00 am to
9.00 pm); 9.00 am to 5.00 pm Saturday.
Branch library opening times vary.

Open access
General reference and loans. Books, pamphlets, periodicals and newspapers; videos, framed prints, CDs and cassettes; arts equipment lending service; recording studio; DTP, Internet and WP for public access; photographs of the Aberdeen area; census records, maps; on-line database, patents and standards. The library offers special services to housebound readers. Non-resident administrative fee for audiovisual services.

Armitt Library

Ambleside, Cumbria LA22 9BL
☎015394 31212   Fax 015394 31313

Open 10.00 am to 12.30 pm and 1.30 pm to
4.00 pm Monday, Tuesday, Wednesday,
Friday.

Free Access To view original material (please give prior notice)
A small but unique reference library of rare books, manuscripts, pictures, antiquarian prints and museum items, mainly about the Lake District. It includes early guidebooks and topographical works, books and papers relating to Wordsworth, Ruskin, H. Martineau and others; fine art including work by W. Green, J. B. Pyne, John Harden, K. Schwitters, and Victorian photographs by Herbert Bell; also a major collection of Beatrix Potter's scientific watercolour drawings and microscope studies. Museum and Exhibition open seven days per week from 10.00 am to 5.00 pm. Entry fee.

The Athenaeum, Liverpool

Church Alley, Liverpool L1 3DD
☎0151 709 7770   Fax 0151 709 0418

Open 9.00 am to 4.00 pm Monday to Friday

Access To club members; researchers by application only
General collection, with books dating from the 15th century, now concentrated mainly on local history with a long run of Liverpool directories and guides. *Special collections* Liverpool playbills; William Roscoe; Blanco White; Robert Gladstone; 18th-century plays; 19th-century economic pamphlets; the Norris books; Bibles; Yorkshire and other genealogy. Some original drawings, portraits, topographical material and local maps.

Bank of England Library and Information Services

Threadneedle Street, London EC2R 8AH
☎0171 601 4715   Fax 0171 601 4356

Open 9.30 am to 5.30 pm Monday to Friday

Access For research workers by prior arrangement only, when material is not readily available elsewhere
50,000 volumes of books and periodicals. 3000 periodicals taken. UK and overseas coverage of banking, finance and economics. *Special collections* Central bank reports; UK 17th–19th-century economic tracts; Government reports in the field of banking.

Barbican Library

Barbican Centre, London EC2Y 8DS
☎0171 638 0569

Open 9.30 am to 5.30 pm Monday,
Wednesday, Thursday, Friday; 9.30 am to
7.30 pm Tuesday; 9.30 am to 12.30 pm
Saturday

Open access
Situated on Level 2 of the Barbican Centre, this is the Corporation of London's largest lending library. Limited study facilities are available. In addition to a large general lending department, the library seeks to reflect the Centre's emphasis on the arts and includes strong collections, including videos, on painting, sculpture, theatre, cinema and ballet, as well as a large music library with books, scores, cassettes and CDs (sound recording loans available at a small charge). Also houses the City's main children's library and has special collections on finance, natural resources, conservation, socialism and the history of London. Service available for housebound readers.

Barnsley Public Library

Central Library, Shambles Street, Barnsley,
South Yorkshire S70 2JF
☎01226 773930   Fax 01226 773955

Open Lending & Reference: 9.30 am to

7.00 pm Monday and Wednesday; 9.30 am to 5.30 pm Tuesday and Friday; 9.30 am to 1.00 pm Thursday; 9.30 am to 4.00 pm Saturday. Please telephone to check hours of other departments.

Open access
General library, lending and reference. Archive collection of family history and local firms; local studies: coalmining, local authors, Yorkshire and Barnsley; European Business Information Unit; music library (books, CDs, records, tapes); large junior library. (Specialist departments are closed on certain weekday evenings and Saturday afternoons.)

BBC Written Archives Centre
Peppard Road, Caversham Park, Reading, Berkshire RG4 8TZ
☎0118 946 9280/1/2   Fax 0118 946 1145
Contact *Jacqueline Kavanagh*
Open 9.30 am to 5.30 pm Monday to Friday

Access For reference, by appointment only on Wednesday to Friday.

Holds the written records of the BBC, including internal papers from 1922 to 1974 and published material to date. Charges for certain services.

Bedford Central Library
Harpur Street, Bedford MK40 1PG
☎01234 350931   Fax 01234 342163
Open 9.30 am to 7.00 pm Monday and Wednesday; 9.30 am to 5.30 pm Tuesday, Thursday, Friday; 9.30 am to 4.00 pm Saturday

Open Access
Reference and lending library with a wide range of stock, including books, music (CD-ROMs and cassettes), audio books and videos, information services, children's library, local history library, Internet facilities, gallery and coffee bar.

Belfast Public Libraries: Central Library
Royal Avenue, Belfast BT1 1EA
☎01232 243233   Fax 01232 332819
Open 9.30 am to 8.00 pm Monday and Thursday; 9.30 am to 5.30 pm Tuesday, Wednesday, Friday; 9.30 am to 1.00 pm Saturday

Open access To lending libraries; reference libraries by application only
Over 2 million volumes for lending and reference. *Special collections* United Nations/UNESCO

depository; complete British Patent Collection; Northern Ireland Newspaper Library; British and Irish government publications. The Central Library offers the following reference departments: Humanities and General Reference; Irish and Local Studies; Business and Law; Science and Technology; Fine Arts, Language and Literature; Music and Recorded Sound. The lending library, supported by twenty branch libraries and two mobile libraries, offers special services to hospitals, prisons and housebound readers.

BFI National Library
21 Stephen Street, London W1P 2LN
☎0171 255 1444   Fax 0171 436 2338
Open 10.30 am to 5.30 pm Monday and Friday; 10.30 am to 8.00 pm Tuesday and Thursday; 1.00 pm to 8.00 pm Wednesday; Telephone Enquiry Service operates from 10.00 am to 5.00 pm

Access For reference only; annual and limited day membership available
The world's largest collection of information on film and television including periodicals, cuttings, scripts, related documentation, personal papers. Information available through SIFT (Summary of Information on Film and Television).

Birmingham and Midland Institute
9 Margaret Street, Birmingham B3 3BS
☎0121 236 3591   Fax 0121 212 4577
Administrator & General Secretary
Philip Fisher
Access For research, to students (loans restricted to members)
ESTABLISHED 1855. Later merged with the Birmingham Library (now renamed the Priestley Library), which was founded in 1779. The Priestley Library specialises in the humanities, with approximately 100,000 volumes in stock. Founder member of the **Association of Independent Libraries**. Meeting-place of many affiliated societies including many devoted to poetry and literature.

Birmingham Library Services
Central Library, Chamberlain Square, Birmingham B3 3HQ
☎0121 235 2615   Fax 0121 233 4458
Open 9.00 am to 8.00 pm Monday to Friday; 9.00 am to 5.00 pm Saturday

Over a million volumes. *Research collections* include the Shakespeare Library; War Poetry Collection; Parker Collection of Children's

Books and Games; Johnson Collection; Milton Collection; Cervantes Collections; Early and Fine Printing Collection (including the William Ridler Collection of Fine Printing); Joseph Priestley Collection; Loudon Collection; Railway Collection; Wingate Bett Transport Ticket Collection; Labour, Trade Union and Co-operative Collections. Photographic Archives: Sir John Benjamin Stone; Francis Bedford; Francis Frith; Warwickshire Photographic Survey; Boulton and Watt Archive; Charles Parker Archive; Birmingham Repertory Theatre Archive and Sir Barry Jackson Library; Local Studies (Birmingham); Patents Collection; Song Sheets Collection; Oberammergau Festival Collection.

Bradford Central Library

Princes Way, Bradford, West Yorkshire
BD1 1NN
☎01274 753600   Fax 01274 395108
Open 9.00 am to 7.30 pm Monday to Friday;
9.00 am to 5.00 pm Saturday

Open access
Wide range of books and media loan services. Comprehensive reference and information services, including major local history collections and specialised business information service. Bradford Libraries runs its own publishing programme, and has a number of creative writing projects – *In Your Own Write* (for local writers), *The Writeplace* (DTP facility for writers), *Poem of the Month*, and an annual programme of performance events.

Brighton Central Library

Church Street, Brighton, East Sussex BN1 1UE
☎01273 290800   Fax 01273 296951
Open 10.00 am to 7.00 pm Monday to Friday
(closed Wednesday); 10.00 am to 4.00 pm
Saturday
Reference Library ☎01273 296969
Fax 01273 296965

Access Limited stock on open access; all material for reference use only
FOUNDED 1869, the library has a large stock covering most subjects. Specialisations include art and antiques, history of Brighton and Sussex, family history, local illustrations, HMSO, business and large bequests of antiquarian books and ecclesiastical history.

Bristol Central Library

College Green, Bristol BS1 5TL
☎0117 9276121   Fax 0117 9221081
Open 9.30 am to 7.30 pm Monday, Tuesday

and Thursday; 9.30 am to 5.00 pm
Wednesday, Friday and Saturday
Open Access
Lending, reference, art, music, commerce and local studies are particularly strong.

British Architectural Library

Royal Institute of British Architects,
66 Portland Place, London W1N 4AD
☎0171 580 5533   Fax 0171 631 1802
Members' Information Line (Premium rate): 0891 234 444; Public Information Line (Premium rate): 0891 234 400
Open 1.30 pm to 5.00 pm Monday; 10.00 am to 8.00 pm Tuesday; 10.00 am to 5.00 pm Wednesday, Thursday, Friday; 10.00 am to 1.30 pm Saturday

Access Free to RIBA members; non-members must buy a day ticket (£10/£5 concessions, but on Tuesdays between 5–8.00 pm and Saturdays £5/£2.50); annual membership (£96/£48 concessions); loans available to RIBA and library members only
Collection of books, drawings, manuscripts, photographs and periodicals, 400 of which are indexed. All aspects of architecture, current and historical. Material both technical and aesthetic, covering related fields including: interior design, landscape architecture, topography, the construction industry and applied arts. Brochure available; queries by telephone, letter or in person. Charge for research (min. charge £15).

The British Library Business Information Service (BIS)

25 Southampton Buildings, London
WC2A 1AW
☎0171 412 7977 (free)/0171 412 7457 (priced enquiry service)   Fax 0171 412 7453
Open 9.30 am to 9.00 pm Monday to Friday; 10.00 am to 1.00 pm Saturday; Free Enquiry Service: 9.00 am to 5.00 pm Monday to Friday; Priced Enquiry Service: 9.00 am to 5.00 pm Monday to Friday

Open access
BIS holds the most comprehensive collection of business information literature in the UK. This includes market research reports and journals, directories, company annual reports, trade and business journals, house journals, trade literature and CD-ROM services.
For information on British Library collections and services, visit the Web page at: http://www.bl.uk
To access British Library catalogues, go to http://opac97.bl.uk

British Library
Department of Manuscripts

From 4 Jan. 1999: 96 Euston Road, London
NW1 2DB

☎0171 412 7513   Fax 0171 412 7511

Open The Library is closed from 28 August
1998 until it reopens at its new location in
Euston Road on 4 January 1999. Opening
times to be confirmed

Access Reading facilities only, by British Library
reader's pass and supplementary mss pass, for
which a written letter of recommendation is
required

Two useful publications, *Index of Manuscripts
in the British Library,* Cambridge 1984–6, 10 vols,
and *The British Library: Guide to the Catalogues and
Indexes of the Department of Manuscripts* by M. A.
E. Nickson, help to guide the researcher through
this vast collection of manuscripts dating from
Ancient Greece to the present day. Approximately 300,000 mss, charters, papyri and seals are
housed here.

For information on British Library collections and services, visit the Web page at:
http://www.bl.uk

To access British Library catalogues, go to
http://opac97.bl.uk

British Library Map Library

96 Euston Road, London NW1 2DB

☎0171 412 7700/7747   Fax 0171 412 7780
E-mail: maps@bl.uk

Open At the time of going to press, times of
opening at the new St Pancras location
were not confirmed. Telephone for details

Access By British Library reader's pass or Map
Library day pass

A collection of two million maps, charts and
globes with particular reference to the history of
British cartography. Maps for all parts of the
world in wide range of scales and dates, including
the most comprehensive collection of Ordnance
Survey maps and plans. *Special collections* King
George III Topographical Collection and Maritime Collection, and the Crace Collection of
maps and plans of London.

For information on British Library collections and services, visit the Web page at:
http://www.bl.uk

To access British Library catalogues, go to
http://opac97.bl.uk

British Library Music Library

96 Euston Road, London NW1 2DP

☎0171 412 7752   Fax 0171 412 7751

Open At the time of going to press, times of

opening at the new St Pancras location
were not confirmed. Telephone for details

Access By British Library reader's pass

Special collections The Royal Music Library
(containing almost all Handel's surviving auto-
graph scores) and the Paul Hirsch Music
Library. Also a large collection (about one and
a quarter million items) of printed music, both
British and foreign.

For information on British Library collections and services, visit the Web page at:
http://www.bl.uk

To access British Library catalogues, go to
http://opac97.bl.uk

British Library
National Sound Archive

96 Euston Road, London NW1 2DB

☎0171 412 7440   Fax 0171 412 7441

Open 9.30 am to 8.00 pm Monday to Friday;
9.30 am to 5.00 pm Saturday

Listening service (by appointment)

Northern Listening Service
British Library Document Supply Centre,
Boston Spa, West Yorkshire: 9.15 am to 4.30
pm Monday to Friday

Open access
An archive of over 1,000,000 discs and more
than 170,000 tape recordings, including all
types of music, oral history, drama, wildlife,
selected BBC broadcasts and BBC Sound
Archive material. Produces a thrice-yearly
newsletter, *Playback.*

For information on British Library collections and services, visit the Web page at:
http://www.bl.uk

To access British Library catalogues, go to
http://opac97.bl.uk

British Library Newspaper Library

Colindale Avenue, London NW9 5HE

☎0171 412 7353   Fax 0171 412 7379
E-mail: newspaper@bl.uk

Open 10.00 am to 4.45 pm Monday to
Saturday (last newspaper issue 4.15 pm)

Access By British Library reader's pass or
Newspaper Library pass (available from and
valid only for Colindale)

English provincial, Scottish, Welsh, Irish,
Commonwealth and selected overseas foreign
newspapers from *c.*1700 are housed here.
London newspapers from 1801 and many
weekly periodicals are also in stock. (London
newspapers pre-dating 1801 are housed at the
new library building in St Pancras – 96 Euston

Road, NW1 2DB – though many are available at Colindale Avenue on microfilm.) Readers are advised to check availability of material in advance.

For information on British Library collections and services, visit the Web page at: http://www.bl.uk

To access British Library catalogues, go to http://opac97.bl.uk

British Library Oriental and India Office Collections

96 Euston Road, London NW1 2DB
☎0171 412 7873   Fax 0171 412 7641

Open 9.30 am to 5.45 pm Monday to Friday; 9.30 am to 12.45 pm Saturday

Open access By British Library reader's pass or day pass (identification required)

A comprehensive collection of printed volumes and manuscripts in the languages of North Africa, the Near and Middle East and all of Asia, plus official records of the East India Company and British government in India until 1947. Also prints, drawings and paintings by British artists of India.

For information on British Library collections and services, visit the Web page at: http://www.bl.uk

To access British Library catalogues, go to http://opac97.bl.uk

British Library Reading Room

96 Euston Road, London NW1 2DB
☎0171 412 7676 (Reading Room/ Bibliographical holdings enquiries)
Fax 0171 412 755
☎0171 412 7677 (Admissions)

Open 9.30 am to 6.00 pm Monday and Thursday; 9.30 am to 8.00 pm Tuesday and Wednesday; 9.30 am to 5.00 pm Friday and Saturday. The Admissions Office is open 10.00 am to 5.00 pm Monday and Thursday; 10.00 am to 6.00 pm Tuesday and Wednesday; 10.00am to 4.30 pm Friday and Saturday.

Access By British Library reader's pass

Large and comprehensive stock of books and periodicals relating to the humanities and social sciences for reference and research which cannot easily be done elsewhere. Leaflet *Applying for a Reader's Pass* available for guidance. A permanent exhibition on the history of printing and binding is on display. Telephone for details.

For information on British Library collections and services, visit the Web page at: http://www.bl.uk

To access British Library catalogues, go to http://opac97.bl.uk

British Library Science Reference and Information Service

Holborn Reading Room: 25 Southampton Buildings, London WC2A 1AW
☎0171 412 7494/7496 (General Enquiries)
Fax 0171 412 7495
British/EPO patent equiries: 0171 412 7919
Business enquiries: 0171 412 7454/7977
(Business quick enquiry line available 9.00 am to 5.00 pm Monday to Friday)
E-mail sris-centre-desk@bl.uk

Open 9.30 am to 8.00 pm Monday to Friday (check before visiting); 10.00 am to 1.00 pm Saturday

Engineering, business information on companies, markets and products, physical science and technologies. British, European and Patent Co-operation Treaty patents and trade marks.

Chancery House Reading Room
(Opposite 25 Southampton Buildings in the basement of Chancery House)
☎0171 412 7901/2   Fax 0171 412 7912
E-mail: patents-information@bl.uk

Open 9.30 am to 5.30 pm Monday to Friday

Covers foreign patent specifications from 38 countries and patent journals from more than 100 countries.

Aldwych Reading Room
9 Kean Street, London WC2B 4AT
☎0171 412 7288   Fax 0171 412 7217
E-mail: sris-aldwych-desk@bl.uk

Open 9.30 am to 5.30 pm Monday to Friday

Covers life sciences and technologies, especially biotechnology, medicine and agriculture, mathematics, astronomy and earth sciences.

Reading Room for Official Publications and Social Sciences
Great Russell Street, London WC1B 3DG
☎0171 412 7536 (enquiries)/412 7728 (issue desk)   Fax 0171 412 7761
E-mail: jennie-grimshaw@bl.uk

Open 9.30 am to 4.15 pm Monday to Friday

Covers UK and foreign official publications and social science material, including education, law and theoretical management.

Open access

The British Library Science Reference and Information Service (SRIS) is a world leader for information in science, technology, business, patents and the social sciences. SRIS is unique in offering access to a wide range of books, journals and CD-ROMs on these topics along with a superb collection of patents from almost every issuing authority in the world. To access the collections and specialist information services users can go into the Library's reading rooms in Central London or contact SRIS by letter, phone, fax or e-mail.

The Library has a range of free and priced services – including online searching and document delivery services; it runs training courses and publishes a wide range of publications from newsletters and directories to definitive bibliographies.

PRICED RESEARCH SERVICE CONTACT DETAILS:
Business Information Service
☎0171 412 7457   Fax 0171 412 7453
E-mail: sris-business-info@bl.uk

Dialtech (National Centre for European Information Network Services):
☎0171 412 7946/51   Fax 0171 412 7954
E-mail: roy.kitley@bl.uk

Environmental Information Service
☎0171 412 7955   Fax 0171 412 7954
E-mail: eis@bl.uk

Health Care Information Service
☎0171 412 7477   Fax 0171 412 7954
E-mail: hcis@bl.uk

Patents Online
☎0171 412 7903   Fax 0171 412 7480
E-mail: patents-information@bl.uk

Social Policy Information Service
☎0171 412 7536   Fax 0171 412 7761
E-mail: jennie.grimshaw@bl.uk

STM search (science, technology and medicine)
☎Tel 0171 412 7477   Fax 0171 412 7954
E-mail: stm-search@bl.uk

NB During 1999, SRIS will be moving to the Library's new building in St Pancras (96 Euston Road, London NW1 2DB).

For information on British Library collections and services, visit the Web page at: http://www.bl.uk

To access British Library catalogues, including the SRIS catalogue, go to http://opac97.bl.uk

British Library Social Policy Information Service

Great Russell Street, London WC1B 3DG
☎0171 412 7536   Fax 0171 412 7761

Leaves the above address on 27 November 1998 and reopens at the new St Pancras building, 96 Euston Road, London NW1 2DB, in March 1999.

Open Great Russell Street: 9.30 am to 4.45 pm (last admissions 4.30 pm) Monday to Friday; Euston Road: 9.30 am to 8.00 pm Monday to Friday; 9.30 am to 5.00 pm Saturday (to be confirmed)

Access By British Library reader's pass

Provides an information service on social policy, public administration, and current and international affairs, and access to current and historical official publications from all countries and intergovernmental bodies, including House of Commons sessional papers, UK legislation, UK electoral registers, up-to-date reference books on official publications and on the social sciences, a major collection of statistics and a browsing collection of recent social science books and periodicals. Also offers a priced research service providing literature surveys, current awareness and topic briefings for clients on demand.

For information on British Library collections and services, visit the Web page at: http://www.bl.uk

To access British Library catalogues, go to http://opac97.bl.uk

British Psychological Society Library

c/o Psychology Library, University of London, Senate House, Malet Street, London WC1E 7HU
☎0171 636 8000 ext. 5060 Fax 0171 436 1494

Open Term-time: 9.00 am to 9.00 pm Monday to Thursday; 9.00 am to 6.30 pm Friday; 9.30 am to 5.30 pm Saturday (Holidays: 9.00 am to 6.00 pm Monday to Friday; 9.30 am to 5.30 pm Saturday)

Access Members only; Non-members £6 day ticket

Reference library, containing the British Psychological Society collection of periodicals – over 140 current titles housed alongside the University of London's collection of books and journals. Largely for academic research. General queries referred to **Swiss Cottage Library** which has a very good psychology collection.

Bromley Central Library

London Borough of Bromley - Leisure & Community Services, High Street, Bromley, Kent BR1 1EX
☎0181 460 9955   Fax 0181 313 9975

Open 9.30 am to 6.00 pm Monday, Wednesday, Friday; 9.30 am to 8.00 pm Tuesday and Thursday; 9.30 am to 5.00 pm Saturday

Open Access

A large selection of fiction and non-fiction books for loan, both adult and children's. Also videos, CDs, cassettes, language courses, open learning packs for hire. Other facilities include a business information service, CD-ROM, computer hire, internet, local studies library, 'Upfront' teenage section, large reference library with photocopying, fax, microfiche and film facilities and specialist 'Healthpoint' and 'Careerpoint' sections. Specialist collections include: H. G. Wells, Walter de la Mare, Crystal Palace, The Harlow Bequest, and the history and geography of Asia, America, Australasia and the Polar regions.

CAA Library and Information Centre

Aviation House, Gatwick Airport, West Sussex RH6 0YR
☎01293 573725   Fax 01293 573181
Open 9.30 am to 4.30 pm Monday to Friday; 10.00 am to 4.30 pm first Wednesday of the month

Open Access
Books, periodicals and reports on air transport, air traffic control, electronics, radar and computing.

Cambridge Central Library (Reference Library & Information Service)

7 Lion Yard, Cambridge CB2 3QD
☎01223 712014   Fax 01223 712018
E-mail: cambridge.central.library@ camcnty.gov.uk
Open 9.30 am to 7.00 pm Monday, Wednesday, Thursday; 9.30 am to 5.00 pm Tuesday and Friday; 12 noon to 7.00 pm Wednesday; 9.30 am to 5.00 pm Saturday

Access Open
Large stock of books, periodicals, newspapers, maps, plus comprehensive collection of directories and annuals covering UK, Europe and the world. Microfilm and fiche reading and printing services. On-line access to news and business databases. News databases on CD-ROM; Internet access. Monochrome and colour photocopiers.

Camomile Street Library

12–20 Camomile Street, London EC3A 7EX
☎0171 247 8895   Fax 0171 377 2972
Open 9.30 am to 5.30 pm Monday to Friday

Open access
City of London lending library. Wide range

of fiction and non-fiction books and language courses on cassette, foreign fiction, paperbacks, maps and guides for travel at home and abroad, children's books, a selection of large print, and collections of music CDs and of videos.

Cardiff Central Library

Frederick Street, St David's Link, Cardiff CF1 4DT
☎01222 382116   Fax 01222 871599
Open 9.00 am to 6.00 pm Monday, Tuesday, Wednesday, Friday; 9.00 am to 7.00 pm Thursday; 9.00 am to 5.30 pm Saturday
General lending library with the following departments: leisure, music, children's, local studies, information, science and humanities.

Carmarthen Public Library

St Peter's Street, Carmarthen SA31 1LN
☎01267 224830   Fax 01267 221839
Open 9.30 am to 7.00 pm Monday, Tuesday, Wednesday Friday; 9.30 am to 5.00 pm Thursday and Saturday

Open access
Comprehensive range of fiction, non-fiction, children's books and reference works in English and in Welsh. Large local history library – newspapers/census returns on microfilm. Large Print books, books on tape, CDs, cassettes, and videos available for loan.

Catholic Central Library

Lancing Street, London NW1 1ND
☎0171 383 4333   Fax 0171 388 6675
Open 10.30 am to 5.00 pm Monday, Tuesday, Thursday, Friday; 10.30 am to 8.00 pm Wednesday

Open access For reference (non-members must sign in; loans restricted to members)
Contains books, many not readily available elsewhere, on theology, religions worldwide, scripture and the history of churches of all denominations.

The Centre for the Study of Cartoons and Caricature

See entry under **Picture Libraries**

City Business Library

1 Brewers Hall Garden, London EC2V 5BX
☎0171 638 8215   Fax 0171 332 1847
☎0171 480 7638 (recorded information)
Open 9.30 am to 5.00 pm Monday to Friday

Open access
Local authority public reference library run by the Corporation of London. Books, pamphlets,

periodicals and newspapers of current business interest, mostly financial. Aims to satisfy the day-to-day information needs of the City's business community, and in so doing has become one of the leading public resource centres in Britain in its field. Strong collection of directories for both the UK and overseas, plus companies information, market research sources, management, law, banking, insurance, statistics and investment. No academic journals or textbooks.

City of London Libraries

See **Barbican Library; Camomile Street Library; City Business Library; Guildhall**

Commonwealth Institute

Commonwealth Resource Centre,
Kensington High Street, London W8 6NQ
☎0171 603 4535   Fax 0171 602 7374
E-mail: info@commonwealth.org
Website: http://www.commonwealth.org.uk

Open 10.00 am to 6.00 pm Monday to Saturday

Access For reference (Loan service available to 'Friends' of the CI)

The Commonwealth Literature Library includes fiction, poems, drama and critical writings. *Special collection* Books and periodicals on the 54 Commonwealth countries. Also a collection of directories and reference books on the Commonwealth and information on arts, geography, history and literature, cultural organisations and bibliography.

Commonwealth Secretariat Library

Marlborough House, Pall Mall, London SW1Y 5HX
☎0171 747 6164   Fax 0171 747 6168

Open 9.15 am to 5.00 pm Monday to Friday

Access For reference only, by appointment

Extensive reference source concerned with economy, development, trade, production and industry of Commonwealth countries; also human resources including women, youth, health, management and education.

Coventry Central Library

Smithford Way, Coventry, Warwickshire CV1 1FY
☎01203 832314   Fax 01203 832440

Open 9.00 am to 8.00 pm Monday, Tuesday, Thursday; 9.30 am to 8.00 pm Wednesday; 9.00 am to 5.00 pm Friday; 9.00 am to 4.30 pm Saturday

Open access

Located in the middle of the city's main shopping centre. Approximately 120,000 items (CDs, books, cassettes) for loan; plus reference collection of business information and local history. *Special collections* Cycling and motor industries; George Eliot; Angela Brazil; Tom Mann Collection (trade union and labour studies); local newspapers on microfilm from 1740 onwards. Over 500 periodicals taken. 'Peoplelink' community information database available.

Derby Central Library

Wardwick, Derby DE1 1HS
☎01332 255398   Fax 01332 369570

Open 9.30 am to 7.00 pm Monday, Tuesday, Thursday, Friday; 9.30 am to 1.00 pm Wednesday and Saturday

LOCAL STUDIES LIBRARY
25B Irongate, Derby DE1 3GL

Open 9.30 am to 7.00 pm Monday and Tuesday; 9.30 am to 5.00 pm Wednesday, Thursday, Friday; 9.30 am to 1.00 pm Saturday

Open access

General library for lending, information and Children's Services. The Central Library also houses specialist private libraries: Derbyshire Archaeological Society; Derby Philatelic Society. The Local Studies Library houses the largest multimedia collection of resources in existence relating to Derby and Derbyshire. The collection includes mss deeds, family papers, business records including the Derby Canal Company, Derby Board of Guardians and the Derby China Factory.

Devon & Exeter Institution Library

7 Cathedral Close, Exeter, Devon EX1 1EZ
☎01392 251017

Open 9.00 am to 5.00 pm Monday to Friday

Access Members only (Temporary membership available)

FOUNDED 1813. Contains over 36,000 volumes, including long runs of 19th-century journals, theology, history, topography, early science, biography and literature. A large and growing collection of books, journals, newspapers, prints and maps relating to the South-West.

Doncaster Libraries and Information Services

Central Library, Waterdale, Doncaster, South Yorkshire DN1 3JE
☎01302 734305   Fax 01302 369749

Open 9.30 am to 6.00 pm Monday to Friday; 9.30 am to 4.00 pm Saturday

Open Access
Books, cassettes, CDs, videos, picture loans. Reading aids unit for people with visual handicap; activities for children during school holidays, including visits by authors, etc. Occasional funding available to support literature activities.

Dorchester Library (part of Dorset County Library)
Colliton Park, Dorchester, Dorset DT1 1XJ
☎01305 224440/224448   Fax 01305 266120

Open 10.00 am to 7.00 pm Monday; 9.30 am to 7.00 pm Tuesday, Wednesday, Friday; 9.30 am to 5.00 pm Thursday; 9.00 am to 1.00 pm Saturday

Open Access
General lending and reference library, including Local Studies Collection, special collections on Thomas Hardy, The Powys Family, William Barnes and T. E. Lawrence. Periodicals, children's library, playsets.

Dundee District Libraries
Central Library, The Wellgate, Dundee DD1 1DB
☎01382 434000 (434866 after 5.00pm)
Fax 01382 434642

Open Lending Departments: 9.30 am to 7.00 pm Monday, Tuesday, Thursday, Friday; 10.00 am to 7.00 pm Wednesday; 9.30 am to 5.00 pm Saturday.
General Reference Department: 9.30 am to 9.00 pm Monday, Tuesday, Thursday, Friday; 10.00 am to 7.00 pm Wednesday; 9.30 am to 5.00 pm Saturday.
Local History Department: 9.30 am to 5.00 pm Monday, Tuesday, Friday, Saturday; 10.00 am to 7.00 pm Wednesday; 9.30 am to 7.00 pm Thursday.

Access Reference services available to all; lending services to those who live, work or study within Dundee City
Adult lending, reference and children's services. Art, music, audio and video lending services. Schools service (Agency). Housebound and mobile services. *Special collections*: The Wighton Collection of National Music; The Wilson Photographic Collection; The Lamb Collection.

English Nature
Northminster House, Peterborough, Cambridgeshire PE1 1UA
☎01733 455000   Fax 01733 568834

Open 8.30 am to 5.00 pm Monday to

Thursday; 8.30 am to 4.30 pm Friday;

Access To *bona fide* students only. Telephone library for appointment on 01733 455094
Information on nature conservation, nature reserves, SSSIs, planning, legislation, etc.

Equal Opportunities Commission Library
Overseas House, Quay Street, Manchester M3 3HN
☎0161 833 9244   Fax 0161 835 1657

Open 10.00 am to 12.00 pm & 2.00 pm to 4.00 pm Monday to Friday

Access For reference
Books and journals on equal opportunities and gender issues. Equal Opportunities Commission publications.

Essex County Council Libraries
County Library Headquarters, Goldlay Gardens, Chelmsford, Essex CM2 0EW
☎01245 284981   Fax 01245 492780

Essex County Council Libraries has 90 static libraries throughout Essex as well as 15 mobile libraries and four special-needs mobiles. Services to the public include books, newspapers, periodicals, CDs, cassettes, videos, pictures, CD-ROM and Internet access as well as postal cassettes for the blind and subtitled videos. Specialist subjects and collections are listed below at the relevant library.

Chelmsford Library
PO Box 882, Market Road, Chelmsford, Essex CM1 1LH
☎01245 492758   Fax 01245 492536

Open: 9.00 am to 7.00 pm Monday to Friday; 9.00 am to 5.00 pm Saturday
Science and technology, business information, social sciences and medical.

Colchester Library
Trinity Square, Colchester, Essex CO1 1JB
☎01206 562243   Fax 01206 562413

Open: 9.00 am to 7.30 pm Monday, Tuesday, Wednesday, Friday; 9.00 am to 5.00 pm Thursday and Saturday
Local studies, music scores and education. Harsnett collection (early theological works 16th/17th-century); Castle collection (18th-century subscription library); Cunnington collection; Margaret Lazell collection; Taylor collection.

Harlow Library
The High, Harlow, Essex CM20 1HA
☎01279 413772   Fax 01279 424612

Open: 9.00 am to 7.30 pm Monday, Tuesday,

Thursday, Friday; 9.00 am to 5.00 pm
Wednesday and Saturday
Fiction, language and literature. Sir John
Newson Memorial collection; Maurice Hughes
Memorial collection.

Loughton Library
Traps Hill, Loughton, Essex IG10 1HD
☎0181 502 0181   Fax 0181 508 5041
Open: 9.00 am to 7.30 pm Monday, Tuesday,
Wednesday, Friday; 9.00 am to 5.00 pm
Saturday (closed Thursday)
National Jazz Foundation Archive.

Saffron Walden Library
2 King Street, Saffron Walden, Essex CB10 1ES
☎01799 523178   Fax 01799 513642
Open: 9.00 am to 7.00 pm Monday, Tuesday,
Thursday, Friday; 9.00 am to 5.00 pm
Saturday (closed Wednesday)
Victorian studies collection.

Witham Library
18 Newland Street, Witham, Essex CM8 2AQ
☎01376 519625   Fax 01376 501913
Open: 9.00 am to 7.00 pm Monday, Tuesday,
Thursday, Friday; 9.00 am to 5.00 pm
Saturday (closed Wednesday)
Drama. Dorothy L. Sayers and Maskell collec-
tions.

The Fawcett Library
London Guildhall University, Calcutta House,
Old Castle Street, London E1 7NT
☎0171 320 1189   Fax 0171 320 1188
E-mail: fawcett@lgu.ac.uk
Website: http://www.lgu.ac.uk/phil/
fawcett.htm
Open University term-time: 10.15 am to 8.30
pm Monday; 9.00 am to 8.30 pm
Wednesday; 9.00 am to 5.00 pm Thursday
and Friday. During University vacation:
9.00 am to 5.00 pm Monday, Wednesday
to Friday
Open access
Members of staff and students at London
Guildhall University and to *bona fide* researchers
employed in higher education institutions
funded by the (UK) Funding Councils and
DENI. Otherwise, full membership including
borrowing rights £30 or £7 for full-time students and the unwaged. Day fee (reference only)
£3 or £1.50 for students and the unwaged.
Bring a student ID card or similar to claim concessionary rate and two passport-type photographs if intending to join as an annual member
The Fawcett Library, national research library
for women's history, is the UK's oldest and most

comprehensive research library on all aspects of
women in society, with both historical and contemporary coverage. The Library includes materials on feminism, work, education, health, the
family, law, arts, sciences, technology, language,
sexuality, fashion and the home. The main
emphasis is on Britain but many other countries
are represented, especially the Commonwealth
and the Third World. Established in 1926 as the
library of the London Society of Women's Service (formerly Suffrage), a non-militant organisation led by Millicent Fawcett. In 1953 the
Society was renamed after her and the library
became the Fawcett Library.
Collections include: women's suffrage, work,
education; women and the church, the law,
sport, art, music; abortion, prostitution. Mostly
British materials but some American and Commonwealth works. Books, journals, pamphlets,
archives, photographs, posters, postcards, audiovisual materials, artefacts, scrapbooks, albums and
press cuttings dating mainly from the 19th century although some materials date from the 17th
century.

Foreign and Commonwealth Office Library
King Charles Street, London SW1A 2AH
☎0171 270 3925   Fax 0171 270 3270
Access By appointment only
An extensive stock of books, pamphlets and
other reference material on all aspects of historical, socio-economic and political subjects relating to countries covered by the Foreign and
Commonwealth Office. Particularly strong on
colonial history, early works on travel, and
photograph collections, mainly of Commonwealth countries and former colonies, *c*.1850s–
1960s.

Forestry Commission Library
Forest Research Station, Alice Holt Lodge,
Wrecclesham, Farnham, Surrey GU10 4LH
☎01420 22255   Fax 01420 23653
E-mail: library@forestry.gov.uk
Website: www.forestry.gov.uk
Open 9.00 am to 5.00 pm Monday to
Thursday; 9.00 am to 4.30 pm Friday
Access By appointment for personal visits
Approximately 20,000 books on forestry and
arboriculture, plus 500 current journals. CD-
ROMS include TREECD (1939 onwards).
Offers a Research Advisory Service for advice
and enquiries on forestry (☎01402 23000)
with a charge for consultations and diagnosis of
tree problems exceeding 10 minutes.

French Institute Library

17 Queensberry Place, London SW7 2DT
☎0171 838 2144   Fax 0171 838 2145
E-mail: library@fr-inst-gov.uk
Head Librarian *Odile Grandet*
Deputy Head Librarian *Pascale Mukerjee*
Open 12.00 pm to 7.00 pm Tuesday to
Friday; 12 noon to 6.00 pm Saturday

Open access For reference and consultation
(loans restricted to members)
A collection of over 40,000 volumes mainly
centred on French cultural interests with special emphasis on language, literature and history. Books in French and English. Collection
of 1000 videos; 250 periodicals; 1000 CDs
(French music); 50 CD-ROMs; Children's
library (8000 books); also a special collection
about 'France Libre'. Inter-library loans; quick
information service; Internet access. Group visits on request.

John Frost Newspapers

8 Monks Avenue, Barnet, Hertfordshire
EN5 1DB
☎0181 440 3159   Fax 0181 440 3159
Contact *John Frost, Andrew Frost*

A collection of 60,000 original newspapers (1630
to the present day) and 100,000 press cuttings
available, on loan, for research and rostrum work
(TV and audiovisual documentaries/presenta-
tions). Historic events, politics, sports, royalty,
crime, wars, personalities etc., plus many in-
depth files.

Gloucestershire County Library Arts & Museums Service

Quayside House, Shire Hall, Gloucester
GL1 2HY
☎01452 425020   Fax 01452 425042
E-mail: gclams@gloscc.gov.uk
Open access
The service includes 39 local libraries – call the
number above for opening hours; and seven
mobile libraries telephone 01452 425039 for
timetable/route enquiries.

Goethe-Institut Library

50 Princes Gate, Exhibition Road, London
SW7 2PH
☎0171 411 3452   Fax 0171 584 3180
E-mail: Library@London.goethe.org
Librarian *Marilen Daum*
Open 11.00 am to 8.00 pm Monday to
Thursday; 10.00 am to 1.00 pm Saturday
Library specialising in German literature and

books/audiovisual material on German culture
and history: 27,000 books (4,800 of them in
English), 134 periodicals, 14 newspapers, 2,600
audiovisual media (including 800 videos),
selected press clippings on German affairs from
the German and UK press, information service,
photocopier, video facility for six viewers. Also
German language teaching material for teachers
and students of German.

Greater London Record Office

See **London Metropolitan Archives**

Guildford Institute of University of Surrey Library

Ward Street, Guildford, Surrey GU1 4LH
☎01483 562142
Librarian *Clare Miles*
Open 10.00 am to 3.00 pm Tuesday,
Thursday, Friday; 10.00 am to 4.00 pm
Wednesday (occasionally closed at
lunchtime)

Open access To members only but open to
enquirers for research purposes
FOUNDED 1834. Some 10,000 volumes of
which 7500 were printed before the First World
War. The remaining stock consists of recently
published works of fiction, biography and travel.
Newspapers and periodicals also available. *Special
collections* include an almost complete run of the
Illustrated London News from 1843-1906, a collection of Victorian scrapbooks, and about 400
photos and other pictures relating to the
Institute's history and the town of Guildford.

Guildhall Library

Aldermanbury, London EC2P 2EJ
☎See below   Fax 0171 600 3384
Access For reference (but much of the
material is kept in storage areas and is
supplied to readers on request; proof of
identity is required for consultation of
certain categories of stock)
Part of the Corporation of London libraries.
Seeks to provide a basic general reference service but its major strength, acknowledged
worldwide, is in its historical collections. The
library is divided into three sections, each with
its own catalogues and enquiry desks. These
are: Printed Books; Manuscripts; the Print
Room.

PRINTED BOOKS
Open 9.30 am to 5 pm Monday to Saturday
☎0171 332 1868/1870

Strong on all aspects of London history, with
wide holdings of English history, topography

and genealogy, including local directories, poll books and parish register transcripts. Also good collections of English statutes, law reports, parliamentary debates and journals, and House of Commons papers. Home of several important collections deposited by London institutions: the Marine collection of the Corporation of Lloyd's, the Stock Exchange's historical files of reports and prospectuses, the Clockmakers' Company library and museum, the Gardeners' Company, Fletchers' Company, the Institute of Masters of Wine, International Wine and Food Society and Gresham College.

MANUSCRIPTS
Open 9.30 am to 4.45 pm Monday to Saturday (no requests for records after 4.30 pm) ☎0171 332 1863

The official repository for historical records relating to the City of London (except those of the Corporation of London itself, which are housed at the Corporation Records Office). Records date from the 11th century to the present day. They include archives of most of the City's parishes, wards and livery companies, and of many individuals, families, estates, schools, societies and other institutions, notably the Diocese of London and St Paul's Cathedral, as well as the largest collection of business archives in any public repository in the UK. Although mainly of City interest, holdings include material for the London area as a whole and beyond.

PRINT ROOM
Open 9.30 am to 5.00 pm Monday to Friday ☎0171 332 1839

An unrivalled collection of prints and drawings relating to London and the adjacent counties. The emphasis is on topography, but there are strong collections of portraits and satirical prints. The map collection includes maps of the capital from the mid-16th century to the present day and various classes of Ordnance Survey maps. Other material includes photographs, theatre bills and programmes, trade cards, book plates and playing cards as well as a sizeable collection of Old Master prints.

Guille–Alles Library
Market Street, St Peter Port, Guernsey,
Channel Islands GY1 1HB
☎01481 720392   Fax 01481 712425
Open 9.00 am to 5.00 pm Monday, Tuesday, Thursday, Friday, Saturday; 9.00 am to 8.00 pm Wednesday

Open Access For residents; payment of returnable deposit by visitors
Lending, reference and information services.

Health Information Library (Westminster)
Marylebone Library, Marylebone Road,
London NW1 5PS
☎0171 641 1039   Fax 0171 641 1028
Open 9.30 am to 8.00 pm Monday, Tuesday, Thursday, Friday; 10.00 am to 8.00 pm Wednesday; 9.30 am to 5.00 pm Saturday; 1.30 pm to 5.00 pm Sunday

Open access
Located in Westminster's Marylebone public library. Books, pamphlets and periodicals covering all aspects of medicine and the health services.

Hereford Libraries and Information Service
Shirehall, Hereford HR1 2HY
☎01432 359830/278254   Fax 01432 359668
Website:
http://www.hereford-worcester.gov.uk
Open Opening hours vary in the libraries across the county

Access Information and reference services open to anyone; loans to members only (membership criteria: resident, being educated, working, or an elector in the county or neighbouring authorities; temporary membership to visitors. Proof of identity and address required)

Information service, reference and lending libraries. Non-fiction and fiction for all age groups, including normal and large print, spoken word cassettes, sound recordings (CD and cassette), videos, maps, local history, CD-ROMs at Hereford and Leominster Libraries, online information service including Internet access to certain specified (public information) websites. *Special collections* Cidermaking; Beekeeping; Alfred Watkins; John Masefield; Pilley.

University of Hertfordshire Library
College Lane, Hatfield, Hertfordshire
AL10 9AD
☎01707 284677   Fax 01707 284670
Open Term-time: 8.30 am to 2.00 am Monday to Friday; 11.00 pm to 10.00 pm Saturday and Sunday; Holidays: 9.00 am to 5.00 pm Monday to Friday

Access For reference; loans available to members of HERTIS.

280,000 volumes and 2000 journals in science technology and social science, including law, across all five of the university's campuses. There are four other site libraries: at the Business School at Hertford, at the Watford campus near Radlett (education and humanities), at the Art & Design building in Hatfield and at the Law School in St Albans. Desk research, postal interlibrary loans and consultancy undertaken by HERTIS Information and Research Unit which is based at Hatfield and has capacity for up to 300 subscribing companies and organisations.

HERTIS
See **University of Hertfordshire Library**

Highgate Literary and Scientific Institution Library
11 South Grove, London N6 6BS
☎0181 340 3343   Fax 0181 340 5632
Open 10.00 am to 5.00 pm Tuesday to Friday; 10.00 am to 4.00 pm Saturday (closed Sunday and Monday)
Annual membership £35 single; £55 household
    25,000 volumes of general fiction and non-fiction, with a children's section and extensive local archives. *Special collections* on local history, London, and local poets Samuel Taylor Coleridge and John Betjeman.

Highland Libraries, The Highland Council, Cultural and Leisure Services
Library Support, 31A Harbour Road, Inverness IV1 1UA
☎01463 235713   Fax 01463 236986
Open Library opening hours vary to suit local needs. Contact Administration and support services for details (8.00 am to 6.00 pm Monday to Friday)
Open access
    Comprehensive range of lending and reference stock: books, pamphlets, periodicals, newspapers, compact discs, audio and video cassettes, maps, census records, genealogical records, photographs, educational materials, etc. Highland Libraries provides the public library service throughout the Highlands with a network of 40 static and 12 mobile libraries.

Holborn Library
32–38 Theobalds Road, London WC1X 8PA
☎0171 413 6345/6
Open 10.00 am to 7.00 pm Monday and Thursday; 10.00 am to 6.00 pm Tuesday and Friday; 10.00 am to 5.00 pm Saturday (closed all day Wednesday)
Open access
    London Borough of Camden public library,

specialising in law. Also includes the London Borough of Camden Local Studies and Archive Centre.

Sherlock Holmes Collection (Westminster)
Marylebone Library, Marylebone Road, London NW1 5PS
☎0171 641 1206   Fax 0171 641 1019
E-mail: c.cooke@dial.pipex.com
Open 9.30 am to 5.00 pm Monday, Tuesday, Thursday, Friday; 10.00 am to 5.00 pm Wednesday (closed Saturday)
Telephone for Access By appointment only
    Located in Westminster's Marylebone Library. An extensive collection of material from all over the world, covering Sherlock Holmes and Sir Arthur Conan Doyle. Books, pamphlets, journals, newspaper cuttings and photos, much of which is otherwise unavailable in this country. Some background material.

Imperial College Library
See **Science Museum Library**

Imperial War Museum
Department of Printed Books, Lambeth Road, London SE1 6HZ
☎0171 416 5000   Fax 0171 416 5374
Open 10.00 am to 5.00 pm Monday to Saturday (restricted service Saturday; closed on Bank Holiday Saturdays and last two full weeks of November for annual stock check)
Access For reference (but at least 24 hours' notice must be given for intended visits)
    A large collection of material on 20th-century life with detailed coverage of the two world wars and other conflicts. Books, pamphlets and periodicals, including many produced for short periods in unlikely wartime settings; also maps, biographies and privately printed memoirs, and foreign language material. Additional research material available in the following departments: Art, Documents, Exhibits and Firearms, Film, Sound Records, Photographs. Active publishing programme based on reprints of rare books held in library. Catalogue available.

Instituto Cervantes
102 Eaton Square, London SW1W 9AN
☎0171 235 0324   Fax 0171 235 0329
E-mail: iclondre@globalnet.co.uk
Open 12.30 pm to 6.30 pm Monday; 9.30 am to 6.30 pm Tuesday to Thursday; 9.30 am to 5.00 pm Friday; 9.30 am to 1.30 pm Saturday

Open access For reference and lending
Spanish literature, history, art, philosophy.
The library houses a collection of books, periodicals, videos, slides, tapes, CDs, cassettes, films and CD-ROMs specialising entirely in Spain and Latin America.

Italian Institute Library
39 Belgrave Square, London SW1X 8NX
☎0171 235 1461   Fax 0171 235 4618
Open 10.00 am to 1.00 pm and 2.00 pm to
5.00 pm Monday to Friday

Open access For reference
A collection of over 21,000 volumes relating to all aspects of Italian culture. Texts are mostly in Italian, with some in English.

Jersey Library
Halkett Place, St Helier, Jersey JE2 4WH
☎01534 59991 (Lending)/59992 (Reference)
Fax 01534 69444
Open 9.30 am to 5.30 pm Monday,
Wednesday, Thursday, Friday; 9.30 am to
7.30 pm Tuesday; 9.30 am to 4.00 pm
Saturday

Open access
Books, periodicals, newspapers, CDs, cassettes, CD-ROMs, videos, microfilm, specialised local studies collection.

Kent County Central Library
Kent County Council Arts & Libraries,
Springfield, Maidstone, Kent ME14 2LH
☎01622 696511   Fax 01622 753338
Open 10.00 am to 5.30 pm Monday,
Wednesday, Friday; 10.00 am to 6.00 pm
Tuesday; 10.00 am to 7.00 pm Thursday;
10.00 am to 5.00 pm Saturday

Open access
50,000 volumes available on the floor of the library plus 250,000 volumes of non-fiction, mostly academic, available on request to staff. English literature, poetry, classical literature, drama (including playsets), music (including music sets). Strong, too, in sociology, art and history. Loans to all who live or work in Kent; those who do not may consult stock for reference or arrange loans via their own local library service.

Lansdowne Library
Meyrick Road, Bournemouth, Dorset
BH1 3DJ
☎01202 556603   Fax 01202 291781
Open 10.00 am to 7.00 pm Monday; 9.30 am
to 7.00 pm Tuesday, Thursday, Friday;

9.30 am to 5.00 pm Wednesday; 9.00 am to
1.00 pm Saturday

Open access
Main library for Bournemouth with separate lending, reference and music departments. Collection of government publications; children's section, periodicals.

The Law Society
113 Chancery Lane, London WC2A 1PL
☎0171 320 5810/5811/5884
Fax 0171 242 1309

Head of Press Office *David McNeill*
Press Relations Manager *Catherine Slaytor*
Open 8.30 am to 5.30 pm with out-of-hours
answerphone and mobile phone back-up

Access Library restricted to solicitors/members but press office available to all journalists for advice, information and assistance.
Provides all information about solicitors, the legal profession in general, law reform issues etc.

Leeds Central Library
Calverley Street, Leeds, West Yorkshire
LS1 3AB
☎0113 2478274   Fax 0113 2478426
Open 9.00 am to 8.00 pm Monday and
Wednesday; 9.00 am to 5.30 pm Tuesday
and Friday; 9.30 am to 5.30 pm Thursday;
10.00 am to 5.00 pm Saturday

Open Access to lending libraries; Reference material on request

Lending Library covering all subjects.

Music Library contains scores, books and audio.

Information for Business Library holds company information, market research, statistics, directories, journals and computer-based information.

Art Library (in Art Gallery) has a major collection of material on fine and applied arts.

Local Studies Library contains an extensive collection on Leeds and Yorkshire, including maps, books, pamphlets, local newspapers, illustrations and playbills. Census returns for the whole of Yorkshire also available. International Genealogical Index and parish registers.

Research & Study Library with over 270,000 volumes, including extensive files of newspapers and periodicals plus all government publications since 1960. *Special collections* include military history, Judaic, early gardening books, and mountaineering.

Leeds City Libraries has an extensive network of 65 branch and mobile libraries.

Leeds Library

18 Commercial Street, Leeds, West Yorkshire LS1 6AL
☎0113 2453071

Open 9.00 am to 5.00 pm Monday to Friday

Access To members; research use upon application to the librarian
FOUNDED 1768. Contains over 120,000 books and periodicals from the 15th century to the present day. *Special collections* include Reformation pamphlets, Civil War tracts, Victorian and Edwardian children's books and fiction, European language material, spiritualism and psychical research, plus local material.

Lincoln Central Library

Free School Lane, Lincoln LN2 1EZ
☎01522 549160 (Reference)/510800 (Lending)
Fax 01522 535882

Open 9.30 am to 7.00 pm Monday to Friday; 9.30 am to 4.00 pm Saturday

Linen Hall Library

17 Donegall Square North, Belfast BT1 5GD
☎01232 321707   Fax 01232 438586

Librarian *John Gray*

Open 9.30 am to 5.30 pm Monday to Friday; 9.30 am to 4.00 pm Saturday

Open access For reference (loans restricted to members)
FOUNDED 1788. Contains about 200,000 books. Major Irish and local studies collections, including the Northern Ireland Political Collection relating to the current troubles (c. 90,000 items).

Literary & Philosophical Society of Newcastle upon Tyne

23 Westgate Road, Newcastle upon Tyne NE1 1SE
☎0191 232 0192   Fax 0191 261 2885

Librarian *Pat Southern*

Open 9.30 am to 7.00 pm Monday, Wednesday, Thursday, Friday; 9.30 am to 8.00 pm Tuesday; 9.30 am to 1.00 pm Saturday

Access Members; research facilities for *bona fide* scholars on application to the Librarian
200-year-old library of 140,000 volumes, periodicals (including 130 current titles), classical music on vinyl recordings and CD, plus a collection of scores. A programme of lectures and recitals provided. Recent publications include:

The Reverend William Turner: Dissent and Reform in Georgian Newcastle upon Tyne Stephen Harbottle; *History of the Literary and Philosophical Society of Newcastle upon Tyne, Vol. 2 (1896–1989)* Charles Parish; *Bicentenary Lectures 1993* ed. John Philipson.

Liverpool City Libraries

William Brown Street, Liverpool LE3 8EW
☎0151 225 5429   Fax 0151 207 1342
E-mail: central@lvpublib.demon.co.uk

Open 9.00 am to 7.30 pm Monday to Thursday; 9.00 am to 5.00 pm Friday; 10.00 am to 4.00 pm Saturday

Open access

Humanities Reference Library A total stock in excess of 120,000 volumes and 24,000 maps, plus book plates, prints and autographed letters. *Special collections* Walter Crane and Edward Lear illustrations, Kolmscott Press, Audubon.

Business and Technology Reference Library Extensive stock dealing with all aspects of science, commerce and technology, including British and European standards and patents and trade directories.

Music Library Extensive stock relating to all aspects of music. Includes 128,000 volumes and music scores, 18,500 records, and over 3000 cassettes and CDs. *Special collections* Carl Rosa Opera Company Collection and Earl of Sefton's early printed piano music.

Record Office and Local History Department Printed and audiovisual material relating to Liverpool, Merseyside, Lancashire and Cheshire, together with archive material mainly on Liverpool. Some restrictions on access, with 30-year rule applying to archives.

London College of Printing & Distributive Trades: Department of Learning Resources

Elephant and Castle, London SE1 6SB
☎0171 514 6527   Fax 0171 514 6597

Access By arrangement
The Department of Learning Resources operates from the three sites of the college at: Elephant & Castle; Davies Street (W1); Back Hill (Clerkenwell). Books, periodicals, slides, CD-ROM, videos and computer software on all aspects of the art of the book, printing, management, film/photography, graphic arts, plus retailing. *Special collections* Private Press books and the history and development of printing and books.

The London Library
14 St James's Square, London SW1Y 4LG
☎0171 930 7705/6   Fax 0171 766 4766
Librarian Mr A. S. Bell
Open 9.30 am to 5.30 pm Monday to
Saturday (Thursday till 7.30 pm)
Access For members only (£135 p.a., 1998)

With over a million books and 8300 members, The London Library 'is the most distinguished private library in the world; probably the largest, certainly the best loved'. Founded in 1841, it is a registered charity and wholly independent of public funding. Its permanent collection embraces most European languages as well as English. Its subject range is predominantly within the humanities, with emphasis on literature, history, fine and applied art, architecture, bibliography, philosophy, religion, and topography and travel. Some 6000–7000 titles are added yearly. Most of the stock is on open shelves to which members have free access. Members may take out up to 10 volumes; 15 if they live more than 20 miles from the Library. The comfortable Reading Room has an annexe for users of personal computers. There are photocopiers and CD-ROM workstations, and the Library also offers a postal loans service.

Prospective members are required to submit a refereed application form in advance of admission, but there is at present no waiting list for membership. The London Library Trust may make grants to those who are unable to afford the full annual fee; details on application.

London Metropolitan Archives
40 Northampton Road, London
EC1R 0HB
☎0171 332 3820   Fax 0171 833 9136
Minicom 0171 278 8703
E-mail: lma@ms.corpoflondon.gov.uk
Open 9.30 am to 4.45 pm Monday,
Wednesday, Friday; 9.30 pm to 7.30 pm
Tuesday and Thursday
Access For reference only

Formerly, the Greater London Record Office Library. Covers all aspects of the life and development of London, specialising in the history and organisation of local government in general, and London in particular. Books on London history and topography, covering many subjects. Also London directories dating back to 1677, plus other source material including Acts of Parliament, Hansard reports, statistical returns, atlases, yearbooks and many complete sets of newspapers and magazines.

Lord Louis Library
Orchard Street, Newport, Isle of Wight
PO30 1LL
☎01983 527655/823800 (Reference Library)
Fax 01983 825972
Open 9.30 am to 5.30 pm Monday to Friday
(Saturday till 5.00 pm)
Open access

General adult and junior fiction and non-fiction collections; local history collection and periodicals. Also the county's main reference library.

Manchester Central Library
St Peters Square, Manchester M2 5PD
☎0161 234 1900   Fax 0161 234 1963
Open 10.00 am to 8.00 pm Monday to
Thursday; 10.00 am to 5.00 pm Friday and
Saturday; Commercial and European Units:
10.00 am to 6.00 pm Monday to Thursday;
10.00 am to 5.00 pm Friday and Saturday
Open access

One of the country's leading reference libraries with extensive collections covering all subjects. Departments include: Commercial, European, Technical, Social Sciences, Arts, Music, Local Studies, Chinese, General Readers, Language & Literature. Large lending stock and VIP (visually impaired) service available.

Marylebone Library (Westminster)
See **Health Information Library; Sherlock Holmes Collection**

Ministry of Agriculture, Fisheries and Food
Whitehall Place Library, 3 Whitehall Place,
London SW1A 2HH
☎0171 270 8000/8421   Fax 0171 270 8419
MAFF Helpline 0645 335577 (local call rate) – general contact point which can provide information on the work of MAFF, either directly or by referring callers to appropriate contacts. Available 9.00 am to 5.00 pm Monday to Friday (excluding Bank Holidays)
Open 9.30 am to 5.00 pm Monday to Friday
Access For reference (but at least 24 hours notice must be given for intended visits)

Large stock of volumes on temperate agriculture.

The Mitchell Library
North Street, Glasgow G3 7DN
☎0141 287 2999   Fax 0141 287 2815
E-mail: fionna.macpherson@gcl.glasgow.
gov.uk

Contact *Mrs F. MacPherson*
Open 9.00 am to 8.00 pm Monday to
Thursday; 9.00 am to 5.00 pm Friday and
Saturday

Open access
Europe's largest public reference library with
stock of over 1,200,000 volumes. It subscribes to
46 newspapers and more than 2,000 periodicals.
There are collections in microform, records,
tapes and videos, as well as CD-ROM, illustrations, photographs, postcards etc.

The library is divided into a number of subject
departments including the Arts department
which contains a number of special collections,
e.g. the Robert Burns Collection (5000 vols),
the Scottish Poetry Collection (12,000 items)
and the Scottish Drama Collection (1,650 items).

Morrab Library
Morrab House, Morrab Gardens, Penzance,
Cornwall TR18 4DA
☎01736 364474
Librarian *L. Lowdon, BA,ALA*
Open 10.00 am to 4.00 pm Tuesday to
Friday; 10.00 am to 1.00 pm Saturday

Access Non-members may use the library for
a small daily fee, but may not borrow books

Formerly known as the Penzance Library.
An indepedent subscription lending library of
over 60,000 volumes covering virtually all subjects except modern science and technology,
with large collections on history, literature and
religion. There is a comprehensive Cornish collection of books, newspapers and manuscripts
including the Borlase letters; a West Cornwall
photographic archive; many runs of 18th- and
19th-century periodicals; a collection of over
2000 books published before 1800.

National Library of Scotland
George IV Bridge, Edinburgh EH1 1EW
☎0131 226 4531/459 4531
Fax 0131 220 6662

Open Main Reading Room: 9.30 am to 8.30
pm Monday, Tuesday, Thursday, Friday;
10.00 am to 8.30 pm Wednesday; 9.30 am
to 1.00 pm Saturday. Map Library: 9.30 am
to 5.00 pm Monday, Tuesday, Thursday,
Friday; 10.00 am to 5.00 pm Wednesday;
9.30 am to 1.00 pm Saturday. Scottish
Science Library: 9.30 am to 5.00 pm
Monday, Tuesday, Thursday, Friday; 10.00
am to 8.30 pm Wednesday.

Access To reading rooms and Map Library,
for research not easily done elsewhere, by
reader's ticket

Collection of over 6 million volumes. The
library receives all British and Irish publications. Large stock of newspapers and periodicals. Many special collections, including early
Scottish books, theology, polar studies, baking,
phrenology and liturgies. Also large collections
of maps, music and manuscripts including personal archives of notable Scottish persons.

National Library of Wales
Aberystwyth, Ceredigion SY23 3BU
☎01970 623800   Fax 01970 615709

Open 9.30 am to 6.00 pm Monday to Friday;
9.30 am to 5.00 pm Saturday (closed Bank
Holidays and first week of October)

Access To reading rooms and map room by
reader's ticket, available on application

Collection of over 4 million books and
including large collections of periodicals, maps,
manuscripts and audiovisual material. Particular
emphasis on humanities in printed foreign
material, and on Wales and other Celtic areas
in all collections.

National Meteorological Library and Archive
London Road, Bracknell, Berkshire
RG12 2SZ
☎01344 854843   Fax 01344 854840

Open Library & Archive: 8.30 am to 4.30 pm
Monday to Friday; Archive closed between
1.00 pm and 2.00 pm

Access By Visitor's Pass available from the
reception desk; advance notice of a planned
visit is appreciated

The major repository of most of the important
literature on the subjects of meteorology, clima-
tology and related sciences. The Library houses a
collection of books, journals, articles and scientific papers, plus published climatological data
from many parts of the world. The Technical
Archive (The Scott Building, Sterling Centre,
Eastern Road, Bracknell, Berks RG12 2PW)
holds the document collection of meteorological
data and charts from England, Wales and British
overseas bases, including ships' weather logs.
Records from Scotland are stored in Edinburgh
and those from Northern Ireland in Belfast.

The Natural History Museum Library
Cromwell Road, London SW7 5BD
☎0171 938 9191   Fax 0171 938 9290
E-mail: library@nhm.ac.uk
Website: http://www.nhm.ac.uk/info/
library/index.html

Open 10.00 am to 4.30 pm Monday to Friday
Access To *bona fide* researchers, by reader's ticket on presentation of identification (telephone first to make an appointment)

The library is in five sections: general; botany; zoology; entomology; earth sciences. The subdepartment of ornithology is housed at Zoological Museum, Akeman Street, Tring, Herts HP23 6AP (☎01442 834181). Resources available include books, journals, maps, manuscripts, drawings and photographs covering all aspects of natural history, including palaeontology and mineralogy, from the 14th century to the present day. Also archives and historical collection on the museum itself.

Newcastle upon Tyne City Library

Princess Square, Newcastle upon Tyne
NE99 1DX
☎0191 261 0691   Fax 0191 261 1435
Open 9.30 am to 8.00 pm Monday and Thursday; 9.30 am to 5.00 pm Tuesday, Wednesday, Friday; 9.00 am to 5.00 pm Saturday
Open access
Extensive local studies collection, including newspapers, illustrations and genealogy. Also business, science, humanities and arts, educational guidance unit, open learning resource centre, marketing advice centre. Patents advice centre.

Norfolk Library & Information Service

Norfolk and Norwich Central Library, Central Lending Service, 71 Ber Street, Norwich, Norfolk NR1 3AD
☎01603 215215
Central Reference & Information Service and Norfolk Studies
Gildengate House, Upper Green Lane, Norwich, Norfolk NR3 1AX
☎01603 215222   Fax 01603 215258
Open Lending Library, Reference and Information Service and Norfolk Studies: 10.00 am to 8.00 pm Monday to Friday; 9.00 am to 5.00 pm Saturday
Open access
Reference and lending library with wide range of stock for loan, including books, recorded music, music scores, plays and videos. Houses the 2nd Air Division Memorial Library and has a strong Local Studies Library. Extensive range of reference stock including business information. On-line database and CD-ROM services. Public fax and colour photocopying, access to the Internet. Information brokerage provides in-depth research services.

Northamptonshire Libraries & Information Service

Library HQ, PO Box 259, 27 Guildhall Road, Northampton NN1 1BA
☎01604 620262   Fax 01604 626789
Since 1991, the Libraries and Information Service have run two to three programmes of literary events for adults each year. Programmes so far have included visiting authors, poetry readings, workshops and other events and activities. The programmes are supported by regular touring fiction displays, writers' advice sessions and dedicated notice boards in libraries across the county.

Northumberland Central Library

The Willows, Morpeth, Northumberland
NE61 1TA
☎01670 512385   Fax 01670 519985
Open 10.00 am to 8.00 pm Monday, Tuesday, Wednesday, Friday; 9.30 am to 12.30 pm Saturday (closed Thursday)
Open access
Books, periodicals, newspapers, cassettes, CDs, video, microcomputers, CD-ROM, Internet access, prints, microforms, vocal scores, playsets, community resource equipment. *Special collections* **Northern Poetry Library**: 13,000 volumes of modern poetry (see entry under **Organisations of Interest to Poets**); Cinema: comprehensive collection of about 5000 volumes covering all aspects of the cinema; Family History.

Nottingham Central Library

Angel Row, Nottingham NG1 6HP
☎0115 9412121   Fax 0115 9504207
Open 9.30 am to 7.00 pm Monday to Friday; 9.00 am to 1.00 pm Saturday
Open access
General public lending library: business information, the arts, local studies, religion, literature. Videos, periodicals, spoken word, recorded music, search service – textual information on CD-ROM on public access machines. *Special collection* on D. H. Lawrence. Extensive back-up reserve stocks. Drama and music sets for loan to groups.

Nottingham Subscription Library Ltd

Bromley House, Angel Row, Nottingham
NG1 6HL
☎0115 9473134

Librarian *Julia Wilson*
Open 9.30 am to 5.00 pm Monday to Friday;
also first Saturday of each month from
10.00 am to 12.30 pm

Access For members only
FOUNDED 1816. Collection of 30,000 books
including local history, topography, biography,
travel and fiction.

Office for National Statistics

1 Drummond Gate, London SW1V 2QQ
☎0171 533 6262   Fax 0171 533 6261
E-mail: info@ons.gov.uk
Open 9.30 am to 4.30 pm Monday to Friday
All published Census data from 1801
onwards for the UK. Population and health
statistics from 1837 onwards. Some foreign
censuses and statistics (incomplete; most are
out-housed and require one week's notice for
retrieval). International statistics (WHO, UN,
etc). Government Social Survey reports, 1941
onwards. Wide range of other Government
statistical publications, business and economic
statistics, EUROSTAT publications. Small
stock of books on demography, vital registration, epidemology, survey methodology, census taking.

Orkney Library

Laing Street, Kirkwall, Orkney
KW15 1NW
☎01856 873166   Fax 01856 875260
Open 9.00 am to 8.00 pm Monday to Friday;
9.00 am to 5.00 pm Saturday. Archives:
9.00 am to 1.00 pm and 2.00 pm to 4.45
pm Monday to Friday

Open access
Local studies collection. Archive includes
sound and photographic departments.

Oxford Central Library

Westgate, Oxford OX1 1DJ
☎01865 815549   Fax 01865 721694
Open Call 01865 815509 for details
General lending and reference library
including the Centre for Oxfordshire Studies.
Also periodicals, audio visual materials, music
library, children's library and Business
Information Point.

PA News Library

292 Vauxhall Bridge Road, London
SW1V 1AE
☎0171 963 7012   Fax 0171 963 7065
Open 8.00 am to 8.00 pm Monday to Friday;
8.00 am to 6.00 pm Saturday; 9.00 am to
5.00 pm Sunday

Open Access
PA News, the 24-hour national news and
information group, offers public access to its
press cutting archive. Covering a wide range of
subjects, the library includes over 14 million cuttings dating back to 1928. Personal callers welcome or research undertaken by in-house staff.

Penzance Library

See **Morrab Library**

City of Plymouth Library and Information Services

Central Library, Drake Circus, Plymouth,
Devon PL4 8AL   Fax 01752 385905
Open Access

CENTRAL LIBRARY LENDING DEPARTMENTS:
Lending ☎01752 385912
Children's Department ☎01752 385916
Music & Drama Department ☎01752
385914
Open 9.30 am to 7.00 pm Monday, Friday;
9.30 am to 5.30 pm Tuesday, Wednesday,
Thursday; 9.30 am to 4.00 pm Saturday
The Lending departments offer books on all
subjects; language courses on cassette and foreign language books; the Holcenberg Jewish
Collection; books on music and musicians,
drama and theatre; music parts and sets of
music parts; play sets; videos; song index; cassettes and CDs.

CENTRAL LIBRARY REFERENCE
DEPARTMENTS:
Reference ☎01752 385907/8
Business Information ☎01752 385906
**Local Studies & Naval History
Department** ☎01752 985909
Open 9.00 am to 7.00 pm Monday to Friday;
9.00 am to 4.00 pm Saturday
The Reference departments include an
extensive collection of Ordnance Survey maps
and town guides; community and census infor-
mation; marketing and statistical information;
Patents and British Standards; books on every
aspect of Plymouth; naval history; Mormon
Index on microfilm; Baring Gould manuscript
of 'Folk Songs of the West'.

Plymouth Proprietary Library
Alton Terrace, 111 North Hill, Plymouth, Devon PL4 8JY
☎01752 660515

Librarian *Camilla M. Blackman*
Open Monday to Saturday from 9.30 am (closing time varies)

Access To members; visitors by appointment only
FOUNDED 1810. The library contains approximately 17,000 volumes of mainly 20th-century work. Member of the Association of Independent Libraries.

The Poetry Library
See entry under **Organisations of Interest to Poets**

Polish Library
238–246 King Street, London W6 0RF
☎0181 741 0474   Fax 0181 746 3798

Open 10.00 am to 8.00 pm Monday and Wednesday; 10.00 am to 5.00 pm Friday; 10.00 am to 1.00 pm Saturday (library closed Tuesday and Thursday)

Access For reference to all interested in Polish affairs; limited loans to members and *bona fide* scholars only through inter-library loans
Books, pamphlets, periodicals, maps, music, photographs on all aspects of Polish history and culture. *Special collections* Emigré publications; Joseph Conrad and related works; Polish underground publications; bookplates.

Poole Central Library
Dolphin Centre, Poole, Dorset BH15 1QE
☎01202 673910   Fax 01202 670253

Open 10.00 am to 7.00 pm Monday; 9.30 am to 7.00 pm Tuesday to Friday; 9.00 am to 1.00 pm Saturday

Open Access
General lending and reference library, including Healthpoint health information centre, HATRICS business information centre, children's library, periodicals.

Press Association Library
See **PA News Library**

Harry Price Library of Magical Literature
University of London Library, Senate House, Malet Street, London WC1E 7HU
☎0171 636 8000 ext 5031 Fax 0171 436 1494

Open 9.30 am to 5.15 pm Monday to Friday;
9.30 am to 1.00 pm, 2.00 pm to 5.15 pm Saturday (by prior appointment only); Monday evenings in term time (by prior appointment only)

Restricted access For reference only, restricted to members of the University and *bona fide* researchers (apply in writing); items must be requested from, and consulted in, the Special Collections Reading Room
Over 14,000 volumes and pamphlets on psychic phenomena and pseudo-phenomena; books relating to spiritualism and its history, to hypnotism, telepathy, astrology, conjuring and quackery.

Public Record Office
Ruskin Avenue, Kew, Richmond, Surrey TW9 4DU
☎0181 876 3444   Fax 0181 878 8905

Also at: The Family Record Centre, 1 Myddleton Street, London EC1 1UW

Open 9.30 am to 5.00 pm Monday, Wednesday, Friday; 10.00 am to 7.00 pm Tuesday; 9.30 am to 7.00 pm Thursday; 9.30 am to 5.00 pm Saturday

Access For reference, by reader's ticket, available free of charge on production of proof of identity (UK citizens: banker's card or driving licence; non-UK: passport or national identity card. Telephone for further information)
Over 168 kilometres of shelving house the national repository of records of central Government in the UK and law courts of England and Wales, which extend in time from the 11th–20th century. Medieval records and the records of the State Paper Office from the early 16th–late 18th century, plus the records of the Privy Council Office and the Lord Chamberlain's and Lord Steward's departments. Modern government department records, together with those of the Copyright Office dating mostly from the late 18th century. Under the Public Records Act, records are normally only open to inspection when they are 30 years old.

Reading Central Library
Abbey Square, Reading, Berkshire RG1 3BQ
☎0118 901 5955   Fax 0118 958 9039

Open 9.30 am to 5.00 pm Monday and Wednesday; 9.30 am to 7.00 pm Tuesday, Thursday, Friday; 9.30 am to 4.00 pm Saturday

Open access
Lending library; reference library; local studies library, bringing together every aspect of the

local environment and human activity in Berkshire; business library; music and drama library. Special collections: Mary Russell Mitford; local illustrations.
Public meeting room available.

Religious Society of Friends Library
Friends House, 173 Euston Road, London NW1 2BJ
☎0171 387 3601   Fax 0171 388 1977
Open 1.00 pm to 5.00 pm Monday, Tuesday, Thursday, Friday; 10.00 am to 5.00 pm Wednesday

Open Acess A letter of introduction from someone in good standing is required for researchers who are not members of the Society
Quaker history, thought and activities from the 17th century onwards. Supporting collections on peace, anti-slavery and other subjects in which Quakers have maintained long-standing interest. Also archives and manuscripts relating to the Society of Friends.

Richmond Central Reference Library
Old Town Hall, Whittaker Avenue, Richmond, Surrey TW9 1TP
☎0181 940 5529   Fax 0181 940 6899
Open 10.00 am to 6.00 pm Monday, Thursday, Friday (Tuesday till 1.00 pm; Wednesday till 8.00 pm and Saturday till 5.00 pm)

Open access
General reference library serving the needs of local residents and organisations.

Royal Geographical Society Library (with the Institute of British Geographers)
1 Kensington Gore, London SW7 2AR
☎0171 591 3040   Fax 0171 591 3001
Open 11.00 am to 5.00 pm Monday to Friday

Access to the library and reading rooms restricted to use by Fellows and members
Books and periodicals on geography, topography, cartography, voyages and travels. The Map Room, open since 1854 to the general public for reference purposes only, houses map and chart sheets, atlases and RGS-sponsored expedition reports. Photographs on travel and exploration are housed in the picture library, for which an appointment is necessary. (See entry under Picture Libraries.)

Royal Society Library
6 Carlton House Terrace, London SW1Y 5AG
☎0171 451 2606   Fax 0171 930 2170
Open 10.00 am to 5.00 pm Monday to Friday

Access For research only, to bona fide researchers; contact the Library in advance of first visit
History of science, scientists' biographies, science policy reports, and publications of international scientific unions and national academies from all over the world.

RSA (Royal Society for the Encouragement of Arts, Manufactures & Commerce)
8 John Adam Street, London WC2N 6EZ
☎0171 930 5115   Fax 0171 839 5805
Archivist Susan Bennett
Open 10.00 am to 1.00 pm Monday, Tuesday, Wednesday, Thursday and 2.00pm to 5.00 pm Wednesdays only; 10.00 am to 1.00 pm Friday

Access to Fellows of RSA; by application and appointment to non-Fellows
Archives of the Society since 1754. A collection of approximately 5000 volumes; international exhibition material.

Royal Society of Medicine Library
1 Wimpole Street, London W1M 8AE
☎0171 290 2940   Fax 0171 290 2939
Open 9.00 am to 8.30 pm Monday to Friday; 10.00 am to 5.00 pm Saturday

Access For reference only, on introduction by Fellow of the Society (temporary membership may also be granted)
Books and periodicals on general medicine, biochemistry and biomedical science. Extensive historical material.

Royal Statistical Society Library
University College London, Gower Street, London WC1E 6BT
☎0171 387 7050 ext. 2628
Fax 0171 380 7727/7373
E-mail: d.chatarji@ucl.ac.uk
Contact D Chatarji
Access RSS Fellows registered with University College London Library
Statistics (theory and methodology), mathematical statistics, applied statistics, econometrics.

Science Fiction Foundation Research Library
Liverpool University Library, PO Box 123, Liverpool L69 3DA
☎0151 794 2696/2733   Fax 0151 794 2681
Contact *Andy Sawyer*
Access For research, by appointment only (telephone first)
This is the largest collection outside the US of science fiction and related material – including autobiographies and critical works. *Special collection* Runs of 'pulp' magazines dating back to the 1920s. Foreign-language material (including a large Russian collection), and the papers of the Flat Earth Society. The collection also features a growing range of archive and manuscript material, including the Eric Frank Russell archive.

Science Museum Library
Imperial College Road, off Exhibition Road, London SW7 5NH
☎0171 938 8234   Fax 0171 938 9714
Open 9.30 am to 9.00 pm Monday to Friday (closes 5.30 pm outside academic terms); 9.30 am to 5.30 pm Saturday
Open access Reference only; no loans
National reference library for the history and public understanding of science and technology, with a large collection of source material. Operates jointly with Imperial College Central Library.

Scottish Poetry Library
See entry under **Organisations of Interest to Poets**

Sheffield Libraries and Information Services
Central Library, Surrey Street, Sheffield S1 1XZ
☎0114 2734711   Fax 0114 2735009
Sheffield Archives
52 Shoreham Street, Sheffield S1 4SP
☎0114 2734756   Fax 0114 2735066
Open 9.30 am to 5.30 pm Monday to Thursday; 9.00 am to 1.00 pm and 2.00 pm to 4.30 pm Saturday (documents should be ordered by 5.00 pm Thursday for Saturday)
Access By reader's pass
Holds documents relating to Sheffield and South Yorkshire, dating from the 12th century to the present day, including records of the City Council, churches, businesses, landed estates, families and individuals, institutions and societies.

Arts and Social Sciences Reference Service
☎0114 2734747/8
Open 10.00 am to 8.00 pm Monday; 9.30 am to 5.30 pm Tuesday and Friday; 9.30 am to 8.00 pm Wednesday; 9.30 am to 4.30 pm Saturday (closed Thursday)
Access For reference only
A comprehensive collection of books, periodicals and newspapers covering all aspects of arts (excluding music) and social sciences.

Music and Video Service
☎0114 2734733
Open as for Arts and Social Services above
Access For reference (loans to ticket holders only)
An extensive range of books, CDs, cassettes, scores, etc. related to music. Also a video cassette loan service.

Local Studies Service
☎0114 2734753
Open as for Arts & Social Sciences above (except Wednesday 9.30 am to 5.30 pm)
Access For reference (but advance notice advisable)
Extensive material covering all aspects of Sheffield and its population, including maps, photos and videos.

Business, Science and Technology Reference Services
☎0114 2734736–7
Open as for Arts & Social Sciences above
Access For reference only
Extensive coverage of science and technology as well as commerce and commercial law. British patents and British and European standards with emphasis on metals. Hosts the World Metal Index. The business section holds a large stock of business and trade directories, plus overseas telephone directories and reference works with business emphasis.

Sheffield Information Service
☎0114 2734760/1
Open 10.00 am to 5.30 pm Monday; 9.30 am to 5.30 pm Tuesday, Wednesday, Friday; 9.30 am to 4.30 pm Saturday (closed Thursday)
Full local information service covering all aspects of the Sheffield community and a generalist advice service on a sessional basis.

Shetland Library
Lower Hillhead, Lerwick, Shetland ZE1 0EL
☎01595 693868   Fax 01595 694430
E-mail: info@shetland-library.gov.uk

Website: http://www.shetland-library.gov.uk

Open 10.00 am to 7.00 pm Monday, Wednesday, Friday; 10.00 am to 5.00 pm Tuesday, Thursday, Saturday

General lending and reference library; extensive local interest collection including complete set of *The Shetland Times, The Shetland News* and other local newspapers on microfilm and many old and rare books; audio collection including *Linguaphone* courses and talking books/newspapers. Junior room for children. Disabled access and Housebound Readers Service (delivery to reader's home). Mobile library services to rural areas. Open Learning Service. Same day photocopying service. Publishing programme of books in dialect, history, literature.

Shoe Lane Library

Hill House, Little New Street, London EC4A 3JR
☎0171 583 7178

Open 9.30 am to 5.30 pm Monday, Wednesday, Thursday, Friday; 9.30 am to 6.30 pm Tuesday

Open access

Corporation of London general lending library, with a comprehensive stock of 48,000 volumes, most of which are on display. Some specialisation in graphics, advertising and illustrated works.

Shrewsbury Library

Castlegates, Shrewsbury, Shropshire SY1 2AS
☎01743 255300   Fax 01743 255309

Open 9.30 am to 5.00 pm Monday and Wednesday; 9.30 am to 1.00 pm Thursday; 9.30 am to 7.30 pm Tuesday and Friday; 9.30 am to 4.00 pm Saturday

Open access

The largest public lending library in Shropshire. Books, cassettes, CDs, talking books, videos, language courses. Public Internet access. Strong music, literature and art book collection. Reference and local studies provision in adjacent buildings.

Southend-on-Sea Libraries

Central Library, Victoria Avenue, Southend-on-Sea, Essex SS2 6EX
☎01702 612621   Fax 01702 469241
E-mail: sos@dial.pipex.com

Open 9.00 am to 7.00 pm Monday to Friday; 9.00 am to 5.00 pm Saturday

Open Access

There are seven libraries and two mobile

libraries. The Central Library has a major arts collection and also specialist collections on history and travel.

Spanish Institute Library

See **Instituto Cervantes**

St Bride Printing Library

Bride Lane, London EC4Y 8EE
☎0171 353 4660   Fax 0171 583 7073

Open 9.30 am to 5.30 pm Monday to Friday

Open access

Corporation of London public reference library. Appointments advisable for consultation of special collections. Every aspect of printing and related matters: publishing and bookselling, newspapers and magazines, graphic design, calligraphy and type, papermaking and bookbinding. One of the world's largest specialist collections in its field, with over 40,000 volumes, over 3000 periodicals (200 current titles), and extensive collection of drawings, manuscripts, prospectuses, patents and materials for printing and typefounding. Noted for its comprehensive holdings of historical and early technical literature.

Suffolk County Council Libraries & Heritage

St Andrew House, County Hall, St Helens Street, Ipswich, Suffolk IP4 1LJ
☎01473 583000   Fax 01473 584549
E-mail (general enquiries):infolink@libher.suffolkcc.gov.uk
Website: http://www.suffolkcc.gov.uk/libraries_and_heritage/

Open Details on application to St Andrew House above. Major libraries open six days a week

Access A single user registration card gives access to the lending service of 41 libraries across the county

Full range of lending and reference services. Free public access to the Internet and multimedia CD-ROMs in larger libraries. Catalogue with self-service facilities for registered borrowers available on the website. *Special collections* include Suffolk Archives and Local History Collection; Benjamin Britten Collection; Edward Fitzgerald Collection; Seckford Collection and Racing Collection (Newmarket). The Suffolk Infolink service gives details of local groups and societies and is available in libraries throughout the county.

Sunderland City Library and Arts Centre

28–30 Fawcett Street, Sunderland, Tyne & Wear SR1 1RE
☎0191 514 1235   Fax 0191 514 8444
Open 9.30 am to 7.30 pm Monday and Wednesday; 9.30 am to 5.00 pm Tuesday, Thursday, Friday; 9.30 am to 4.00 pm Saturday
The city's main lending and reference library. Local studies and children's sections, plus sound and vision department (CDs, cassettes, videos, talking books). The City of Sunderland also maintains community libraries of varying size, offering a range of services. Special services available to housebound readers, hospitals and schools, plus mobile libraries.

Swansea Central Reference Library

Alexandra Road, Swansea SA1 5DX
☎01792 655521   Fax 01792 645751
Open 9.00 am to 7.00 pm Monday, Tuesday, Wednesday, Friday; 9.00 am to 5.00 pm Thursday and Saturday. The library has a lending service but hours tend to be shorter – check in advance (☎01792 654065).

Access For reference only (Local Studies closed access: items must be requested on forms provided)
General reference material (approx. 100,000 volumes); also British standards, statutes, company information, maps, European Community information. Local studies: comprehensive collections on Wales; Swansea & Gower; Dylan Thomas. Local maps, periodicals, illustrations, local newspapers from 1804. B&w and colour photocopying facilities, access to the Internet and microfilm/microfiche copying facility.

Swiss Cottage Library

88 Avenue Road, London NW3 3HA
☎0171 413 6533/4
Open 10.00 am to 7.00 pm Monday and Thursday; 10.00 am to 6.00 pm Tuesday and Friday; 10.00 am to 5.00 pm Saturday (closed all day Wednesday)

Open access
Over 300,000 volumes in the lending and reference libraries and 300 periodicals (200 current titles). Home of the London Borough of Camden's Information and Reference Services.

Theatre Museum Library & Archive

1e Tavistock Street, London WC2E 7PA
☎0171 836 7891   Fax 0171 836 5148
Open 10.30 am to 4.30 pm Tuesday to Friday

Access By appointment only
The Theatre Museum was founded as a separate department of the Victoria & Albert Museum in 1974 and moved to its own building in Covent Garden in 1987. The museum (open Tuesday to Sunday 11.00 am to 7.00 pm) houses permanent displays, temporary exhibitions, a studio theatre, and organises a programme of special events, performances, lectures and guided visits. The library houses the UK's largest performing arts research collections, including books, photographs, designs, engravings, programmes, press cuttings, etc. All the performing arts are covered but strengths are in the areas of theatre history, ballet, circus and stage design. The Theatre Museum has acquired much of the British Theatre Association's library and is providing reference access to its collections of play texts and critical works.

Thurrock Council Leisure, Libraries & Cultural Services Department

Grays Library, Orsett Road, Grays, Essex RM17 5DX
☎01375 383611   Fax 01375 370806
Open 9.00 am to 7.00 pm Monday, Tuesday, Thursday; 9.00 am to 5.00 pm Wednesday, Friday, Saturday; branch library opening times vary

Open Access
General library lending and reference through nine libraries and a mobile library. Services include books, magazines, newspapers, audiocassettes, CDs, videos, pictures and language courses. Large collection of Thurrock materials. Periodicals collection (not on public access).

Truro Library

Union Place, Pydar Street, Truro, Cornwall TR1 1EP
☎01872 279205 (Lending)/272702 (Reference
Open 9.30 am to 5.00 pm Monday to Thursday; 9.30 am to 7.00 pm Friday; 9.30 am to 1.00 pm Saturday
Books, cassettes, CDs and videos for loan through branch or mobile networks. Reference, music and drama. *Special collections* on local studies.

United Nations Library and Information Centre

Millbank Tower (21st Floor), 21–24 Millbank, London SW1P 4QH
☎0171 630 1981   Fax 0171 976 6478

Open Library: 9.00 am to 1.00 pm and 2.00 pm to 5.00 pm Monday to Thursday; Information Centre: 9.30 am to 1.00 pm and 2.00 pm to 5.30 pm Monday to Friday

Open access To Information Centre only; Reference Library by appointment only
A full stock of official publications and documentation from the United Nations.

Western Isles Libraries

Public Library, Keith Street, Stornoway, Isle of Lewis HS1 2QG
☎01851 703064   Fax 01851 705657

Open 10.00 am to 5.00 pm Monday to Thursday; 10.00 am to 7.00 pm Friday; 10.00 am to 1.00 pm Saturday

Open access
General public library stock, plus local history and Gaelic collections including maps, printed music and cassettes; census records and Council minutes; music collection (cassettes). Branch libraries on the isles of Barra, Benbecula, Harris and Lewis.

City of Westminster Archives Centre

10 St Ann's Street, London SW1P 2XR
☎0171 641 5180   Fax 0171 641 5179

Open 9.30 am to 7.00 pm Monday to Friday; 9.30 am to 5.00 pm Saturday

Access For reference
Comprehensive coverage of the history of Westminster and selective coverage of general London history. 22,000 books, together with a large stock of maps, prints, photographs, and theatre programmes.

Westminster Music Library

Victoria Library, 160 Buckingham Palace Road, London SW1W 9UD
☎0171 641 2192   Fax 0171 641 2181

Open 1.00 pm to 7.00 pm Monday to Friday; 10 am to 5.00 pm Saturday

Open access
Located at Victoria Library, this is the largest public music library in the South of England, with extensive coverage of all aspects of music, including books, periodicals and printed scores. No recorded material, notated only. Lending library includes a small collection of CDs, cassettes and videos.

Westminster Reference Library

35 St Martin's Street, London WC2H 7HP
☎0171 641 4636 (General Reference & Performing Arts)   Fax 0171 641 4640
Business and Official Publications
☎0171 641 4634
Information for Business Service
☎0171 641 4603 (fee-based service)

Open 10.00 am to 7.00 pm Monday to Friday; 10.00 am to 5.00 pm Saturday

Access For reference only
A general reference library with emphasis on the following: Art & Design (see separate entry); Performing Arts – theatre, cinema, radio, television and dance; Official Publications – major collection of HMSO publications from 1947, plus parliamentary papers dating back to 1906, and a ten-year file of key statistical publications from OECD, UN, UNESCO, etc.; Business – UK directories, trade directories, company and market data; Official EU Depository Library – carries all official EU material; Periodicals – long files of many titles. One working day's notice is required for some monographs and most older periodicals.

Westminster Reference Library (Art & Design Department)

Westminster Reference Library, St Martin's Street, London WC2H 7HP
☎0171 641 4638   Fax 0171 641 4640

Open 10.00 am to 7.00 pm Monday to Friday; 10.00 am to 5.00 pm Saturday

Access For reference only (stacks are closed to the public)
Located on the second floor of the City of Westminster's main reference library. An excellent reference source for fine and applied arts, including antiques, architecture, ceramics, coins, costume, crafts, design, furniture, garden history, interior decoration, painting, sculpture, textiles. Complete runs of major English Language periodicals such as *Studio*; exhibition catalogues; guidebooks to historic houses, castles, gardens and churches. Some older books and most periodicals earlier than 1980 are in storage and at least one day's notice is required before they can be obtained.

The Wiener Library

4 Devonshire Street, London W1N 2BH
☎0171 636 7247   Fax 0171 436 6428
E-mail: lib@wl.v-net.com

Open 10.00 am to 5.30 pm Monday to Friday

Access By letter of introduction (readers needing to use the Library for any length of time should become members)

Private library – one of the leading research centres on European history since the First World War, with special reference to the era of totalitarianism and to Jewish affairs. Founded by Dr Alfred Wiener in Amsterdam in 1933, it holds material that is not available elsewhere. Books, periodicals, press archives, documents, pamphlets, leaflets and brochures. Much of the material can be consulted on microfilm.

Vaughan Williams Memorial Library

English Folk Dance and Song Society, Cecil Sharp House, 2 Regent's Park Road, London NW1 7AY
☎0171 284 0523   Fax 0171 284 0523

Open 9.30 am to 5.30 pm Monday to Friday

Access For reference to the general public, on payment of a daily fee; members may borrow books and use the library free of charge

A multi-media collection: books, periodicals, manuscripts, tapes, records, CDs, films, videos. Mostly British folk culture and how this has developed around the world. Some foreign language material, and some books in English about foreign cultures. Also, the history of the English Folk Dance and Song Society.

Dr Williams's Library

14 Gordon Square, London WC1H 0AG
☎0171 387 3727   Fax 0171 388 1142

Open 10.00 am to 5.00 pm Monday, Wednesday, Friday; 10.00 am to 6.30 pm Tuesday and Thursday

Open access To reading room (loans restricted to subscribers) **Annual subscription** £10; ministers of religion and certain students £5

Primarily a library of theology, religion and ecclesiastical history. Also philosophy, history (English and Byzantine). Particularly important for the study of English Nonconformity.

Wolverhampton Central Library

Snow Hill, Wolverhampton WV1 3AX
☎01902 552025   Fax 01902 714579

Open 10.00 am to 7.00 pm Monday to Thursday; 10.00 am to 5.00 pm Friday and Saturday

Archives & Local Studies Collection

42–50 Snow Hill, Wolverhampton WV2 4AB
☎01902 717703

Open 10.00 am to 5.00 pm Monday, Tuesday, Friday, Saturday (limited archive production between 12.00 pm and 2.00 pm; archives must be booked in advance on Saturdays); 10.00 am to 7.00 pm Wednesday (closed Thursday)

General lending and reference libraries, plus children's library. Also audiovisual library holding cassettes, CDs, videos and music scores.

Worcestershire Libraries and Information Service

County Hall, Spetchley Road, Worcester WR5 2NP
☎01905 766231   Fax 01905 766240

Website: http://www.worcestershire.gov.uk

Open Opening hours vary in the 22 libraries and mobile libraries covering the county; all full-time libraries open at least one evening a week until 7.00 pm or 8.00 pm, and on Saturday until 1 pm; part-time libraries vary

Access Information and reference services open to anyone; loans to members only (membership criteria: resident, being educated, working, or an elector in the county or neighbouring authorities; temporary membership to visitors. Proof of identity and address required)

Information service, and reference and lending libraries. Non-fiction and fiction for all age groups, including normal and large print, spoken word cassettes, sound recordings (CD, cassette, some vinyl), videos, maps, local history, CD-ROMs for reference at main libraries, online information service including Internet access to certain specified (public information) websites. *Special collections* Carpets and Textiles; Needles & Needlemaking; Stuart Period; A. E. Housman.

York Central Library

Museum Street, York YO1 2DS
☎01904 655631   Fax 01904 611025

Lending Library

Open 9.30 am to 8.00 pm Monday, Tuesday, Friday; 9.30 am to 5.30 pm Wednesday and Thursday; 9.30 am to 4.00 pm Saturday

General lending library including videos, CDs, music cassettes, audio books and children's storytapes.

Reference Library

Open 9.00 am to 8.00 pm Monday, Tuesday, Wednesday, Friday; 9.00 am to 5.30 pm Thursday; 9.00 am to 4.00 pm Saturday

General reference library; organisations database; local studies library for York and surrounding area; business information service; microfilm/ fiche readers for national and local newspapers; census returns and family history resource; general reference collection. Maintains strong links with other local history resource centres, namely the Borthwick Institute, York City Archive and York Minster Library. CD-ROM and Internet facilities.

Young Book Trust Children's Reference Library

Book House, 45 East Hill, London SW18 2QZ
☎0181 516 2977   Fax 0181 516 2978
Open 9.00 am to 5.00 pm Monday to Friday (by appointment only)
Access For reference only
 A comprehensive collection of children's literature, related books and periodicals. Aims to hold most of all children's titles published within the last two years. An information service covers all aspects of children's literature, including profiles of authors and illustrators. Reading room facilities.

Zoological Society Library

Regent's Park, London NW1 4RY
☎0171 449 6293   Fax 0171 586 5743
Open 9.30 am to 5.30 pm Monday to Friday
Access To members and staff; non-members by application and on payment of fee
 160,000 volumes on zoology including 5000 journals (1300 current) and a wide range of books on animals and particular habitats. Slide collection available and many historic zoological prints.

Picture Libraries

A–Z Botanical Collection Ltd
82–84 Clerkenwell Road, London EC1M 5RJ
☎0171 336 7942   Fax 0171 336 7942
E-mail: alasdair@image-data.com
Website: www.a-z.picture-library.com

Contact *Alasdair McCombe*

200,000 transparencies, specialising in plants and related subjects.

Acme
See **Popperfoto**

Action Plus
54–58 Tanner Street, London SE1 3PH
☎0171 403 1558   Fax 0171 403 1526

Specialist sports and action library with a vast comprehensive collection of small-format colour and b&w images covering all aspects of over 120 professional and amateur sports from around the world. As well as personalities, events, venues, etc, also covers themes such as success, celebration, dejection, teamwork, effort and exhaustion. Offers same-day despatch of pictures or alternatively, clients with Macintosh and modem or ISDN links can receive digital images direct.

Lesley & Roy Adkins Picture Library
Longstone Lodge, Aller, Langport, Somerset TA10 0QT
☎01458 250075   Fax 01458 250858

Colour coverage of archaeology, heritage and related subjects in the UK, Europe, Egypt and Turkey. Subjects include towns, tillages, housing, landscape and countryside, churches, temples, castles, monasteries, art and architecture, gravestones and tombs, and antiquarian views. Prompt service. No service charge if pictures are used. Catalogue and rates available.

The Advertising Archive Limited
45 Lyndale Avenue, London NW2 2QB
☎0171 435 6540   Fax 0171 794 6584

Contact *Suzanne or Larry Viner*

With half a million images, the largest collection of British and American press ads and magazine cover illustrations in Europe. Material from 1870 to the present day. Visitors by appointment. Research undertaken; rapid service, competitive rates. Exclusive UK agents for *Saturday Evening*

Post cover illustrations including artwork of Norman Rockwell and Josef Leyendecker.

AKG London Ltd, Arts and History Picture Library
10 Plato Place, 72–74 St Dionis Road, London SW6 4TU
☎0171 610 6103   Fax 0171 610 6125
E-mail: enquiries@akg-london.co.uk
Website: www.akg-london.co.uk

Contact *Julia Engelhardt*

Collection of 125,000 images with computerised access to nine million more kept in the Berlin AKG Library. *Specialises* in art, archaeology, history, topography, music, personalities and film.

Bryan & Cherry Alexander Photography
Higher Cottage, Manston, Sturminster Newton, Dorset DT10 1EZ
☎01258 473006   Fax 01258 473333
E-mail: arcticfoto@aol.com
Website: http://members.aol.com/arcticfoto/

Contact *Cherry Alexander*

Artic and Antartic specialists; indigenous peoples, wildlife and science in polar regions; Norway, Iceland, Siberia and Alaska.

Allsport (UK) Ltd
3 Greenlea Park, Prince George's Road, London SW19 2JD
☎0181 685 1010   Fax 0181 648 5240

Contact *Lee Martin*

A large specialist library with 6 million colour transparencies, covering 140 different sports and top sports personalities. Represented in 27 countries worldwide. Digital wiring facilities through Macintosh picture desk. Online digital archive access available via ISDN and Internet.

Alphastock Picture Library
Greenheys Business Centre, 10 Pencroft Way, Manchester M15 6JJ
☎0161 226 8000   Fax 0161 226 2022
Website: http://www.alphastock.co.uk

Wide selection of subjects from the UK and abroad. Mostly colour, some b&w. Industry, business, sport, farming, scenic, personalities, jazz musicians (and some classical), space, and many more. Special collection on the North West of England. Commissions undertaken.

Alvey & Towers

9 Rosebank Road, Countesthorpe,
Leicestershire LE8 5YA
☎0116 2779184   Fax 0116 2779184

Contact *Emma Rowen*

Houses two separate collections; one covering the modern railway industry and all related supporting industries, the other features a more general 'lifestyle' collection with the emphasis on people and day-to-day living plus a substantial selection of transport images.

Andalucia Slide Library

Apto 499, Estepona, Malaga 29 680, Spain
☎00 34 952 793647   Fax 00 34 952 793647

Contact *Chris Chaplow*

Specialist library covering all aspects of Spain and Spanish life and culture. Cities, white villages, landscapes, festivals, art, gastronomy, leisure, tourism. Commissions undertaken.

Andes Press Agency

26 Padbury Court, London E2 7EH
☎0171 613 5417   Fax 0171 739 3159

Contact *Val Baker, Carlos Reyes*

80,000 colour transparencies and 300,000 b&w, specialising in social documentary, world religions, Latin America and Britain.

Heather Angel/Biofotos

Highways, 6 Vicarage Hill, Farnham, Surrey GU9 8HJ
☎01252 716700   Fax 01252 727464

Contacts *Lindsay Bamford, Valerie West*

Constantly expanding worldwide natural history, wildlife and landscapes: polar regions, tropical rainforest flora and fauna, all species of plants and animals in natural habitats from Africa, Asia (notably China and Malaysia), Australasia, South America and USA, urban wildlife, pollution, biodiversity, global warming. Catalogue available. Commissions undertaken. Complete picture/text packages a speciality.

Animal Photography

4 Marylebone Mews, New Cavendish Street, London W1M 7LF
☎0171 935 0503   Fax 0171 487 3038
E-mail: thompson@animal-photography.co.uk

Colour and b&w coverage of horses, dogs, cats,

zoos, the Galapagos Islands, East Africa. Pictures from other photographers are not accepted.

Aquarius Picture Library

PO Box 5, Hastings, East Sussex
TN34 1HR
☎01424 721196   Fax 01424 717704

Contact *David Corkill*

Over one million images specialising in cinema past and present, television, pop music, ballet, opera, theatre, etc. The library includes various American showbiz collections. Film stills date back to the beginning of the century. Interested in film stills, the older the better. Current material is supplied by own suppliers.

Aquila Wildlife Images

PO Box 1, Studley, Warwickshire B80 7JG
☎0152785 2357   Fax 0152785 7507

Natural history library specialising in birds, British and European wildlife, North America, Africa and Australia, environmental subjects, farming, habitats and related subjects, domestic animals and pets.

Arcaid

The Factory, 2 Acre Road, Kingston upon Thames, Surrey KT2 6EF
☎0181 546 4352   Fax 0181 541 5230

The built environment, historic and contemporary architecture and interior design by leading architectural photographers. Covers international and British subjects, single images and series, with background information. Visitors welcome by appointment. Commissions undertaken.

Architectural Association Photo Library

34–36 Bedford Square, London
WC1B 3ES
☎0171 887 4078/4086   Fax 0171 414 0782

Contact *Valerie Bennett, Vanessa Norwood*

200,000 35mm transparencies on architecture, historical and contemporary. Archive of large-format b&w negatives from the 1920s and 1930s.

Ardea London Ltd

35 Brodrick Road, London SW17 7DX
☎0181 672 2067   Fax 0181 672 8787

Wildlife, natural history, conservation and environmental topics in colour and b&w. Animals, birds, plants and fish in their natural habitat worldwide.

Art Directors & Tripp Photo Library

57 Burdon Lane, Cheam, Surrey SM2 7BY
☎0181 642 3593/661 7104
Fax 0181 395 7230
E-mail: images@tripphoto.demon.co.uk
Website: http://www.tripphoto.demon.co.uk

Contact *Helene Rogers, Bob Turner*

Englarged newly-merged library with more than 750,000 images. Extensive coverage of all countries, lifestyles, religion, peoples, etc. Backgrounds a speciality. Two new catalogues available free to professionals.

Artbank Illustration Library

8 Woodcroft Avenue, London NW7 2AG
☎0181 906 2288   Fax 0181 906 2289

Illustration and art library holding thousands of images by many renowned contemporary illustrators. Large-format transparencies. Catalogue available on faxed request. Represents a diverse group of UK and American illustrators for commissioned work. Portfolios available for viewing.

Aspect Picture Library Ltd

40 Rostrevor Road, London SW6 5AD
☎0171 736 1998/731 7362
Fax 0171 731 7362
E-mail: Aspect.Ldn@btinternet.com

Colour and b&w worldwide coverage of countries, events, industry and travel, with large files on art, namely paintings, space, China and the Middle East.

Audio Visual Services

Imperial College School of Medicine at St Mary's, London W2 1PG
☎0171 725 1739   Fax 0171 724 7349

Contact *B. Tallon*

Colour and b&w, mostly 35mm colour. Clinical medicine, contemporary and historical, including HIV-AIDS material and history of penicillin. Commissions undertaken.

Australia Pictures

28 Sheen Common Drive, Richmond TW10 5BN
☎0181 898 0150/876 3637
Fax 0181 898 0150/876 3637

Contact *John Miles*

Collection of 4000 transparencies covering all aspects of Australia: Aboriginal people, paintings, Ayers Rock, Kakadu, Tasmania, underwater, reefs, Arnhem Land, Sydney. Also Africa, Middle East and Asia.

Aviation Images – Mark Wagner

42B Queens Road, London SW19 8LR
☎0181 944 5225   Fax 0181 944 5335

Contact *Mark Wagner*

250,000+ aviation images, civil and military, technical and generic. Mark Wagner is the photographer for *Flight International* magazine. Member of **BAPLA** and RAeS.

Aviation Photographs International

15 Downs View Road, Swindon, Wiltshire SN3 1NS
☎01793 497179   Fax 01793 434030

The 250,000 colour photos comprise a comprehensive coverage of army, naval and airforce hardware ranging from early pistols to the latest ships. Extensive coverage of military and civil aviation includes modern together with many air-to-air views of vintage/warbird types. Commissions undertaken for additional photography and research.

Aviation Picture Library

116 The Avenue, St Stephens, West Ealing, London W13 8JX
☎0181 566 7712   Fax 0181 566 7714
E-mail: avpix@aviationpictures.com

Contact *Austin John Brown, Chris Savill*

Specialists in the aviation field but also a general library which includes travel, architecture, transport, landscapes and skyscapes. *Special collections*: aircraft and all aspects of the aviation industry; aerial obliques of Europe, USA, Caribbean and West Africa; architectural and town planning. Commissions undertaken on the ground and in the air.

Axel Poignant Archive

115 Bedford Court Mansions, Bedford Avenue, London WC1B 3AG
☎0171 636 2555   Fax 0171 636 2555

Contact *Roslyn Poignant*

Anthropological and ethnographic subjects, especially Australia and the South Pacific. Also Scandinavia (early history and mythology), Sicily and England.

Barnaby's Picture Library

Barnaby House, 19 Rathbone Street, London W1P 1AF
☎0171 636 6128   Fax 0171 637 4317

Contact *Mary Buckland*

Colour and b&w coverage of a wide range of subjects: nature, transport, industry and historical, including a collection on Hitler. Etchings throughout history.

Barnardos Photographic and Film Archive

Tanners Lane, Barkingside, Ilford, Essex
IG6 1QG
☎0181 550 8822   Fax 0181 550 0429
Contact *John Kirkham*

Specialises in social history (1874 to present day), child care, education, war years, emigration/migration. Half a million prints, slides, negatives. Images are mainly b&w, colour since late 1940s/early 50s. Archive of 200 films dating back to 1905. Visitors by appointment Mon–Fri 9.30 am to 4.30 pm.

Colin Baxter Photography Limited

Woodlands Industrial Estate, Grantown-on-Spey PH26 3NA
☎01479 873999   Fax 01479 873888
E-mail: colin.baxter@zetnet.co.uk
Contact *Colin B. Kirkwood (Marketing),*
Mike Rensner (Editorial)

Over 50,000 images specialising in Scotland. Also the Lake District, Yorkshire, the Cotswolds, France, Iceland and a special collection on Charles Rennie Mackintosh's work. *Publishes* books, calendars, postcards and greetings cards on landscape, cityscape and natural history containing images which are primarily, but not exclusively, Colin Baxter's. Also publishers of the *Worldlife Library* of natural history books.

BBC Natural History Unit Picture Library

Broadcasting House, Whiteladies Road, Bristol BS8 2LR
☎0117 9746720   Fax 0117 9238166
E-mail: nhu.picture.library@bbc.co.uk
Contacts *Helen Gilks, Sue Fogden*

A collection of 80,000 transparencies of wildlife of the world. Other subjects covered include plants, landscapes, environmental issues and photos relating to the making of the Natural History Unit's films. Wildlife sound recordings and film footage also available.

The Photographic Library Beamish, The North of England Open Air Museum

Beamish, The North of England Open Air Museum, Beamish, County Durham DH9 0RG
☎01207 231811   Fax 01207 290933
Assistant Keeper, Resource Collections
Jim Lawson

Comprehensive collection; images relate to the North East of England and cover agricultural, industrial, topography, advertising and shop scenes, people at work and play. Also on laser disk for rapid searching. Visitors by appointment weekdays.

Francis Bedford

See **Birmingham Library Services** under **Library Services**

Ivan J. Belcher Colour Picture Library

57 Gibson Close, Abingdon, Oxfordshire OX14 1XS
☎01235 521524   Fax 01235 521524

Extensive colour picture library specialising in top-quality medium-format transparencies depicting the British scene. Particular emphasis on tourist, holiday and heritage locations, including famous cities, towns, picturesque harbours, rivers, canals, castles, cottages, rural scenes and traditions photographed throughout the seasons. Mainly of recent origin, and constantly updated.

Andrew Besley PhotoLibrary

2 Reawla Lane, Reawla, Near Hayle, Cornwall TR27 5HQ
☎01736 850086   Fax 01736 850086
E-mail: bes.pix@btinternet.com
Contact *Andrew Besley*

Specialist library of 20,000 images of West Country faces, places and moods.

BFI Stills, Posters and Designs

British Film Institute, 21 Stephen Street, London W1P 2LN
☎0171 255 1444   Fax 0171 323 9260

Holds images from more than 60,000 films and TV programmes on 6 million b&w prints and over 500,000 colour transparencies. A further 20,000 files hold portraits of film and TV personalities and cover related general subjects such as studios, equipment, awards. Also holds original posters and set and costume designs. Visitors welcome by appointment only (from 11.00 am to 5.00 pm).

Birmingham Repertory Theatre Archive and Sir Barry Jackson Library

See **Birmingham Library Services** under **Library Services**

Blackwoods Picture Library

See **Geoslides Photography**

Anthony Blake Photo Library
54 Hill Rise, Richmond, Surrey TW10 6UB
☎0181 940 7583   Fax 0181 948 1224
'Europe's premier source' of food and wine-related images. From the farm and the vineyard to the plate and the bottle. Cooking and kitchens, top chefs and restaurants, country trades and markets, worldwide travel. Extensive new Italian section. Many recipes available to accompany transparencies. Commissions accepted. Free brochure available.

Boats & Boating Features (Keith Pritchard)
9 High Street, Southwell, Portland, Dorset DT5 2EH
☎01305 861006/0378 307301
Fax 01305 861006
E-mail: keith@boating-features.demon.co.uk
Contact *Keith Pritchard*

Around 20,000 colour transparencies of small craft, historic and modern boats up to 100ft, boating events, people and places in Britain and overseas.

Chris Bonington Picture Library
Badger Hill, Nether Row, Hesket
Newmarket, Wigton, Cumbria CA7 8LA
☎016974 78286   Fax 016974 78238
E-mail: frances@bonington.com
Contact *Frances Daltrey*

Based on the personal collection of climber and author Chris Bonington and his extensive travels and mountaineering achievements; also work by Doug Scott and other climbers, including the Peter Boardman and Joe Tasker Collections. Full coverage of the world's mountains, from British hills to Everest, depicting expedition planning and management stages, the approach march showing inhabitants of the area, flora and fauna, local architecture and climbing action shots on some of the world's highest mountains.

Boulton and Watt Archive
See **Birmingham Library Services** under **Library Services**

The Bridgeman Art Library
17–19 Garway Road, London W2 4PH
☎0171 727 4065   Fax 0171 792 8509
Website: www.bridgeman.co.uk
Rights & Marketing Executive *Gail Finn*

Fine art photo archive acting as an agent to more than 700 museums, galleries and picture owners around the world. Large-format colour transparencies of paintings, sculptures, prints, manuscripts, antiquities and the decorative arts. The Library is currently expanding at the rate of 500 new images each week. Collections represented by the library include the British Library, the National Galleries of Scotland, the National Library of Australia, and the National Gallery of South Africa. Catalogues of stock are available in printed form and on CD-ROM. Please call for a free brochure or visit the website on the Internet.

British Library Reproductions
British Library, 96 Euston Road, London
NW1 2DB
☎0171 412 7614   Fax 0171 412 7771
E-mail: bl-repro@bl.uk
Website: www.bl.uk

Twelve million books and approximately five million other items available for photography, microfilming or photocopying by Library staff. Specialist subjects include illuminated manuscripts, stamps, music, maps, botanical and zoological illustration, portraits of historical figures, history of India and South East Asia. All copies should be ordered as far in advance as possible. However, for photographs for commercial reproduction a picture library service is available which enables orders to be processed more quickly. Customers are welcome to browse.

Brooklands Museum Picture Library
Brooklands Museum, Brooklands Road,
Weybridge, Surrey KT13 0QN
☎01932 857381   Fax 01932 855465
Contact *John Pulford, Curator of Collections; Julian Temple, Curator of Aviation*

About 40,000 b&w and colour prints and slides. Subjects include: Brooklands Motor Racing 1907–1939; British aviation and aerospace 1908–present day – particularly BAC, Hawker, Sopwith and Vickers aircraft built at Brooklands.

Hamish Brown Scottish Photographic
26 Kirkcaldy Road, Burntisland, Fife KY3 9HQ
☎01592 873546
Contact *Hamish M. Brown*

Colour and b&w coverage of most topics and areas of Scotland (sites, historic, buildings, landscape, mountains), also travel and mountains abroad, Ireland and Morocco. Commissions undertaken.

Simon Brown, Nature and Landscape Photographer
36 Sandymount Road, Wath–upon–Dearne, Rotherham, South Yorkshire S63 7AE
☎01709 874322/0966 538821 (mobile)
Fax 01709 874322

Contact *Simon Brown*

5000 images of natural history and landscape of the British Isles with a particular focus on the Peak District, Northumberland and north Wales. Also some rock climbing pictures. Can work to commission; full research service in life sciences, landscape, mountaineering and photography. Info pack on using a library (£1.50) and catalogue (£5) – both refundable against fees for reproduction. Free brochure also available.

Bubbles Photolibrary
23A Benwell Road, London N7 7BL
☎0171 609 4547   Fax 0171 607 1410
E-mail: bubblesphotos@compuserve.com

Pregnancy, babies, children, teenagers, general lifestyle, health, old age, medical, still lives of food.

Camera Press
21 Queen Elizabeth Street, London SE1 2PD
☎0171 378 1300   Fax 0171 278 5126

High-quality photofeatures and up-to-date coverage of international events, celebrities, royals, fashion and beauty, and general stock.

Camera Ways Ltd Picture Library
Court View, Stonebridge Green Road, Egerton, Ashford, Kent TN27 9AN
☎01233 756454   Fax 01233 756242

Contacts *Derek, Caryl, Jonathan, Steve*

Founded by award-winning film-maker and photographer, Derek Budd, the library specialises in rural activities and natural history. It contains 35mm and 6x4.5mm, colour and b&w images as well as 16mm film and video footage on Beta SP. Coverage includes: wildlife habitats, flora and fauna of Britain and Europe, traditional country crafts and people, village scenes, landscapes, gardens, coastal and aquatic life, dinosaurs, aerial surveys, storm damage and M.O.D. reserves. A creative service is available from their Technical Artist & Wildlife Illustrator; commissions undertaken in all aspects of commercial multi-media photography, 16mm film, broadcast and corporate video production.

Capital Pictures
54a Clerkenwell Road, London EC1M 5PS
☎0171 253 1122   Fax 0171 253 1414

Contact *Phil Loftus*

450,000 images. *Specialises* in famous people from the worlds of showbusiness, rock and pop, television, politics, royalty and film stills.

The Casement Collection
Erin Lodge, Jigs Lane South, Warfield, Berkshire RG42 3DR
☎01344 302067   Fax 01344 303158

Colour and b&w travel library, particularly strong on North America and the Gulf. Not just beaches and palm trees. Based on Jack Casement's collection, with additions by other photographers. Digitised images available.

J. Allan Cash Ltd
74 South Ealing Road, London W5 4QB
☎0181 840 4141   Fax 0181 566 2568

Colour and b&w coverage of travel, natural history, people, space, sport, industry, agriculture and many other subjects. New material regularly contributed by 300-plus photographers.

The Centre for the Study of Cartoons and Caricature
The Templeman Library, University of Kent at Canterbury, Canterbury, Kent CT2 7NU
☎01227 823127   Fax 01227 823127

Contacts *Jane Newton*

A national research archive of over 85,000 20th century cartoons and caricatures, supported by a library of books, papers, journals, catalogues and assorted ephemera. A computer database provides for quick and easy catalogued access. A source for exhibitions and displays as well as a picture library service. *Specialises* in historical, political and social cartoons – British and international.

Cephas Picture Library
Hurst House, 157 Walton Road, East Molesey, Surrey KT8 0DX
☎0181 979 8647   Fax 0181 224 8095
E-mail: mickrock@cephas.co.uk
Website: http://www.cephas.co.uk

The wine industry and vineyards of the world is the subject on which Cephas has made its reputation. 80,000 images, mainly original 6x7s, make this the most comprehensive and up-to-date archive in Britain. Almost all wine-producing countries and all aspects of the industry are covered in depth. Spirits, beer and cider also included. A major food and drink collection now also exists, through preparation and cooking, to eating and drinking. Call for free 114-page catalogue.

Christel Clear Marine Photography
Roselea, Church Lane, Awbridge,
Near Romsey, Hampshire SO51 0HN
☎01794 341081   Fax 01794 340890
Contact *Nigel Dowden, Christel Dowden*

Over 60,000 images on 35mm and 645 transparency: yachting and boating from Grand Prix sailing to small dinghies, cruising locations and harbours. Recent additions include angling, fly fishing and travel. Visitors by appointment.

Christian Aid Photo Section
PO Box 100, London SE1 7RT
☎0171 523 2235   Fax 0171 620 0719

Pictures are mainly from Africa, Asia and Latin America, relating to small-scale, community-based programmes. Mostly development themes: agriculture, health, education, urban and rural life.

Christie's Images
1 Langley Lane, London SW8 1TH
☎0171 582 1282   Fax 0171 582 5632
E-mail: chrisimage@earthlink.net
Contact *Camilla Young*

The UK's largest fine art photo library. 150,000 images of fine and decorative art. An extensive list of subjects is covered through paintings, drawings and prints of all periods as well as silver, ceramics, jewellery, sculpture, textiles and many other decorative and collectable items. Staff will search files and database to locate specific requests or supply a selection for consideration. No search fee. Visits by appointment.

The Cinema Museum
The Master's House, Old Lambeth
Workhouse, off Renfrew Road, London
SE11 4TH
☎0171 840 2200   Fax 0171 840 2299

Colour and b&w coverage (including stills) of the motion picture industry throughout its history, including the Ronald Grant Archive. Smaller collections on theatre, variety, television and popular music.

John Cleare/Mountain Camera
Hill Cottage, Fonthill Gifford, Salisbury,
Wiltshire SP3 6QW
☎01747 820320   Fax 01747 820320

E-mail: cleare@btinternet.com

Colour and b&w coverage of mountains and wild places, climbing, ski-touring, trekking, expeditions, wilderness travel, landscapes, people and geographical features from all continents. *Specialises* in the Himalaya, Andes, Antarctic, Alps and the British countryside, and a range of topics from reindeer in Lapland to camels in Australia, from whitewater rafting in Utah to ski-mountaineering in China. Commissions and consultancy work undertaken. Researchers welcome by appointment. Member of **BAPLA** and the OWG.

The Clifton Archive
Suite 314, 28 Old Brompton Road, South
Kensington, London SW7 3DL
Fax 0171 581 4851   .
Contact *Alan Clifton*

Established in 1956 by photographer Alan Clifton. A collection of 300,000 b&w 35mm negatives and 200,000 colour 35mm transparencies which includes a large travel section and over 500 personalities.

Close-Up Picture Library
14 Burnham Wood, Fareham, Hampshire
PO16 7UD
☎01329 239053
Director *David Stent*

Specialises in the close-up angle of all aspects of life: people, places, animal and bird-life and the environment in general. Also a wide range of pictures covering travel in Europe and the Orient, multicultural, ethnic and educational issues. Photographers with quality material always welcome: no minimum initial submission; 50% commission on 35mm.

Stephanie Colasanti
38 Hillside Court, 409 Finchley Road,
London NW3 6HQ
☎0171 435 3695   Fax 0171 435 9995
E-mail: stephani@photosource.co.uk
Website: http://www.photosource.co.uk/
   photosource/stephanie.htm

Colour coverage of Europe, Africa, Asia, United Arab Emirates, the Caribbean, USA, Australia, New Zealand, the Pacific Islands and South America: people, animals, towns, agriculture, landscapes, carnivals, markets, archaeology, religion and ancient civilisations. Travel assignments undertaken. Medium-format transparencies (2″ square).

Michael Cole Camerawork

The Coach House, 27 The Avenue,
Beckenham, Kent BR3 2DP
☎0181 658 6120   Fax 0181 658 6120
Contact *Michael Cole, Derrick Bentley*

Probably the largest and most comprehensive collection of tennis pictures in the world; incorporating the library of Le Roye Productions, a company which covered Wimbledon from 1945–70, and MCC coverage of all major tennis events, worldwide, since 1970. Also small travel picture library: English countryside, Venice, Moscow, USA, etc. 200,000 35mm colour slides, 3,600 2¼" and 6x7cm colour transparencies, 270,000 b&w negatives and a vast quantity of b&w movie film.

Collections

13 Woodberry Crescent, London N10 1PJ
☎0181 883 0083   Fax 0181 883 9215
Contact *Laura Boswell, Brian Shuel*

250,000 colour and b&w images making a collection of collections about the British Isles. 'Our "area" collections aim to cover Great Britain, Ireland and the many smaller islands eventually – and we are doing well so far.' Subjects include two of Britain's major collections on pregnancy, birth, childhood and education by Anthea Sieveking and Sandra Lousada, the customs of Britain by Brian Shuel, landscapes by Fay Godwin, large collections of castles, waterways, railways, bridges and London, and a large variety of smaller specialities. Also building an unusual collection on the emergency services. Visitors welcome by appointment.

COMSTOCK Photolibrary

28 Chelsea Wharf, 15 Lots Road, London
SW10 0QQ
☎0171 351 4448   Fax 0171 352 8414
Contact *Helena Kovac*

Extensive coverage of business, people, industry, science, futuristic, world travel, landscapes, medical and natural history. Also desktop photography and CD-ROM. Free catalogues on request. Provides access to over four million images.

Concannon Golf History Library

Cairns Business Centre, 2 Cairns Road,
Battersea, London SW11 1ES
☎0171 801 7020   Fax 0171 801 7070
Contact *Dale Concannon*

Private collection of historic golfing images 1750–1950. Players, courses, Ryder Cup, Open championship, golf architecture, memorabilia, US golf. Specialist advice. Commissions undertaken.

Corbis UK Ltd

12 Regents Wharf, All Saints Street, London
N1 7RL
☎0171 843 4444   Fax 0171 278 1408
Contacts *Helen Menzies, Anna Calvert*

Access to a digital archive of over one million images, plus one of the world's largest picture sources, Bettmann. With over 17 million images, the archive is home to scores of individual collections including two of the most important news libraries: UPI (1907–1990) and Reuters (1985 to the present day, from the original negatives). Specialist subjects include news events, sports, cinema, war, social history, entertainment, people, geography, and early coverage of the Wild West, native Americans and the American Civil War. Other major components provide comprehensive coverage of world history from woodcuts and engravings to early photographs. A 6000-image directory has been published and a free catalogue is available.

Sylvia Cordaiy Photo Library

72 East Ham Road, Littlehampton, West
Sussex BN17 7BQ
☎01903 715297   Fax 01903 715297
E-mail: 113023.2732@compuserve.com

Over 130 countries on file from the obscure to main stock images – Africa, North, Central and South America, Asia, Atlantic, Indian and Pacific Ocean islands, Australasia, Europe, polar regions. Covers travel, architecture, ancient civilisations, people worldwide, environment, wildlife, natural history, Antarctica, domestic pets, livestock, marine biology, veterinary treatment, equestrian, ornithology, flowers. UK files cover cities, towns villages, coastal and rural scenes, London. Transport, railways, shipping and aircraft (military and civilian). Aerial photography. Backgrounds and abstracts. Also the Paul Kaye B/W archive.

Country Life Picture Library

King's Reach Tower, Stamford Street,
London SE1 9LS
☎0171 261 6337   Fax 0171 261 6216
Contact *Camilla Costello*

Over 150,000 b&w negatives dating back to 1897, and 15,000 colour transparencies. Country houses, stately homes, churches and town houses in Britain and abroad, interiors of architectural interest (ceilings, fireplaces, furniture, paintings, sculpture), and exteriors showing many land-scaped gardens, sporting and social events, crafts, people and animals. Visitors by appointment. Open Tuesday to Friday.

Country Matters Picture Library
27 Camwood, Clayton Green, Bamber Bridge, Preston, Lancashire PR5 8LA
☎01772 321243   Fax 01772 321243
E-mail: terrymarsh@countrymatters.demon. co.uk

Contact *Terry Marsh*

35mm colour coverage of landscapes and countryside features generally throughout the UK and France, in particular Cumbria, North Yorkshire, Lancashire, southern Scotland, Isle of Skye, Wales, Cornwall, French Alps, French Pyrenees and Provence. Commissions undertaken.

Philip Craven
Worldwide Photo-Library
Surrey Studios, 21 Nork Way, Nork, Banstead, Surrey SM7 1PB
☎01737 373737   Fax 01737 373737

Contact *Philip Craven*

Extensive coverage of British scenes, cities, villages, English countryside, gardens, historic buildings and wildlife. Worldwide travel and wildlife subjects on medium- and large-format transparencies.

CTC Picture Library
CTC Publicity, Longfield, Midhurst Road, Fernhurst, Haslemere, Surrey GU27 3HA
☎01428 655007   Fax 01428 641071
E-mail: ctcpub@globalnet.co.uk

Contact *Neil Crighton*

One of the biggest specialist libraries in the UK with 250,000 slides covering world and UK agriculture, horticulture, and environmental subjects. Also a small section on travel.

Sue Cunningham Photographic
56 Chatham Road, Kingston upon Thames, Surrey KT1 3AA
☎0181 541 3024   Fax 0181 541 5388
E-mail: scphotographic@btinternet.com

Extensive coverage of many geographical areas: South America (especially Brazil), Eastern Europe from the Baltic to the Balkans, Zambia, Gambia, Western Europe including the UK. Colour and b&w. Member of **BAPLA**.

Dalton–Watson Collection
See **The Ludvigsen Library Limited**

James Davis Travel Photography
65 Brighton Road, Shoreham, West Sussex BN43 6RE
☎01273 452252   Fax 01273 440116

Travel collection: people, places, emotive scenes and tourism. Constantly updated by James Davis and a team of photographers, both at home and abroad. Same-day service available.

The Defence Picture Library
Sherwell House, 54 Staddiscombe Road, Plymouth, Devon PL9 9NB
☎01752 401800   Fax 01752 402800

Contact *David Reynolds, Jessica Kelly*

Leading source of military photography covering all areas of the UK Armed Forces, supported by a research agency of facts and figures. More than 100,000 images. Campaigns in Aden, the Falklands, Ulster, the Gulf and Yugoslavia covered. Specialist collections include the Royal Marine Commandos and Parachute Regiment training. Visitors welcome by appointment.

Douglas Dickins Photo Library
2 Wessex Gardens, Golders Green, London NW11 9RT
☎0181 455 6221

Worldwide colour and b&w coverage, specialising in Asia, particularly India, Indonesia and Japan. Meeting educational requirements on landscape, archaeology, history, religions, customs, people and folklore.

C M Dixon
The Orchard, Marley Lane, Kingston, Canterbury, Kent CT4 6HJ
☎01227 830075   Fax 01227 831135

Colour coverage of ancient civilisations, archaeology and art, ethnology, mythology, world religion, museum objects, geography, geology, meteorology, landscapes, people and places from many countries including most of Europe, former USSR, Ethiopia, Iceland, Jordan, Morocco, Sri Lanka, Tunisia, Turkey, Egypt, Uzbekistan.

Dominic Photography
4B Moore Park Road, London SW6 2JT
☎0171 381 0007   Fax 0171 381 0008

Contact *Zoë Dominic, Catherine Ashmore*

Colour and b&w coverage of the entertainment world from 1957 onwards: dance, opera, theatre, ballet, musicals and personalities.

Philip Dunn Picture Library
18 Tyning Terrace, Bath, Somerset BA1 6ET
☎01225 461741/0860 523599
E-mail: philip.dunn@btinternet.com

Contact *Philip Dunn*

Constantly expanding collection of some 50,000 b&w/colour images of travel, people, activities and places in Britain and overseas. Commissions undertaken.

E. T. Archive

4th Floor, 184 Drummond Street, London NW1 3HP
☎0171 388 8848   Fax 0171 388 8849
E-mail: et.archive@dial.pipex.com

22,000 colour transparencies covering fine art and history.

Patrick Eagar Photography

5 Ennerdale Road, Kew Gardens, Surrey TW9 3PG
☎0181 940 9269   Fax 0181 332 1229

Colour and b&w coverage of cricket from 1965. Test matches, overseas tours and all aspects of the sport. Also a constantly expanding wine library (colour) of vineyards, grapes, cellars and winemakers of France, Italy, Germany, Lebanon, Australia, New Zealand, South Africa (and England). Digital photograph transmission by modem.

Ecoscene

The Oasts, Headley Lane, Passfield, Liphook, Hampshire GU30 7RX
☎01428 751056   Fax 01428 751057
Contact *Sally Morgan*

Expanding colour library of over 80,000 transparencies specialising in all aspects of the environment: pollution, conservation, recycling, restoration, natural history, habitats, education, landscapes, industry and agriculture. All parts of the globe are covered with specialist collections covering Antarctica, Australia, North America. Sally Morgan, who runs the library, is a professional ecologist and expert source of information on all environmental topics. Photographic and writing commissions undertaken.

Edifice

14 Doughty Street, London WC1N 2PL
☎0171 405 9395   Fax 0171 267 3632
Contact *Philippa Lewis, Gillian Darley*

Colour coverage of architecture, buildings of all possible descriptions, gardens, urban and rural landscape. *Specialises* in details of ornament, period style and material. British Isles, USA, Africa, Europe and Japan all covered. Detailed list available, visits by appointment.

English Heritage Photographic Library

23 Savile Row, London W1X 1AB
☎0171 973 3338   Fax 0171 973 3027
Contact *Celia Sterne*

Images of English castles, abbeys, houses, gardens, Roman remains, ancient monuments, battlefields, industrial and post-war buildings, interiors, paintings, artifacts, architectural details, conservation, archaeology.

Mary Evans Picture Library

59 Tranquil Vale, Blackheath, London SE3 0BS
☎0181 318 0034   Fax 0181 852 7211
E-mail: lib@mepl.co.uk

Collection of historical illustrations documenting social, political, cultural, technical, geographical and biographical themes from ancient times to the recent past (up to mid-20th century). Photographs, prints and ephemera backed by large book and magazine collection. Many special collections including Sigmund Freud, the **Fawcett Library** (women's rights), the paranormal, the Meledin Collection (20th-century Russian history) and individual photographers such as Roger Mayne. Brochure sent on request. Compilers of the *Picture Researcher's Handbook* every three years by PIRA.

Express Newspapers Syndication

Ludgate House, 245 Blackfriars Road, London SE1 9UX
☎0171 922 7902/3/4/5/6 Fax 0171 922 7871
Syndication Manager *Jamie Maskey*

Two million images updated daily, with strong collections on personalities, royalty, showbiz, sport, fashion, nostalgia and events. Electronic transmission available.

Eye Ubiquitous

65 Brighton Road, Shoreham, East Sussex BN43 6RE
☎01273 440113   Fax 01273 440116
Contact *Paul Seheult*

General stock specialising in social documentary worldwide, including the work of Tim Page, and now incorporating the **James Davis Travel Library** (see entry).

Chris Fairclough Colour Library

See **Image Select International**

Falklands Pictorial

Vision House, 16 Broadfield Road, Heeley, Sheffield, South Yorkshire S8 0XJ

☎0114 2589299   Fax 0114 2550113

Colour and b&w photographs showing all aspects of Falklands life from 1880 to the present day.

Famous Pictures and Features

Studio 4, Limehouse Cut, 46 Morris Road, London E14 6NQ
☎0171 510 2500   Fax 0171 510 2510
E-mail: famous:compuserve.com
Website: www.famous.uk.com

Pictures and features agency with a growing library of colour transparencies dating back to 1985. Portrait, party and concert shots of rock and pop stars plus international entertainers, film and TV celebrities. The library is supplied by a team of photographers from the UK and around the world, keeping it up-to-date on a daily basis.

Farmers Weekly Picture Library

Quadrant House, The Quadrant, Sutton, Surrey SM2 5AS
☎0181 652 4914   Fax 0181 652 4005
E-mail: farmers.library@rbi.co.uk
Website: http://www.fwi.co.uk

Library Manager *Barry Dixon*

Britain's largest agricultural picture library holds more than 200,000 transparencies covering all aspects of farming, country life and the environment. The collection is continually updated.

ffotograff

10 Kyveilog Street, Pontcanna, Cardiff CF1 9JA
☎01222 236879   Fax 01222 229326
Contact *Patricia Aithie*

Library and agency specialising in travel, exploration, the arts, architecture, traditional culture, archaeology and landscape. Based in Wales but specialising in the Middle and Far East; Yemen and Wales are unusually strong aspects of the library. Churches and cathedrals of Britain and Crusader castles. Abstract paintings and detailed photographic textures suitable for book covers. Digital transfer by ISDN and modem available.

Financial Times Pictures

1 Southwark Bridge, London SE1 9HL
☎0171 873 3671   Fax 0171 873 4606
E-mail: suzie.kew@ft.com

Photographs from around the world ranging from personalities in business, politics and the arts, people at work and other human interests and activities. 'FT Graphics are outstanding in their ability to make complex issues compre-

hensible.' Delivery via Modem, ISDN, E-mail or Newscom.

Fine Art Photographic Library Ltd

2A Milner Street, London SW3 2PU
☎0171 589 3127   Fax 0171 584 1944
Contact *Linda Hammerbeck*

Over 20,000 large-format transparencies, with a specialist collection of 19th-century paintings.

Fire-Pix International

68 Arkles Lane, Anfield, Liverpool, Merseyside L4 2SP
☎0151 260 0111   Fax 0151 250 0111
E-mail: tonymyers@firepixint.demon.co.uk
Website: www.firepixint.demon.co.uk
Contact *Tony Myers*

The UK's only fire photo library. 15000 images of fire, firefighters, fire equipment manufacturers. Member of **BAPLA**.

Fogden Natural History Photos

Basement, 10 Bellevue, Bristol BS8 1DA
☎0117 923 8849   Fax 0117 923 8543
Contact *Susan Fogden*

Natural history collection, with special reference to rain forests and deserts. Emphasis on quality rather than quantity; growing collection of around 10,000 images.

Food Features

Hardwicke Court, Waverley Lane, Farnham, Surrey GU9 8ES
☎01252 781433   Fax 01252 784091
Contacts *Steve Moss, Alex Barker*

Specialised high-quality food and drink photography, features and tested recipes. Clients' specific requirements can be incorporated into regular shooting schedules.

Ron & Christine Foord Colour Picture Library

155B City Way, Rochester, Kent ME1 2BE
☎01634 847348   Fax 01634 847348

Specialist library with over 1000 species of British and European wild flowers, plus garden flowers, trees, indoor plants, pests and diseases, mosses, lichen, cacti and the majority of larger British insects.

The Football Archive

14–15 Perseverance Works, 38 Kingsland Road, London E2 8DD
☎0171 613 1400   Fax 0171 613 1800
Contacts *Peter Robinson*

FOUNDED in 1995 as a specialist football library. Based on the work of FIFA's former director of photography, Peter Robinson, the library consists of over 100,000 colour and b&w images dating from the 1960s to the present day.

Forest Life Picture Library
231 Corstorphine Road, Edinburgh EH12 7AT
☎0131 314 6411   Fax 0131 314 6285
Contact *Douglas Green, Neill Campbell*

The official image bank of the Forestry Commission, the library provides a single source for all aspects of forest and woodland management. The comprehensive subject list includes tree species, scenic landscapes, employment, wildlife, flora and fauna, conservation, sport and leisure.

Werner Forman Archive Ltd
36 Camden Square, London NW1 9XA
☎0171 267 1034   Fax 0171 267 6026

Colour and b&w coverage of ancient civilisations, oriental and primitive societies around the world. A number of rare collections. Subject lists available.

Formula One Pictures
Suite 8, King Harold Court, Sun Street, Waltham Abbey, Essex EN9 1ER
☎01992 787800   Fax 01992 714366
E-mail: jt@f1pictures.demon.co.uk
Website: www.f1pictures.demon.co.uk
Contacts *John Townsend, Erika Townsend*

500,000 35mm colour slides, b&w and colour negatives of all aspects of Formula One grand prix racing including driver profiles and portraits.

Robert Forsythe Picture Library
16 Lime Grove, Prudhoe, Northumberland NE42 6PR
☎01661 834511
Website: http://www.forsythe.demon.co.uk/
Contact *Robert Forsythe, Fiona Forsythe*

25,000 transparencies of industrial and transport heritage; plus a unique collection of 50,000 items of related publicity ephemera from 1945. Image finding service available. Robert Forsythe is a transport/industrial heritage historian and consultant. Nationwide coverage, particularly strong on Northern Britain. A bibliography of published material is available.

Fortean Picture Library
Henblas, Mwrog Street, Ruthin LL15 1LG
☎01824 707278   Fax 01824 705324
Contact *Janet Bord*

30,000 colour and 45,000 b&w images: mysteries and strange phenomena worldwide, including ghosts, UFOs, witchcraft and monsters; also antiquities, folklore and mythology. Subject list available.

The Fotomas Index
12 Pickhurst Rise, West Wickham, Kent BR4 0AL
☎0181 776 2772   Fax 0181 776 2772
Contact *John Freeman*

General historical collection, mostly pre-1900. Subjects include London, topography, art, satirical, social and political history. Large portrait section.

The Francis Frith Collection
The Old Rectory, Bimport, Shaftesbury, Dorset SP7 8AT
☎01747 855669   Fax 01747 855065
Contact *John Buck*

330,000 b&w and sepia photographs of British topography from 1860 to 1969 depicting 7000 British towns and villages.

John Frost Newspapers
See under **Library Services**

Andrew N. Gagg's Photo Flora
Fordbank Court, Henwick Road, Worcester WR2 5PF
☎01905 748575   E-mail: gagg@mcmail.com
Website: http://www.gagg.mcmail.com/
    photoflora.htm

Specialist in British and European wild plants, flowers, ferns, grasses, trees, shrubs etc. with colour coverage of most British and many European species (rare and common) and habitats; also travel in India, Nepal, Egypt, China, Thailand and Tibet.

Galaxy Picture Library
1 Milverton Drive, Ickenham, Uxbridge, Middlesex UB10 8PP
☎01895 637463   Fax 01895 623277
E-mail: galaxypix@compuserve.com
Website: http://ourworld.compuserve.com/
    homepages/galaxypix/
Contact *Robin Scagell*

Specialises in astronomy, space, telescopes, observatories, the sky, clouds and sunsets. Composites of foregrounds, stars, moon and planets prepared to commission. Editorial service available.

Garden and Wildlife Matters Photo Library

'Marlham', Henley's Down, Battle, East
Sussex TN33 9BN
☎01424 830566   Fax 01424 830224
Contact *Dr John Feltwell*

Collection of 80,000 6x4 and 35mm images. General gardening techniques and design; cottage gardens and USA designer gardens. 6000 species of garden plants. Flowers, wild and house plants, trees and crops. Environmental, ecological and conservation pictures, including sea, air, noise and freshwater pollution, SE Asian and Central American rainforests; Eastern Europe, Mediterranean. Recycling, agriculture, forestry, horticulture and oblique aerial habitat shots from Europe, USA and. High-quality images required.

The Garden Picture Library

Unit 12, Ransome's Dock, 35 Parkgate Road, London SW11 4NP
☎0171 228 4332   Fax 0171 924 3267
Contact *Sally Wood*

'Our inspirational images of gardens, plants and gardening offer plenty of scope for writers looking for original ideas to write about.' Special collections include al fresco food, floral graphics and the still life photography of Linda Burgess. From individual stock photos to complete features, photographers submit material from the UK, Europe, USA and Australia on 35mm and medium formats. In-house picture research can be undertaken on request. Visitors to the library are welcome by appointment and copies of promotional literature are available on request.

Leslie Garland Picture Library

69 Fern Avenue, Jesmond, Newcastle upon Tyne, Tyne & Wear NE2 2QU
☎0191 281 3442   Fax 0191 209 1094
E-mail: garland@cableinet.co.uk
Contact *Leslie Garland, ABIPP, ARPS*

Subjects areas: Northumberland, Durham, Tyne & Wear, Cumbria, North Yorkshire, with growing collections of Lancashire, Merseyside, Greater Manchester and Derbyshire. Also Scotland, Norway and Sweden. Major cities, towns, sights and scenes, heritage, etc. Applied science and engineering – bridges, cranes, ship building, chemical plants, field studies, geography and geology, physics and chemistry experiments, etc., and a range of still-life studies of miscellaneous subjects – household objects, cats

eyes, hydraulic rams, galvanised steel, crash barriers, etc. Most on medium format. Brochure available. Commissions undertaken.

Ed Geldard Picture Collection

7 Ellergreen House, Nr Burnside, Kendal, Cumbria LA9 5SD
☎01539 728609
Contact *Ed Geldard*

Approximately 15,000 colour transparencies and b&w negs, all by Ed Geldard, specialising in mountain landscapes: particularly, the mountain regions of the Lake District; and the Yorkshire limestone areas, from valley to summit. Commissions undertaken. Books published: *Wainwright's Tour of the Lake District* and *Wainwright in the Limestone Dales*.

Genesis Space Photo Library

Greenbanks, Robins Hill, Raleigh, Bideford, Devon EX39 3PA
☎01237 471960   Fax 01237 472060
E-mail: tim@spaceport.co.uk
Website: http://www.spaceport.co.uk
Contact *Tim Furniss*

Contemporary and historical colour and b&w spaceflight collection including rockets, spacecraft, spacemen, Earth, moon and planets. Stock list available on request.

Geo Aerial Photography

4 Christian Fields, London SW16 3JZ
☎0181 764 6292/0115 9819418 Fax 0181 764 6292/0115 9815474/9819418
Contact *Kelly White*

Established 1990 and now a growing collection of aerial oblique photographs from the UK, Scandinavia, Asia and Africa – landscapes, buildings, industrial sites, etc. Commissions undertaken.

GeoScience Features

6 Orchard Drive, Wye, Kent TN25 5AU
☎01233 812707   Fax 01233 812707
E-mail: gsf@geoscience.demon.co.uk

Fully computerised and comprehensive library containing the world's principal source of volcanic phenomena. Extensive collections, providing scientific detail with technical quality, of rocks, minerals, fossils, microsections of botanical and animal tissues, animals, biology, birds, botany, chemistry, earth science, ecology, environment, geology, geography, habitats, landscapes, macro/microbiology, peoples, sky, weather, wildlife and zoology. Over 300,000 original colour transparencies in medium- and 35mm-format. Subject lists and CD-ROM catalogue available on application. Incorporates the RIDA photolibrary.

Geoslides Photography
4 Christian Fields, London SW16 3JZ
☎0181 764 6292   Fax 0181 764 6292/0115 9819418

Contact *John Douglas*

Established in 1968. Landscape and human interest subjects from the Arctic, Antarctica, Scandinavia, UK, Africa (south of Sahara), Middle East, Asia (south and southeast); also Australia, via Blackwoods Picture Library. Also specialist collections of images from British India (the Raj) and Boer War.

Getty Images (incorporating Tony Stone Images & The Hulton Getty Collection)
101 Bayham Street, London NW1 0AY
☎0171 544 3333   Fax 0171 544 3334
E-mail: info@getty-images.com

Contact *Sales Dept.*

With over 15 million images, the collection is the largest picture resource in Europe with images from ancient history through the early years of photography up to the present day. As well as many old newspaper archives, the extensive contemporary collections cover lifestyles, travel, science, business.

Martin and Dorothy Grace
40 Clipstone Avenue, Mapperley, Nottingham NG3 5JZ
☎0115 9208248   Fax 0115 9626802
E-mail: graces@lineone.net

Colour coverage of Britain's natural history, specialising in trees, shrubs and wild flowers. Also ferns, birds and butterflies, habitats, landscapes, ecology. Subject lists available. Member of **BAPLA**.

Ronald Grant Archive
See **The Cinema Museum**

Greater London Photograph Library
London Metropolitan Archives, 40 Northampton Road, London EC1R 0HB
☎0171 332 3820/Minicom: 0171 278 8703
Fax 0171 833 9136
E-mail: lma@ms.corpoflondon.gov.uk

Contact *The Senior Librarian*

Approximately 500,000 images of London, mostly topographical and architectural. Subjects include education, local authority housing, transport, the Thames, parks, churches, hospitals, war damage, pubs, theatres and cinemas. Also major redevelopments like the South Bank, The City, Covent Garden and Docklands.

Sally and Richard Greenhill
357A Liverpool Road, London N1 1NL
☎0171 607 8549   Fax 0171 607 7151

Photo Librarian *Denise Lalonde*

Colour and b&w photos of a social documentary nature: child development, pregnancy and birth, education and urban scenes in London and Northern England. Also Modern China 1971–95, Hong Kong, USA, longhouse life in Sarawak, and other material from around the world.

V. K. Guy Ltd
Silver Birches, Troutbeck, Windermere, Cumbria LA23 1PN
☎015394 33519   Fax 015394 32971

Contact *Vic Guy, Pauline Guy, Mike Guy, Paul Guy, Nicola Guy*

British landscapes and architectural heritage. 20,000 5"x4" transparencies, suitable for tourism brochures, calendars, etc. Colour catalogue available.

Hamlyn Books Picture Library
Michelin House, 81 Fulham Road, London SW3 6RB
☎0171 225 9212   Fax 0171 225 9053

Contact *Sally Claxton, Christine Junemann*

400,000 images of cookery and gardening.

Angela Hampton 'Family Life Picture Library'
Holly Tree House, The Street, Walberton, Arundel, West Sussex BN18 0PH
☎01243 555952   Fax 01243 555952

Contact *Angela Hampton*

Over 50,000 transparencies on all aspects of contemporary lifestyle, including pregnancy, childbirth, babies, children, parenting, behaviour, education, medical, holidays, pets, family life, relationships, teenagers, women and men's health, over-50's and retirement. Also comprehensive stock on domestic and farm animal life. Isle of Wight travel pictures in 35mm. Commissions undertaken. Offers fully illustrated text packages on most subjects and welcomes ideas for collaboration from writers with proven, successful background.

Tom Hanley
61 Stephendale Road, London SW6 2LT
☎0171 731 3525   Fax 0171 731 3525
Colour and b&w coverage of London, England, Europe, Canada, India, the Philippines, Brazil, China, Japan, Korea, Taiwan, the Seychelles, Cayman Islands, USA. Also pop artists of the 60s, First World War trenches, removal of London Bridge to America, and much more. Current preoccupation with Greece, Turkey, Spain and Egypt, ancient and modern.

Robert Harding Picture Library
58–59 Great Marlborough Street, London W1V 1DD
☎0171 287 5414   Fax 0171 631 1070
Over two million colour images covering a wide range of subjects – travel, people, architecture, scenics, sport, lifestyle, food, industry and agriculture. Syndication of many titles from IPC Magazines, BBC Magazines and Burda Group.

Harpur Garden Library
44 Roxwell Road, Chelmsford, Essex CM1 2NB
☎01245 257527   Fax 01245 344101
Contact *Jerry Harpur, Marcus Harpur*
Jerry Harpur's personal collection of gardens in Britain, France, Australia, South Africa, the US, Morocco, Argentina, Chile and Japan (35mm and 6x7, colour). Inspired partly by contemporary designers and horticulturalists but also includes historic gardens: formal gardens, front and back gardens, plant associations, gardens in all four seasons, garden containers, fences, hedges, herbs, hillsides, seaside, lawns, paths, paving, rock, arbours, scented, fruit and vegetables, ornaments, water and integrated gardens.

Jim Henderson Photographer & Publisher
Crooktree, Kincardine O'Neil, Aboyne, Aberdeenshire AB34 4JD
☎01339 882149   Fax 01339 882149
Contact *Jim Henderson, AMPA, ARPS*
Scenic and general activity coverage of the North-East Scotland-Grampian region and Highlands for tourist, holiday and activity illustration. Specialist collection of over 100 Aurora Borealis displays from 1989–1998 in Grampian and co-author of *The Aurora* (pub. 1997). Large collection of recent images of Egypt: Cairo through to Abu-Simbel. Commissions undertaken.

Heritage and Natural History Photographic Library
37 Plainwood Close, Summersdale, Chichester, West Sussex PO19 4YB
☎01243 533822   Fax 01243 533822
Contact *Dr John B. Free*
Specialises in insects (particularly bees and beekeeping), tropical and temperate agriculture and crops, archaeology and history worldwide.

John Heseltine Picture Library
Hill House, Tetbury Hill, Avening, Gloucestershire GL8 8LT
☎01453 835792   Fax 01453 835858
E-mail: Johnhes@aol.com
Contact *John Heseltine*
Over 100,000 colour transparencies of landscapes, architecture, food and travel with particular emphasis on Italy and the UK.

Christopher Hill Photographic Library
17 Clarence Street, Belfast BT2 8DY
☎01232 245038   Fax 01232 231942
Contact *Janet Smyth*
A comprehensive collection of landscapes of Northern Ireland, from Belfast to the Giant's Causeway, updated daily. Images of farming, food and industry. 'We will endeavour to supply images overnight.'

Hobbs Golf Collection
5 Winston Way, New Ridley, Stocksfield, Northumberland NE43 7RF
☎01661 842933   Fax 01661 842933
Contact *Michael Hobbs*
Specialist golf collection: players, courses, art, memorabilia and historical topics (1300–present). 40,000+ images – mainly 35mm colour transparencies and b&w prints. Commissions undertaken. Author of 30 golf books.

David Hoffman Photo Library
21 Norman Grove, London E3 5EG
☎0181 981 5041/0468 402932
Fax 0181 980 2041
E-mail: info:hoffmanphotos.demon.co.uk
Contact *David Hoffman*
Commissioned photography and stock library with a strong emphasis on social issues built up from 35mm journalistic and documentary work dating from the late 1970s. Files on drugs and drug use, policing, disorder, riots, major strikes, youth protest, homelessness, housing, environ-

mental demonstrations and events, waste disposal, alternative energy, industry and pollution. Wide range of images especially from UK and Europe but also USA, Venezuela and Thailand. General files on topical issues and current affairs plus specialist files from leisure cycling to local authority services.

Holt Studios International Ltd
The Courtyard, 24 High Street, Hungerford, Berkshire RG17 0NF
☎01488 683523　　　　　Fax 01488 683511
Commercial Director *Andy Morant*

Specialist photo library covering world agriculture and horticulture both from a pictorial and a technical point of view. Commissions undertaken worldwide.

The Bill Hopkins Collection
See **The Special Photographers Library**

Houghton's Horses/Kit Houghton Photography
Radlet Cottage, Spaxton, Bridgwater, Somerset TA5 1DE
☎01278 671362　　　　　Fax 01278 671739
E-mail: kit@enterprise.net
Contact *Kit Houghton, Debbie Cook*

Specialist equestrian library of over 200,000 transparencies on all aspects of the horse world, with images ranging from the romantic to the practical, step-by-step instructional and competition pictures in all equestrian disciplines worldwide. On-line picture delivery with ISDN facility.

Houses and Interiors
82–84 Clerkenwell Road, London EC1M 5RJ
☎0171 336 7942　　　　　Fax 0171 336 7943

40,000 images of houses and gardens. Large format and 35mm. Specialises in reselling of illustrated articles and features for magazines. Member of **BAPLA**.

Chris Howes/Wild Places Photography
51 Timbers Square, Roath, Cardiff CF2 3SH
☎01222 486557　　　　　Fax 01222 486557
Contact *Chris Howes, Judith Calford*

Expanding collection of over 50,000 colour transparencies and b&w prints covering travel, topography and natural history worldwide, plus action sports such as climbing. *Specialist areas* include caves, caving and mines (with historical

coverage using engravings and early photographs), wildlife, landscapes and the environment, including pollution and conservation. Europe (including Britain), USA, Africa and Australia are all well represented within the collection. Commissions undertaken.

The Hulton Getty Picture Collection
See **Getty Images**

Huntley Film Archive
78 Mildmay Park, Islington, London N1 4PR
☎0171 923 0990　　　　　Fax 0171 241 4929
Contact *Amanda Huntley*

Originally a private collection, the library is now a comprehensive archive of rare and vintage documentary film dating from 1895. 30,000–35,000 films on all subjects of a documentary nature, plus 50,000 feature film stills. Hollywood and the British film studios plus a television archive of rare stills and films.

Jacqui Hurst
66 Richford Street, Hammersmith, London W6 7HP
☎0181 743 2315/07970 781336
Fax 0181 743 2315
Contact *Jacqui Hurst*

A specialist library of traditional and contemporary designers and crafts, regional food producers and markets. The photos form illustrated essays of how something is made and finish with a still life of the completed object. The collection is always being extended and a list is available on request. Commissions undertaken.

Hutchison Picture Library
118B Holland Park Avenue, London W11 4UA
☎0171 229 2743　　　　　Fax 0171 792 0259

Worldwide contemporary images from the straight-forward to the esoteric and quirky. With over half a million documentary colour photographs on file and more than 200 photographers continually adding new work, this is an ever-growing resource covering people, places, customs and faiths, agriculture, industry and transport. *Special collections* include the environment and climate, family life (including pregnancy and birth), ethnic minorities worldwide (including Disappearing World archive), conventional and alternative medicine, and music around the world. Search service available.

Illustrated London News Picture Library

20 Upper Ground, London SE1 9PF
☎0171 805 5585   Fax 0171 805 5905

Engravings, photographs and illustrations from 1842 to the present day, taken from magazines published by Illustrated Newspapers: *Illustrated London News; Graphic; Sphere; Tatler; Sketch; Illustrated Sporting and Dramatic News; Illustrated War News 1914–18; Bystander; Britannia & Eve.* Social history, London, Industrial Revolution, wars, travel. Brochure available. Visitors by appointment.

The Image Bank

17 Conway Street, London W1P 6EE
☎0171 312 0300   Fax 0171 391 9111
4 Jordan Street, Manchester M15 4PY
☎0161 236 9226   Fax 0161 236 8723
14 Alva Street, Edinburgh EH2 4QG
☎0131 225 1770   Fax 0131 225 1660

Contact, London *Joanne Rees*
Contact, Manchester *Rowan Young*
Contact, Edinburgh *Roddy McRae*

Stock photography, illustration and film footage. Over 20 million constantly updated images from 450 photographers and 337 illustrators. Free catalogue available. Creative advertising, editorial and corporate commissions undertaken. For magazines, partworks and books, contact the publishing department. Visitors welcome.

Image Select International

19 Radnor Road, Harrow, Middlesex HA1 1RY
☎0181 861 1122   Fax 0181 861 4755

Contact *Darren Wisden*

History archive plus the Chris Fairclough Colour Library, a general colour library with special collections on religion, education, travel, children, people and places.

Images Colour Library

15/17 High Court Lane, The Calls, Leeds, West Yorkshire LS2 7EU
☎0113 2433389   Fax 0113 2425605
12–14 Argyll Street, London W1V 1AB
☎0171 734 7344   Fax 0171 287 3933

A general contemporary library specialising in top-quality advertising, editorial and travel photography. Catalogues available. Visitors welcome. Also holds the **Landscape Only** collection (see entry).

Images of Africa Photobank

11 The Windings, Lichfield, Staffordshire WS13 7EX
☎01543 262898   Fax 01543 417154

Contact *Jacquie Shipton*
Owner *David Keith Jones, ABIPP, FRPS*

Over 135,000 images covering 14 African countries: Botswana, Egypt, Ethiopia, Kenya, Malawi, Namibia, Rwanda, South Africa, Swaziland, Tanzania, Uganda, Zaire, Zambia and Zimbabwe. 'Probably the best collection of photographs of Kenya in Europe.' Wide range of topics covered. Particularly strong on African wildlife with over 80 species of mammals including many sequences showing action and behaviour. Popular animals like lions and elephants are covered in encyclopedic detail. More than 100 species of birds and many reptiles are included. Other strengths include National Parks & Reserves, natural beauty, tourism facilities, traditional and modern people. Most work is by David Keith Jones, ABIPP, FRPS; several other photographers are represented. Colour brochure available.

Imperial War Museum Photograph Archive

Lambeth Road, London SE1 6HZ
☎0171 416 5333   Fax 0171 416 5355
E-mail: photos@iwm.org.uk

A national archive of photographs of war in this century. Mostly the two world wars but also other conflicts involving Britain and the Commonwealth. Mostly b&w. Visitors welcome to the Museum's All Saints Annexe, Austral Street, five minutes walk from main building. Appointments preferred.

The Interior Archive Ltd

7 Chelsea Studios, 410 Fulham Road, London SW6 1EB
☎0171 370 0595   Fax 0171 385 5403

Contact *Karen Howes*

Several thousand images of interiors, architecture, design and gardens.

International Photobank

Loscombe Barn Farmhouse, West Knighton, Dorchester, Dorset DT2 8LS
☎01305 854145   Fax 01305 853065

Over 300,000 transparencies, mostly medium-format. Colour coverage of travel subjects: places, people, folklore, events. Assignments undertaken for guide books and brochure photography.

The Isle of Wight Photo Library

The Old Rectory, Calbourne, Isle of Wight
PO30 4JE
☎01983 531247   Fax 01983 531253
Contact *The Librarian*

Stock material represents all that is best on the Isle of Wight – landscapes, seascapes, architecture, gardens, boats.

Robbie Jack Photography

45 Church Road, Hanwell, London W7 3BD
☎0181 567 9616   Fax 0181 567 9616
Contact *Robbie Jack*

Built up over the last 14 years, the library contains over 250,000 colour transpa:ncies of the performing arts – theatre, dance, opera and music. Includes West End shows, the RSC and Royal National Theatre productions, English National Opera and Royal Opera. The dance section contains images of the Royal Ballet, English National Ballet, the Rambert Dance Company, plus many foreign companies. Also holds the largest selection of colour material from the Edinburgh International Festival. Researchers are welcome to visit by appointment.

Jayawardene Travel Photo Library

7A Napier Road, Wembley, Middlesex HA0 4UA
☎0181 902 3588   Fax 0181 902 7114
Contacts *Marion Jayawardene, Rohith Jayawardene*

100,000 colour transparencies, specialising in worldwide travel and travel-related subjects. Most topics featured have been covered in depth, with more than 500 different images per destination. Regularly updated, all are originals and shot in 35mm- and medium-format. Commissions undertaken. New photographers welcome (please telephone first) – minimum initial submission: 100 transparencies per destination.

Trevor Jones Thoroughbred Photography

The Hornbeams, 2 The Street, Worlington, Suffolk IP28 8RU
☎01638 713944   Fax 01638 713945
Contact *Trevor Jones, Gill Jones*

Extensive library of high-quality colour transparencies depicting all aspects of thoroughbred horse racing dating from 1987. Major group races, English classics, studs, stallions, mares and foals, early morning scenes, personalities, jockeys, trainers and prominent owners. Also international work: USA Breeders Cup, Arc de Triomphe, French Classics, Irish Derby, Dubai racing scene, Japan Cup and Hokkaido stud farms; and more unusual scenes such as racing on the sands at low tide, Ireland, and on the frozen lake at St Moritz. Visitors by appointment.

Katz Pictures

Zetland House, 5–25 Scrutton Street, London EC2A 4LP
☎0171 377 5888   Fax 0171 377 5558
Contact *Alyson Whalley*

Contains an extensive collection of colour and b&w material covering a multitude of subjects from around the world – business, environment, industry, lifestyles, politics plus celebrity portraits from the entertainment world. Also Hollywood portraits and film stills dating back to the twenties. Represents *Life* and *Time* magazines for syndication in the UK and can offer a complete selection of material spanning over 50 years; also the Mansell Collection.

David King Collection

90 St Pauls Road, London N1 2QP
☎0171 226 0149   Fax 0171 354 8264
Contact *David King*

250,000 b&w original and copy photographs and colour transparencies of historical and present-day images. Russian history and the Soviet Union from 1900 to the fall of Khrushchev; the lives of Lenin, Trotsky and Stalin; the Tzars, Russo-Japanese War, 1917 Revolution, World War I, Red Army, Great Patriotic War, etc. Special collections on China, Eastern Europe, the Weimar Republic, American labour struggles, Spanish Civil War. Open to qualified researchers by appointment, Monday to Friday, 10 – 6. Staff will undertake research; negotiable fee for long projects. David King's latest photographic book, *The Commissar Vanishes*, documents the falsification of photographs and art in Stalin's Russia.

The Kobal Collection

4th Floor, 184 Drummond Street, London NW1 3HP
☎0171 383 0011   Fax 0171 383 0044
Colour and b&w coverage of Hollywood films: portraits, stills, publicity shots, posters, ephemera. Visitors by appointment.

Kos Picture Source Ltd

7 Spice Court, Ivory Square, Plantation Wharf, London SW11 3UE
☎0171 801 0044   Fax 0171 801 0055

Specialists in water-related images, from yachting and superyachts to windsurfing, canoeing and ice skeeting. Seascapes, underwater images and a worldwide travel section.

Landscape Only
12–14 Argyll Street, London W1V 1AB
☎0171 734 7344   Fax 0171 287 3933

Part of the **Images Colour Library**. A premier landscape collection, featuring the work of top photographers Charlie Waite, Nick Meers, Joe Cornish and many others. Colour brochure available.

Frank Lane Picture Agency Ltd
Pages Green House, Wetheringsett, Stowmarket, Suffolk IP14 5QA
☎01728 860789   Fax 01728 860222
E-mail: pictures@flpa-images.co.uk
Website: www.flpa-images.co.uk

Colour and b&w coverage of natural history and weather. Represents Silvestris Fotoservice, Germany, and works closely with Eric and David Hosking, plus 200 freelance photographers.

Last Resort Picture Library
Manvers Studios, 12 Ollerton Road, Tuxford, Newark, Nottinghamshie NG22 0LF
☎01777 870166   Fax 01777 871739
E-mail: dickmakin@compuserve.com
Contact *Jo Makin*

Approximately 10,000 pictures of agriculture, architecture, education, landscapes, industry, people at work, new technology, food. Images cover a wide variety of areas rather than specialising, ranging from the everyday to the unusual.

LAT Photographic
Somerset House, Somerset Road, Teddington TW11 8RU
☎0181 251 3000   Fax 0181 251 3001

Motor sport collection of over 30 million images dating from 1920 to the present day.

André Laubier Picture Library
4 St James Park, Bath, Avon BA1 2SS
☎01225 420688   Fax 01225 420688

An extensive library of photographs from 1935 to the present day in 35mm- and medium-format. Main subjects are: archaeology and architecture; art and artists (wood carving, sculptures, contemporary glass); botany; historical buildings, sites and events; landscapes; nature; leisure sports; events; experimental artwork and photography; people;

and travel. Substantial stock of many other subjects including: birds, buildings and cities, folklore, food and drink, gardens, transport. Special collection: *Images d'Europe* (Austria, Britain, France, Greece, S. W. Ireland, Italy, Spain, Turkey and former Yugoslavia) and Norway. Private collection: World War II to D-Day. List available on request. Photo assignments, artwork, design, and line drawings undertaken. Correspondence welcome in English, French or German.

Lebrecht Music Collection
58b Carlton Hill, London NW8 0ES
☎0171 625 5341/372 8233
Fax 0171 625 5341
E-mail: lebrechtcoll@claranet
Contact *Elbie Lebrecht*

30,000 b&w prints and transparencies covering classical music, from antiquity to 21st century minimalists. Instruments, opera singers, concert halls and opera houses, composers and musicians.

The Erich Lessing Archive of Fine Art & Culture
c/o AKG London Ltd, Arts and History Picture Library, 10 Plato Place, 72–74 St Dionis Road, London SW6 4TU
☎0171 610 6103   Fax 0171 610 6125
E-mail: enquiries@akg-london.co.uk
Website: akg-london.co.uk

Computerised archive of large-format transparencies depicting the contents of many of the world's finest art galleries as well as ancient archaeological and biblical sites. Over 70,000 pictures can be viewed on microfiche. Represented by AKG London Ltd.

Life File Ltd
76 Streathbourne Road, London SW17 8QY
☎0181 767 8832   Fax 0181 672 8879
Contact *Simon Taylor*

300,000 images of people and places, lifestyles, industry, environmental issues, natural history and customs, from Afghanistan to Zimbabwe. Stocks most of the major tourist destinations throughout the world, including the UK.

Lindley Library, Royal Horticultural Society
80 Vincent Square, London SW1P 2PE
☎0171 821 3050   Fax 0171 828 3022
Contact *Jennifer Vine*

18,0000 original drawings and approx. 8000 books with hand-coloured plates of botanical illustrations. Appointment is absolutely essential; all photography is done by own photographer.

Link Picture Library
33 Greyhound Road, London W6 8NH
☎0171 381 2261/2433   Fax 0171 385 6244
E-mail: lib@linkpics.demon.co.uk

Contacts *Orde Eliason*

40,000 images of South Africa, India and Israel. A more general collection of colour transparencies from 100 countries worldwide, including an archive on musicians. Link Picture Library has an international network and can source material not in its file from Japan, USA, Holland, Scandinavia, Germany and South Africa. Original photographic commissions undertaken.

London Aerial Photo Library
PO Box 25, Ashwellthorpe, Norwich,
Norfolk NR16 1HL
☎01508 488320   Fax 01508 488282

Contact *Sandy Stockwell*

60,000 colour negatives of aerial photographs covering most of Britain, with particular emphasis on London and surrounding counties. No search fee. Photocopies of library prints are supplied free of charge to enquirers. Welcomes enquiries in respect of either general subjects or specific sites and buildings.

The London Film Archive
78 Mildmay Park, Islington, London
N1 4PR
☎0171 923 4074   Fax 0171 241 4929

Contact *Robert Dewar*

A newly-established archive which concentrates on all aspects of commercial, political and social life in the City and suburbs of London. The collection is primarily a film collection but also has stills, glass plate negatives, posters, advertising and documents of London interest.

London Transport Museum Photographic Library
39 Wellington Street, London WC2E 7BB
☎0171 379 6344   Fax 0171 497 3527

Contacts *Hugh Robertson, Simon Murphy,*
  Martin Harrison-Putnam

Around 100,000 b&w images from the 1860s and 10,000 colour images from c.1975. *Specialist collections* poster archive, underground construction, corporate design and architecture, street scenes, London Transport during the war. Collection available for viewing by appointment

on Monday, Wednesday and Friday. No loans system but prints and transparences can be purchased.

The Ludvigsen Library Limited
73 Collier Street, London N1 9BE
☎0171 837 1700   Fax 0171 837 1776
E-mail: ludvigsen@mail.bogo.co.uk
Website: http://www.ludvigsen.com

Contact *Paul Parker, Neil King*

Approximately 250,000 images (both b&w and many colour transparencies) of automobiles and motorsport, from 1920s through 1970s. Glass plate negatives from the early 1900s; Formula One, Le Mans, motor car shows, vintage, antique and classic cars from all countries. Includes the Dalton-Watson Collection and noted photographers such as Max le Grand, Rodolfo Mailander, Edward Eves and others. Extensive information research facilities for writers and publishers.

Lupe Cunha Photos
19 Ashfields Parade, London N14 5EH
☎0181 882 6441   Fax 0181 882 6303
E-mail: lupe.cunha@btinternet.com

Children, health, pregnancy and general women's interest. Also special collection on Brazil. Commissions undertaken.

MacQuitty International Photographic Collection
7 Elm Lodge, River Gardens, Stevenage Road, London SW6 6NZ
☎0171 385 6031/384 1781
Fax 0171 384 1781

Contact *Dr Miranda MacQuitty*

Colour and b&w collection on aspects of life in over 70 countries: dancing, music, religion, death, archaeology, buildings, transport, food, drink, nature. Visitors by appointment.

Magnum Photos Ltd
Moreland Buildings, 2nd Floor, 5 Old Street, London EC1V 9HL
☎0171 490 1771   Fax 0171 608 0020

Head of Library *Heather Vickers*

FOUNDED 1947 by Cartier Bresson, George Rodger, Robert Capa and David 'Chim' Seymour. Represents over 50 of the world's leading photo-journalists. Coverage of all major world events from the Spanish Civil War to present day. Also a large collection of personalities.

The Raymond Mander & Joe Mitchenson Theatre Collection

The Mansion, Beckenham Place Park, Beckenham, Kent BR3 2BP
☎0181 658 7725   Fax 0181 663 0313
Contact *Richard Mangan*

Enormous collection covering all aspects of the theatre: plays, actors, dramatists, music hall, theatres, singers, composers, etc. Visitors welcome by appointment.

Mansell Collection
See **Katz Pictures**

S & O Mathews Photography
The Old Rectory, Calbourne, Isle of Wight PO30 4JE
☎01983 531247   Fax 01983 531253
Library of colour transparencies of landscapes, gardens and flowers.

Institution of Mechanical Engineers
1 Birdcage Walk, London SW1H 9JJ
☎0171 973 1289   Fax 0171 222 4557
Head of Marketing & Corporate Communications *James Kelly*

800 contemporary images on mechanical engineering can be borrowed free of charge.

Medimage
32 Brooklyn Road, Coventry CV1 4JT
☎01203 668652   Fax 01203 668562
Contact *Anthony King, Catherine King*

10,000 medium format colour transparencies of Mediterranean countries covering a wide range of subjects – agriculture, archaeology, architecture, arts, crafts, education, festivals, flora, geography, history, industry, landscapes, markets, recreation, seascapes, sports and transport. The collection is added to on a regular basis and photographic commissions are undertaken. No search fees. Pictures by other photographers are not accepted.

Meledin Collection
See **Mary Evans Picture Library**

Lee Miller Archives
Burgh Hill House, Chiddingly, Near Lewes, East Sussex BN8 6JF
☎01825 872691   Fax 01825 872733
E-mail: archives@leemiller.co.uk
Website: http://www.leemiller.co.uk
The work of Lee Miller (1907–77). As a photojournalist she covered the war in Europe from early in 1944 to VE Day with further reporting from the Balkans. Collection includes photographic portraits of prominent Surrealist artists: Ernst, Eluard, Miró, Picasso, Penrose, Carrington, Tanning, and others. Surrealist and contemporary art, poets and writers, fashion, the Middle East, Egypt, the Balkans in the 1930s, London during the Blitz, war in Europe and the liberation of Dachau and Buchenwald.

Mirror Syndication International
20th Floor, 1 Canada Square, Canary Wharf, London E14 5AP
☎0171 293 3700   Fax 0171 293 2712
E-mail: desk@mirpix.com
Managing Director *Frank Walker*

Major photo library specialising in current affairs, personalities, royalty, sport, pop and glamour, plus extensive British and world travel pictures. Major motion picture archive up to 1965. Agents for Mirror Group Newspapers. Syndicator of photos and text for news/features.

Monitor Syndication
17 Old Street, London EC1V 9HL
☎0171 253 7071   Fax 0171 250 0966

Colour and b&w coverage of leading international personalities. Politics, entertainment, royals, judicial, commerce, religion, trade unions, well-known buildings. Also an archive library dating back to 1870, and a specialist file on Lotus cars. Syndication to international, national and local media.

Moroccan Scapes
Seend Park, Seend, Wiltshire SN12 6NZ
☎01380 828533   Fax 01380 828630
Contact *Chris Lawrence*

Specialist collection of Moroccan material: scenery, towns, people, markets and places, plus the Atlas Mountains. Over 16,000 images.

Motoring Picture Library
National Motor Museum, Beaulieu, Hampshire SO42 7ZN
☎01590 612345   Fax 01590 612655
Contact *Jonathan Day*

A quarter of a million b&w images, plus 50,000 colour transparencies covering all forms of motoring history from the 1880s to the present day. Commissions undertaken. Own studio.

Mountain Camera
See **John Cleare**

Moving Image Communications Ltd

The Basement, 2–4 Dean Street, London
W1V 5RN
☎0171 437 5688   Fax 0171 437 5649

Contact *Michael Maloney*

11,000 hours of quality archive and contemporary images; computer catalogued for immediate access. Collections include: Britain 1925–98, The Cuban Archive, Medical Technology, 1950s Classic Travelogues, Subaqua Films, Space Exploration, Vintage Slapstick, British Airways 1984–98, Seascapes and Landscapes, TVAM Interviews/Funnies 1983–92. In addition, Moving Image provides an external research and copyright clearance service. In-house researchers can locate images using long-established contacts with footage sources worldwide.

Museum of Antiquities Picture Library

University and Society of Antiquaries of
Newcastle upon Tyne, Newcastle upon Tyne
NE1 7RU
☎0191 222 7846   Fax 0191 222 8561

Contact *Lindsay Allason-Jones*

25,000 images, mostly b&w, of special collections including: Hadrian's Wall Archive (b&ws taken over the last 100 years); Gertrude Bell Archive (during her travels in the Near East, 1900–26); and aerial photographs of archaeological sites in the North of England. Visitors welcome by appointment.

Museum of London Picture Library

London Wall, London EC2Y 5HN
☎0171 600 3699 ext. 254 Fax 0171 600 1058

Contact *Oona Wills, Anna Payne*

Comprehensive coverage of the history and archaeology of London represented in paintings, photographs and historic artefacts. Special files include Roman and medieval archaeology, costume, suffragettes and the River Thames in London.

National Galleries of Scotland Picture Library

National Galleries of Scotland, Belford Road,
Edinburgh EH4 3DR
☎0131 624 6319   Fax 0131 315 2963

Contacts *Deborah Hunter, Helen Nicoll*

Over 30,000 b&w and several thousand images in colour of works of art from the Renaissance to present day. Specialist subjects cover fine art (painting, sculpture, drawing), portraits, Scottish, historical, still life, photography and landscape. Colour leaflet, scale of charges and application forms available on request.

National Maritime Museum Picture Library

Greenwich, London SE10 9NF
☎0181 312 6631/6704   Fax 0181 312 6533

Contact *David Taylor, Lindsey Macfarlane*

Over 3 million maritime-related images and artefacts, including oil paintings from the 16th century to present day, prints and drawings, historic photographs, plans of ships built in the UK since the beginning of the 18th Century, models, rare maps and charts, instruments, etc. Over 50,000 items within the collection are now photographed and with the Historic Photographs Collection form the basis of the picture library's stock.

National Medical Slide Bank

Wellcome Trust Medical Photo Library, 210
Euston Road, London NW1 2BE
☎0171 611 8746   Fax 0171 611 8577

Contact *Julie Dorrington*

Specialist section of the **Wellcome Trust Medical Photographic Library**, it comprises 200,000 slides covering clinical and general medicine with associated pathology and medical imaging. 12,000 images on videodisc.

National Meteorological Library and Archive

See under **Library Services**

National Monuments Record

National Monuments Record Centre, Kemble
Drive, Swindon, Wiltshire SN2 2GZ
☎01793 414600   Fax 01793 414606

The National Monuments Record is the first stop for photographs and information on England's heritage. Over 7 million photographs, documents and drawings are held. English architecture from the first days of photography to the present, air photographs covering every inch of England from the first days of flying to the present, and archaeological sites. The record is the public archive of the Royal Commission on the Historical Monuments of England, which surveys buildings and archaeological sites. The London office specialises in the architecture of the capital city – for more information phone 0171 208 8200.

National Portrait Gallery Picture Library

St Martin's Place, London WC2H 0HE
☎0171 306 0055 exts. 259/260/261
Fax 0171 306 0092/0056
E-mail: spatel@npg.org.uk
Contact *Shruti Patel*

Over 700,000 images – portraits of famous British men and women dating from medieval times to the present day. Various formats/media.

National Railway Museum Picture Library

Leeman Road, York YO2 4XJ
☎01904 621261   Fax 01904 611112

1.5 million images, mainly b&w, covering every aspect of railways from 1866 to the present day. Visitors by appointment.

The National Trust Photographic Library

36 Queen Anne's Gate, London SW1H 9AS
☎0171 447 6788   Fax 0171 447 6767
Contact *Ed Gibbons*

Collection of mixed-format transparencies covering landscape and coastline throughout England, Wales and Northern Ireland; also architecture, interiors, gardens, paintings and conservation. Brochure available on request. Profits from the picture library are reinvested in continuing the work of the Trust.

Natural History Museum Picture Library

Cromwell Road, London SW7 5BD
☎0171 938 9122/9035   Fax 0171 938 9169
Contact *Martin Pulsford, Lodvina Mascarenhas*

12,000 large-format transparencies on natural history and related subjects: extinct animals, dinosaurs, fossils, anthropology, minerals, gemstones, fauna and flora. No wildlife pictures but many images of historic natural history art. Commissions of museum specimens undertaken.

Natural History Photographic Agency

See **NHPA**

Natural Science Photos

33 Woodland Drive, Watford, Hertfordshire WD1 3BY
☎01923 245265   Fax 01923 246067

Colour coverage of natural history subjects worldwide. The work of some 150 photographers, it includes angling, animals, birds, reptiles, amphibia, fish, insects and other invertebrates, habitats, plants, fungi, geography, weather, scenics, horticulture, agriculture, farm animals and registered dog breeds. Researched by experienced scientists Peter and Sondra Ward. Visits by appointment. Commissions undertaken.

Nature Photographers Ltd

West Wit, New Road, Little London, Tadley, Hampshire RG26 5EU
☎01256 850661   Fax 01256 851157
E-mail: nature.photos@clara.net
Contact *Dr Paul Sterry*

Over 150,000 images on worldwide natural history and environmental subjects. The library is run by a trained biologist and experienced author on his subject.

Peter Newark's Pictures

3 Barton Buildings, Queen Square, Bath BA1 2JR
☎01225 334213   Fax 01225 334213/480554

Over 1 million images covering world history from ancient times to the present day. Incorporates two special collections: American history in general with strong Wild West collection; and the military collection: military/naval personalities and events. Subject list available. Visitors welcome by appointment.

NHPA (Natural History Photographic Agency)

Little Tye, 57 High Street, Ardingly, West Sussex RH17 6TB
☎01444 892514   Fax 01444 892168
Library Manager *Tim Harris*

Extensive coverage on all aspects of natural history – animals, plants, landscapes, environmental issues, gardens and pets. 120 photographers worldwide provide a steady input of high-quality transparencies. Specialist files include the unique high-speed photography of Stephen Dalton, extensive coverage of African and American wildlife, also rainforests, marine life and the polar regions. UK agents for the ANT collection of Australasian material. Loans are generally made direct to publishers; individual writers must request material via their publisher.

NRSC – Air Photo Group

Arthur Street, Barwell, Leicestershire LE9 8GZ
☎01455 849227   Fax 01455 841785
Contact *Kate Pallett*

Leading supplier of earth observation data, including satellite imagery, aerial photography and airborne remote sensing.

Observer Colour Library
See **Topham Picturepoint**

Odhams Periodicals Library
See **Poppefoto**

Only Horses Picture Agency
27 Greenway Gardens, Greenford, Middlesex UB6 9TU
☎0181 578 9047   Fax 0181 575 7244

Colour and b&w coverage of all aspects of the horse. Foaling, retirement, racing, show jumping, eventing, veterinary, polo, breeds, personalities.

Open University Photo Library
Room 163 A Block, Walton Hall, Milton Keynes MK7 6AA
☎01908 658408   Fax 01908 653313
Contact *Debbie Nicholls-Brien*

Education, industry and social welfare collection. 65000 mainly b&w images dating from the early 1970s.

Oxford Picture Library
1 North Hinksey Village, Oxford OX2 0NA
☎01865 723404   Fax 01865 725294
Contact *Annabel Webb, Chris Andrews, Angus Palmer*

Specialist collection on Oxford: the city, university and colleges, events, people, spires and shires; also the Cotswolds, architecture and landscape from Stratford-upon-Avon to Bath; the Chilterns and Henley on Thames, with aerial views of all of the above; plus Channel Islands, especially Guernsey and Sark. General collection includes wildlife, trees, plants, clouds, sun, sky, water and teddy bears. Commissions undertaken.

Oxford Scientific Films
Photo Library
Long Hanborough, Witney, Oxfordshire OX8 8LL
☎01993 881881   Fax 01993 882808
Senior Account Manager *Suzanne Aitzetmuller*
Account Managers *Dee Williams*

Collection of 300,000 colour transparencies of wildlife and natural science images supplied by over 300 photographers worldwide, covering all aspects of wildlife plus landscapes, weather, seasons, plants, environment, anthropology, habitats, industry, space, creative textures and backgrounds, and geology. Macro and micro photography. UK agents for Animals Animals, USA, Okapia, Germany and Dinodia, India. Research by experienced researchers for specialist and creative briefs. Visits welcome, by appointment.

PA News Photo Library
PA News Centre, 292 Vauxhall Bridge Road, London SW1V 1AE
☎0171 963 7038/7039   Fax 0171 963 7066

PA News, the 24-hour national news and information group, offers public access to its photographic archives. Photographs, dating from 1890 to the present day, cover everything from news and sport to entertainment and royalty, with around 50 new pictures added daily. Personal callers welcome (10.00am to 4.00pm weekdays) or research undertaken by in-house staff.

Hugh Palmer
Knapp House, Shenington, Near Banbury, Oxfordshire OX15 6NE
☎01295 670433   Fax 01295 670709

Extensive coverage of gardens from Britain and Europe, as well as rural landscapes and architecture. Medium-format transparencies from numerous specialist commissions for books and magazines.

Panos Pictures
1 Chapel Court, Borough High Street, London SE1 1HH
☎0171 234 0010   Fax 0171 357 0094

Documentary colour and b&w library specialising in Third World and Eastern Europe, with emphasis on environment and development issues. Leaflet available. Fifty per cent of all profits from this library go to the Panos Institute to further its work in international sustainable development.

Papilio Natural History & Travel Library
44 Palestine Grove, Merton, London SW19 2QN
☎0181 687 2202   Fax 0181 687 2202
E-mail: justine@papilio.demon.co.uk
Contact *Robert Pickett, Justine Bowler*

100,000 colour transparencies of natural history, including birds, animals, insects, flowers, plants, fungi and landscapes; plus travel worldwide including people, places and cultures. Commissions undertaken. Full company information pack available. Visits by appointment only. Member of **BAPLA**.

Charles Parker Archive

See **Birmingham Library Services** under **Library Services**

David Paterson Photo-Library

88 Cavendish Road, London SW12 0DF
☎0181 673 2414   Fax 0181 675 9197
E-mail: paterson@ndirect.co.uk
Website: http://www.ndirect.co.uk/npaterson

Travel, landscapes, nature from the UK, Europe, North Africa, the Himalayas, Japan, Scotland and the USA.

Ann & Bury Peerless Picture Library

St David's, 22 King's Avenue, Minnis Bay, Birchington-on-Sea, Kent CT7 9QL
☎01843 841428   Fax 01843 848321

Contact *Ann or Bury Peerless*

Specialist collection on world religions: Hinduism, Buddhism, Jainism, Christianity, Islam, Sikhism. Geographical areas covered: India, Pakistan, Bangladesh, Sri Lanka, Cambodia, Thailand, Russia, Republic of China, Spain, Poland. 10,000 35mm colour transparencies.

Performing Arts Library

52 Agate Road, London W6 0AH
☎0181 748 2002   Fax 0181 563 0538
E-mail: performingartslibrary@compuserve.com

Colour and b&w pictures of all aspects of the performing arts, including classical music, opera, theatre, ballet and contemporary dance, musicals, concert halls, opera houses and festivals.

Photo Library International Ltd

PO Box 75, Leeds, West Yorkshire
LS7 3NX
☎0113 2623005   Fax 0113 2625366

Contemporary colour coverage of most subjects, including industry.

Photo Resources

The Orchard, Marley Lane, Kingston, Canterbury, Kent CT4 6JH
☎01227 830075   Fax 01227 831135

Colour and b&w coverage of archaeology, art, ancient art, ethnology, mythology, world religion, museum objects.

Photofusion

17A Electric Lane, London SW9 8LA
☎0171 738 5774   Fax 0171 738 5509

Contact *Liz Somerville*

Colour and b&w coverage of contemporary social issues including babies and children, disability, education, the elderly, environment, family, health, housing, homelessness, people and work. Brochure available.

The Photographers' Library

81A Endell Street, London WC2H 9AJ
☎0171 836 5591   Fax 0171 379 4650

Covers people, lifestyles, commerce, holiday people, travel destinations, industry, landscapes, health. Brochure available.

Photomax

118–122 Magdalen Road, Oxford OX4 1RQ
☎01865 241825   Fax 01865 794511
E-mail: photomax@compuserve.com

Contact *Max Gibbs, Barry Allday*

All aspects of the aquarium hobby are covered: aquarium fish, tropical freshwater, tropical marine, coldwater, marine invertebrates (tropical), freshwater invertebrates, aquarium plants, fish diseases/parasites, water lilies. Commissions undertaken.

Photos Horticultural

169 Valley Road, Ipswich, Suffolk IP1 4PJ
☎01473 257329   Fax 01473 233974

Colour coverage of all aspects of gardening in Britain and abroad, including extensive files on plants in cultivation and growing wild.

PictureBank Photo Library Ltd

Parman House, 30–36 Fife Road, Kingston upon Thames, Surrey KT1 1SY
☎0181 547 2344   Fax 0181 974 5652

Over 400,000 colour transparencies covering people (girls, couples, families, children), travel and scenic (UK and world), moods (sunsets, seascapes, deserts, etc.), industry and technology, environments and general. Commissions undertaken. Visitors welcome. Member of **BAPLA**. New material on medium/large format welcome.

Pictures Colour Library

4th Floor, The Italian Building, 41 Dockhead, London SE1 2BS
☎0171 252 3300   Fax 0171 252 3345

Location, lifestyle, food, still life, sport, animals, industry and business. Visitors welcome.

Pitkin Guides Ltd
Healey House, Dene Road, Andover,
Hampshire SP10 2AA
☎01264 334303   Fax 01264 334110
Contact *Jan Kean*

Colour transparencies of English cathedrals; plus a large collection of b&w prints. Also London and a few other cities. No visitors.

H. G. Ponting
See **Popperfoto**

Popperfoto
The Old Mill, Overstone Farm, Overstone, Northampton NN6 0AB
☎01604 670670   Fax 01604 670635
Home to over 13 million images, covering 150 years of photographic history. Renowned for its archival material, a world-famous sports library and stock photography. Popperfoto's credit line includes Reuters, Bob Thomas Sports Photography, UPI, Acme, INP, Planet, Paul Popper, Exclusive News Agency, Victory Archive, Odhams Periodicals Library, Illustrated, Harris Picture Agency, and H. G. Ponting which holds the Scott 1910–1912 Antarctic expedition. Colour from 1940, b&w from 1870 to the present. Major subjects covered worldwide include events, personalities, wars, royalty, sport, politics, transport, crime, history and social conditions. Material available on the same day to clients throughout the world. Mac-desk available. Researchers welcome by appointment. Free catalogue available.

PPL Photo Agency Ltd
68 East Ham Road, Littlehampton, West Sussex BN17 7BE
☎01903 730614   Fax 01903 730618
Contacts *Barry Pickthall, Eunice Bergin*

2 million pictures of sailing and boating, watersports, travel, water and coastal scenes. British Steel Multimedia Library – all aspects of steel and steel making. Construction, science and technology, transport, mining and industry.

Premaphotos Wildlife
Amberstone, 1 Kirland Road, Bodmin, Cornwall PL30 5JQ
☎01208 78258   Fax 01208 72302
E-mail: premaphotos@compuserve.com
Contact *Jean Preston-Mafham, Library Manager*

Natural history worldwide. Subjects include flowering and non-flowering plants, fungi, slime moulds, fruits and seeds, galls, leaf mines,

seashore life, mammals, birds, reptiles, amphibians, insects, spiders, habitats, scenery and cultivated cacti. Commissions undertaken. Visitors welcome. 'Make sure your name is on our mailing list to receive regular, colourful mailers.'

Professional Sport International Ltd
8 Apollo Studios, Charlton Kings Mews, London NW5 2SA
☎0171 482 2311   Fax 0171 482 2441
Colour and b&w coverage of tennis, soccer, athletics, golf, cricket, boxing, winter sports and many minor sports. Major international events including the Olympic Games, World Cup soccer and all Grand Slam tennis events. Also news and feature material supplied worldwide. Computerised library with in-house processing and studio facilities; Macintosh photo transmission services available for editorial and advertising.

Public Record Office
Image Library
Ruskin Avenue, Kew, Richmond, Surrey TW9 4DU
☎0181 392 5225   Fax 0181 392 5266
E-mail: enterprises.pro.kew@gtnet.gov.uk
Contact *Jo Matthews, Paul Johnson*

British and colonial history from the Domesday Book to the 1960s, shown in photography, maps, illuminations, posters, advertisements, textiles and original manuscripts. Approximately 20,000 5"x4" and 35mm colour transparencies and b&w negatives. Open: 9.00am to 5.30pm, Monday to Friday.

PWA International Ltd
City Gate House, 399–425 Eastern Avenue, Gants Hill, Ilford, Essex IG2 6LR
☎0181 518 2057   Fax 0181 518 2241
E-mail: pwaint@dircon.co.uk
Contact *Terry Allen*

Leading comprehensive library of story illustrations comprising work by some of the UK's best-known illustrators, including book covers and magazines. Also over half a million images of beauty, cookery and craft.

Railfotos
Millbrook House Ltd., Unit 1, Oldbury Business Centre, Pound Road, Oldbury, West Midlands B68 8NA
☎0121 544 2970
Fax 0121 253 6808 (quote Millbrook House)
One of the largest specialist libraries dealing

comprehensively with railway subjects world-wide. Colour and b&w dating from the turn of the century to present day. Up-to-date material on UK, South America and Far East (except Japan), especially China. Visitors by appointment.

Redferns Music Picture Library

7 Bramley Road, London W10 6SZ
☎0171 792 9914   Fax 0171 792 0921
E-mail: info@redferns.com

Music picture library covering every aspect of popular music from 1920's jazz to present day. Over 12,000 artists on file plus other subjects including musical instruments, recording studios, crowd scenes, festivals, etc. Brochure available.

Remote Source

See **Royal Geographical Society Picture Library**

Retna Pictures Ltd

1 Fitzroy Mews, Cleveland Street, London W1P 5DQ
☎0171 209 0200   Fax 0171 383 7151

Colour and b&w coverage of international rock and pop performers, actors, actresses, entertainers and celebrities. Also a general stock library covering a wide range of subjects, including travel, people, sport and leisure, flora and fauna, and the environment.

Retrograph Archive Ltd

164 Kensington Park Road, London W11 2ER
☎0171 727 9378/9426   Fax 0171 229 3395
E-mail: mbreese999@aol.com

Contact *Jilliana Ranicar-Breese*

'Number One for nostalgia!' A vast archive of commercial and decorative art (1860–1960). Worldwide labels and packaging for food, wine, chocolate, soap, perfume, cigars and cigarettes; fine art and commercial art journals, fashion and lifestyle magazines, posters, Victorian greetings cards, scraps, Christmas cards, Edwardian post-cards, wallpaper and gift-wrap sample books, music sheets, folios of decorative design and ornament – Art Nouveau and Deco; hotel, air-line and shipping labels; memorabilia, tourism, leisure, food and drink, transport and entertainment. Lasers for book dummies, packaging, mock-ups, film/TV action props. Colour brochure on request. Medium format. Picture research service. Design consultancy service. Victorian-style montages conceived, designed and styled (RetroMontages).

Rex Features Ltd

18 Vine Hill, London EC1R 5DX
☎0171 278 7294/3362   Fax 0171 696 0974

Established in the 1950s. Colour and b&w coverage of news, politics, personalities, show business, glamour, humour, art, medicine, science, landscapes, royalty, etc.

Royal Air Force Museum

Grahame Park Way, Hendon, London NW9 5LL
☎0181 205 2266   Fax 0181 200 1751

Contact *Christine Gregory*

About a quarter of a million images, mostly b&w, with around 1500 colour in all formats, on the history of aviation. Particularly strong on the activities of the Royal Air Force from the 1870s to 1970s. Researchers are requested to enquire in writing only.

The Royal Collection

Windsor Castle, Windsor, Berks SL4 1NJ
☎01753 868286   Fax 01753 620046

Contact *Gwyneth Campling, Nicole Tetzner*

Photographic material of items in the Royal Collection, particularly oil paintings, drawings and watercolours, works of art, and interiors and exteriors of royal residences. 35,000 colour transparencies plus 25,000 b&w negatives.

Royal Geographical Society Picture Library

1 Kensington Gore, London SW7 2AR
☎0171 591 3060   Fax 0171 591 3061

Contact *Joanna Scadden, Sharon Martins*

A strong source of geographical and historical images, both archival and modern, showing the world through the eyes of photographers and explorers dating from the 1830s to the present day. The Remote Source Collection provides up-to-date transparencies from around the world, highlighting aspects of cultural activity, environmental phenomena, anthropology, architectural design, travel, mountaineering and exploration. Offers a professional and comprehensive service for both commercial and academic use.

Royal Opera House Archives

Royal Opera House, Covent Garden, London WC2E 9DD
☎0171 240 1200   Fax 0171 212 9489

Closed 'until further notice' while the rebuilding of the Royal Opera House takes place.

The Royal Photographic Society
The Octagon, Milsom Street, Bath BA1 1DN
☎01225 462841   Fax 01225 448688
Contact *Debbie Ireland*

History of photography, with an emphasis on pictorial photography as an art rather than a documentary record. Photographic processes and cameras, landscape, portraiture, architecture, India, Victorian and Edwardian life.

RSPB Images
21-22 Great Sutton Street, London EC1V 0DN
☎0171 608 7325   Fax 0171 608 0770
Contact *Zoe Beech*

Colour and b&w images of birds, butterflies, moths, mammals, reptiles and their habitats. Also colour images of all RSPB reserves. Growing selection of various habitats. Total number of slides now 52,000, available digitally or in any desired format.

RSPCA Photolibrary
RSPCA Trading Limited, Causeway, Horsham, West Sussex RH12 1HG
☎01403 223150   Fax 01403 241048
E-mail: photolibrary@rspca.org.uk
Photolibrary Manager *Andrew Forsyth*

Over 35,000 colour transparencies and over 5000 b&w/colour prints. A comprehensive collection of natural history images whose subjects include mammals, birds, domestic and farm animals, amphibians, insects and the environment, as well as a unique photographic record of the RSPCA's work. Catalogue available. No search fees.

Russia and and Eastern Images
'Sonning', Cheapside Lane, Denham, Uxbridge, Middlesex UB9 5AE
☎01895 833508/0956 304384 (mobile)
Fax 01895 834028

Architecture, cities, landscapes, people and travel images of Russia and the former Soviet Union. Considerable background knowledge available and Russian language spoken.

Salamander Picture Library
8 Blenheim Court, Brewery Road, London N7 9NT
☎0171 700 7799   Fax 0171 700 3918/3572
Contact *Terry Forshaw*

Approximately 250,000 images, colour and b&w, of American history, collectibles, cookery, crafts, military, natural history, space and transport.

Peter Sanders Photography
24 Meades Lane, Chesham, Buckinghamshire HP5 1ND
☎01494 773674   Fax 01494 773674/771372
E-mail: petersanders.photography@
  btinternet.com
Contact *Peter Sanders, Hafsa Garwatuk*

The world of Islam in all its aspects from religion and industry to culture and arts. Areas included are Saudi Arabia, Africa, Asia, Europe and USA. Now expanding to all religions.

Science & Society Picture Library
Science Museum, Exhibition Road, London SW7 2DD
☎0171 938 9750   Fax 0171 938 9751
E-mail: piclib@nmsi.ac.uk
Website: http://www.nmsi.ac.uk/piclib/
Contact *Angela Murphy, Venita Paul*

25,000 reference prints and 100,000 colour transparencies, incorporating many from collections at the Science Museum, the National Railway Museum and the National Museum of Film, Photography and Television. Collections illustrate the history of: science, industry, technology, medicine, transport and the media. Plus three archives documenting British society in the twentieth century.

The Scottish Highland Photo Library
Croft Roy, Crammond Brae, Tain, Ross-shire IV19 1JG
☎01862 892298   Fax 01862 892298
Contact *Hugh Webster*

120,000 colour transparencies of the Scottish Highlands and Islands. Not just a travel library; images cover industry, agriculture, fisheries and many other subjects of the Highlands and Islands. Submissions from photographers welcome. Commissions undertaken.

Scottish Media Newspapers
195 Albion Street, Glasgow G1 1QP
☎0141 552 6255   Fax 0141 553 2642

Over 6 million images: b&w and colour photographs from *c.*1900 from the *Herald* (Glasgow) and *Evening Times*. Current affairs, Scotland, Glasgow, Clydeside shipbuilding and engineering, personalities, World Wars I and II, sport.

Seaco Picture Library
Sea Containers House, 20 Upper Ground, London SE1 9PF
☎0171 805 5831   Fax 0171 805 5926

Contact *Maureen Elliott*

Approx. 250,000 images of containerisation, shipping, fast ferries, manufacturing, fruit farming, ports, hotels and leisure.

Mick Sharp Photography

Eithinog, Waun, Penisarwaun, Caernarfon, Gwynedd LL55 3PW

☎01286 872425   Fax 01286 872425

Contacts *Mick Sharp, Jean Williamson*

Colour transparencies (6x4.5cm and 35mm) and black & white prints (5[dq]x4[dq] and 6x4.5cm negatives) of subjects connected with archaeology, ancient monuments, buildings, churches, countryside, environment, history, landscape, past cultures and topography from Britain and abroad. Photographs by Mick Sharp and Jean Williamson, plus access to other specialist collections on related subjects. Commissions undertaken.

Phil Sheldon Golf Picture Library

40 Manor Road, Barnet, Hertfordshire EN5 2JQ

☎0181 440 1986   Fax 0181 440 9348

An expanding collection of over 400,000 quality images of the 'world of golf'. In-depth worldwide tournament coverage including every Major championship & Ryder Cup since 1976. Instruction, portraits, trophies and over 300 golf courses from around the world. Also the Dale Concannon collection covering the period 1870 to 1940 and the classic 1960s collection by photographer Sidney Harris.

Skishoot–Offshoot

Hall Place, Upper Woodcott, Whitchurch, Hampshire RG28 7PY

☎01635 255527   Fax 01635 255528

Contact *Felice Eyston, Peter Hardy*

Predominantly skiing and snowboarding, but also a travel library specialising in France. Commissions undertaken.

The Skyscan Photolibrary

Oak House, Toddington, Cheltenham, Gloucestershire GL54 5BY

☎01242 621357   Fax 01242 621343

E-mail: info@skyscan.co.uk

Website: www.skyscan.co.uk

As well as the Skyscan Photolibrary collection of unique balloon's-eye views of Britain, the library now includes the work of photographers from across the aviation spectrum; air to ground, aviation, aerial sports – 'in fact, anything aerial!'.

Links have been built with photographers across the world; photographs can be handled on an agency basis and held in house, or as a brokerage where the collection stays with the photographer; terms 50/50 for both. Commissioned photography undertaken. Enquiries welcome.

Snookerimages (Eric Whitehead Photography)

PO Box 33, Kendal, Cumbria LA9 4SU

☎015394 48894   Fax 015394 48294

E-mail: eric@snookerimages.co.uk

Website: www.snookerimages.co.uk

Over 20,000 images of snooker. Also holds the Cumbria Picture Library; the agency covers local news events, PR and commercial material.

SOA Photo Library

87 York Street, London W1H 1DU

☎0171 258 0202   Fax 0171 258 01881

Contact *Brigitte Bott, Lorna Allen, Emma Davies*

75,000 colour slides, 10,000 b&w photos covering *Stern* productions, sports, travel & geographic, advertising, social subjects. Representatives of Voller Ernst, Interfoto and many freelance photographers. Catalogues available.

Solo Syndication Ltd

49–53 Kensington High Street, London W8 5ED

☎0171 376 2166   Fax 0171 938 3165

Syndication Manager *Trevor York*

Photo Sales *Danny Howell, Nick York*

Online transmissions *Geoff Malyon* (☎0171 937 3866)

Three million images from the archives of the *Daily Mail, Mail on Sunday, Evening Standard* and *Evening News*. Also photo portfolios from Australia, South Africa and 1000 colour travel slides of Spain. Main library encompassing celebrities, royalty, political figures, crime, sports, beauty, cuisine, health, fashion and general. Hard prints or Mac-to-mac delivery. 24-hour service.

Sotheby's Picture Library

34–35 New Bond Street, London W1A 2AA

☎0171 293 5383   Fax 0171 293 5062

Contact *Joanna Ling*

The library mainly consists of several thousand selected transparencies of pictures sold at Sotheby's. Images from the 15th to the 20th century. Oils, drawings, watercolours and prints. 'Happy to do searches or, alternatively, visitors are welcome by appointment.'

South American Pictures
48 Station Road, Woodbridge, Suffolk
IP12 4AT
☎01394 383963/383279   Fax 01394 380176
E-mail: morrison@south-american-pic.com
Website: http://www.south-american-pic.com

Contact *Marion Morrison*

Colour and b&w images of South/Central America, Cuba, Mexico and New Mexico (USA), including archaeology and the Amazon. Frequently updated. There is an archival section, with pictures and documents from most countries.

The Special Photographers Library
21 Kensington Park Road, London W11 2EU
☎0171 221 3489   Fax 0171 792 9112

Contacts *Chris Kewbank*

Represents over 100 contemporary fine art photographers who are unusual in style, technique or subject matter. Also has exclusive access to the Bill Hopkins Collection – an archive of thousands of vintage pictures dating back to the early 20th century.

Spectrum Colour Library
41–42 Berners Street, London W1P 3AA
☎0171 637 1587   Fax 0171 637 3681

A large collection including travel, sport, people, pets, scenery, industry, British and European cities, etc. All pictures are also available in digital format. Visitors welcome by appointment.

Frank Spooner Pictures Ltd
Unit B7, Hatton Square, 16–16A Baldwin's Gardens, London EC1N 7US
☎0171 632 5800   Fax 0171 632 5828

Subjects include current affairs, show business, fashion, politics, travel, adventure, sport, personalities, films, animals and the Middle East. Represented in more than 30 countries and handles UK distribution of Harry Benson, and Gamma Presse Images and Roger-Viollet of Paris. Commissions undertaken.

The Still Moving Picture Co.
67A Logie Green Road, Edinburgh EH7 4HF
☎0131 557 9697   Fax 0131 557 9699
E-mail: stillmovingpictures@compuserve.com

Contact *John Hutchinson, Sue Hall*

250,000 colour, b&w and 16mm film coverage of Scotland and sport. The largest photo and film library in Scotland, holding the Scottish Tourist Board library among its files. Scottish agents for **Allsport (UK) Ltd**.

Still Pictures' Whole Earth Photolibrary
199 Shooters Hill Road, Blackheath, London SE3 8UL
☎0181 858 8307   Fax 0181 858 2049

Contacts *Theresa de Salis, Mark Edwards*

FOUNDED 1970, the library is a leading source of pictures illustrating the human impact on the environment, Third World development issues, industrial ecology, wildlife, endangered species and habitats. 250,000 colour medium-format transparencies, 100,000 b&w prints. Over 300 leading photographers from around the world supply the library with stock pictures. Write, phone or fax for Still Pictures' Environment and Third World catalogue and Still Pictures' Wildlife and Nature catalogue.

Stockfile
5 High Street, Sunningdale, Berkshire SL5 0LX
☎01344 872249   Fax 01344 872263

Contact *Jill Behr, Steven Behr*

Specialist cycling- and skiing-based collection covering most aspects of these activities, with emphasis on mountain biking. Expanding adventure sports section.

Sir John Benjamin Stone
See **Birmingham Library Services** under **Library Services**

Tate Gallery Picture Library
Tate Gallery Publishing Ltd, Millbank, London SW1P 4RG
☎0171 887 8867/90   Fax 0171 887 8900
E-mail: carlotta.gelmetti@tate.org.uk and christopher.webster@tate.org.uk

Contact *Carlotta Gelmetti, Chris Webster*

Approximately 8000 images of British art from the 16th century; international 20th century painting and sculpture. Artists include William Blake, William Hogarth, J. M. W. Turner, Dante Gabriel Rossetti, Barbara Hepworth, Henry Moore, Stanley Spencer, Pablo Picasso, Mark Rothko, Salvador Dali, Lucien Freud and David Hockney. Colour transparencies of more than half the works in the main collection are available for hire. For a fee, new photography is available depending on the location and condition of the art work. B&w prints of nearly all the works in the collection can be purchased. Colour slides and prints can be made on request providing a colour transparency exists. Picture researchers must make an appointment to visit the library. All applications must be made by fax or letter.

Telegraph Colour Library

The Innovation Centre, 225 Marsh Wall,
London E14 9FX
☎0171 987 1212   Fax 0171 538 3309
Contact *Lynn Mears*

Leading stock photography agency covering a wide subject range: business, sport, people, industry, animals, medical, nature, space, travel and graphics. Free catalogue available. Same-day service to UK clients.

3rd Millennium Music Ltd

22 Avon, Hockley, Tamworth, Staffordshire
B77 5QA
☎01827 286086   Fax 01827 286086
E-mail: neil3mmltd@aol.com
Website: http://home.aol.com/Neil3MMLtd
Managing Director *Neil Williams*

Archive specialising in classical music ephemera, particularly portraits of composers, musicians, conductors and opera singers comprising of old and sometimes very rare photographs, postcards, antique prints, cigarette cards, stamps, First Day Covers, concert programmes, Victorian newspapers, etc. Also modern photos of composer references such as museums, statues, busts, paintings, monuments, memorials and graves. Other subjects covered include ballet and dance, musical instruments, concert halls, opera houses, bandstands, 'music in art', manuscripts, church organs, opera scenes, music–cartoons, ethnic music, jazz, military bands, orchestras and other music groups.

Bob Thomas Sports Photography

See **Popperfoto**

Patrick Thurston Photolibrary

10 Willis Road, Cambridge CB1 2AQ
☎01223 352547   Fax 01223 366274

Colour photography of Britain: scenery, people, museums, churches, coastline. Also various countries abroad. Commissions undertaken.

Rick Tomlinson Marine Photo Library

18 Hamble Yacht Services, Port Hamble,
Hamble, Southampton, Hampshire
SO31 4NN
☎01703 458450   Fax 01703 458350
Contacts *Rick Tomlinson, Julie Birchall*

ESTABLISHED 1985. *Specialises* in marine subjects. 60,000 35mm transparencies of yachting, racing, cruising, Whitbread Round the World

Race, Tall Ships, RNLI Lifeboats, Antarctica, wildlife and locations.

Topham Picturepoint

PO Box 33, Edenbridge, Kent TN8 5PB
☎01342 850313   Fax 01342 850244
Contact *Alan Smith*

Eight million contemporary and historical images, ideal for advertisers, publishers and the travel trade. Includes half a million pictures from the *Observer* magazine, from 1962 to end 1992. Delivery on line.

B. M. Totterdell Photography

Constable Cottage, Burlings Lane, Knockholt,
Kent TN14 7PE
☎01959 532001   Fax 01959 532001
Contact *Barbara Totterdell*

Specialist volleyball library covering all aspects of the sport.

Tessa Traeger Library

7 Rossetti Studios, 72 Flood Street, London
SW3 5TF
☎0171 352 3641   Fax 0171 352 4846

Food, gardens, travel and artists.

Travel Ink Photo & Feature Library

The Old Coach House, 14 High Street,
Goring on Thames, Nr Reading, Berkshire
RG8 9AR
☎01491 873011   Fax 01491 875558
Website: http://www.photosource.co.uk/
    photosource/travink.htm
Contact *Abbie Enock*

Around 100,000 colour images covering about 130 countries (including the UK). Close links with other specialist libraries mean most topics can be accessed. Subjects include travel, tourism, lifestyles, business, industry, transport, children, religion, history, activities. Specialist collections on Hong Kong (including construction of the Tsing Ma bridge), Greece, North Wales, Germany, the Cotswolds, France, and many others.

Peter Trenchard's Image Store Ltd

The Studio, West Hill, St Helier, Jersey,
Channel Islands JE2 3HB
☎01534 69933   Fax 01534 89191
Contact *Peter Trenchard, FBIPP, AMPA, PPA*

Slide library of the Channel Islands – mainly tourist and financial-related. Commissions undertaken.

Tropix Photographic Library

156 Meols Parade, Meols, Wirral, Merseyside
L47 6AN
☎0151 632 1698   Fax 0151 632 1698
Website: http://www.merseyworld.com/
tropix/

Contact *Veronica Birley*

Leading specialists on the developing world in all its aspects. Environmental topics widely covered. Assignment photography undertaken at home and overseas. New collections welcome, especially parts of Africa and Latin America, and environmental; please write with details enclosing four first-class stamps. All submissions (35mm + colour transparencies only) must be accompanied by detailed accurate captions, prepared according to Tropix specifications.

True North Picture Source

5 Brunswick Street, Hebden Bridge, West Yorkshire HX7 6AJ
☎01422 845532   Fax 01422 845532
Contact *John Morrison*

30,000 transparencies on 35mm and 6x4.5cm format on the life and landscape of the north of England, photographed by John Morrison.

Ulster Museum

Botanic Gardens, Belfast BT9 5AB
☎01232 383000 ext 3113   Fax 01232 383103
Contact *Mrs Pat McLean*

The Ulster Museum is a national museum for Northern Ireland. Specialist subjects: art – fine and decorative, late 17th–20th century, particularly Irish art, archaeology, ethnography, treasures from the Armada shipwrecks, geology, botany, zoology, local history and industrial archaeology. Commissions welcome for objects not already photographed.

Universal Pictorial Press & Agency Ltd

29–31 Saffron Hill, London EC1N 8FH
☎0171 421 6000   Fax 0171 421 6006
News Editor *Peter Dare*

Photo archive dates back to 1944 and contains approximately four million pictures. Colour and b&w coverage of news, royalty, politics, sport, arts, and many other subjects. Commissions undertaken for press and public relations. Fully interactive digital photo archive in addition to bulletin board accessible via ISDN or modem. Full digital scanning, retouching and transmission facilities.

UPI

See **Popperfoto**

V & A Picture Library

Victoria and Albert Museum, South Kensington, London SW7 2RL
☎0171 938 8352/8354/8452/9645
Fax 0171 938 8353
E-mail: picture.library@vam.ac.uk

47,000 colour and half a million b&w photos of decorative and applied arts, including ceramics, ivories, furniture, costumes, textiles, stage, musical instruments, toys, Indian, Far Eastern, Islamic objects, sculpture, painting and prints, from medieval to present day.

Valley Green

Barn Ley, Valley Lane, Buxhall, Stowmarket, Suffolk IP14 3EB
☎01449 736090   Fax 01449 736090
Contact *Joseph Barrere*

Masses of perennials – 'all correctly labelled'. Over 10,000 hardy plant transparencies in stock, plus watercolours and line drawings available. Commissions undertaken as well as commercial copywriting.

Venice Picture Library

2a Milner Street, London SW3 2PU
☎0171 589 3127   Fax 0171 584 1944

25,000 35mm images of Venice, its buildings, people, animals and atmosphere. Member of **BAPLA**.

Victory Archive

See **Popperfoto**

The Vintage Magazine Company Ltd

203–213 Mare Street, London E8 3QE
☎0181 533 7588   Fax 0181 533 7283

A large collection of movie stills and posters, photographs, illustrations and advertisements covering music, glamour, social history, theatre posters, ephemera, postcards.

The Charles Walker Collection

12–14 Argyll Street, London W1V 1AB
☎0171 734 7344   Fax 0171 287 3933

One of the foremost collections in the world on subjects popularly listed as 'Mystery, myth and magic'. The collection includes astrology, occultism, witchcraft and many other related areas. Catalogue available.

John Walmsley Photo Library

April Cottage, Warners Lane, Albury Heath, Guildford, Surrey GU5 9DE
☎01483 203846   Fax 01483 203846
E-mail: johnwalmsleyphotos@ compuserve.com

Specialist library of learning/training/working subjects. Comprehensive coverage of learning environments such as playgroups, schools, colleges and universities. Images reflect a multiracial Britain. Plus a section on complementary medicine with over 30 therapies from acupuncture and yoga to more unusual ones like moxibustion and metamorphic technique. Commissions undertaken. Subject list available on request.

Warwickshire Photographic Survey

See **Birmingham Library Services** under **Library Services**

Waterways Photo Library

39 Manor Court Road, Hanwell, London W7 3EJ
☎0181 840 1659   Fax 0181 567 0605

A specialist photo library on all aspects of Britain's inland waterways. Top-quality 35mm- and medium-format colour transparencies, plus a large collection of b&w. Rivers and canals, bridges, locks, aqueducts, tunnels and waterside buildings. Town and countryside scenes, canal art, waterway holidays, boating, fishing, windmills, watermills, watersports and wildlife.

Philip Way Photography

2 Green Moor Link, Winchmore Hill, London N21 2ND
☎0181 360 5876
Contact *Philip Way*

Over 1000 images of St Paul's Cathedral – historical exteriors, interiors and events (1982–1997).

Wellcome Trust Medical Photographic Library

210 Euston Road, London NW1 2BE
☎0171 611 8348   Fax 0171 611 8577
Contact *Catherine Draycott, Heather Ercilla, Michele Minto, Julie Dorrington*

Approximately 160,000 images on the history of medicine and human culture worldwide, including modern clinical medicine. Incorporates the **National Medical Slide Bank**.

Wilderness Photographic Library

Mill Barn, Broad Raine, Sedbergh, Cumbria LA10 5ED
☎015396 20196   Fax 015396 21293
Contact *John Noble*

Striking colour images from around the world, from polar wastes to the Himalayas and Amazon jungle. Subjects: mountains, Arctic, deserts, icebergs, wildlife, rainforests, glaciers, geysers, exploration, caves, rivers, eco-tourism, people and cultures, canyons, seascapes, marine life, weather, volcanoes, mountaineering, skiing, geology, conservation, adventure sports, national parks.

David Williams Picture Library

50 Burlington Avenue, Glasgow G12 0LH
☎0141 339 7823   Fax 0141 337 3031

Colour coverage of Scotland and Iceland. Smaller collections of the Faroes, France and Western USA. Landscapes, historical sites, buildings, geology and physical geography. Medium format and 35mm. Catalogue available. Commissions undertaken.

Vaughan Williams Memorial Library

English Folk Dance and Song Society, Cecil Sharp House, 2 Regent's Park Road, London NW1 7AY
☎0171 284 0523   Fax 0171 284 0523

Mainly b&w coverage of traditional/folk music, dance and customs worldwide, focusing on Britain and other English-speaking nations. Photographs date from the late 19th century to the 1970s.

The Wilson Photographic Collection

See **Dundee District Libraries** under **Library Services**

Windrush Photos, Wildlife and Countryside Picture Agency

99 Noah's Ark, Kemsing, Sevenoaks, Kent TN15 6PD
☎01732 763486   Fax 01732 763285
Contact *David Tipling*

Specialists in birds (worldwide) and British wildlife. A large collection of black and white images covering British wildlife and angling, and shooting scenes dating back to the 1930s. High quality photographic and features commissions are regularly undertaken for publications in the UK and overseas. The agency acts as ornithological consultants for all aspects of the media.

The Wingfield Sporting Art Library

25 Montrose Court, Princes Gate, Exhibition Road, London SW7 2QQ
☎0171 581 2964   Fax 0171 581 2964

Contact *Mary Ann Wingfield*

Sporting works of art, both historical and contemporary, covering 50 different sports. Commissions undertaken.

Woodfall Wild Images

17 Bull Lane, Denbigh, Denbighshire LL16 3SN
☎01745 815903   Fax 01745 814581

Contacts *David Woodfall, David Hill*

Environmental, conservation, landscape and wildlife photographic library. A constantly-expanding collection of images reflecting a wide range of subjects, 'from mammals to marine, insects to industry, rivers to rainforest, and pollution to people changing our world, for the better and for the worse'.

World Pictures

85a Great Portland Street, London W1N 5RA
☎0171 437 2121/436 0440
Fax 0171 439 1307

Contacts *David Brenes, Carlo Irek*

600,000 colour transparencies of travel and emotive material.

WWF UK Photolibrary

Panda House, Weyside Park, Catteshall Lane, Godalming, Surrey GU7 1XR
☎01483 426444   Fax 01483 426409

Contact *Amanda Freestone*

Specialist library covering natural history, endangered species, conservation, environment, forests, habitats, habitat destruction, and pollution in the UK and abroad. 10,000 colour slides (35mm).

Yemen Pictures

28 Sheen Common Drive, Richmond TW10 5BN
☎0181 898 0150/876 3637
Fax 0181 898 0150

Large collection (4000 transparencies) covering all aspects of Yemen – culture, people, architecture, dance, qat, music. Also Africa, Australia, Middle East, and Asia.

York Archaeological Trust Picture Library

Cromwell House, 13 Ogleforth, York YO1 2JG
☎01904 663000   Fax 01904 640029

Specialist library of rediscovered artifacts, historic buildings and excavations, presented by the creators of the highly acclaimed Jorvik Viking Centre. The main emphasis is on the Roman, Anglo-Saxon and Viking periods.

The John Robert Young Collection

61 De Montfort Road, Lewes, East Sussex BN7 1SS
☎01273 475216   Fax 01273 475216

Contact *Jennifer Barrett*

50,000 transparencies and monochrome prints on travel, religion and military subjects.

Balancing the Books –
Tax and the Writer

'No man in the country is under the smallest obligation, moral or other, to arrange his affairs as to enable the Inland Revenue to put the largest possible shovel in his stores.

The Inland Revenue is not slow, and quite rightly, to take every advantage which is open to it ... for the purpose of depleting the taxpayer's pockets. And the taxpayer is, in like manner, entitled to be astute to prevent as far as he honestly can the depletion of his means by the Inland Revenue.'

Lord Clyde, *Ayrshire Pullman v Inland Revenue Commissioners, 1929*

Income Tax

What is a professional writer for tax purposes?
Writers are professionals while they are writing regularly with the intention of making a profit; or while they are gathering material, researching or otherwise preparing a publication.

A professional freelance writer is taxed under Case II of Schedule D of the *Income and Corporation Taxes Act 1988*. The taxable income is the amount received, either directly or by an agent, on his behalf, less expenses wholly and exclusively laid out for the purpose of the profession. If expenses exceed income, the loss can either be carried forward and set against future income from writing or set against other income which is subject to tax in the same year. If tax has been paid on that other income, a repayment can be obtained, or the sum can be offset against other tax liabilities. Special loss relief can apply in the opening year of the profession. Losses made in the first four years can be set against income of up to three earlier years.

Where a writer receives very occasional payments for isolated articles, it may not be possible to establish that these are profits arising from carrying on a continuing profession. In such circumstances these 'isolated transactions' may be assessed under Case VI of Schedule D of the *Income and Corporation Taxes Act 1988*. Again, expenses may be deducted in arriving at the taxable income, but, if expenses exceed income, the loss can only be set against the profits from future isolated transactions, or other income assessable under Case VI.

In the tax year 1996/97 a new tax system came into effect called Self Assessment. Under Self Assessment the onus is on the individual to declare income and expenses correctly. Each writer therefore has to decide whether profits arise from a professional or occasional activity. The consequences of getting it wrong can be expensive by way of interest, penalties and surcharges on additional tax subsequently found to be due. If in any doubt the writer should seek professional advice.

Income

A writer's income includes fees, advances, royalties, commissions, sale of copyrights, reimbursed expenses, etc., from any source anywhere in the world whether or not brought to the UK (non UK resident or domiciled writers should seek professional advice).

Expenses

A writer can normally claim the following expenses:

(a) Secretarial, typing, proofreading, research. Where payment for these is made to the author's wife or husband they should be recorded and entered in the spouse's tax return as earned income which is subject to the usual personal allowances. If payments reach relevant levels, PAYE should be operated.

(b) Telephone, faxes, Internet costs, computer software, postage, stationery, printing, equipment maintenance, insurance, dictation tapes, batteries, any equipment or office requisites used for the profession.

(c) Periodicals, books (including presentation copies and reference books) and other publications necessary for the profession, but amounts received from the sale of books should be deducted.

(d) Hotels, fares, car running expenses (including repairs, petrol, oil, garaging, parking, cleaning, insurance, road fund tax, depreciation), hire of cars or taxis in connection with:

  (i) business discussions with agents, publishers, co-authors, collaborators, researchers, illustrators, etc.

  (ii) travel at home and abroad to collect background material.

  As an alternative to keeping details of full car running costs, a mileage rate can be claimed for business use. This rate depends on the engine size and varies from year to year. This is known as the Fixed Profit Car Scheme and is available to writers whose turnover does not exceed the VAT registration limit, currently £50,000.

(e) Publishing and advertising expenses, including costs of proof corrections, indexing, photographs, etc.

(f) Subscriptions to societies and associations, press cutting agencies, libraries, etc., incurred wholly for the purpose of the profession.

(g) Rent, council tax and water rates, etc., the proportion being determined by the ratio of the number of rooms used exclusively for the profession, to the total number of rooms in the residence. But see note on *Capital Gains Tax* below.

(h) Lighting, heating and cleaning. A carefully calculated figure of the business use of these costs can be claimed as a proportion of the total.

(i) Agent's commission, accountancy charges and legal charges incurred wholly in the course of the profession including cost of defending libel actions, damages in so far as they are not covered by insurance, and libel insurance premiums. However, where in a libel case damages are awarded to punish the author for having acted maliciously the action becomes quasi-criminal and costs and damages may not be allowed.

(j) TV and video rental (which may be apportioned for private use), and cinema or theatre tickets, if wholly for the purpose of the profession.

(k) Capital allowances for business equipment, e.g. car, TV, radio, hi-fi sets, tape and video recorders, dictaphones, computers, printers, scanners, typewriters, office furniture, photographic equipment. Allowances vary in the Finance Acts. At present there is a First Year Allowance (for the year to 30 June 1998, 50%, and 1999, 40%) of the cost of equipment purchased in those years. Subsequently there is an annual Writing Down Allowance of 25% of the reducing balance. On motor cars the allowance is 25% in the first year and 25% of the reducing balance in each successive year limited to £3000 each year. (In the case of motor cars bought before 11 March 1992 the limit is £2000 each year.) The total allowances claimed over the lifetime of any asset must not exceed the difference between the cost and eventual sale price. Allowances will be reduced to exclude personal (non-professional) use where necessary.

(l) Lease rent. The cost of lease rent of equipment is allowable; also on cars, subject to restrictions for private use, and for expensive cars.

(m) Other expenses incurred wholly and exclusively for professional purposes. (Entertaining expenses are not allowable in any circumstances.)

NB It is always advisable to keep detailed records. Diary entries of appointments, notes of fares and receipted bills are much more convincing to the Inland Revenue than round figure estimates.

The Self Assessment regime makes it a legal requirement for proper accounting records to be kept. These records must be sufficient to support the figures declared in the tax return.

In addition to the above, tax relief is available on:

(a) Premiums to pension schemes such as the *Society of Authors Retirement Benefits Scheme*. Depending on age, up to 40% of net earned income can be paid into a personal pension plan.

(b) Covenants to charities.

(c) Gift Aid payments to charities. Currently single payment of £250 or more.

Capital Gains Tax

The exemption from Capital Gains Tax which applies to an individual's main residence does not apply to any part of that residence which is used exclusively for business purposes. The effect of this is that the appropriate proportion of any increase in value of the residence since 31 March 1982 can be taxed when the residence is sold, subject to adjustment for inflation to March 1998 and subsequent length of ownership, at the individual's highest rate of tax.

Writers who own their houses should bear this in mind before claiming expenses for the use of a room for writing purposes. Arguments in favour of making such claims are that they afford some relief now, while Capital Gains Tax in its present form may not stay for ever. Also, where a new house is bought in place of an old one, the gain made on the sale of the first study may be set off against the cost of the study in the new house, thus postponing the tax payment until the final sale. For this relief to apply, each house must have a study and the author must continue his profession throughout. On death there is an exemption of the total Capital Gains of the estate.

Alternatively, writers can claim that their use is non-exclusive and restrict their claim to the cost of extra lighting, heating and cleaning to avoid any Capital Gains Tax liability.

Can a writer average out his income over a number of years for tax purposes?

Under Section 534 of the *Income and Corporation Taxes Act 1988*, a writer may in certain circumstances spread over two or three fiscal years lump sum payments whenever received and royalties received during two years from the date of first publication or performance of work. Points to note are:

(a) If the period of preparing and writing the work exceeds twelve months but does not exceed twenty-four months, one-half of the advances and/or royalties will be regarded as income from the year preceding that of receipt. If the period of preparing and writing exceeds twenty-four months, one-third of the amount received would be regarded as income from each of the two years preceding that of receipt.

(b) For a writer on a very large income, who otherwise fulfils the conditions required, a claim under these sections could result in a tax saving. If his income is not large he should consider the implication, in the various fiscal years concerned, of possible loss of benefit from personal and other allowances and changes in the standard rate of income tax.

It is also possible to average out income within the terms of publishers' contracts, but professional advice should be taken before signature. Where a husband and wife collaborate as writers, advice should be taken as to whether a formal partnership agreement should be made or whether the publishing agreement should be in joint names.

Is a lump sum paid for an outright sale of the copyright or is part of the copyright exempt from tax?

No. All the money received from the marketing of literary work, by whatever means, is taxable. Some writers, in spite of clear judicial decisions to the contrary, still seem to think that an outright sale of, for instance, the film rights in a book is not subject to tax.

Remaindering

To avoid remaindering authors can usually purchase copies of their own books from the publishers. Monies received from sales are subject to income tax but the cost of books sold should be deducted because tax is only payable on the profit made.

Is there any relief where old copyrights are sold?

Section 535 of the *Income and Corporation Taxes Act 1988* gives relief where not less than ten years after the first publication of the work the author of a literary, dramatic, musical or artistic work assigns the copyright therein wholly or partially, or grants any interest in the copyright by licence, and:

(a) the consideration for the assignment or grant consists wholly or partially of a lump sum payment, the whole amount of which would, but for this section, be included in computing the amount of his/her profits or gains for a single year of assessment, and

(b) the copyright of interest is not assigned or granted for a period of less than two years.

In such cases, the amount received may be spread forward in equal yearly instalments for a maximum of six years, or, where the copyright or interest is assigned or granted for a period of less than six years, for the number of whole years in that period. A 'lump sum payment' is defined to include a non-returnable advance on account of royalties.

It should be noted that a claim may not be made under this section in respect of a payment if a prior claim has been made under Section 534 of the *Income and Corporation Taxes Act 1988* (see section on spreading lump sum payments over two or three years) or vice versa.

Are royalties payable on publication of a book abroad subject to both foreign tax as well as UK tax?

Where there is a Double Taxation Agreement between the country concerned and the UK, then on the completion of certain formalities no tax is deductible at source by the foreign payer, but such income is taxable in the UK in the ordinary way. When there is no Double Taxation Agreement, credit will be given against UK tax for overseas tax paid. A complete list of countries with which the UK has conventions for the avoidance of double taxation may be obtained from FICO, Inland Revenue, St John's House, Merton Road, Bootle, Merseyside L69 9BB, or the local tax office.

Residence abroad

Writers residing abroad will, of course, be subject to the tax laws ruling in their country of residence, and as a general rule royalty income paid from the United Kingdom can be exempted from deduction of UK tax at source, providing the author is carrying on his profession abroad. A writer who is intending to go and live abroad should make early application for future royalties to be paid without deduction of tax to FICO, address as above. In certain circumstances writers resident in the Irish Republic are exempt from Irish Income Tax on their authorship earnings.

Are grants or prizes taxable?
The law is uncertain. Some Arts Council grants are now deemed to be taxable, whereas most prizes and awards are not, though it depends on the conditions in each case. When submitting the Self Assessment annual returns, such items should be excluded, but reference made to them in the 'Additional Information' box on the self-employment (or partnership) pages.

What is the item 'Class 4 N.I.C.' which appears on my Self Assessment return?
All taxpayers who are self-employed pay an additional national insurance contribution if their earned income exceeds a figure which varies each year. This contribution is described as Class 4 and is calculated when preparing the return. It is additional to the self-employed Class 2 (stamp) contribution but confers no additional benefits and is a form of levy. It applies to men aged under 65 and women under 60.

Value Added Tax

Value Added Tax (VAT) is a tax currently levied at 17.5% on:

(a) the total value of taxable goods and services supplied to consumers,
(b) the importation of goods into the UK,
(c) certain services or goods from abroad if a taxable person receives them in the UK for the purpose of their business.

Who is taxable?
A writer resident in the UK whose turnover from writing and any other business, craft or art on a self-employed basis is greater than £50,000 annually, before deducting agent's commission, must register with HM Customs & Excise as a taxable person. Turnover includes fees, royalties, advances, commissions, sale of copyright, reimbursed expenses, etc. A business is required to register:

●   at the end of any month if the value of taxable supplies in the past twelve months has exceeded the annual threshold; or
●   if there are reasonable grounds for believing that the value of taxable supplies in the next twelve months will exceed the annual threshold.

Penalties will be claimed in the case of late registration. A writer whose turnover is below these limits is exempt from the requirements to register for VAT, but may apply for voluntary registration, and this will be allowed at the discretion of HM Customs & Excise.

A taxable person collects VAT on outputs (turnover) and deducts VAT paid on inputs (taxable expenses) and where VAT collected exceeds VAT paid, must remit the difference to HM Customs & Excise. In the event that input exceeds output, the difference will be refunded by HM Customs & Excise.

Inputs (Expenses)

NB The following lists are not exhaustive.

Taxable at the standard rate if supplier is registered	Taxable at the zero or special rate	Not liable to VAT
Rent of certain commercial premises	Books (zero)	Rent of non-commercial premises
Advertisements in newspapers, magazines, journals and periodicals	Coach, rail, and air travel (zero)	Postage
Agent's commission (unless it relates to monies from overseas)	Agent's commission (on monies from overseas)	Services supplied by unregistered persons
Accountant's fees and solicitor's fees for business matters	Domestic gas and electricity (5%)	Subscriptions to the Society of Authors, PEN, NUJ, etc.
Agency services (typing, copying, etc.)		Wages and salaries
Word processors, typewriters and stationery		Insurance
Artists' materials		
Photographic equipment		
Tape recorders and tapes		
Hotel accommodation		*Outside the scope of VAT*
Taxi fares		PLR (Public Lending Right)
Motor-car expenses		Profit shares
Telephone		Investment income
Theatres and concerts		

Outputs (Turnover)

A writer's outputs are taxable services supplied to publishers, broadcasting organisations, theatre managements, film companies, educational institutions, etc. A taxable writer must invoice, i.e. collect from, all the persons (either individuals or organisations) in the UK for whom supplies have been made, for fees, royalties or other considerations plus VAT. An unregistered writer cannot and must not invoice for VAT. A taxable writer is not obliged to collect VAT on royalties or other fees paid by publishers or others overseas. In practice, agents usually collect VAT for the registered author.

Remit to Customs

The taxable writer adds up the VAT which has been paid on taxable inputs, deducts it from the VAT received and remits the balance to Customs. Business with HM Customs is conducted through the local VAT offices of HM Customs which are listed in local telephone directories, except for VAT returns which are sent direct to the Customs & Excise VAT Central Unit, Alexander House, 21 Victoria Avenue, Southend on Sea, Essex SS99 1AA.

Accounting

A taxable writer is obliged to account to HM Customs & Excise at quarterly intervals. Returns must be completed and sent to VAT Central Unit by the dates shown on the return. Penalties can be charged if the returns are late.

It is possible to account for the VAT liability under the Cash Accounting Scheme (leaflet 731), whereby the author accounts for the output tax when the invoice is paid or royalties, etc., are received. The same applies to the input tax, but as most purchases are probably on a 'cash basis', this will not make a considerable difference to the author's input tax. This scheme is only applicable to those with a taxable turnover of less than £350,000 and, therefore, is available to the majority of authors. The advantage of this scheme is that the author does not have to account for VAT before receiving payments, thereby relieving the author of a cash flow problem.

It is also possible to pay VAT by nine estimated direct debits, with a final balance at the end of the year (see leaflet 732). This annual accounting method also means that only one VAT return is submitted.

Registration

A writer will be given a VAT registration number which must be quoted on all VAT correspondence. It is the responsibility of those registered to inform those to whom they make supplies of their registration number. The taxable turnover limit which determines whether a person who is registered for VAT may apply for cancellation of registration is £48,000.

Voluntary registration

A writer whose turnover is below the limits may apply to register. If the writer is paying a relatively large amount of VAT on taxable inputs – agent's commission, accountant's fees, equipment, materials, or agency services, etc. – it may make a significant improvement in the net income to be able to offset the VAT on these inputs. A writer who pays relatively little VAT may find it easier, and no more expensive, to remain unregistered.

Fees and royalties

A taxable writer must notify those to whom he makes supplies of the Tax Registration Number at the first opportunity. One method of accounting for and paying VAT on fees and royalties is the use of multiple stationery for 'self-billing', one copy of the royalty statement being used by the author as the VAT invoice. A second method is for the recipient of taxable outputs to pay fees, including authors' royalties, without VAT. The taxable writer then renders a tax invoice for the VAT element and a second payment, of the VAT element, will be made. This scheme is cumbersome but will involve only taxable authors. Fees and royalties from abroad will count as payments of the exported services and will accordingly be zero-rated.

Agents and accountants

A writer is responsible to HM Customs for making VAT returns and payments. Neither an agent nor an accountant nor a solicitor can remove the responsibility, although they can be helpful in preparing and keeping VAT returns and accounts. Their professional fees or commission will, except in rare cases where the adviser or agent is himself unregistered, be taxable at the standard rate and will represent some of a writer's taxable inputs.

Income Tax – Schedule D

An unregistered writer can claim some of the VAT paid on taxable inputs as a business expense allowable against income tax. However, certain taxable inputs fall into categories which cannot be claimed under the income tax regulations. A taxable writer, who has already claimed VAT on inputs, cannot charge it as a business expense for the purposes of income tax.

Certain services from abroad

A taxable author who resides in the United Kingdom and who receives certain services from abroad must account for VAT on those services at the appropriate tax rate on the sum paid for them. Examples of the type of services concerned include: services of lawyers, accountants, consultants, provision of information and copyright permissions.

Inheritance Tax

Inheritance Tax was introduced in 1984 to replace Capital Transfer Tax, which had in turn replaced Estate Duty, the first of the death taxes of recent times. Paradoxically, Inheritance Tax has reintroduced a number of principles present under the old Estate Duty.

The general principle now is that all assets owned at death are chargeable to tax (currently 40%) except the first £223,000 of the estate and any assets passed to a surviving spouse or a charity. Gifts made more than seven years before death are exempt, but those made within this period are taxed on a sliding scale. No tax is payable at the time of making the gift.

In addition, each individual may currently make gifts of up to £3000 in any year and these will be considered to be exempt. A further exemption covers any number of annual gifts not exceeding £250 to any one person.

If the £3000 is not fully utilised in one year, any unused balance can be carried forward to the following year (but no later). Gifts out of income, which do not reduce one's living standards, are also exempt if they are part of normal expenditure.

At death all assets are valued; they will include any property, investments, life policies, furniture and personal possessions, bank balances and, in the case of authors, the value of copyrights. All, with the sole exception of copyrights, are capable (as assets) of accurate valuation and, if necessary, can be turned into cash. The valuation of copyright is, of course, complicated and frequently gives rise to difficulty. Except where they are bequeathed to the owner's husband or wife, very real problems can be left behind by the author.

Experience has shown that a figure based on two to three years' past royalties may be proposed by the Inland Revenue in their valuation of copyright. However, this may not be reasonable and may require negotiation. If a book is running out of print or if, as in the case of educational books, it may need revision at the next reprint, these factors must be taken into account. In many cases the fact that the author is no longer alive and able to make personal appearances, or provide publicity, or write further works, will result in lower or slower sales. Obviously, this is an area in which help can be given by the publishers, and in particular one needs to know what their future intentions are, what stocks of the books remain, and what likelihood there will be of reprinting.

There is a further relief available to authors who have established that they have been carrying on a business, normally assessable under Case II of Schedule D, for at least two years prior to death. It has been possible to establish that copyrights are treated as business property and in these circumstances, Inheritance Tax 'business property relief' is available. This relief at present is 100% so that the tax saving can be quite substantial. The Inland Revenue may wish to be assured that the business is continuing and consideration should therefore be given to the appointment, in the author's will, of a literary executor who should be a qualified business person or, in certain circumstances, the formation of partnership between the author and spouse, or other relative, to ensure that it is established the business is continuing after the author's death.

If the author has sufficient income, consideration should be given to building up a fund to cover future Inheritance Tax liabilities. One of a number of ways would be to take out a whole life assurance policy which is assigned to the children, or other beneficiaries, the premiums on which are within the annual exemption of £3000. The capital sum payable on the death of the assured is exempt from inheritance tax.

Anyone wondering how best to order his affairs for tax purposes should consult an accountant with specialised knowledge in this field. Experience shows that a good accountant is well worth his fee which, incidentally, so far as it relates to professional matters, is an allowable expense.

The information contained in this section has been prepared by Pat Kernon and Ian Spring of Moore Stephens, Chartered Accountants, who will be pleased to answer questions on tax problems. Please write to Pat Kernon, c/o The Writer's Handbook, 34 Ufton Road, London N1 5BX.

Company Index

The following codes have been used to classify the index entries:

A	UK Publishers	L	Film, TV and Video Production
A1	Irish Publishers		Companies
AB	Writer's Courses, Circles and Workshops	M	Theatre Producers
AA	European Publishers	N	US Publishers
AU	Audio Books	O	US Agents
B	Poetry Presses	P	US Media Contacts in the UK
C	Poetry Magazines	Q	Professional Associations
D	Organisations of Interest to Poets	R	Arts Councils and Regional Arts
E	UK Packagers		Boards
EE	Book Clubs	S	Bursaries, Fellowships and Grants
F	UK Agents	T	Prizes
G	National Newspapers	U	Library Services
H	Regional Newspapers	V	Picture Libraries
HH	News Agencies	W	Small Presses
I	Magazines	X	Festivals
J	National and Regional Television and	Y	Editorial, Research and other Services
	Radio	YY	Press Cuttings Agencies
K	European Television Companies	Z	Literary Societies

Subject Index